ALL SPORTS

ALPHABETICAL
PRICE GUIDE

Published by

 **krause
publications**

700 E. State Street • Iola, WI 54990-0001

Please call or write for our free catalog of sports publications. Our toll-free number
to place an order or obtain a free catalog is 800-258-0929
or please use our regular business telephone 715-445-2214
for editorial comment and further information.

Library of Congress Catalog Number: 95-76546
ISBN: 0-87341-361-X

Printed in the United States of America

Table of Contents

Football

Basketball

Hockey

Baseball

　　* Editor's note: Some cards which have been used to illustrate certain hockey players are from the 1994 Parkhurst Missing Link and the 1964 Parkhurst "Tall Boys" set. However, since values for these cards were undetermined at press time, they have not been listed in the players' checklists.

Introduction

In today's hobby market, the shelves are overflowing with an abundance of new cards. Many collectors, faced with difficult, sometimes costly choices, are instead opting to collect cards of certain players, rather than choosing from among the proliferation of complete sets to be assembled wax pack by wax pack. The All Sport Alphabetical Price Guide, believed to be the first alphabetical guide which has included prices in it, is a handy reference for those pursuing cards of their favorite players.

For this book, 743 athletes were selected from the four main sports - baseball, basketball, football and hockey. Two-sportstar Deion Sanders, however, is listed in baseball and football. The total of his 101 selected baseball cards is $227.38, compared to only $109.29 for his 96 selected football cards in Mint condition.

There were 251 baseball players selected for this guide. If one added up the most expensive rookie card from each player (or the most expensive card listed, if a rookie card is not designated), those cards would be worth $294,918.95.

The cards for the 186 basketball players selected would be worth $20,749.70, while the 127 hockey players would be worth $19,802.50. The 180 football players would be worth $10,496.30. Collectively, the cards for all 743 players would total $345,967.45.

Krause Publications' sports collectibles database has

assigned more than 1.2 million prices to more than 500,000 items, ranging from cards to stickers, from stamps to coins, covering all sports. To give you a better idea of the scope of the database, if we were to print out Roger Clemens' entire database, it would have stretched over four pages in this book, compared to the two he was given for the cards we selected.

There are 831 collectibles manufacturers represented in the database. Early in the 1995 collecting season, those manufacturers had produced 7,176 sets, dating back to the late 1800s. More than 50,000 players are represented in the database, including Ken Griffey Jr., whose 1989 Upper Deck rookie card, at

$70, is more valuable than all of his father's listed cards combined. Ken Sr.'s cards total $61.17.

HOW TO USE THIS CATALOG

This catalog has been uniquely designed to serve the needs of beginning and advanced collectors. It provides an alphabetical listing of more than 700 players' key card issues, arranged so that even the most novice collector can consult it with confidence and ease.

Each player is listed alphabetically within his sport according to the name he most commonly used during his playing career. Within the player listing is a chronological list of the player's cards, with the manufacturers' names listed alphabetically within each year. The card number and three grades are also provided for each card. See the section on grading for more information about that topic.

An (R) after the card number indicates the card is a player's rookie card - the first appearance of a player in one of the major sets, excluding update and traded sets. It may or may not be issued during the player's actual rookie season.

Fillers used in the baseball section were taken from three Krause Publications sports books - 101 Sports Card Investments, The Sports Card Explosion, and Getting Started in Card Collecting.

The following explanations summarize the general practices used in preparing this catalog's listings:

ARRANGEMENT

Because the most important feature in identifying, and pricing, a sports card is its set of origin, this catalog has been arranged chronologically, then alphabetically according to the name by which the set is most popularly known to collectors. Within each set, the cards are listed by their designated card number.

IDENTIFICATION

While most modern sports cards are well identified on front, back or both, as to date and issue, such has not always been the case. In general, the back of the card is more useful in identifying the set of origin than the front. The issuer or sponsor's name will usually appear on the back since, after all, sports cards were first produced as a promotional item to stimulate sales of other products. As often as not, that issuer's name is the name by which the set is known to collectors and under which it will be found listed in this catalog.

A sports card's general age, if not specific year of issue, can usually be fixed by studying the biological or statistical information on the back of the card. The last year mentioned in either the biography or stats is usually the year which preceded the year of issue.

PHOTOGRAPHS

A photograph of the front of a selected card for each player has been provided. Photographs have been printed in reduced size; standard size cards are 2 1/2" by 3 1/2".

DATING

The dating of sports cards by year of issue on the front or back of the card itself is a relatively new phenomenon. In most cases, to accurately determine a date of issue for an unidentified card, it must be studied for clues. As mentioned, the biography, career summary or statistics on the back of the card are the best way to pinpoint a year of issue. In most cases, the year of issue will be the year after the last season mentioned on the card.

Luckily for today's collector, earlier generations have done much of the research in determining year of issue for those cards which bear no clues. The painstaking task of matching players' listed and/or pictured team against their career records often allowed an issue date to be determined.

In some cases, particular card sets were issued over a period of more than one calendar year, but since they are collected together as a single set, their specific year of issue is not important. Such sets will be listed with their complete known range of issue years.

NUMBERING

While many sports card issues as far back as the 1880s have contained card numbers assigned by the issuer, to facilitate the collecting of a complete set, the practice has by no means been universal. Even today, not every set bears card numbers.

Logically, those sports cards which were numbered by their manufacturer are presented in that numerical order within the listings of this catalog. The many unnumbered issues, however, have been assigned Sports Collectors Digest Sports Card Price Guide numbers to facilitate their universal identification within the hobby, especially when buying and selling by mail.

In all cases, numbers which have been assigned, or which otherwise do not appear on the card through error or by design, are shown in this catalog within parentheses. In virtually all cases, unless a more natural system suggested itself by the unique matter of a particular set, the assignment of Sports Collectors Digest Sports Card Price Guide numbers by the cataloging staff has been done by alphabetical arrangement of the players' last names or the card's principal title.

Significant collectible variations for any particular card are noted within the listings by the application of a suffix letter within parentheses. In instances of variations, the suffix "a" is assigned to the variation which was created first. (Editor's note: Some cards have suffixes attached to them. These are cards, generally from insert sets, which use the letters as prefixes or suffixes, along with a number.)

NAMES

The identification of a player by full name on the front of his sports card has been a common practice only since the 1920s. Prior to that, the player's last name and team were the usual information found on the card front.

The listings in this book are those which the player is most commonly known. His actual cards, however, may identify the player on the card by several different methods, such as using his formal name, nicknames, or combinations thereof.

GRADING

It is necessary that some sort of card grading standard be used so that buyer and seller (especially when dealing by mail) may reach an informed agreement on the value of a card.

Each card set's listings are generally priced in Krause Publications' price guides in three grades of preservation in which those cards are most commonly encountered in the daily buying and selling of the hobby marketplace.

Older cards (pre-1981) are listed in grades of Near Mint (NR MT), Excellent (EX) and Very Good (VG), reflecting the basic fact that few cards were able to survive for 25, 50 or even 100 years in close semblance to the condition of their issue.

The pricing of cards in these three conditions will allow readers to accurately price cards which fall in intermediate grades, such as EX-MT, or VG-EX.

More recent issues, which have been preserved in top condition in considerable number, are listed in the grades of Mint (MT), Near Mint and Excellent, reflective of the fact that there exists in the current market little or no demand for cards of the recent past in grades below Excellent.

In general, although grades below Very Good are not generally priced in price guides, close approximations of low-grade card values may be figured on the following formula: Good condition cards are valued at about 50 percent of VG price, with Fair cards about 50 percent of Good.

Cards in Poor condition have no market value except in the cases of the rarest and most expensive cards. In such cases, value has to be negotiated individually.

For the benefit of the reader, we present herewith the grading guide which was originally formulated by Baseball Cards magazine and Sports Collectors Digest in 1981, and has been continually refined since that time.

These grading definitions have been used in the pricing of cards in this book, but they are by no means a universally-accepted grading standard.

The potential buyer of a baseball card should keep that in mind when encountering cards of nominally the same grade, but at a price which differs widely from that quoted in this book.

Ultimately, the collector himself must formulate his own personal grading standards in deciding whether cards available for purchase meet the needs of his own collection.

No collector is required to adhere to the grading standards presented herewith - or to any other published grading standards - but all are invited to do so. The editors of Krause Publications' sports books and price guides are eager to work toward the development of a standardized system of card grading that will be consistent with the realities of the hobby marketplace. Contact the editors.

Mint (MT): A perfect card. Well-centered, with parallel borders which appear equal to the naked eye. Four sharp, square corners. No creases, edge dents, surface scratches, paper flaws, loss of luster, yellowing or fading, regardless of age. No imperfectly printed card - out of register, badly cut or ink flawed - or card stained by contact with gum, wax or other substances can be considered truly Mint, even if new out of the pack.

Near Mint (NR MT): A nearly perfectly card. At first glance, a Near Mint card appears perfect; upon closer examination, however, a minor flaw will be discovered. On well-centered cards, three of the four corners must be perfectly sharp; only one corner shows a minor imperfection upon close inspection. A slightly off-center card with one or more borders being noticeably unequal - but still present - would also fit this grade.

Excellent (EX): Corners are still fairly sharp with only moderate wear. Card borders may be off center. No creases. May have very minor gum, wax or product stains, front or back. Surfaces may show slight loss of luster from rubbing across other cards.

Very Good (VG): Show obvious handling. Corners rounded and/or perhaps showing minor creases. Other minor creases may be visible. Surfaces may exhibit loss of luster, but all printing is intact. May show major gum, wax or other packaging stains. No major creases, tape marks or extraneous markings or writing. Exhibit honest wear.

Good (G - generally 50% of the VG price): A well-worn card, but exhibits no intentional damage or abuse. May have major or multiple creases. Corners rounded well beyond the border.

Fair (F - generally 50% of the Good price): Shows excessive wear, along with damage or abuse. Will show all the wear characteristics of a Good card, along with such damage as thumb tack holes in or near margins, evidence of having been taped or pasted, perhaps small tears around the edges, or creases so heavy as to break the cardboard. Backs may show minor added pen or pencil writing, or be missing small bits of paper. Still, basically a complete card.

Poor (P): A card that has been tortured to death. Corners or other areas may be torn off. Card may have been trimmed, show holes from paper punch or have been used for BB gun practice. Front may have extraneous pen or pencil writing, or other defacement. Major portions of front or back design may be missing. Not a pretty sight.

In addition to these terms, collectors may encounter intermediate grades, such as VG-EX or EX-MT. These cards usually have characteristics of both the lower and higher grades, and are generally priced midway between those two values.

VALUATIONS

Values quoted in this book represent the current retail market and are compiled from recommendations provided and verified through the authors' daily involvement in the publication of the hobby's leading advertising periodicals, as well as the input of specialized consultants.

It should be stressed, however, that this book is intended to serve only as an aid in evaluating cards; actual market conditions are constantly changing. This is especially true of the cards of current players, whose on-field performance during the course of a season can greatly affect the value of their cards - upwards or downwards.

Publication of this book is not intended as a solicitation to buy or sell the listed cards by the editors, publishers or contributors.

Again, the values here are retail prices - what a collector can expect to pay when buying a card from a dealer. The wholesale price, that which a collector can expect to receive from a dealer when selling cards, will be significantly lower.

Most dealers operate on a 100 percent mark-up, generally paying about 50 percent of a card's retail value. On some high-demand cards, dealers will pay up to 75 percent or even 100 percent or more of retail value, anticipating continued price increases. Conversely, for many low-demand cards, such as common players' cards of recent years, dealers may pay 25 percent or even less of retail.

It should also be noted that with several hundred thousand valuations quoted in this book, there are bound to be a few compilations or typographical errors which will creep into the final product, a fact readers should remember if they encounter a listing at a fraction of, or several times, the card's actual current retail price. The editors welcome the correction of any such errors discovered.

ERRORS/VARIATIONS

It is often hard for the beginning collector to understand that an error on a sports card, in and of itself, does not usually add premium value to that card. It is usually only when the correcting of an error in a subsequent printing creates a variation that premium value attaches to an error.

Minor errors, such as wrong stats or personal data, misspellings, inconsistencies, etc. - usually affecting the back of the card - are very common, especially in recent years. These errors are not noted in the listings of this book because they are not generally perceived by collectors to have premium value.

On the other hand, major effort has been expended to include the most complete listings ever for collectible variation cards. Many scarce and valuable variations are included in these listings because they are widely collected and have significant premium value.

COUNTERFEITS/ REPRINTS

As the value of sports cards has risen in the past 10-20 years, certain cards and sets have become too expensive for the average collector to obtain. This, along with changes in technology of color printing, have given rise to increasing numbers of counterfeit and reprint cards.

While both terms describe essentially the same thing - a modern copy which attempts to duplicate as closely as possible an original card - there are differences which are important to a collector.

Generally, a counterfeit is made with the intention of deceiving somebody into believing it is genuine, and thus paying large amounts of money for it. The counterfeiter takes every pain to try to make his fakes look as authentic as possible.

A reprint, on the other hand, while it may have been made to look as close as possible to an original card, is made with the intention of allowing collectors to buy them as substitutes for cards they may never be otherwise able to afford. The big difference is that a reprint is generally marked as such, usually on the back of the card. In other cases, the replicas are printed in a size markedly different from the originals.

Collectors should be aware, however, that unscrupulous persons will sometimes cut off or otherwise obliterate the distinguishing word - "Reprint," 'Copy," - or modern copyright date on the back of a reprint card in an attempt to pass it as genuine.

A collector's best defense against reprints and counterfeits is to acquire a knowledge of the "look" and "feel" of genuine sports cards of various eras and issues.

UNLISTED CARDS

We recognize that not all cards for every player are listed, but we have attempted to list all the major sets and corresponding insert sets.

Major sets listed include: Batter-Up, Bowman, DeLong, Diamond Stars, Donruss, Double Play, Fleer, GameDay, Goudey, Home Run Derby, Leaf, NBA Hoops, O-Pee-Chee, Pacific, Parkhurst, Philadelphia, Pinnacle, Play Ball, Post, Pro Set, Red Heart, Red Man, Score, SkyBox, Sportflics, Star Co., Studio, Topps and Upper Deck.

(Editor's note: Honus Wagner has a sampling of tobacco cards (E and T sets) listed. His 1909-11 T206 card is $230,000.)

Some cards may have slipped through the cracks, due to an uncommon spelling or variation of a player name on the card, or due to the fact he shares it with another player. Readers who have cards or sets which are not covered in this edition are invited to correspond with the editor for the purposes of adding to the compilation work now in progress. Also, general comments and suggestions on which players should be featured in future editions is also welcome. Contact Krause Publications' sports book editor at 700 E. State St., Iola, Wis. 54990.

COLLECTOR ISSUES

There exists within the hobby a great body of cards which do not fall under the scope of this catalog by virtue of their nature of having been issued solely for the collector market. Known as "collector issues," these cards and sets are distinguished from "legitimate" issues in not having been created as a sales promotional item for another product or service - bubble gum, soda, snack cakes, dog food, cigarettes, gasoline, etc.

By their nature, and principally because the person issuing them is always free to print and distribute more of the same if they should ever attain any real value, collector issues are generally regarded by collectors as having little or no premium value.

ACKNOWLEDGMENTS

This book, created from a redesigned, enhanced computer database which facilitated the process, is the collective efforts of many people at Krause Publications, all of whom deserve a thanks. These employees, in particular, played key roles in working out the bugs during the production of this book, the first to be done using the new database publishing system developed at Krause Publications: Mike Ross and Mark Rosicky, computer programmers; Bonnie Tetzlaff, operations technician; Dawn Van Epern, data entry; Joe Clemens and Bruce Tieves, price guide analysts; Barb Lefeber, book production; Tom Dupuis, graphic design; and Mark K. Larson, sports book editor.

FOOTBALL

Herb Adderley

Set	Card #	NM	EX	VG
1964 Philadelphia	71 (R)	30.00	15.00	9.00
1965 Philadelphia	72	8.00	4.00	2.50
1966 Philadelphia	80	5.00	2.50	1.50
1967 Philadelphia	74	4.50	2.25	1.25
1968 Topps	131	3.00	1.50	.90
1969 Topps	255	4.00	2.00	1.25
1969 Topps Four In Ones	(36)	2.00	1.00	.60
1972 Topps	66	2.50	1.25	.70
1973 Topps	243	2.25	1.25	.70

Troy Aikman

Set	Card #	MT	NM	EX
1989 Pro Set	490 (R)	6.50	5.00	2.50
1989 Score	270 (R)	55.00	41.00	22.00
1989 Topps Traded	70 (R)	3.50	2.75	1.50
1990 Fleer	384	1.50	1.25	.60
1990 Pro Set	78	1.00	.70	.40
1990 Score	21	1.25	.90	.50
1990 Score Young Superstars	8	.75	.60	.30
1990 Score 100 Hottest	14	2.00	1.50	.80
1990 Topps	3	.50	.40	.20
1990 Topps	482	1.25	.90	.50
1991 Bowman	113	1.00	.70	.40
1991 Fleer	228	1.50	1.25	.60
1991 Fleer Ultra	162	1.00	.70	.40
1991 Pacific	93	1.00	.70	.40

1991 Pinnacle	6	5.50	4.25	2.25
1991 Pinnacle	383	1.00	.70	.40
1991 Pro Set	128	1.00	.70	.40
1991 Pro Set	372	.25	.20	.10
1991 Pro Set Platinum	24	1.00	.70	.40
1991 Score	225	1.00	.70	.40
1991 Score	631	.50	.40	.20
1991 Topps	371	1.00	.70	.40
1991 Topps Stadium Club	228	10.00	7.50	4.00
1991 Upper Deck	152	1.00	.70	.40
1992 GameDay	227	5.00	3.75	2.00
1992 Pro Set	401	.60	.45	.25
1992 Pro Set	473	1.25	.90	.50
1992 Pro Set Power	8	2.50	2.00	1.00
1992 SkyBox Impact	232	1.50	1.25	.60
1992 SkyBox Impact Major Impact	11	7.00	5.25	2.75
1992 SkyBox Primetime	8	3.00	2.25	1.25
1992 SkyBox Primetime	313	1.50	1.25	.60
1992 SkyBox Primetime Poster Cards	14	15.00	11.00	6.00
1992 Topps	744	1.50	1.25	.60
1992 Topps Stadium Club	602	8.00	6.00	3.25
1992 Topps Stadium Club	695	18.00	13.50	7.25
1992 Upper Deck	597	1.25	.90	.50
1992 Upper Deck Gold	22	1.50	1.25	.60
1992 Upper Deck Gold	40	2.00	1.50	.80
1992 Upper Deck NFL Fanimation	5	10.00	7.50	4.00
1993 Bowman	1	8.00	6.00	3.25
1993 Fleer	253	.40	.30	.15
1993 Fleer	273	1.50	1.25	.60
1993 Fleer Ultra	85	2.50	2.00	1.00
1993 Fleer Ultra Award Winners	1	35.00	26.00	14.00
1993 GameDay	1	3.50	2.75	1.50
1993 GameDay Game Breakers	1	6.00	4.50	2.50
1993 Pacific	2	1.25	.90	.50
1993 Pacific Gold Prisms	1	50.00	37.00	20.00
1993 Pacific Prism Inserts	1	20.00	15.00	8.00
1993 Pacific Prisms	18	15.00	11.00	6.00
1993 Pacific Triple Folder Superstars	1	3.50	2.75	1.50
1993 Pinnacle	281	3.75	2.75	1.50
1993 Pinnacle Team Pinnacle	1	120.00	90.00	48.00
1993 Pro Set	30	1.75	1.25	.70
1993 Pro Set Power	8	1.50	1.25	.60
1993 Pro Set Power Update Combos	8	8.00	6.00	3.25
1993 Score	238	1.50	1.25	.60
1993 Score	411	.65	.50	.25
1993 Score Select	7	9.00	6.75	3.50
1993 Score Select Gridiron Skills	5	110.00	82.00	44.00
1993 SkyBox Impact	66	1.00	.70	.40
1993 SkyBox Premium	10	3.00	2.25	1.25
1993 SkyBox Thunder and Lightning	6	18.00	13.50	7.25
1993 Topps	530	1.25	.90	.50
1993 Topps Black Gold	8	7.00	5.25	2.75
1993 Topps Stadium Club	50	3.00	2.25	1.25
1993 Topps Stadium Club	242	1.25	.90	.50
1993 Upper Deck	140	1.50	1.25	.60
1993 Upper Deck America's Team	8	35.00	26.00	14.00
1993 Upper Deck America's Team	14	15.00	11.00	6.00
1993 Upper Deck Dallas Cowboys	23	3.00	2.25	1.25

Marcus Allen

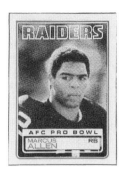

Set	Card #	MT	NM	EX
1983 Topps	205	.80	.60	.30
1983 Topps	293	1.00	.70	.40
1983 Topps	294 (R)	15.00	11.00	6.00
1984 Topps	98	4.00	3.00	1.50
1984 Topps	99	1.50	1.25	.60
1985 Topps	281	.30	.25	.12
1985 Topps	282	2.00	1.50	.80
1986 Topps	1	.65	.50	.25
1986 Topps	60	.25	.20	.10
1986 Topps	62	1.25	.90	.50
1986 Topps	227	.25	.20	.10
1986 Topps 1000 Yard Club	1	.40	.30	.15
1987 Topps	213	.15	.11	.06
1987 Topps	215	.90	.70	.35
1988 Topps	328	.30	.25	.12
1988 Topps 1000 Yard Club	27	.30	.25	.12
1989 Pro Set	182	.35	.25	.14
1989 Score	234	.75	.60	.30
1989 Score	284	.75	.60	.30
1989 Topps	264	.05	.04	.02
1989 Topps	267	.12	.09	.05
1990 Fleer	249	.08	.06	.03
1990 Pro Set	538	.03	.02	.01
1990 Pro Set Super Bowl MVPs	18	.20	.15	.08
1990 Score	230	.04	.03	.02
1990 Score 100 Hottest	31	.30	.25	.12
1990 Topps	289	.04	.03	.02
1991 Bowman	238	.03	.02	.01
1991 Fleer	102	.15	.11	.06
1991 Fleer Ultra	75	.08	.06	.03
1991 Pacific	225	.04	.03	.02
1991 Pinnacle	232	.50	.40	.20
1991 Pinnacle	398	.10	.08	.04
1991 Pro Set	45	.04	.03	.02
1991 Pro Set	541	.03	.02	.01
1991 Pro Set Platinum	209	.05	.04	.02
1991 Score	420	.05	.04	.02
1991 Topps	87	.04	.03	.02
1991 Topps Stadium Club	8	.75	.60	.30
1991 Upper Deck	446	.05	.04	.02
1991 Upper Deck Game Breaker Holograms	9	.75	.60	.30
1992 Bowman	132	.75	.60	.30
1992 Fleer	188	.08	.06	.03
1992 Fleer Ultra	185	.08	.06	.03
1992 Pacific	153	.05	.04	.02
1992 Pinnacle	120	.05	.04	.02
1992 Pro Set	27	.08	.06	.03
1992 Pro Set	208	.08	.06	.03
1992 Pro Set Power	32	.05	.04	.02
1992 Score	161	.05	.04	.02
1992 Topps	25	.05	.04	.02
1992 Topps Stadium Club	129	.08	.06	.03
1992 Upper Deck	94	.05	.04	.02
1992 Upper Deck	211	.05	.04	.02
1993 Bowman	229	.65	.50	.25

Set	Card #	MT	NM	EX
1993 Upper Deck Dallas Cowboys	25	2.00	1.50	.80
1993 Upper Deck Future Heroes	40	5.00	3.75	2.00
1993 Upper Deck NFL Experience	34	2.00	1.50	.80
1993 Upper Deck Pro Bowl	13	23.00	17.00	9.25
1993 Upper Deck SP	64	15.00	11.00	6.00
1993 Upper Deck SP All Pro	3	90.00	67.00	36.00
1993 Upper Deck Team MVP	11	6.00	4.50	2.50
1994 Bowman	95	2.75	2.00	1.00
1994 Fleer	107	1.25	.90	.50
1994 Fleer All-Pro	1	4.50	3.50	1.75
1994 Fleer Pro-Visions	5	1.75	1.25	.70
1994 Fleer Ultra	67	2.25	1.75	.90
1994 Fleer Ultra Hot Numbers	1	5.50	4.25	2.25
1994 Fleer Ultra Ultra Stars	1	45.00	34.00	18.00
1994 GameDay	91	2.75	2.00	1.00
1994 GameDay Game Breakers	1	5.00	3.75	2.00
1994 Pacific Crown	1	1.75	1.25	.70
1994 Pacific Crown Gems of the Crown	1	18.00	13.50	7.25
1994 Pacific Marquee	1	6.00	4.50	2.50
1994 Pacific Prisms	1	15.00	11.00	6.00
1994 Pinnacle	150	2.50	2.00	1.00
1994 Pinnacle Performers	1	10.00	7.50	4.00
1994 Pinnacle Sportflics Head-to-Head	6	35.00	26.00	14.00
1994 Pinnacle Sportflics	31	3.50	2.75	1.50
1994 Pinnacle Sportflics	178	2.00	1.50	.80
1994 Pinnacle Team Pinnacle	1	90.00	67.00	36.00
1994 Score	2	1.25	.90	.50
1994 Score Dream Team	1	40.00	30.00	16.00
1994 Score Select	40	3.00	2.25	1.25
1994 Score Select Canton Bound	11	60.00	45.00	24.00
1994 SkyBox Impact	57	1.25	.90	.50
1994 SkyBox Impact Ultimate Impact	1	15.00	11.00	6.00
1994 SkyBox Premium	37	2.00	1.50	.80
1994 SkyBox Premium Revolution	3	22.00	16.50	8.75
1994 SkyBox Premium SkyTech Stars	1	12.00	9.00	4.75
1994 Topps	200	1.00	.70	.40
1994 Topps	316	.65	.50	.25
1994 Topps	400	2.25	1.75	.90
1994 Topps All-Pros	9	35.00	26.00	14.00
1994 Topps Finest	202	20.00	15.00	8.00
1994 Topps Finest Inserts	30	40.00	30.00	16.00
1994 Topps Stadium Club	520	1.50	1.25	.60
1994 Topps Stadium Club	540	3.00	2.25	1.25
1994 Upper Deck	277	2.50	2.00	1.00
1994 Upper Deck Collector's Choice Crash Game	2	11.00	8.25	4.50
1994 Upper Deck Collector's Choice	342	1.25	.90	.50
1994 Upper Deck Retail Predictor	1	10.00	7.50	4.00
1994 Upper Deck SP	117	5.00	3.75	2.00
1994 Upper Deck SP All-Pro	9	20.00	15.00	8.00

Year / Set	Card #			
1993 Fleer Ultra	193	.40	.30	.15
1993 GameDay	105	.10	.08	.04
1993 Pacific	402	.05	.04	.02
1993 Pinnacle	116	.10	.08	.04
1993 Pro Set	203	.05	.04	.02
1993 Pro Set Power Power Moves	33	.75	.60	.30
1993 Score Select	125	.10	.08	.04
1993 SkyBox Impact	150	.06	.05	.02
1993 SkyBox Premium	102	.15	.11	.06
1993 Topps	618	.07	.05	.03
1993 Topps Stadium Club	471	.15	.11	.06
1993 Upper Deck	457	.05	.04	.02
1993 Upper Deck Kansas City Chiefs	3	1.00	.70	.40
1993 Upper Deck SP	118	.25	.20	.10
1994 Bowman	195	.20	.15	.08
1994 Fleer	215	.15	.11	.06
1994 Fleer League Leaders	1	1.00	.70	.40
1994 Fleer Living Legends	1	12.00	9.00	4.75
1994 Fleer Scoring Machines	1	4.50	3.50	1.75
1994 Fleer Ultra	137	.25	.20	.10
1994 Fleer Ultra Achievement Awards	1	.75	.60	.30
1994 Fleer Ultra Scoring Power	1	2.00	1.50	.80
1994 Fleer Ultra Touchdown Kings	1	9.00	6.75	3.50
1994 GameDay	185	.10	.08	.04
1994 GameDay Game Breakers	2	.75	.60	.30
1994 Pacific Crown	46	.08	.06	.03
1994 Pacific Crown Crystalline Collection	15	2.00	1.50	.80
1994 Pacific Crown Gems of the Crown	2	3.00	2.25	1.25
1994 Pacific Marquee	2	1.25	.90	.50
1994 Pacific Prisms	2	1.50	1.25	.60
1994 Pinnacle	186	.15	.11	.06
1994 Pinnacle Sportflics	108	.20	.15	.08
1994 Score	19	.10	.08	.04
1994 Score Select	107	.12	.09	.05
1994 SkyBox Impact	115	.10	.08	.04
1994 SkyBox Premium	72	.15	.11	.06
1994 Topps	214	.15	.11	.06
1994 Topps	273	.05	.04	.02
1994 Topps Finest	63	3.00	2.25	1.25
1994 Topps Stadium Club	260	.10	.08	.04
1994 Topps Stadium Club	521	.10	.08	.04
1994 Upper Deck	253	.15	.11	.06
1994 Upper Deck Collector's Choice	55	.10	.08	.04
1994 Upper Deck Collector's Choice	315	.10	.08	.04
1994 Upper Deck SP	89	.30	.25	.12

Grading Guide

Mint (MT): A perfect card. Well-centered with all corners sharp and square. No creases, stains, edge nicks, surface marks, yellowing or fading.

Near Mint (NM): A nearly perfect card. At first glance, a NM card appears to be perfect. May be slightly off-center. No surface marks, creases or loss of gloss.

Excellent (EX): Corners are still fairly sharp with only moderate wear. Borders may be off-center. No creases or stains on fronts or backs, but may show slight loss of surface luster.

Very Good (VG): Shows obvious handling. May have rounded corners, minor creases, major gum or wax stains. No major creases, tape marks, writing, etc.

Good (G): A well-worn card, but exhibits no intentional damage. May have major or multiple creases. Corners may be rounded well beyond card border.

Lance Alworth

Set	Card #	NM	EX	VG
1963 Fleer	72 (R)	250.00	125.00	75.00
1964 Topps	155	40.00	20.00	12.00
1965 Topps	155	65.00	32.00	19.50
1966 Topps	119	30.00	15.00	9.00
1967 Topps	123	22.00	11.00	6.50
1968 Topps	193	13.00	6.50	4.00
1969 Topps	69	8.00	4.00	2.50
1969 Topps Four In Ones	(3)	3.00	1.50	.90
1970 Topps	240	6.00	3.00	1.75
1971 Topps	10	5.00	2.50	1.50
1972 Topps	248	6.00	3.00	1.75
1973 Topps	61	3.50	1.75	1.00

Morten Andersen

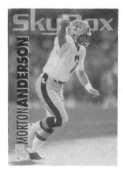

Set	Card #	MT	NM	EX
1984 Topps	300 (R)	3.00	2.25	1.25
1985 Topps	101	.75	.60	.30
1986 Topps	344	.35	.25	.14
1987 Topps	277	.35	.25	.14
1988 Topps	61	.15	.11	.06
1989 Pro Set	261	.03	.02	.01
1989 Score	227	.10	.08	.04
1989 Topps	153	.05	.04	.02
1990 Fleer	183	.03	.02	.01
1990 Fleer All-Pro	23	.25	.20	.10
1990 Pro Set	210	.03	.02	.01
1990 Score	108	.04	.03	.02
1990 Topps	245	.04	.03	.02
1991 Bowman	340	.03	.02	.01
1991 Fleer	291	.05	.04	.02
1991 Fleer Ultra	204	.04	.03	.02
1991 Pacific	321	.10	.08	.04
1991 Pinnacle	2	.10	.08	.04
1991 Pinnacle	361	.10	.08	.04
1991 Pro Set	402	.03	.02	.01
1991 Pro Set	586	.03	.02	.01
1991 Pro Set Platinum	233	.05	.04	.02

Set	Card #	MT	NM	EX
1991 Score	166	.06	.05	.02
1991 Topps	316	.04	.03	.02
1991 Topps Stadium Club	379	.30	.25	.12
1991 Upper Deck	226	.05	.04	.02
1992 Bowman	140	.30	.25	.12
1992 Bowman	337	1.00	.70	.40
1992 Fleer	269	.03	.02	.01
1992 Fleer Ultra	256	.05	.04	.02
1992 Pacific	199	.05	.04	.02
1992 Pinnacle	38	.05	.04	.02
1992 Pro Set	253	.05	.04	.02
1992 Score	33	.05	.04	.02
1992 Topps	427	.05	.04	.02
1992 Topps Stadium Club	495	.08	.06	.03
1992 Upper Deck	477	.05	.04	.02
1993 Bowman	262	.15	.11	.06
1993 Fleer	149	.05	.04	.02
1993 Fleer Ultra	297	.08	.06	.03
1993 GameDay	33	.10	.08	.04
1993 Pacific	155	.05	.04	.02
1993 Pacific Prisms	66	1.25	.90	.50
1993 Pacific Triple Folders	23	.45	.35	.20
1993 Pinnacle	5	.10	.08	.04
1993 Pro Set	285	.05	.04	.02
1993 Pro Set Power	107	.08	.06	.03
1993 Score	97	.04	.03	.02
1993 Score Dream Team	12	.65	.50	.25
1993 Score Select	102	.10	.08	.04
1993 SkyBox Impact	207	.03	.02	.01
1993 SkyBox Impact Kelly's Heroes/ Magic's Kingdom	12	1.25	.90	.50
1993 Topps	367	.06	.05	.02
1993 Topps Stadium Club	441	.10	.08	.04
1993 Upper Deck SP	172	.25	.20	.10
1994 Bowman	376	.10	.08	.04
1994 Fleer	318	.05	.04	.02
1994 Fleer Scoring Machines	2	25.00	18.50	10.00
1994 Fleer Ultra	455	.08	.06	.03
1994 GameDay	271	.10	.08	.04
1994 Pacific Crown	225	.06	.05	.02
1994 Pacific Prisms	3	1.00	.70	.40
1994 Pinnacle	53	.09	.07	.04
1994 Score	234	.05	.04	.02
1994 Score Select	194	.10	.08	.04
1994 SkyBox Impact	174	.04	.03	.02
1994 SkyBox Premium	103	.10	.08	.04
1994 Topps	255	.07	.05	.03
1994 Topps Finest	71	.65	.50	.25
1994 Topps Stadium Club	355	.10	.08	.04
1994 Upper Deck Collector's Choice	100	.07	.05	.03
1990 Fleer	33	.03	.02	.01
1990 Pro Set	162	.10	.08	.04
1990 Score	125	.10	.08	.04
1990 Score	593	.04	.03	.02
1990 Score Young Superstars	33	.15	.11	.06
1990 Score 100 Hottest	71	.15	.11	.06
1990 Topps	2	.04	.03	.02
1990 Topps	68	.15	.11	.06
1990 Topps 1000 Yard Club	18	.10	.08	.04
1991 Bowman	255	.03	.02	.01
1991 Bowman	283	.03	.02	.01
1991 Fleer	264	.10	.08	.04
1991 Fleer Ultra	181	.04	.03	.02
1991 Pacific	245	.04	.03	.02
1991 Pinnacle	349	.10	.08	.04
1991 Pro Set	550	.05	.04	.02
1991 Score	425	.04	.03	.02
1991 Topps	525	.04	.03	.02
1991 Topps Stadium Club	308	.30	.25	.12
1991 Topps 1000 Yard Club	11	.25	.20	.10
1991 Upper Deck	237	.05	.04	.02
1992 Bowman	207	.30	.25	.12
1992 Fleer	207	.03	.02	.01
1992 Fleer Ultra	203	.05	.04	.02
1992 GameDay	73	.12	.09	.05
1992 Pacific	155	.05	.04	.02
1992 Pro Set	217	.05	.04	.02
1992 Pro Set Power	282	.05	.04	.02
1992 Score	182	.05	.04	.02
1992 SkyBox Impact	78	.05	.04	.02
1992 SkyBox Primetime	41	.10	.08	.04
1992 Topps	604	.05	.04	.02
1992 Topps Stadium Club	582	.08	.06	.03
1992 Upper Deck	122	.05	.04	.02
1993 Bowman	152	.15	.11	.06
1993 Fleer	454	.05	.04	.02
1993 Fleer Ultra	231	.08	.06	.03
1993 GameDay	122	.10	.08	.04
1993 Pacific	194	.05	.04	.02
1993 Pinnacle	312	.10	.08	.04
1993 Pro Set	225	.05	.04	.02
1993 Score	228	.04	.03	.02
1993 Score Select	100	.10	.08	.04
1993 SkyBox Impact	163	.03	.02	.01
1993 SkyBox Premium	167	.10	.08	.04
1993 Topps	48	.05	.04	.02
1993 Topps Stadium Club	230	.10	.08	.04
1993 Upper Deck	446	.05	.04	.02
1993 Upper Deck SP	136	.25	.20	.10
1994 Bowman	268	.12	.09	.05
1994 Fleer	251	.15	.11	.06
1994 Fleer Ultra	160	.08	.06	.03
1994 GameDay	214	.10	.08	.04
1994 Pacific Crown	343	.06	.05	.02
1994 Pinnacle	57	.09	.07	.04
1994 Pinnacle Sportflics	3	.15	.11	.06
1994 Score	103	.05	.04	.02
1994 Score Select	88	.10	.08	.04
1994 SkyBox Impact	137	.10	.08	.04
1994 Topps	535	.05	.04	.02
1994 Topps Finest	213	.65	.50	.25
1994 Topps Stadium Club	281	.10	.08	.04

A card number in parentheses () indicates the set is unnumbered.

Values for recent cards and sets are listed in Mint (MT), Near Mint (NM), reflecting the fact that many cards from recent years have been preserved in to condition. Recent cards and sets in less than Excellent condition have little collector interest.

Flipper Anderson

Willie ANDERSON

Set	Card #	MT	NM	EX
1989 Pro Set	545 (R)	.40	.30	.15
1989 Topps Traded	14 (R)	.30	.25	.12

Ken Anderson

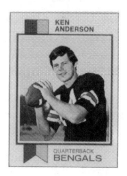

Set	Card #	NM	EX	VG
1973 Topps	34 (R)	25.00	12.50	7.50
1974 Topps	401	6.50	3.25	2.00
1975 Topps	160	3.50	1.75	1.00
1976 Topps	10	2.00	1.00	.60
1977 Topps	235	1.75	.90	.50
1978 Topps	205	1.25	.60	.40
1979 Topps	115	1.25	.60	.40
1980 Topps	388	.75	.40	.25

Set	Card #	MT	NM	EX
1981 Topps	115	.75	.60	.30
1982 Topps	1	.50	.40	.20
1982 Topps	38	.50	.40	.20
1982 Topps	39	.20	.15	.08
1983 Topps	1	.25	.20	.10
1983 Topps	202	.20	.15	.08
1983 Topps	232	.25	.20	.10
1984 Topps	34	.25	.20	.10
1984 Topps	35	.10	.08	.04
1985 Topps	209	.10	.08	.04
1985 Topps	210	.20	.15	.08

Neal Anderson

Set	Card #	MT	NM	EX
1988 Topps	71 (R)	.75	.60	.30
1989 Pro Set	35	.10	.08	.04
1989 Score	62	.50	.40	.20
1989 Topps	64	.30	.25	.12
1989 Topps 1000 Yard Club	14	.20	.15	.08
1990 Fleer	288	.08	.06	.03
1990 Pro Set	49	.03	.02	.01
1990 Pro Set	380	.03	.02	.01
1990 Score	47	.10	.08	.04
1990 Score	326	.04	.03	.02
1990 Score 100 Hottest	6	.15	.11	.06
1990 Topps	367	.15	.11	.06

1990 Topps 1000 Yard Club	8	.25	.20	.10
1991 Bowman	63	.10	.08	.04
1991 Fleer	212	.20	.15	.08
1991 Fleer All-Pro	11	.10	.08	.04
1991 Fleer Ultra	151	.08	.06	.03
1991 Pacific	38	.10	.08	.04
1991 Pinnacle	8	.10	.08	.04
1991 Pinnacle	369	.10	.08	.04
1991 Pro Set	389	.03	.02	.01
1991 Pro Set	451	.03	.02	.01
1991 Pro Set Platinum	11	.08	.06	.03
1991 Pro Set Platinum PC	6	.50	.40	.20
1991 Score	270	.08	.06	.03
1991 Score	621	.05	.04	.02
1991 Topps	157	.10	.08	.04
1991 Topps Stadium Club	96	.25	.20	.10
1991 Topps 1000 Yard Club	12	.35	.25	.14
1991 Upper Deck	244	.10	.08	.04
1991 Upper Deck	453	.05	.04	.02
1991 Upper Deck Game Breaker Holograms	6	.60	.45	.25
1992 Bowman	270	.35	.25	.14
1992 Fleer	35	.10	.08	.04
1992 Fleer Team Leaders	2	6.50	5.00	2.50
1992 Fleer Ultra	34	.20	.15	.08
1992 GameDay	428	.20	.15	.08
1992 Pacific	27	.10	.08	.04
1992 Pinnacle	123	.05	.04	.02
1992 Pro Set	118	.05	.04	.02
1992 Pro Set Gold MVPs	17	.45	.35	.20
1992 Pro Set Ground Force	118	2.00	1.50	.80
1992 Pro Set Power	35	.10	.08	.04
1992 Score	170	.07	.05	.03
1992 SkyBox Primetime	23	.10	.08	.04
1992 SkyBox Primetime	277	.20	.15	.08
1992 SkyBox Primetime Poster Cards	3	1.25	.90	.50
1992 Topps	153	.10	.08	.04
1992 Topps Stadium Club	35	.08	.06	.03
1992 Topps Stadium Club	305	.15	.11	.06
1992 Upper Deck	256	.05	.04	.02
1993 Bowman	137	.20	.15	.08
1993 Fleer	378	.05	.04	.02
1993 Fleer Ultra	38	.08	.06	.03
1993 GameDay	57	.10	.08	.04
1993 Pacific	127	.05	.04	.02
1993 Pacific Prisms	9	1.25	.90	.50
1993 Pinnacle	280	.07	.05	.03
1993 Pro Set	75	.05	.04	.02
1993 Pro Set College Connections	3	15.00	11.00	6.00
1993 Pro Set Power	135	.05	.04	.02
1993 Score	223	.06	.05	.02
1993 Score Select	18	.10	.08	.04
1993 SkyBox Impact	31	.05	.04	.02
1993 SkyBox Premium	67	.10	.08	.04
1993 Topps	432	.06	.05	.02
1993 Topps Stadium Club	5	.10	.08	.04
1993 Upper Deck	135	.05	.04	.02
1993 Upper Deck SP	37	.25	.20	.10
1993 Upper Deck Team MVP	1	.50	.40	.20
1994 Fleer	54	.05	.04	.02
1994 Pacific Crown	271	.06	.05	.02
1994 Pinnacle	13	.09	.07	.04
1994 Pinnacle Sportflics	60	.15	.11	.06
1994 Score	180	.05	.04	.02
1994 SkyBox Impact	32	.04	.03	.02
1994 Topps Finest	53	.65	.50	.25
1994 Upper Deck Collector's Choice	115	.05	.04	.02

Ottis Anderson

Set	Card #	NM	EX	VG
1980 Topps	1	1.00	.50	.30
1980 Topps	170 (R)	5.00	2.50	1.50

Set	Card #	MT	NM	EX
1981 Topps	12	.75	.60	.30
1981 Topps	365	1.50	1.25	.60
1982 Topps	463	1.00	.70	.40
1982 Topps	464	.60	.45	.25
1983 Topps	152	.20	.15	.08
1983 Topps	153	.40	.30	.15
1984 Topps	337	.15	.11	.06
1984 Topps	338	.50	.40	.20
1985 Topps	138	.30	.25	.12
1986 Topps	329	.20	.15	.08
1989 Pro Set	554	.03	.02	.01
1989 Score	348	.10	.08	.04
1990 Fleer	62	.03	.02	.01
1990 Pro Set	7	.03	.02	.01
1990 Pro Set	591	.03	.02	.01
1990 Score	531	.04	.03	.02
1990 Score	562	.04	.03	.02
1990 Topps	59	.04	.03	.02
1990 Topps 1000 Yard Club	29	.20	.15	.08
1991 Fleer	305	.03	.02	.01
1991 Fleer Ultra	214	.04	.03	.02
1991 Pinnacle	216	.10	.08	.04
1991 Pro Set	20	.03	.02	.01
1991 Pro Set	51	.03	.02	.01
1991 Pro Set	595	.03	.02	.01
1991 Pro Set Inserts	25	.50	.40	.20
1991 Pro Set Platinum	80	.05	.04	.02
1991 Score	3B	.05	.04	.02
1991 Score	4B	.05	.04	.02
1991 Score	433	.05	.04	.02
1991 Topps	5	.04	.03	.02
1991 Topps	20	.04	.03	.02
1991 Topps Stadium Club	490	.30	.25	.12
1991 Upper Deck	161	.05	.04	.02
1991 Upper Deck	469	.05	.04	.02
1992 Pacific	541	.05	.04	.02

Lem Barney

Set	Card #	NM	EX	VG
1970 Topps	75 (R)	15.00	7.50	4.50
1972 Topps	42	3.00	1.50	.90
1973 Topps	370	2.50	1.25	.70
1974 Topps	525	2.00	1.00	.60
1975 Topps	365	1.50	.70	.45
1976 Topps	43	1.00	.50	.30
1977 Topps	433	.90	.45	.25
1978 Topps	82	.75	.40	.25

Set	Card #	MT	NM	EX
1992 Pinnacle	346	.05	.04	.02
1992 Pro Set HOF Inductees	1	.40	.30	.15
1992 Score	537	.05	.04	.02

Bobby Bell

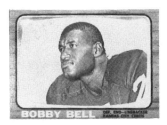

Set	Card #	NM	EX	VG
1964 Topps	90 (R)	35.00	17.50	10.50
1965 Topps	91	25.00	12.50	7.50
1966 Topps	64	8.00	4.00	2.50
1967 Topps	69	5.50	2.75	1.75
1968 Topps	93	3.50	1.75	1.00
1969 Topps	153	4.00	2.00	1.25
1969 Topps Four In Ones	(5)	1.00	.50	.30
1970 Topps	154	3.75	2.00	1.25
1971 Topps	35	2.50	1.25	.70
1972 Topps	177	2.50	1.25	.70
1973 Topps	435	2.00	1.00	.60
1974 Topps	59	1.50	.70	.45
1974 Topps	359	.35	.20	.11
1975 Topps	281	1.50	.70	.45
1977 Topps	241	.20	.10	.06

Cornelius Bennett

Set	Card #	MT	NM	EX
1988 Topps	230 (R)	1.00	.70	.40
1989 Pro Set	17	.20	.15	.08
1989 Score	61	.75	.60	.30
1989 Score	299	.25	.20	.10
1989 Topps	43	.30	.25	.12
1990 Fleer	111	.03	.02	.01
1990 Pro Set	39	.03	.02	.01
1990 Score	256	.04	.03	.02
1990 Score Promos	256	5.00	3.75	2.00
1990 Score Young Superstars	32	.20	.15	.08
1990 Score 100 Hottest	23	.15	.11	.06
1990 Topps	208	.04	.03	.02
1991 Bowman	50	.03	.02	.01
1991 Fleer Ultra Update	6	.10	.08	.04
1991 Pacific	560	.05	.04	.02
1991 Pinnacle	56	.15	.11	.06
1991 Pro Set	74	.20	.15	.08
1991 Pro Set	729	.03	.02	.01
1991 Pro Set Platinum	157	.05	.04	.02
1991 Topps Stadium Club	113	.40	.30	.15
1991 Upper Deck	41	.05	.04	.02
1992 Bowman	72	.30	.25	.12
1992 Bowman	273	1.25	.90	.50
1992 Fleer	20	.03	.02	.01
1992 Fleer Team Leaders	14	8.00	6.00	3.25
1992 Fleer Ultra	19	.05	.04	.02
1992 Fleer Ultra Award Winners	2	1.50	1.25	.60
1992 GameDay	69	.12	.09	.05
1992 Pacific	15	.05	.04	.02
1992 Pinnacle	63	.05	.04	.02
1992 Pro Set	92	.05	.04	.02
1992 Pro Set	376	.05	.04	.02
1992 Pro Set Power	97	.05	.04	.02
1992 Score	70	.07	.05	.03
1992 SkyBox Impact	70	.05	.04	.02
1992 SkyBox Impact	315	.05	.04	.02
1992 SkyBox Impact Major Impact	1	.75	.60	.30
1992 SkyBox Primetime	97	.10	.08	.04
1992 Topps	91	.05	.04	.02
1992 Topps Stadium Club	296	.08	.06	.03
1992 Topps Stadium Club	412	.08	.06	.03
1992 Upper Deck	75	.05	.04	.02
1992 Upper Deck	142	.05	.04	.02
1992 Upper Deck Pro Bowl	8	1.50	1.25	.60
1993 Bowman	357	.15	.11	.06
1993 Fleer	62	.08	.06	.03
1993 Fleer Ultra	21	.08	.06	.03
1993 GameDay	218	.10	.08	.04
1993 Pacific	198	.05	.04	.02
1993 Pinnacle	68	.10	.08	.04
1993 Pro Set	46	.05	.04	.02
1993 Pro Set College Connections	6	1.50	1.25	.60
1993 Pro Set Power	97	.08	.06	.03
1993 Pro Set Power Update Combos	6	1.00	.70	.40
1993 Score	72	.04	.03	.02
1993 Score Select	113	.10	.08	.04
1993 SkyBox Impact	16	.03	.02	.01
1993 SkyBox Premium	202	.10	.08	.04
1993 Topps	157	.05	.04	.02
1993 Topps	291	.05	.04	.02
1993 Topps Stadium Club	480	.10	.08	.04
1993 Upper Deck	373	.05	.04	.02
1993 Upper Deck SP	28	.25	.20	.10
1994 Bowman	119	.10	.08	.04
1994 Fleer	36	.10	.08	.04
1994 Fleer Pro-Visions	8	.25	.20	.10
1994 Fleer Ultra	22	.08	.06	.03
1994 GameDay	29	.10	.08	.04
1994 Pacific Crown	17	.06	.05	.02
1994 Pinnacle	179	.09	.07	.04
1994 Pinnacle Sportflics	52	.15	.11	.06
1994 Score	70	.10	.08	.04
1994 Score Dream Team	3	4.00	3.00	1.50
1994 Score Select	164	.10	.08	.04
1994 SkyBox Impact	23	.08	.06	.03
1994 SkyBox Premium	15	.10	.08	.04
1994 Topps	93	.05	.04	.02
1994 Topps	202	.05	.04	.02
1994 Topps Finest	125	.65	.50	.25
1994 Topps Stadium Club	87	.10	.08	.04
1994 Topps Stadium Club	439	.10	.08	.04
1994 Upper Deck	89	.10	.08	.04
1994 Upper Deck Collector's Choice	318	.05	.04	.02
1994 Upper Deck SP	25	.60	.45	.25

Edgar Bennett

Set	Card #	MT	NM	EX
1992 Fleer	432 (R)	.65	.50	.25
1992 Fleer Ultra	418 (R)	.85	.60	.35
1992 GameDay	498 (R)	1.00	.70	.40
1992 Pinnacle	323 (R)	1.00	.70	.40
1992 Pro Set	501 (R)	.65	.50	.25
1992 Pro Set Power	310 (R)	.50	.40	.20
1992 Score	490 (R)	.50	.40	.20
1992 SkyBox Impact	350 (R)	.60	.45	.25
1992 SkyBox Primetime	98 (R)	1.00	.75	.40
1992 Topps	104 (R)	.45	.35	.20
1992 Topps Stadium Club	388 (R)	1.00	.75	.40
1992 Upper Deck	2 (R)	.50	.40	.20
1992 Upper Deck Coach's Report	9	2.00	1.50	.80
1993 Bowman	287	1.00	.75	.40
1993 Fleer	460	.10	.08	.04
1993 Fleer Ultra	140	.10	.08	.04
1993 Pacific	85	.15	.11	.06
1993 Pro Set	150	.10	.08	.04
1993 Score Select	154	.25	.20	.10
1993 Topps	126	.15	.11	.06
1993 Topps Stadium Club	137	.60	.45	.25
1993 Upper Deck	289	.10	.08	.04

1994 Fleer	164	.15	.11	.06
1994 Fleer Ultra	104	.08	.06	.03
1994 GameDay	141	.10	.08	.04
1994 Pacific Crown	133	.06	.05	.02
1994 Pacific Prisms	6	1.50	1.25	.60
1994 Score	88	.05	.04	.02
1994 SkyBox Impact	89	.15	.11	.06
1994 SkyBox Premium	57	.10	.08	.04
1994 Topps	144	.07	.05	.03
1994 Topps Finest	192	1.50	1.25	.60
1994 Topps Stadium Club	94	.10	.08	.04
1994 Upper Deck	160	.10	.08	.04
1994 Upper Deck Collector's Choice	324	.05	.04	.02

Raymond Berry

Set	Card #	NM	EX	VG
1957 Topps	94 (R)	95.00	47.00	28.00
1958 Topps	120	30.00	15.00	9.00
1959 Topps	55	15.00	7.50	4.50
1960 Topps	4	7.00	3.50	2.00
1961 Fleer	33	10.00	5.00	3.00
1961 Topps	4	7.00	3.50	2.00
1962 Topps	5	20.00	10.00	6.00
1963 Topps	4	7.00	3.50	2.00
1964 Philadelphia	1	20.00	10.00	6.00
1965 Philadelphia	2	6.00	3.00	1.75
1966 Philadelphia	15	7.00	3.50	2.00
1967 Philadelphia	14	5.00	2.50	1.50

Set	Card #	MT	NM	EX
1989 Pro Set	260	.15	.11	.06
1989 Topps	80	.05	.04	.02
1990 Fleer	94	.03	.02	.01
1990 Pro Set	566	.03	.02	.01
1991 Pacific	283	.04	.03	.02
1991 Score	158	.04	.03	.02
1991 Topps	385	.04	.03	.02
1991 Topps Stadium Club	44	.20	.15	.08
1992 Bowman	388	.25	.20	.10
1992 Fleer	239	.03	.02	.01
1992 Fleer Ultra	231	.05	.04	.02
1992 Pacific	506	.05	.04	.02
1992 Score	334	.05	.04	.02
1992 Topps	85	.05	.04	.02
1992 Topps Stadium Club	41	.08	.06	.03
1992 Upper Deck	292	.05	.04	.02

Cards before 1981 are priced in Near Mint (NM), Excellent (EX), and Very Good (VG).
Cards 1981 to present are Mint (MT), Near Mint (NM), and Excellent (EX).

Jerome Bettis

Set	Card #	MT	NM	EX
1993 Bowman	264 (R)	7.00	5.25	2.75
1993 Fleer NFL Prospects	7	20.00	15.00	8.00
1993 Fleer Ultra	232 (R)	5.00	3.75	2.00
1993 Fleer Ultra All-Rookie	2	15.00	11.00	6.00
1993 GameDay	339 (R)	7.00	5.25	2.75
1993 GameDay Rookie Standouts	4	6.00	4.50	2.40
1993 Pacific	434 (R)	2.00	1.50	.80
1993 Pacific Gold Prisms	2	30.00	22.00	12.00
1993 Pacific Prism Inserts	2	17.00	12.50	6.75
1993 Pacific Prisms	48	15.00	11.00	6.00
1993 Pacific Triple Folder Superstars	3 (R)	3.50	2.75	1.50
1993 Pinnacle Rookies	7	85.00	64.00	34.00
1993 Pro Set	226 (R)	2.50	2.00	1.00
1993 Pro Set All-Rookie Forecast	3	12.00	9.00	4.75
1993 Pro Set College Connections	2	10.00	7.50	4.00
1993 Pro Set Power Draft Picks	14	3.00	2.25	1.25
1993 Pro Set Power Update Impact Rookies	3	3.00	2.25	1.25
1993 Pro Set Power Update Prospects	9 (R)	3.50	2.75	1.50
1993 Pro Set Rookie Running Backs	6	4.50	3.50	1.75
1993 Score	306 (R)	2.00	1.50	.80
1993 Score Select	172 (R)	10.00	7.50	4.00
1993 SkyBox Impact	370 (R)	2.50	2.00	1.00
1993 SkyBox Premium	62 (R)	4.50	3.50	1.75
1993 Topps	166 (R)	2.00	1.50	.80
1993 Topps	604	1.00	.75	.40
1993 Topps Stadium Club	108 (R)	4.50	3.50	1.75
1993 Topps Stadium Club	506	1.50	1.25	.60
1993 Upper Deck	20 (R)	3.25	2.45	1.30
1993 Upper Deck Rookie Exchange	7	10.00	7.50	4.00
1993 Upper Deck SP	6 (R)	17.00	12.50	6.75
1994 Bowman	240	2.25	1.75	.90
1994 Fleer	252	1.25	.90	.50
1994 Fleer All-Pro	3	3.50	2.75	1.50
1994 Fleer Award Winners	1	2.50	2.00	1.00
1994 Fleer Pro-Visions	6	1.75	1.25	.70
1994 Fleer Rookie Sensations	1	45.00	34.00	18.00
1994 Fleer Scoring Machines	3	25.00	18.50	10.00
1994 Fleer Ultra	161	1.50	1.25	.60
1994 Fleer Ultra Award Winners	1	5.00	3.75	2.00
1994 Fleer Ultra Hot Numbers	2	1.50	1.25	.60
1994 Fleer Ultra Ultra Stars	2	30.00	22.00	12.00
1994 Fleer Ultra 2nd Year Standouts	1	3.00	2.25	1.25

1994 GameDay	215	1.50	1.25	.60
1994 GameDay Flashing Stars	1	15.00	11.00	6.00
1994 GameDay Second-Year Stars	1	3.50	2.75	1.50
1994 Pacific Crown	344	1.50	1.25	.60
1994 Pacific Crown Crystalline Collection	2	15.00	11.00	6.00
1994 Pacific Crown Gems of the Crown	3	10.00	7.50	4.00
1994 Pacific Crown Knights of the Gridiron	2	20.00	15.00	8.00
1994 Pacific Marquee	3	3.00	2.25	1.25
1994 Pacific Prisms	8	10.00	7.50	4.00
1994 Pinnacle	93	2.25	1.70	.90
1994 Pinnacle Performers	9	7.00	5.25	2.75
1994 Pinnacle Sportflics Head-to-Head	5	12.00	9.00	4.75
1994 Pinnacle Sportflics	72	2.50	2.00	1.00
1994 Pinnacle Sportflics	180	1.25	.90	.50
1994 Pinnacle Team Pinnacle	5	45.00	34.00	18.00
1994 Score	21	1.50	1.25	.60
1994 Score	327	1.00	.75	.40
1994 Score Select	25	1.75	1.25	.70
1994 Score Select Canton Bound	9	25.00	18.50	10.00
1994 Score Select Future Force	3	40.00	30.00	16.00
1994 Score Sophomore Showcase	1	10.00	7.50	4.00
1994 SkyBox Impact	141	1.50	1.25	.60
1994 SkyBox Impact Instant Impact	2	10.00	7.50	4.00
1994 SkyBox Premium	84	1.50	1.25	.60
1994 SkyBox Premium Revolution	10	15.00	11.00	6.00
1994 SkyBox Premium SkyTech Stars	10	7.00	5.25	2.75
1994 Topps	100	1.25	.90	.50
1994 Topps	199	.50	.40	.20
1994 Topps All-Pros	11	15.00	11.00	6.00
1994 Topps Finest	42	15.00	11.00	6.00
1994 Topps Finest Inserts	18	27.00	21.00	11.00
1994 Topps Stadium Club	190	1.25	.90	.50
1994 Topps Stadium Club	410	2.00	1.50	.80
1994 Upper Deck	135	1.75	1.25	.70
1994 Upper Deck Collector's Choice Crash Game	18	9.00	6.75	3.50
1994 Upper Deck Collector's Choice	35	.50	.40	.20
1994 Upper Deck Collector's Choice	116	1.25	.90	.50
1994 Upper Deck Hobby Predictor	3	8.00	6.00	3.25
1994 Upper Deck Pro Bowl	1	20.00	15.00	8.00
1994 Upper Deck Retail Predictor	13	10.00	7.50	4.00
1994 Upper Deck SP	191	3.00	2.25	1.25
1994 Upper Deck SP All-Pro	22	8.00	6.00	3.25
1994 Upper Deck Then And Now	1	8.00	6.00	3.25

Cards before 1981 are priced in Near Mint (NM),
Excellent (EX), and Very Good (VG).
Cards 1981 to present are Mint (MT), Near Mint (NM),
and Excellent (EX).

Values quoted in this guide reflect the
retail price of a card – the price a collector
can expect to pay when buying a card from a dealer.
The wholesale price – that which a collector can expect to
receive from a dealer when selling cards – will be
significantly lower, depending on desirability and condition.

Fred Biletnikoff

Set	Card #	NM	EX	VG
1965 Topps	133 (R)	190.00	95.00	57.00
1966 Topps	104	50.00	25.00	15.00
1967 Topps	106	30.00	15.00	9.00
1968 Topps	168	11.00	5.50	3.25
1969 Topps	201	10.00	5.00	3.00
1969 Topps Four In Ones	(4)	2.25	1.15	.70
1970 Topps	85	7.00	3.50	2.00
1971 Topps	178	6.00	3.00	1.75
1972 Topps	5	1.00	.50	.30
1972 Topps	210	5.00	2.50	1.50
1973 Topps	320	4.00	2.00	1.25
1974 Topps	490	3.50	1.75	1.00
1975 Topps	405	3.00	1.50	.90
1976 Topps	25	3.00	1.50	.90
1977 Topps	295	2.00	1.00	.60
1978 Topps	415	1.50	.70	.45
1979 Topps	305	1.25	.60	.40

Set	Card #	MT	NM	EX
1990 Pro Set Super Bowl MVPs	11	.20	.15	.08
1993 Upper Deck NFL Experience	5	.20	.15	.08
1994 Upper Deck Then And Now	2	3.00	2.25	1.25

George Blanda

Set	Card #	NM	EX	VG
1954 Bowman	23 (R)	180.00	90.00	54.00
1955 Bowman	62	80.00	40.00	24.00
1956 Topps	11	50.00	25.00	15.00
1957 Topps	31	45.00	22.00	13.50
1958 Topps	129	35.00	17.50	10.50
1960 Fleer	58	40.00	20.00	12.00
1961 Fleer	166	45.00	22.00	13.50
1961 Topps	145	26.00	13.00	7.75
1962 Fleer	46	55.00	27.00	16.50

Set	Card #	MT	NM	EX
1963 Fleer	36	55.00	27.00	16.50
1964 Topps	68	60.00	30.00	18.00
1965 Topps	69	90.00	45.00	27.00
1966 Topps	48	40.00	20.00	12.00
1968 Topps	142	23.00	11.50	7.00
1969 Topps	232	20.00	10.00	6.00
1969 Topps Four In Ones	(57)	22.00	11.00	6.50
1971 Topps	39	15.00	7.50	4.50
1972 Topps	235	11.00	5.50	3.25
1972 Topps	348	45.00	22.00	13.50
1973 Topps	25	7.50	3.75	2.25
1974 Topps	245	7.00	3.50	2.00
1975 Topps	7	5.00	2.50	1.50
1975 Topps	8	5.00	2.50	1.50
1975 Topps	351	2.50	1.25	.70
1976 Topps	1	5.50	2.75	1.75
1976 Topps	355	5.00	2.50	1.50

Set	Card #	MT	NM	EX
1992 Topps Stadium Club QB Legends	4	3.00	2.25	1.25

Drew Bledsoe

Set	Card #	MT	NM	EX
1993 Bowman	280 (R)	12.00	9.00	4.75
1993 Fleer NFL Prospects	1	30.00	22.00	12.00
1993 Fleer Ultra	283 (R)	7.00	5.25	2.75
1993 Fleer Ultra All-Rookie	3	22.00	16.50	8.75
1993 GameDay	11 (R)	11.00	8.25	4.50
1993 GameDay Rookie Standouts	1	10.00	7.50	4.00
1993 Pacific	435 (R)	3.75	2.75	1.50
1993 Pacific Gold Prisms	3	45.00	34.00	18.00
1993 Pacific Prism Inserts	3	25.00	18.50	10.00
1993 Pacific Prisms	61	22.00	16.50	8.75
1993 Pacific Triple Folder Superstars	4 (R)	3.50	2.75	1.50
1993 Pacific Triple Folders	10	3.00	2.25	1.25
1993 Pinnacle Rookies	1	125.00	94.00	50.00
1993 Pro Set	270 (R)	3.50	2.75	1.50
1993 Pro Set Power Draft Picks	17	4.00	3.00	1.50
1993 Pro Set Power Update Prospects	1 (R)	3.50	2.75	1.50
1993 Pro Set Power Update Impact Rookies	2	5.00	3.75	2.00
1993 Pro Set Rookie QB's	1	10.00	7.50	4.00
1993 Score	308 (R)	3.50	2.75	1.50
1993 Score Select	166 (R)	14.00	10.50	5.50
1993 SkyBox Impact	361 (R)	3.75	2.80	1.50
1993 SkyBox Premium	7 (R)	10.00	7.50	4.00
1993 SkyBox Primetime Rookies	2	40.00	30.00	16.00
1993 Topps	130 (R)	3.50	2.75	1.50
1993 Topps	400	2.00	1.50	.80
1993 Topps Stadium Club	280 (R)	7.50	5.75	3.00
1993 Topps Stadium Club	504	2.75	2.00	1.00

Set	Card #	MT	NM	EX
1993 Upper Deck	11 (R)	5.00	3.75	2.00
1993 Upper Deck	83	1.50	1.25	.60
1993 Upper Deck Rookie Exchange	2	9.00	6.75	3.50
1993 Upper Deck SP	9 (R)	27.00	20.00	11.00
1994 Bowman	220	3.00	2.25	1.25
1994 Fleer	307	2.00	1.50	.80
1994 Fleer Rookie Sensations	2	60.00	45.00	24.00
1994 Fleer Ultra	196	3.00	2.25	1.25
1994 Fleer Ultra 2nd Year Standouts	2	6.00	4.50	2.50
1994 GameDay	261	3.25	2.50	1.25
1994 GameDay Second-Year Stars	2	7.00	5.25	2.75
1994 Pacific Crown	358	2.50	2.00	1.00
1994 Pacific Crown Gems of the Crown	4	15.00	11.00	6.00
1994 Pacific Crown Knights of the Gridiron	3	30.00	22.00	12.00
1994 Pacific Marquee	4	6.00	4.50	2.50
1994 Pacific Prisms	11	15.00	11.00	6.00
1994 Pinnacle	92	3.75	2.75	1.50
1994 Pinnacle Passer	1	80.00	60.00	32.00
1994 Pinnacle Performers	14	12.00	9.00	4.75
1994 Pinnacle Sportflics	61	4.00	3.00	1.50
1994 Score	321	1.75	1.25	.70
1994 Score Select	4	3.00	2.25	1.25
1994 Score Select Future Force	2	65.00	49.00	26.00
1994 Score Sophomore Showcase	4	12.00	9.00	4.75
1994 SkyBox Impact	166	2.25	1.70	.90
1994 SkyBox Impact Instant Impact	7	14.00	10.50	5.50
1994 SkyBox Premium	98	3.00	2.25	1.25
1994 SkyBox Premium Revolution	12	25.00	18.50	10.00
1994 SkyBox Premium SkyTech Stars	7	7.00	5.25	2.75
1994 Topps	360	2.50	2.00	1.00
1994 Topps Finest	146	20.00	15.00	8.00
1994 Topps Stadium Club	185	2.25	1.75	.90
1994 Topps Stadium Club	360	3.50	2.75	1.50
1994 Upper Deck	168	3.50	2.75	1.50
1994 Upper Deck Collector's Choice Crash Game	9	9.00	6.75	3.50
1994 Upper Deck Collector's Choice	33	.90	.70	.35
1994 Upper Deck Collector's Choice	123	2.00	1.50	.80
1994 Upper Deck Retail Predictor	9	12.00	9.00	4.75
1994 Upper Deck SP	43	5.00	3.75	2.00

Mel Blount

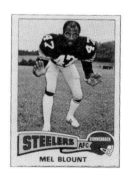

Set	Card #	NM	EX	VG
1975 Topps	12 (R)	25.00	12.50	7.50

Set	Card #	MT	NM	EX
1976 Topps	205	.75	.40	.25
1976 Topps	480	5.00	2.50	1.50
1977 Topps	180	3.00	1.50	.90
1978 Topps	475	1.25	.60	.40
1978 Topps	522	1.00	.50	.30
1979 Topps	275	1.00	.50	.30
1980 Topps	155	.75	.40	.25
Set	Card #	MT	NM	EX
1982 Topps	203	.75	.60	.30
1983 Topps	357	.25	.20	.10

Reggie Brooks

Set	Card #	MT	NM	EX
1993 Bowman	62 (R)	3.50	2.75	1.50
1993 Fleer NFL Prospects	29	5.00	3.75	2.00
1993 Fleer Ultra	479 (R)	2.00	1.50	.80
1993 GameDay	133 (R)	2.50	2.00	1.00
1993 GameDay Rookie Standouts	6	4.00	3.00	1.60
1993 Pacific	422 (R)	1.50	1.25	.60
1993 Pacific Gold Prisms	4	12.00	9.00	4.75
1993 Pacific Prism Inserts	4	6.00	4.50	2.50
1993 Pacific Prisms	103	7.00	5.25	2.75
1993 Pacific Triple Folder Superstars	5 (R)	1.25	.90	.50
1993 Pinnacle Rookies	24	25.00	18.50	10.00
1993 Pro Set	447 (R)	1.00	.70	.40
1993 Pro Set College Connections	2	10.00	7.50	4.00
1993 Pro Set Power Update Prospects	10 (R)	2.00	1.50	.80
1993 Pro Set Rookie Running Backs	2	2.00	1.50	.80
1993 Topps	204 (R)	1.00	.75	.40
1993 Topps	554	.40	.30	.15
1993 Topps Stadium Club	502 (R)	1.00	.70	.40
1993 Upper Deck	7 (R)	1.00	.75	.40
1993 Upper Deck SP	18 (R)	4.50	3.50	1.75
1994 Bowman	234	.50	.40	.20
1994 Fleer	459	.40	.30	.15
1994 Fleer Rookie Sensations	3	12.00	9.00	4.75
1994 Fleer Ultra	308	.75	.60	.30
1994 Fleer Ultra 2nd Year Standouts	3	1.50	1.25	.60
1994 GameDay	403	.75	.60	.30
1994 GameDay Second-Year Stars	3	1.00	.70	.40
1994 Pacific Crown	389	.35	.25	.14
1994 Pacific Crown Crystalline Collection	9	3.00	2.25	1.25
1994 Pacific Crown Gems of the Crown	5	4.00	3.00	1.50
1994 Pacific Crown Knights of the Gridiron	5	3.00	2.25	1.25
1994 Pacific Marquee	5	1.25	.90	.50
1994 Pacific Prisms	13	3.00	2.25	1.25
1994 Pinnacle	109	.75	.60	.30
1994 Pinnacle Performers	12	2.50	2.00	1.00
1994 Pinnacle Sportflics	50	.50	.40	.20
1994 Score	325	.50	.40	.20
1994 Score Select	120	.50	.40	.20
1994 Score Select Future Force	4	20.00	15.00	8.00
1994 Score Sophomore Showcase	3	3.00	2.25	1.25
1994 SkyBox Impact	256	.30	.25	.12
1994 SkyBox Impact Instant Impact	3	4.50	3.50	1.75
1994 SkyBox Premium	153	.75	.60	.30

Terry Bradshaw

Set	Card #	NM	EX	VG
1971 Topps	156 (R)	175.00	87.00	52.00
1972 Topps	120	15.00	7.50	4.50
1972 Topps	150	45.00	22.00	13.50
1973 Topps	15	25.00	12.50	7.50
1974 Topps	470	20.00	10.00	6.00
1975 Topps	461	15.00	7.50	4.50
1976 Topps	75	14.00	7.00	4.25
1977 Topps	245	7.00	3.50	2.00
1978 Topps	65	6.00	3.00	1.75
1979 Topps	500	5.50	2.75	1.75
1980 Topps	200	2.75	1.50	.80
Set	Card #	MT	NM	EX
1981 Topps	88	1.00	.70	.40
1981 Topps	375	2.50	2.00	1.00
1982 Topps	204	1.50	1.25	.60
1982 Topps	205	.75	.60	.30
1983 Topps	358	.75	.60	.30
1984 Topps	162	1.00	.70	.40
1989 Pro Set Announcer Inserts	12	.50	.40	.20
1990 Pro Set Super Bowl MVPs	13	.40	.30	.15
1990 Pro Set Super Bowl MVPs	14	.40	.30	.15
1992 Topps Stadium Club QB Legends	6	7.50	5.75	3.00
1993 Upper Deck NFL Experience	7	.25	.20	.10

Values for recent cards and sets are listed in Mint (MT), Near Mint (NM), reflecting the fact that many cards from recent years have been preserved in to condition. Recent cards and sets in less than Excellent condition have little collector interest.

1994 SkyBox Premium SkyTech Stars	19	1.50	1.25	.60
1994 Topps	270	.50	.40	.20
1994 Topps Finest Inserts	11	8.00	6.00	3.25
1994 Topps Stadium Club	182	.30	.25	.12
1994 Topps Stadium Club	223	.30	.25	.12
1994 Topps Stadium Club	280	.75	.60	.30
1994 Upper Deck	268	.75	.60	.30
1994 Upper Deck Collector's Choice	40	.25	.20	.10
1994 Upper Deck Collector's Choice	48	.10	.08	.04
1994 Upper Deck Collector's Choice	360	.50	.40	.20
1994 Upper Deck Retail Predictor	18	4.00	3.00	1.50
1994 Upper Deck SP	139	.75	.60	.30
1994 Upper Deck SP All-Pro	39	5.00	3.75	2.00

1994 Pacific Prisms	14	1.50	1.25	.60
1994 Pinnacle	78	.20	.15	.08
1994 Pinnacle Sportflics	48	.30	.25	.12
1994 Score	78	.35	.25	.14
1994 Score Select	146	.20	.15	.08
1994 Score Sophomore Showcase	6	4.00	3.00	1.50
1994 SkyBox Impact	175	.20	.15	.08
1994 SkyBox Premium	104	.20	.15	.08
1994 Topps	46	.25	.20	.10
1994 Topps Finest	47	4.00	3.00	1.50
1994 Topps Stadium Club	192	.25	.20	.10
1994 Upper Deck	80	.15	.11	.06
1994 Upper Deck	289	.20	.15	.08
1994 Upper Deck Collector's Choice	106	.30	.25	.12
1994 Upper Deck Collector's Choice	326	.05	.04	.02
1994 Upper Deck SP	175	.35	.25	.14

Derek Brown

Set	Card #	MT	NM	EX
1992 GameDay	12 (R)	.20	.15	.08
1992 Pro Set	591 (R)	.10	.08	.04
1992 Topps	720 (R)	.15	.11	.06
1992 Topps Stadium Club	694 (R)	.20	.15	.08
1993 Bowman	135	1.50	1.25	.60
1993 Fleer	417	.05	.04	.02
1993 Fleer Ultra	318	.08	.06	.03
1993 Pacific	56	.05	.04	.02
1993 Pacific Triple Folder Superstars	6	1.00	.70	.40
1993 Pinnacle	343	.10	.08	.04
1993 Pro Set	296	.75	.60	.30
1993 Pro Set Power Update Impact Rookies	4	1.50	1.25	.60
1993 Pro Set Power Update Prospects	13	1.00	.70	.40
1993 Pro Set Rookie Running Backs	8	1.25	.90	.50
1993 SkyBox Impact	228	.03	.02	.01
1993 SkyBox Premium	97	.10	.08	.04
1993 Topps	653	.06	.05	.02
1993 Topps Stadium Club	283	.10	.08	.04
1993 Topps Stadium Club	516	1.50	1.25	.60
1993 Upper Deck	19	.50	.40	.20
1993 Upper Deck	274	.05	.04	.02
1993 Upper Deck SP	173	1.50	1.25	.60
1993 Upper Deck SP	181	.25	.20	.10
1994 Bowman	229	.15	.11	.06
1994 Fleer	319	.25	.20	.10
1994 Fleer Ultra	207	.20	.15	.08
1994 GameDay	273	.25	.20	.10
1994 Pacific Crown	92	.06	.05	.02
1994 Pacific Crown	227	.20	.15	.08
1994 Pacific Crown Knights of the Gridiron	6	3.00	2.25	1.25

Jim Brown

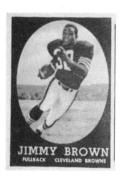

Set	Card #	NM	EX	VG
1958 Topps	62 (R)	360.00	180.00	108.00
1959 Topps	10	125.00	62.00	37.00
1960 Topps	23	85.00	42.00	25.00
1961 Fleer	11	130.00	65.00	39.00
1961 Topps	71	85.00	42.00	25.00
1961 Topps	77	27.50	13.50	8.25
1962 Topps	28	100.00	50.00	30.00
1963 Topps	14	150.00	75.00	45.00
1964 Philadelphia	30	65.00	32.00	19.50
1965 Philadelphia	31	60.00	30.00	18.00
1966 Philadelphia	41	55.00	27.50	16.50
1967 Philadelphia	136	1.50	.70	.45

Grading Guide

Mint (MT): A perfect card. Well-centered with all corners sharp and square. No creases, stains, edge nicks, surface marks, yellowing or fading.

Near Mint (NM): A nearly perfect card. At first glance, a NM card appears to be perfect. May be slightly off-center. No surface marks, creases or loss of gloss.

Excellent (EX): Corners are still fairly sharp with only moderate wear. Borders may be off-center. No creases or stains on fronts or backs, but may show slight loss of surface luster.

Very Good (VG): Shows obvious handling. May have rounded corners, minor creases, major gum or wax stains. No major creases, tape marks, writing, etc.

Good (G): A well-worn card, but exhibits no intentional damage. May have major or multiple creases. Corners may be rounded well beyond card border.

Tim Brown

Set	Card #	MT	NM	EX
1989 Pro Set	183 (R)	2.00	1.50	.80
1989 Score	86 (R)	8.00	6.00	3.25
1989 Score	305	1.00	.70	.40
1989 Score	328	2.25	1.75	.90
1989 Topps	2	.70	.50	.30
1989 Topps	265 (R)	1.50	1.25	.60
1990 Fleer Update	65	1.25	.90	.50
1990 Pro Set	150	.35	.25	.14
1990 Score	373	.45	.35	.20
1990 Score Young Superstars	10	.25	.20	.10
1990 Topps	295	.45	.35	.20
1991 Fleer	104	.07	.05	.03
1991 Fleer Ultra	77	.08	.06	.03
1991 Pacific	228	.20	.15	.08
1991 Pro Set	40	.05	.04	.02
1991 Score	14	.25	.20	.10
1991 Topps	85	.12	.09	.05
1991 Upper Deck	294	.12	.09	.05
1992 Bowman	181	1.75	1.25	.70
1992 Fleer	191	.10	.08	.04
1992 Fleer Ultra	188	.40	.30	.15
1992 Pacific	146	.30	.25	.12
1992 Pinnacle	67	.50	.40	.20
1992 Pinnacle	342	.05	.04	.02
1992 Pro Set	210	.10	.08	.04
1992 Pro Set	377	.05	.04	.02
1992 Pro Set Power	276	.50	.40	.20
1992 Score	76	.35	.25	.14
1992 Topps	612	.35	.25	.14
1992 Topps Stadium Club	515	.40	.30	.15
1992 Upper Deck	218	.05	.04	.02
1992 Upper Deck Pro Bowl	15	1.50	1.25	.60
1993 Bowman	186	.75	.60	.30
1993 Fleer	89	.30	.25	.12
1993 Fleer Ultra	215	.55	.40	.20
1993 GameDay	166	.45	.35	.20
1993 Pacific	372	.30	.25	.12
1993 Pinnacle	186	.60	.45	.25
1993 Pro Set	212	.05	.04	.02
1993 Pro Set College Connections	4	1.75	1.25	.70
1993 Pro Set Power Update Combos	9	2.00	1.50	.80
1993 Score	21	.10	.08	.04
1993 Score Select	14	.85	.60	.35
1993 SkyBox Impact	152	.35	.25	.14
1993 SkyBox Premium	104	.50	.40	.20
1993 Topps	628	.06	.05	.02
1993 Topps Stadium Club	46	.10	.08	.04
1993 Upper Deck	415	.05	.04	.02
1993 Upper Deck SP	127	.70	.50	.30
1993 Upper Deck Team MVP	22	.50	.40	.20
1994 Bowman	369	.15	.11	.06
1994 Fleer	232	.12	.09	.05
1994 Fleer League Leaders	2	1.00	.70	.40
1994 Fleer Scoring Machines	4	4.00	3.00	1.50
1994 Fleer Ultra	149	.12	.09	.05
1994 Fleer Ultra Hot Numbers	3	.75	.60	.30
1994 Fleer Ultra Ultra Stars	3	12.00	9.00	4.75
1994 GameDay	198	.12	.09	.05
1994 GameDay Game Breakers	3	.75	.60	.30
1994 Pacific Crown	107	.25	.20	.10
1994 Pacific Crown Gems of the Crown	7	2.50	2.00	1.00
1994 Pacific Prisms	16	2.00	1.50	.80
1994 Pinnacle	27	.12	.09	.05
1994 Pinnacle Performers	10	3.00	2.25	1.25
1994 Pinnacle Sportflics	79	.25	.20	.10
1994 Pinnacle Team Pinnacle	6	35.00	26.00	14.00
1994 Score	115	.15	.11	.06
1994 Score Dream Team	4	4.00	3.00	1.50
1994 Score Select	73	.10	.08	.04
1994 SkyBox Impact	127	.12	.09	.05
1994 SkyBox Premium	79	.15	.11	.06
1994 SkyBox Premium SkyTech Stars	12	3.00	2.25	1.25
1994 Topps	240	.10	.08	.04
1994 Topps Finest	116	1.50	1.25	.60
1994 Topps Finest Inserts	5	4.00	3.00	1.50
1994 Topps Stadium Club	150	.25	.20	.10
1994 Upper Deck	194	.25	.20	.10
1994 Upper Deck Collector's Choice Crash Game	28	9.00	6.75	3.50
1994 Upper Deck Collector's Choice	42	.10	.08	.04
1994 Upper Deck Collector's Choice	345	.07	.05	.03
1994 Upper Deck Pro Bowl	6	8.50	6.50	3.50
1994 Upper Deck Retail Predictor	25	7.50	5.75	3.00
1994 Upper Deck SP	92	.30	.25	.12
1994 Upper Deck SP All-Pro	20	6.00	4.50	2.50
1994 Upper Deck Then And Now	2	3.00	2.25	1.25

Willie Brown

Set	Card #	NM	EX	VG
1965 Topps	46 (R)	65.00	32.00	19.50
1966 Philadelphia	93	1.50	.70	.45
1970 Topps	144	4.00	2.00	1.25
1971 Topps	207	3.50	1.75	1.00
1972 Topps	28	3.00	1.50	.90
1972 Topps	285	27.50	13.50	8.25
1973 Topps	210	2.00	1.00	.60
1974 Topps	141	1.25	.60	.40
1975 Topps	95	1.25	.60	.40

Buck Buchanan

Set	Card #	NM	EX	VG
1964 Topps	92 (R)	35.00	17.50	10.50
1965 Topps	94	25.00	12.50	7.50
1967 Topps	71	5.50	2.75	1.75
1968 Topps	197	4.00	2.00	1.25
1969 Topps	222	3.50	1.75	1.00
1969 Topps Four In Ones	(59)	1.00	.50	.30
1970 Topps	220	3.75	2.00	1.25
1971 Topps	13	2.50	1.25	.70
1972 Topps	204	2.50	1.25	.70
1973 Topps	497	2.00	1.00	.60
1974 Topps	218	2.00	1.00	.60
1975 Topps	16	1.50	.70	.45

Set	Card #	MT	NM	EX
1990 Pro Set	23	.03	.02	.01
1990 Score	600	.04	.03	.02

Dick Butkus

Set	Card #	NM	EX	VG
1966 Philadelphia	31 (R)	170.00	85.00	51.00
1967 Philadelphia	28	50.00	25.00	15.00
1968 Topps	127	36.00	18.00	11.00
1969 Topps	139	25.00	12.50	7.50
1969 Topps Four In Ones	(21)	4.00	2.00	1.25
1970 Topps	190	13.00	6.50	4.00
1971 Topps	25	10.00	5.00	3.00
1972 Topps	170	10.00	5.00	3.00
1972 Topps	341	50.00	25.00	15.00
1973 Topps	300	6.00	3.00	1.75
1974 Topps	230	6.00	3.00	1.75

Set	Card #	MT	NM	EX
1989 Pro Set Announcer Inserts	15	.50	.40	.20

Marion Butts

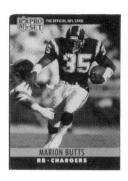

Set	Card #	MT	NM	EX
1989 Pro Set	549 (R)	.50	.40	.20
1989 Topps Traded	23 (R)	.40	.30	.15
1990 Fleer	305	.10	.08	.04
1990 Pro Set	276	.06	.05	.02
1990 Score	97	.10	.08	.04
1990 Topps	383	.15	.11	.06
1991 Bowman	451	.05	.04	.02
1991 Fleer	171	.20	.15	.08
1991 Fleer Ultra	120	.08	.06	.03
1991 Pacific	439	.04	.03	.02
1991 Pinnacle	105	.10	.08	.04
1991 Pro Set	281	.05	.04	.02
1991 Pro Set	416	.05	.04	.02
1991 Pro Set Platinum	102	.08	.06	.03
1991 Score	13	.04	.03	.02
1991 Score	628	.05	.04	.02
1991 Topps	425	.04	.03	.02
1991 Topps Stadium Club	27	.50	.40	.20
1991 Topps 1000 Yard Club	5	.75	.60	.30
1991 Upper Deck	147	.05	.04	.02
1991 Upper Deck Game Breaker Holograms	7	.60	.45	.25
1992 Bowman	102	.35	.25	.14
1992 Bowman	478	.50	.40	.20
1992 Fleer	356	.03	.02	.01
1992 Fleer Team Leaders	23	6.50	5.00	2.50
1992 Fleer Ultra	342	.08	.06	.03
1992 Pacific	600	.10	.08	.04
1992 Pinnacle	34	.05	.04	.02
1992 Pinnacle	348	.05	.04	.02
1992 Pro Set	308	.05	.04	.02
1992 Pro Set	378	.05	.04	.02
1992 Pro Set Gold MVPs	13	.30	.25	.12
1992 Pro Set Power	240	.05	.04	.02
1992 Score	26	.05	.04	.02
1992 Topps	590	.05	.04	.02
1992 Topps Stadium Club	60	.08	.06	.03
1992 Upper Deck	80	.05	.04	.02
1992 Upper Deck	154	.05	.04	.02
1992 Upper Deck Pro Bowl	6	12.00	9.00	4.75
1993 Bowman	277	.20	.15	.08
1993 Fleer	39	.05	.04	.02
1993 Fleer Ultra	407	.08	.06	.03
1993 GameDay	23	.10	.08	.04
1993 Pacific	325	.05	.04	.02
1993 Pinnacle	60	.10	.08	.04
1993 Pro Set	375	.05	.04	.02
1993 Score	112	.04	.03	.02
1993 Score Select	186	.10	.08	.04
1993 SkyBox Impact	282	.05	.04	.02
1993 SkyBox Premium	44	.10	.08	.04
1993 Topps	196	.05	.04	.02
1993 Topps	273	.05	.04	.02
1993 Topps Stadium Club	68	.10	.08	.04
1993 Upper Deck	346	.05	.04	.02
1993 Upper Deck SP	226	.25	.20	.10
1994 Fleer	397	.12	.09	.05

1994 Fleer Ultra	199	.08	.06	.03
1994 Fleer Ultra	448	.08	.06	.03
1994 GameDay	264	.10	.08	.04
1994 Pacific Crown	211	.06	.05	.02
1994 Pacific Crown Crystalline Collection	17	3.50	2.75	1.50
1994 Pacific Prisms	17	1.75	1.25	.70
1994 Pinnacle	66	.12	.09	.05
1994 Pinnacle Sportflics	127	.15	.11	.06
1994 Score	163	.05	.04	.02
1994 Score Select	141	.10	.08	.04
1994 SkyBox Impact	219	.07	.05	.03
1994 SkyBox Premium	102	.12	.09	.05
1994 Topps	224	.06	.05	.02
1994 Topps Finest	43	.65	.50	.25
1994 Upper Deck	56	.15	.11	.06
1994 Upper Deck Collector's Choice	102	.05	.04	.02
1994 Upper Deck SP	44	.20	.15	.08

Earl Campbell

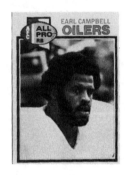

Set	Card #	NM	EX	VG
1979 Topps	331	5.50	2.75	1.75
1979 Topps	390 (R)	30.00	15.00	9.00

Set	Card #	MT	NM	EX
1991 Pro Set	27	.10	.08	.04
1991 Score	674	.10	.08	.04

Harold Carmichael

Set	Card #	NM	EX	VG
1974 Topps	121 (R)	16.00	8.00	4.75
1975 Topps	80	3.00	1.50	.90
1976 Topps	425	1.50	.70	.45
1977 Topps	144	1.00	.50	.30
1978 Topps	379	.75	.40	.25
1978 Topps	521	.50	.25	.15

1979 Topps	250	.60	.30	.20
1980 Topps	2	.15	.08	.05
1980 Topps	420	.50	.25	.15

Set	Card #	MT	NM	EX
1981 Topps	35	.50	.40	.20
1982 Topps	440	.25	.20	.10
1982 Topps	441	.10	.08	.04
1983 Topps	137	.25	.20	.10
1984 Topps	326	.20	.15	.08

Anthony Carter

Set	Card #	MT	NM	EX
1984 Topps USFL	59 (R)	25.00	18.50	10.00
1985 Topps USFL	92	6.00	4.50	2.50
1986 Topps	297 (R)	2.00	1.50	.80
1987 Topps	202	.30	.25	.12
1988 Topps	151	.25	.20	.10
1988 Topps 1000 Yard Club	12	.10	.08	.04
1989 Pro Set	228	.03	.02	.01
1989 Score	20	.10	.08	.04
1989 Topps	79	.05	.04	.02
1989 Topps 1000 Yard Club	7	.10	.08	.04
1990 Fleer	96	.03	.02	.01
1990 Pro Set	187	.03	.02	.01
1990 Score	345	.04	.03	.02
1990 Topps	115	.04	.03	.02
1990 Topps 1000 Yard Club	26	.10	.08	.04
1991 Bowman	305	.03	.02	.01
1991 Fleer	279	.07	.05	.03
1991 Fleer Ultra	193	.08	.06	.03
1991 Pacific	285	.04	.03	.02
1991 Pinnacle	80	.10	.08	.04
1991 Pro Set	569	.05	.04	.02
1991 Pro Set Platinum	223	.05	.04	.02
1991 Score	182	.04	.03	.02
1991 Topps	391	.04	.03	.02
1991 Topps Stadium Club	267	.30	.25	.12
1991 Topps 1000 Yard Club	17	.30	.25	.12
1991 Upper Deck	236	.05	.04	.02
1991 Upper Deck	466	.05	.04	.02
1992 Bowman	456	.30	.25	.12
1992 Fleer	241	.03	.02	.01
1992 Fleer Ultra	232	.05	.04	.02
1992 Pacific	177	.05	.04	.02
1992 Pinnacle	91	.05	.04	.02
1992 Pro Set	236	.05	.04	.02
1992 Pro Set Power	277	.05	.04	.02
1992 Score	108	.07	.05	.03
1992 SkyBox Impact	172	.05	.04	.02
1992 SkyBox Primetime	265	.10	.08	.04
1992 Topps	450	.05	.04	.02
1992 Topps Stadium Club	297	.08	.06	.03
1992 Topps Stadium Club	558	.10	.08	.04
1992 Upper Deck	100	.05	.04	.02

Set	Card #	MT	NM	EX
1992 Upper Deck	187	.05	.04	.02
1993 Bowman	286	.20	.15	.08
1993 Fleer	135	.05	.04	.02
1993 Fleer Ultra	267	.08	.06	.03
1993 GameDay	101	.10	.08	.04
1993 Pacific	72	.05	.04	.02
1993 Pacific Triple Folders	9	.45	.35	.20
1993 Pinnacle	74	.10	.08	.04
1993 Pro Set	255	.05	.04	.02
1993 SkyBox Impact	187	.03	.02	.01
1993 SkyBox Premium	82	.10	.08	.04
1993 Topps	370	.05	.04	.02
1993 Topps Stadium Club	214	.10	.08	.04
1993 Upper Deck	495	.05	.04	.02
1993 Upper Deck SP	154	.25	.20	.10
1994 Fleer	288	.08	.06	.03
1994 Fleer Ultra	383	.08	.06	.03
1994 GameDay	127	.10	.08	.04
1994 Pacific Crown	149	.06	.05	.02
1994 Pacific Prisms	20	1.00	.70	.40
1994 Pinnacle	124	.09	.07	.04
1994 Pinnacle Sportflics	4	.15	.11	.06
1994 Score	239	.05	.04	.02
1994 Score Select	153	.10	.08	.04
1994 SkyBox Impact	155	.06	.05	.02
1994 Topps Finest	155	1.50	1.25	.60
1994 Upper Deck Collector's Choice	332	.05	.04	.02
1992 SkyBox Impact	84	.05	.04	.02
1992 SkyBox Primetime	95	.10	.08	.04
1992 SkyBox Primetime	118	.10	.08	.04
1992 Topps	552	.05	.04	.02
1992 Topps Stadium Club	382	.08	.06	.03
1992 Upper Deck	203	.05	.04	.02
1992 Upper Deck	378	.05	.04	.02
1993 Bowman	68	.15	.11	.06
1993 Fleer	53	.05	.04	.02
1993 Fleer Ultra	268	.08	.06	.03
1993 GameDay	102	.10	.08	.04
1993 Pacific	73	.05	.04	.02
1993 Pinnacle	46	.10	.08	.04
1993 Pro Set	256	.05	.04	.02
1993 Score	211	.04	.03	.02
1993 Score Select	75	.10	.08	.04
1993 SkyBox Impact	188	.03	.02	.01
1993 SkyBox Premium	136	.10	.08	.04
1993 Topps	284	.05	.04	.02
1993 Topps Stadium Club	95	.10	.08	.04
1993 Upper Deck	137	.05	.04	.02
1993 Upper Deck SP	155	.25	.20	.10
1994 Bowman	375	.15	.11	.06
1994 Fleer	289	.10	.08	.04
1994 Fleer Ultra	183	.15	.11	.06
1994 GameDay	245	.12	.09	.05
1994 Pacific Crown	150	.08	.06	.03
1994 Pinnacle	19	.12	.09	.05
1994 Pinnacle Sportflics	99	.25	.20	.10
1994 Score	233	.05	.04	.02
1994 Score Select	50	.12	.09	.05
1994 SkyBox Impact	156	.06	.05	.02
1994 Topps	252	.08	.06	.03
1994 Topps Finest	66	.65	.50	.25
1994 Topps Finest Inserts	16	3.50	2.75	1.50
1994 Topps Stadium Club	85	.10	.08	.04
1994 Topps Stadium Club	513	.10	.08	.04
1994 Upper Deck	227	.15	.11	.06
1994 Upper Deck Collector's Choice	338	.05	.04	.02
1994 Upper Deck SP	148	.30	.25	.12

Cris Carter

Set	Card #	MT	NM	EX
1989 Pro Set	314 (R)	1.25	.90	.50
1989 Score	72 (R)	6.50	4.90	2.60
1989 Topps	121 (R)	2.00	1.50	.80
1990 Fleer	81	.30	.25	.12
1990 Pro Set	246	.35	.25	.14
1990 Pro Set	571	.30	.25	.12
1990 Pro Set	798	.03	.02	.01
1990 Score	193	.35	.25	.14
1990 Score 100 Hottest	30	.40	.30	.15
1990 Topps	92	.30	.25	.12
1990 Topps Update	19	.35	.25	.14
1991 Pacific	286	.25	.20	.10
1991 Pinnacle	125	.12	.09	.05
1991 Pro Set	834	.03	.02	.01
1991 Pro Set Platinum	224	.05	.04	.02
1991 Score	487	.05	.04	.02
1991 Topps	386	.04	.03	.02
1991 Upper Deck	56	.05	.04	.02
1992 Bowman	346	.30	.25	.12
1992 Fleer	242	.03	.02	.01
1992 Fleer Ultra	233	.05	.04	.02
1992 GameDay	142	.10	.08	.04
1992 Pacific	178	.05	.04	.02
1992 Pinnacle	29	.05	.04	.02
1992 Pro Set	564	.05	.04	.02
1992 Pro Set Power	268	.05	.04	.02
1992 Score	19	.05	.04	.02

Gary Clark

Set	Card #	MT	NM	EX
1985 Topps USFL	49 (R)	25.00	18.50	10.00
1986 Topps	176 (R)	4.00	3.00	1.50
1987 Topps	68	1.00	.70	.40
1987 Topps 1000 Yard Club	10	.15	.11	.06
1988 Topps	13	.50	.40	.20
1988 Topps 1000 Yard Club	5	.10	.08	.04
1989 Pro Set	424	.20	.15	.08
1989 Score	108	.50	.40	.20
1989 Topps	258	.15	.11	.06
1990 Fleer	154	.10	.08	.04
1990 Pro Set	321	.15	.11	.06
1990 Score	239	.10	.08	.04
1990 Topps	128	.15	.11	.06

1990 Topps 1000 Yard Club	14	.05	.04	.02
1991 Bowman	545	.10	.08	.04
1991 Fleer	384	.06	.05	.02
1991 Fleer Ultra	270	.10	.08	.04
1991 Pacific	518	.20	.15	.08
1991 Pinnacle	198	.20	.15	.08
1991 Pro Set	317	.08	.06	.03
1991 Pro Set Platinum	279	.10	.08	.04
1991 Score	154	.08	.06	.03
1991 Topps	196	.15	.11	.06
1991 Topps Stadium Club	242	.25	.20	.10
1991 Topps 1000 Yard Club	9	.35	.25	.14
1991 Upper Deck	436	.12	.09	.05
1992 Bowman	153	.35	.25	.14
1992 Fleer	415	.03	.02	.01
1992 Fleer Ultra	400	.05	.04	.02
1992 GameDay	81	.25	.20	.10
1992 Pacific	639	.10	.08	.04
1992 Pinnacle	133	.05	.04	.02
1992 Pinnacle	344	.05	.04	.02
1992 Pro Set	75	.08	.06	.03
1992 Pro Set	406	.05	.04	.02
1992 Pro Set Power	285	.05	.04	.02
1992 Score	190	.08	.06	.03
1992 SkyBox Impact	240	.05	.04	.02
1992 SkyBox Primetime	142	.10	.08	.04
1992 Topps	637	.05	.04	.02
1992 Topps Stadium Club	323	.08	.06	.03
1992 Topps 1000-Yard Club	5	.75	.60	.30
1992 Upper Deck	316	.05	.04	.02
1992 Upper Deck Pro Bowl	2	4.00	3.00	1.50
1993 Fleer	283	.05	.04	.02
1993 Fleer Ultra	376	.08	.06	.03
1993 GameDay	163	.10	.08	.04
1993 Pacific	414	.05	.04	.02
1993 Pacific Prisms	80	1.25	.90	.50
1993 Pinnacle	223	.10	.08	.04
1993 Pro Set	354	.05	.04	.02
1993 Pro Set Power Power Moves	24	.25	.20	.10
1993 Pro Set Power Update Moves	24	.15	.11	.06
1993 Score	256	.04	.03	.02
1993 Score Select	101	.10	.08	.04
1993 SkyBox Impact	266	.05	.04	.02
1993 SkyBox Premium	84	.10	.08	.04
1993 Topps	321	.10	.08	.04
1993 Topps Stadium Club	460	.10	.08	.04
1993 Upper Deck	492	.05	.04	.02
1993 Upper Deck Team MVP	24	.50	.40	.20
1994 Fleer	7	.20	.15	.08
1994 Fleer Ultra	2	.08	.06	.03
1994 GameDay	3	.10	.08	.04
1994 Pacific Crown	305	.06	.05	.02
1994 Pacific Prisms	22	1.00	.70	.40
1994 Pinnacle	121	.09	.07	.04
1994 Pinnacle Sportflics	17	.15	.11	.06
1994 Score	126	.08	.06	.03
1994 Score Select	106	.10	.08	.04
1994 SkyBox Impact	3	.12	.09	.05
1994 SkyBox Premium	2	.10	.08	.04
1994 Topps	82	.07	.05	.03
1994 Topps Finest	106	1.50	1.25	.60
1994 Topps Stadium Club	117	.10	.08	.04
1994 Upper Deck	181	.10	.08	.04
1994 Upper Deck Collector's Choice	197	.05	.04	.02
1994 Upper Deck SP	111	.20	.15	.08

Quentin Coryatt

Set	Card #	MT	NM	EX
1992 GameDay	474 (R)	.60	.45	.25
1992 Pro Set	522 (R)	.40	.30	.15
1992 Pro Set Power	315 (R)	.40	.30	.15
1992 Pro Set Power Power Combos	1	5.00	3.75	2.00
1992 SkyBox Impact	326 (R)	.35	.25	.14
1992 SkyBox Primetime	114 (R)	.50	.40	.20
1992 Topps	701 (R)	.30	.25	.12
1992 Topps Stadium Club	682 (R)	3.00	2.25	1.25
1992 Upper Deck	406	.40	.30	.15
1992 Upper Deck Gold	10 (R)	.50	.40	.20
1993 Bowman	130	.20	.15	.08
1993 Fleer	352	.15	.11	.06
1993 Fleer Rookie Sensations	4	5.00	3.75	2.00
1993 Fleer Ultra	181	.15	.11	.06
1993 GameDay	400	.25	.20	.10
1993 GameDay Second-Year Stars	12	.60	.45	.25
1993 Pacific	228	.12	.09	.05
1993 Pinnacle	321	.20	.15	.08
1993 Pinnacle Team 2001	13	.25	.20	.10
1993 Pro Set	181	.15	.11	.06
1993 Score	281	.08	.06	.03
1993 Score Select	80	.20	.15	.08
1993 SkyBox Impact	134	.08	.06	.03
1993 SkyBox Premium	181	.15	.11	.06
1993 Topps	440	.10	.08	.04
1993 Topps Stadium Club	420	.15	.11	.06
1993 Upper Deck	47	.05	.04	.02
1993 Upper Deck	520	.10	.08	.04
1993 Upper Deck NFL Experience	14	.25	.20	.10
1993 Upper Deck SP	111	.25	.20	.10
1994 Bowman	33	.15	.11	.06
1994 Fleer	205	.08	.06	.03
1994 Fleer Ultra	130	.08	.06	.03
1994 GameDay	175	.10	.08	.04
1994 Pacific Crown	376	.06	.05	.02
1994 Pinnacle	125	.09	.07	.04
1994 Pinnacle Sportflics	21	.15	.11	.06
1994 Score	37	.08	.06	.03
1994 Score Select	49	.10	.08	.04
1994 SkyBox Impact	111	.08	.06	.03
1994 SkyBox Premium	68	.08	.06	.03
1994 Topps	280	.06	.05	.02
1994 Topps Finest	166	1.50	1.25	.60
1994 Topps Stadium Club	120	.10	.08	.04
1994 Upper Deck	312	.10	.08	.04
1994 Upper Deck Collector's Choice	363	.05	.04	.02
1994 Upper Deck SP	30	.20	.15	.08

Roger Craig

Set	Card #	MT	NM	EX
1984 Topps	353 (R)	5.50	4.25	2.25
1985 Topps	151	1.25	.90	.50
1986 Topps	155	.25	.20	.10
1986 Topps	157	.75	.60	.30
1986 Topps	226	.15	.11	.06
1986 Topps 1000 Yard Club	22	.40	.30	.15
1987 Topps	111	.12	.09	.05
1987 Topps	113	.30	.25	.12
1988 Topps	37	.05	.04	.02
1988 Topps	40	.20	.15	.08
1988 Topps 1000 Yard Club	19	.50	.40	.20
1989 Pro Set	372	.03	.02	.01
1989 Score	4	.10	.08	.04
1989 Score	297	.10	.08	.04
1989 Score Promos	4	9.00	9.00	9.00
1989 Topps	8	.05	.04	.02
1989 Topps 1000 Yard Club	3	.40	.30	.15
1990 Fleer	5	.03	.02	.01
1990 Pro Set	287	.03	.02	.01
1990 Pro Set	385	.03	.02	.01
1990 Score	100	.04	.03	.02
1990 Score	329	.04	.03	.02
1990 Score 100 Hottest	9	.20	.15	.08
1990 Topps	12	.04	.03	.02
1990 Topps 1000 Yard Club	28	.20	.15	.08
1991 Fleer Ultra Update	41	.10	.08	.04
1991 Pacific	601	.05	.04	.02
1991 Pinnacle	25	.10	.08	.04
1991 Pro Set	21	.03	.02	.01
1991 Pro Set Platinum	210	.05	.04	.02
1991 Score	222	.04	.03	.02
1991 Score Supplemental	7	.06	.05	.02
1991 Topps	2	.04	.03	.02
1991 Topps	90	.04	.03	.02
1991 Topps Stadium Club	146	.40	.30	.15
1991 Upper Deck	143	.05	.04	.02
1991 Upper Deck	542	.05	.04	.02
1992 Pacific	147	.05	.04	.02
1992 Pro Set	565	.05	.04	.02
1992 Score	171	.05	.04	.02
1992 SkyBox Impact	21	.05	.04	.02
1992 SkyBox Primetime	171	.10	.08	.04
1992 Topps	511	.05	.04	.02
1992 Upper Deck	500	.05	.04	.02
1993 Fleer	81	.05	.04	.02
1993 Fleer Ultra	269	.08	.06	.03
1993 Pacific	74	.05	.04	.02
1993 Pro Set	257	.05	.04	.02
1993 SkyBox Impact	194	.05	.04	.02
1993 SkyBox Impact	351	.05	.04	.02
1993 SkyBox Premium	244	.10	.08	.04
1993 Topps	118	.05	.04	.02
1993 Topps Stadium Club	197	.10	.08	.04
1993 Upper Deck	341	.05	.04	.02
1993 Upper Deck SP	156	.25	.20	.10

1994 Pacific Crown	151	.06	.05	.02
1994 Topps Finest	181	.65	.50	.25

Larry Csonka

Set	Card #	NM	EX	VG
1969 Topps	120 (R)	80.00	40.00	24.00
1969 Topps Four In Ones	(41)	2.00	1.00	.60
1970 Topps	162	25.00	12.50	7.50
1971 Topps	45	12.00	6.00	3.50
1972 Topps	1	3.50	1.75	1.00
1972 Topps	140	7.00	3.50	2.00
1972 Topps	259	3.50	1.75	1.00
1973 Topps	100	5.00	2.50	1.50
1974 Topps	131	3.50	1.75	1.00
1976 Topps	437	3.00	1.50	.90
1977 Topps	505	2.00	1.00	.60
1978 Topps	25	1.50	.70	.45
1979 Topps	22	1.25	.60	.40
1980 Topps	485	1.00	.50	.30

Set	Card #	MT	NM	EX
1990 Pro Set Super Bowl MVPs	8	.30	.25	.12

Randall Cunningham

Set	Card #	MT	NM	EX
1987 Topps	296 (R)	14.00	10.50	5.50
1988 Topps	233	.25	.20	.10
1988 Topps	234	.90	.70	.35
1989 Pro Set	315	.30	.25	.12
1989 Score	75	.90	.70	.35
1989 Score	281	.25	.20	.10
1989 Topps	106	.10	.08	.04
1989 Topps	115	.40	.30	.15
1990 Fleer	82	.20	.15	.08
1990 Pro Set	247	.15	.11	.06
1990 Pro Set	386	.10	.08	.04
1990 Score	563	.08	.06	.03

1990 Score	605	.10	.08	.04
1990 Topps	93	.20	.15	.08
1991 Bowman	278	.10	.08	.04
1991 Bowman	404	.15	.11	.06
1991 Fleer	326	.10	.08	.04
1991 Fleer	409	.08	.06	.03
1991 Fleer Pro Visions	7	.40	.30	.15
1991 Fleer Ultra	230	.15	.11	.06
1991 Fleer Ultra All Stars	4	1.00	.70	.40
1991 Pacific	385	.20	.15	.08
1991 Pinnacle	348	.35	.25	.14
1991 Pro Set	24	.08	.06	.03
1991 Pro Set	256	.10	.08	.04
1991 Pro Set	334	.10	.08	.04
1991 Pro Set	712	.06	.05	.02
1991 Pro Set Platinum	88	.10	.08	.04
1991 Score	12	.10	.08	.04
1991 Score	320	.08	.06	.03
1991 Score	633	.08	.06	.03
1991 Topps	210	.15	.11	.06
1991 Topps Stadium Club	203	.70	.50	.30
1991 Upper Deck	31	.10	.08	.04
1991 Upper Deck	146	.15	.11	.06
1991 Upper Deck	471	.10	.08	.04
1992 Fleer	248	.03	.02	.01
1992 GameDay	275	.25	.20	.10
1992 Pro Set	611	.12	.09	.05
1992 Pro Set Gold MVPs	25	.50	.40	.20
1992 Pro Set Power	12	.20	.15	.08
1992 SkyBox Impact	200	.15	.11	.06
1992 SkyBox Impact Major Impact	12	.75	.60	.30
1992 SkyBox Primetime	300	.25	.20	.10
1992 Topps	700	.05	.04	.02
1992 Topps Stadium Club	604	.65	.50	.25
1992 Topps Stadium Club	639	1.25	.90	.50
1992 Upper Deck	608	.20	.15	.08
1992 Upper Deck Gold	23	.50	.40	.20
1992 Upper Deck Gold	35	.50	.40	.20
1993 Bowman	70	.60	.45	.25
1993 Fleer	354	.15	.11	.06
1993 Fleer Ultra	356	.25	.20	.10
1993 GameDay	25	.30	.25	.12
1993 Pacific	18	.15	.11	.06
1993 Pacific Prisms	78	1.25	.90	.50
1993 Pinnacle	298	.15	.11	.06
1993 Pinnacle Men of Autumn	48	.40	.30	.15
1993 Pro Set	334	.10	.08	.04
1993 Pro Set Power	112	.15	.11	.06
1993 Score	260	.15	.11	.06
1993 Score Select	27	.60	.45	.25
1993 SkyBox Impact	246	.10	.08	.04
1993 SkyBox Premium	26	.25	.20	.10
1993 SkyBox Thunder and Lightning	7	5.00	3.75	2.00
1993 Topps	180	.05	.04	.02
1993 Topps	525	.10	.08	.04
1993 Topps Black Gold	16	1.00	.70	.40
1993 Topps Stadium Club	168	.25	.20	.10
1993 Topps Stadium Club	494	.15	.11	.06
1993 Upper Deck	141	.15	.11	.06
1993 Upper Deck NFL Experience	43	.35	.25	.14
1993 Upper Deck SP	201	.25	.20	.10
1994 Bowman	130	.15	.11	.06
1994 Fleer	369	.25	.20	.10
1994 Fleer Ultra	244	.20	.15	.08
1994 GameDay	317	.20	.15	.08
1994 Pacific Crown	245	.10	.08	.04
1994 Pacific Prisms	27	1.25	.90	.50
1994 Pinnacle	91	.20	.15	.08
1994 Pinnacle Sportflics	11	.25	.20	.10
1994 Score	269	.10	.08	.04
1994 Score Select	18	.10	.08	.04
1994 SkyBox Impact	204	.20	.15	.08
1994 SkyBox Premium	121	.35	.25	.14
1994 Topps	184	.15	.11	.06
1994 Topps Finest	69	3.00	2.25	1.25
1994 Topps Stadium Club	238	.20	.15	.08
1994 Upper Deck	322	.25	.20	.10
1994 Upper Deck Collector's Choice	137	.12	.09	.05
1994 Upper Deck SP	130	.25	.20	.10

Willie Davis

Set	Card #	NM	EX	VG
1964 Philadelphia	72 (R)	30.00	15.00	9.00
1965 Philadelphia	73	8.00	4.00	2.50
1966 Philadelphia	83	5.00	2.50	1.50
1967 Philadelphia	76	4.50	2.25	1.25

Len Dawson

Set	Card #	NM	EX	VG
1963 Fleer	47 (R)	250.00	125.00	75.00
1964 Topps	96	75.00	37.00	22.00
1965 Topps	99	80.00	40.00	24.00
1966 Topps	67	33.00	16.50	10.00
1967 Topps	61	20.00	10.00	6.00
1968 Topps	171	13.00	6.50	4.00
1969 Topps	20	8.00	4.00	2.50
1969 Topps Four In Ones	(56)	2.00	1.00	.60
1970 Topps	1	15.00	7.50	4.50
1971 Topps	180	7.00	3.50	2.00
1972 Topps	3	2.00	1.00	.60
1972 Topps	245	6.50	3.25	2.00
1972 Topps	340	40.00	20.00	12.00
1973 Topps	335	3.50	1.75	1.00
1975 Topps	120	3.50	1.75	1.00
1976 Topps	308	3.00	1.50	.90

Set	Card #	MT	NM	EX
1990 Pro Set Super Bowl MVPs	4	.20	.15	.08
1993 Upper Deck NFL Experience	4	.20	.15	.08
1994 Upper Deck Then And Now	3	10.00	7.50	4.00

Grading Guide

Mint (MT): A perfect card. Well-centered with all corners sharp and square. No creases, stains, edge nicks, surface marks, yellowing or fading.

Near Mint (NM): A nearly perfect card. At first glance, a NM card appears to be perfect. May be slightly off-center. No surface marks, creases or loss of gloss.

Excellent (EX): Corners are still fairly sharp with only moderate wear. Borders may be off-center. No creases or stains on fronts or backs, but may show slight loss of surface luster.

Very Good (VG): Shows obvious handling. May have rounded corners, minor creases, major gum or wax stains. No major creases, tape marks, writing, etc.

Good (G): A well-worn card, but exhibits no intentional damage. May have major or multiple creases. Corners may be rounded well beyond card border.

Richard Dent

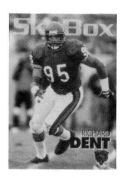

Set	Card #	MT	NM	EX
1985 Topps	24 (R)	5.00	3.75	2.00
1986 Topps	19	1.00	.70	.40
1987 Topps	56	.50	.40	.20
1988 Topps	80	.20	.15	.08
1989 Pro Set	38	.03	.02	.01
1989 Score	114	.10	.08	.04
1989 Topps	60	.05	.04	.02
1990 Fleer	291	.03	.02	.01
1990 Pro Set	52	.03	.02	.01
1990 Pro Set Super Bowl MVPs	20	.10	.08	.04
1990 Score	28	.04	.03	.02
1990 Topps	376	.04	.03	.02
1991 Bowman	56	.03	.02	.01
1991 Fleer	218	.07	.05	.03
1991 Fleer Ultra	155	.04	.03	.02
1991 Pacific	47	.04	.03	.02
1991 Pinnacle	238	.10	.08	.04
1991 Pro Set	103	.03	.02	.01
1991 Pro Set Platinum	13	.05	.04	.02
1991 Score	553	.04	.03	.02
1991 Topps	173	.04	.03	.02
1991 Topps Stadium Club	6	.30	.25	.12
1991 Upper Deck	247	.05	.04	.02
1992 Bowman	235	.35	.25	.14
1992 Bowman	487	8.00	6.00	3.25
1992 Fleer	38	.03	.02	.01
1992 Fleer Ultra	38	.05	.04	.02
1992 Pacific	353	.05	.04	.02
1992 Pinnacle	20	.05	.04	.02
1992 Pro Set	121	.05	.04	.02
1992 Pro Set Power	95	.05	.04	.02
1992 Score	6	.05	.04	.02
1992 Topps	128	.05	.04	.02
1992 Topps Stadium Club	9	.08	.06	.03
1992 Upper Deck	151	.05	.04	.02
1993 Bowman	28	.15	.11	.06
1993 Fleer	80	.05	.04	.02
1993 Fleer Ultra	43	.08	.06	.03
1993 GameDay	95	.10	.08	.04
1993 Pacific	130	.05	.04	.02
1993 Pinnacle	131	.10	.08	.04
1993 Pinnacle Men of Autumn	31	.25	.20	.10
1993 Pro Set	78	.05	.04	.02
1993 Pro Set Power	95	.05	.04	.02
1993 Score	173	.04	.03	.02
1993 Score The Franchise	3	3.50	2.75	1.50
1993 SkyBox Impact	36	.03	.02	.01
1993 SkyBox Impact	348	.03	.02	.01
1993 Topps	172	.05	.04	.02
1993 Topps	601	.05	.04	.02
1993 Topps Stadium Club	139	.10	.08	.04
1993 Upper Deck	291	.05	.04	.02
1993 Upper Deck SP	40	.25	.20	.10
1994 Fleer	60	.05	.04	.02
1994 Fleer Ultra	492	.08	.06	.03
1994 GameDay	361	.10	.08	.04
1994 Pacific Crown	276	.06	.05	.02
1994 Pacific Prisms	31	1.00	.70	.40
1994 Pinnacle	175	.09	.07	.04
1994 Pinnacle Sportflics	66	.15	.11	.06
1994 Score	16	.06	.05	.02
1994 Score Select	6	.10	.08	.04
1994 SkyBox Impact	34	.08	.06	.03
1994 Topps Finest	118	.65	.50	.25
1994 Upper Deck	90	.10	.08	.04
1994 Upper Deck Collector's Choice	151	.05	.04	.02

Eric Dickerson

Set	Card #	MT	NM	EX
1984 Topps	1	.75	.60	.30
1984 Topps	204	.40	.30	.15
1984 Topps	276	.75	.60	.30
1984 Topps	280 (R)	10.00	7.50	4.00
1984 Topps	281	2.00	1.50	.80
1985 Topps	2	.50	.40	.20
1985 Topps	77	.40	.30	.15
1985 Topps	79	2.50	2.00	1.00
1985 Topps	194	.40	.30	.15
1986 Topps	2	.30	.25	.12
1986 Topps	76	.15	.11	.06
1986 Topps	78	1.00	.70	.40
1986 Topps 1000 Yard Club	10	1.25	.90	.50
1987 Topps	144	.15	.11	.06
1987 Topps	146	.50	.40	.20
1987 Topps	229	.25	.20	.10
1987 Topps 1000 Yard Club	1	.75	.60	.30
1988 Topps	116	.15	.11	.06
1988 Topps	118	.30	.25	.12
1988 Topps	217	.15	.11	.06
1988 Topps 1000 Yard Club	2	.75	.60	.30
1989 Pro Set	455	.20	.15	.08
1989 Topps	3	.12	.09	.05
1989 Topps	206	.20	.15	.08
1989 Topps 1000 Yard Club	1	.60	.45	.25
1990 Pro Set	338	4.00	3.00	1.50
1991 Pro Set	175	.20	.15	.08
1992 GameDay	24	.40	.30	.15
1992 Pro Set	537	.10	.08	.04
1992 Pro Set Power	129	.05	.04	.02
1992 SkyBox Impact	46	.05	.04	.02
1992 SkyBox Primetime	213	.10	.08	.04
1992 Topps	709	.05	.04	.02
1992 Topps Stadium Club	619	1.50	1.25	.60
1992 Upper Deck	580	.05	.04	.02
1992 Upper Deck Gold	29	.10	.08	.04
1992 Upper Deck NFL Fanimation	8	2.50	2.00	1.00
1993 Fleer	453	.05	.04	.02
1993 Fleer Ultra	3	.08	.06	.03
1993 GameDay	330	.10	.08	.04

1993 Pacific	367	.05	.04	.02
1993 Pinnacle	349	.07	.05	.03
1993 Pro Set	61	.05	.04	.02
1993 Pro Set Power	129	.05	.04	.02
1993 SkyBox Impact	153	.03	.02	.01
1993 SkyBox Impact	344	.08	.06	.03
1993 SkyBox Premium	184	.10	.08	.04
1993 Topps Stadium Club	18	.10	.08	.04
1993 Upper Deck	84	.05	.04	.02
1993 Upper Deck	231	.05	.04	.02
1993 Upper Deck NFL Experience	33	.20	.15	.08
1993 Upper Deck SP	19	.25	.20	.10
1994 Upper Deck Then And Now	1	8.00	6.00	3.25

The values quoted are intended
to reflect the market price.

Trent Dilfer

Set	Card #	MT	NM	EX
1994 Bowman	5 (R)	2.75	2.00	1.00
1994 Fleer Ultra	511 (R)	2.50	2.00	1.00
1994 Fleer Ultra Wave of the Future	1	3.00	2.25	1.25
1994 GameDay	392 (R)	2.50	2.00	1.00
1994 GameDay Rookie Standouts	4	3.00	2.25	1.25
1994 Pacific Crown	425 (R)	2.50	2.00	1.00
1994 Pacific Crown Knights of the Gridiron	8	8.00	6.00	3.25
1994 Pacific Prisms	32 (R)	11.00	8.25	4.50
1994 Pinnacle	202 (R)	2.75	2.00	1.00
1994 Pinnacle Draft Pick	4	22.00	16.50	8.75
1994 Pinnacle Sportflics Rookie Rivalry	3	15.00	11.00	6.00
1994 Pinnacle Sportflics	175 (R)	2.75	2.00	1.00
1994 Score	294 (R)	2.00	1.50	.80
1994 Score Select	212 (R)	2.50	2.00	1.00
1994 SkyBox Impact	278 (R)	1.50	1.25	.60
1994 SkyBox Premium	162 (R)	2.00	1.50	.80
1994 SkyBox Premium Prime Time Rookies	1	25.00	18.50	10.00
1994 SkyBox Premium QB Autograph Exchange Se	3	10.00	10.00	10.00
1994 Topps	407 (R)	2.00	1.50	.80
1994 Topps Stadium Club	362 (R)	3.00	2.25	1.25
1994 Upper Deck	17 (R)	3.00	2.25	1.25
1994 Upper Deck Collector's Choice Crash Game	4	7.00	5.25	2.75
1994 Upper Deck Collector's Choice	13 (R)	2.00	1.50	.80
1994 Upper Deck Hobby Predictor	12	6.00	4.50	2.50
1994 Upper Deck SP	5 (R)	3.00	2.25	1.25

Mike Ditka

Set	Card #	NM	EX	VG
1962 Topps	17 (R)	160.00	80.00	48.00
1963 Topps	62	50.00	25.00	15.00
1964 Philadelphia	17	32.00	16.00	9.50
1965 Philadelphia	19	25.00	12.50	7.50
1966 Philadelphia	32	15.00	7.50	4.50
1967 Philadelphia	29	15.00	7.50	4.50
1968 Topps	162	9.00	4.50	2.75

Set	Card #	MT	NM	EX
1989 Pro Set	53	.10	.08	.04
1990 Pro Set	59	.03	.02	.01
1991 Pro Set	108	.05	.04	.02
1992 Pro Set	126	.08	.06	.03

Art Donovan

Set	Card #	NM	EX	VG
1952 Bowman Large	46 (R)	225.00	112.00	67.00
1952 Bowman Small	46 (R)	100.00	50.00	30.00
1956 Topps	36	15.00	7.50	4.50
1957 Topps	65	13.00	6.50	4.00
1958 Topps	106	9.00	4.50	2.75
1959 Topps	86	8.00	4.00	2.50
1961 Fleer	39	6.50	3.25	2.00

Values quoted in this guide reflect the
retail price of a card – the price a collector
can expect to pay when buying a card from a dealer.
The wholesale price – that which a collector can expect to
receive from a dealer when selling cards – will be
significantly lower, depending on desirability and condition.

Tony Dorsett

Set	Card #	NM	EX	VG
1978 Topps	315 (R)	35.00	17.50	10.50
1979 Topps	160	8.00	4.00	2.50
1980 Topps	330	4.50	2.25	1.25

Set	Card #	MT	NM	EX
1981 Topps	138	.75	.60	.30
1981 Topps	500	2.50	2.00	1.00
1982 Topps	311	1.00	.70	.40
1982 Topps	312	.60	.45	.25
1983 Topps	2	.40	.30	.15
1983 Topps	42	.25	.20	.10
1983 Topps	46	.75	.60	.30
1983 Topps	204	.40	.30	.15
1984 Topps	235	.25	.20	.10
1984 Topps	238	.60	.45	.25
1984 Topps	239	.25	.20	.10
1985 Topps	37	.25	.20	.10
1985 Topps	40	.60	.45	.25
1986 Topps	126	.50	.40	.20
1986 Topps 1000 Yard Club	6	.50	.40	.20
1987 Topps	260	.15	.11	.06
1987 Topps	263	.40	.30	.15
1988 Topps	262	.20	.15	.08
1989 Pro Set	453	.15	.11	.06
1989 Score	326	.25	.20	.10
1989 Topps	240	.25	.20	.10

Carl Eller

Set	Card #	NM	EX	VG
1965 Philadelphia	105 (R)	26.00	13.00	7.75
1970 Topps	175	3.00	1.50	.90
1972 Topps	20	1.50	.70	.45
1972 Topps	277	30.00	15.00	9.00
1973 Topps	211	1.50	.70	.45
1974 Topps	5	1.00	.50	.30
1975 Topps	290	1.00	.50	.30

1976 Topps	105	.75	.40	.25
1977 Topps	385	.60	.30	.20
1978 Topps	79	.40	.20	.12
1978 Topps	515	.50	.25	.15
1979 Topps	406	.30	.15	.09
1980 Topps	189	.35	.20	.11

John Elway

Set	Card #	MT	NM	EX
1984 Topps	63 (R)	33.00	25.00	13.00
1985 Topps	235	.70	.50	.30
1985 Topps	238	10.00	7.50	4.00
1985 Topps Star Set	3	1.00	.75	.40
1986 Topps	112	6.50	5.00	2.50
1987 Topps	31	3.00	2.25	1.25
1988 Topps	23	.75	.60	.30
1989 Pro Set	100	.30	.25	.12
1989 Score	339	2.00	1.50	.80
1989 Topps	238	.10	.08	.04
1989 Topps	241	.50	.40	.20
1990 Fleer	21	.50	.40	.20
1990 Pro Set	88	.40	.30	.15
1990 Score	25	.40	.30	.15
1990 Score	564	.20	.15	.08
1990 Score 100 Hottest	10	.60	.45	.25
1990 Topps	37	.40	.30	.15
1991 Bowman	127	.40	.30	.15
1991 Fleer	45	.35	.25	.14
1991 Fleer Ultra	35	.40	.30	.15
1991 Pacific	115	.35	.25	.14
1991 Pinnacle	7	1.50	1.25	.60
1991 Pro Set	138	.35	.25	.14
1991 Pro Set	345	.08	.06	.03
1991 Pro Set Platinum	28	.40	.30	.15
1991 Score	410	.35	.25	.14
1991 Topps	554	.40	.30	.15
1991 Topps Stadium Club	294	3.50	2.75	1.50
1991 Upper Deck	124	.35	.25	.14
1992 Bowman	193	5.00	3.75	2.00
1992 Bowman	280	3.00	2.25	1.25
1992 Fleer	94	.50	.40	.20
1992 Fleer	471	.10	.08	.04
1992 Fleer Team Leaders	16	40.00	30.00	16.00
1992 Fleer Ultra	97	.75	.60	.30
1992 GameDay	23	1.00	.70	.40
1992 Pacific	75	.35	.25	.14
1992 Pinnacle	212	.80	.60	.30
1992 Pinnacle	353	.50	.40	.20
1992 Pro Set	25	.10	.08	.04
1992 Pro Set	155	.45	.35	.20
1992 Pro Set Gold MVPs	4	1.75	1.25	.70
1992 Pro Set Power	7	.50	.40	.20
1992 Score	413	.40	.30	.15
1992 SkyBox Impact	10	.45	.35	.20
1992 SkyBox Primetime	50	1.00	.70	.40
1992 SkyBox Primetime	257	.30	.25	.12
1992 Topps	125	.45	.35	.20
1992 Topps Stadium Club	110	1.00	.70	.40
1992 Upper Deck	200	.40	.30	.15

Set	Card #	MT	NM	EX
1992 Upper Deck	514	.20	.15	.08
1993 Bowman	400	2.00	1.50	.80
1993 Fleer	91	.35	.25	.14
1993 Fleer	237	.10	.08	.04
1993 Fleer Team Leaders	4	10.00	7.50	4.00
1993 Fleer Ultra	111	1.00	.70	.40
1993 GameDay	10	1.00	.70	.40
1993 Pacific	352	.35	.25	.14
1993 Pacific Prisms	23	8.00	6.00	3.20
1993 Pinnacle	103	.80	.60	.30
1993 Pinnacle Men of Autumn	7	1.50	1.25	.60
1993 Pro Set	4	.15	.11	.06
1993 Pro Set	123	.40	.30	.15
1993 Pro Set Power	7	.40	.30	.15
1993 Score	40	.40	.30	.15
1993 Score Select	34	2.00	1.50	.80
1993 Score Select Gridiron Skills	4	75.00	56.00	30.00
1993 Score The Franchise	7	20.00	15.00	8.00
1993 SkyBox Impact	83	.40	.30	.15
1993 SkyBox Impact	341	.10	.08	.04
1993 SkyBox Premium	139	1.00	.70	.40
1993 Topps	100	.30	.25	.12
1993 Topps	264	.10	.08	.04
1993 Topps Stadium Club	70	1.00	.70	.40
1993 Topps Stadium Club	241	.40	.30	.15
1993 Upper Deck	357	.40	.30	.15
1993 Upper Deck SP	76	2.00	1.50	.80
1993 Upper Deck Team MVP	4	2.00	1.50	.80
1994 Bowman	80	.50	.40	.20
1994 Fleer	135	.60	.45	.25
1994 Fleer League Leaders	3	2.50	2.00	1.00
1994 Fleer Living Legends	2	15.00	11.00	6.00
1994 Fleer Ultra	86	.60	.45	.25
1994 Fleer Ultra Achievement Awards	2	2.00	1.50	.80
1994 Fleer Ultra Hot Numbers	4	2.00	1.50	.80
1994 GameDay	118	.60	.45	.25
1994 GameDay Game Breakers	4	2.00	1.50	.80
1994 Pacific Crown	124	.35	.25	.14
1994 Pacific Crown Gems of the Crown	9	8.00	6.00	3.25
1994 Pacific Marquee	10	2.50	2.00	1.00
1994 Pacific Prisms	36	4.50	3.50	1.75
1994 Pinnacle	12	.40	.30	.15
1994 Pinnacle Canton Bound Box Set	7	.15	.15	.15
1994 Pinnacle Performers	7	6.00	4.50	2.50
1994 Pinnacle Sportflics Head-to-Head	10	9.00	6.75	3.50
1994 Pinnacle Sportflics	28	1.00	.70	.40
1994 Pinnacle Sportflics	181	.40	.30	.15
1994 Score	7	.50	.40	.20
1994 Score Select	10	.50	.40	.20
1994 SkyBox Impact	72	.40	.30	.15
1994 SkyBox Impact Ultimate Impact	10	3.00	2.25	1.25
1994 SkyBox Premium	46	.35	.25	.14
1994 SkyBox Premium Revolution	6	12.00	9.00	4.75
1994 SkyBox Premium SkyTech Stars	4	5.00	3.75	2.00
1994 Topps	196	.40	.30	.15
1994 Topps	540	.65	.50	.25
1994 Topps Finest	119	8.00	6.00	3.25
1994 Topps Finest Inserts	21	15.00	11.00	6.00
1994 Topps Stadium Club	90	.60	.45	.25
1994 Upper Deck	218	.75	.60	.30
1994 Upper Deck Collector's Choice Crash Game	6	10.00	7.50	4.00
1994 Upper Deck Collector's Choice	300	.35	.25	.14
1994 Upper Deck Pro Bowl	12	15.00	11.00	6.00
1994 Upper Deck SP	80	1.00	.70	.40
1994 Upper Deck SP All-Pro	11	10.00	7.50	4.00

Boomer Esiason

Set	Card #	MT	NM	EX
1986 Topps	255 (R)	9.00	6.75	3.50
1987 Topps	185	2.00	1.50	.80
1988 Topps	339	.15	.11	.06
1988 Topps	340	.50	.40	.20
1989 Pro Set	58	.20	.15	.08
1989 Score	3	.50	.40	.20
1989 Score	298	.20	.15	.08
1989 Topps	23	.05	.04	.02
1989 Topps	25	.30	.25	.12
1989 Topps	217	.05	.04	.02
1990 Fleer	214	.10	.08	.04
1990 Pro Set	341	.06	.05	.02
1990 Pro Set	463	.10	.08	.04
1990 Score	40	.20	.15	.08
1990 Score	316	.10	.08	.04
1990 Score 100 Hottest	37	.20	.15	.08
1990 Topps	270	.20	.15	.08
1991 Bowman	84	.15	.11	.06
1991 Fleer	19	.15	.11	.06
1991 Fleer Ultra	15	.20	.15	.08
1991 Pacific	63	.15	.11	.06
1991 Pinnacle	152	.25	.20	.10
1991 Pinnacle	378	.15	.11	.06
1991 Pro Set	111	.10	.08	.04
1991 Pro Set	327	.03	.02	.01
1991 Pro Set	371	.05	.04	.02
1991 Pro Set Platinum	16	.08	.06	.03
1991 Score	7	.10	.08	.04
1991 Topps	248	.15	.11	.06
1991 Topps Stadium Club	91	.50	.40	.20
1991 Upper Deck	245	.15	.11	.06
1991 Upper Deck	454	.05	.04	.02
1992 GameDay	405	.20	.15	.08
1992 Pro Set	456	.15	.11	.06
1992 Pro Set	681	.05	.04	.02
1992 Pro Set Power	107	.25	.20	.10
1992 SkyBox Impact	73	.10	.08	.04
1992 SkyBox Primetime	7	.20	.15	.08
1992 Topps	722	.05	.04	.02
1992 Topps Stadium Club	615	.85	.60	.35
1992 Upper Deck	569	.10	.08	.04
1992 Upper Deck Gold	47	.10	.08	.04
1993 Bowman	100	.40	.30	.15
1993 Fleer	349	.10	.08	.04
1993 Fleer Ultra	336	.10	.08	.04
1993 GameDay	180	.20	.15	.08
1993 Pacific	393	.15	.11	.06
1993 Pinnacle	314	.20	.15	.08
1993 Pro Set	317	.10	.08	.04
1993 Pro Set Power Power Moves	19	.30	.25	.12

Set	Card #	MT	NM	EX
1993 Pro Set Power Update Moves	19	.20	.15	.08
1993 Score Select	76	.40	.30	.15
1993 SkyBox Impact	235	.10	.08	.04
1993 SkyBox Premium	160	.25	.20	.10
1993 Topps	410	.08	.06	.03
1993 Topps Stadium Club	113	.30	.25	.12
1993 Upper Deck	471	.05	.04	.02
1993 Upper Deck NFL Experience	23	.35	.25	.14
1993 Upper Deck SP	191	.20	.15	.08
1994 Bowman	210	.12	.09	.05
1994 Fleer	353	.15	.11	.06
1994 Fleer Ultra	230	.08	.06	.03
1994 GameDay	300	.10	.08	.04
1994 Pacific Crown	198	.06	.05	.02
1994 Pacific Crown Gems of the Crown	10	2.50	2.00	1.00
1994 Pacific Prisms	38	1.25	.90	.50
1994 Pinnacle	94	.09	.07	.04
1994 Pinnacle Sportflics	23	.15	.11	.06
1994 Score	44	.08	.06	.03
1994 Score Select	134	.10	.08	.04
1994 SkyBox Impact	194	.12	.09	.05
1994 SkyBox Premium	115	.08	.06	.03
1994 Topps	220	.07	.05	.03
1994 Topps Finest	99	1.50	1.25	.60
1994 Topps Finest Inserts	32	3.50	2.75	1.50
1994 Topps Stadium Club	330	.10	.08	.04
1994 Topps Stadium Club	514	.10	.08	.04
1994 Upper Deck Collector's Choice	130	.07	.05	.03
1994 Upper Deck SP	51	.25	.20	.10

Jim Everett

Set	Card #	MT	NM	EX
1987 Topps	145 (R)	5.00	3.75	2.00
1988 Topps	287	.15	.11	.06
1988 Topps	288	.40	.30	.15
1989 Pro Set	199	.08	.06	.03
1989 Score	244	.50	.40	.20
1989 Topps	129	.15	.11	.06
1990 Fleer	36	.03	.02	.01
1990 Pro Set	165	.03	.02	.01
1990 Score	4	.04	.03	.02
1990 Score	312	.04	.03	.02
1990 Score 100 Hottest	50	.15	.11	.06
1990 Topps	75	.04	.03	.02
1991 Bowman	269	.03	.02	.01
1991 Fleer	267	.15	.11	.06
1991 Fleer Ultra	186	.04	.03	.02
1991 Pacific	250	.04	.03	.02
1991 Pinnacle	15	.10	.08	.04
1991 Pro Set	200	.03	.02	.01
1991 Pro Set	374	.04	.03	.02
1991 Pro Set Platinum	58	.05	.04	.02
1991 Score	367	.06	.05	.02
1991 Topps	8	.10	.08	.04
1991 Topps	532	.04	.03	.02
1991 Topps Stadium Club	107	.20	.15	.08

Set	Card #	MT	NM	EX
1991 Upper Deck	30	.05	.04	.02
1991 Upper Deck	164	.05	.04	.02
1992 Bowman	176	.45	.35	.20
1992 Fleer	211	.03	.02	.01
1992 Fleer Team Leaders	6	6.50	5.00	2.50
1992 Fleer Ultra	206	.05	.04	.02
1992 GameDay	301	.20	.15	.08
1992 Pinnacle	111	.05	.04	.02
1992 Pro Set	547	.05	.04	.02
1992 Pro Set Power	207	.05	.04	.02
1992 Score	141	.05	.04	.02
1992 SkyBox Impact	7	.05	.04	.02
1992 SkyBox Primetime	43	.10	.08	.04
1992 Topps	420	.05	.04	.02
1992 Topps Stadium Club	210	.08	.06	.03
1992 Upper Deck	111	.05	.04	.02
1993 Bowman	369	.15	.11	.06
1993 Fleer	98	.05	.04	.02
1993 Fleer Ultra	237	.08	.06	.03
1993 GameDay	469	.10	.08	.04
1993 Pacific	187	.05	.04	.02
1993 Pacific Prisms	50	1.25	.90	.50
1993 Pinnacle	20	.10	.08	.04
1993 Pinnacle Men of Autumn	42	.25	.20	.10
1993 Pro Set	229	.05	.04	.02
1993 Pro Set Power	111	.05	.04	.02
1993 Score	55	.04	.03	.02
1993 Score Select	73	.10	.08	.04
1993 SkyBox Impact	165	.05	.04	.02
1993 SkyBox Premium	113	.10	.08	.04
1993 Topps	27	.05	.04	.02
1993 Topps Stadium Club	206	.10	.08	.04
1993 Upper Deck	349	.05	.04	.02
1993 Upper Deck SP	141	.35	.25	.14
1993 Upper Deck Team MVP	23	.50	.40	.20
1994 Bowman	65	.10	.08	.04
1994 Fleer	323	.10	.08	.04
1994 Fleer Ultra	210	.08	.06	.03
1994 Fleer Ultra	456	.08	.06	.03
1994 GameDay	275	.10	.08	.04
1994 Pacific Crown	349	.06	.05	.02
1994 Pinnacle	15	.09	.07	.04
1994 Pinnacle Sportflics	136	.15	.11	.06
1994 Score	137	.08	.06	.03
1994 Score Select	8	.10	.08	.04
1994 SkyBox Impact	139	.10	.08	.04
1994 SkyBox Premium	109	.12	.09	.05
1994 Topps	346	.05	.04	.02
1994 Topps Finest	64	.65	.50	.25
1994 Topps Stadium Club	465	.10	.08	.04
1994 Upper Deck	43	.10	.08	.04
1994 Upper Deck Collector's Choice	152	.05	.04	.02
1994 Upper Deck SP	176	.25	.20	.10

Grading Guide

Mint (MT): A perfect card. Well-centered with all corners sharp and square. No creases, stains, edge nicks, surface marks, yellowing or fading.

Near Mint (NM): A nearly perfect card. At first glance, a NM card appears to be perfect. May be slightly off-center. No surface marks, creases or loss of gloss.

Excellent (EX): Corners are still fairly sharp with only moderate wear. Borders may be off-center. No creases or stains on fronts or backs, but may show slight loss of surface luster.

Very Good (VG): Shows obvious handling. May have rounded corners, minor creases, major gum or wax stains. No major creases, tape marks, writing, etc.

Good (G): A well-worn card, but exhibits no intentional damage. May have major or multiple creases. Corners may be rounded well beyond card border.

Fair (F): Shows excessive wear and damage such as thumb tack holes, tape marks, small tears, or creases so heavy as to break the cardboard. Backs may have ink or pencil marks, or missing small bits of paper.

Poor (P). A card that has been tortured to death. Card may have been trimmed, or show holes from a paper punch. Front may have ink or pencil marks or other defacement. Portions of the front or back design may be missing.

Marshall Faulk

Brett Favre

Set	Card #	MT	NM	EX
1994 Bowman	2 (R)	8.00	6.00	3.25
1994 Fleer NFL Prospects	7	9.50	7.15	3.80
1994 Fleer Ultra	133 (R)	7.50	5.75	3.00
1994 Fleer Ultra	408	3.50	2.75	1.50
1994 Fleer Ultra First Rounders	4	10.00	7.50	4.00
1994 Fleer Ultra Wave of the Future	2	8.00	6.00	3.25
1994 GameDay	179 (R)	9.00	6.75	3.50
1994 GameDay Rookie Standouts	5	12.00	9.00	4.75
1994 Pacific Crown	426 (R)	6.50	5.00	2.50
1994 Pacific Crown Knights of the Gridiron	10	35.00	26.00	14.00
1994 Pacific Marquee	11	12.00	9.00	4.75
1994 Pacific Prisms	39 (R)	22.00	16.50	8.75
1994 Pinnacle	198 (R)	7.50	5.75	3.00
1994 Pinnacle Draft Pick	2	50.00	37.00	20.00
1994 Pinnacle Sportflics Rookie Rivalry	1	25.00	18.50	10.00
1994 Pinnacle Sportflics	152 (R)	10.00	7.50	4.00
1994 Score	277 (R)	6.00	4.50	2.50
1994 Score Select	200 (R)	8.00	6.00	3.25
1994 Score Select Select Rookies	1	125.00	94.00	50.00
1994 SkyBox Impact	274 (R)	5.50	4.15	2.20
1994 SkyBox Premium	158 (R)	6.00	4.50	2.50
1994 SkyBox Premium Prime Time Rookies	3	100.00	75.00	40.00
1994 SkyBox Premium SkyTech Stars	21	20.00	15.00	8.00
1994 Topps	445 (R)	5.50	4.25	2.25
1994 Topps Stadium Club	327 (R)	9.00	6.75	3.50
1994 Upper Deck	7 (R)	8.00	6.00	3.25
1994 Upper Deck Collector's Choice Crash Game	11	18.00	13.50	7.25
1994 Upper Deck Collector's Choice	14 (R)	5.00	3.75	2.00
1994 Upper Deck Hobby Predictor	6	8.00	6.00	3.25
1994 Upper Deck Hobby Predictor	11	40.00	30.00	16.00
1994 Upper Deck Retail Predictor	16	12.00	9.00	4.75
1994 Upper Deck SP	3 (R)	12.00	9.00	4.75

Values for recent cards and sets are listed in Mint (MT), Near Mint (NM), reflecting the fact that many cards from recent years have been preserved in to condition. Recent cards and sets in less than Excellent condition have little collector interest.

Set	Card #	MT	NM	EX
1991 Fleer Ultra	283 (R)	2.50	2.00	1.00
1991 Fleer Ultra Update	1	7.00	5.25	2.75
1991 Pacific	551 (R)	1.75	1.25	.70
1991 Pro Set	762 (R)	1.75	1.25	.70
1991 Pro Set Platinum	290 (R)	1.75	1.25	.70
1991 Score	611 (R)	1.75	1.25	.70
1991 Topps Stadium Club	94 (R)	13.00	9.75	5.25
1991 Upper Deck	13 (R)	1.75	1.25	.70
1991 Upper Deck	627	.30	.25	.12
1991 Upper Deck	647	1.25	.90	.50
1992 Pinnacle	303	2.50	2.00	1.00
1992 Pinnacle Team 2000	23	3.00	2.25	1.25
1992 Pro Set	505	1.25	.90	.50
1992 Pro Set Gold MVPs	20	4.00	3.00	1.50
1992 Pro Set Power	104	2.50	2.00	1.00
1992 Topps	696	1.00	.70	.40
1992 Topps Stadium Club	683	17.00	12.50	6.75
1992 Upper Deck	484	1.00	.70	.40
1992 Upper Deck Coach's Report	5	6.00	4.50	2.50
1993 Bowman	335	4.00	3.00	1.50
1993 Fleer	103	1.00	.75	.40
1993 Fleer Team Leaders	1	13.00	9.75	5.25
1993 Fleer Ultra	146	1.50	1.25	.60
1993 Fleer Ultra Ultra Stars	1	10.00	7.50	4.00
1993 GameDay	100	1.75	1.25	.70
1993 GameDay Game Breakers	2	3.50	2.75	1.50
1993 Pacific	89	1.00	.70	.40
1993 Pacific Gold Prisms	5	30.00	22.00	12.00
1993 Pacific Prism Inserts	5	12.00	9.00	4.75
1993 Pacific Prisms	31	8.00	6.00	3.25
1993 Pacific Triple Folder Superstars	9	2.00	1.50	.80
1993 Pacific Triple Folders	21	1.50	1.25	.60
1993 Pinnacle	1	1.50	1.25	.60
1993 Pinnacle Men of Autumn	37	3.00	2.25	1.25
1993 Pinnacle Team 2001	7	4.00	3.00	1.50
1993 Pro Set	152	1.00	.70	.40
1993 Pro Set Power	4	.75	.60	.30
1993 Score	25	1.00	.70	.40
1993 Score Select	43	3.00	2.25	1.25
1993 SkyBox Impact	108	.85	.60	.35
1993 SkyBox Premium	122	1.50	1.25	.60
1993 SkyBox Thunder and Lightning	2	12.00	9.00	4.75
1993 Topps	250	1.00	.70	.40
1993 Topps Black Gold	39	4.00	3.00	1.50
1993 Topps Stadium Club	210	1.50	1.25	.60
1993 Topps Stadium Club	498	1.00	.70	.40
1993 Upper Deck	82	.50	.40	.20
1993 Upper Deck	360	1.00	.70	.40
1993 Upper Deck	439	.50	.40	.20
1993 Upper Deck Future Heroes	44	2.25	1.75	.90

Set	Card #	MT	NM	EX
1993 Upper Deck Pro Bowl	14	13.00	9.75	5.25
1993 Upper Deck SP	93	4.50	3.50	1.75
1994 Bowman	295	1.00	.70	.40
1994 Fleer	168	.50	.40	.20
1994 Fleer Pro-Visions	4	.75	.60	.30
1994 Fleer Ultra	107	.65	.50	.25
1994 GameDay	147	.80	.60	.30
1994 Pacific Crown	140	.50	.40	.20
1994 Pacific Crown Gems of the Crown	11	5.00	3.75	2.00
1994 Pacific Marquee	12	2.50	2.00	1.00
1994 Pacific Prisms	40	7.00	5.25	2.75
1994 Pinnacle	36	.65	.50	.25
1994 Pinnacle Performers	13	5.00	3.75	2.00
1994 Pinnacle Sportflics	27	1.25	.90	.50
1994 Pinnacle Sportflics	183	.50	.40	.20
1994 Pinnacle Team Pinnacle	2	45.00	34.00	18.00
1994 Score	142	.60	.45	.25
1994 Score Select	142	.85	.60	.35
1994 SkyBox Impact	92	.35	.25	.14
1994 SkyBox Impact Ultimate Impact	15	4.50	3.50	1.75
1994 SkyBox Premium	58	.45	.35	.20
1994 SkyBox Premium SkyTech Stars	14	5.00	3.75	2.00
1994 Topps	530	.60	.45	.25
1994 Topps Finest	124	10.00	7.50	4.00
1994 Topps Finest Inserts	22	15.00	11.00	6.00
1994 Topps Stadium Club	536	.75	.60	.30
1994 Upper Deck	250	1.00	.70	.40
1994 Upper Deck Collector's Choice	309	.45	.35	.20
1994 Upper Deck Pro Bowl	9	10.00	7.50	4.00
1994 Upper Deck Retail Predictor	5	10.00	7.50	4.00
1994 Upper Deck SP	163	1.50	1.25	.60
1994 Upper Deck SP All-Pro	15	12.00	9.00	4.75

Set	Card #	MT	NM	EX
1994 Pinnacle Sportflics Rookie Rivalry	1	25.00	18.50	10.00
1994 Pinnacle Sportflics	148 (R)	2.00	1.50	.80
1994 Score	289 (R)	1.00	.75	.40
1994 Score Select	208 (R)	1.75	1.25	.70
1994 SkyBox Impact	300 (R)	.65	.50	.25
1994 SkyBox Premium	184 (R)	1.00	.70	.40
1994 SkyBox Premium Prime Time Rookies	7	10.00	7.50	4.00
1994 Topps	618 (R)	.60	.45	.25
1994 Topps Stadium Club	35 (R)	1.50	1.25	.60
1994 Upper Deck	26 (R)	1.50	1.25	.60
1994 Upper Deck Collector's Choice	16 (R)	.90	.70	.35
1994 Upper Deck SP	14 (R)	2.50	2.00	1.00
1994 Upper Deck SP All-Pro	35	6.00	4.50	2.50

Barry Foster

Set	Card #	MT	NM	EX
1990 Fleer Update	25 (R)	5.50	4.15	2.20
1990 Score	308 (R)	1.25	.90	.50
1990 Score Update	110	8.00	6.00	3.20
1990 Topps	174 (R)	.85	.60	.35
1990 Topps Update	51	.90	.70	.35
1991 Pinnacle	17	.85	.60	.35
1991 Pro Set	844	.45	.35	.20
1991 Pro Set Platinum	258	.50	.40	.20
1991 Score	484	.45	.35	.20
1992 Bowman	409	4.50	3.50	1.75
1992 Fleer	343	.40	.30	.15
1992 Fleer Ultra	331	.65	.50	.25
1992 Pacific	589	.45	.35	.20
1992 Pinnacle	121	.90	.70	.35
1992 Pinnacle Team 2000	11	1.25	.90	.50
1992 Pro Set	627	.30	.25	.12
1992 Pro Set Power	29	.50	.40	.20
1992 Score	166	.45	.35	.20
1992 Topps	526	.40	.30	.15
1992 Topps Stadium Club	380	.85	.60	.35
1992 Upper Deck	57	.40	.30	.15
1993 Bowman	310	1.25	.90	.50
1993 Fleer	55	.30	.25	.12
1993 Fleer	238	.15	.11	.06
1993 Fleer	241	.15	.11	.06
1993 Fleer	248	.25	.20	.10
1993 Fleer All-Pro	5	3.00	2.25	1.25
1993 Fleer Ultra	393	.75	.60	.30
1993 Fleer Ultra Award Winners	5	7.00	5.25	2.75
1993 Fleer Ultra Ultra Stars	2	6.00	4.50	2.50
1993 GameDay	5	.75	.60	.30
1993 GameDay Game Breakers	9	1.50	1.25	.60
1993 Pacific	269	.35	.25	.14
1993 Pacific Gold Prisms	6	15.00	11.00	6.00
1993 Pacific Picks the Pros Gold	10	6.00	4.50	2.50

William Floyd

Set	Card #	MT	NM	EX
1994 Bowman	169 (R)	2.50	2.00	1.00
1994 Fleer NFL Prospects	8	3.00	2.25	1.25
1994 Fleer Ultra	276 (R)	1.75	1.25	.70
1994 Fleer Ultra	493	.50	.40	.20
1994 Fleer Ultra First Rounders	5	2.00	1.50	.80
1994 GameDay	362 (R)	2.00	1.50	.80
1994 Pacific Crown	428 (R)	.60	.45	.25
1994 Pacific Crown Knights of the Gridiron	11	8.00	6.00	3.25
1994 Pacific Prisms	41 (R)	5.50	4.25	2.25
1994 Pinnacle	208 (R)	1.75	1.25	.70
1994 Pinnacle Draft Pick	8	12.00	9.00	4.75

1993 Pacific Prism Inserts	6	8.00	6.00	3.25
1993 Pacific Prisms	84	3.50	2.75	1.50
1993 Pacific Triple Folder Superstars	10	.75	.60	.30
1993 Pacific Triple Folders	12	1.00	.70	.40
1993 Pinnacle	6	.75	.60	.30
1993 Pinnacle Men of Autumn	23	1.50	1.25	.60
1993 Pinnacle Team Pinnacle	3	25.00	18.50	10.00
1993 Pinnacle Team 2001	22	1.50	1.25	.60
1993 Pro Set	361	.45	.35	.20
1993 Pro Set Power	29	.35	.25	.14
1993 Score	20	.25	.20	.10
1993 Score Dream Team	3	2.50	2.00	1.00
1993 Score Select	93	.90	.70	.35
1993 SkyBox Impact	277	.40	.30	.15
1993 SkyBox Poster Art Cards	3	1.75	1.25	.70
1993 SkyBox Premium	239	.75	.60	.30
1993 Topps	140	.35	.25	.14
1993 Topps	219	.50	.40	.20
1993 Topps	272	.10	.08	.04
1993 Topps Black Gold	29	2.00	1.50	.80
1993 Topps Stadium Club	140	.75	.60	.30
1993 Topps Stadium Club	245	.30	.25	.12
1993 Upper Deck	89	.10	.08	.04
1993 Upper Deck	345	.35	.25	.14
1993 Upper Deck	435	.10	.08	.04
1993 Upper Deck Future Heroes	37	1.50	1.25	.60
1993 Upper Deck Pro Bowl	5	7.00	5.25	2.75
1993 Upper Deck SP	218	1.00	.70	.40
1993 Upper Deck SP All Pro	6	15.00	11.00	6.00
1993 Upper Deck Team MVP	27	2.50	2.00	1.00
1994 Bowman	45	.45	.35	.20
1994 Fleer	384	.35	.25	.14
1994 Fleer All-Pro	4	1.00	.70	.40
1994 Fleer Scoring Machines	5	6.50	5.00	2.50
1994 Fleer Ultra	253	.40	.30	.15
1994 GameDay	332	.25	.20	.10
1994 Pacific Crown	166	.20	.15	.08
1994 Pacific Crown Crystalline Collection	19	6.00	4.50	2.50
1994 Pacific Marquee	13	2.00	1.50	.80
1994 Pacific Prisms	43	2.00	1.50	.80
1994 Pinnacle	37	.45	.35	.20
1994 Pinnacle Sportflics	103	.40	.30	.15
1994 Pinnacle Team Pinnacle	4	40.00	30.00	16.00
1994 Score	94	.15	.11	.06
1994 Score Select	111	.35	.25	.14
1994 SkyBox Impact	214	.35	.25	.14
1994 SkyBox Premium	128	.35	.25	.14
1994 SkyBox Premium SkyTech Stars	23	4.00	3.00	1.50
1994 Topps	510	.30	.25	.12
1994 Topps Finest	18	5.00	3.75	2.00
1994 Topps Stadium Club	340	.45	.35	.20
1994 Upper Deck	115	.40	.30	.15
1994 Upper Deck Collector's Choice Crash Game	13	7.50	5.75	3.00
1994 Upper Deck Collector's Choice	333	.10	.08	.04
1994 Upper Deck Retail Predictor	17	12.00	9.00	4.75
1994 Upper Deck SP	73	.60	.45	.25
1994 Upper Deck SP All-Pro	30	8.00	6.00	3.25

Dan Fouts

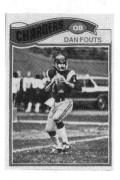

Set	Card #	NM	EX	VG
1975 Topps	367 (R)	50.00	25.00	15.00
1976 Topps	128	20.00	10.00	6.00
1977 Topps	274	8.50	4.25	2.50
1978 Topps	499	5.00	2.50	1.50
1979 Topps	387	4.00	2.00	1.25
1980 Topps	3	1.00	.50	.30
1980 Topps	520	2.00	1.00	.60

Set	Card #	MT	NM	EX
1981 Topps	153	.60	.45	.25
1981 Topps	265	1.50	1.25	.60
1982 Topps	2	.50	.40	.20
1982 Topps	230	1.00	.70	.40
1982 Topps	231	.50	.40	.20
1983 Topps	3	.20	.15	.08
1983 Topps	374	.75	.60	.30
1984 Topps	179	.75	.60	.30
1984 Topps	180	.50	.40	.20
1985 Topps	372	.60	.45	.25
1986 Topps	230	.20	.15	.08
1986 Topps	231	.60	.45	.25
1987 Topps	340	.50	.40	.20
1989 Pro Set Announcer Inserts	14	.30	.25	.12
1993 Pinnacle	353	.10	.08	.04
1993 Score	438	.04	.03	.02

Willie Gault

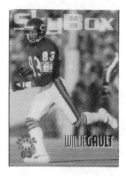

Set	Card #	MT	NM	EX
1984 Topps	224 (R)	1.00	.70	.40
1985 Topps	29	.40	.30	.15
1986 Topps	13	.10	.08	.04
1987 Topps	48	.15	.11	.06
1988 Topps	68	.05	.04	.02
1988 Topps	72	.10	.08	.04
1989 Pro Set	184	.03	.02	.01
1989 Score	218	.25	.20	.10

Set	Card #	MT	NM	EX
1989 Topps	272	.05	.04	.02
1990 Fleer Update	66	.15	.11	.06
1990 Pro Set	153	.03	.02	.01
1990 Score	37	.04	.03	.02
1990 Topps	288	.04	.03	.02
1991 Bowman	249	.03	.02	.01
1991 Fleer	107	.07	.05	.03
1991 Fleer Ultra	79	.04	.03	.02
1991 Pacific	232	.04	.03	.02
1991 Pacific Flash Cards	95	.10	.05	.05
1991 Pro Set	190	.03	.02	.01
1991 Pro Set Platinum	52	.05	.04	.02
1991 Score	147	.06	.05	.02
1991 Topps	94	.04	.03	.02
1991 Topps Stadium Club	257	.30	.25	.12
1991 Upper Deck	292	.05	.04	.02
1992 Bowman	411	.30	.25	.12
1992 Fleer	195	.03	.02	.01
1992 GameDay	259	.12	.09	.05
1992 Pacific	469	.05	.04	.02
1992 Pinnacle	288	.05	.04	.02
1992 Pro Set	538	.05	.04	.02
1992 Score	345	.05	.04	.02
1992 SkyBox Impact	173	.05	.04	.02
1992 SkyBox Primetime	249	.10	.08	.04
1992 Topps	566	.05	.04	.02
1992 Upper Deck	436	.05	.04	.02
1993 Fleer	413	.05	.04	.02
1993 Fleer Ultra	216	.08	.06	.03
1993 GameDay	459	.10	.08	.04
1993 Pacific	371	.05	.04	.02
1993 Pinnacle	16	.10	.08	.04
1993 Pro Set	213	.05	.04	.02
1993 SkyBox Impact	154	.03	.02	.01
1993 SkyBox Impact	345	.05	.04	.02
1993 SkyBox Premium	77	.10	.08	.04
1993 Topps	374	.05	.04	.02
1993 Topps Stadium Club	119	.10	.08	.04
1993 Upper Deck	146	.05	.04	.02
1994 Pacific Crown	108	.06	.05	.02
1991 Topps	349	.30	.25	.12
1991 Topps Stadium Club	178	2.00	1.50	.80
1991 Upper Deck	345	.30	.25	.12
1992 GameDay	221	.35	.25	.14
1992 Pro Set	524	.30	.25	.12
1992 Pro Set Power	111	.40	.30	.15
1992 SkyBox Impact	226	.25	.20	.10
1992 SkyBox Primetime	104	.35	.25	.14
1992 Topps	678	.05	.04	.02
1992 Topps Stadium Club	691	1.50	1.25	.60
1992 Topps Stadium Club No. 1 Draft Picks	1	32.00	24.00	12.80
1992 Upper Deck	590	.05	.04	.02
1992 Upper Deck Gold	42	.50	.40	.20
1993 Fleer	478	.10	.08	.04
1993 Fleer Ultra	184	.35	.25	.14
1993 GameDay	293	.25	.20	.10
1993 Pacific	227	.12	.09	.05
1993 Pacific Prisms	39	2.50	2.00	1.00
1993 Pinnacle	326	.20	.15	.08
1993 Pinnacle	358	.10	.08	.04
1993 Pro Set	186	.15	.11	.06
1993 Score	246	.10	.08	.04
1993 Score Select	115	.50	.40	.20
1993 SkyBox Impact	131	.15	.11	.06
1993 SkyBox Premium	19	.25	.20	.10
1993 Topps	35	.20	.15	.08
1993 Topps	266	.10	.08	.04
1993 Topps Stadium Club	218	.25	.20	.10
1993 Upper Deck	72	.05	.04	.02
1993 Upper Deck	251	.10	.08	.04
1993 Upper Deck NFL Experience	39	.20	.15	.08
1993 Upper Deck SP	113	.20	.15	.08
1994 Bowman	303	.10	.08	.04
1994 Fleer	21	.25	.20	.10
1994 Fleer Ultra	14	.20	.15	.08
1994 Fleer Ultra	335	.15	.11	.06
1994 GameDay	19	.10	.08	.04
1994 Pacific Crown	379	.06	.05	.02
1994 Pacific Prisms	45	1.50	1.25	.60
1994 Pinnacle	98	.25	.20	.10
1994 Pinnacle Sportflics	130	.35	.25	.14
1994 Score	75	.08	.06	.03
1994 SkyBox Impact	109	.18	.14	.07
1994 SkyBox Premium	14	.25	.20	.10
1994 SkyBox Premium SkyTech Stars	13	2.00	1.50	.80
1994 Topps	580	.08	.06	.03
1994 Topps Finest	28	2.50	2.00	1.00
1994 Topps Stadium Club	310	.15	.11	.06
1994 Upper Deck	50	.20	.15	.08
1994 Upper Deck Collector's Choice	254	.07	.05	.03
1994 Upper Deck SP	182	.65	.50	.25

Jeff George

Set	Card #	MT	NM	EX
1990 Fleer	347 (R)	1.00	.70	.40
1990 Fleer Update	4	3.00	2.25	1.25
1990 Pro Set	669 (R)	2.00	1.50	.80
1990 Score	634 (R)	1.00	.70	.40
1990 Score Update	78	6.00	4.50	2.50
1990 Topps	298 (R)	1.00	.70	.40
1990 Topps Update	41	.75	.60	.30
1991 Bowman	1	.10	.08	.04
1991 Bowman	212	.25	.20	.10
1991 Fleer	81	.25	.20	.10
1991 Fleer Ultra	59	.25	.20	.10
1991 Pacific	193	.30	.25	.12
1991 Pinnacle	92	.50	.40	.20
1991 Pro Set	177	.20	.15	.08
1991 Pro Set Platinum	45	.30	.25	.12
1991 Score	502	.20	.15	.08
1991 Score	630	.10	.08	.04

Grading Guide

Mint (MT): A perfect card. Well-centered with all corners sharp and square. No creases, stains, edge nicks, surface marks, yellowing or fading.

Near Mint (NM): A nearly perfect card. At first glance, a NM card appears to be perfect. May be slightly off-center. No surface marks, creases or loss of gloss.

Excellent (EX): Corners are still fairly sharp with only moderate wear. Borders may be off-center. No creases or stains on fronts or backs, but may show slight loss of surface luster.

Very Good (VG): Shows obvious handling. May have rounded corners, minor creases, major gum or wax stains. No major creases, tape marks, writing, etc.

Good (G): A well-worn card, but exhibits no intentional damage. May have major or multiple creases. Corners may be rounded well beyond card border.

Fair (F): Shows excessive wear and damage such as thumb tack holes, tape marks, small tears, or creases so heavy as to break the cardboard. Backs may have ink or pencil marks, or missing small bits of paper.

Poor (P): A card that has been tortured to death. Card may have been trimmed, or show holes from a paper punch. Front may have ink or pencil marks or other defacement. Portions of the front or back design may be missing.

Frank Gifford

Set	Card #	NM	EX	VG
1952 Bowman Large	16 (R)	475.00	237.00	142.00
1952 Bowman Small	16 (R)	425.00	212.00	127.00
1953 Bowman	43	340.00	170.00	102.00
1954 Bowman	55	125.00	62.00	37.00
1955 Bowman	7	90.00	45.00	27.00
1956 Topps	53	115.00	57.00	34.00
1957 Topps	88	85.00	42.00	25.00
1958 Topps	73	60.00	30.00	18.00
1959 Topps	20	50.00	25.00	15.00
1960 Topps	74	45.00	22.50	13.50
1962 Topps	104	50.00	25.00	15.00
1964 Philadelphia	117	45.00	22.00	13.50

Set	Card #	MT	NM	EX
1989 Pro Set Announcer Inserts	2	.75	.60	.30

Ernest Givins

Set	Card #	MT	NM	EX
1987 Topps	310 (R)	2.00	1.50	.80
1987 Topps 1000 Yard Club	20	.20	.15	.08
1988 Topps	107	.40	.30	.15
1988 Topps 1000 Yard Club	11	.10	.08	.04
1989 Pro Set	143	.10	.08	.04
1989 Score	194	.40	.30	.15
1989 Topps	103	.20	.15	.08
1990 Fleer	127	.03	.02	.01
1990 Pro Set	119	.03	.02	.01
1990 Score	352	.04	.03	.02
1990 Topps	228	.04	.03	.02
1991 Bowman	190	.03	.02	.01
1991 Fleer	61	.07	.05	.03
1991 Fleer Ultra	47	.08	.06	.03
1991 Pacific	173	.04	.03	.02
1991 Pinnacle	145	.10	.08	.04

Set	Card #	NM	EX	VG
1991 Pro Set	164	.03	.02	.01
1991 Pro Set Platinum	41	.05	.04	.02
1991 Score	81	.04	.03	.02
1991 Topps	224	.04	.03	.02
1991 Topps Stadium Club	389	.40	.30	.15
1991 Upper Deck	312	.05	.04	.02
1992 Bowman	104	.40	.30	.15
1992 Fleer	146	.03	.02	.01
1992 Fleer Ultra	144	.05	.04	.02
1992 GameDay	264	.20	.15	.08
1992 Pacific	117	.05	.04	.02
1992 Pinnacle	116	.05	.04	.02
1992 Pro Set	510	.05	.04	.02
1992 Pro Set Power	272	.05	.04	.02
1992 Score	155	.06	.05	.02
1992 SkyBox Impact	165	.05	.04	.02
1992 SkyBox Primetime	169	.10	.08	.04
1992 Topps	187	.05	.04	.02
1992 Topps Stadium Club	293	.08	.06	.03
1992 Topps Stadium Club	451	.08	.06	.03
1992 Upper Deck	120	.05	.04	.02
1993 Bowman	8	.15	.11	.06
1993 Fleer	142	.05	.04	.02
1993 Fleer Ultra	164	.08	.06	.03
1993 GameDay	61	.10	.08	.04
1993 Pacific	282	.05	.04	.02
1993 Pacific Prisms	34	1.25	.90	.50
1993 Pinnacle	134	.10	.08	.04
1993 Pro Set	178	.05	.04	.02
1993 Score Select	191	.10	.08	.04
1993 SkyBox Impact	119	.03	.02	.01
1993 SkyBox Premium	173	.10	.08	.04
1993 Topps	485	.05	.04	.02
1993 Topps Stadium Club	20	.10	.08	.04
1993 Upper Deck	375	.05	.04	.02
1994 Bowman	76	.10	.08	.04
1994 Fleer	185	.20	.15	.08
1994 Fleer Ultra	399	.08	.06	.03
1994 GameDay	163	.10	.08	.04
1994 Pacific Crown	65	.06	.05	.02
1994 Pinnacle	4	.09	.07	.04
1994 Pinnacle Sportflics	107	.15	.11	.06
1994 Score	132	.05	.04	.02
1994 Score Select	130	.10	.08	.04
1994 SkyBox Impact	99	.15	.11	.06
1994 Topps	122	.05	.04	.02
1994 Topps Finest	144	.65	.50	.25
1994 Topps Stadium Club	232	.10	.08	.04
1994 Upper Deck	191	.10	.08	.04
1994 Upper Deck Collector's Choice	279	.05	.04	.02

Joe Greene

Set	Card #	NM	EX	VG
1971 Topps	245 (R)	48.00	24.00	14.50
1972 Topps	230	17.00	8.50	5.00
1973 Topps	280	6.00	3.00	1.75
1974 Topps	40	6.00	3.00	1.75
1975 Topps	425	4.00	2.00	1.25

Set	Card #	MT	NM	EX
1976 Topps	245	3.25	1.75	1.00
1977 Topps	405	2.00	1.00	.60
1978 Topps	295	1.50	.70	.45
1979 Topps	65	1.25	.60	.40
1980 Topps	175	1.00	.50	.30
Set	Card #	MT	NM	EX
1981 Topps	495	1.00	.70	.40

L.C. Greenwood

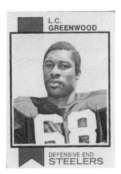

Set	Card #	NM	EX	VG
1972 Topps	101 (R)	20.00	10.00	6.00
1972 Topps	257	3.00	1.50	.90
1973 Topps	165	3.50	1.75	1.00
1974 Topps	496	1.50	.70	.45
1976 Topps	180	.85	.45	.25
1977 Topps	355	.60	.30	.20
1978 Topps	145	.50	.25	.15
1979 Topps	255	.40	.20	.12
1980 Topps	375	.30	.15	.09

Regional interest may affect the value of a card.

Forrest Gregg

Set	Card #	NM	EX	VG
1960 Topps	56 (R)	28.00	14.00	8.50
1961 Fleer	94 (R)	8.50	4.25	2.50
1962 Topps	70	7.50	3.75	2.25
1963 Topps	89	5.25	2.75	1.50
1964 Philadelphia	73	4.00	2.00	1.25
1965 Philadelphia	75	4.00	2.00	1.25
1966 Philadelphia	85	4.00	2.00	1.25
1967 Philadelphia	77	4.00	2.00	1.25

Bob Griese

Set	Card #	NM	EX	VG
1968 Topps	196 (R)	85.00	42.50	25.50
1969 Topps	161	30.00	15.00	9.00
1969 Topps Four In Ones	(18)	4.00	2.00	1.25
1970 Topps	10	15.00	7.50	4.50
1971 Topps	160	12.00	6.00	3.50
1972 Topps	3	2.00	1.00	.60
1972 Topps	80	8.00	4.00	2.50
1972 Topps	132	3.50	1.75	1.00
1972 Topps	272	75.00	37.00	22.00
1973 Topps	295	7.00	3.50	2.00
1974 Topps	200	5.00	2.50	1.50
1975 Topps	100	5.00	2.50	1.50
1976 Topps	255	4.00	2.00	1.25
1977 Topps	515	4.00	2.00	1.25
1978 Topps	120	3.00	1.50	.90
1979 Topps	440	2.00	1.00	.60
1980 Topps	35	1.75	.90	.50

Set	Card #	MT	NM	EX
1981 Topps	482	1.00	.70	.40
1990 Pro Set	24	.03	.02	.01
1992 Pacific Legends of the Game Bob Griese	10	.50	.40	.20
1992 Pacific Legends of the Game Bob Griese	11	.50	.40	.20
1992 Pacific Legends of the Game Bob Griese	12	.50	.40	.20
1992 Pacific Legends of the Game Bob Griese	13	.50	.40	.20
1992 Pacific Legends of the Game Bob Griese	14	.50	.40	.20
1992 Pacific Legends of the Game Bob Griese	15	.50	.40	.20
1992 Pacific Legends of the Game Bob Griese	16	.50	.40	.20
1992 Pacific Legends of the Game Bob Griese	17	.50	.40	.20
1992 Pacific Legends of the Game Bob Griese	18	.50	.40	.20
1994 Upper Deck Then And Now	5	10.00	7.50	4.00

Cards before 1981 are priced in Near Mint (NM),
Excellent (EX), and Very Good (VG).
Cards 1981 to present are Mint (MT), Near Mint (NM),
and Excellent (EX).

Paul Gruber

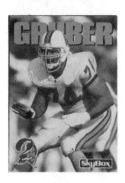

Set	Card #	MT	NM	EX
1989 Pro Set	411 (R)	.10	.08	.04
1989 Score	77 (R)	.20	.15	.08
1989 Topps	333 (R)	.12	.09	.05
1990 Fleer	345	.03	.02	.01
1990 Pro Set	310	.03	.02	.01
1990 Score	351	.04	.03	.02
1990 Topps	406	.04	.03	.02
1991 Bowman	512	.03	.02	.01
1991 Pacific	503	.04	.03	.02
1991 Pinnacle	276	.10	.08	.04
1991 Pro Set	670	.03	.02	.01
1991 Pro Set Platinum	278	.05	.04	.02
1991 Score	249	.04	.03	.02
1991 Topps	487	.04	.03	.02
1991 Topps Stadium Club	214	.30	.25	.12
1991 Upper Deck	388	.05	.04	.02
1992 Bowman	473	.30	.25	.12
1992 GameDay	410	.12	.09	.05
1992 Pacific	307	.05	.04	.02
1992 Pro Set	666	.05	.04	.02
1992 Pro Set Power	74	.05	.04	.02
1992 Score	152	.05	.04	.02
1992 SkyBox Impact	69	.05	.04	.02
1992 SkyBox Primetime	18	.10	.08	.04
1992 Topps	63	.05	.04	.02
1992 Topps Stadium Club	433	.08	.06	.03
1992 Upper Deck	235	.05	.04	.02
1993 Fleer	319	.05	.04	.02
1993 Fleer Ultra	470	.08	.06	.03
1993 GameDay	396	.10	.08	.04
1993 Pinnacle	254	.10	.08	.04
1993 Pro Set Power	74	.05	.04	.02
1993 Score	76	.04	.03	.02
1993 Topps	89	.05	.04	.02
1993 Topps	406	.05	.04	.02
1993 Topps Stadium Club	143	.10	.08	.04
1994 Bowman	176	.10	.08	.04
1994 Fleer	453	.05	.04	.02
1994 Fleer Ultra	302	.08	.06	.03
1994 GameDay	396	.10	.08	.04
1994 Score	46	.05	.04	.02
1994 SkyBox Impact	255	.04	.03	.02
1994 SkyBox Premium	152	.08	.06	.03
1994 Topps	94	.05	.04	.02
1994 Topps Stadium Club	218	.10	.08	.04

Jack Ham

Set	Card #	NM	EX	VG
1973 Topps	115 (R)	25.00	12.50	7.50
1974 Topps	137	7.00	3.50	2.00
1975 Topps	125	5.00	2.50	1.50
1976 Topps	420	3.25	1.75	1.00
1977 Topps	140	2.50	1.25	.70
1978 Topps	450	1.50	.70	.45
1979 Topps	320	1.25	.60	.40
1980 Topps	10	1.00	.50	.30

Set	Card #	MT	NM	EX
1981 Topps	235	.60	.45	.25
1982 Topps	210	.75	.60	.30

Rodney Hampton

Set	Card #	MT	NM	EX
1990 Fleer Update	11 (R)	5.00	3.75	2.00
1990 Pro Set	692 (R)	1.25	.90	.50
1990 Score	307 (R)	1.25	.90	.50
1990 Score Update	71	8.00	6.00	3.25
1990 Topps	48 (R)	1.50	1.25	.60
1990 Topps Update	30	1.00	.70	.40
1991 Bowman	367	.50	.40	.20
1991 Fleer	311	.50	.40	.20
1991 Fleer Ultra	218	.75	.60	.30
1991 Pacific	346	.50	.40	.20
1991 Pinnacle	23	1.50	1.25	.60
1991 Pinnacle	371	.50	.40	.20
1991 Pinnacle	375	.25	.20	.10
1991 Pro Set	62	.75	.60	.30
1991 Pro Set Platinum	240	.50	.40	.20
1991 Score	378	.75	.60	.30
1991 Topps	18	.75	.60	.30
1991 Topps Stadium Club	58	4.00	3.00	1.50
1991 Upper Deck	269	.75	.60	.30
1992 Bowman	290	2.00	1.50	.80
1992 Bowman	415	6.00	4.50	2.50
1992 Fleer	292	.40	.30	.15

1992 Fleer Team Leaders	9	20.00	15.00	8.00
1992 Fleer Ultra	277	.75	.60	.30
1992 Pacific	211	.40	.30	.15
1992 Pacific Prism Inserts	8	2.00	1.50	.80
1992 Pinnacle	102	.75	.60	.30
1992 Pinnacle Team 2000	2	1.50	1.25	.60
1992 Pro Set	264	.50	.40	.20
1992 Pro Set Gold MVPs	24	2.00	1.50	.80
1992 Pro Set Power	27	.50	.40	.20
1992 Score	123	.50	.40	.20
1992 Topps	210	.45	.35	.20
1992 Topps Stadium Club	247	.75	.60	.30
1992 Topps Stadium Club	310	.40	.30	.15
1992 Topps 1000-Yard Club	11	2.50	2.00	1.00
1992 Upper Deck	88	.10	.08	.04
1992 Upper Deck	172	.35	.25	.14
1992 Upper Deck	366	.10	.08	.04
1993 Bowman	350	1.00	.70	.40
1993 Fleer	40	.30	.25	.12
1993 Fleer Ultra	323	.50	.40	.20
1993 Fleer Ultra Touchdown Kings	1	2.00	1.50	.80
1993 GameDay	38	.75	.60	.30
1993 Pacific	43	.35	.25	.14
1993 Pacific Prisms	70	2.50	2.00	1.00
1993 Pacific Triple Folders	25	1.00	.70	.40
1993 Pinnacle	126	.75	.60	.30
1993 Pinnacle Men of Autumn	19	1.00	.75	.40
1993 Pinnacle Team Pinnacle	3	25.00	18.50	10.00
1993 Pinnacle Team 2001	9	1.25	.90	.50
1993 Pro Set	303	.25	.20	.10
1993 Pro Set College Connections	5	2.00	1.50	.80
1993 Pro Set Power	27	.35	.25	.14
1993 Score	5	.25	.20	.10
1993 Score Select	37	1.00	.70	.40
1993 Score The Franchise	19	15.00	11.00	6.00
1993 SkyBox Impact	224	.25	.20	.10
1993 SkyBox Premium	16	.65	.50	.25
1993 Topps	25	.35	.25	.14
1993 Topps	179	.10	.08	.04
1993 Topps Black Gold	41	2.00	1.50	.80
1993 Topps Stadium Club	105	.80	.60	.30
1993 Upper Deck	78	.10	.08	.04
1993 Upper Deck	352	.40	.30	.15
1993 Upper Deck Pro Bowl	16	7.00	5.25	2.75
1993 Upper Deck SP	184	1.00	.70	.40
1993 Upper Deck Team MVP	16	1.50	1.25	.60
1994 Bowman	50	.40	.30	.15
1994 Fleer	343	.30	.25	.12
1994 Fleer Pro-Visions	1	.40	.30	.15
1994 Fleer Scoring Machines	6	8.00	6.00	3.25
1994 Fleer Ultra	223	.45	.35	.20
1994 Fleer Ultra Hot Numbers	5	.75	.60	.30
1994 GameDay	292	.40	.30	.15
1994 Pacific Crown	96	.30	.25	.12
1994 Pacific Crown Crystalline Collection	7	6.00	4.50	2.50
1994 Pacific Crown Gems of the Crown	12	4.00	3.00	1.50
1994 Pacific Marquee	14	1.75	1.25	.70
1994 Pacific Prisms	47	2.50	2.00	1.00
1994 Pinnacle	177	.40	.30	.15
1994 Pinnacle Performers	17	2.50	2.00	1.00
1994 Pinnacle Sportflics	57	.40	.30	.15
1994 Score	147	.30	.25	.12
1994 Score Select	144	.35	.25	.14
1994 SkyBox Impact	187	.30	.25	.12
1994 SkyBox Premium	111	.35	.25	.14
1994 Topps	5	.30	.25	.12
1994 Topps Finest	214	3.50	2.75	1.50
1994 Topps Finest Inserts	17	10.00	7.50	4.00
1994 Topps Stadium Club	470	.40	.30	.15
1994 Upper Deck	230	.45	.35	.20
1994 Upper Deck Collector's Choice Crash Game	17	9.00	6.75	3.50
1994 Upper Deck Collector's Choice	83	.30	.25	.12
1994 Upper Deck Retail Predictor	14	4.00	3.00	1.50
1994 Upper Deck SP	125	.60	.45	.25
1994 Upper Deck SP All-Pro	27	10.00	7.50	4.00

John Hannah

Set	Card #	NM	EX	VG
1974 Topps	383 (R)	15.00	7.50	4.50
1975 Topps	318	4.00	2.00	1.25
1976 Topps	16	2.00	1.00	.60
1977 Topps	460	1.25	.60	.40
1978 Topps	35	.75	.40	.25
1979 Topps	485	.60	.30	.20
1980 Topps	230	.50	.25	.15

Set	Card #	MT	NM	EX
1981 Topps	80	.40	.30	.15
1982 Topps	150	.25	.20	.10
1982 Topps	151	.10	.08	.04
1982 Topps	267	.20	.15	.08
1983 Topps	330	.25	.20	.10
1984 Topps	137	.15	.11	.06
1985 Topps	326	.20	.15	.08
1986 Topps	36	.20	.15	.08
1991 Pro Set	28	.03	.02	.01
1991 Score	672	.05	.04	.02

Jim Harbaugh

Set	Card #	MT	NM	EX
1989 Topps Traded	91 (R)	.30	.25	.12

1990 Fleer	293	.15	.11	.06
1990 Pro Set	452	.10	.08	.04
1990 Score	232	.10	.08	.04
1990 Topps	366	.20	.15	.08
1991 Bowman	62	.10	.08	.04
1991 Fleer	220	.15	.11	.06
1991 Fleer Ultra	157	.08	.06	.03
1991 Pacific	49	.10	.08	.04
1991 Pinnacle	101	.25	.20	.10
1991 Pro Set	104	.08	.06	.03
1991 Pro Set	716	.04	.03	.02
1991 Pro Set Platinum	10	.08	.06	.03
1991 Score	264	.08	.06	.03
1991 Topps	159	.10	.08	.04
1991 Topps Stadium Club	396	.30	.25	.12
1991 Upper Deck	322	.10	.08	.04
1992 Bowman	316	.35	.25	.14
1992 Fleer	40	.03	.02	.01
1992 Fleer Ultra	40	.05	.04	.02
1992 GameDay	8	.15	.11	.06
1992 Pacific	30	.05	.04	.02
1992 Pinnacle	189	.05	.04	.02
1992 Pro Set	449	.05	.04	.02
1992 Pro Set Power	4	.05	.04	.02
1992 Score	306	.07	.05	.03
1992 SkyBox Impact	206	.08	.06	.03
1992 SkyBox Primetime	325	.10	.08	.04
1992 Topps	185	.05	.04	.02
1992 Topps Stadium Club	81	.08	.06	.03
1992 Upper Deck	273	.05	.04	.02
1992 Upper Deck	351	.05	.04	.02
1993 Bowman	337	.20	.15	.08
1993 Fleer	289	.05	.04	.02
1993 Fleer Ultra	45	.10	.08	.04
1993 GameDay	372	.10	.08	.04
1993 Pacific	134	.05	.04	.02
1993 Pacific Prisms	10	1.25	.90	.50
1993 Pinnacle	308	.10	.08	.04
1993 Pro Set	79	.10	.08	.04
1993 Pro Set Power	104	.05	.04	.02
1993 Score	268	.05	.04	.02
1993 Score Select	130	.10	.08	.04
1993 SkyBox Impact	37	.05	.04	.02
1993 SkyBox Premium	40	.15	.11	.06
1993 Topps	191	.10	.08	.04
1993 Topps Stadium Club	62	.10	.08	.04
1993 Upper Deck	158	.05	.04	.02
1993 Upper Deck SP	42	.25	.20	.10
1994 Bowman	211	.10	.08	.04
1994 Fleer	209	.08	.06	.03
1994 Fleer Ultra	134	.08	.06	.03
1994 Fleer Ultra	409	.08	.06	.03
1994 GameDay	181	.10	.08	.04
1994 Pacific Crown	278	.06	.05	.02
1994 Pacific Prisms	48	1.50	1.25	.60
1994 Pinnacle Sportflics	134	.15	.11	.06
1994 Score Select	102	.10	.08	.04
1994 SkyBox Impact	35	.06	.05	.02
1994 SkyBox Premium	70	.08	.06	.03
1994 Topps	610	.05	.04	.02
1994 Topps Finest	209	1.25	.90	.50
1994 Topps Stadium Club	392	.10	.08	.04
1994 Upper Deck	109	.10	.08	.04
1994 Upper Deck	193	.05	.04	.02
1994 Upper Deck Collector's Choice				
1994 Upper Deck SP	28	.20	.15	.08

Values for recent cards and sets are listed in Mint (MT), Near Mint (NM), reflecting the fact that many cards from recent years have been preserved in to condition. Recent cards and sets in less than Excellent condition have little collector interest.

Alvin Harper

Set	Card #	MT	NM	EX
1991 Bowman	122 (R)	1.50	1.25	.60
1991 Pro Set	741 (R)	1.50	1.25	.60
1991 Score	589 (R)	1.50	1.25	.60
1991 Score Supplemental	71	.80	.60	.30
1991 Topps	375 (R)	1.75	1.25	.70
1991 Upper Deck	24 (R)	1.25	.90	.50
1991 Upper Deck	634	.60	.45	.25
1992 Bowman	335	3.75	2.75	1.50
1992 Fleer	80	.45	.35	.20
1992 Fleer Ultra	80	.60	.45	.25
1992 GameDay	467	.75	.60	.30
1992 Pacific	394	.50	.40	.20
1992 Pinnacle	299	.75	.60	.30
1992 Pro Set Power	265	.60	.45	.25
1992 SkyBox Impact	170	.40	.30	.15
1992 SkyBox Primetime	339	.75	.60	.30
1992 Topps	28	.50	.40	.20
1992 Topps Stadium Club	549	.85	.60	.35
1992 Upper Deck	34	.30	.25	.12
1992 Upper Deck	470	.40	.30	.15
1992 Upper Deck Coach's Report	6	6.00	4.50	2.50
1993 Bowman	222	1.25	.90	.50
1993 Fleer	101	.30	.25	.12
1993 Fleer Ultra	90	.85	.60	.35
1993 GameDay	326	.60	.45	.25
1993 Pacific	6	.30	.25	.12
1993 Pacific Prisms	19	4.50	3.50	1.75
1993 Pinnacle	90	.70	.50	.30
1993 Pinnacle Super Bowl XXVII	9	15.00	11.00	6.00
1993 Pro Set	33	.25	.20	.10
1993 Pro Set Power Update Combos	4	2.50	2.00	1.00
1993 Score	371	.50	.40	.20
1993 SkyBox Impact	69	.25	.20	.10
1993 SkyBox Premium	253	.75	.60	.30
1993 Topps	225	.30	.25	.12
1993 Topps Stadium Club	17	.60	.45	.25
1993 Upper Deck	239	.25	.20	.10
1993 Upper Deck Dallas Cowboys	1	1.00	.70	.40
1994 Fleer	111	.30	.25	.12
1994 Fleer Ultra	370	.15	.11	.06
1994 GameDay	95	.10	.08	.04
1994 Pacific Crown	3	.10	.08	.04
1994 Pacific Crown Gems of the Crown	13	2.50	2.00	1.00
1994 Pacific Prisms	49	1.50	1.25	.60
1994 Pinnacle	30	.15	.11	.06
1994 Pinnacle Sportflics	19	.50	.40	.20
1994 Score	231	.10	.08	.04
1994 Score Select	85	.10	.08	.04
1994 SkyBox Impact	58	.20	.15	.08
1994 SkyBox Premium	38	.12	.09	.05
1994 Topps	548	.08	.06	.03
1994 Topps	650	.05	.04	.02
1994 Topps Stadium Club	282	.15	.11	.06
1994 Upper Deck	217	.15	.11	.06

1994 Upper Deck	328	.08	.06	.03
Collector's Choice				
1994 Upper Deck SP	119	.40	.30	.15

Franco Harris

Set	Card #	NM	EX	VG
1973 Topps	89 (R)	50.00	25.00	15.00
1974 Topps	220	20.00	10.00	6.00
1975 Topps	300	12.00	6.00	3.50
1976 Topps	100	7.00	3.50	2.00
1977 Topps	300	4.00	2.00	1.25
1978 Topps	500	2.50	1.25	.70
1979 Topps	300	2.00	1.00	.60
1980 Topps	400	1.75	.90	.50

Set	Card #	MT	NM	EX
1981 Topps	220	1.50	1.25	.60
1982 Topps	211	.75	.60	.30
1982 Topps	212	.50	.40	.20
1983 Topps	355	.25	.20	.10
1983 Topps	362	.75	.60	.30
1984 Topps	3	.25	.20	.10
1984 Topps	159	.25	.20	.10
1984 Topps	165	.75	.60	.30
1984 Topps	166	.30	.25	.12
1989 Score Franco Harris	1A	80.00	60.00	32.00
1989 Score Franco Harris	1B	65.00	49.00	26.00
1990 Pro Set	25	.03	.02	.01
1990 Pro Set Super Bowl MVPs	9	.30	.25	.12
1990 Score	595	.08	.06	.03
1990 Score Franco Harris	1	125.00	94.00	50.00
1991 Pinnacle	387	.15	.11	.06

Michael Haynes

Set	Card #	MT	NM	EX
1990 Pro Set	431 (R)	.75	.60	.30
1990 Topps	471 (R)	1.00	.70	.40

1991 Bowman	17	.30	.25	.12
1991 Fleer	202	.25	.20	.10
1991 Pro Set	95	.03	.02	.01
1991 Topps	578	.35	.25	.14
1991 Topps Stadium Club	447	2.00	1.50	.80
1991 Upper Deck	567	.30	.25	.12
1992 Bowman	11	1.00	.70	.40
1992 Fleer	7	.25	.20	.10
1992 Fleer Ultra	8	.50	.40	.20
1992 GameDay	429	.15	.11	.06
1992 Pacific	4	.30	.25	.12
1992 Pinnacle	283	.40	.30	.15
1992 Pro Set	57	.08	.06	.03
1992 Pro Set	112	.35	.25	.14
1992 Pro Set Power	181	.60	.45	.25
1992 Score	44	.25	.20	.10
1992 SkyBox Impact	213	.30	.25	.12
1992 SkyBox Primetime	324	.50	.40	.20
1992 Topps	265	.25	.20	.10
1992 Topps Stadium Club	30	.60	.45	.25
1992 Topps 1000-Yard Club	7	1.50	1.25	.60
1992 Upper Deck	171	.30	.25	.12
1992 Upper Deck Game Breaker Holograms	7	2.00	1.50	.80
1993 Fleer	99	.20	.15	.08
1993 Fleer Ultra	7	.30	.25	.12
1993 GameDay	28	.35	.25	.14
1993 Pacific	181	.15	.11	.06
1993 Pinnacle	201	.35	.25	.14
1993 Pro Set	64	.15	.11	.06
1993 Pro Set Power	181	.30	.25	.12
1993 Pro Set Power Update Combos	1	1.00	.70	.40
1993 Score	403	.20	.15	.08
1993 SkyBox Impact	2	.10	.08	.04
1993 SkyBox Premium	76	.30	.25	.12
1993 Topps	59	.20	.15	.08
1993 Topps Stadium Club	318	.15	.11	.06
1993 Upper Deck	261	.10	.08	.04
1993 Upper Deck SP	21	.25	.20	.10
1994 Bowman	186	.10	.08	.04
1994 Fleer	324	.25	.20	.10
1994 Fleer Ultra	211	.12	.09	.05
1994 Fleer Ultra	457	.08	.06	.03
1994 GameDay	276	.10	.08	.04
1994 Pacific Crown	290	.06	.05	.02
1994 Pinnacle	145	.12	.09	.05
1994 Pinnacle Sportflics	137	.15	.11	.06
1994 Score	109	.15	.11	.06
1994 Score Select	189	.10	.08	.04
1994 SkyBox Impact	12	.20	.15	.08
1994 SkyBox Premium	105	.25	.20	.10
1994 Topps	435	.05	.04	.02
1994 Topps Finest	180	1.50	1.25	.60
1994 Topps Stadium Club	226	.12	.09	.05
1994 Topps Stadium Club	407	.12	.09	.05
1994 Upper Deck	45	.15	.11	.06
1994 Upper Deck Collector's Choice	103	.08	.06	.03
1994 Upper Deck SP	177	.20	.15	.08

Grading Guide

Mint (MT): A perfect card. Well-centered with all corners sharp and square. No creases, stains, edge nicks, surface marks, yellowing or fading.

Near Mint (NM): A nearly perfect card. At first glance, a NM card appears to be perfect. May be slightly off-center. No surface marks, creases or loss of gloss.

Excellent (EX): Corners are still fairly sharp with only moderate wear. Borders may be off-center. No creases or stains on fronts or backs, but may show slight loss of surface luster.

Very Good (VG): Shows obvious handling. May have rounded corners, minor creases, major gum or wax stains. No major creases, tape marks, writing, etc.

Good (G): A well-worn card, but exhibits no intentional damage. May have major or multiple creases. Corners may be rounded well beyond card border.

Garrison Hearst

Set	Card #	MT	NM	EX
1993 Bowman	20 (R)	1.25	.90	.50
1993 Fleer NFL Prospects	2	3.00	2.25	1.25
1993 Fleer Ultra	380 (R)	.75	.60	.30
1993 Fleer Ultra All-Rookie	5	4.00	3.00	1.50
1993 GameDay	257 (R)	.75	.60	.30
1993 GameDay Rookie Standouts	3	3.00	2.25	1.25
1993 Pacific	423 (R)	.50	.40	.20
1993 Pacific Gold Prisms	7	10.00	7.50	4.00
1993 Pacific Prism Inserts	7	6.00	4.50	2.50
1993 Pacific Prisms	82	5.00	3.75	2.00
1993 Pacific Triple Folder Superstars	11 (R)	.75	.60	.30
1993 Pacific Triple Folders	27	1.00	.70	.40
1993 Pinnacle Rookies	2	25.00	18.50	10.00
1993 Pro Set	351 (R)	.50	.40	.20
1993 Pro Set All-Rookie Forecast	2	25.00	18.50	10.00
1993 Pro Set College Connections	5	2.00	1.50	.80
1993 Pro Set Power Draft Picks	22	1.00	.70	.40
1993 Pro Set Power Update Prospects	8 (R)	1.00	.70	.40
1993 Pro Set Rookie Running Backs	3	2.00	1.50	.80
1993 Score	315 (R)	.50	.40	.20
1993 Score Select	171 (R)	2.00	1.50	.80
1993 SkyBox Impact	363 (R)	.50	.40	.20
1993 SkyBox Premium	196 (R)	1.00	.70	.40
1993 SkyBox Primetime Rookies	4	10.00	7.50	4.00
1993 Topps	101 (R)	.75	.60	.30
1993 Topps	385	.50	.40	.20
1993 Topps Stadium Club	82 (R)	1.00	.70	.40
1993 Upper Deck	23 (R)	.50	.40	.20
1993 Upper Deck	69	.40	.30	.15
1993 Upper Deck Rookie Exchange	4	4.00	3.00	1.50
1993 Upper Deck SP	13 (R)	1.50	1.25	.60
1994 Bowman	241	1.35	1.00	.50
1994 Fleer	8	.10	.08	.04
1994 Fleer Rookie Sensations	7	7.00	5.25	2.75
1994 Fleer Ultra	326	.15	.11	.06
1994 GameDay	4	.25	.20	.10
1994 Pacific Crown	308	.06	.05	.02
1994 Pacific Prisms	51	2.00	1.50	.80
1994 Pinnacle	95	.25	.20	.10
1994 Pinnacle Performers	16	2.50	2.00	1.00
1994 Pinnacle Sportflics	85	.25	.20	.10
1994 Score	320	.20	.15	.08
1994 Score Select	17	.25	.20	.10
1994 Score Select Future Force	12	8.00	6.00	3.25
1994 Score Sophomore Showcase	14	5.00	3.75	2.00
1994 SkyBox Impact	4	.08	.06	.03
1994 SkyBox Impact Instant Impact	12	2.25	1.75	.90
1994 SkyBox Premium	3	.25	.20	.10
1994 Topps	340	.25	.20	.10
1994 Topps Finest	218	5.00	3.75	2.00
1994 Upper Deck	269	.20	.15	.08
1994 Upper Deck Collector's Choice	155	.10	.08	.04

Ted Hendricks

Set	Card #	NM	EX	VG
1972 Topps	93 (R)	20.00	10.00	6.00
1972 Topps	281	45.00	22.00	13.50
1973 Topps	430	4.00	2.00	1.25
1974 Topps	385	3.00	1.50	.90
1975 Topps	315	1.50	.70	.45
1976 Topps	76	1.25	.60	.40
1978 Topps	68	.75	.40	.25
1979 Topps	345	.50	.25	.15
1980 Topps	489	.50	.25	.15

Set	Card #	MT	NM	EX
1981 Topps	200	.15	.11	.06
1982 Topps	190	.05	.04	.02
1983 Topps	302	.15	.11	.06
1984 Topps	110	.20	.15	.08
1990 Pro Set	26	.03	.02	.01
1990 Score	599	.04	.03	.02

Drew Hill

Set	Card #	MT	NM	EX
1982 Topps	379 (R)	3.00	2.25	1.25
1986 Topps	353	.30	.25	.12
1986 Topps 1000 Yard Club	14	.10	.08	.04

Set	Card #	NM	EX	VG
1987 Topps	309	.25	.20	.10
1987 Topps 1000 Yard Club	16	.15	.11	.06
1988 Topps	106	.20	.15	.08
1988 Topps 1000 Yard Club	7	.10	.08	.04
1989 Pro Set	146	.03	.02	.01
1989 Score	95	.10	.08	.04
1989 Topps	95	.05	.04	.02
1989 Topps 1000 Yard Club	11	.10	.08	.04
1990 Fleer	130	.03	.02	.01
1990 Pro Set	122	.03	.02	.01
1990 Pro Set	792	.03	.02	.01
1990 Score	185	.04	.03	.02
1990 Topps	217	.04	.03	.02
1991 Bowman	195	.03	.02	.01
1991 Fleer	62	.10	.08	.04
1991 Fleer Ultra	49	.08	.06	.03
1991 Pacific	174	.04	.03	.02
1991 Pinnacle	189	.10	.08	.04
1991 Pro Set	516	.03	.02	.01
1991 Pro Set Platinum	196	.05	.04	.02
1991 Score	215	.04	.03	.02
1991 Topps	231	.04	.03	.02
1991 Topps Stadium Club	440	.30	.25	.12
1991 Topps 1000 Yard Club	15	.25	.20	.10
1991 Upper Deck	33	.10	.08	.04
1991 Upper Deck	260	.05	.04	.02
1992 Pacific	112	.05	.04	.02
1992 Pinnacle	242	.05	.04	.02
1992 Pro Set	430	.05	.04	.02
1992 Score	360	.05	.04	.02
1992 Topps	483	.05	.04	.02
1992 Topps 1000-Yard Club	8	.50	.40	.20
1992 Upper Deck	533	.05	.04	.02
1992 Upper Deck Game Breaker Holograms	2	1.75	1.25	.70
1993 GameDay	120	.10	.08	.04
1993 Pacific	171	.05	.04	.02
1993 Pro Set Power Update Combos	1	1.00	.70	.40
1993 Topps	403	.05	.04	.02
1993 Upper Deck	453	.05	.04	.02

Paul Hornung

Set	Card #	NM	EX	VG
1957 Topps	151 (R)	400.00	200.00	120.00
1959 Topps	82	60.00	30.00	18.00
1960 Topps	54	35.00	17.50	10.50
1961 Fleer	90	42.00	21.00	12.50
1961 Topps	40	28.00	14.00	8.50
1962 Topps	64	45.00	22.00	13.50
1964 Philadelphia	74	25.00	12.50	7.50
1965 Philadelphia	76	25.00	12.50	7.50
1967 Philadelphia	123	18.00	9.00	5.50

Jeff Hostetler

Set	Card #	MT	NM	EX
1990 Fleer	67 (R)	.75	.60	.30
1990 Pro Set	596 (R)	.75	.60	.30
1991 Bowman	363	.15	.11	.06
1991 Fleer	312	.10	.08	.04
1991 Fleer Ultra Update	64	.25	.20	.10
1991 Pacific	347	.20	.15	.08
1991 Pinnacle	50	.50	.40	.20
1991 Pro Set	63	.15	.11	.06
1991 Pro Set Platinum	79	.25	.20	.10
1991 Score	1B	.25	.20	.10
1991 Score	475	.20	.15	.08
1991 Topps	28	.25	.20	.10
1991 Topps Stadium Club	110	1.00	.70	.40
1991 Upper Deck	156	.20	.15	.08
1992 Bowman	66	.75	.60	.30
1992 Fleer	293	.10	.08	.04
1992 Fleer Ultra	278	.25	.20	.10
1992 GameDay	87	.25	.20	.10
1992 Pacific	212	.15	.11	.06
1992 Pinnacle	126	.25	.20	.10
1992 Pro Set	265	.20	.15	.08
1992 Pro Set Power	15	.35	.25	.14
1992 Score	179	.20	.15	.08
1992 SkyBox Impact	67	.20	.15	.08
1992 SkyBox Primetime	207	.25	.20	.10
1992 Topps	96	.15	.11	.06
1992 Topps Stadium Club	341	.30	.25	.12
1992 Upper Deck	326	.20	.15	.08
1993 Bowman	165	.20	.15	.08
1993 Fleer	493	.15	.11	.06
1993 Fleer Ultra	220	.10	.08	.04
1993 GameDay	382	.20	.15	.08
1993 Pacific	409	.20	.15	.08
1993 Pinnacle	272	.15	.11	.06
1993 Pro Set	215	.10	.08	.04
1993 Pro Set Power	115	.10	.08	.04
1993 Pro Set Power Power Moves	12	.25	.20	.10
1993 Pro Set Power Update Moves	12	.15	.11	.06
1993 Score	221	.10	.08	.04
1993 Score Select	99	.25	.20	.10
1993 SkyBox Impact	161	.10	.08	.04
1993 SkyBox Premium	23	.15	.11	.06
1993 Topps	475	.08	.06	.03
1993 Topps Stadium Club	330	.15	.11	.06
1993 Upper Deck	528	.10	.08	.04
1993 Upper Deck SP	129	.30	.25	.12
1994 Bowman	255	.15	.11	.06
1994 Fleer	234	.15	.11	.06
1994 Fleer Ultra	152	.12	.09	.05
1994 GameDay	202	.10	.08	.04
1994 Pacific Crown	111	.06	.05	.02
1994 Pacific Crown Gems of the Crown	14	2.50	2.00	1.00
1994 Pacific Prisms	54	1.00	.70	.40
1994 Pinnacle	10	.10	.08	.04
1994 Pinnacle Sportflics	7	.25	.20	.10
1994 Score	184	.06	.05	.02

1994 Score Select	46	.10 .08 .04
1994 SkyBox Impact	130	.15 .11 .06
1994 SkyBox Premium	81	.10 .08 .04
1994 Topps	155	.15 .11 .06
1994 Topps Finest	162	1.50 1.25 .60
1994 Topps Finest Inserts	31	3.50 2.75 1.50
1994 Topps Stadium Club	450	.12 .09 .05
1994 Upper Deck	134	.12 .09 .05
1994 Upper Deck	296	.07 .05 .03
Collector's Choice		
1994 Upper Deck SP	93	.30 .25 .12

A card number in parentheses ()
indicates the set is unnumbered.

Ken Houston

Set	Card #	NM	EX	VG
1971 Topps	113 (R)	20.00	10.00	6.00
1972 Topps	78	4.00	2.00	1.25
1972 Topps	287	27.50	13.50	8.25
1973 Topps	415	1.75	.90	.50
1974 Topps	235	1.50	.70	.45
1975 Topps	354	.60	.30	.20
1975 Topps	519	1.25	.60	.40
1976 Topps	170	1.00	.50	.30
1977 Topps	450	.75	.40	.25
1978 Topps	10	.75	.40	.25
1978 Topps	528	1.00	.50	.30
1979 Topps	350	.50	.25	.15
1980 Topps	145	.50	.25	.15

Michael Irvin

Set	Card #	MT	NM	EX
1989 Pro Set	89 (R)	3.50	2.75	1.50

1989 Score	18 (R)	22.00	16.50	8.75
1989 Topps	383 (R)	4.50	3.50	1.75
1990 Fleer	389	.60	.45	.25
1990 Pro Set	79	.85	.60	.35
1991 Bowman	120	.55	.40	.20
1991 Fleer Ultra	163	.45	.35	.20
1991 Pacific	97	.50	.40	.20
1991 Pinnacle	199	2.25	1.75	.90
1991 Pro Set	132	.55	.40	.20
1991 Pro Set Platinum	178	.60	.45	.25
1991 Score	452	.65	.50	.25
1991 Topps	368	.65	.50	.25
1991 Topps Stadium Club	37	4.50	3.50	1.75
1991 Upper Deck	107	.65	.50	.25
1992 Bowman	13	9.50	7.25	3.75
1992 Bowman	258	6.50	5.00	2.50
1992 Fleer	83	.40	.30	.15
1992 Fleer	455	.20	.15	.08
1992 Fleer All-Pro	6	2.00	1.50	.80
1992 Fleer Ultra	83	.75	.60	.30
1992 Fleer Ultra Award	6	6.50	4.90	2.60
Winners				
1992 GameDay	373	1.50	1.25	.60
1992 Pacific	65	.75	.60	.30
1992 Pinnacle	42	1.00	.70	.40
1992 Pinnacle Team	6	10.00	7.50	4.00
Pinnacle				
1992 Pro Set	10	.20	.15	.08
1992 Pro Set	49	.10	.08	.04
1992 Pro Set	348	.30	.25	.12
1992 Pro Set	409	.35	.25	.14
1992 Pro Set	476	.60	.45	.25
1992 Pro Set Power	88	1.00	.70	.40
1992 Pro Set Power	5	30.00	22.00	12.00
Power Combos				
1992 Score	40	.60	.45	.25
1992 Score Dream Team	1	17.00	12.50	6.75
1992 SkyBox Impact	11	.50	.40	.20
1992 SkyBox Impact	310	.30	.25	.12
1992 SkyBox Impact	13	3.00	2.25	1.25
Major Impact				
1992 SkyBox Primetime	88	1.50	1.25	.60
1992 SkyBox Primetime	176	.50	.40	.20
1992 SkyBox Primetime	344	.50	.40	.20
1992 SkyBox Primetime	13	7.50	5.63	3.00
Poster Cards				
1992 Topps	340	.55	.40	.20
1992 Topps Stadium Club	299	1.25	.90	.50
1992 Topps Stadium Club	447	1.75	1.25	.70
1992 Topps 1000-Yard	3	3.50	2.75	1.50
Club				
1992 Upper Deck	303	.25	.20	.10
1992 Upper Deck	345	.50	.40	.20
1992 Upper Deck	361	.25	.20	.10
1992 Upper Deck Game	9	3.50	2.75	1.50
Breaker Holograms				
1992 Upper Deck Pro	1	4.00	3.00	1.50
Bowl				
1993 Bowman	170	2.75	2.00	1.00
1993 Fleer	127	.40	.30	.15
1993 Fleer	246	.25	.20	.10
1993 Fleer Ultra	91	.80	.60	.30
1993 Fleer Ultra Ultra	3	15.00	11.00	6.00
Stars				
1993 GameDay	50	1.00	.70	.40
1993 GameDay Game	11	1.25	.90	.50
Breakers				
1993 Pacific	7	.50	.40	.20
1993 Pacific Gold Prisms	8	20.00	15.00	8.00
1993 Pacific Prism Inserts	8	12.00	9.00	4.75
1993 Pacific Prisms	20	7.50	5.63	3.00
1993 Pinnacle	133	1.00	.70	.40
1993 Pinnacle Men of	6	1.00	.75	.40
Autumn				
1993 Pinnacle Super	5	20.00	15.00	8.00
Bowl XXVII				
1993 Pinnacle Team	5	30.00	22.00	12.00
Pinnacle				
1993 Pro Set	34	.35	.25	.14
1993 Pro Set Power	88	.40	.30	.15

1993 Pro Set Power Update Combos	4	2.50	2.00	1.00
1993 Score	10	.35	.25	.14
1993 Score Select	83	2.25	1.75	.90
1993 Score Select Gridiron Skills	10	50.00	37.00	20.00
1993 SkyBox Impact	71	.40	.30	.15
1993 SkyBox Premium	91	1.00	.70	.40
1993 SkyBox Thunder and Lightning	6	18.00	13.50	7.25
1993 Topps	630	.35	.25	.14
1993 Topps Black Gold	7	3.75	2.75	1.50
1993 Topps Stadium Club	129	1.00	.70	.40
1993 Upper Deck	337	.40	.30	.15
1993 Upper Deck America's Team	13	20.00	15.00	8.00
1993 Upper Deck Dallas Cowboys	17	1.50	1.25	.60
1993 Upper Deck Pro Bowl	10	16.00	12.00	6.50
1993 Upper Deck SP	66	3.00	2.25	1.25
1994 Bowman	332	.10	.08	.04
1994 Fleer	112	.50	.40	.20
1994 Fleer All-Pro	5	1.50	1.25	.60
1994 Fleer Scoring Machines	7	15.00	11.00	6.00
1994 Fleer Ultra	71	.65	.50	.25
1994 Fleer Ultra Hot Numbers	6	1.50	1.25	.60
1994 Fleer Ultra Ultra Stars	4	20.00	15.00	8.00
1994 GameDay	96	.50	.40	.20
1994 GameDay Game Breakers	5	1.50	1.25	.60
1994 Pacific Crown	4	.35	.25	.14
1994 Pacific Marquee	15	2.50	2.00	1.00
1994 Pacific Prisms	55	5.00	3.75	2.00
1994 Pinnacle	7	.65	.50	.25
1994 Pinnacle Performers	8	6.00	4.50	2.50
1994 Pinnacle Sportflics	76	1.00	.70	.40
1994 Pinnacle Team Pinnacle	8	30.00	22.00	12.00
1994 Score	60	.35	.25	.14
1994 Score Dream Team	5	15.00	11.00	6.00
1994 Score Select	95	.65	.50	.25
1994 SkyBox Impact	59	.45	.35	.20
1994 SkyBox Impact Ultimate Impact	3	4.00	3.00	1.50
1994 SkyBox Premium	39	.60	.45	.25
1994 SkyBox Premium Revolution	4	7.00	5.25	2.75
1994 SkyBox Premium SkyTech Stars	3	5.00	3.75	2.00
1994 Topps	203	.20	.15	.08
1994 Topps	318	.15	.11	.06
1994 Topps	328	.30	.25	.12
1994 Topps All-Pros	1	12.00	9.00	4.75
1994 Topps Finest	79	9.00	6.75	3.50
1994 Topps Finest Inserts	14	13.00	9.75	5.25
1994 Topps Stadium Club	270	.50	.40	.20
1994 Topps Stadium Club Ring Leaders	10	15.00	11.00	6.00
1994 Upper Deck	307	.60	.45	.25
1994 Upper Deck Collector's Choice Crash Game	23	10.00	7.50	4.00
1994 Upper Deck Collector's Choice	307	.35	.25	.14
1994 Upper Deck Retail Predictor	24	6.00	4.50	2.50
1994 Upper Deck SP	120	1.00	.70	.40

Qadry Ismail

Set	Card #	MT	NM	EX
1993 Bowman	321 (R)	1.00	.70	.40
1993 Fleer NFL Prospects	24	5.00	3.75	2.00
1993 Fleer Ultra	272 (R)	1.00	.70	.40
1993 Fleer Ultra All-Rookie	6	2.50	2.00	1.00
1993 GameDay	470 (R)	1.25	.90	.50
1993 GameDay Rookie Standouts	8	1.75	1.25	.70
1993 Pacific	438 (R)	.50	.40	.20
1993 Pro Set	261 (R)	.50	.40	.20
1993 Pro Set Power Draft Picks	7	.50	.40	.20
1993 Pro Set Power Update Prospects	23 (R)	.75	.60	.30
1993 Topps	448 (R)	.50	.40	.20
1993 Topps Stadium Club	526 (R)	.75	.60	.30
1993 Upper Deck	24 (R)	.50	.40	.20
1993 Upper Deck SP	158 (R)	1.25	.90	.50
1994 Bowman	231	.20	.15	.08
1994 Fleer	295	.30	.25	.12
1994 Fleer Ultra	440	.30	.25	.12
1994 GameDay	249	.25	.20	.10
1994 Pacific Crown	156	.20	.15	.08
1994 Pacific Prisms	56	1.25	.90	.50
1994 Pinnacle	63	.25	.20	.10
1994 SkyBox Impact	159	.25	.20	.10
1994 SkyBox Premium	93	.20	.15	.08
1994 Topps	90	.50	.40	.20
1994 Topps Finest	128	2.75	2.05	1.10
1994 Topps Stadium Club	18	.25	.20	.10
1994 Topps Stadium Club	72	.10	.08	.04
1994 Upper Deck	287	.25	.20	.10
1994 Upper Deck Collector's Choice	297	.20	.15	.08
1994 Upper Deck SP	144	.50	.40	.20

Grading Guide

Mint (MT): A perfect card. Well-centered with all corners sharp and square. No creases, stains, edge nicks, surface marks, yellowing or fading.

Near Mint (NM): A nearly perfect card. At first glance, a NM card appears to be perfect. May be slightly off-center. No surface marks, creases or loss of gloss.

Excellent (EX): Corners are still fairly sharp with only moderate wear. Borders may be off-center. No creases or stains on fronts or backs, but may show slight loss of surface luster.

Very Good (VG): Shows obvious handling. May have rounded corners, minor creases, major gum or wax stains. No major creases, tape marks, writing, etc.

Good (G): A well-worn card, but exhibits no intentional damage. May have major or multiple creases. Corners may be rounded well beyond card border.

Raghib Ismail

Keith Jackson

Set	Card #	MT	NM	EX
1991 Pro Set	36 (R)	2.00	1.50	.80
1992 Topps Stadium Club No. 1 Draft Picks	4	28.00	21.00	11.50
1993 Bowman	101	1.00	.70	.40
1993 Pro Set	218	.30	.25	.12
1993 Pro Set All-Rookie Forecast	7	25.00	18.50	10.00
1993 Pro Set College Connections	4	1.75	1.25	.70
1993 Pro Set Power Update Combos	9	2.00	1.50	.80
1993 Pro Set Power Update Prospects	22	.40	.30	.15
1993 Topps	395	.50	.40	.20
1993 Topps Stadium Club	532	.75	.60	.30
1993 Upper Deck SP	131	1.00	.70	.40
1994 Bowman	201	.35	.25	.14
1994 Fleer	235	.12	.09	.05
1994 Fleer Ultra	153	.25	.20	.10
1994 GameDay	203	.25	.20	.10
1994 Pacific Crown	112	.20	.15	.08
1994 Pacific Crown Knights of the Gridiron	12	3.00	2.25	1.25
1994 Pacific Prisms	57	1.50	1.25	.60
1994 Pinnacle	159	.20	.15	.08
1994 Pinnacle Sportflics	122	.25	.20	.10
1994 Score	266	.15	.11	.06
1994 Score Select	112	.20	.15	.08
1994 Score Sophomore Showcase	12	5.00	3.75	2.00
1994 SkyBox Impact	128	.15	.11	.06
1994 SkyBox Premium	80	.15	.11	.06
1994 Topps	458	.20	.15	.08
1994 Topps Finest	8	3.00	2.25	1.25
1994 Topps Stadium Club	306	.25	.20	.10
1994 Upper Deck	224	.40	.30	.15
1994 Upper Deck Collector's Choice	50	.20	.15	.08
1994 Upper Deck Collector's Choice	310	.15	.11	.06
1994 Upper Deck SP	95	.40	.30	.15

The values quoted are intended
to reflect the market price.

Values quoted in this guide reflect the
retail price of a card – the price a collector
can expect to pay when buying a card from a
dealer. The wholesale price – that which a collector
can expect to receive from a dealer when selling
cards – will be significantly lower, depending on
desirability and condition.

Set	Card #	MT	NM	EX
1989 Pro Set	318 (R)	1.50	1.25	.60
1989 Score	101 (R)	5.00	3.75	2.00
1989 Score	281	.25	.20	.10
1989 Score	293	2.00	1.50	.80
1989 Topps	107 (R)	1.25	.90	.50
1990 Fleer	86	.20	.15	.08
1990 Fleer All-Pro	3	.50	.40	.20
1990 Fleer Stars 'n Stripes	75	.25	.20	.10
1990 Pro Set	248	.25	.20	.10
1990 Pro Set	396	.08	.06	.03
1990 Score	210	.25	.20	.10
1990 Score	588	.08	.06	.03
1990 Score Young Superstars	6	.25	.20	.10
1990 Score 100 Hottest	46	.30	.25	.12
1990 Topps	85	.25	.20	.10
1991 Bowman	396	.15	.11	.06
1991 Fleer	329	.06	.05	.02
1991 Fleer All-Pro	12	.30	.20	.12
1991 Fleer Ultra	233	.15	.11	.06
1991 Fleer Ultra All Stars	2	.75	.60	.30
1991 Pacific	388	.20	.15	.08
1991 Pinnacle	343	.35	.25	.14
1991 Pro Set	386	.05	.04	.02
1991 Pro Set	618	.10	.08	.04
1991 Pro Set Platinum	249	.10	.08	.04
1991 Score	371	.08	.06	.03
1991 Score	681	.05	.04	.02
1991 Topps	220	.15	.11	.06
1991 Topps Stadium Club	230	.50	.40	.20
1991 Upper Deck	31	.10	.08	.04
1991 Upper Deck	127	.15	.11	.06
1992 Bowman	191	.75	.60	.30
1992 Fleer	320	.10	.08	.04
1992 Fleer Ultra	309	.15	.11	.06
1992 GameDay	88	.15	.11	.06
1992 Pacific	563	.15	.11	.06
1992 Pinnacle	88	.10	.08	.04
1992 Pro Set	283	.10	.08	.04
1992 Pro Set	558	.05	.04	.02
1992 Pro Set Power	200	.15	.11	.06
1992 Score	104	.15	.11	.06
1992 SkyBox Impact	168	.10	.08	.04
1992 SkyBox Primetime	59	.25	.20	.10
1992 Topps	489	.15	.11	.06
1992 Topps Stadium Club	242	.15	.11	.06
1992 Upper Deck	85	.05	.04	.02
1992 Upper Deck	282	.05	.04	.02
1993 Bowman	85	.25	.20	.10
1993 Fleer	360	.15	.11	.06
1993 Fleer Ultra	256	.15	.11	.06
1993 GameDay	137	.15	.11	.06
1993 Pacific	215	.15	.11	.06
1993 Pacific Prisms	54	1.25	.90	.50
1993 Pinnacle	300	.15	.11	.06
1993 Pinnacle Men of Autumn	43	.30	.25	.12

1993 Pinnacle Team Pinnacle	6	10.00	7.50	4.00
1993 Pro Set	249	.05	.04	.02
1993 Pro Set Power	188	.05	.04	.02
1993 Score	229	.10	.08	.04
1993 Score Dream Team	6	.75	.60	.30
1993 Score Select	142	.25	.20	.10
1993 SkyBox Impact	181	.10	.08	.04
1993 SkyBox Impact Kelly's Heroes/ Magic's Kingdom	3	2.00	1.50	.80
1993 SkyBox Premium	215	.15	.11	.06
1993 Topps	645	.08	.06	.03
1993 Topps Stadium Club	186	.20	.15	.08
1993 Upper Deck	240	.05	.04	.02
1993 Upper Deck SP	148	.25	.20	.10
1994 Fleer	278	.12	.09	.05
1994 Fleer Ultra	437	.08	.06	.03
1994 GameDay	238	.10	.08	.04
1994 Pacific Crown	187	.06	.05	.02
1994 Pinnacle	184	.09	.07	.04
1994 Pinnacle Sportflics	110	.15	.11	.06
1994 Score	223	.08	.06	.03
1994 Score Select	160	.10	.08	.04
1994 SkyBox Impact	150	.10	.08	.04
1994 SkyBox Premium	88	.10	.08	.04
1994 Topps	43	.10	.08	.04
1994 Topps Finest	73	2.50	2.00	1.00
1994 Topps Stadium Club	137	.12	.09	.05
1994 Upper Deck	286	.12	.09	.05
1994 Upper Deck Collector's Choice	171	.05	.04	.02

1992 Pacific	375	.10	.08	.04
1992 Pro Set	138	.20	.15	.08
1992 Pro Set Power	101	.30	.25	.12
1992 Topps	77	.10	.08	.04
1992 Topps Stadium Club	225	.25	.20	.10
1992 Upper Deck	68	.15	.11	.06
1993 Fleer	4	.05	.04	.02
1993 Fleer Ultra	77	.08	.06	.03
1993 GameDay	316	.10	.08	.04
1993 Pacific	304	.05	.04	.02
1993 Pacific Prisms	15	1.25	.90	.50
1993 Pro Set	108	.05	.04	.02
1993 Pro Set Power	101	.10	.08	.04
1993 SkyBox Impact	56	.05	.04	.02
1993 SkyBox Premium	31	.15	.11	.06
1993 Topps	534	.06	.05	.02
1993 Topps Stadium Club	4	.10	.08	.04
1993 Upper Deck	335	.05	.04	.02
1994 Bowman	182	.10	.08	.04
1994 Fleer	95	.25	.20	.10
1994 Fleer Ultra	57	.08	.06	.03
1994 GameDay	80	.10	.08	.04
1994 Pacific Crown	258	.06	.05	.02
1994 Pinnacle	140	.09	.07	.04
1994 Pinnacle Sportflics	18	.15	.11	.06
1994 Score	49	.08	.06	.03
1994 Score Select	44	.10	.08	.04
1994 SkyBox Impact	50	.20	.15	.08
1994 SkyBox Premium	33	.12	.09	.05
1994 Topps	483	.05	.04	.02
1994 Topps Finest	189	1.50	1.25	.60
1994 Topps Stadium Club	370	.10	.08	.04
1994 Upper Deck	246	.12	.09	.05
1994 Upper Deck Collector's Choice	182	.07	.05	.03
1994 Upper Deck SP	60	.20	.15	.08

Values for recent cards and sets are listed in Mint (MT), Near Mint (NM), reflecting the fact that many cards from recent years have been preserved in to condition. Recent cards and sets in less than Excellent condition have little collector interest.

Michael Jackson

Set	Card #	MT	NM	EX
1991 Fleer Ultra Update	16 (R)	1.25	.90	.50
1991 Pacific	570 (R)	.75	.60	.30
1991 Pro Set	819 (R)	.60	.45	.25
1991 Pro Set Platinum	292 (R)	.60	.45	.25
1991 Score Supplemental	66 (R)	.50	.40	.20
1991 Upper Deck	610 (R)	.65	.50	.25
1992 Bowman	53	.75	.60	.30
1992 Fleer	69	.15	.11	.06
1992 Fleer Rookie Sensations	8	3.00	2.25	1.25
1992 Fleer Ultra	68	.15	.11	.06
1992 GameDay	423	.30	.25	.12

Tom Jackson

Set	Card #	NM	EX	VG
1978 Topps	240 (R)	4.00	2.00	1.25
1979 Topps	83	.75	.40	.25
1980 Topps	323	.50	.25	.15

Set	Card #	MT	NM	EX
1982 Topps	80	.25	.20	.10
1984 Topps	65	.15	.11	.06
1985 Topps	241	.15	.11	.06
1989 Pro Set Announcer Inserts	6	.15	.11	.06

Cards before 1981 are priced in Near Mint (NM), Excellent (EX), and Very Good (VG). Cards 1981 to present are Mint (MT), Near Mint (NM), and Excellent (EX).

Haywood Jeffires

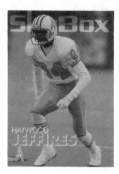

Set	Card #	MT	NM	EX
1990 Fleer Update	34 (R)	2.75	2.05	1.10
1990 Pro Set	511 (R)	.85	.60	.35
1990 Score	506 (R)	.85	.60	.35
1990 Topps	225 (R)	.85	.60	.35
1991 Bowman	189	.25	.20	.10
1991 Fleer	63	.15	.11	.06
1991 Fleer	412	.06	.05	.02
1991 Fleer Ultra	50	.20	.15	.08
1991 Pacific	175	.20	.15	.08
1991 Pinnacle	111	.35	.25	.14
1991 Pro Set	517	.10	.08	.04
1991 Score	377	.15	.11	.06
1991 Topps	10	.25	.20	.10
1991 Topps	230	.15	.11	.06
1991 Topps Stadium Club	479	1.00	.70	.40
1991 Topps 1000 Yard Club	13	.45	.35	.20
1991 Upper Deck	258	.25	.20	.10
1992 Bowman	424	.50	.40	.20
1992 Bowman	519	5.00	3.75	2.00
1992 Fleer	147	.15	.11	.06
1992 Fleer	454	.08	.06	.03
1992 Fleer Ultra	145	.15	.11	.06
1992 GameDay	235	.15	.11	.06
1992 Pacific	430	.15	.11	.06
1992 Pinnacle	26	.20	.15	.08
1992 Pinnacle Team Pinnacle	5	11.00	8.25	4.50
1992 Pro Set	8	.08	.06	.03
1992 Pro Set	19	.10	.08	.04
1992 Pro Set	386	.05	.04	.02
1992 Pro Set	512	.12	.09	.05
1992 Pro Set Power	84	.25	.20	.10
1992 Score	15	.10	.08	.04
1992 Score Dream Team	2	2.25	1.75	.90
1992 SkyBox Impact	229	.10	.08	.04
1992 SkyBox Impact	309	.05	.04	.02
1992 SkyBox Impact Major Impact	3	1.00	.70	.40
1992 SkyBox Primetime	84	.25	.20	.10
1992 Topps	360	.15	.11	.06
1992 Topps Stadium Club	373	.15	.11	.06
1992 Topps 1000-Yard Club	6	.75	.60	.30
1992 Upper Deck	91	.05	.04	.02
1992 Upper Deck	302	.05	.04	.02
1992 Upper Deck	314	.15	.11	.06
1992 Upper Deck	369	.10	.08	.04
1992 Upper Deck Game Breaker Holograms	3	1.75	1.25	.70
1992 Upper Deck Pro Bowl	1	4.00	3.00	1.50
1993 Bowman	289	.25	.20	.10
1993 Fleer	88	.10	.08	.04
1993 Fleer Ultra	166	.10	.08	.04
1993 Fleer Ultra League Leaders	1	3.00	2.25	1.25
1993 GameDay	327	.10	.08	.04
1993 GameDay Game Breakers	20	.60	.45	.25
1993 Pacific	284	.12	.09	.05
1993 Pacific Prisms	35	1.50	1.25	.60
1993 Pinnacle	111	.15	.11	.06
1993 Pinnacle Team Pinnacle	5	30.00	22.00	12.00
1993 Pro Set	170	.10	.08	.04
1993 Score	28	.10	.08	.04
1993 Score	413	.08	.06	.03
1993 Score Select	56	.25	.20	.10
1993 Score Select Gridiron Skills	9	23.00	17.00	9.25
1993 SkyBox Impact	120	.10	.08	.04
1993 SkyBox Premium	200	.15	.11	.06
1993 SkyBox Thunder and Lightning	5	6.00	4.50	2.50
1993 Topps	41	.15	.11	.06
1993 Topps Stadium Club	329	.15	.11	.06
1993 Upper Deck	129	.10	.08	.04
1993 Upper Deck SP	104	.25	.20	.10
1993 Upper Deck SP All Pro	12	9.00	6.75	3.50
1994 Bowman	189	.10	.08	.04
1994 Fleer	186	.20	.15	.08
1994 Fleer Ultra	121	.15	.11	.06
1994 GameDay	165	.10	.08	.04
1994 Pacific Crown	66	.06	.05	.02
1994 Score	208	.05	.04	.02
1994 Score Select	192	.10	.08	.04
1994 SkyBox Impact	100	.15	.11	.06
1994 SkyBox Premium	63	.10	.08	.04
1994 Topps	496	.07	.05	.03
1994 Topps Stadium Club	490	.10	.08	.04
1994 Upper Deck	221	.12	.09	.05
1994 Upper Deck Collector's Choice	285	.07	.05	.03
1994 Upper Deck SP	65	.20	.15	.08

Charles Johnson

Set	Card #	MT	NM	EX
1994 Bowman	16 (R)	1.75	1.25	.70
1994 Fleer NFL Prospects	13	3.50	2.75	1.50
1994 Fleer Ultra	255 (R)	1.75	1.25	.70
1994 Fleer Ultra	482	.65	.50	.25
1994 Fleer Ultra First Rounders	9	3.00	2.25	1.25
1994 Fleer Ultra Wave of the Future	4	2.00	1.50	.80
1994 GameDay	336 (R)	2.00	1.50	.80
1994 GameDay Rookie Standouts	7	3.00	2.25	1.25
1994 Pacific Crown	433 (R)	1.25	.90	.50
1994 Pacific Prisms	59 (R)	8.00	6.00	3.25
1994 Pinnacle	204 (R)	1.75	1.25	.70
1994 Pinnacle Draft Pick	5	12.00	9.00	4.75
1994 Pinnacle Sportflics	157 (R)	2.50	2.00	1.00

1994 Score	278 (R)	1.25	.90	.50
1994 Score Select	201 (R)	1.75	1.25	.70
1994 SkyBox Impact	289 (R)	1.00	.70	.40
1994 SkyBox Premium	173 (R)	1.25	.90	.50
1994 SkyBox Premium Prime Time Rookies	8	15.00	11.00	6.00
1994 Topps	349 (R)	1.25	.90	.50
1994 Topps Stadium Club	386 (R)	1.75	1.25	.70
1994 Upper Deck	4 (R)	1.75	1.25	.70
1994 Upper Deck Collector's Choice	24 (R)	1.25	.90	.50
1994 Upper Deck Collector's Choice Crash Game	29	7.50	5.75	3.00
1994 Upper Deck Hobby Predictor	15	4.00	3.00	1.50
1994 Upper Deck Retail Predictor	29	4.00	3.00	1.50
1994 Upper Deck SP	10 (R)	2.25	1.75	.90
1994 Upper Deck SP All-Pro	31	5.00	3.75	2.00

Charlie Joiner

Set	Card #	NM	EX	VG
1972 Topps	244 (R)	25.00	12.50	7.50
1973 Topps	467	6.00	3.00	1.75
1976 Topps	89	2.00	1.00	.60
1977 Topps	167	1.50	.70	.45
1978 Topps	338	1.00	.50	.30
1978 Topps	524	.50	.25	.15
1979 Topps	419	.75	.40	.25
1980 Topps	28	.65	.35	.20

Set	Card #	MT	NM	EX
1981 Topps	312	.25	.20	.10
1981 Topps	496	.60	.45	.25
1982 Topps	233	.40	.30	.15
1982 Topps	234	.20	.15	.08
1983 Topps	377	.25	.20	.10
1984 Topps	181	.25	.20	.10
1985 Topps	3	.15	.11	.06
1985 Topps	377	.30	.25	.12
1986 Topps	236	.25	.20	.10
1987 Topps	4	.10	.08	.04

Values for recent cards and sets are listed in Mint (MT), Near Mint (NM), reflecting the fact that many cards from recent years have been preserved in to condition. Recent cards and sets in less than Excellent condition have little collector interest.

Deacon Jones

Set	Card #	NM	EX	VG
1963 Topps	44 (R)	50.00	25.00	15.00
1965 Philadelphia	89	8.00	4.00	2.50
1966 Philadelphia	96	6.00	3.00	1.75
1967 Philadelphia	90	5.00	2.50	1.50
1969 Topps	238	4.00	2.00	1.25
1970 Topps	125	3.50	1.75	1.00
1971 Topps	209	3.00	1.50	.90
1972 Topps	209	2.50	1.25	.70
1973 Topps	38	2.50	1.25	.70
1974 Topps	390	2.25	1.25	.70

Values quoted in this guide reflect the retail price of a card – the price a collector can expect to pay when buying a card from a dealer. The wholesale price – that which a collector can expect to receive from a dealer when selling cards – will be significantly lower, depending on desirability and condition.

Sonny Jurgensen

Set	Card #	NM	EX	VG
1958 Topps	90 (R)	100.00	50.00	30.00
1961 Topps	95	20.00	10.00	6.00
1962 Topps	115	24.00	12.00	7.25
1963 Topps	110	22.00	11.00	6.50
1964 Philadelphia	186	18.00	9.00	5.40
1965 Philadelphia	188	15.00	7.50	4.50
1966 Philadelphia	185	9.00	4.50	2.75
1967 Philadelphia	185	10.00	5.00	3.00
1968 Topps	88	6.50	3.25	2.00
1969 Topps	227	7.00	3.50	2.00
1969 Topps Four In Ones	(30)	3.00	1.50	.90
1970 Topps	200	6.50	3.25	2.00
1971 Topps	50	6.00	3.00	1.75
1972 Topps	195	4.50	2.25	1.25

Jim Kelly

Set	Card #	MT	NM	EX
1984 Topps USFL	36 (R)	150.00	112.00	60.00
1985 Topps USFL	45	50.00	37.00	20.00
1987 Topps	362 (R)	10.00	7.50	4.00
1988 Topps	220	.30	.25	.12
1988 Topps	221	1.00	.70	.40
1989 Pro Set	22	.50	.40	.20
1989 Score	223	2.00	1.50	.80
1989 Topps	40	.15	.11	.06
1989 Topps	46	.50	.40	.20
1990 Fleer	113	.20	.15	.08
1990 Pro Set	40	.35	.25	.14
1990 Score	112	.30	.25	.12
1990 Score	318	.10	.08	.04
1990 Score 100 Hottest	34	.60	.45	.25
1990 Topps	207	.35	.25	.14
1991 Pro Set	8	.15	.25	.14
1991 Pro Set	78	.35	.25	.14
1992 GameDay	1	.75	.60	.30
1992 Pro Set	442	.25	.20	.10
1992 Pro Set Power	100	.40	.30	.15
1992 SkyBox Impact	1	.25	.20	.10
1992 SkyBox Impact	305	.10	.08	.04
1992 SkyBox Primetime	1H	5.00	3.75	2.00
1992 SkyBox Primetime	12	.50	.40	.20
1992 Topps	733	.30	.25	.12
1992 Topps Stadium Club	605	2.00	1.50	.80
1992 Topps Stadium Club	640	2.50	2.00	1.00
1992 Upper Deck	566	.25	.20	.10
1992 Upper Deck Gold	21	.50	.40	.20
1992 Upper Deck Gold	30	.75	.60	.30
1992 Upper Deck NFL Fanimation	1	4.50	3.50	1.75
1993 Bowman	330	.75	.60	.30
1993 Fleer	436	.25	.20	.10
1993 Fleer Ultra	26	.40	.30	.15
1993 GameDay	12	.35	.25	.14
1993 GameDay Game Breakers	6	1.00	.70	.40
1993 Pacific	206	.30	.25	.12
1993 Pacific Prisms	6	2.00	1.50	.80
1993 Pinnacle	276	.50	.40	.20
1993 Pro Set	49	.25	.20	.10
1993 Pro Set College Connections	10	8.00	6.00	3.25
1993 Pro Set Power	12	.30	.25	.12
1993 Pro Set Power Update Combos	3	2.00	1.50	.80
1993 Score	251	.25	.20	.10
1993 Score Select	57	.75	.60	.30
1993 SkyBox Impact	19	.25	.20	.10
1993 SkyBox Impact	342	.10	.08	.04
1993 SkyBox Impact Kelly's Heroes/ Magic's Kingdom	2	4.00	3.00	1.50
1993 SkyBox Premium	68	.40	.30	.15
1993 SkyBox Thunder and Lightning	1	6.00	4.50	2.50
1993 Topps	170	.25	.20	.10
1993 Topps	261	.10	.08	.04
1993 Topps Stadium Club	75	.50	.40	.20
1993 Upper Deck	65	.10	.08	.04
1993 Upper Deck	179	.20	.15	.08
1993 Upper Deck NFL Experience	21	.80	.60	.30
1993 Upper Deck SP	31	1.00	.70	.40
1994 Bowman	70	.40	.30	.15
1994 Fleer	43	.25	.20	.10
1994 Fleer Ultra	27	.40	.30	.15
1994 GameDay	37	.30	.25	.12
1994 Pacific Crown	23	.25	.20	.10
1994 Pacific Crown Gems of the Crown	15	6.00	4.50	2.50
1994 Pacific Prisms	63	2.50	2.00	1.00
1994 Pinnacle	21	.45	.35	.20
1994 Pinnacle Sportflics	86	.45	.35	.20
1994 Score	108	.25	.20	.10
1994 Score Select	92	.35	.25	.14
1994 SkyBox Impact	26	.25	.20	.10
1994 SkyBox Impact Ultimate Impact	12	2.00	1.50	.80
1994 SkyBox Premium	16	.45	.35	.20
1994 SkyBox Premium Revolution	1	5.00	3.75	2.00
1994 SkyBox Premium SkyTech Stars	28	3.00	2.25	1.25
1994 Topps	204	.20	.15	.08
1994 Topps	600	.20	.15	.08
1994 Topps Finest	5	5.00	3.75	2.00
1994 Topps Finest Inserts	23	5.00	3.75	2.00
1994 Topps Stadium Club	170	.35	.25	.14
1994 Upper Deck	273	.50	.40	.20
1994 Upper Deck Collector's Choice	61	.15	.11	.06
1994 Upper Deck Retail Predictor	3	4.00	3.00	1.50
1994 Upper Deck SP	24	.25	.20	.10

Cortez Kennedy

Set	Card #	MT	NM	EX
1990 Fleer Update	85 (R)	2.50	2.00	1.00
1990 Pro Set	671 (R)	.60	.45	.25
1990 Score	299 (R)	1.00	.70	.40
1990 Score	616	.40	.30	.15
1990 Score Update	68	4.00	3.00	1.50
1990 Topps	334 (R)	.75	.60	.30
1990 Topps Update	44	.75	.60	.30
1991 Bowman	503	.25	.20	.10
1991 Fleer	190	.20	.15	.08
1991 Pacific	482	.30	.25	.12
1991 Pinnacle	242	1.00	.70	.40
1991 Pro Set	302	.20	.15	.08
1991 Pro Set Platinum	114	.30	.25	.12
1991 Score	279	.25	.20	.10
1991 Topps	287	.30	.25	.12
1991 Topps Stadium Club	194	1.50	1.25	.60
1991 Upper Deck	491	.30	.25	.12
1992 Bowman	50	1.00	.70	.40
1992 Fleer	394	.15	.11	.06

1992 Fleer Ultra	379	.25	.20	.10
1992 GameDay	370	.25	.20	.10
1992 Pacific	294	.15	.11	.06
1992 Pinnacle	107	.25	.20	.10
1992 Pro Set	329	.10	.08	.04
1992 Pro Set Power	196	.05	.04	.02
1992 Score	131	.10	.08	.04
1992 SkyBox Impact	16	.10	.08	.04
1992 SkyBox Primetime	113	.25	.20	.10
1992 Topps	8	.15	.11	.06
1992 Topps Stadium Club	300	.15	.11	.06
1992 Topps Stadium Club	585	.25	.20	.10
1992 Upper Deck	376	.05	.04	.02
1992 Upper Deck	495	.15	.11	.06
1993 Bowman	375	.25	.20	.10
1993 Fleer	156	.10	.08	.04
1993 Fleer	239	.08	.06	.03
1993 Fleer All-Pro	7	1.50	1.25	.60
1993 Fleer Ultra	453	.15	.11	.06
1993 Fleer Ultra Award Winners	7	2.50	2.00	1.00
1993 Fleer Ultra Ultra Stars	4	4.00	3.00	1.50
1993 GameDay	99	.15	.11	.06
1993 Pacific	382	.10	.08	.04
1993 Pacific Gold Prisms	9	8.00	6.00	3.25
1993 Pacific Picks the Pros Gold	14	3.00	2.25	1.25
1993 Pacific Prism Inserts	9	5.00	3.75	2.00
1993 Pacific Prisms	94	1.25	.90	.50
1993 Pacific Triple Folder Superstars	12	.50	.40	.20
1993 Pacific Triple Folders	14	.75	.60	.30
1993 Pinnacle	230	.15	.11	.06
1993 Pinnacle Men of Autumn	26	.30	.25	.14
1993 Pinnacle Team Pinnacle	9	12.00	9.00	4.75
1993 Pinnacle Team 2001	2	.25	.20	.10
1993 Pro Set	18	.08	.06	.03
1993 Pro Set	408	.10	.08	.04
1993 Pro Set College Connections	7	2.00	1.50	.80
1993 Pro Set Power	99	.10	.08	.04
1993 Pro Set Power All-Power Defense	6	.25	.20	.10
1993 Score	18	.08	.06	.03
1993 Score Dream Team	18	1.00	.70	.40
1993 Score Select	68	.25	.20	.10
1993 Score The Franchise	26	3.50	2.75	1.50
1993 SkyBox Impact	311	.10	.08	.04
1993 SkyBox Premium	101	.15	.11	.06
1993 Topps	205	.10	.08	.04
1993 Topps	299	.05	.04	.02
1993 Topps Stadium Club	45	.20	.15	.08
1993 Upper Deck	60	.05	.04	.02
1993 Upper Deck	242	.05	.04	.02
1993 Upper Deck	436	.10	.08	.04
1993 Upper Deck Pro Bowl	7	4.50	3.50	1.75
1993 Upper Deck SP	247	.25	.20	.10
1993 Upper Deck Team MVP	26	.50	.40	.20
1994 Bowman	245	.10	.08	.04
1994 Fleer	437	.10	.08	.04
1994 Fleer All-Pro	6	.50	.40	.20
1994 Fleer Ultra	290	.08	.06	.03
1994 GameDay	381	.10	.08	.04
1994 Pacific Crown	321	.06	.05	.02
1994 Pacific Prisms	64	1.00	.70	.40
1994 Pinnacle	8	.12	.09	.05
1994 Pinnacle Sportflics	113	.15	.11	.06
1994 Pinnacle Team Pinnacle	10	12.00	9.00	4.75
1994 Score	10	.08	.06	.03
1994 Score Select	32	.12	.09	.05
1994 SkyBox Impact	240	.08	.06	.03
1994 SkyBox Premium	144	.15	.11	.06
1994 SkyBox Premium SkyTech Stars	16	1.50	1.25	.60
1994 Topps	112	.10	.08	.04
1994 Topps All-Pros	15	3.00	2.25	1.25
1994 Topps Finest	101	2.00	1.50	.80
1994 Topps Stadium Club	30	.12	.09	.05
1994 Topps Stadium Club	436	.15	.11	.06
1994 Topps Stadium Club Dynasty and Destiny	3	5.00	3.75	2.00
1994 Upper Deck	206	.15	.11	.06
1994 Upper Deck Collector's Choice	192	.07	.05	.03
1994 Upper Deck SP	107	.25	.20	.10

Terry Kirby

Set	Card #	MT	NM	EX
1993 Bowman	320 (R)	3.50	2.75	1.50
1993 Fleer Ultra	257 (R)	1.50	1.25	.60
1993 GameDay	299 (R)	2.00	1.50	.80
1993 Pro Set	246 (R)	1.00	.75	.40
1993 Pro Set Power Update Prospects	15 (R)	1.50	1.25	.60
1993 Pro Set Rookie Running Backs	10	2.00	1.50	.80
1993 SkyBox Primetime Rookies	6	15.00	11.00	6.00
1993 Topps Stadium Club	520 (R)	2.00	1.50	.80
1993 Upper Deck	25 (R)	1.00	.75	.40
1993 Upper Deck SP	149 (R)	3.00	2.25	1.25
1994 Bowman	224	.15	.11	.06
1994 Fleer	279	.35	.25	.14
1994 Fleer Rookie Sensations	11	10.00	7.50	4.00
1994 Fleer Ultra	178	.45	.35	.20
1994 Fleer Ultra 2nd Year Standouts	9	1.50	1.25	.60
1994 GameDay	239	.60	.45	.25
1994 GameDay Second-Year Stars	9	1.00	.70	.40
1994 Pacific Crown	188	.50	.40	.20
1994 Pacific Crown Knights of the Gridiron	13	3.00	2.25	1.25
1994 Pacific Marquee	16	1.25	.90	.50
1994 Pacific Prisms	65	4.00	3.00	1.50
1994 Pinnacle	14	.40	.30	.15
1994 Pinnacle Sportflics	49	.40	.30	.15
1994 Score	90	.50	.40	.20
1994 Score Select	190	.35	.25	.14
1994 Score Select Future Force	7	12.00	9.00	4.75
1994 Score Sophomore Showcase	8	5.00	3.75	2.00
1994 SkyBox Impact	151	.40	.30	.15
1994 SkyBox Impact Instant Impact	4	4.50	3.50	1.75
1994 SkyBox Premium	89	.35	.25	.14
1994 Topps	375	.60	.45	.25
1994 Topps Finest	217	4.00	3.00	1.60

		MT	NM	EX
1994 Topps Stadium Club	399	.85	.60	.35
1994 Upper Deck	316	.40	.30	.15
1994 Upper Deck Collector's Choice	141	.20	.15	.08
1994 Upper Deck SP	37	1.00	.70	.40

		MT	NM	EX
1994 SkyBox Premium	27	.10	.08	.04
1994 Topps	265	.15	.11	.06
1994 Topps Finest	160	2.50	2.00	1.00
1994 Topps Stadium Club	115	.25	.20	.10
1994 Upper Deck	275	.10	.08	.04
1994 Upper Deck Collector's Choice	362	.05	.04	.02
1994 Upper Deck SP	55	.25	.20	.10

David Klingler

Set	Card #	MT	NM	EX
1992 GameDay	48 (R)	1.00	.70	.40
1992 Pro Set	459 (R)	.40	.30	.15
1992 Pro Set Power	115 (R)	.60	.45	.25
1992 Pro Set Power	300	.50	.40	.20
1992 SkyBox Impact	323 (R)	.40	.30	.15
1992 SkyBox Primetime	238 (R)	.60	.45	.25
1992 Topps	694 (R)	.65	.50	.25
1992 Upper Deck	415	.35	.25	.14
1992 Upper Deck Gold	7 (R)	.75	.60	.30
1993 Bowman	19	.50	.40	.20
1993 Fleer	470	.25	.20	.10
1993 Fleer Rookie Sensations	12	9.00	6.75	3.50
1993 Fleer Ultra	59	.35	.25	.14
1993 GameDay	15	.45	.35	.20
1993 GameDay Second-Year Stars	2	1.25	.90	.50
1993 Pacific	315	.15	.11	.06
1993 Pacific Gold Prisms	10	8.00	6.00	3.25
1993 Pacific Prism Inserts	10	5.00	3.75	2.00
1993 Pacific Prisms	12	3.00	2.25	1.25
1993 Pinnacle	235	.35	.25	.14
1993 Pinnacle Team 2001	4	.60	.45	.25
1993 Pro Set	94	.15	.11	.06
1993 Pro Set Power	15	.12	.09	.05
1993 Score	276	.15	.11	.06
1993 Score Select	30	.65	.50	.25
1993 SkyBox Impact	45	.15	.11	.06
1993 SkyBox Premium	261	.35	.25	.14
1993 Topps	123	.15	.11	.06
1993 Topps Stadium Club	51	.30	.25	.12
1993 Upper Deck	31	.20	.15	.08
1993 Upper Deck	250	.15	.11	.06
1993 Upper Deck Future Heroes	41	1.50	1.25	.60
1993 Upper Deck NFL Experience	11	.60	.45	.25
1993 Upper Deck SP	48	.60	.45	.25
1994 Bowman	101	.15	.11	.06
1994 Fleer	79	.20	.15	.08
1994 Fleer Ultra	47	.12	.09	.05
1994 GameDay	67	.10	.08	.04
1994 Pacific Crown	408	.06	.05	.02
1994 Pacific Prisms	66	1.25	.90	.50
1994 Pinnacle	79	.12	.09	.05
1994 Pinnacle Sportflics	63	.15	.11	.06
1994 Score	153	.15	.11	.06
1994 Score Select	116	.12	.09	.05
1994 SkyBox Impact	43	.15	.11	.06

Bernie Kosar

Set	Card #	MT	NM	EX
1986 Topps	185	.40	.30	.15
1986 Topps	187 (R)	5.00	3.75	2.00
1987 Topps	80	1.00	.70	.40
1988 Topps	85	.05	.04	.02
1988 Topps	86	.05	.04	.02
1989 Pro Set	77	.08	.06	.03
1989 Score	9	.50	.40	.20
1989 Score	138	.05	.04	.02
1989 Topps	141	.20	.15	.08
1990 Fleer	51	.03	.02	.01
1990 Pro Set	72	.03	.02	.01
1990 Score	60	.04	.03	.02
1990 Score	319	.04	.03	.02
1990 Score 100 Hottest	80	.20	.15	.08
1990 Topps	163	.04	.03	.02
1991 Pro Set	121	.03	.02	.01
1992 GameDay	245	.15	.11	.06
1992 Pro Set	467	.05	.04	.02
1992 Pro Set Power	19	.05	.04	.02
1992 SkyBox Impact	250	.05	.04	.02
1992 SkyBox Primetime	19	.10	.08	.04
1992 SkyBox Primetime	184	.10	.08	.04
1992 SkyBox Primetime	190	.10	.08	.04
1992 SkyBox Primetime Poster Cards	1	1.50	1.25	.60
1992 Topps	702	.05	.04	.02
1992 Topps Stadium Club	672	.75	.60	.30
1992 Upper Deck	588	.05	.04	.02
1992 Upper Deck Gold	24	.10	.08	.04
1992 Upper Deck Gold	31	.10	.08	.04
1993 Bowman	291	.20	.15	.08
1993 Fleer	274	.05	.04	.02
1993 Fleer Ultra	79	.08	.06	.03
1993 GameDay	214	.10	.08	.04
1993 Pacific	300	.05	.04	.02
1993 Pacific Prisms	16	1.25	.90	.50
1993 Pinnacle	313	.10	.08	.04
1993 Pinnacle	359	.10	.08	.04
1993 Pro Set	110	.05	.04	.02
1993 Pro Set College Connections	10	8.00	6.00	3.25
1993 Pro Set Power	19	.05	.04	.02
1993 Score Select	88	.10	.08	.04
1993 SkyBox Impact	57	.05	.04	.02
1993 SkyBox Premium	85	.10	.08	.04
1993 Topps	50	.05	.04	.02

1993 Topps Stadium Club	98	.10	.08	.04
1993 Upper Deck	155	.05	.04	.02
1993 Upper Deck NFL Experience	24	.25	.20	.10
1993 Upper Deck SP	61	.25	.20	.10
1994 Bowman	18	.12	.09	.05
1994 Fleer	280	.10	.08	.04
1994 Score	245	.05	.04	.02
1994 SkyBox Impact	70	.06	.05	.02
1994 SkyBox Premium	92	.08	.06	.03
1994 Topps	616	.05	.04	.02
1994 Upper Deck SP	39	.20	.15	.08

Jerry Kramer

Set	Card #	NM	EX	VG
1959 Topps	116 (R)	25.00	12.50	7.50
1961 Fleer	95	7.50	3.75	2.25
1964 Philadelphia	76	5.00	2.50	1.50

Paul Krause

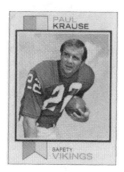

Set	Card #	NM	EX	VG
1965 Philadelphia	189 (R)	16.00	8.00	4.75
1966 Philadelphia	186	5.00	2.50	1.50
1968 Topps	166	1.35	.70	.40
1971 Topps	158	2.00	1.00	.60
1973 Topps	380	1.25	.60	.40
1974 Topps	82	1.00	.50	.30
1975 Topps	496	.75	.40	.25
1976 Topps	65	.60	.30	.20
1976 Topps	205	.75	.40	.25
1977 Topps	125	.50	.25	.15
1978 Topps	378	.15	.08	.05
1979 Topps	489	.15	.08	.05
1980 Topps	4	.15	.08	.05

Dave Krieg

Set	Card #	MT	NM	EX
1984 Topps	195 (R)	3.50	2.75	1.50
1985 Topps	388	.75	.60	.30
1986 Topps	201	.25	.20	.10
1987 Topps	173	.20	.15	.08
1988 Topps	131	.15	.11	.06
1989 Pro Set	395	.03	.02	.01
1989 Score	100	.10	.08	.04
1989 Topps	181	.05	.04	.02
1989 Topps	188	.05	.04	.02
1990 Fleer	269	.03	.02	.01
1990 Pro Set	349	.03	.02	.01
1990 Pro Set	648	.03	.02	.01
1990 Score	61	.04	.03	.02
1990 Score 100 Hottest	16	.10	.08	.04
1990 Topps	338	.04	.03	.02
1991 Bowman	500	.03	.02	.01
1991 Fleer	191	.10	.08	.04
1991 Fleer Ultra	140	.04	.03	.02
1991 Pacific	483	.04	.03	.02
1991 Pinnacle	236	.10	.08	.04
1991 Pro Set	664	.03	.02	.01
1991 Pro Set Platinum	112	.05	.04	.02
1991 Score	362	.04	.03	.02
1991 Topps	268	.04	.03	.02
1991 Topps Stadium Club	19	.30	.25	.12
1991 Upper Deck	170	.05	.04	.02
1992 Pro Set	330	.05	.04	.02
1992 Pro Set	531	.05	.04	.02
1992 Pro Set Power	17	.05	.04	.02
1992 Score	210	.05	.04	.02
1992 Topps	574	.05	.04	.02
1992 Upper Deck	508	.05	.04	.02
1993 Fleer	455	.05	.04	.02
1993 Fleer Ultra	200	.08	.06	.03
1993 GameDay	251	.10	.08	.04
1993 Pacific	340	.05	.04	.02
1993 Pinnacle	225	.10	.08	.04
1993 Pro Set	208	.05	.04	.02
1993 Pro Set Power	17	.05	.04	.02
1993 Score	258	.04	.03	.02
1993 SkyBox Impact	140	.03	.02	.01
1993 SkyBox Premium	263	.10	.08	.04
1993 Topps	147	.05	.04	.02
1993 Topps Stadium Club	53	.10	.08	.04
1993 Upper Deck	166	.05	.04	.02
1993 Upper Deck Kansas City Chiefs	9	.25	.20	.10
1994 Pacific Crown	52	.06	.05	.02
1994 Upper Deck Collector's Choice	64	.15	.11	.06

Cards before 1981 are priced in Near Mint (NM),
Excellent (EX), and Very Good (VG).
Cards 1981 to present are Mint (MT), Near Mint (NM),
and Excellent (EX).

Jack Lambert

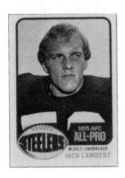

Set	Card #	NM	EX	VG
1976 Topps	220 (R)	28.00	14.00	8.50
1977 Topps	480	7.00	3.50	2.00
1978 Topps	165	2.25	1.25	.70
1979 Topps	475	2.00	1.00	.60
1980 Topps	280	1.25	.60	.40

Set	Card #	MT	NM	EX
1981 Topps	155	1.00	.70	.40
1982 Topps	213	.75	.60	.30
1982 Topps	214	.50	.40	.20
1983 Topps	363	.60	.45	.25
1984 Topps	167	.60	.45	.25
1984 Topps	168	.25	.20	.10
1985 Topps	357	.40	.30	.15
1990 Pro Set	27	.03	.02	.01
1990 Score	598	.04	.03	.02

Jim Langer

Set	Card #	NM	EX	VG
1973 Topps	341 (R)	13.00	6.50	4.00
1974 Topps	397	2.50	1.25	.70
1975 Topps	196	1.50	.70	.45
1976 Topps	210	1.25	.60	.40
1977 Topps	390	1.00	.50	.30
1978 Topps	70	.75	.40	.25
1979 Topps	425	.40	.20	.12

Values quoted in this guide reflect the
retail price of a card – the price a collector
can expect to pay when buying a card from a dealer.
The wholesale price – that which a collector can expect to
receive from a dealer when selling cards – will be
significantly lower, depending on desirability and condition.

Willie Lanier

Set	Card #	NM	EX	VG
1971 Topps	114 (R)	20.00	10.00	6.00
1972 Topps	35	4.00	2.00	1.25
1972 Topps	283	27.50	13.50	8.25
1973 Topps	410	2.00	1.00	.60
1974 Topps	480	1.50	.70	.45
1975 Topps	218	1.00	.50	.30
1975 Topps	325	1.50	.70	.45
1976 Topps	24	1.00	.50	.30
1977 Topps	155	.75	.40	.25

Steve Largent

Set	Card #	NM	EX	VG
1977 Topps	177 (R)	55.00	41.00	22.00
1978 Topps	443	17.00	12.50	6.75
1978 Topps	526	1.50	.70	.45
1979 Topps	198	8.00	6.00	3.25
1980 Topps	450	4.50	3.50	1.75

Set	Card #	MT	NM	EX
1981 Topps	271	1.75	1.25	.70
1981 Topps	343	.85	.60	.35
1982 Topps	249	1.75	1.25	.70
1982 Topps	250	.90	.70	.35
1983 Topps	389	.85	.60	.35
1984 Topps	196	.80	.60	.30
1984 Topps	197	.60	.45	.25
1985 Topps	389	.80	.60	.35
1986 Topps	4	.30	.25	.12
1986 Topps	203	.65	.50	.25
1986 Topps 1000 Yard Club	8	1.00	.70	.40
1987 Topps	5	.25	.20	.10
1987 Topps	177	.60	.45	.25
1987 Topps 1000 Yard Club	18	.60	.45	.25
1988 Topps	3	.15	.11	.06
1988 Topps	135	.30	.25	.12

1988 Topps 1000 Yard Club	14	.75	.60	.30
1989 Pro Set	396	.15	.11	.06
1989 Score	225	.85	.60	.35
1989 Score	327	.25	.20	.10
1989 Topps	4	.12	.09	.05
1989 Topps	183	.25	.20	.10
1990 Score	592	.10	.08	.04
1994 Topps Stadium Club Dynasty and Destiny	2	6.00	4.50	2.50

Thomas Lewis

Set	Card #	MT	NM	EX
1994 Bowman	22 (R)	.90	.70	.35
1994 Fleer Ultra	224 (R)	.75	.60	.30
1994 Fleer Ultra	465	.25	.20	.10
1994 GameDay	294 (R)	.80	.60	.30
1994 Pacific Crown Knights of the Gridiron	14	3.00	2.25	1.25
1994 Pinnacle	206 (R)	.85	.60	.35
1994 Pinnacle Sportflics Rookie Rivalry	7	10.00	7.50	4.00
1994 Pinnacle Sportflics	159 (R)	.85	.60	.35
1994 Score	303 (R)	.50	.40	.20
1994 Score Select	221 (R)	.70	.50	.30
1994 SkyBox Impact	296 (R)	.40	.30	.15
1994 SkyBox Premium	180 (R)	.75	.60	.30
1994 Topps	433 (R)	.50	.40	.20
1994 Topps Stadium Club	417 (R)	.75	.60	.30
1994 Upper Deck	19 (R)	.75	.60	.30
1994 Upper Deck	32	.25	.20	.10
1994 Upper Deck Collector's Choice	26 (R)	.75	.60	.30
1994 Upper Deck SP	19 (R)	1.00	.70	.40
1994 Upper Deck SP All-Pro	28	4.00	3.00	1.50

Grading Guide

Mint (MT): A perfect card. Well-centered with all corners sharp and square. No creases, stains, edge nicks, surface marks, yellowing or fading.

Near Mint (NM): A nearly perfect card. At first glance, a NM card appears to be perfect. May be slightly off-center. No surface marks, creases or loss of gloss.

Excellent (EX): Corners are still fairly sharp with only moderate wear. Borders may be off-center. No creases or stains on fronts or backs, but may show slight loss of surface luster.

Very Good (VG): Shows obvious handling. May have rounded corners, minor creases, major gum or wax stains. No major creases, tape marks, writing, etc.

Good (G): A well-worn card, but exhibits no intentional damage. May have major or multiple creases. Corners may be rounded well beyond card border.

Bob Lilly

Set	Card #	NM	EX	VG
1963 Topps	82 (R)	95.00	47.00	28.00
1964 Philadelphia	48	30.00	15.00	9.00
1965 Philadelphia	47	15.00	7.50	4.50
1966 Philadelphia	60	10.00	5.00	3.00
1967 Philadelphia	55	8.00	4.00	2.50
1968 Topps	181	7.00	3.50	2.00
1969 Topps	53	6.00	3.00	1.75
1969 Topps Four In Ones	(34)	4.00	2.00	1.25
1970 Topps	87	4.50	2.25	1.25
1971 Topps	144	4.50	2.25	1.25
1972 Topps	145	4.00	2.00	1.25
1972 Topps	280	45.00	22.00	13.50
1973 Topps	450	4.00	2.00	1.25
1974 Topps	250	4.00	2.00	1.25
1975 Topps	175	3.50	1.75	1.00

Set	Card #	MT	NM	EX
1993 Upper Deck America's Team	5	6.00	4.50	2.50

Larry Little

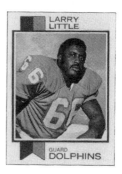

Set	Card #	NM	EX	VG
1972 Topps	240 (R)	17.00	8.50	5.00
1972 Topps	267	40.00	20.00	12.00
1973 Topps	440	3.00	1.50	.90
1974 Topps	123	1.50	.70	.45
1975 Topps	499	1.00	.50	.30
1976 Topps	33	.75	.40	.25
1977 Topps	172	.60	.30	.20
1978 Topps	322	.50	.25	.15
1979 Topps	60	.35	.20	.11
1980 Topps	406	.25	.13	.08

Set	Card #	MT	NM	EX
1993 Pinnacle	356	.10	.08	.04
1993 Score	439	.04	.03	.02

James Lofton

Set	Card #	NM	EX	VG
1979 Topps	310 (R)	20.00	10.00	6.00
1980 Topps	78	4.00	2.00	1.25

Set	Card #	MT	NM	EX
1981 Topps	361	2.00	1.50	.80
1981 Topps	430	3.50	2.75	1.50
1982 Topps	364	1.75	1.25	.70
1982 Topps	365	.75	.60	.30
1983 Topps	83	1.00	.70	.40
1984 Topps	263	.25	.20	.10
1984 Topps	272	1.50	1.25	.60
1984 Topps	273	.75	.60	.30
1985 Topps	75	1.00	.70	.40
1986 Topps	218	.60	.45	.25
1986 Topps 1000 Yard Club	15	.20	.15	.08
1987 Topps	354	.50	.40	.20
1988 Topps	329	.20	.15	.08
1988 Topps 1000 Yard Club	16	.10	.08	.04
1989 Score	213	.40	.30	.15
1989 Topps Traded	109	.15	.11	.06
1990 Pro Set	753	.03	.02	.01
1991 Bowman	42	.03	.02	.01
1991 Fleer	4	.10	.08	.04
1991 Fleer Ultra Update	10	.10	.08	.04
1991 Pacific	25	.04	.03	.02
1991 Pinnacle	136	.10	.08	.04
1991 Pro Set	46	.04	.03	.02
1991 Pro Set	444	.03	.02	.01
1991 Score	180	.04	.03	.02
1991 Topps	43	.04	.03	.02
1991 Topps Stadium Club	89	.60	.45	.25
1991 Upper Deck	358	.05	.04	.02
1992 Bowman	4	.35	.25	.14
1992 Fleer	24	.03	.02	.01
1992 Fleer Ultra	24	.05	.04	.02
1992 GameDay	232	.20	.15	.08
1992 Pacific	18	.05	.04	.02
1992 Pinnacle	269	.05	.04	.02
1992 Pro Set	21	.05	.04	.02
1992 Pro Set	98	.05	.04	.02
1992 Pro Set	387	.05	.04	.02
1992 Pro Set Power	271	.05	.04	.02
1992 Score	425	.07	.05	.03
1992 SkyBox Impact	18	.05	.04	.02
1992 SkyBox Primetime	227	.10	.08	.04
1992 Topps	633	.05	.04	.02
1992 Topps Stadium Club	385	.10	.08	.04
1992 Topps 1000-Yard Club	10	1.00	.70	.40
1992 Upper Deck	585	.05	.04	.02
1993 Fleer Ultra	221	.08	.06	.03
1993 GameDay	282	.10	.08	.04
1993 Pacific	395	.05	.04	.02
1993 Pinnacle	106	.10	.08	.04
1993 Score	33	.04	.03	.02
1993 Score	434	.04	.03	.02
1993 SkyBox Impact	160	.03	.02	.01
1993 SkyBox Premium	158	.10	.08	.04
1993 Topps	345	.05	.04	.02
1993 Upper Deck	104	.05	.04	.02

Ronnie Lott

Set	Card #	MT	NM	EX
1982 Topps	486 (R)	22.00	16.50	8.75
1982 Topps	487	8.00	6.00	3.25
1983 Topps	168	4.00	3.00	1.50
1984 Topps	357	1.50	1.25	.60
1985 Topps	156	1.00	.70	.40
1985 Topps Star Set	5	.40	.30	.20
1986 Topps	168	.75	.60	.30
1987 Topps	123	.30	.25	.12
1987 Topps	231	.07	.05	.03
1988 Topps	51	.30	.25	.12
1989 Pro Set	379	.10	.08	.04
1989 Score	215	.40	.30	.15
1989 Topps	9	.15	.11	.06
1990 Fleer	9	.03	.02	.01
1990 Fleer All-Pro	19	.50	.40	.20
1990 Pro Set	291	.10	.08	.04
1990 Pro Set	400	.06	.05	.02
1990 Pro Set	793	.03	.02	.01
1990 Pro Set	799	.03	.02	.01
1990 Score	170	.10	.08	.04
1990 Score	566	.04	.03	.02
1990 Score 100 Hottest	40	.20	.15	.08
1990 Topps	9	.10	.08	.04
1991 Fleer Ultra Update	42	.10	.08	.04
1991 Pacific	602	.10	.08	.04
1991 Pinnacle	13	.25	.20	.10
1991 Pinnacle	381	.15	.11	.06
1991 Pro Set	348	.05	.04	.02
1991 Pro Set	400	.05	.04	.02
1991 Pro Set	546	.08	.06	.03
1991 Pro Set Platinum	211	.10	.08	.04
1991 Score	200	.10	.08	.04
1991 Score	651A	.08	.06	.03
1991 Score	651B	.05	.04	.02
1991 Score Supplemental	1	.10	.08	.04
1991 Topps	97	.10	.08	.04
1991 Topps Stadium Club	341	.25	.20	.10
1991 Upper Deck	355	.10	.08	.04
1991 Upper Deck	544	.10	.08	.04
1992 Bowman	137	7.50	5.75	3.00
1992 Bowman	200	.35	.25	.14
1992 Fleer	200	.03	.02	.01
1992 Fleer	462	.03	.02	.01
1992 Fleer	472	.03	.02	.01
1992 Fleer All-Pro	21	.30	.20	.12
1992 Fleer Ultra	195	.05	.04	.02
1992 GameDay	262	.12	.09	.05
1992 Pinnacle	36	.05	.04	.02
1992 Pinnacle Team Pinnacle	1	8.50	6.50	3.50
1992 Pro Set	16	.08	.06	.03

Nick Lowery

Set	Card #			
1992 Pro Set	41	.05	.04	.02
1992 Pro Set	212	.05	.04	.02
1992 Pro Set	388	.05	.04	.02
1992 Pro Set Power	42	.05	.04	.02
1992 Score	30	.07	.05	.03
1992 SkyBox Impact	235	.07	.05	.03
1992 SkyBox Impact	313	.07	.05	.03
1992 SkyBox Impact	317	.05	.04	.02
1992 SkyBox Impact Major Impact	4	.75	.60	.30
1992 SkyBox Primetime	42	.10	.08	.04
1992 SkyBox Primetime	305	.10	.08	.04
1992 Topps	350	.05	.04	.02
1992 Topps Stadium Club	167	.12	.09	.05
1992 Upper Deck	157	.10	.08	.04
1992 Upper Deck	307	.05	.04	.02
1992 Upper Deck	515	.10	.08	.04
1992 Upper Deck Pro Bowl	11	1.50	1.25	.60
1993 Bowman	125	.20	.15	.08
1993 Fleer	268	.05	.04	.02
1993 Fleer Ultra	342	.08	.06	.03
1993 GameDay	171	.10	.08	.04
1993 Pacific	400	.05	.04	.02
1993 Pacific Prisms	73	1.25	.90	.50
1993 Pinnacle	275	.10	.08	.04
1993 Pro Set	321	.05	.04	.02
1993 Pro Set Power Power Moves	20	.25	.20	.10
1993 Pro Set Power Update Moves	20	.15	.11	.06
1993 Score	227	.04	.03	.02
1993 Score Select	50	.10	.08	.04
1993 SkyBox Impact	234	.05	.04	.02
1993 SkyBox Premium	79	.10	.08	.04
1993 Topps	605	.06	.05	.02
1993 Topps Stadium Club	364	.10	.08	.04
1993 Upper Deck	58	.05	.04	.02
1993 Upper Deck	463	.05	.04	.02
1993 Upper Deck SP	193	.25	.20	.10
1994 Bowman	94	.10	.08	.04
1994 Fleer	359	.08	.06	.03
1994 Fleer Ultra	236	.08	.06	.03
1994 GameDay	306	.10	.08	.04
1994 Pacific Crown	202	.06	.05	.02
1994 Pinnacle	133	.09	.07	.04
1994 Pinnacle Sportflics	112	.15	.11	.06
1994 Score	161	.08	.06	.03
1994 Score Select	155	.10	.08	.04
1994 Score Select Canton Bound	6	12.00	9.00	4.75
1994 SkyBox Impact	193	.09	.07	.04
1994 SkyBox Premium	114	.08	.06	.03
1994 Topps	101	.08	.06	.03
1994 Topps	274	.05	.04	.02
1994 Topps	541	.05	.04	.02
1994 Topps Finest	26	1.25	.90	.50
1994 Topps Stadium Club	46	.10	.08	.04
1994 Topps Stadium Club Ring Leaders	11	10.00	7.50	4.00
1994 Upper Deck	171	.12	.09	.05
1994 Upper Deck Collector's Choice	54	.05	.04	.02
1994 Upper Deck Collector's Choice	160	.05	.04	.02
1994 Upper Deck SP	52	.20	.15	.08

The values quoted are intended
to reflect the market price.

Values for recent cards and sets are listed in Mint
(MT), Near Mint (NM), reflecting the fact that many
cards from recent years have been preserved in to
condition. Recent cards and sets in
less than Excellent condition
have little collector interest.

Set	Card #	MT	NM	EX
1981 Topps	213 (R)	4.00	3.00	1.50
1982 Topps	120	1.50	1.25	.60
1982 Topps	121	.60	.45	.25
1983 Topps	290	.60	.45	.25
1984 Topps	94	.25	.20	.10
1985 Topps	277	.30	.25	.12
1986 Topps	308	.20	.15	.08
1987 Topps	165	.15	.11	.06
1989 Pro Set	174	.03	.02	.01
1989 Score	208	.10	.08	.04
1989 Topps	358	.05	.04	.02
1990 Fleer	202	.03	.02	.01
1990 Pro Set	144	.03	.02	.01
1990 Score	372	.04	.03	.02
1990 Topps	255	.04	.03	.02
1991 Bowman	230	.03	.02	.01
1991 Bowman	279	.03	.02	.01
1991 Fleer	94	.03	.02	.01
1991 Fleer All-Pro	23	.10	.08	.04
1991 Fleer Ultra	67	.04	.03	.02
1991 Pacific	210	.04	.03	.02
1991 Pinnacle	51	.10	.08	.04
1991 Pro Set	14	.03	.02	.01
1991 Pro Set	184	.03	.02	.01
1991 Pro Set	429	.03	.02	.01
1991 Pro Set Platinum	128	.05	.04	.02
1991 Score	11	.04	.03	.02
1991 Score	333	.04	.03	.02
1991 Topps	136	.04	.03	.02
1991 Topps Stadium Club	233	.20	.15	.08
1991 Upper Deck	160	.05	.04	.02
1991 Upper Deck	405	.05	.04	.02
1992 Bowman	445	.30	.25	.12
1992 GameDay	163	.12	.09	.05
1992 Pacific	137	.05	.04	.02
1992 Pinnacle	125	.05	.04	.02
1992 Pinnacle	355	.05	.04	.02
1992 Pro Set	24	.05	.04	.02
1992 Pro Set	202	.05	.04	.02
1992 Pro Set	533	.05	.04	.02
1992 Score	176	.05	.04	.02
1992 SkyBox Primetime	73	.10	.08	.04
1992 Topps	90	.05	.04	.02
1992 Topps Stadium Club	268	.10	.08	.04
1992 Upper Deck	494	.05	.04	.02
1992 Upper Deck	582	.05	.04	.02
1993 Bowman	305	.15	.11	.06
1993 Fleer	138	.05	.04	.02
1993 Fleer All-Pro	8	1.00	.70	.40
1993 Fleer Ultra	201	.08	.06	.03
1993 GameDay	324	.10	.08	.04
1993 Pacific Picks the Pros Gold	11	2.50	2.00	1.00
1993 Pinnacle	139	.10	.08	.04
1993 Pinnacle Men of Autumn	40	.25	.20	.10
1993 Pro Set	207	.05	.04	.02
1993 Score	391	.04	.03	.02

1993 Score Select	82	.10	.08	.04
1993 SkyBox Impact	145	.03	.02	.01
1993 SkyBox Impact Kelly's Heroes/ Magic's Kingdom	12	1.25	.90	.50
1993 Topps	16	.05	.04	.02
1993 Topps Stadium Club	375	.10	.08	.04
1993 Upper Deck Kansas City Chiefs	1	.25	.20	.10
1994 Fleer	224	.07	.05	.03
1994 Fleer Scoring Machines	8	4.00	3.00	1.50
1994 Pacific Crown	54	.06	.05	.02
1994 Pinnacle	143	.09	.07	.04
1994 Score	131	.05	.04	.02
1994 Score Select	151	.10	.08	.04
1994 SkyBox Impact	121	.06	.05	.02
1994 Topps	314	.05	.04	.02
1994 Topps	471	.08	.06	.03
1994 Topps Finest	132	.65	.50	.25
1994 Topps Stadium Club	25	.12	.09	.05

Tommy Maddox

Set	Card #	MT	NM	EX
1992 GameDay	244 (R)	1.00	.70	.40
1992 Pro Set	486 (R)	.40	.30	.15
1992 SkyBox Impact	336 (R)	.40	.30	.15
1992 SkyBox Primetime	166 (R)	.75	.60	.30
1992 Topps	686 (R)	.50	.40	.20
1992 Upper Deck	416 (R)	.40	.30	.15
1992 Upper Deck Gold	9	1.00	.70	.40
1993 Fleer	338	.20	.15	.08
1993 Fleer Ultra	114	.25	.20	.10
1993 GameDay	65	.40	.30	.15
1993 Pacific	355	.15	.11	.06
1993 Pacific Prisms	24	2.50	2.00	1.00
1993 Pinnacle Team 2001	21	.50	.40	.20
1993 Score	225	.15	.11	.06
1993 SkyBox Impact	91	.15	.11	.06
1993 SkyBox Premium	59	.25	.20	.10
1993 Topps	124	.10	.08	.04
1993 Topps Stadium Club	12	.25	.20	.10
1993 Upper Deck	32	.10	.08	.04
1993 Upper Deck	199	.10	.08	.04
1993 Upper Deck NFL Experience	15	.50	.40	.20
1993 Upper Deck SP	78	.40	.30	.15
1994 Pacific Crown	127	.06	.05	.02

Cards before 1981 are priced in Near Mint (NM),
Excellent (EX), and Very Good (VG).
Cards 1981 to present are Mint (MT), Near Mint (NM),
and Excellent (EX).

Dan Marino

Set	Card #	MT	NM	EX
1984 Topps	123 (R)	80.00	60.00	32.00
1984 Topps	124	12.00	9.00	4.75
1984 Topps	202	4.00	3.00	1.50
1985 Topps	4	5.00	3.75	2.00
1985 Topps	314	20.00	15.00	8.00
1986 Topps	45	15.00	11.00	6.00
1987 Topps	6	2.00	1.50	.80
1987 Topps	233	8.00	6.00	3.25
1988 Topps	190	1.50	1.25	.60
1989 Pro Set	220	1.00	.70	.40
1989 Score	13	4.00	3.00	1.50
1989 Topps	5	.60	.45	.25
1989 Topps	293	1.25	.90	.50
1990 Fleer	244	.75	.60	.30
1990 Pro Set	181	.75	.60	.30
1990 Score	13	.75	.60	.30
1990 Score	320	.40	.30	.15
1990 Score Hot Card	9	8.00	6.00	3.25
1990 Score 100 Hottest	4	1.25	.90	.50
1990 Topps	323	.75	.60	.30
1991 Bowman	285	.80	.60	.30
1991 Fleer	124	.75	.60	.30
1991 Fleer Pro Visions	5	1.75	1.25	.70
1991 Fleer Ultra	88	.75	.60	.30
1991 Fleer Ultra All Stars	5	3.50	2.75	1.50
1991 Pacific	269	.70	.50	.30
1991 Pinnacle	70	3.50	2.75	1.50
1991 Pinnacle	385	1.00	.70	.40
1991 Pro Set	25	.40	.30	.15
1991 Pro Set	210	.75	.60	.30
1991 Pro Set	726	.40	.30	.15
1991 Pro Set Platinum	62	.75	.60	.30
1991 Score	385	.75	.60	.30
1991 Score	632	.25	.20	.10
1991 Topps	112	.75	.60	.30
1991 Topps Stadium Club	264	7.50	5.75	3.00
1991 Upper Deck	34	.20	.15	.08
1991 Upper Deck	255	.75	.60	.30
1991 Upper Deck	465	.40	.30	.15
1992 GameDay	254	2.75	2.00	1.00
1992 Pro Set	559	.75	.60	.30
1992 Pro Set Power	13	1.25	.90	.50
1992 SkyBox Impact	150	.80	.60	.30
1992 SkyBox Impact Major Impact	5	4.50	3.50	1.75
1992 SkyBox Primetime	13	1.75	1.25	.70
1992 SkyBox Primetime	272	.85	.60	.35
1992 SkyBox Primetime	332	.75	.60	.30
1992 SkyBox Primetime Poster Cards	9	10.00	7.50	4.00
1992 Topps	682	.65	.50	.25
1992 Topps Stadium Club	603	6.00	4.50	2.50
1992 Topps Stadium Club	660	12.00	9.00	4.75
1992 Upper Deck	598	.65	.50	.25
1992 Upper Deck Gold	25	1.00	.70	.40
1992 Upper Deck Gold	45	1.00	.70	.40
1992 Upper Deck Marino Heroes	28	3.50	2.50	1.50

1992 Upper Deck Marino Heroes	29	3.50	2.50	1.50
1992 Upper Deck Marino Heroes	30	3.50	2.50	1.50
1992 Upper Deck Marino Heroes	31	3.50	2.50	1.50
1992 Upper Deck Marino Heroes	32	3.50	2.50	1.50
1992 Upper Deck Marino Heroes	33	3.50	2.50	1.50
1992 Upper Deck Marino Heroes	34	3.50	2.50	1.50
1992 Upper Deck Marino Heroes	35	3.50	2.50	1.50
1992 Upper Deck Marino Heroes	36	3.50	2.50	1.50
1992 Upper Deck NFL Fanimation	2	6.00	4.50	2.75
1993 Bowman	150	5.00	3.75	2.00
1993 Fleer	278	.75	.60	.30
1993 Fleer Ultra	258	1.50	1.25	.60
1993 Fleer Ultra Touchdown Kings	2	18.00	13.50	7.25
1993 GameDay	13	1.75	1.25	.70
1993 GameDay Game Breakers	4	3.00	2.25	1.25
1993 Pacific	218	.75	.60	.30
1993 Pacific Gold Prisms	11	40.00	30.00	16.00
1993 Pacific Prism Inserts	11	20.00	15.00	8.00
1993 Pacific Prisms	55	13.00	9.75	5.25
1993 Pacific Triple Folders	8	2.50	2.00	1.00
1993 Pinnacle	302	1.75	1.25	.70
1993 Pinnacle Men of Autumn	15	2.00	1.50	.80
1993 Pro Set	6	.20	.15	.08
1993 Pro Set	250	.75	.60	.30
1993 Pro Set Power	13	.75	.60	.30
1993 Score	265	.75	.60	.30
1993 Score Select	16	4.50	3.50	1.75
1993 Score Select Gridiron Skills	3	95.00	71.00	38.00
1993 Score The Franchise	15	50.00	37.00	20.00
1993 SkyBox Impact	174	.85	.60	.35
1993 SkyBox Impact	343	.20	.15	.08
1993 SkyBox Impact Kelly's Heroes/ Magic's Kingdom	2	4.00	3.00	1.50
1993 SkyBox Premium	108	1.50	1.25	.60
1993 Topps	269	.40	.30	.15
1993 Topps	290	.90	.70	.35
1993 Topps Black Gold	33	5.00	3.75	2.00
1993 Topps Stadium Club	60	1.50	1.25	.60
1993 Topps Stadium Club	246	.85	.60	.35
1993 Upper Deck	74	.40	.30	.15
1993 Upper Deck	139	.75	.60	.30
1993 Upper Deck	426	.25	.20	.10
1993 Upper Deck NFL Experience	10	.85	.60	.35
1993 Upper Deck NFL Experience	22	1.00	.70	.40
1993 Upper Deck Pro Bowl	2	25.00	18.50	10.00
1993 Upper Deck SP	150	10.00	7.50	4.00
1993 Upper Deck SP All Pro	4	90.00	67.00	36.00
1993 Upper Deck Team MVP	12	5.00	3.75	2.00
1994 Bowman	140	1.50	1.25	.60
1994 Fleer	281	1.00	.70	.40
1994 Fleer Scoring Machines	9	35.00	26.00	14.00
1994 Fleer Ultra	179	1.50	1.25	.60
1994 Fleer Ultra Achievement Awards	3	4.00	3.00	1.50
1994 Fleer Ultra Hot Numbers	7	4.50	3.50	1.75
1994 Fleer Ultra Touchdown Kings	2	35.00	26.00	14.00
1994 GameDay	240	1.25	.90	.50

1994 GameDay Game Breakers	6	4.00	3.00	1.50
1994 Pacific Crown	189	1.00	.70	.40
1994 Pacific Crown Gems of the Crown	16	16.00	12.00	6.50
1994 Pacific Marquee	17	5.00	3.75	2.00
1994 Pacific Prisms	70	15.00	11.00	6.00
1994 Pinnacle	120	1.50	1.25	.60
1994 Pinnacle Performers	18	9.00	6.75	3.50
1994 Pinnacle Sportflics Head-to-Head	3	35.00	26.00	14.00
1994 Pinnacle Sportflics	120	2.00	1.50	.80
1994 Pinnacle Sportflics	182	1.50	1.25	.60
1994 Score	65	.80	.60	.30
1994 Score Select	127	2.00	1.50	.80
1994 SkyBox Impact	152	.85	.60	.35
1994 SkyBox Impact Ultimate Impact	14	15.00	11.00	6.00
1994 SkyBox Premium	90	1.25	.90	.50
1994 SkyBox Premium Revolution	11	25.00	18.50	10.00
1994 SkyBox Premium SkyTech Stars	30	10.00	7.50	4.00
1994 Topps	160	.70	.50	.30
1994 Topps	275	.40	.30	.15
1994 Topps	545	.30	.25	.12
1994 Topps Finest	142	18.00	13.50	7.25
1994 Topps Stadium Club	200	1.25	.90	.50
1994 Upper Deck	136	1.50	1.25	.60
1994 Upper Deck Collector's Choice Crash Game	5	10.00	7.50	4.00
1994 Upper Deck Collector's Choice	147	.65	.50	.25
1994 Upper Deck Hobby Predictor	5	25.00	18.50	10.00
1994 Upper Deck Retail Predictor	7	12.00	9.00	4.75
1994 Upper Deck SP	36	4.50	3.50	1.75
1994 Upper Deck SP All-Pro	23	18.00	13.50	7.25
1994 Upper Deck SP Commemorative	1	150.00	112.00	60.00
1994 Upper Deck Then And Now	5	10.00	7.50	4.00
1994 Upper Deck Then And Now	6	6.00	4.50	2.50

Russell Maryland

RUSSELL MARYLAND

Set	Card #	MT	NM	EX
1991 Bowman	104 (R)	.50	.40	.20
1991 Fleer	423 (R)	.45	.35	.20
1991 Fleer Ultra	288 (R)	.40	.30	.15
1991 Fleer Ultra Update	21	.75	.60	.30
1991 Pacific	536	.50	.40	.20
1991 Pacific	572	.15	.11	.06
1991 Pinnacle	288 (R)	1.00	.70	.40
1991 Pro Set	32 (R)	.40	.30	.15
1991 Pro Set	730	.20	.15	.08

1991 Pro Set Platinum	298 (R)	.35	.25	.14
1991 Score	565A (R)	.40	.30	.15
1991 Score	565B (R)	.40	.30	.15
1991 Score Supplemental	61	.25	.20	.10
1991 Topps	353 (R)	.50	.40	.20
1991 Topps Stadium Club	231 (R)	1.50	1.25	.60
1991 Upper Deck	5 (R)	.50	.40	.20
1991 Upper Deck	636	.20	.15	.08
1992 GameDay	230	.30	.25	.12
1992 Pro Set	478	.12	.09	.05
1992 Pro Set Power	67	.25	.20	.10
1992 SkyBox Impact	190	.15	.11	.06
1992 SkyBox Primetime	221	.50	.40	.20
1992 Topps	739	.05	.04	.02
1992 Topps Stadium Club	624	1.25	.90	.50
1992 Topps Stadium Club No. 1 Draft Picks	2	10.00	7.50	4.00
1992 Upper Deck	579	.15	.11	.06
1993 Bowman	35	.25	.20	.10
1993 Fleer	300	.05	.04	.02
1993 Fleer Ultra	96	.08	.06	.03
1993 GameDay	323	.10	.08	.04
1993 Pacific Prisms	21	1.25	.90	.50
1993 Pinnacle	273	.10	.08	.04
1993 Pinnacle Team 2001	26	.35	.25	.14
1993 Pro Set	36	.05	.04	.02
1993 Pro Set College Connections	7	2.00	1.50	.80
1993 Pro Set Power	67	.08	.06	.03
1993 Score	259	.08	.06	.03
1993 SkyBox Impact	72	.03	.02	.01
1993 SkyBox Premium	172	.10	.08	.04
1993 Topps	249	.05	.04	.02
1993 Topps Stadium Club	204	.10	.08	.04
1993 Upper Deck America's Team	11	6.00	4.50	2.50
1993 Upper Deck Dallas Cowboys	24	.50	.40	.20
1993 Upper Deck NFL Experience	45	.40	.30	.15
1993 Upper Deck SP	69	.25	.20	.10
1994 Bowman	206	.12	.09	.05
1994 Fleer	116	.08	.06	.03
1994 Fleer Ultra	372	.08	.06	.03
1994 GameDay	99	.10	.08	.04
1994 Pacific Crown	9	.08	.06	.03
1994 Pinnacle	172	.20	.15	.08
1994 Pinnacle Sportflics	53	.15	.11	.06
1994 Score	206	.08	.06	.03
1994 SkyBox Impact	61	.07	.05	.03
1994 Topps	86	.06	.05	.02
1994 Topps Finest	145	2.50	2.00	1.00
1994 Topps Stadium Club	168	.10	.08	.04
1994 Upper Deck Collector's Choice	60	.10	.08	.04
1994 Upper Deck Collector's Choice	79	.06	.05	.02

Grading Guide

Mint (MT): A perfect card. Well-centered with all corners sharp and square. No creases, stains, edge nicks, surface marks, yellowing or fading.

Near Mint (NM): A nearly perfect card. At first glance, a NM card appears to be perfect. May be slightly off-center. No surface marks, creases or loss of gloss.

Excellent (EX): Corners are still fairly sharp with only moderate wear. Borders may be off-center. No creases or stains on fronts or backs, but may show slight loss of surface luster.

Very Good (VG): Shows obvious handling. May have rounded corners, minor creases, major gum or wax stains. No major creases, tape marks, writing, etc.

Good (G): A well-worn card, but exhibits no intentional damage. May have major or multiple creases. Corners may be rounded well beyond card border.

Bruce Matthews

Set	Card #	MT	NM	EX
1989 Pro Set	148 (R)	.30	.25	.12
1989 Score	109 (R)	1.00	.70	.40
1989 Score	286	.10	.08	.04
1989 Topps	91 (R)	.30	.25	.12
1990 Fleer	131	.03	.02	.01
1990 Pro Set	352	.03	.02	.01
1990 Pro Set	514	.03	.02	.01
1990 Score	93	.04	.03	.02
1990 Score	584	.04	.03	.02
1990 Score 100 Hottest	97	.10	.08	.04
1990 Topps	215	.04	.03	.02
1991 Bowman	187	.03	.02	.01
1991 Fleer	67	.05	.04	.02
1991 Pacific	178	.04	.03	.02
1991 Pinnacle	74	.10	.08	.04
1991 Pro Set	166	.03	.02	.01
1991 Pro Set	410	.03	.02	.01
1991 Pro Set Platinum	197	.05	.04	.02
1991 Score	242	.04	.03	.02
1991 Score	684	.04	.03	.02
1991 Topps	238	.04	.03	.02
1991 Topps Stadium Club	358	.20	.15	.08
1992 Bowman	372	.25	.20	.10
1992 Fleer	150	.03	.02	.01
1992 Fleer All-Pro	10	.25	.20	.10
1992 Fleer Ultra	148	.05	.04	.02
1992 Pacific	113	.05	.04	.02
1992 Pinnacle	203	.05	.04	.02
1992 Pinnacle Team Pinnacle	7	8.50	6.50	3.50
1992 Pro Set	513	.05	.04	.02
1992 Score	340	.05	.04	.02
1992 Topps	239	.05	.04	.02
1992 Topps Stadium Club	218	.08	.06	.03
1992 Upper Deck	112	.05	.04	.02
1993 Bowman	372	.15	.11	.06
1993 Fleer	161	.05	.04	.02
1993 Fleer All-Pro	10	1.00	.70	.40
1993 Fleer Ultra	169	.08	.06	.03
1993 GameDay	74	.10	.08	.04
1993 Pacific	287	.05	.04	.02
1993 Pinnacle	72	.10	.08	.04
1993 Pinnacle Men of Autumn	38	.25	.20	.10
1993 Pro Set Power	174	.05	.04	.02
1993 Score	36	.04	.03	.02
1993 Score Dream Team	11	.65	.50	.25
1993 Score Select	10	.10	.08	.04
1993 SkyBox Impact	128	.03	.02	.01
1993 Topps	19	.05	.04	.02
1993 Topps Stadium Club	305	.10	.08	.04
1993 Upper Deck	400	.05	.04	.02
1994 Bowman	160	.10	.08	.04
1994 Fleer	189	.05	.04	.02
1994 Fleer Ultra	122	.08	.06	.03
1994 GameDay	166	.10	.08	.04
1994 Pinnacle	60	.09	.07	.04
1994 Score	8	.05	.04	.02

Set		MT	NM	EX
1994 Score Dream Team	6	4.00	3.00	1.50
1994 Score Select	75	.10	.08	.04
1994 Topps	85	.05	.04	.02
1994 Topps Stadium Club	269	.10	.08	.04

O.J. McDuffie

Set	Card #	MT	NM	EX
1993 Bowman	273 (R)	3.50	2.75	1.50
1993 Fleer NFL Prospects	15	7.00	5.25	2.75
1993 Fleer Ultra	259 (R)	3.00	2.25	1.25
1993 GameDay	188 (R)	2.00	1.50	.80
1993 GameDay Rookie Standouts	7	2.50	2.00	1.00
1993 Pacific	420 (R)	1.25	.90	.50
1993 Pinnacle Rookies	18	25.00	18.50	10.00
1993 Pro Set	251 (R)	1.25	.90	.50
1993 Pro Set All-Rookie Forecast	5	3.00	2.25	1.25
1993 Pro Set Power Draft Picks	15	1.00	.75	.40
1993 Pro Set Power Update Impact Rookies	10	1.75	1.25	.70
1993 Pro Set Power Update Prospects	21 (R)	1.25	.90	.50
1993 Score Select	177 (R)	3.25	2.50	1.25
1993 SkyBox Impact	383 (R)	1.50	1.25	.60
1993 SkyBox Premium	223 (R)	2.50	2.00	1.00
1993 Topps	326 (R)	1.50	1.25	.60
1993 Topps	463	.50	.40	.20
1993 Topps Stadium Club	56 (R)	2.25	1.75	.90
1993 Upper Deck	16 (R)	1.25	.90	.50
1993 Upper Deck SP	7 (R)	4.50	3.50	1.75
1994 Bowman	232	.20	.15	.08
1994 Fleer	282	.40	.30	.15
1994 Pacific Crown	190	.25	.20	.10
1994 Pacific Crown Gems of the Crown	18	2.50	2.00	1.00
1994 Pacific Prisms	71	2.00	1.50	.80
1994 Pinnacle	62	.30	.25	.12
1994 Score	210	.30	.25	.12
1994 SkyBox Impact	153	.35	.25	.14
1994 SkyBox Impact Instant Impact	11	2.50	2.00	1.00
1994 Topps	136	.40	.30	.15
1994 Topps Finest	115	5.00	3.75	2.00
1994 Topps Stadium Club	99	.45	.35	.20
1994 Upper Deck	149	.25	.20	.10
1994 Upper Deck Collector's Choice	177	.30	.25	.12
1994 Upper Deck SP All-Pro	24	4.00	3.00	1.50

The values quoted are intended to reflect the market price.

A card number in parentheses () indicates the set is unnumbered.

Jim McMahon

Set	Card #	MT	NM	EX
1983 Topps	33 (R)	4.50	3.50	1.75
1984 Topps	227	1.50	1.25	.60
1985 Topps	31	.60	.45	.25
1986 Topps	10	.30	.25	.12
1987 Topps	44	.25	.20	.10
1988 Topps	69	.15	.11	.06
1989 Pro Set	44	.03	.02	.01
1989 Pro Set	478	.03	.02	.01
1989 Score	145	.10	.08	.04
1989 Score	353	.10	.08	.04
1989 Topps	62	.05	.04	.02
1989 Topps Traded	97	.05	.04	.02
1990 Fleer	310	.03	.02	.01
1990 Fleer Update	16	.15	.11	.06
1990 Pro Set	610	.03	.02	.01
1990 Topps Update	111	.07	.05	.03
1991 Fleer Ultra Update	72	.10	.08	.04
1991 Pacific	627	.05	.04	.02
1991 Pinnacle	237	.10	.08	.04
1991 Pro Set	842	.05	.04	.02
1991 Pro Set Platinum	250	.05	.04	.02
1993 Bowman	349	.20	.15	.08
1993 Pinnacle	345	.07	.05	.03
1993 Pro Set	262	.05	.04	.02
1993 Pro Set Power Power Moves	32	.25	.20	.10
1993 Topps	482	.06	.05	.02
1993 Topps Stadium Club	324	.10	.08	.04
1994 Bowman	326	.10	.08	.04
1994 Fleer Ultra	329	.08	.06	.03
1994 Pacific Crown	159	.06	.05	.02
1994 Pinnacle	244	.09	.07	.04
1994 Topps Finest	90	1.25	.90	.50

Natrone Means

Set	Card #	MT	NM	EX
1993 Bowman	162 (R)	9.00	6.75	3.50

		MT	NM	EX
1993 Fleer NFL Prospects	23	25.00	18.50	10.00
1993 Fleer Ultra	416 (R)	6.00	4.50	2.50
1993 GameDay	434 (R)	8.00	6.00	3.25
1993 Pacific	433 (R)	3.00	2.25	1.25
1993 Pinnacle Rookies	23	100.00	75.00	40.00
1993 Pro Set	380 (R)	3.00	2.25	1.25
1993 Pro Set Power Draft Picks	24	1.00	.75	.40
1993 Pro Set Power Update Prospects	18 (R)	1.50	1.25	.60
1993 Pro Set Rookie Running Backs	13	6.00	4.50	2.50
1993 Score Select	174 (R)	9.00	6.75	3.50
1993 SkyBox Impact	399 (R)	2.50	2.00	1.00
1993 SkyBox Premium	183 (R)	7.00	5.25	2.75
1993 SkyBox Primetime Rookies	7	30.00	18.50	10.00
1993 Topps	243 (R)	3.00	2.25	1.25
1993 Topps	477	1.00	.75	.40
1993 Topps Stadium Club	21 (R)	6.00	4.50	2.50
1993 Upper Deck	479 (R)	4.00	3.00	1.50
1993 Upper Deck SP	14 (R)	20.00	15.00	8.00
1994 Bowman	242	2.00	1.50	.80
1994 Fleer Ultra	268	2.25	1.70	.90
1994 Fleer Ultra Scoring Power	2	5.00	3.75	2.00
1994 Fleer Ultra 2nd Year Standouts	10	4.00	3.00	1.50
1994 GameDay	354	2.00	1.50	.80
1994 GameDay Second-Year Stars	10	4.00	3.00	1.50
1994 Pacific Crown	219	.85	.60	.35
1994 Pacific Crown Gems of the Crown	19	13.00	9.75	5.25
1994 Pacific Crown Knights of the Gridiron	15	20.00	15.00	8.00
1994 Pacific Marquee	18	5.00	3.75	2.00
1994 Pacific Prisms	72	12.00	9.00	4.75
1994 Pinnacle	134	2.00	1.50	.80
1994 Pinnacle Sportflics	73	3.00	2.25	1.25
1994 Pinnacle Team Pinnacle	5	45.00	34.00	18.00
1994 Score	237	.80	.60	.30
1994 Score Select	184	3.00	2.25	1.25
1994 Score Select Future Force	5	50.00	37.00	20.00
1994 SkyBox Impact	225	.85	.60	.35
1994 SkyBox Impact Instant Impact	9	10.00	7.50	4.00
1994 SkyBox Premium	134	2.00	1.50	.80
1994 Topps	450	.85	.60	.35
1994 Topps Finest	188	14.00	10.50	5.50
1994 Topps Stadium Club	40	2.00	1.50	.80
1994 Upper Deck SP	100	3.25	2.50	1.25

Anthony Miller

Set	Card #	MT	NM	EX
1989 Pro Set	363 (R)	1.50	1.25	.60
1989 Score	178 (R)	5.50	4.25	2.25
1989 Score	311	1.25	.90	.50
1989 Topps	313 (R)	2.00	1.50	.80
1990 Fleer	311	.30	.25	.12
1990 Pro Set	356	.06	.25	.12
1990 Pro Set	630	.30	.25	.12
1990 Score	220	.30	.25	.12
1990 Score Young Superstars	35	.20	.15	.08
1990 Score 100 Hottest	24	.15	.11	.06
1990 Topps	390	.30	.25	.12
1990 Topps 1000 Yard Club	10	.20	.15	.08
1991 Bowman	460	.06	.05	.02
1991 Fleer	176	.15	.11	.06
1991 Fleer Ultra	125	.08	.06	.03
1991 Pacific	448	.04	.03	.02
1991 Pinnacle	184	.50	.40	.20
1991 Pro Set	285	.03	.02	.01
1991 Pro Set	407	.03	.02	.01
1991 Pro Set	717	.03	.02	.01
1991 Pro Set Platinum	264	.05	.04	.02
1991 Score	370	.05	.04	.02
1991 Topps	422	.04	.03	.02
1991 Topps Stadium Club	367	.85	.60	.35
1991 Upper Deck	126	.05	.04	.02
1991 Upper Deck	474	.05	.04	.02
1992 GameDay	386	.12	.09	.05
1992 Pro Set	639	.05	.04	.02
1992 Pro Set Power	280	.05	.04	.02
1992 SkyBox Impact	223	.05	.04	.02
1992 SkyBox Primetime	105	.10	.08	.04
1992 Topps	707	.05	.04	.02
1992 Topps Stadium Club	664	.60	.45	.25
1992 Upper Deck	606	.10	.08	.04
1992 Upper Deck Gold	33	.10	.08	.04
1993 Bowman	328	.45	.35	.20
1993 Fleer	399	.25	.20	.10
1993 Fleer Ultra	417	.10	.08	.04
1993 GameDay	93	.35	.25	.14
1993 Pacific	335	.05	.04	.02
1993 Pinnacle	258	.35	.25	.14
1993 Pinnacle Team Pinnacle	4	40.00	30.00	16.00
1993 Pro Set	381	.05	.04	.02
1993 Pro Set Power	183	.15	.11	.06
1993 Score	243	.04	.03	.02
1993 Score Select	46	.50	.40	.20
1993 SkyBox Impact	285	.05	.04	.02
1993 SkyBox Premium	232	.10	.08	.04
1993 Topps	217	.20	.15	.08
1993 Topps	336	.05	.04	.02
1993 Topps Black Gold	22	.75	.60	.30
1993 Topps Stadium Club	466	.15	.11	.06
1993 Upper Deck	70	.05	.04	.02
1993 Upper Deck	252	.05	.04	.02
1993 Upper Deck NFL Experience	42	.30	.25	.12
1993 Upper Deck Pro Bowl	4	4.50	3.50	1.75
1993 Upper Deck SP	231	.25	.20	.10
1993 Upper Deck SP All Pro	11	8.00	6.00	3.25
1994 Fleer	140	.20	.15	.08
1994 Fleer Ultra	89	.20	.15	.08
1994 Fleer Ultra	379	.10	.08	.04
1994 GameDay	121	.10	.08	.04
1994 Pacific Crown	220	.10	.08	.04
1994 Pacific Prisms	75	1.50	1.25	.60
1994 Pinnacle	41	.12	.09	.05
1994 Pinnacle Sportflics	133	.20	.15	.08
1994 Pinnacle Team Pinnacle	7	40.00	30.00	16.00
1994 Score	167	.15	.11	.06
1994 Score Dream Team	8	5.00	3.75	2.00
1994 Score Select	114	.12	.09	.05
1994 SkyBox Impact	226	.08	.06	.03
1994 SkyBox Premium	51	.20	.15	.08
1994 Topps	425	.08	.06	.03
1994 Topps	614	.10	.08	.04
1994 Topps Finest	23	1.25	.90	.50

Set	Card #	MT	NM	EX
1994 Topps Finest Inserts	8	4.00	3.00	1.50
1994 Upper Deck	59	.15	.11	.06
1994 Upper Deck Collector's Choice	150	.07	.05	.03
1994 Upper Deck Pro Bowl	7	5.00	3.75	2.00
1994 Upper Deck SP	78	.30	.25	.12

Chris Miller

Set	Card #	MT	NM	EX
1989 Pro Set	12 (R)	.60	.45	.25
1989 Score	60 (R)	2.50	2.00	1.00
1989 Topps	341 (R)	.60	.45	.25
1990 Fleer	381	.10	.08	.04
1990 Pro Set	35	.06	.05	.02
1990 Score	70	.10	.08	.04
1990 Score Young Superstars	37	.35	.25	.14
1990 Score 100 Hottest	93	.30	.25	.12
1990 Topps	472	.25	.20	.10
1991 Bowman	18	.03	.02	.01
1991 Fleer	207	.15	.11	.06
1991 Fleer Ultra	146	.10	.08	.04
1991 Pacific	16	.04	.03	.02
1991 Pinnacle	24	.10	.08	.04
1991 Pro Set	97	.03	.02	.01
1991 Pro Set Platinum	1	.05	.04	.02
1991 Score	219	.04	.03	.02
1991 Topps	585	.04	.03	.02
1991 Topps Stadium Club	63	.30	.25	.12
1991 Upper Deck	193	.05	.04	.02
1992 Bowman	150	.30	.25	.12
1992 Fleer	12	.03	.02	.01
1992 Fleer Team Leaders	1	6.50	5.00	2.50
1992 Fleer Ultra	12	.05	.04	.02
1992 GameDay	363	.15	.11	.06
1992 Pacific	8	.05	.04	.02
1992 Pinnacle	241	.05	.04	.02
1992 Pro Set	113	.08	.06	.03
1992 Pro Set	415	.05	.04	.02
1992 Pro Set Power	112	.05	.04	.02
1992 Score	390	.07	.05	.03
1992 SkyBox Impact	211	.05	.04	.02
1992 SkyBox Primetime	297	.10	.08	.04
1992 Topps	156	.05	.04	.02
1992 Topps Stadium Club	79	.08	.06	.03
1992 Upper Deck	291	.05	.04	.02
1992 Upper Deck	364	.05	.04	.02
1993 Fleer	153	.10	.08	.04
1993 Fleer Ultra	13	.10	.08	.04
1993 GameDay	119	.10	.08	.04
1993 Pacific	173	.05	.04	.02
1993 Pacific Prisms	1	1.25	.90	.50
1993 Pinnacle	160	.10	.08	.04
1993 Pro Set	67	.05	.04	.02
1993 Score	386	.04	.03	.02

Set	Card #	MT	NM	EX
1993 Score Select	129	.10	.08	.04
1993 SkyBox Impact	8	.03	.02	.01
1993 SkyBox Premium	22	.10	.08	.04
1993 Topps	10	.05	.04	.02
1993 Topps Stadium Club	15	.10	.08	.04
1993 Upper Deck	325	.05	.04	.02
1993 Upper Deck SP	24	.25	.20	.10
1994 Bowman	40	.15	.11	.06
1994 Fleer	260	.15	.11	.06
1994 Fleer Ultra	167	.08	.06	.03
1994 GameDay	222	.10	.08	.04
1994 Pacific Crown	293	.06	.05	.02
1994 Pinnacle	67	.10	.08	.04
1994 Pinnacle Sportflics	139	.15	.11	.06
1994 Score	98	.10	.08	.04
1994 Score Select	181	.10	.08	.04
1994 SkyBox Impact	144	.15	.11	.06
1994 SkyBox Premium	85	.10	.08	.04
1994 Topps	364	.05	.04	.02
1994 Topps Stadium Club	385	.10	.08	.04
1994 Upper Deck	48	.20	.15	.08
1994 Upper Deck Collector's Choice	133	.05	.04	.02
1994 Upper Deck SP	188	.20	.15	.08

Rick Mirer

Set	Card #	MT	NM	EX
1993 Bowman	50 (R)	7.50	5.65	3.00
1993 Fleer Ultra	456 (R)	5.00	3.75	2.00
1993 Fleer Ultra All-Rookie	9	17.00	12.50	6.75
1993 GameDay	402 (R)	7.50	5.65	3.00
1993 GameDay Rookie Standouts	2	6.00	4.50	2.50
1993 Pacific	385 (R)	2.00	1.50	.80
1993 Pacific Gold Prisms	12	30.00	22.00	12.00
1993 Pacific Prism Inserts	12	17.00	12.50	6.75
1993 Pacific Prisms	95	15.00	11.00	6.00
1993 Pacific Triple Folder Superstars	13 (R)	2.50	2.00	1.00
1993 Pacific Triple Folders	15	2.25	1.75	.90
1993 Pinnacle Rookies	12	85.00	64.00	34.00
1993 Pro Set	411 (R)	2.25	1.70	.90
1993 Pro Set All-Rookie Forecast	1	12.00	9.00	4.75
1993 Pro Set College Connections	8	30.00	22.00	12.00
1993 Pro Set Power Update Impact Rookies	1	3.00	2.25	1.25
1993 Pro Set Power Update Prospects	2 (R)	3.50	2.75	1.50
1993 Pro Set Rookie QB's	2	6.00	4.50	2.50
1993 Score Select	179 (R)	10.00	7.50	4.00
1993 SkyBox Impact	362 (R)	2.50	2.00	1.00

Set	Card #	MT	NM	EX
1993 SkyBox Premium	89 (R)	4.50	3.50	1.75
1993 SkyBox Primetime Rookies	8	25.00	18.50	10.00
1993 Topps	285 (R)	2.50	2.00	1.00
1993 Topps	600	1.25	.90	.50
1993 Topps Stadium Club	180 (R)	4.50	3.50	1.75
1993 Topps Stadium Club	510	1.50	1.25	.60
1993 Upper Deck	3 (R)	2.75	2.05	1.10
1993 Upper Deck	88	1.00	.70	.40
1993 Upper Deck Rookie Exchange	3	9.00	6.75	3.50
1993 Upper Deck SP	16 (R)	15.00	11.00	6.00
1994 Bowman	235	2.00	1.50	.80
1994 Fleer	439	1.25	.90	.50
1994 Fleer Award Winners	2	2.50	2.00	1.00
1994 Fleer Pro-Visions	3	1.75	1.25	.70
1994 Fleer Rookie Sensations	13	40.00	30.00	16.00
1994 Fleer Ultra	291	1.75	1.25	.70
1994 Fleer Ultra Award Winners	2	5.00	3.75	2.00
1994 Fleer Ultra Ultra Stars	5	25.00	18.50	10.00
1994 Fleer Ultra 2nd Year Standouts	11	3.00	2.25	1.25
1994 GameDay	383	2.00	1.50	.80
1994 GameDay Flashing Stars	2	15.00	11.00	6.00
1994 GameDay Second-Year Stars	11	4.00	3.00	1.50
1994 Pacific Crown	324	1.75	1.25	.70
1994 Pacific Crown Gems of the Crown	20	10.00	7.50	4.00
1994 Pacific Crown Knights of the Gridiron	16	20.00	15.00	8.00
1994 Pacific Marquee	19	2.75	2.00	1.00
1994 Pacific Prisms	76	10.00	7.50	4.00
1994 Pinnacle	104	2.25	1.70	.90
1994 Pinnacle Sportflics	115	2.50	2.00	1.00
1994 Pinnacle Team Pinnacle	2	45.00	34.00	18.00
1994 Score	329	1.25	.90	.50
1994 Score Select	20	1.75	1.25	.70
1994 Score Select Future Force	1	40.00	30.00	16.00
1994 Score Sophomore Showcase	2	8.00	6.00	3.25
1994 SkyBox Impact	242	1.50	1.25	.60
1994 SkyBox Impact Instant Impact	1	10.00	7.50	4.00
1994 SkyBox Premium	146	1.50	1.25	.60
1994 SkyBox Premium Revolution	15	13.00	9.75	5.25
1994 SkyBox Premium SkyTech Stars	8	6.00	4.50	2.50
1994 Topps	480	1.50	1.25	.60
1994 Topps Finest	41	15.00	11.00	6.00
1994 Topps Stadium Club	188	1.25	.90	.50
1994 Topps Stadium Club	380	2.00	1.50	.80
1994 Upper Deck	266	2.25	1.70	.90
1994 Upper Deck Collector's Choice Crash Game	3	8.00	6.00	3.25
1994 Upper Deck Collector's Choice	49	.40	.30	.15
1994 Upper Deck Collector's Choice	162	1.25	.90	.50
1994 Upper Deck Retail Predictor	8	5.00	3.75	2.00
1994 Upper Deck SP	106	2.50	2.00	1.00
1994 Upper Deck SP All-Pro	37	8.00	6.00	3.25

Cards before 1981 are priced in Near Mint (NM),
Excellent (EX), and Very Good (VG).
Cards 1981 to present are Mint (MT), Near Mint (NM),
and Excellent (EX).

Johnny Mitchell

Set	Card #	MT	NM	EX
1992 GameDay	35 (R)	1.25	.90	.50
1992 Pro Set	603 (R)	.60	.45	.25
1992 Pro Set Power	324 (R)	.75	.60	.30
1992 Topps Stadium Club	662 (R)	4.50	3.50	1.75
1992 Upper Deck	417 (R)	.50	.40	.20
1993 Fleer	280	.20	.15	.08
1993 Fleer Rookie Sensations	17	9.00	6.75	3.50
1993 Fleer Ultra	344	.50	.40	.20
1993 GameDay	83	.50	.40	.20
1993 GameDay Second-Year Stars	16	1.00	.75	.40
1993 Pacific	248	.30	.25	.12
1993 Pacific Prisms	74	2.50	2.00	1.00
1993 Pinnacle	285	.50	.40	.20
1993 Pinnacle Team 2001	15	.50	.40	.20
1993 Pro Set	323	.25	.20	.10
1993 Score Select	8	.60	.45	.25
1993 SkyBox Impact	239	.25	.20	.10
1993 Topps	129	.25	.20	.10
1993 Topps Stadium Club	33	.40	.30	.15
1993 Upper Deck	469	.25	.20	.10
1993 Upper Deck SP	194	.75	.60	.30
1994 Bowman	299	.10	.08	.04
1994 Fleer	361	.10	.08	.04
1994 Fleer Ultra	471	.08	.06	.03
1994 GameDay	307	.10	.08	.04
1994 Pacific Crown	205	.06	.05	.02
1994 Pacific Prisms	77	1.00	.70	.40
1994 Pinnacle	161	.09	.07	.04
1994 Pinnacle Sportflics	6	.20	.15	.08
1994 Score	79	.10	.08	.04
1994 Score Select	37	.10	.08	.04
1994 SkyBox Impact	199	.10	.08	.04
1994 SkyBox Premium	119	.08	.06	.03
1994 Topps	15	.10	.08	.04
1994 Topps Finest	173	.65	.50	.25
1994 Topps Stadium Club	172	.15	.11	.06
1994 Upper Deck	201	.10	.08	.04
1994 Upper Deck Collector's Choice	166	.07	.05	.03
1994 Upper Deck SP	49	.20	.15	.08

Grading Guide

Mint (MT): A perfect card. Well-centered with all corners sharp and square. No creases, stains, edge nicks, surface marks, yellowing or fading.

Near Mint (NM): A nearly perfect card. At first glance, a NM card appears to be perfect. May be slightly off-center. No surface marks, creases or loss of gloss.

Excellent (EX): Corners are still fairly sharp with only moderate wear. Borders may be off-center. No creases or stains on fronts or backs, but may show slight loss of surface luster.

Very Good (VG): Shows obvious handling. May have rounded corners, minor creases, major gum or wax stains. No major creases, tape marks, writing, etc.

Good (G): A well-worn card, but exhibits no intentional damage. May have major or multiple creases. Corners may be rounded well beyond card border.

Art Monk

Set	Card #	MT	NM	EX
1981 Topps	194 (R)	32.00	24.00	13.80
1982 Topps	515	6.50	4.90	2.60
1983 Topps	193	2.00	1.50	.80
1984 Topps	384	1.00	.70	.40
1985 Topps	5	.30	.25	.12
1985 Topps	185	1.00	.70	.40
1985 Topps	193	.35	.25	.14
1986 Topps	175	.75	.60	.30
1986 Topps 1000 Yard Club	12	.20	.15	.08
1987 Topps	69	.50	.40	.20
1987 Topps 1000 Yard Club	19	.15	.11	.06
1988 Topps	12	.25	.20	.10
1989 Pro Set	433	.10	.08	.04
1989 Score	130	.40	.30	.15
1989 Topps	260	.15	.11	.06
1990 Fleer	164	.06	.05	.02
1990 Pro Set	328	.03	.02	.01
1990 Score	12	.04	.03	.02
1990 Score	557	.04	.03	.02
1990 Score 100 Hottest	49	.30	.25	.12
1990 Topps	126	.04	.03	.02
1990 Topps 1000 Yard Club	16	.15	.11	.06
1991 Bowman	536	.08	.06	.03
1991 Fleer	391	.06	.05	.02
1991 Fleer Ultra	274	.08	.06	.03
1991 Pacific	529	.04	.03	.02
1991 Pinnacle	280	.10	.08	.04
1991 Pinnacle	411	.10	.08	.04
1991 Pro Set	22	.05	.04	.02
1991 Pro Set	682	.05	.04	.02
1991 Pro Set Platinum PC	2	.50	.40	.20
1991 Score	181	.04	.03	.02
1991 Topps	187	.04	.03	.02
1991 Topps Stadium Club	179	.25	.20	.10
1991 Upper Deck	123	.05	.04	.02
1992 Bowman	255	.35	.25	.14
1992 Bowman	349	.30	.25	.12
1992 Fleer	427	.03	.02	.01
1992 Fleer	473	.03	.02	.01
1992 Fleer Ultra	411	.05	.04	.02
1992 GameDay	472	.15	.11	.06
1992 Pacific	311	.05	.04	.02
1992 Pinnacle	138	.05	.04	.02
1992 Pro Set	22	.08	.06	.03
1992 Pro Set	42	.08	.06	.03
1992 Pro Set	85	.05	.04	.02
1992 Pro Set Power	81	.10	.08	.04
1992 Pro Set Power Power Combos	7	4.00	3.00	1.50
1992 Score	200	.07	.05	.03
1992 SkyBox Primetime	54	.10	.08	.04
1992 Topps	345	.05	.04	.02
1992 Topps Stadium Club	244	.08	.06	.03
1992 Topps 1000-Yard Club	14	1.00	.70	.40
1992 Upper Deck	344	.05	.04	.02

Set	Card #	MT	NM	EX
1992 Upper Deck Game Breaker Holograms	1	1.75	1.25	.70
1993 Fleer	102	.08	.06	.03
1993 Fleer Ultra	493	.10	.08	.04
1993 Fleer Ultra Touchdown Kings	3	1.50	1.25	.60
1993 GameDay	81	.10	.08	.04
1993 Pacific	36	.05	.04	.02
1993 Pacific Prisms	106	1.25	.90	.50
1993 Pinnacle	81	.07	.05	.03
1993 Pro Set	443	.05	.04	.02
1993 Pro Set Power	81	.10	.08	.04
1993 Pro Set Power Update Combos	10	1.00	.70	.40
1993 Score	368	.04	.03	.02
1993 Score	433	.06	.05	.02
1993 Score Select	63	.10	.08	.04
1993 SkyBox Impact	339	.05	.04	.02
1993 SkyBox Poster Art Cards	4	.50	.40	.20
1993 SkyBox Premium	110	.10	.08	.04
1993 Topps	1	.05	.04	.02
1993 Topps	590	.07	.05	.03
1993 Topps Stadium Club	124	.10	.08	.04
1993 Upper Deck	150	.05	.04	.02
1993 Upper Deck SP	268	.25	.20	.10
1994 Fleer	471	.10	.08	.04
1994 Fleer Ultra	472	.08	.06	.03
1994 GameDay	308	.10	.08	.04
1994 Score	259	.05	.04	.02
1994 Score Select	197	.10	.08	.04
1994 SkyBox Impact	263	.08	.06	.03
1994 Topps	473	.08	.06	.03
1994 Topps Finest	113	2.00	1.50	.80
1994 Upper Deck SP	50	.20	.15	.08

Joe Montana

Set	Card #	MT	NM	EX
1981 Topps	216 (R)	210.00	157.00	84.00
1982 Topps	488	36.00	27.00	14.50
1982 Topps	489	10.00	7.50	4.00
1983 Topps	4	2.00	1.50	.80
1983 Topps	169	15.00	11.00	6.00
1984 Topps	358	9.00	6.75	3.50
1984 Topps	359	4.00	3.00	1.50
1985 Topps	157	7.00	5.25	2.75
1985 Topps	192	7.00	5.25	2.75
1986 Topps	156	6.00	4.50	2.50
1986 Topps	225	1.00	.70	.40
1987 Topps	112	3.75	2.75	1.50
1988 Topps	4	.80	.60	.30
1988 Topps	38	1.50	1.25	.60
1989 Pro Set	381	1.50	1.25	.60
1989 Score	1	4.00	3.00	1.50
1989 Score	275	2.00	1.50	.80
1989 Score	279	1.50	1.25	.60
1989 Score	329	2.00	1.50	.80
1989 Topps	12	1.50	1.25	.60
1990 Fleer	10	.03	.02	.01

Set	#			
1990 Fleer	397	.70	.50	.30
1990 Fleer All-Pro	1	1.50	1.25	.60
1990 Pro Set	2	.50	.40	.20
1990 Pro Set	8	.50	.40	.20
1990 Pro Set	293	1.00	.70	.40
1990 Pro Set	408	.50	.40	.20
1990 Pro Set Super Bowl MVPs	16	.50	.40	.20
1990 Pro Set Super Bowl MVPs	19	.50	.40	.20
1990 Pro Set Super Bowl MVPs	24	.50	.40	.20
1990 Score	1	1.00	.70	.40
1990 Score	311	.50	.40	.20
1990 Score	582	.50	.40	.20
1990 Score	594	.50	.40	.20
1990 Score Hot Card	1	10.00	7.50	4.00
1990 Score 100 Hottest	2	2.00	1.50	.80
1990 Topps	1	.50	.40	.20
1990 Topps	13	1.00	.70	.40
1991 Bowman	479	1.25	.90	.50
1991 Fleer	360	1.00	.70	.40
1991 Fleer	408	.50	.40	.20
1991 Fleer All-Pro	19	2.00	1.50	.75
1991 Fleer Pro Visions	1	2.00	1.50	.80
1991 Fleer Ultra	251	1.00	.70	.40
1991 Fleer Ultra Performances	4	10.00	7.50	4.00
1991 Pacific	464	1.00	.70	.40
1991 Pinnacle	66	3.50	2.75	1.50
1991 Pro Set	3	.50	.40	.20
1991 Pro Set	387	.50	.40	.20
1991 Pro Set	653	1.00	.70	.40
1991 Pro Set Platinum	139	1.00	.70	.40
1991 Score	1	1.00	.70	.40
1991 Score	620	.50	.40	.20
1991 Topps	73	1.00	.70	.40
1991 Topps Stadium Club	327	9.00	6.75	3.50
1991 Upper Deck	35	.40	.30	.15
1991 Upper Deck	54	1.00	.70	.40
1991 Upper Deck Heroes Joe Montana	1	1.00	.70	.40
1991 Upper Deck Heroes Joe Montana	2	1.00	.70	.40
1991 Upper Deck Heroes Joe Montana	3	1.00	.70	.40
1991 Upper Deck Heroes Joe Montana	4	1.00	.70	.40
1991 Upper Deck Heroes Joe Montana	5	1.00	.70	.40
1991 Upper Deck Heroes Joe Montana	6	1.00	.70	.40
1991 Upper Deck Heroes Joe Montana	7	1.00	.70	.40
1991 Upper Deck Heroes Joe Montana	8	1.00	.70	.40
1991 Upper Deck Heroes Joe Montana	9	1.00	.70	.40
1991 Upper Deck Heroes Joe Montana	----	10.00	7.50	4.00
1992 GameDay	5	3.50	2.75	1.50
1992 Pro Set	649	1.25	.90	.50
1992 Pro Set Power	16	2.00	1.50	.80
1992 SkyBox Impact	227	1.00	.70	.40
1992 SkyBox Impact Major Impact	15	5.00	3.75	2.00
1992 SkyBox Primetime	16	2.50	2.00	1.00
1992 SkyBox Primetime	67	1.25	.90	.50
1992 SkyBox Primetime Poster Cards	6	10.00	7.50	4.00
1992 Topps	719	1.00	.70	.40
1992 Topps Stadium Club	650	16.00	12.00	6.50
1992 Upper Deck	560	1.00	.70	.40
1992 Upper Deck Gold	36	2.00	1.50	.80
1993 Bowman	200	8.00	6.00	3.25
1993 Fleer	475	1.00	.70	.40
1993 Fleer Ultra	203	3.00	2.25	1.25
1993 Fleer Ultra Touchdown Kings	4	25.00	18.50	10.00
1993 GameDay	36	3.00	2.25	1.25
1993 GameDay Game Breakers	5	5.00	3.75	2.00
1993 Pacific	412	1.00	.70	.40
1993 Pacific Gold Prisms	13	50.00	37.00	20.00
1993 Pacific Prism Inserts	13	22.00	16.50	8.75
1993 Pacific Prisms	42	15.00	11.00	6.00
1993 Pacific Triple Folders	6	3.50	2.75	1.50
1993 Pacific Triple Folder Superstars	14	4.00	3.00	1.50
1993 Pinnacle	277	3.75	2.75	1.50
1993 Pinnacle Team Pinnacle	1	120.00	90.00	48.00
1993 Pro Set	198	1.50	1.25	.60
1993 Pro Set College Connections	8	30.00	22.00	12.00
1993 Pro Set Power	200	1.50	1.25	.60
1993 Pro Set Power Power Moves	10	3.00	2.25	1.25
1993 Pro Set Power Update Moves	10	2.50	2.00	1.00
1993 Score	253	1.50	1.25	.60
1993 Score Select	155	9.00	6.75	3.50
1993 SkyBox Impact	139	1.00	.70	.40
1993 SkyBox Premium	48	2.00	1.50	.80
1993 Topps	200	1.25	.90	.50
1993 Topps	340	1.50	1.25	.60
1993 Topps Stadium Club	250	1.00	.70	.40
1993 Topps Stadium Club	440	3.00	2.25	1.25
1993 Upper Deck	460	1.25	.90	.50
1993 Upper Deck Kansas City Chiefs	15	3.00	2.25	1.25
1993 Upper Deck Kansas City Chiefs	25	2.00	1.50	.80
1993 Upper Deck NFL Experience	1	1.25	.90	.50
1993 Upper Deck SP	122	15.00	11.00	6.00
1994 Bowman	100	3.00	2.25	1.25
1994 Fleer	226	1.50	1.25	.60
1994 Fleer All-Pro	7	4.50	3.50	1.75
1994 Fleer Living Legends	3	45.00	34.00	18.00
1994 Fleer Pro-Visions	7	1.75	1.25	.70
1994 Fleer Scoring Machines	10	50.00	37.00	20.00
1994 Fleer Ultra	145	2.50	2.00	1.00
1994 Fleer Ultra Achievement Awards	4	5.00	3.75	2.00
1994 Fleer Ultra Hot Numbers	8	5.50	4.25	2.25
1994 Fleer Ultra Touchdown Kings	3	40.00	30.00	16.00
1994 GameDay	194	2.50	2.00	1.00
1994 GameDay Game Breakers	7	5.00	3.75	2.00
1994 Pacific Crown	55	1.75	1.25	.70
1994 Pacific Crown Gems of the Crown	21	15.00	11.00	6.00
1994 Pacific Marquee	20	5.50	4.25	2.25
1994 Pacific Prisms	79	13.00	9.75	5.25
1994 Pinnacle	102	2.50	2.00	1.00
1994 Pinnacle Performers	11	10.00	7.50	4.00
1994 Pinnacle Sportflics Head-to-Head	9	45.00	34.00	18.00
1994 Pinnacle Sportflics	123	3.75	2.75	1.50
1994 Pinnacle Sportflics	176	2.25	1.75	.90
1994 Pinnacle Team Pinnacle	1	90.00	67.00	36.00
1994 Score	67	1.50	1.25	.60
1994 Score Select	79	3.00	2.25	1.25
1994 Score Select Canton Bound	3	70.00	52.00	28.00
1994 SkyBox Impact	122	1.50	1.25	.60
1994 SkyBox Impact Ultimate Impact	4	16.00	12.00	6.50
1994 SkyBox Premium	75	1.75	1.25	.70
1994 SkyBox Premium Revolution	9	28.00	21.00	11.00
1994 SkyBox Premium SkyTech Stars	6	12.00	9.00	4.75
1994 Topps	520	1.75	1.25	.70

Set	Card #	MT	NM	EX
1994 Topps Finest	172	23.00	17.00	9.25
1994 Topps Stadium Club	160	2.25	1.75	.90
1994 Upper Deck	133	2.00	1.50	.80
1994 Upper Deck Collector's Choice Crash Game	8	12.00	9.00	4.75
1994 Upper Deck Collector's Choice	36	.50	.40	.20
1994 Upper Deck Collector's Choice	47	.05	.04	.02
1994 Upper Deck Collector's Choice	70	1.75	1.25	.70
1994 Upper Deck Hobby Predictor	4	10.00	7.50	4.00
1994 Upper Deck Retail Predictor	4	10.00	7.50	4.00
1994 Upper Deck SP	88	4.00	3.00	1.50
1994 Upper Deck SP All-Pro	17	20.00	15.00	8.00
1994 Upper Deck Then And Now	3	10.00	7.50	4.00
1994 Upper Deck Then And Now	4	10.00	7.50	4.00

Warren Moon

Set	Card #	MT	NM	EX
1985 Topps	251 (R)	22.00	16.50	8.75
1986 Topps	350	4.00	3.00	1.50
1987 Topps	306	.35	.25	.14
1987 Topps	307	2.25	1.75	.90
1988 Topps	102	.20	.15	.08
1988 Topps	103	.75	.60	.30
1989 Pro Set	149	.25	.20	.10
1989 Score	15	1.50	1.25	.60
1989 Topps	93	.40	.30	.15
1990 Fleer	133	.20	.15	.08
1990 Pro Set	4	.10	.08	.04
1990 Pro Set	359	.08	.06	.03
1990 Pro Set	517	.20	.15	.08
1990 Score	105	.25	.20	.10
1990 Score	317	.10	.08	.04
1990 Score 100 Hottest	96	.50	.40	.20
1990 Topps	216	.25	.20	.10
1991 Bowman	180	.25	.20	.10
1991 Bowman	277	.15	.11	.06
1991 Fleer	70	.20	.15	.08
1991 Fleer	410	.08	.06	.03
1991 Fleer Ultra	53	.20	.15	.08
1991 Fleer Ultra Performances	5	1.00	.70	.40
1991 Pacific	181	.15	.11	.06
1991 Pinnacle	1	.40	.30	.15
1991 Pinnacle	356	.25	.20	.10
1991 Pro Set	9	.08	.11	.06
1991 Pro Set	167	.15	.11	.04
1991 Pro Set	337	.10	.08	.04
1991 Pro Set	370	.08	.08	.03
1991 Pro Set	414	.10	.08	.04
1991 Pro Set Platinum	40	.15	.11	.06
1991 Pro Set Platinum	138	.10	.08	.04
1991 Score	201	.20	.15	.08
1991 Score	330	.10	.08	.04
1991 Score	619	.10	.08	.04
1991 Score	638	.08	.06	.03
1991 Score	676	.10	.08	.04
1991 Topps	7	.10	.08	.04
1991 Topps	8	.10	.08	.04
1991 Topps	233	.25	.20	.10
1991 Topps Stadium Club	137	1.25	.90	.50
1991 Upper Deck	33	.10	.08	.04
1991 Upper Deck	256	.20	.15	.08
1991 Upper Deck	403	.10	.08	.04
1991 Upper Deck	460	.10	.08	.04
1992 Bowman	59	6.00	4.50	2.50
1992 Bowman	70	1.00	.70	.40
1992 Fleer	153	.20	.15	.08
1992 Fleer	474	.10	.08	.04
1992 Fleer Team Leaders	17	12.00	9.00	4.75
1992 Fleer Ultra	151	.40	.30	.15
1992 GameDay	27	.40	.30	.15
1992 Pacific	431	.20	.15	.08
1992 Pacific Statistical Leaders	10	1.00	1.00	1.00
1992 Pinnacle	51	.30	.25	.12
1992 Pinnacle	357	.10	.08	.04
1992 Pro Set	6	.10	.08	.04
1992 Pro Set	186	.20	.15	.08
1992 Pro Set	390	.10	.08	.04
1992 Pro Set Gold MVPs	5	.60	.45	.25
1992 Pro Set Power	1	.30	.25	.12
1992 Score	50	.20	.15	.08
1992 Score	548	.10	.08	.04
1992 SkyBox Impact	50	.25	.20	.10
1992 SkyBox Impact Major Impact	6	1.00	.70	.40
1992 SkyBox Primetime	100	.25	.20	.10
1992 SkyBox Primetime	178	.15	.11	.06
1992 SkyBox Primetime	211	.15	.11	.06
1992 SkyBox Primetime Poster Cards	12	3.00	2.25	1.25
1992 Topps	70	.20	.15	.08
1992 Topps Stadium Club	120	.40	.30	.15
1992 Upper Deck	146	.25	.20	.10
1992 Upper Deck	304	.15	.11	.06
1992 Upper Deck	513	.10	.08	.04
1992 Upper Deck Pro Bowl	4	4.00	3.00	1.50
1993 Bowman	180	.65	.50	.25
1993 Fleer	220	.15	.11	.06
1993 Fleer	242	.10	.08	.04
1993 Fleer Ultra	171	.25	.20	.10
1993 Fleer Ultra League Leaders	4	5.00	3.75	2.00
1993 GameDay	121	.35	.25	.14
1993 Pacific	283	.25	.20	.10
1993 Pacific Prisms	36	1.25	.90	.50
1993 Pinnacle	226	.35	.25	.14
1993 Pinnacle Men of Autumn	10	.35	.25	.14
1993 Pro Set	174	.15	.11	.06
1993 Pro Set Power	1	.20	.15	.08
1993 Pro Set Power Combos	6	.50	.40	.20
1993 Score	216	.15	.11	.06
1993 Score	413	.08	.06	.03
1993 Score Select	107	.40	.30	.15
1993 Score Select Gridiron Skills	1	23.00	17.00	9.25
1993 Score The Franchise	10	6.50	5.00	2.50
1993 SkyBox Impact	122	.15	.11	.06
1993 SkyBox Premium	146	.25	.20	.10
1993 SkyBox Thunder and Lightning	5	6.00	4.50	2.50
1993 Topps	80	.15	.11	.06
1993 Topps	220	.12	.09	.05
1993 Topps	265	.10	.08	.04
1993 Topps Black Gold	28	1.00	.70	.40
1993 Topps Stadium Club	101	.35	.25	.14
1993 Upper Deck	81	.15	.11	.06
1993 Upper Deck	308	.20	.15	.08
1993 Upper Deck	437	.15	.11	.06

1993 Upper Deck Pro Bowl	3	7.50	5.75	3.00
1993 Upper Deck SP	106	.50	.40	.20
1993 Upper Deck SP All Pro	2	8.00	6.00	3.25
1993 Upper Deck Team MVP	19	1.00	.75	.40
1994 Bowman	145	.15	.11	.06
1994 Fleer	193	.20	.15	.08
1994 Fleer Scoring Machines	11	5.00	3.75	2.00
1994 Fleer Ultra	187	.20	.15	.08
1994 Fleer Ultra	442	.08	.06	.03
1994 GameDay	252	.10	.08	.04
1994 Pacific Crown	69	.10	.08	.04
1994 Pacific Marquee	21	1.50	1.25	.60
1994 Pacific Prisms	80	1.00	.70	.40
1994 Pinnacle	77	.12	.09	.05
1994 Pinnacle Sportflics	142	.35	.25	.14
1994 Score	32	.10	.08	.04
1994 Score Select	188	.12	.09	.05
1994 SkyBox Impact	101	.15	.11	.06
1994 SkyBox Premium	97	.15	.11	.06
1994 Topps	27	.15	.11	.06
1994 Topps Finest	21	3.00	2.25	1.25
1994 Topps Finest Inserts	24	5.00	3.75	2.00
1994 Topps Stadium Club	484	.12	.09	.05
1994 Topps Stadium Club Ring Leaders	4	10.00	7.50	4.00
1994 Upper Deck	42	.25	.20	.10
1994 Upper Deck Collector's Choice Crash Game	10	6.50	5.00	2.50
1994 Upper Deck Collector's Choice	301	.10	.08	.04
1994 Upper Deck Pro Bowl	13	10.00	7.50	4.00
1994 Upper Deck SP	145	.50	.40	.20

1992 SkyBox Primetime	70	1.00	.70	.40
1992 Topps Stadium Club	235	1.00	.75	.40
1992 Upper Deck Coach's Report	8	5.00	3.75	2.00
1993 Fleer	126	.30	.25	.12
1993 Fleer Ultra	131	.60	.45	.25
1993 GameDay	431	.50	.40	.20
1993 Pacific	107	.30	.25	.12
1993 Pacific Prisms	26	5.00	3.75	2.00
1993 Pinnacle	132	.75	.60	.30
1993 Pinnacle Team 2001	23	1.00	.75	.40
1993 Pro Set	146	.25	.20	.10
1993 Score	129	.40	.30	.15
1993 Score Select	148	1.25	.90	.50
1993 SkyBox Impact	98	.40	.30	.15
1993 SkyBox Premium	201	.50	.40	.20
1993 Topps	453	.25	.20	.10
1993 Upper Deck	390	.30	.25	.12
1993 Upper Deck SP	86	1.00	.70	.40
1994 Bowman	207	.20	.15	.08
1994 Fleer	156	.15	.11	.06
1994 Fleer Ultra	98	.25	.20	.10
1994 GameDay	133	.12	.09	.05
1994 Pacific Crown	82	.15	.11	.06
1994 Pacific Crown Gems of the Crown	22	2.50	2.00	1.00
1994 Pacific Prisms	82	1.50	1.25	.60
1994 Pinnacle	103	.15	.11	.06
1994 Pinnacle Sportflics	70	.45	.35	.20
1994 Score	155	.15	.11	.06
1994 Score Select	110	.15	.11	.06
1994 SkyBox Impact	79	.12	.09	.05
1994 SkyBox Premium	52	.20	.15	.08
1994 Topps	259	.10	.08	.04
1994 Topps Finest	161	1.50	1.25	.60
1994 Topps Stadium Club	393	.15	.11	.06
1994 Upper Deck	249	.12	.09	.05
1994 Upper Deck Collector's Choice	308	.08	.06	.03
1994 Upper Deck SP	155	.35	.25	.14

Herman Moore

Set	Card #	MT	NM	EX
1991 Bowman	158 (R)	2.00	1.50	.80
1991 Fleer Ultra	291 (R)	2.00	1.50	.80
1991 Fleer Ultra Update	27	4.00	3.00	1.50
1991 Pacific	580 (R)	1.75	1.25	.70
1991 Pro Set	739 (R)	1.25	.90	.50
1991 Score	568 (R)	1.50	1.25	.60
1991 Topps	397 (R)	1.75	1.25	.70
1991 Upper Deck	17 (R)	1.50	1.25	.60
1991 Upper Deck	639	.60	.45	.25
1992 Bowman	564	5.00	3.75	2.00
1992 Fleer	119	.45	.35	.20
1992 GameDay	465	1.00	.70	.40
1992 Pacific	90	.50	.40	.20
1992 Pinnacle	181	.90	.70	.35
1992 Pinnacle Team 2000	5	.75	.60	.30
1992 Pro Set	495	.50	.40	.20
1992 Pro Set Power	287	.65	.50	.25
1992 Score	212	.60	.45	.25
1992 SkyBox Impact	4	.40	.30	.15

Rob Moore

Set	Card #	MT	NM	EX
1990 Fleer Update	77 (R)	2.00	1.50	.80
1990 Pro Set	694 (R)	.75	.60	.30
1990 Score Update	62 (R)	4.00	3.00	1.50
1990 Topps Update	31 (R)	1.00	.75	.40
1991 Bowman	7	.15	.11	.06
1991 Bowman	392	.15	.11	.06
1991 Fleer	153	.20	.15	.08
1991 Fleer Ultra	104	.20	.15	.08
1991 Pacific	372	.25	.20	.10
1991 Pinnacle	174	.45	.35	.20
1991 Pro Set	608	.08	.06	.03
1991 Pro Set Platinum	246	.20	.15	.08
1991 Score	403	.10	.08	.04
1991 Topps	463	.20	.15	.08
1991 Topps Stadium Club	223	.25	.20	.10
1991 Upper Deck	435	.15	.11	.06
1992 Bowman	111	.30	.25	.12

Set	Card #	MT	NM	EX
1992 Fleer	310	.10	.08	.04
1992 Fleer Ultra	299	.05	.04	.02
1992 GameDay	248	.20	.15	.08
1992 Pacific	230	.20	.15	.08
1992 Pinnacle	182	.15	.11	.06
1992 Pinnacle	337	.05	.04	.02
1992 Pinnacle Team 2000	6	.40	.30	.15
1992 Pro Set	277	.05	.04	.02
1992 Pro Set Gold MVPs	11	.30	.25	.12
1992 Pro Set Power	185	.05	.04	.02
1992 Score	295	.05	.04	.02
1992 SkyBox Impact	208	.08	.06	.03
1992 SkyBox Primetime	255	.10	.08	.04
1992 Topps	182	.05	.04	.02
1992 Topps Stadium Club	389	.08	.06	.03
1992 Upper Deck	89	.05	.04	.02
1993 Bowman	17	.20	.15	.08
1993 Fleer	209	.10	.08	.04
1993 Fleer Ultra	345	.15	.11	.06
1993 GameDay	416	.15	.11	.06
1993 Pacific	241	.10	.08	.04
1993 Pacific Prisms	75	1.25	.90	.50
1993 Pacific Triple Folders	11	.75	.60	.30
1993 Pinnacle	32	.10	.08	.04
1993 Pinnacle	360	.10	.08	.04
1993 Pro Set	324	.05	.04	.02
1993 Pro Set Power	185	.05	.04	.02
1993 Score	134	.07	.05	.03
1993 SkyBox Impact	237	.05	.04	.02
1993 SkyBox Premium	214	.10	.08	.04
1993 Topps	244	.10	.08	.04
1993 Topps Stadium Club	144	.20	.15	.08
1993 Upper Deck SP	195	.25	.20	.10
1993 Upper Deck Team MVP	17	.50	.40	.20
1994 Bowman	267	.12	.09	.05
1994 Fleer	362	.15	.11	.06
1994 Fleer Ultra	237	.08	.06	.03
1994 GameDay	309	.10	.08	.04
1994 Pacific Crown	206	.06	.05	.02
1994 Pacific Prisms	83	1.50	1.25	.60
1994 Pinnacle	108	.09	.07	.04
1994 Pinnacle Sportflics	54	.20	.15	.08
1994 Score	220	.10	.08	.04
1994 Score Select	83	.10	.08	.04
1994 SkyBox Impact	195	.07	.05	.03
1994 SkyBox Premium	116	.08	.06	.03
1994 Topps	591	.05	.04	.02
1994 Topps Finest	141	1.25	.90	.50
1994 Topps Stadium Club	532	.25	.20	.10
1994 Upper Deck	261	.10	.08	.04
1994 Upper Deck Collector's Choice	196	.05	.04	.02
1994 Upper Deck SP	48	.25	.20	.10
1993 Pro Set Power Update Prospects	6 (R)	2.00	1.50	.80
1993 Pro Set Rookie Running Backs	4	2.00	1.50	.80
1994 Bowman	225	.15	.11	.06
1994 Fleer	11	.40	.30	.15
1994 Fleer Rookie Sensations	14	10.00	7.50	4.00
1994 Fleer Ultra	6	.30	.25	.12
1994 Fleer Ultra 2nd Year Standouts	12	2.00	1.50	.80
1994 GameDay	10	.45	.35	.20
1994 GameDay Second-Year Stars	12	1.00	.70	.40
1994 Pacific Crown	311	.30	.25	.12
1994 Pacific Crown Crystalline Collection	10	1.50	1.25	.60
1994 Pacific Crown Gems of the Crown	23	3.00	2.25	1.25
1994 Pacific Marquee	22	1.25	.90	.50
1994 Pacific Prisms	84	3.50	2.75	1.50
1994 Pinnacle	131	.15	.11	.06
1994 Pinnacle Sportflics	114	.50	.40	.20
1994 Score	265	.35	.25	.14
1994 Score Select	62	.30	.25	.12
1994 Score Sophomore Showcase	5	4.00	3.00	1.50
1994 SkyBox Impact	5	.30	.25	.12
1994 SkyBox Premium	4	.20	.15	.08
1994 Topps	225	.50	.40	.20
1994 Topps Finest Inserts	13	4.00	3.00	1.50
1994 Topps Stadium Club	10	.40	.30	.15
1994 Topps Stadium Club	186	.25	.20	.10
1994 Upper Deck	121	.35	.25	.14
1994 Upper Deck Collector's Choice Crash Game	20	7.50	5.75	3.00
1994 Upper Deck Collector's Choice	44	.25	.20	.10
1994 Upper Deck Collector's Choice	167	.50	.40	.20
1994 Upper Deck SP	113	.35	.25	.14

Ron Moore

Set	Card #	MT	NM	EX
1993 Pro Set	355 (R)	1.25	.90	.50

Anthony Munoz

Set	Card #	MT	NM	EX
1982 Topps	51 (R)	7.00	5.25	2.75
1983 Topps	240	1.50	1.25	.60
1984 Topps	45	.75	.60	.30
1985 Topps	219	.40	.30	.15
1986 Topps	261	.25	.20	.10
1987 Topps	192	.20	.15	.08
1988 Topps	345	.12	.09	.05
1989 Pro Set	66	.03	.02	.01
1989 Score	96	.10	.08	.04
1989 Score	309	.10	.08	.04
1989 Topps	28	.05	.04	.02
1990 Fleer	220	.03	.02	.01
1990 Fleer All-Pro	8	.25	.20	.10

1990 Pro Set	361	.03	.02	.01
1990 Pro Set	467	.03	.02	.01
1990 Score	178	.04	.03	.02
1990 Score	587	.04	.03	.02
1990 Score 100 Hottest	51	.15	.11	.06
1990 Topps	278	.04	.03	.02
1991 Bowman	79	.03	.02	.01
1991 Fleer	26	.07	.05	.03
1991 Fleer All-Pro	25	.10	.08	.04
1991 Fleer Ultra	21	.04	.03	.02
1991 Pacific	72	.04	.03	.02
1991 Pinnacle	167	.10	.08	.04
1991 Pinnacle	357	.10	.08	.04
1991 Pro Set	116	.03	.02	.01
1991 Pro Set	375	.06	.05	.02
1991 Pro Set	408	.03	.02	.01
1991 Pro Set Platinum	169	.05	.04	.02
1991 Score	115	.04	.03	.02
1991 Topps	259	.04	.03	.02
1991 Topps Stadium Club	119	.30	.25	.12
1991 Upper Deck	209	.05	.04	.02
1992 Bowman	86	.35	.25	.14
1992 Fleer	61	.03	.02	.01
1992 Fleer Ultra	62	.05	.04	.02
1992 Fleer Ultra Award Winners	9	1.50	1.25	.60
1992 GameDay	376	.12	.09	.05
1992 Pacific	44	.05	.04	.02
1992 Pinnacle	21	.05	.04	.02
1992 Pinnacle Team Pinnacle	11	13.00	9.75	5.25
1992 Pro Set	4	.05	.04	.02
1992 Pro Set	132	.05	.04	.02
1992 Pro Set	391	.05	.04	.02
1992 Pro Set Gold MVPs	2	.35	.25	.14
1992 Pro Set Power	78	.05	.04	.02
1992 Score	7	.05	.04	.02
1992 SkyBox Impact	119	.05	.04	.02
1992 SkyBox Primetime	78	.10	.08	.04
1992 Topps	380	.05	.04	.02
1992 Topps Stadium Club	410	.08	.06	.03
1992 Upper Deck	109	.05	.04	.02
1992 Upper Deck Pro Bowl	3	1.50	1.25	.60
1993 Pinnacle	348	.10	.08	.04
1993 SkyBox Impact	325	.03	.02	.01
1993 SkyBox Premium	45	.10	.08	.04
1993 Topps Stadium Club	122	.10	.08	.04

Joe Namath

Set	Card #	NM	EX	VG
1965 Topps	122 (R)	1650.	825.00	495.00
1966 Topps	96	325.00	162.00	97.00
1967 Topps	98	185.00	92.00	55.00
1968 Topps	65	80.00	40.00	24.00
1969 Topps	100	80.00	40.00	24.00
1970 Topps	150	50.00	25.00	15.00
1971 Topps	250	50.00	25.00	15.00

1972 Topps	100	35.00	17.50	10.50
1972 Topps	343	335.00	167.00	100.00
1973 Topps	400	30.00	15.00	9.00

Set	Card #	MT	NM	EX
1989 Pro Set Announcer Inserts	25	.65	.50	.25
1990 Pro Set Super Bowl MVPs	3	.50	.40	.20
1991 Upper Deck Heroes Joe Namath	10	1.00	.70	.40
1991 Upper Deck Heroes Joe Namath	11	1.00	.70	.40
1991 Upper Deck Heroes Joe Namath	12	1.00	.70	.40
1991 Upper Deck Heroes Joe Namath	13	1.00	.70	.40
1991 Upper Deck Heroes Joe Namath	14	1.00	.70	.40
1991 Upper Deck Heroes Joe Namath	15	1.00	.70	.40
1991 Upper Deck Heroes Joe Namath	16	1.00	.70	.40
1991 Upper Deck Heroes Joe Namath	17	1.00	.70	.40
1991 Upper Deck Heroes Joe Namath	18	1.00	.70	.40
1991 Upper Deck Heroes Joe Namath	----	8.00	6.00	3.25

The values quoted are intended
to reflect the market price.

Ozzie Newsome

Set	Card #	NM	EX	VG
1979 Topps	308 (R)	17.00	8.50	5.00
1980 Topps	110	4.00	2.00	1.25

Set	Card #	MT	NM	EX
1981 Topps	435	3.00	2.25	1.25
1982 Topps	67	1.50	1.25	.60
1982 Topps	68	.75	.60	.30
1983 Topps	254	.60	.45	.25
1984 Topps	58	.50	.40	.20
1984 Topps	59	.20	.15	.08
1985 Topps	193	.35	.25	.14
1985 Topps	232	.35	.25	.14
1986 Topps	191	.30	.25	.12
1987 Topps	85	.25	.20	.10
1988 Topps	92	.20	.15	.08
1989 Pro Set	451	.15	.11	.06
1989 Score	124	.10	.08	.04
1989 Topps	151	.20	.15	.08
1990 Pro Set	75	.05	.04	.02
1990 Score	443	.10	.08	.04
1990 Topps	168	.10	.08	.04
1991 Pro Set	699	.08	.06	.03

Ray Nitschke

Set	Card #	NM	EX	VG
1963 Topps	96 (R)	70.00	35.00	21.00
1965 Philadelphia	79	11.00	5.50	3.25
1966 Philadelphia	87	8.00	4.00	2.50
1967 Philadelphia	79	6.00	3.00	1.75
1968 Topps	157	5.00	2.50	1.50
1969 Topps	55	5.00	2.50	1.50
1969 Topps Four In Ones	(35)	1.00	.50	.30
1970 Topps	55	4.00	2.00	1.25
1971 Topps	133	4.50	2.25	1.25

Jay Novacek

Set	Card #	MT	NM	EX
1989 Pro Set	335 (R)	1.00	.70	.40
1989 Topps	282 (R)	1.00	.70	.40
1990 Pro Set	757	.40	.30	.15
1990 Score Update	11	2.50	2.00	1.00
1990 Topps Update	72	.50	.40	.20
1991 Bowman	108	.15	.11	.06
1991 Fleer Ultra Update	22	.25	.20	.10
1991 Pacific	104	.15	.11	.06
1991 Pinnacle	350	.35	.25	.14
1991 Pinnacle	404	.20	.15	.08
1991 Pro Set	12	.05	.04	.02
1991 Pro Set	484	.10	.08	.04
1991 Pro Set Platinum	179	.15	.11	.06
1991 Score	31	.15	.11	.06
1991 Topps	358	.25	.20	.10
1991 Topps Stadium Club	120	.75	.60	.30
1991 Upper Deck	109	.25	.20	.10
1992 Bowman	307	.75	.60	.30
1992 Fleer	88	.15	.11	.06
1992 Fleer Ultra	87	.20	.15	.08
1992 GameDay	458	.15	.11	.06
1992 Pacific	63	.15	.11	.06
1992 Pinnacle	79	.20	.15	.08
1992 Pro Set	479	.12	.09	.05

1992 Pro Set Power	184	.25	.20	.10
1992 Score	94	.10	.08	.04
1992 SkyBox Impact	22	.10	.08	.04
1992 SkyBox Primetime	153	.40	.30	.15
1992 Topps	518	.15	.11	.06
1992 Topps Stadium Club	489	.15	.11	.06
1992 Upper Deck	106	.05	.04	.02
1993 Bowman	405	.25	.20	.10
1993 Fleer	214	.05	.04	.02
1993 Fleer All-Pro	14	1.00	.70	.40
1993 Fleer Ultra	99	.08	.06	.03
1993 GameDay	424	.10	.08	.04
1993 Pacific Gold Prisms	14	8.00	6.00	3.25
1993 Pacific Prism Inserts	14	5.00	3.75	2.00
1993 Pinnacle	57	.10	.08	.04
1993 Pinnacle Super Bowl XXVII	6	5.00	3.75	2.00
1993 Pinnacle Team Pinnacle	6	10.00	7.50	4.00
1993 Pro Set	9	.05	.04	.02
1993 Pro Set	38	.05	.04	.02
1993 Pro Set Power	184	.05	.04	.02
1993 Score	29	.08	.06	.03
1993 Score Select	110	.10	.08	.04
1993 SkyBox Impact	73	.03	.02	.01
1993 SkyBox Impact Kelly's Heroes/ Magic's Kingdom	3	2.00	1.50	.80
1993 SkyBox Premium	145	.10	.08	.04
1993 Topps	468	.06	.05	.02
1993 Topps Stadium Club	174	.10	.08	.04
1993 Upper Deck	517	.05	.04	.02
1993 Upper Deck America's Team	12	6.00	4.50	2.50
1993 Upper Deck Dallas Cowboys	10	.40	.30	.15
1994 Bowman	158	.10	.08	.04
1994 Fleer	119	.12	.09	.05
1994 Fleer Ultra	74	.08	.06	.03
1994 GameDay	101	.10	.08	.04
1994 Pacific Crown	11	.06	.05	.02
1994 Pinnacle	82	.09	.07	.04
1994 Score	176	.05	.04	.02
1994 Score Select	133	.10	.08	.04
1994 SkyBox Impact	62	.08	.06	.03
1994 SkyBox Premium	40	.10	.08	.04
1994 Topps	300	.08	.06	.03
1994 Topps Finest	107	2.50	2.00	1.00
1994 Topps Stadium Club	52	.10	.08	.04
1994 Upper Deck	127	.12	.09	.05
1994 Upper Deck Collector's Choice	91	.07	.05	.03
1994 Upper Deck Pro Bowl	2	4.00	3.00	1.50

Neil O'Donnell

Set	Card #	MT	NM	EX
1991 Fleer Ultra Update	79 (R)	3.00	2.25	1.25
1991 Pro Set	845 (R)	1.50	1.25	.60

1992 Bowman	46	2.00	1.50	.80
1992 Fleer	351	.50	.40	.20
1992 Fleer Ultra	339	.60	.45	.25
1992 GameDay	113	1.00	.70	.40
1992 Pacific	259	.50	.40	.20
1992 Pinnacle	178	1.00	.70	.40
1992 Pro Set	304	.40	.30	.15
1992 Pro Set Power	114	.70	.50	.30
1992 Score	286	.50	.40	.20
1992 SkyBox Impact	222	.50	.40	.20
1992 SkyBox Primetime	64	1.00	.70	.40
1992 Topps	122	.50	.40	.20
1992 Topps Stadium Club	205	1.00	.70	.40
1992 Upper Deck	338	.40	.30	.15
1993 Bowman	377	1.00	.70	.40
1993 Fleer	140	.25	.20	.10
1993 Fleer Ultra	402	.40	.30	.15
1993 GameDay	106	.40	.30	.15
1993 Pacific	274	.25	.20	.10
1993 Pacific Prisms	86	3.00	2.25	1.25
1993 Pinnacle	190	.40	.30	.15
1993 Pro Set	367	.25	.20	.10
1993 Pro Set Power	14	.25	.20	.10
1993 Score	327	.25	.20	.10
1993 SkyBox Impact	269	.25	.20	.10
1993 SkyBox Premium	156	.50	.40	.20
1993 Topps	555	.25	.20	.10
1993 Topps Stadium Club	65	.50	.40	.20
1993 Upper Deck	369	.25	.20	.10
1993 Upper Deck SP	224	.75	.60	.30
1994 Bowman	377	.12	.09	.05
1994 Fleer	392	.20	.15	.08
1994 Fleer Ultra	258	.15	.11	.06
1994 GameDay	340	.10	.08	.04
1994 Pacific Crown	174	.10	.08	.04
1994 Pacific Crown Gems of the Crown	24	2.50	2.00	1.00
1994 Pacific Prisms	86	1.25	.90	.50
1994 Pinnacle	106	.20	.15	.08
1994 Pinnacle Sportflics	116	.15	.11	.06
1994 Score	202	.15	.11	.06
1994 Score Select	67	.10	.08	.04
1994 SkyBox Impact	210	.15	.11	.06
1994 SkyBox Premium	124	.20	.15	.08
1994 Topps	211	.08	.06	.03
1994 Topps Finest	49	2.00	1.50	.80
1994 Topps Finest Inserts	27	4.00	3.00	1.50
1994 Topps Stadium Club	88	.15	.11	.06
1994 Upper Deck	143	.15	.11	.06
1994 Upper Deck Collector's Choice	66	.10	.08	.04
1994 Upper Deck SP	72	.25	.20	.10

1989 Score	43	.25	.20	.10
1989 Topps	353	.12	.09	.05
1990 Fleer	206	.03	.02	.01
1990 Fleer All-Pro	5	.25	.20	.10
1990 Pro Set	9	.03	.02	.01
1990 Pro Set	363	.03	.02	.01
1990 Pro Set	532	.03	.02	.01
1990 Score	2	.04	.03	.02
1990 Score	321	.04	.03	.02
1990 Score	581	.04	.03	.02
1990 Score Hot Card	7	1.75	1.25	.70
1990 Score 100 Hottest	75	.15	.11	.06
1990 Topps	253	.04	.03	.02
1990 Topps 1000 Yard Club	2	.15	.11	.06
1991 Bowman	217	.03	.02	.01
1991 Fleer	96	.15	.11	.06
1991 Fleer Ultra	69	.06	.05	.02
1991 Pacific	214	.04	.03	.02
1991 Pinnacle	32	.10	.08	.04
1991 Pinnacle	367	.10	.08	.04
1991 Pro Set	185	.03	.02	.01
1991 Pro Set Platinum	49	.05	.04	.02
1991 Score	70	.04	.03	.02
1991 Topps	149	.04	.03	.02
1991 Topps Stadium Club	72	.60	.45	.25
1991 Upper Deck	176	.05	.04	.02
1991 Upper Deck	658	.05	.04	.02
1992 Bowman	190	.30	.25	.12
1992 Fleer	176	.03	.02	.01
1992 Fleer Ultra	174	.05	.04	.02
1992 GameDay	352	.12	.09	.05
1992 Pacific	139	.05	.04	.02
1992 Pacific Prism Inserts	3	2.75	2.00	1.00
1992 Pinnacle	76	.05	.04	.02
1992 Pro Set	37	.05	.04	.02
1992 Pro Set	534	.05	.04	.02
1992 Pro Set Power	135	.05	.04	.02
1992 Pro Set Power Power Combos	2	3.00	2.25	1.25
1992 Score	90	.05	.04	.02
1992 SkyBox Impact	203	.05	.04	.02
1992 SkyBox Impact Major Impact	7	.60	.45	.25
1992 SkyBox Primetime	35	.10	.08	.04
1992 SkyBox Primetime	197	.10	.08	.04
1992 SkyBox Primetime Poster Cards	11	1.25	.90	.50
1992 Topps	395	.05	.04	.02
1992 Topps Stadium Club	487	.08	.06	.03
1992 Topps 1000-Yard Club	17	.50	.40	.20
1992 Upper Deck	81	.05	.04	.02
1992 Upper Deck	135	.05	.04	.02
1993 Fleer	197	.05	.04	.02
1993 Fleer Ultra	204	.08	.06	.03
1993 GameDay	48	.10	.08	.04
1993 Pacific	343	.05	.04	.02
1993 Pinnacle	167	.10	.08	.04
1993 Score	160	.04	.03	.02
1993 SkyBox Impact	144	.03	.02	.01
1993 SkyBox Premium	236	.10	.08	.04
1993 Topps	73	.05	.04	.02
1993 Topps Stadium Club	102	.10	.08	.04
1993 Upper Deck	396	.05	.04	.02
1993 Upper Deck Kansas City Chiefs	6	.25	.20	.10

Christian Okoye

Set	Card #	MT	NM	EX
1988 Topps	363 (R)	.25	.20	.10
1989 Pro Set	176	.10	.08	.04

Merlin Olsen

Set	Card #	NM	EX	VG
1964 Philadelphia	91 (R)	50.00	25.00	15.00
1965 Philadelphia	94	17.00	8.50	5.00
1966 Philadelphia	102	9.00	4.50	2.75
1967 Philadelphia	94	7.00	3.50	2.00
1969 Topps	34	5.00	2.50	1.50
1969 Topps Four In Ones	(61)	2.00	1.00	.60
1970 Topps	237	4.50	2.25	1.25
1971 Topps	125	4.00	2.00	1.25
1972 Topps	181	3.50	1.75	1.00
1973 Topps	479	3.50	1.75	1.00
1974 Topps	205	3.50	1.75	1.00
1975 Topps	525	3.00	1.50	.90

Set	Card #	MT	NM	EX
1989 Pro Set Announcer Inserts	27	.25	.20	.10

The values quoted are intended to reflect the market price.

Jim Otto

Set	Card #	NM	EX	VG
1961 Fleer	197 (R)	60.00	30.00	18.00
1961 Topps	182 (R)	40.00	20.00	12.00
1962 Fleer	72	25.00	12.50	7.50
1963 Fleer	62	30.00	15.00	9.00
1964 Topps	148	25.00	12.50	7.50
1965 Topps	145	25.00	12.50	7.50
1966 Topps	115	15.00	7.50	4.50
1967 Topps	105	6.00	3.00	1.75
1969 Topps	163	3.75	2.00	1.25
1969 Topps Four In Ones	(43)	1.00	.50	.30
1970 Topps	116	2.50	1.25	.70
1971 Topps	151	3.00	1.50	.90
1972 Topps	86	2.00	1.00	.60
1973 Topps	461	2.25	1.25	.70
1974 Topps	409	2.00	1.00	.60
1975 Topps	497	2.00	1.00	.60

Alan Page

Set	Card #	NM	EX	VG
1970 Topps	59 (R)	33.00	16.50	10.00
1971 Topps	71	8.00	4.00	2.50
1972 Topps	279	40.00	20.00	12.00
1972 Topps	300	35.00	17.50	10.50
1973 Topps	30	3.00	1.50	.90
1974 Topps	134	2.25	1.25	.70
1975 Topps	214	.50	.25	.15
1975 Topps	520	1.75	.90	.50
1976 Topps	150	1.50	.70	.45
1977 Topps	230	1.25	.60	.40
1978 Topps	406	.75	.40	.25
1979 Topps	15	.75	.40	.25
1980 Topps	205	.50	.25	.15

Set	Card #	MT	NM	EX
1981 Topps	160	.50	.40	.20

Walter Payton

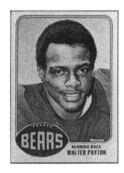

Set	Card #	NM	EX	VG
1976 Topps	148 (R)	200.00	100.00	60.00
1977 Topps	360	30.00	15.00	9.00
1978 Topps	3	4.00	2.00	1.25
1978 Topps	200	17.00	8.50	5.00
1979 Topps	335	3.00	1.50	.90
1979 Topps	480	12.00	6.00	3.50
1980 Topps	160	8.00	4.00	2.40

Set	Card #	MT	NM	EX
1981 Topps	202	2.00	1.50	.80
1981 Topps	400	4.50	3.50	1.75
1982 Topps	269	1.00	.70	.40
1982 Topps	302	3.50	2.75	1.50
1982 Topps	303	1.50	1.25	.60
1983 Topps	28	.75	.60	.30
1983 Topps	36	2.00	1.50	.80
1984 Topps	221	.75	.60	.30
1984 Topps	228	2.00	1.50	.80

1984 Topps	229	1.00	.70	.40
1985 Topps	6	1.00	.70	.40
1985 Topps	33	1.75	1.25	.70
1986 Topps	7	.75	.60	.30
1986 Topps	11	1.00	.70	.40
1986 Topps 1000 Yard Club	3	1.00	.70	.40
1987 Topps	46	1.25	.90	.50
1987 Topps 1000 Yard Club	7	.90	.70	.35
1988 Topps	5	.30	.25	.12
1991 Pro Set	(1)	.03	.02	.01
1991 Pro Set Inserts	1	1.50	1.25	.60
1992 Upper Deck Payton Heroes	19	3.50	2.50	1.50
1992 Upper Deck Payton Heroes	20	3.50	2.50	1.50
1992 Upper Deck Payton Heroes	21	3.50	2.50	1.50
1992 Upper Deck Payton Heroes	22	3.50	2.50	1.50
1992 Upper Deck Payton Heroes	23	3.50	2.50	1.50
1992 Upper Deck Payton Heroes	24	3.50	2.50	1.50
1992 Upper Deck Payton Heroes	25	3.50	2.50	1.50
1992 Upper Deck Payton Heroes	26	3.50	2.50	1.50
1992 Upper Deck Payton Heroes	27	3.50	2.50	1.50
1994 Topps Stadium Club Dynasty and Destiny	1	17.00	12.50	6.75

Cards before 1981 are priced in Near Mint (NM),
Excellent (EX), and Very Good (VG).
Cards 1981 to present are Mint (MT), Near Mint (NM),
and Excellent (EX).

Drew Pearson

Set	Card #	NM	EX	VG
1975 Topps	65 (R)	12.00	6.00	3.50
1976 Topps	313	4.00	2.00	1.25
1977 Topps	2	.50	.25	.15
1977 Topps	130	2.00	1.00	.60
1978 Topps	350	1.00	.50	.30
1978 Topps	507	2.00	1.00	.60
1979 Topps	70	.75	.40	.25
1980 Topps	250	.50	.25	.15

Set	Card #	MT	NM	EX
1981 Topps	95	.60	.45	.25
1982 Topps	321	.40	.30	.15
1983 Topps	51	.25	.20	.10
1984 Topps	243	.20	.15	.08
1992 Pro Set	348	.30	.25	.12
1993 Upper Deck America's Team	6	6.00	4.50	2.50

Andre Reed

Set	Card #	MT	NM	EX
1986 Topps	388 (R)	7.00	5.25	2.75
1987 Topps	365	2.00	1.50	.80
1988 Topps	224	.50	.40	.20
1988 Topps 1000 Yard Club	28	.10	.08	.04
1989 Pro Set	26	.20	.15	.08
1989 Score	152	.75	.60	.30
1989 Topps	52	.30	.25	.12
1990 Fleer	119	.20	.15	.08
1990 Fleer All-Pro	24	1.00	.75	.40
1990 Pro Set	366	.06	.05	.02
1990 Pro Set	440	.15	.11	.06
1990 Score	57	.20	.15	.08
1990 Score	559	.08	.06	.03
1990 Score Young Superstars	18	.30	.25	.12
1990 Score 100 Hottest	95	.25	.20	.10
1990 Topps	204	.20	.15	.08
1990 Topps 1000 Yard Club	7	.25	.20	.10
1991 Bowman	30	.10	.08	.04
1991 Fleer	8	.20	.15	.08
1991 Fleer All-Pro	1	.35	.25	.15
1991 Fleer Ultra	6	.15	.11	.06
1991 Pacific	27	.20	.15	.08
1991 Pinnacle	34	.25	.20	.10
1991 Pro Set	81	.08	.06	.03
1991 Pro Set	406	.05	.04	.02
1991 Pro Set Platinum	158	.10	.08	.04
1991 Score	53	.10	.08	.04
1991 Score	679	.06	.05	.02
1991 Topps	54	.15	.11	.06
1991 Topps Stadium Club	417	.75	.60	.30
1991 Upper Deck	43	.15	.11	.06
1992 GameDay	210	.15	.11	.06
1992 Pro Set	444	.15	.11	.06
1992 Pro Set Power	83	.25	.20	.10
1992 SkyBox Impact	54	.15	.11	.06
1992 SkyBox Impact Major Impact	8	1.00	.70	.40
1992 SkyBox Primetime	260	.25	.20	.10
1992 Topps	741	.05	.04	.02
1992 Topps Stadium Club	601	.20	.15	.08
1992 Topps Stadium Club	623	1.50	1.25	.60
1992 Upper Deck	570	.15	.11	.06
1992 Upper Deck Game Breaker Holograms	8	2.00	1.50	.80
1992 Upper Deck Gold	26	.35	.25	.14
1993 Bowman	386	.25	.20	.10
1993 Fleer	264	.05	.04	.02
1993 Fleer	476	.10	.08	.04
1993 Fleer Ultra	29	.20	.15	.08
1993 GameDay	464	.10	.08	.04
1993 Pacific	204	.12	.09	.05
1993 Pacific Prisms	7	1.25	.90	.50
1993 Pinnacle	329	.25	.20	.10
1993 Pro Set	50	.10	.08	.04
1993 Pro Set Power	83	.20	.15	.08
1993 Score	237	.10	.08	.04

1993 Score Select	2	.20	.15	.08
1993 SkyBox Impact	22	.10	.08	.04
1993 SkyBox Impact Kelly's Heroes/ Magic's Kingdom	7	4.00	3.00	1.50
1993 SkyBox Premium	256	.15	.11	.06
1993 Topps	420	.07	.05	.03
1993 Topps Stadium Club	107	.20	.15	.08
1993 Upper Deck	227	.10	.08	.04
1993 Upper Deck NFL Experience	28	.35	.25	.14
1993 Upper Deck Pro Bowl	1	5.00	3.75	2.00
1993 Upper Deck SP	33	.25	.20	.10
1994 Bowman	291	.10	.08	.04
1994 Fleer	46	.20	.15	.08
1994 Fleer Ultra	29	.15	.11	.06
1994 GameDay	40	.10	.08	.04
1994 Pacific Crown	25	.08	.06	.03
1994 Pacific Prisms	93	1.25	.90	.50
1994 Pinnacle	116	.15	.11	.06
1994 Pinnacle Sportflics	93	.15	.11	.06
1994 Score	136	.08	.06	.03
1994 Score Select	143	.10	.08	.04
1994 SkyBox Impact	27	.15	.11	.06
1994 SkyBox Premium	17	.15	.11	.06
1994 Topps	183	.10	.08	.04
1994 Topps	543	.08	.06	.03
1994 Topps Finest	174	2.50	2.00	1.00
1994 Topps Stadium Club	122	.12	.09	.05
1994 Upper Deck	303	.20	.15	.08
1994 Upper Deck Collector's Choice Crash Game	27	7.50	5.75	3.00
1994 Upper Deck Collector's Choice	67	.20	.15	.08
1994 Upper Deck Retail Predictor	27	7.50	5.75	3.00
1994 Upper Deck SP	21	.25	.20	.10

Errict Rhett

Set	Card #	MT	NM	EX
1994 Bowman	64 (R)	3.00	2.25	1.25
1994 Fleer NFL Prospects	20	6.00	4.50	2.50
1994 Fleer Ultra	306 (R)	3.00	2.25	1.25
1994 Fleer Ultra	514	1.50	.70	.35
1994 GameDay	401 (R)	3.50	2.75	1.50
1994 GameDay Rookie Standouts	12	5.00	3.75	2.00
1994 Pacific Crown	443 (R)	2.50	2.00	1.00
1994 Pacific Crown Knights of the Gridiron	18	15.00	11.00	6.00
1994 Pacific Marquee	24	3.00	2.25	1.25
1994 Pacific Prisms	94 (R)	12.00	9.00	4.75
1994 Pinnacle	212 (R)	3.25	2.45	1.30
1994 Pinnacle Draft Pick	9	15.00	11.00	6.00
1994 Pinnacle Sportflics	155 (R)	4.00	3.00	1.50
1994 Score	287 (R)	2.00	1.50	.80

1994 Score Select	207 (R)	4.00	3.00	1.50
1994 SkyBox Premium	188 (R)	2.75	2.05	1.10
1994 SkyBox Premium Prime Time Rookies	5	40.00	30.00	16.00
1994 Topps	127 (R)	2.00	1.50	.80
1994 Topps Stadium Club	252 (R)	3.50	2.75	1.50
1994 Upper Deck	27 (R)	3.00	2.25	1.20
1994 Upper Deck Hobby Predictor	18	10.00	7.50	4.00
1994 Upper Deck SP	17 (R)	5.00	3.75	2.00
1994 Upper Deck SP All-Pro	38	10.00	7.50	4.00

Jerry Rice

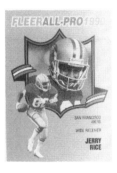

Set	Card #	MT	NM	EX
1986 Topps	161 (R)	75.00	56.00	30.00
1987 Topps	115	14.00	10.50	5.50
1987 Topps 1000 Yard Club	2	.75	.60	.30
1988 Topps	6	.70	.50	.30
1988 Topps	43	2.00	1.50	.80
1988 Topps	218	.30	.25	.12
1988 Topps 1000 Yard Club	4	.75	.60	.30
1989 Pro Set	383	1.00	.70	.40
1989 Score	221	3.50	2.75	1.50
1989 Score	275	2.00	1.50	.80
1989 Score	279	1.50	1.25	.60
1989 Score	292	1.50	1.25	.60
1989 Topps	7	1.25	.90	.50
1989 Topps 1000 Yard Club	5	.60	.45	.25
1990 Fleer	13	.75	.60	.30
1990 Fleer	397	.70	.50	.30
1990 Fleer All-Pro	2	1.50	1.25	.60
1990 Pro Set	295	.75	.60	.30
1990 Pro Set	411	.40	.30	.15
1990 Pro Set Super Bowl MVPs	23	.30	.25	.12
1990 Score	200	.75	.60	.30
1990 Score	556	.40	.30	.15
1990 Score	590	.40	.30	.15
1990 Score Hot Card	4	6.00	4.50	2.50
1990 Score 100 Hottest	100	1.25	.90	.50
1990 Topps	8	.75	.60	.30
1990 Topps 1000 Yard Club	1	.50	.40	.20
1991 Bowman	274	.40	.30	.15
1991 Bowman	470	.75	.60	.30
1991 Fleer	363	.75	.60	.30
1991 Fleer All-Pro	20	1.00	.75	.40
1991 Fleer Ultra	254	.75	.60	.30
1991 Fleer Ultra Performances	9	5.00	3.75	2.00
1991 Fleer Ultra Update	99	1.75	1.25	.70
1991 Pacific	467	.70	.50	.30
1991 Pinnacle	103	2.00	1.50	.80
1991 Pinnacle	359	.75	.60	.30
1991 Pro Set	11	.40	.30	.15

Card	#			
1991 Pro Set	329	.25	.20	.10
1991 Pro Set	379	.25	.20	.10
1991 Pro Set	654	.75	.60	.30
1991 Pro Set Platinum	140	.75	.60	.30
1991 Score	380	.75	.60	.30
1991 Score	665	.40	.30	.15
1991 Topps	6	.30	.25	.12
1991 Topps	10	.25	.20	.10
1991 Topps	81	.80	.60	.30
1991 Topps Stadium Club	71	6.00	4.50	2.50
1991 Topps 1000 Yard Club	1	1.50	1.25	.60
1991 Upper Deck	35	.40	.30	.15
1991 Upper Deck	57	.75	.60	.30
1991 Upper Deck	402	.35	.25	.14
1991 Upper Deck	475	.35	.25	.14
1991 Upper Deck	655	.20	.15	.08
1992 GameDay	336	2.25	1.75	.90
1992 Pro Set	418	.30	.25	.12
1992 Pro Set	651	.60	.45	.25
1992 Pro Set Gold MVPs	27	3.00	2.25	1.25
1992 Pro Set Power	80	1.25	.90	.50
1992 SkyBox Impact	25	.50	.40	.20
1992 SkyBox Impact Major Impact	14	4.00	3.00	1.50
1992 SkyBox Primetime	80	1.25	.90	.50
1992 SkyBox Primetime	159	.60	.45	.25
1992 SkyBox Primetime	236	.60	.45	.25
1992 SkyBox Primetime Poster Cards	7	8.00	6.00	3.25
1992 Topps	665	.50	.40	.20
1992 Topps Stadium Club	608	5.00	3.75	2.00
1992 Topps Stadium Club	645	8.00	6.00	3.25
1992 Upper Deck	616	.50	.40	.20
1992 Upper Deck Game Breaker Holograms	6	3.50	2.75	1.50
1992 Upper Deck Gold	46	1.00	.70	.40
1992 Upper Deck NFL Fanimation	9	7.00	6.00	3.50
1993 Bowman	340	4.00	3.00	1.50
1993 Fleer	315	.65	.50	.25
1993 Fleer All-Pro	15	8.00	6.00	3.20
1993 Fleer Ultra	437	1.00	.70	.40
1993 Fleer Ultra Touchdown Kings	5	15.00	11.00	6.00
1993 GameDay	80	1.75	1.25	.70
1993 GameDay Game Breakers	14	2.00	1.50	.80
1993 Pacific	147	.65	.50	.25
1993 Pacific Gold Prisms	15	30.00	22.00	12.00
1993 Pacific Picks the Pros Gold	1	15.00	11.00	6.00
1993 Pacific Prism Inserts	15	15.00	11.00	6.00
1993 Pacific Prisms	91	9.00	6.75	3.50
1993 Pacific Triple Folder Superstars	15	2.50	2.00	1.00
1993 Pacific Triple Folders	28	2.00	1.50	.80
1993 Pinnacle	292	1.75	1.25	.70
1993 Pro Set	395	.60	.45	.25
1993 Pro Set Power	80	.75	.60	.30
1993 Pro Set Power Update Combos	2	2.50	2.00	1.00
1993 Score	235	.50	.40	.20
1993 Score	431	.25	.20	.10
1993 Score Dream Team	5	5.00	3.75	2.00
1993 Score Select	21	3.50	2.75	1.50
1993 Score Select Gridiron Skills	7	80.00	60.00	32.00
1993 SkyBox Impact	293	.50	.40	.20
1993 SkyBox Impact Kelly's Heroes/ Magic's Kingdom	6	5.00	3.75	2.00
1993 SkyBox Impact Kelly's Heroes/ Magic's Kingdom	7	4.00	3.00	1.50
1993 SkyBox Poster Art Cards	5	2.00	1.50	.80
1993 SkyBox Premium	60	1.00	.70	.40
1993 SkyBox Thunder and Lightning	8	12.00	9.00	4.75
1993 Topps	2	.30	.25	.12
1993 Topps	182	.20	.15	.08
1993 Topps	500	.60	.45	.25
1993 Topps Black Gold	12	4.00	3.00	1.50
1993 Topps Stadium Club	232	1.50	1.25	.60
1993 Upper Deck	241	.75	.60	.30
1993 Upper Deck	433	.25	.20	.10
1993 Upper Deck NFL Experience	8	.75	.60	.30
1993 Upper Deck NFL Experience	32	1.00	.70	.40
1993 Upper Deck Pro Bowl	9	17.00	12.50	6.75
1993 Upper Deck San Francisco 49ers	12	2.00	1.50	.80
1993 Upper Deck SP	240	7.00	5.25	2.75
1993 Upper Deck SP All Pro	9	55.00	41.00	22.00
1994 Bowman	200	1.00	.70	.40
1994 Fleer	420	.50	.40	.20
1994 Fleer All-Pro	9	2.50	2.00	1.00
1994 Fleer League Leaders	5	3.00	2.25	1.25
1994 Fleer Living Legends	4	25.00	18.50	10.00
1994 Fleer Scoring Machines	13	25.00	18.50	10.00
1994 Fleer Ultra	280	.75	.60	.30
1994 Fleer Ultra Achievement Awards	5	3.00	2.25	1.25
1994 Fleer Ultra Hot Numbers	9	3.50	2.75	1.50
1994 Fleer Ultra Scoring Power	3	5.00	3.75	2.00
1994 Fleer Ultra Touchdown Kings	4	25.00	18.50	10.00
1994 Fleer Ultra Ultra Stars	6	30.00	22.00	12.00
1994 GameDay	368	.85	.60	.35
1994 GameDay Flashing Stars	3	25.00	18.50	10.00
1994 GameDay Game Breakers	8	3.00	2.25	1.25
1994 Pacific Crown	41	.60	.45	.25
1994 Pacific Crown Gems of the Crown	27	10.00	7.50	4.00
1994 Pacific Marquee	25	4.00	3.00	1.50
1994 Pacific Prisms	95	7.00	5.25	2.75
1994 Pinnacle	181	.75	.60	.30
1994 Pinnacle Performers	5	8.00	6.00	3.25
1994 Pinnacle Sportflics Head-to-Head	4	30.00	22.00	12.00
1994 Pinnacle Sportflics	45	1.75	1.25	.70
1994 Pinnacle Team Pinnacle	7	40.00	30.00	16.00
1994 Score	11	.50	.40	.20
1994 Score Dream Team	9	22.00	16.50	8.75
1994 Score Select	21	1.00	.70	.40
1994 Score Select Canton Bound	5	45.00	34.00	18.00
1994 SkyBox Impact	232	.60	.45	.25
1994 SkyBox Impact Ultimate Impact	5	5.00	3.75	2.00
1994 SkyBox Premium	137	.60	.45	.25
1994 SkyBox Premium Revolution	13	18.00	13.50	7.25
1994 SkyBox Premium SkyTech Stars	25	6.00	4.50	2.50
1994 Topps	116	.45	.35	.20
1994 Topps	320	.50	.40	.20
1994 Topps	550	.35	.25	.14
1994 Topps All-Pros	8	25.00	18.50	10.00
1994 Topps Finest	12	9.00	6.75	3.50
1994 Topps Finest Inserts	1	20.00	15.00	8.00
1994 Topps Stadium Club	101	.50	.40	.20
1994 Topps Stadium Club	500	.80	.60	.30
1994 Topps Stadium Club	519	.60	.45	.25
1994 Topps Stadium Club Ring Leaders	6	25.00	18.50	10.00
1994 Upper Deck	205	.85	.60	.35

1994 Upper Deck Collector's Choice Crash Game	21	13.00	9.75	5.25
1994 Upper Deck Collector's Choice	45	.25	.20	.10
1994 Upper Deck Collector's Choice	348	.65	.50	.25
1994 Upper Deck Pro Bowl	8	20.00	15.00	8.00
1994 Upper Deck Retail Predictor	21	12.00	9.00	4.75
1994 Upper Deck SP	194	1.25	.90	.50
1994 Upper Deck SP All-Pro	33	15.00	11.00	6.00
1994 Upper Deck SP Commemorative	2	120.00	90.00	48.00

John Riggins

Set	Card #	NM	EX	VG
1972 Topps	13 (R)	32.00	16.00	9.50
1972 Topps	126	8.00	4.00	2.50
1973 Topps	245	9.00	4.50	2.75
1974 Topps	280	6.00	3.00	1.75
1975 Topps	313	5.00	2.50	1.50
1976 Topps	305	4.00	2.00	1.25
1977 Topps	55	2.50	1.25	.70
1978 Topps	215	2.00	1.00	.60
1979 Topps	10	1.50	.70	.45
1980 Topps	390	1.25	.60	.40

Set	Card #	MT	NM	EX
1982 Topps	520	1.00	.70	.40
1983 Topps	8	.25	.20	.10
1983 Topps	10	.10	.08	.04
1983 Topps	12	.25	.20	.10
1983 Topps	186	.25	.20	.10
1983 Topps	198	.60	.45	.25
1984 Topps	5	.25	.20	.10
1984 Topps	375	.20	.15	.08
1984 Topps	388	.60	.45	.25
1984 Topps	389	.25	.20	.10
1985 Topps	177	.20	.15	.08
1985 Topps	189	.50	.40	.20
1985 Topps Star Set	9	.35	.27	.15
1990 Pro Set Super Bowl MVPs	17	.20	.15	.08
1992 Pinnacle	347	.05	.04	.02
1992 Pro Set HOF Inductees	4	.50	.40	.20
1992 Score	536	.05	.04	.02

Values quoted in this guide reflect the retail price of a card – the price a collector can expect to pay when buying a card from a dealer. The wholesale price – that which a collector can expect to receive from a dealer when selling cards – will be significantly lower, depending on desirability and condition.

Andre Rison

Set	Card #	MT	NM	EX
1989 Pro Set	497 (R)	2.50	2.00	1.00
1989 Score	272 (R)	9.00	6.75	3.50
1989 Topps Traded	102 (R)	1.00	.70	.40
1990 Fleer	231	.25	.20	.10
1990 Fleer Update	60	1.25	.90	.50
1990 Pro Set	134	.20	.15	.08
1990 Pro Set	434	.25	.20	.10
1990 Score	87	.25	.20	.10
1990 Score Update	20	2.00	1.50	.80
1990 Topps	300	.25	.20	.10
1990 Topps Update	2	.15	.11	.06
1991 Bowman	12	.25	.20	.10
1991 Fleer	208	.25	.20	.10
1991 Fleer	411	.08	.06	.03
1991 Fleer All-Pro	8	.40	.30	.15
1991 Fleer Ultra	148	.30	.25	.12
1991 Fleer Ultra Performances	2	1.50	1.25	.60
1991 Pacific	17	.25	.20	.10
1991 Pinnacle	45	.45	.35	.20
1991 Pro Set	380	.10	.08	.04
1991 Pro Set	439	.30	.25	.12
1991 Pro Set Platinum	2	.25	.20	.10
1991 Score	26	.25	.20	.10
1991 Score	329	.15	.11	.06
1991 Score	634	.08	.06	.03
1991 Score	680	.15	.11	.06
1991 Topps	575	.25	.20	.10
1991 Topps Stadium Club	398	1.50	1.25	.60
1991 Topps 1000 Yard Club	7	.50	.40	.20
1991 Upper Deck	173	.25	.20	.10
1991 Upper Deck	451	.12	.09	.05
1992 Bowman	251	1.75	1.25	.70
1992 Bowman	505	9.00	6.75	3.50
1992 Fleer	15	.25	.20	.10
1992 Fleer All-Pro	7	.60	.45	.25
1992 Fleer Ultra	15	.50	.40	.20
1992 GameDay	468	.50	.40	.20
1992 Pacific	336	.30	.25	.12
1992 Pinnacle	99	.35	.25	.14
1992 Pinnacle	335	.15	.11	.06
1992 Pro Set	48	.08	.06	.03
1992 Pro Set	116	.25	.20	.10
1992 Pro Set	419	.10	.08	.04
1992 Pro Set Power	180	.50	.40	.20
1992 Score	120	.25	.20	.10
1992 SkyBox Impact	2	.25	.20	.10
1992 SkyBox Primetime	226	.45	.35	.20
1992 Topps	440	.25	.20	.10
1992 Topps Stadium Club	65	.50	.40	.20
1992 Upper Deck	86	.10	.08	.04
1992 Upper Deck	156	.25	.20	.10
1992 Upper Deck	517	.20	.15	.08
1992 Upper Deck Game Breaker Holograms	4	2.50	2.00	1.00
1993 Bowman	45	.60	.45	.25
1993 Fleer	192	.25	.20	.10
1993 Fleer Ultra	15	.40	.30	.15

Set	Card #	MT	NM	EX
1993 Fleer Ultra Touchdown Kings	6	2.00	1.50	.80
1993 GameDay	213	.40	.30	.15
1993 GameDay Game Breakers	15	.75	.60	.30
1993 Pacific	177	.30	.25	.12
1993 Pacific Prisms	3	1.75	1.25	.70
1993 Pinnacle	77	.30	.25	.12
1993 Pinnacle Men of Autumn	1	.40	.30	.15
1993 Pro Set	68	.25	.20	.10
1993 Pro Set Power	180	.30	.25	.12
1993 Pro Set Power Update Combos	1	1.00	.70	.40
1993 Score	71	.25	.20	.10
1993 Score Select	79	.75	.60	.30
1993 Score Select Gridiron Skills	8	23.00	17.00	9.25
1993 Score The Franchise	1	7.00	5.25	2.75
1993 SkyBox Impact	11	.20	.15	.08
1993 SkyBox Premium	49	.35	.25	.14
1993 Topps	480	.30	.25	.12
1993 Topps Black Gold	18	1.25	.90	.50
1993 Topps Stadium Club	162	.40	.30	.15
1993 Upper Deck	406	.25	.20	.10
1993 Upper Deck	440	.15	.11	.06
1993 Upper Deck SP	26	.80	.60	.30
1993 Upper Deck Team MVP	14	1.00	.75	.40
1994 Bowman	110	.20	.15	.08
1994 Fleer	30	.25	.20	.10
1994 Fleer All-Pro	10	.65	.50	.25
1994 Fleer Scoring Machines	12	4.00	3.00	1.50
1994 Fleer Scoring Machines	14	5.50	4.25	2.25
1994 Fleer Ultra	19	.30	.25	.12
1994 Fleer Ultra Hot Numbers	10	.75	.60	.30
1994 Fleer Ultra Scoring Power	4	2.00	1.50	.80
1994 Fleer Ultra Touchdown Kings	5	12.00	9.00	4.75
1994 GameDay	24	.20	.15	.08
1994 GameDay Game Breakers	9	1.00	.70	.40
1994 Pacific Crown	297	.15	.11	.06
1994 Pacific Prisms	96	1.50	1.25	.60
1994 Pinnacle	31	.30	.25	.12
1994 Pinnacle Sportflics	92	.45	.35	.20
1994 Score	30	.10	.08	.04
1994 Score Dream Team	10	8.00	6.00	3.25
1994 Score Select	31	.12	.09	.05
1994 SkyBox Impact	16	.30	.25	.12
1994 SkyBox Premium	9	.25	.20	.10
1994 SkyBox Premium SkyTech Stars	26	2.00	1.50	.80
1994 Topps	80	.20	.15	.08
1994 Topps	612	.10	.08	.04
1994 Topps Finest	27	3.00	2.25	1.25
1994 Topps Finest Inserts	12	4.00	3.00	1.50
1994 Topps Stadium Club	457	.20	.15	.08
1994 Upper Deck	272	.40	.30	.15
1994 Upper Deck Collector's Choice Crash Game	22	11.00	8.25	4.50
1994 Upper Deck Collector's Choice	139	.25	.20	.10
1994 Upper Deck Pro Bowl	5	8.00	6.00	3.25
1994 Upper Deck Retail Predictor	23	12.00	9.00	4.75
1994 Upper Deck SP	183	.65	.50	.25
1994 Upper Deck SP All-Pro	2	8.00	6.00	3.25

Definitions for grading conditions are located
in the Introduction of this price guide.

Leonard Russell

Set	Card #	MT	NM	EX
1991 Fleer Ultra Update	56 (R)	2.50	2.00	1.00
1991 Pacific	612 (R)	1.00	.70	.40
1991 Pinnacle	336 (R)	2.25	1.75	.90
1991 Pro Set	743 (R)	1.00	.70	.40
1991 Pro Set Platinum	308 (R)	1.00	.70	.40
1991 Score Supplemental	109 (R)	1.25	.90	.50
1991 Topps Stadium Club	435 (R)	3.50	2.75	1.50
1991 Upper Deck	622 (R)	1.00	.70	.40
1992 Bowman	30	3.00	2.25	1.25
1992 Fleer	266	.25	.20	.10
1992 Fleer Rookie Sensations	15	9.00	6.75	3.50
1992 Fleer Ultra	252	.35	.25	.14
1992 Fleer Ultra Award Winners	10	2.00	1.50	.75
1992 Pacific	192	.25	.20	.10
1992 Pacific Prism Inserts	4	2.50	2.00	1.00
1992 Pinnacle	163	.50	.40	.20
1992 Pinnacle Team 2000	4	.75	.60	.30
1992 Pro Set	249	.35	.25	.14
1992 Pro Set	351	.10	.08	.04
1992 Pro Set Gold MVPs	10	.75	.60	.30
1992 Pro Set Ground Force	249	5.00	3.75	2.00
1992 Pro Set Power	233	.50	.40	.20
1992 Score	259	.35	.25	.14
1992 Score	520	.10	.08	.04
1992 Topps	163	.25	.20	.10
1992 Topps Stadium Club	220	.50	.40	.20
1992 Topps Stadium Club	304	.30	.25	.12
1992 Upper Deck	245	.30	.25	.12
1992 Upper Deck	371	.05	.04	.02
1992 Upper Deck Coach's Report	17	2.50	2.00	1.00
1993 Bowman	25	.20	.15	.08
1993 Fleer	106	.15	.11	.06
1993 Fleer Ultra	291	.10	.08	.04
1993 GameDay	108	.15	.11	.06
1993 Pacific	259	.12	.09	.05
1993 Pacific Prisms	64	1.25	.90	.50
1993 Pinnacle	136	.15	.11	.06
1993 Pro Set	275	.15	.11	.06
1993 Score	138	.10	.08	.04
1993 Score Select	103	.20	.15	.08
1993 SkyBox Impact	203	.10	.08	.04
1993 SkyBox Premium	150	.15	.11	.06
1993 Topps	238	.12	.09	.05
1993 Topps Stadium Club	110	.15	.11	.06
1993 Upper Deck	381	.15	.11	.06
1993 Upper Deck SP	169	.20	.15	.08
1994 Fleer	314	.15	.11	.06
1994 Fleer Ultra	381	.08	.06	.03
1994 Pacific Crown	368	.06	.05	.02
1994 Pacific Crown Crystalline Collection	6	1.00	.70	.40
1994 Pacific Prisms	99	1.00	.70	.40
1994 Pinnacle	127	.09	.07	.04
1994 Pinnacle Sportflics	41	.15	.11	.06

Set	Card #	MT	NM	EX
1994 Score	66	.10	.08	.04
1994 SkyBox Impact	169	.10	.08	.04
1994 SkyBox Premium	100	.12	.09	.05
1994 Topps	444	.05	.04	.02
1994 Topps Finest	111	2.00	1.50	.80
1994 Topps Finest Inserts	3	4.00	3.00	1.50
1994 Upper Deck	258	.12	.09	.05
1994 Upper Deck Collector's Choice	159	.07	.05	.03

Mark Rypien

Set	Card #	MT	NM	EX
1989 Pro Set	434 (R)	.50	.40	.20
1989 Score	105 (R)	1.50	1.25	.60
1989 Topps	253 (R)	.40	.30	.15
1990 Fleer	166	.15	.11	.06
1990 Pro Set	330	.10	.08	.04
1990 Pro Set	412	.03	.02	.01
1990 Score	313	.08	.06	.03
1990 Score	350	.15	.11	.06
1990 Score 100 Hottest	92	.20	.15	.08
1990 Topps	133	.25	.20	.10
1991 Bowman	531	.10	.08	.04
1991 Fleer	393	.15	.11	.06
1991 Fleer Ultra	276	.10	.08	.04
1991 Pacific	531	.12	.09	.05
1991 Pinnacle	173	.20	.15	.08
1991 Pro Set	322	.08	.06	.03
1991 Pro Set Platinum	126	.10	.08	.04
1991 Score	111	.10	.08	.04
1991 Topps	192	.15	.11	.06
1991 Topps Stadium Club	393	.30	.25	.12
1991 Upper Deck	280	.15	.11	.06
1992 Bowman	188	.30	.25	.12
1992 Bowman	295	.30	.25	.12
1992 Fleer	428	.10	.08	.04
1992 Fleer All-Pro	11	.35	.25	.15
1992 Fleer Mark Rypien	1	.40	.30	.15
1992 Fleer Mark Rypien	2	.40	.30	.15
1992 Fleer Mark Rypien	3	.40	.30	.15
1992 Fleer Mark Rypien	4	.40	.30	.15
1992 Fleer Mark Rypien	5	.40	.30	.15
1992 Fleer Mark Rypien	6	.40	.30	.15
1992 Fleer Mark Rypien	7	.40	.30	.15
1992 Fleer Mark Rypien	8	.40	.30	.15
1992 Fleer Mark Rypien	9	.40	.30	.15
1992 Fleer Mark Rypien	10	.40	.30	.15
1992 Fleer Mark Rypien	11	.40	.30	.15
1992 Fleer Mark Rypien	12	.40	.30	.15
1992 Fleer Team Leaders	13	6.50	5.00	2.50
1992 Fleer Ultra	412	.15	.11	.06
1992 Fleer Ultra Award Winners	1	1.75	1.25	.60
1992 GameDay	109	.15	.11	.06
1992 Pacific	313	.20	.15	.08
1992 Pinnacle	40	.10	.08	.04
1992 Pinnacle	334	.05	.04	.02
1992 Pinnacle Team Pinnacle	1	8.50	6.50	3.50

Set	Card #	MT	NM	EX
1992 Pro Set	63	.05	.04	.02
1992 Pro Set	66	.05	.04	.02
1992 Pro Set	87	.08	.06	.03
1992 Pro Set	420	.08	.06	.03
1992 Pro Set	700	.10	.08	.04
1992 Pro Set Gold MVPs	29	.45	.35	.20
1992 Pro Set Power	11	.10	.08	.04
1992 Score	35	.10	.08	.04
1992 Score	534	.05	.04	.02
1992 Score Dream Team	25	2.00	1.50	.80
1992 SkyBox Impact	276	.10	.08	.04
1992 SkyBox Impact Major Impact	16	.60	.45	.25
1992 SkyBox Primetime	11	.12	.09	.05
1992 SkyBox Primetime	77	.10	.08	.04
1992 Topps	295	.15	.11	.06
1992 Topps Stadium Club	1	.15	.11	.06
1992 Topps Stadium Club	307	.10	.08	.04
1992 Upper Deck	96	.05	.04	.02
1992 Upper Deck	246	.10	.08	.04
1992 Upper Deck	374	.05	.04	.02
1992 Upper Deck	520	.05	.04	.02
1992 Upper Deck Pro Bowl	4	4.00	3.00	1.50
1993 Bowman	413	.20	.15	.08
1993 Fleer	74	.10	.08	.04
1993 Fleer Ultra	494	.15	.11	.06
1993 GameDay	72	.15	.11	.06
1993 Pacific	35	.10	.08	.04
1993 Pacific Prisms	107	1.00	.70	.40
1993 Pinnacle	135	.10	.08	.04
1993 Pinnacle Men of Autumn	28	.30	.25	.14
1993 Pro Set	444	.10	.08	.04
1993 Pro Set Power	11	.10	.08	.04
1993 Score	184	.06	.05	.02
1993 Score Select	139	.15	.11	.06
1993 Score The Franchise	28	3.50	2.75	1.50
1993 SkyBox Impact	340	.08	.06	.03
1993 SkyBox Premium	83	.10	.08	.04
1993 Topps	335	.08	.06	.03
1993 Topps Stadium Club	352	.15	.11	.06
1993 Upper Deck	395	.10	.08	.04
1993 Upper Deck SP	269	.25	.20	.10
1994 Fleer	473	.07	.05	.03
1994 Pacific Crown	400	.06	.05	.02
1994 Topps Finest	9	1.25	.90	.50
1994 Upper Deck SP	61	.20	.15	.08

Barry Sanders

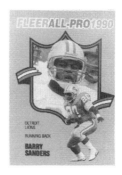

Set	Card #	MT	NM	EX
1989 Pro Set	494 (R)	4.50	3.50	1.75
1989 Score	257 (R)	40.00	30.00	16.00
1989 Topps Traded	83 (R)	3.50	2.75	1.50
1990 Fleer	284	.90	.70	.35
1990 Fleer All-Pro	4	3.00	2.25	1.25
1990 Pro Set	1	.60	.45	.25
1990 Pro Set	102	1.25	.90	.50
1990 Pro Set	413	.60	.45	.25

Card	#			
1990 Pro Set	794	.45	.35	.20
1990 Score	20	1.25	.90	.50
1990 Score	325	.60	.45	.25
1990 Score	580	.60	.45	.25
1990 Score Hot Card	3	6.00	4.50	2.50
1990 Score Promos	20	14.00	10.50	5.50
1990 Score Young Superstars	1	1.50	1.25	.60
1990 Score 100 Hottest	5	1.00	.70	.40
1990 Topps	352	1.00	.70	.40
1990 Topps 1000 Yard Club	3	.75	.60	.30
1991 Bowman	153	.85	.60	.35
1991 Bowman	273	.45	.35	.20
1991 Fleer	247	.85	.60	.35
1991 Fleer	415	.30	.25	.12
1991 Fleer All-Pro	9	2.00	1.50	.75
1991 Fleer Pro Visions	2	2.00	1.50	.80
1991 Fleer Ultra	169	.85	.60	.35
1991 Fleer Ultra All Stars	1	4.50	3.50	1.75
1991 Pacific	144	.85	.60	.35
1991 Pinnacle	250	4.00	3.00	1.50
1991 Pinnacle	358	1.75	1.25	.70
1991 Pinnacle	366	1.25	.90	.50
1991 Pro Set	10	.50	.40	.20
1991 Pro Set	39	.45	.35	.20
1991 Pro Set	388	.45	.35	.20
1991 Pro Set	502	.85	.60	.35
1991 Pro Set Platinum	33	.90	.70	.35
1991 Pro Set Platinum PC	8	3.00	2.25	1.25
1991 Score	20	.80	.60	.30
1991 Score	637	.30	.25	.12
1991 Score	663	.25	.20	.10
1991 Score	677	.40	.30	.15
1991 Topps	9	.30	.25	.12
1991 Topps	415	.85	.60	.35
1991 Topps Stadium Club	361	6.00	4.50	2.50
1991 Topps 1000 Yard Club	2	1.75	1.25	.70
1991 Upper Deck	401	.40	.30	.15
1991 Upper Deck	444	.90	.70	.35
1991 Upper Deck	458	.40	.30	.15
1991 Upper Deck	656	.25	.20	.10
1991 Upper Deck Game Breaker Holograms	1	4.00	3.00	1.60
1992 Bowman	170	9.00	6.75	3.50
1992 Bowman	221	20.00	15.00	8.00
1992 Fleer	123	.75	.60	.30
1992 Fleer	457	.40	.30	.15
1992 Fleer All-Pro	9	3.00	2.25	1.25
1992 Fleer Ultra	122	2.50	2.00	1.00
1992 Fleer Ultra Award Winners	8	8.00	6.00	3.25
1992 Pacific	417	.80	.60	.30
1992 Pacific Prism Inserts	7	6.00	4.50	2.50
1992 Pinnacle	15	2.75	2.00	1.00
1992 Pinnacle Team Pinnacle	2	20.00	15.00	8.00
1992 Pinnacle Team 2000	21	3.00	2.25	1.25
1992 Pro Set	13	.35	.25	.14
1992 Pro Set	169	.80	.60	.30
1992 Pro Set	349	.25	.20	.10
1992 Pro Set	421	.30	.25	.12
1992 Pro Set Gold MVPs	19	5.00	3.75	2.00
1992 Pro Set Power	20	1.50	1.25	.60
1992 Score	1	.75	.60	.30
1992 Score	528	.25	.20	.10
1992 Score Dream Team	4	30.00	22.00	12.00
1992 SkyBox Primetime	243	.10	.08	.04
1992 Topps	300	.75	.60	.30
1992 Topps Stadium Club	38	2.50	2.00	1.00
1992 Topps Stadium Club	301	2.50	2.00	1.00
1992 Topps 1000-Yard Club	2	4.00	3.00	1.50
1992 Upper Deck	155	.85	.60	.35
1992 Upper Deck	306	.40	.30	.15
1992 Upper Deck	368	.30	.25	.12
1992 Upper Deck	511	.40	.30	.15
1992 Upper Deck Pro Bowl	5	8.00	6.00	3.25
1993 Bowman	140	3.00	2.25	1.25
1993 Fleer	213	.75	.60	.30
1993 Fleer Ultra	135	1.25	.90	.50
1993 Fleer Ultra Touchdown Kings	7	12.00	9.00	4.75
1993 GameDay	20	2.00	1.50	.80
1993 GameDay Game Breakers	10	3.50	2.75	1.50
1993 Pacific	106	.80	.60	.30
1993 Pacific Gold Prisms	16	30.00	22.00	12.00
1993 Pacific Prism Inserts	16	17.00	12.50	6.75
1993 Pacific Prisms	28	10.00	7.50	4.00
1993 Pacific Triple Folder Superstars	16	2.50	2.00	1.00
1993 Pacific Triple Folders	20	2.50	2.00	1.00
1993 Pinnacle	200	1.75	1.25	.70
1993 Pinnacle Men of Autumn	8	2.50	2.00	1.00
1993 Pro Set	142	1.00	.70	.40
1993 Pro Set College Connections	1	4.00	3.00	1.50
1993 Pro Set Power	20	.80	.60	.30
1993 Pro Set Power Combos	1	3.50	2.75	1.50
1993 Score	1	.75	.60	.30
1993 Score Select	90	4.50	3.50	1.75
1993 Score The Franchise	8	25.00	18.50	10.00
1993 SkyBox Impact	101	.80	.60	.30
1993 SkyBox Impact Kelly's Heroes/ Magic's Kingdom	4	6.00	4.50	2.50
1993 SkyBox Impact Kelly's Heroes/ Magic's Kingdom	5	10.00	7.50	4.00
1993 SkyBox Poster Art Cards	6	2.50	2.00	1.00
1993 SkyBox Premium	39	1.75	1.25	.70
1993 Topps	174	.35	.25	.14
1993 Topps	190	.90	.70	.35
1993 Topps Black Gold	32	4.00	3.00	1.60
1993 Topps Stadium Club	120	1.75	1.25	.70
1993 Topps Stadium Club	496	1.00	.70	.40
1993 Upper Deck	80	.40	.30	.15
1993 Upper Deck	441	.40	.30	.15
1993 Upper Deck	454	.75	.60	.30
1993 Upper Deck Future Heroes	43	3.50	2.75	1.50
1993 Upper Deck Pro Bowl	17	15.00	11.00	6.00
1993 Upper Deck SP	88	7.50	5.75	3.00
1993 Upper Deck SP All Pro	5	60.00	45.00	24.00
1993 Upper Deck Team MVP	18	4.00	3.00	1.50
1994 Bowman	180	1.25	.90	.50
1994 Fleer	160	.65	.50	.25
1994 Fleer All-Pro	11	2.25	1.75	.90
1994 Fleer Scoring Machines	15	30.00	22.00	12.00
1994 Fleer Ultra	101	1.00	.70	.40
1994 Fleer Ultra Achievement Awards	6	2.50	2.00	1.00
1994 Fleer Ultra Hot Numbers	11	3.50	2.75	1.50
1994 Fleer Ultra Ultra Stars	7	30.00	22.00	12.00
1994 GameDay	137	1.00	.70	.40
1994 GameDay Game Breakers	10	3.00	2.25	1.25
1994 Pacific Crown	85	.65	.50	.25
1994 Pacific Crown Crystalline Collection	5	20.00	15.00	8.00
1994 Pacific Crown Gems of the Crown	28	12.00	9.00	4.75
1994 Pacific Marquee	27	3.50	2.75	1.50
1994 Pacific Prisms	100	8.00	6.00	3.25
1994 Pinnacle	3	.75	.60	.30
1994 Pinnacle Performers	4	8.00	6.00	3.25
1994 Pinnacle Sportflics	12	2.00	1.50	.80
1994 Pinnacle Sportflics	184	1.25	.90	.50

Set	Card #	MT	NM	EX
1994 Pinnacle Team Pinnacle	4	40.00	30.00	16.00
1994 Score	1	.50	.40	.20
1994 Score Dream Team	11	25.00	18.50	10.00
1994 Score Select	11	1.25	.90	.50
1994 Score Select Canton Bound	4	45.00	34.00	18.00
1994 SkyBox Impact	81	.60	.45	.25
1994 SkyBox Impact Ultimate Impact	9	6.00	4.50	2.50
1994 SkyBox Premium	53	.50	.40	.20
1994 SkyBox Premium Revolution	7	14.00	10.50	5.50
1994 SkyBox Premium SkyTech Stars	27	8.00	6.00	3.25
1994 Topps	542	.25	.20	.10
1994 Topps	570	.65	.50	.25
1994 Topps	615	.35	.25	.14
1994 Topps All-Pros	10	25.00	18.50	10.00
1994 Topps Finest	44	10.00	7.50	4.00
1994 Topps Finest Inserts	15	25.00	18.50	10.00
1994 Topps Stadium Club	71	.60	.45	.25
1994 Topps Stadium Club	165	1.25	.90	.50
1994 Topps Stadium Club Ring Leaders	8	20.00	15.00	8.00
1994 Upper Deck	129	.75	.60	.30
1994 Upper Deck Collector's Choice Crash Game	16	12.00	9.00	4.75
1994 Upper Deck Collector's Choice	86	.75	.60	.30
1994 Upper Deck Hobby Predictor	2	30.00	22.00	12.00
1994 Upper Deck Retail Predictor	12	12.00	9.00	4.75
1994 Upper Deck SP	158	5.00	3.75	2.00
1994 Upper Deck SP All-Pro	12	18.00	13.50	7.25

Deion Sanders

Set	Card #	MT	NM	EX
1989 Pro Set	486 (R)	3.00	2.25	1.25
1989 Score	246 (R)	12.50	9.50	5.00
1989 Topps Traded	30 (R)	1.75	1.25	.70
1990 Fleer	382	.35	.25	.14
1990 Pro Set	36	.30	.25	.12
1990 Score	95	.35	.25	.14
1990 Score Young Superstars	15	.50	.40	.20
1990 Score 100 Hottest	3	.50	.40	.20
1990 Topps	469	.35	.25	.14
1991 Bowman	15	.25	.20	.10
1991 Fleer	210	.25	.20	.10
1991 Fleer Ultra	150	.25	.20	.10
1991 Pacific	1	.25	.20	.10
1991 Pinnacle	147	.65	.50	.25
1991 Pro Set	98	.20	.15	.08
1991 Pro Set Platinum	141	.30	.25	.12
1991 Score	395	.30	.25	.12
1991 Topps	582	.35	.25	.14
1991 Topps Stadium Club	3	2.50	2.00	1.00
1991 Upper Deck	154	.25	.20	.10
1992 GameDay	49a	.50	.40	.20
1992 GameDay	49b	.40	.30	.15
1992 Pro Set	422	.05	.04	.02
1992 Pro Set	434	.12	.09	.05
1992 Pro Set Gold MVPs	16	.75	.60	.30
1992 Pro Set Power	21	.40	.30	.15
1992 SkyBox Impact	100	.15	.11	.06
1992 SkyBox Impact	314	.07	.05	.03
1992 SkyBox Impact Major Impact	17	1.00	.70	.40
1992 SkyBox Primetime	1	.25	.20	.10
1992 SkyBox Primetime	101	.10	.08	.04
1992 SkyBox Primetime	161	.10	.08	.04
1992 SkyBox Primetime Poster Cards	5	2.50	2.00	1.00
1992 Topps	692	.05	.04	.02
1992 Topps Stadium Club	606	1.25	.90	.50
1992 Topps Stadium Club	637	1.75	1.25	.70
1992 Upper Deck	567	.30	.25	.12
1992 Upper Deck Gold	27	.50	.40	.20
1992 Upper Deck NFL Fanimation	4	5.00	3.75	2.00
1993 Fleer	261	.05	.04	.02
1993 Fleer	263	.05	.04	.02
1993 Fleer	385	.15	.11	.06
1993 Fleer Ultra	16	.08	.06	.03
1993 Fleer Ultra League Leaders	6	5.00	3.75	2.00
1993 Fleer Ultra Ultra Stars	5	6.00	4.50	2.50
1993 GameDay	21	.50	.40	.20
1993 GameDay Game Breakers	16	.75	.60	.30
1993 Pacific	178	.15	.11	.06
1993 Pacific Prisms	4	1.75	1.25	.70
1993 Pacific Triple Folders	16	1.50	1.25	.60
1993 Pinnacle	315	.30	.25	.12
1993 Pinnacle Men of Autumn	29	.40	.30	.15
1993 Pinnacle Team Pinnacle	12	18.00	13.50	7.25
1993 Pro Set	69	.15	.11	.06
1993 Pro Set College Connections	9	1.50	1.25	.60
1993 Pro Set Power	21	.12	.09	.05
1993 Pro Set Power All-Power Defense	17	.75	.60	.30
1993 Pro Set Power Combos	4	.50	.40	.20
1993 Score	222	.10	.08	.04
1993 Score	425	.08	.06	.03
1993 Score Dream Team	14	1.00	.70	.40
1993 Score Select	3	.90	.70	.35
1993 SkyBox Impact	12	.10	.08	.04
1993 SkyBox Poster Art Cards	7	.75	.60	.30
1993 SkyBox Premium	238	.35	.25	.14
1993 Topps	171	.05	.04	.02
1993 Topps	254	.15	.11	.06
1993 Topps Black Gold	35	1.00	.70	.40
1993 Topps Stadium Club	100	.40	.30	.15
1993 Topps Stadium Club	493	.20	.15	.08
1993 Upper Deck	76	.05	.04	.02
1993 Upper Deck	228	.15	.11	.06
1993 Upper Deck NFL Experience	26	.30	.25	.12
1993 Upper Deck SP	27	1.25	.90	.50
1994 Fleer	31	.10	.08	.04
1994 Fleer All-Pro	12	.60	.45	.25
1994 Fleer Award Winners	3	.50	.40	.20
1994 Fleer Ultra	20	.08	.06	.03
1994 Fleer Ultra	498	.12	.09	.05
1994 GameDay	25	.20	.15	.08
1994 GameDay Game Breakers	11	1.00	.70	.40
1994 Pacific Crown	298	.15	.11	.06
1994 Pacific Prisms	101	1.50	1.25	.60

1994 Pinnacle	1	.12	.09	.05
1994 Pinnacle Sportflics	1	.50	.40	.20
1994 Score	4	.15	.11	.06
1994 Score Dream Team	12	8.00	6.00	3.25
1994 Score Select	57	.20	.15	.08
1994 SkyBox Impact	17	.10	.08	.04
1994 SkyBox Premium	10	.15	.11	.06
1994 Topps	544	.10	.08	.04
1994 Topps Finest	206	3.00	2.25	1.25
1994 Topps Stadium Club Ring Leaders	3	8.00	6.00	3.25
1994 Upper Deck	302	.20	.15	.08
1994 Upper Deck Collector's Choice	145	.10	.08	.04
1994 Upper Deck SP	196	.50	.40	.20

Gale Sayers

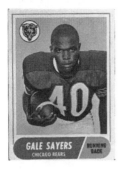

Set	Card #	NM	EX	VG
1966 Philadelphia	38 (R)	200.00	100.00	60.00
1966 Philadelphia	39	20.00	10.00	6.00
1967 Philadelphia	35	75.00	37.00	22.00
1968 Topps	75	60.00	30.00	18.00
1969 Topps	51	50.00	25.00	15.00
1969 Topps Four In Ones	(1)	6.00	3.00	1.75
1970 Topps	70	35.00	17.50	10.50
1971 Topps	150	30.00	15.00	9.00
1972 Topps	110	22.00	11.00	6.50

Junior Seau

Set	Card #	MT	NM	EX
1990 Fleer Update	102 (R)	3.50	2.75	1.50
1990 Pro Set	673 (R)	.75	.60	.30
1990 Score	302 (R)	.75	.60	.30
1990 Score Update	65	5.00	3.75	2.00
1990 Topps	381 (R)	1.00	.70	.40
1990 Topps Update	28	1.00	.70	.40
1991 Bowman	455	.25	.20	.10

1991 Fleer	179	.25	.20	.10
1991 Fleer Ultra	129	.30	.25	.12
1991 Pacific	451	.30	.25	.12
1991 Pinnacle	195	1.00	.70	.40
1991 Pro Set	645	.20	.15	.08
1991 Pro Set Platinum	265	.25	.20	.10
1991 Score	354	.25	.20	.10
1991 Topps	427	.30	.25	.12
1991 Topps Stadium Club	317	3.00	2.25	1.25
1991 Upper Deck	343	.30	.25	.12
1992 GameDay	433	.50	.40	.20
1992 Pro Set	643	.15	.11	.06
1992 Pro Set Power	55	.10	.08	.04
1992 SkyBox Impact	175	.15	.11	.06
1992 SkyBox Primetime	318	.35	.25	.14
1992 Topps	674	.05	.04	.02
1992 Topps Stadium Club	607	1.50	1.25	.60
1992 Topps Stadium Club	635	1.50	1.25	.60
1992 Upper Deck	610	.15	.11	.06
1992 Upper Deck Gold	41	.50	.40	.20
1992 Upper Deck NFL Fanimation	6	4.50	3.50	2.00
1993 Bowman	30	.40	.30	.15
1993 Fleer	371	.15	.11	.06
1993 Fleer All-Pro	16	1.50	1.25	.60
1993 Fleer Ultra	422	.15	.11	.06
1993 Fleer Ultra Ultra Stars	6	4.00	3.00	1.50
1993 GameDay	55	.15	.11	.06
1993 Pacific	329	.20	.15	.08
1993 Pacific Picks the Pros Gold	18	2.50	2.00	1.00
1993 Pacific Prisms	89	1.50	1.25	.60
1993 Pinnacle	327	.25	.20	.10
1993 Pinnacle Men of Autumn	24	.40	.30	.15
1993 Pinnacle Team Pinnacle	11	15.00	11.00	6.00
1993 Pinnacle Team 2001	1	.40	.30	.15
1993 Pro Set	385	.10	.08	.04
1993 Pro Set Power	55	.15	.11	.06
1993 Pro Set Power All-Power Defense	10	.25	.20	.10
1993 Pro Set Power Combos	3	.50	.40	.20
1993 Score	272	.15	.11	.06
1993 Score Select	24	.25	.20	.10
1993 SkyBox Impact	287	.15	.11	.06
1993 SkyBox Poster Art Cards	8	.75	.60	.30
1993 SkyBox Premium	71	.15	.11	.06
1993 Topps	60	.15	.11	.06
1993 Topps	298	.05	.04	.02
1993 Topps Stadium Club	320	.15	.11	.06
1993 Upper Deck	57	.05	.04	.02
1993 Upper Deck	247	.15	.11	.06
1993 Upper Deck Future Heroes	38	1.25	.90	.50
1993 Upper Deck NFL Experience	50	.50	.40	.20
1993 Upper Deck Pro Bowl	8	7.00	5.25	2.75
1993 Upper Deck SP	234	.20	.15	.08
1993 Upper Deck SP All Pro	13	6.00	4.50	2.50
1993 Upper Deck Team MVP	8	.75	.60	.30
1994 Bowman	297	.15	.11	.06
1994 Fleer	409	.10	.08	.04
1994 Fleer All-Pro	13	.35	.25	.14
1994 Fleer Ultra	272	.12	.09	.05
1994 GameDay	358	.12	.09	.05
1994 Pacific Crown	224	.06	.05	.02
1994 Pacific Prisms	103	1.25	.90	.50
1994 Pinnacle	188	.09	.07	.04
1994 Pinnacle Sportflics	95	.20	.15	.08
1994 Score	81	.08	.06	.03
1994 Score Select	19	.10	.08	.04
1994 SkyBox Impact	228	.08	.06	.03
1994 SkyBox Premium	135	.10	.08	.04

1994 SkyBox Premium SkyTech Stars	9	2.00	1.50	.80
1994 Topps	205	.10	.08	.04
1994 Topps	250	.10	.08	.04
1994 Topps Finest	149	2.50	2.00	1.00
1994 Topps Stadium Club	74	.12	.09	.05
1994 Topps Stadium Club	390	.12	.09	.05
1994 Topps Stadium Club	440	.12	.09	.05
1994 Topps Stadium Club	522	.10	.08	.04
1994 Upper Deck	234	.12	.09	.05
1994 Upper Deck Collector's Choice	52	.05	.04	.02
1994 Upper Deck Collector's Choice	186	.10	.08	.04
1994 Upper Deck SP	102	.25	.20	.10

1994 SkyBox Premium SkyTech Stars	18	1.50	1.25	.60
1994 Topps	70	.15	.11	.06
1994 Topps All-Pros	7	4.00	3.00	1.50
1994 Topps Finest	93	.65	.50	.25
1994 Topps Stadium Club	107	.12	.09	.05
1994 Topps Stadium Club	350	.12	.09	.05
1994 Topps Stadium Club	372	.10	.08	.04
1994 Upper Deck	188	.12	.09	.05
1994 Upper Deck Collector's Choice Crash Game	25	8.00	6.00	3.25
1994 Upper Deck Collector's Choice	212	.08	.06	.03
1994 Upper Deck Pro Bowl	3	5.00	3.75	2.00
1994 Upper Deck Retail Predictor	26	5.00	3.75	2.00
1994 Upper Deck SP	81	.30	.25	.12

Shannon Sharpe

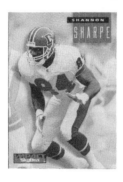

Set	Card #	MT	NM	EX
1991 Bowman	131 (R)	.50	.40	.20
1991 Pacific	126 (R)	.50	.40	.20
1991 Topps	563 (R)	.75	.60	.30
1992 GameDay	385	.50	.40	.20
1992 Pacific	80	.05	.04	.02
1992 Pro Set	487	.10	.08	.04
1992 SkyBox Impact	245	.15	.11	.06
1992 Upper Deck	499	.30	.25	.12
1993 Bowman	83	.40	.30	.15
1993 Fleer Ultra	119	.35	.25	.14
1993 GameDay	240	.15	.11	.06
1993 Pacific	363	.25	.20	.10
1993 Pacific Prisms	25	1.50	1.25	.60
1993 Pinnacle	124	.40	.30	.15
1993 Pro Set	127	.05	.04	.02
1993 Score	154	.30	.25	.12
1993 Score Select	91	.50	.40	.20
1993 SkyBox Impact	86	.08	.06	.03
1993 SkyBox Premium	5	.35	.25	.14
1993 Topps	155	.05	.04	.02
1993 Topps Stadium Club	290	.40	.30	.15
1993 Upper Deck	397	.05	.04	.02
1993 Upper Deck SP	81	.80	.60	.30
1994 Bowman	310	.10	.08	.04
1994 Fleer	142	.20	.15	.08
1994 Fleer All-Pro	14	.75	.60	.30
1994 Fleer Scoring Machines	16	5.50	4.25	2.25
1994 Fleer Ultra	90	.15	.11	.06
1994 GameDay	123	.10	.08	.04
1994 Pacific Crown	131	.06	.05	.02
1994 Pacific Crown Gems of the Crown	29	3.00	2.25	1.25
1994 Pacific Marquee	28	1.25	.90	.50
1994 Pacific Prisms	104	1.50	1.25	.60
1994 Pinnacle	148	.15	.11	.06
1994 Pinnacle Sportflics	105	.15	.11	.06
1994 Score	50	.15	.11	.06
1994 Score Select	34	.10	.08	.04
1994 SkyBox Impact	73	.15	.11	.06
1994 SkyBox Premium	47	.12	.09	.05

Sterling Sharpe

Set	Card #	MT	NM	EX
1989 Pro Set	550 (R)	4.00	3.00	1.50
1989 Score	333 (R)	21.00	15.50	8.50
1989 Topps	379 (R)	4.00	3.00	1.50
1990 Fleer	180	.85	.60	.35
1990 Pro Set	13	.40	.30	.15
1990 Pro Set	114	.60	.45	.25
1990 Pro Set	415	.35	.25	.14
1990 Score	245	.75	.60	.30
1990 Score	560	.30	.25	.12
1990 Score	589	.30	.25	.12
1990 Score Hot Card	10	5.00	3.75	2.00
1990 Score Young Superstars	7	.25	.20	.10
1990 Score 100 Hottest	64	.65	.50	.25
1990 Topps	140	.75	.60	.30
1990 Topps 1000 Yard Club	4	.40	.30	.15
1991 Bowman	172	.50	.40	.20
1991 Fleer	261	.50	.40	.20
1991 Fleer Ultra	178	.50	.40	.20
1991 Pacific	166	.60	.45	.25
1991 Pinnacle	11	1.75	1.25	.70
1991 Pro Set	161	.50	.40	.20
1991 Pro Set	715	.08	.06	.03
1991 Pro Set Platinum	36	.50	.40	.20
1991 Score	42	.50	.40	.20
1991 Score	639	.25	.20	.10
1991 Topps	456	.60	.45	.25
1991 Topps Stadium Club	79	5.50	4.15	2.20
1991 Topps 1000 Yard Club	10	1.25	.90	.50
1991 Upper Deck	136	.60	.45	.25
1991 Upper Deck	459	.30	.25	.12
1992 Bowman	20	6.00	4.50	2.50
1992 Fleer	135	.50	.40	.20
1992 Fleer Ultra	136	1.00	.70	.40
1992 GameDay	272	1.50	1.25	.60

Card	#			
1992 Pacific	104	.45	.35	.20
1992 Pinnacle	95	1.25	.90	.50
1992 Pinnacle	343	.40	.30	.15
1992 Pro Set	176	.50	.40	.20
1992 Pro Set Power	286	.75	.60	.30
1992 Score	114	.50	.40	.20
1992 SkyBox Impact	75	.60	.45	.25
1992 SkyBox Primetime	123	1.00	.70	.40
1992 Topps	490	.50	.40	.20
1992 Topps Stadium Club	592	1.75	1.25	.70
1992 Upper Deck	92	.15	.11	.06
1992 Upper Deck	252	.50	.40	.20
1993 Bowman	260	3.00	2.25	1.25
1993 Fleer	196	.50	.40	.20
1993 Fleer	243	.20	.15	.08
1993 Fleer All-Pro	17	5.00	3.75	2.00
1993 Fleer Ultra	153	.75	.60	.30
1993 Fleer Ultra League Leaders	7	10.00	7.50	4.00
1993 Fleer Ultra Touchdown Kings	8	7.00	5.25	2.75
1993 GameDay	6	.90	.70	.35
1993 GameDay Game Breakers	13	1.50	1.25	.60
1993 Pacific	91	.50	.40	.20
1993 Pacific Gold Prisms	17	20.00	15.00	8.00
1993 Pacific Picks the Pros Gold	2	10.00	7.50	4.00
1993 Pacific Prism Inserts	17	10.00	7.50	4.00
1993 Pacific Prisms	32	6.00	4.50	2.50
1993 Pacific Triple Folder Superstars	17	1.50	1.25	.60
1993 Pinnacle	75	.75	.60	.30
1993 Pinnacle Men of Autumn	9	1.75	1.25	.70
1993 Pinnacle Team Pinnacle	4	40.00	30.00	16.00
1993 Pro Set	8	.15	.11	.06
1993 Pro Set	10	.15	.11	.06
1993 Pro Set	155	.40	.30	.15
1993 Pro Set Power	84	.45	.35	.20
1993 Pro Set Power Combos	2	1.00	.70	.40
1993 Score	91	.40	.30	.15
1993 Score	432	.20	.15	.08
1993 Score Dream Team	4	5.00	3.75	2.00
1993 Score Select	137	2.50	2.00	1.00
1993 Score Select Gridiron Skills	6	60.00	45.00	24.00
1993 Score The Franchise	9	20.00	15.00	8.00
1993 SkyBox Impact	109	.40	.30	.15
1993 SkyBox Impact Kelly's Heroes/ Magic's Kingdom	6	5.00	3.75	2.00
1993 SkyBox Premium	149	.75	.60	.30
1993 SkyBox Thunder and Lightning	2	12.00	9.00	4.75
1993 Topps	160	.40	.30	.15
1993 Topps	175	.25	.20	.10
1993 Topps	217	.20	.15	.08
1993 Topps Black Gold	26	4.00	3.00	1.50
1993 Topps Stadium Club	1	1.00	.70	.40
1993 Topps Stadium Club	495	.40	.30	.15
1993 Upper Deck	248	.40	.30	.15
1993 Upper Deck	423	.20	.15	.08
1993 Upper Deck	424	.20	.15	.08
1993 Upper Deck Pro Bowl	11	14.00	10.50	5.50
1993 Upper Deck SP	95	3.50	2.75	1.50
1993 Upper Deck SP All Pro	10	25.00	18.50	10.00
1993 Upper Deck Team MVP	20	3.00	2.25	1.25
1994 Bowman	340	.65	.50	.25
1994 Fleer	176	.45	.35	.20
1994 Fleer All-Pro	15	2.00	1.50	.80
1994 Fleer League Leaders	6	2.50	2.00	1.00
1994 Fleer Scoring Machines	17	15.00	11.00	6.00
1994 Fleer Ultra	110	.80	.60	.30
1994 Fleer Ultra Achievement Awards	7	2.00	1.50	.80
1994 Fleer Ultra Hot Numbers	12	2.00	1.50	.80
1994 Fleer Ultra Touchdown Kings	6	15.00	11.00	6.00
1994 GameDay	151	.50	.40	.20
1994 GameDay Game Breakers	12	1.50	1.25	.60
1994 Pacific Crown	143	.40	.30	.15
1994 Pacific Crown Gems of the Crown	30	6.00	4.50	2.50
1994 Pacific Marquee	29	2.00	1.50	.80
1994 Pacific Prisms	105	4.00	3.00	1.50
1994 Pinnacle	11	.60	.45	.25
1994 Pinnacle Performers	3	5.00	3.75	2.00
1994 Pinnacle Sportflics Head-to-Head	8	12.00	9.00	4.75
1994 Pinnacle Sportflics	40	1.25	.90	.50
1994 Pinnacle Team Pinnacle	6	35.00	26.00	14.00
1994 Score	3	.35	.25	.14
1994 Score Dream Team	13	20.00	15.00	8.00
1994 Score Select	12	.65	.50	.25
1994 Score Select Canton Bound	2	15.00	11.00	6.00
1994 SkyBox Impact	94	.40	.30	.15
1994 SkyBox Impact Ultimate Impact	6	3.50	2.75	1.50
1994 SkyBox Premium	59	.50	.40	.20
1994 SkyBox Premium Revolution	8	8.00	6.00	3.25
1994 SkyBox Premium SkyTech Stars	5	15.00	11.00	6.00
1994 Topps	310	.35	.25	.14
1994 Topps	554	.12	.09	.05
1994 Topps Finest	31	7.50	5.75	3.00
1994 Topps Finest Inserts	19	15.00	11.00	6.00
1994 Topps Stadium Club	108	.30	.25	.12
1994 Topps Stadium Club	240	.60	.45	.25
1994 Topps Stadium Club	523	.40	.30	.15
1994 Topps Stadium Club Ring Leaders	7	8.00	6.00	3.25
1994 Upper Deck	280	.65	.50	.25
1994 Upper Deck Collector's Choice Crash Game	24	10.00	7.50	4.00
1994 Upper Deck Collector's Choice	32	.25	.20	.10
1994 Upper Deck Collector's Choice	217	.45	.35	.20
1994 Upper Deck Hobby Predictor	8	6.00	4.50	2.50
1994 Upper Deck Retail Predictor	22	10.00	7.50	4.00
1994 Upper Deck SP	162	.80	.60	.30

Grading Guide

Mint (MT): A perfect card. Well-centered with all corners sharp and square. No creases, stains, edge nicks, surface marks, yellowing or fading.

Near Mint (NM): A nearly perfect card. At first glance, a NM card appears to be perfect. May be slightly off-center. No surface marks, creases or loss of gloss.

Excellent (EX): Corners are still fairly sharp with only moderate wear. Borders may be off-center. No creases or stains on fronts or backs, but may show slight loss of surface luster.

Very Good (VG): Shows obvious handling. May have rounded corners, minor creases, major gum or wax stains. No major creases, tape marks, writing, etc.

Good (G): A well-worn card, but exhibits no intentional damage. May have major or multiple creases. Corners may be rounded well beyond card border.

Art Shell

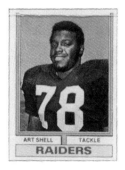

Set	Card #	NM	EX	VG
1973 Topps	77 (R)	25.00	12.50	7.50
1974 Topps	272	6.00	3.00	1.75
1976 Topps	380	2.00	1.00	.60
1977 Topps	270	1.50	.70	.45
1978 Topps	460	1.00	.50	.30
1979 Topps	210	1.00	.50	.30
1980 Topps	382	.50	.25	.15

Set	Card #	MT	NM	EX
1981 Topps	43	.50	.40	.20
1982 Topps	198	.40	.30	.15
1989 Pro Set	541	.10	.08	.04
1990 Pro Set	161	.03	.02	.01
1991 Pro Set	4	.03	.02	.01
1991 Pro Set	198	.03	.02	.01
1991 Pro Set	432	.03	.02	.01
1991 Pro Set Platinum	149	.05	.04	.02
1992 Pro Set	216	.05	.04	.02

Phil Simms

Set	Card #	NM	EX	VG
1980 Topps	225 (R)	15.00	7.50	4.50

Set	Card #	MT	NM	EX
1981 Topps	55	5.00	3.75	2.00
1982 Topps	433	1.50	1.25	.60
1984 Topps	320	1.00	.70	.40
1985 Topps	123	.60	.45	.25
1986 Topps	138	.40	.30	.15
1987 Topps	8	.15	.11	.06
1987 Topps	10	.35	.25	.14
1988 Topps	272	.30	.25	.12
1989 Pro Set	291	.15	.11	.06
1989 Score	6	.40	.30	.15
1989 Topps	172	.15	.11	.06

1990 Fleer	76	.10	.08	.04
1990 Pro Set	230	.10	.08	.04
1990 Pro Set Super Bowl MVPs	21	.20	.15	.08
1990 Score	5	.10	.08	.04
1990 Score	314	.08	.06	.03
1990 Score 100 Hottest	7	.20	.15	.08
1990 Topps	51	.10	.08	.04
1991 Bowman	364	.08	.06	.03
1991 Fleer	318	.08	.06	.03
1991 Fleer	414	.08	.06	.03
1991 Fleer Ultra	223	.10	.08	.04
1991 Pacific	355	.10	.08	.04
1991 Pinnacle	235	.25	.20	.10
1991 Pro Set	601	.05	.04	.02
1991 Score	555	.10	.08	.04
1991 Topps	32	.10	.08	.04
1991 Topps Stadium Club	140	.25	.20	.10
1991 Upper Deck	181	.10	.08	.04
1992 Fleer	300	.10	.08	.04
1992 Fleer Ultra	286	.10	.08	.04
1992 GameDay	471	.15	.11	.06
1992 Pacific	536	.10	.08	.04
1992 Pinnacle	4	.15	.11	.06
1992 Pro Set	595	.10	.08	.04
1992 Pro Set Power	206	.15	.11	.06
1992 Score	388	.10	.08	.04
1992 SkyBox Impact	214	.10	.08	.04
1992 SkyBox Primetime	215	.10	.08	.04
1992 Topps	750	.05	.04	.02
1992 Topps Stadium Club	620	.90	.70	.35
1992 Upper Deck	561	.05	.04	.02
1993 Bowman	185	.20	.15	.08
1993 Fleer	314	.10	.08	.04
1993 Fleer Ultra	330	.15	.11	.06
1993 GameDay	254	.15	.11	.06
1993 Pacific	55	.15	.11	.06
1993 Pacific Prisms	71	1.00	.70	.40
1993 Pinnacle	239	.15	.11	.06
1993 Pro Set	308	.10	.08	.04
1993 Score	240	.08	.06	.03
1993 Score Select	19	.25	.20	.10
1993 SkyBox Impact	225	.10	.08	.04
1993 SkyBox Premium	43	.15	.11	.06
1993 Topps	350	.10	.08	.04
1993 Topps Stadium Club	220	.15	.11	.06
1993 Upper Deck	219	.05	.04	.02
1993 Upper Deck SP	187	.20	.15	.08
1994 Fleer	349	.10	.08	.04
1994 Pacific Crown	102	.06	.05	.02
1994 Pacific Prisms	107	1.25	.90	.50
1994 Pinnacle	5	.09	.07	.04
1994 Pinnacle Sportflics	64	.15	.11	.06
1994 Score	27	.10	.08	.04
1994 SkyBox Impact	188	.08	.06	.03
1994 Topps	260	.10	.08	.04
1994 Topps Finest	152	1.50	1.25	.60
1994 Topps Finest Inserts	25	4.00	3.00	1.50
1994 Topps Stadium Club	210	.10	.08	.04
1994 Upper Deck	290	.10	.08	.04
1994 Upper Deck Collector's Choice	233	.05	.04	.02

Cards before 1981 are priced in Near Mint (NM),
Excellent (EX), and Very Good (VG).
Cards 1981 to present are priced in Mint (MT), Near Mint (NM),
and Excellent (EX).

Values for recent cards and sets are listed in Mint
(MT), Near Mint (NM), reflecting the fact that many
cards from recent years have been preserved in to
condition. Recent cards and sets in
less than Excellent condition
have little collector interest.

O.J. Simpson

Set	Card #	NM	EX	VG
1970 Topps	90 (R)	175.00	87.00	52.00
1971 Topps	260	60.00	30.00	18.00
1972 Topps	160	37.00	18.50	11.00
1973 Topps	500	30.00	15.00	9.00
1974 Topps	1	28.00	14.00	8.40
1974 Topps	130	20.00	10.00	6.00
1975 Topps	355	7.00	3.50	2.00
1975 Topps	500	15.00	7.50	4.50
1976 Topps	6	6.00	3.00	1.75
1976 Topps	300	13.00	6.50	4.00
1977 Topps	100	13.00	6.50	4.00
1977 Topps	453	5.00	2.50	1.50
1978 Topps	4	4.50	2.25	1.25
1978 Topps	400	10.00	5.00	3.00
1979 Topps	170	10.00	5.00	3.00

Set	Card #	MT	NM	EX
1989 Pro Set Announcer Inserts	29	2.00	1.50	.80

Set	Card #	MT	NM	EX
1990 Score	554	.04	.03	.02
1990 Score	570	.04	.03	.02
1990 Score 100 Hottest	44	.20	.15	.08
1990 Topps	368	.04	.03	.02
1991 Bowman	58	.03	.02	.01
1991 Fleer	225	.07	.05	.03
1991 Fleer	402	.05	.04	.02
1991 Fleer All-Pro	22	.10	.08	.04
1991 Fleer Pro Visions	4	.25	.20	.10
1991 Fleer Ultra	160	.10	.08	.04
1991 Fleer Ultra Performances	6	.50	.40	.20
1991 Pacific	53	.04	.03	.02
1991 Pinnacle	210	.10	.08	.04
1991 Pro Set	5	.03	.02	.01
1991 Pro Set	396	.03	.02	.01
1991 Pro Set	458	.05	.04	.02
1991 Pro Set	728	.05	.04	.02
1991 Pro Set Platinum	165	.05	.04	.02
1991 Score	6	.04	.03	.02
1991 Topps	176	.04	.03	.02
1991 Topps Stadium Club	314	.30	.25	.12
1991 Upper Deck	229	.05	.04	.02
1992 GameDay	108	.12	.09	.05
1992 Pro Set	424	.05	.04	.02
1992 Pro Set	452	.05	.04	.02
1992 Pro Set Power	50	.05	.04	.02
1992 SkyBox Impact	196	.05	.04	.02
1992 SkyBox Primetime	85	.10	.08	.04
1992 Topps	687	.05	.04	.02
1992 Topps Stadium Club	673	.75	.60	.30
1992 Upper Deck	568	.05	.04	.02
1992 Upper Deck Gold	32	.10	.08	.04
1992 Upper Deck NFL Fanimation	7	2.50	2.00	1.00
1993 Upper Deck NFL Experience	27	.20	.15	.08

Definitions for grading conditions are located
in the Introduction of this price guide.

Mike Singletary

Set	Card #	MT	NM	EX
1983 Topps	38 (R)	7.00	5.25	2.75
1984 Topps	232	1.75	1.25	.70
1985 Topps	34	.75	.60	.30
1986 Topps	24	.60	.45	.25
1987 Topps	58	.50	.40	.20
1988 Topps	82	.20	.15	.08
1989 Pro Set	50	.03	.02	.01
1989 Score	50	.15	.11	.06
1989 Score	303	.10	.08	.04
1989 Topps	58	.10	.08	.04
1990 Fleer	299	.03	.02	.01
1990 Pro Set	57	.03	.02	.01
1990 Pro Set	416	.03	.02	.01
1990 Score	3	.04	.03	.02

Bruce Smith

Set	Card #	MT	NM	EX
1986 Topps	389 (R)	7.00	5.25	2.75
1987 Topps	369	1.50	1.25	.60
1988 Topps	227	.50	.40	.20
1989 Pro Set	28	.15	.11	.06
1989 Score	19	.50	.40	.20
1989 Score	307	.15	.11	.06
1989 Score	325	.25	.20	.10
1989 Topps	44	.15	.11	.06
1990 Fleer	121	.03	.02	.01
1990 Pro Set	371	.06	.05	.02
1990 Pro Set	443	.03	.02	.01
1990 Score	16	.04	.03	.02
1990 Score 100 Hottest	33	.15	.11	.06
1990 Topps	205	.04	.03	.02
1991 Bowman	44	.03	.02	.01

Emmitt Smith

1991 Fleer	11	.15	.11	.06
1991 Fleer	396	.03	.02	.01
1991 Fleer All-Pro	5	.10	.08	.04
1991 Fleer Pro Visions	8	.25	.20	.10
1991 Fleer Ultra	8	.08	.06	.03
1991 Fleer Ultra All Stars	3	.50	.40	.20
1991 Pacific	29	.04	.03	.02
1991 Pinnacle	221	.15	.11	.06
1991 Pro Set	6	.04	.03	.02
1991 Pro Set	47	.08	.02	.03
1991 Pro Set	83	.03	.02	.01
1991 Pro Set	417	.03	.02	.01
1991 Pro Set Platinum	8	.05	.04	.02
1991 Score	278	.08	.06	.03
1991 Score	345	.06	.05	.02
1991 Score	660	.08	.06	.03
1991 Score	667	.08	.06	.03
1991 Topps	59	.04	.03	.02
1991 Topps Stadium Club	12	.25	.20	.10
1991 Upper Deck	174	.05	.04	.02
1992 GameDay	53	.12	.09	.05
1992 Pro Set	445	.08	.06	.03
1992 Pro Set Power	178	.05	.04	.02
1992 SkyBox Impact	237	.07	.05	.03
1992 SkyBox Primetime	76	.10	.08	.04
1992 Topps	693	.05	.04	.02
1992 Topps Stadium Club	609	.75	.60	.30
1992 Topps Stadium Club	686	.75	.60	.30
1992 Upper Deck	586	.15	.11	.06
1992 Upper Deck Gold	48	.10	.08	.04
1993 Bowman	175	.20	.15	.08
1993 Fleer	416	.05	.04	.02
1993 Fleer Ultra	32	.08	.06	.03
1993 GameDay	412	.10	.08	.04
1993 Pacific	202	.05	.04	.02
1993 Pinnacle	269	.07	.05	.03
1993 Pinnacle Men of Autumn	30	.25	.20	.10
1993 Pro Set	51	.05	.04	.02
1993 Pro Set Power	78	.10	.08	.04
1993 Pro Set Power All-Power Defense	5	.25	.20	.10
1993 Pro Set Power Combos	5	.50	.40	.20
1993 Pro Set Power Update Combos	6	1.00	.70	.40
1993 Score	267	.08	.06	.03
1993 Score Select	28	.10	.08	.04
1993 SkyBox Impact	24	.04	.03	.02
1993 SkyBox Premium	175	.10	.08	.04
1993 Topps	75	.05	.04	.02
1993 Topps Stadium Club	54	.10	.08	.04
1993 Upper Deck	136	.05	.04	.02
1993 Upper Deck NFL Experience	35	.45	.35	.20
1993 Upper Deck SP	34	.25	.20	.10
1994 Bowman	144	.10	.08	.04
1994 Fleer	48	.10	.08	.04
1994 Fleer All-Pro	16	.35	.25	.14
1994 Fleer Ultra	30	.08	.06	.03
1994 GameDay	41	.10	.08	.04
1994 Pacific Crown	27	.06	.05	.02
1994 Pacific Prisms	109	1.00	.70	.40
1994 Pinnacle	96	.09	.07	.04
1994 Pinnacle Sportflics	35	.15	.11	.06
1994 Score	5	.10	.08	.04
1994 Score Select	2	.12	.09	.05
1994 Score Select Canton Bound	10	12.00	9.00	4.75
1994 SkyBox Impact	28	.10	.08	.04
1994 SkyBox Premium	18	.12	.09	.05
1994 Topps	30	.10	.08	.04
1994 Topps All-Pros	17	3.50	2.75	1.50
1994 Topps Finest	91	1.50	1.25	.60
1994 Topps Stadium Club	400	.10	.08	.04
1994 Topps Stadium Club	435	.10	.08	.04
1994 Topps Stadium Club	515	.10	.08	.04
1994 Upper Deck	243	.10	.08	.04
1994 Upper Deck Collector's Choice	205	.07	.05	.03
1994 Upper Deck SP	23	.70	.50	.30

Set	Card #	MT	NM	EX
1990 Fleer Update	40 (R)	40.00	30.00	16.00
1990 Pro Set	685 (R)	3.00	2.25	1.25
1990 Pro Set	800	1.00	.70	.40
1990 Score Update	101 (R)	85.00	64.00	34.00
1990 Topps Update	27 (R)	7.00	5.25	2.75
1991 Bowman	3	1.00	.70	.40
1991 Bowman	117	2.00	1.50	.80
1991 Fleer	237	2.00	1.50	.80
1991 Fleer	418	1.00	.70	.40
1991 Fleer Ultra	165	2.00	1.50	.80
1991 Fleer Ultra Performances	1	10.00	7.50	4.00
1991 Pacific	107	2.50	2.00	1.00
1991 Pinnacle	42	8.00	6.00	3.25
1991 Pinnacle	364	3.00	2.25	1.25
1991 Pro Set	1	1.00	.70	.40
1991 Pro Set	485	2.00	1.50	.80
1991 Pro Set Platinum	25	2.00	1.50	.80
1991 Pro Set Platinum PC	9	5.00	3.75	2.00
1991 Score	15	2.00	1.50	.80
1991 Score	675	.25	.20	.10
1991 Topps	360	2.50	2.00	1.00
1991 Topps Stadium Club	2	22.00	16.50	8.75
1991 Upper Deck	172	2.00	1.50	.80
1991 Upper Deck	456	1.00	.70	.40
1991 Upper Deck Game Breaker Holograms	5	4.50	3.50	1.75
1992 Bowman	100	30.00	22.00	12.00
1992 Bowman	180	100.00	75.00	40.00
1992 Fleer	89	2.00	1.50	.80
1992 Fleer	453	1.00	.70	.40
1992 Fleer	475	1.00	.70	.40
1992 Fleer Team Leaders	3	130.00	97.00	52.00
1992 Fleer Ultra	88	5.00	3.75	2.00
1992 GameDay	490	7.00	5.25	2.75
1992 Pacific	68	2.25	1.75	.90
1992 Pacific Prism Inserts	6	8.00	6.00	3.25
1992 Pinnacle	58	4.75	3.50	2.00
1992 Pinnacle Team 2000	19	5.00	3.75	2.00
1992 Pro Set	1AU	180.00	135.00	72.00
1992 Pro Set	7	1.00	.70	.40
1992 Pro Set	150	2.00	1.50	.80
1992 Pro Set	425	1.00	.70	.40
1992 Pro Set Gold MVPs	18	10.00	7.50	4.00
1992 Pro Set Ground Force	150	35.00	26.00	14.00
1992 Pro Set Power	22	3.75	2.87	1.50
1992 Pro Set Power Power Combos	5	30.00	22.00	12.00
1992 Score	65	2.00	1.50	.80
1992 Score Dream Team	3	50.00	37.00	20.00
1992 SkyBox Impact	275	2.00	1.50	.80
1992 SkyBox Impact	308	1.00	.70	.40
1992 SkyBox Impact Major Impact	18	8.00	6.00	3.25
1992 SkyBox Primetime	22	5.50	4.25	2.25
1992 SkyBox Primetime	165	3.00	2.25	1.25
1992 SkyBox Primetime Poster Cards	15	20.00	15.00	8.00

1992 Topps	180	2.50	2.00	1.00
1992 Topps Stadium Club	190	5.00	3.75	2.00
1992 Topps Stadium Club	303	5.00	3.75	2.00
1992 Topps 1000-Yard Club	1	8.00	6.00	3.25
1992 Upper Deck	83	1.00	.70	.40
1992 Upper Deck	254	2.00	1.50	.80
1992 Upper Deck	301	1.00	.70	.40
1992 Upper Deck	516	1.00	.70	.40
1992 Upper Deck Pro Bowl	6	12.00	9.00	4.75
1993 Bowman	300	10.00	7.50	4.00
1993 Fleer	233	2.00	1.50	.80
1993 Fleer	244	1.00	.70	.40
1993 Fleer All-Pro	19	25.00	18.50	10.00
1993 Fleer Ultra	101	4.00	3.00	1.50
1993 Fleer Ultra League Leaders	9	60.00	45.00	24.00
1993 Fleer Ultra Touchdown Kings	9	35.00	26.00	14.00
1993 GameDay	22	5.00	3.75	2.00
1993 GameDay Game Breakers	7	10.00	7.50	4.00
1993 Pacific	1	2.00	1.50	.80
1993 Pacific Gold Prisms	18	75.00	56.00	30.00
1993 Pacific Picks the Pros Gold	9	30.00	22.00	12.00
1993 Pacific Prism Inserts	18	28.00	21.00	11.00
1993 Pacific Prisms	22	20.00	15.00	8.00
1993 Pacific Triple Folder Superstars	18	5.00	3.75	2.00
1993 Pacific Triple Folders	19	4.50	3.50	1.75
1993 Pinnacle	100	5.00	3.75	2.00
1993 Pinnacle Men of Autumn	34	5.00	3.75	2.00
1993 Pinnacle Super Bowl XXVII	3	50.00	37.00	20.00
1993 Pinnacle Team Pinnacle	2	75.00	60.00	30.00
1993 Pro Set	7	1.20	.90	.50
1993 Pro Set	39	1.75	1.25	.70
1993 Pro Set Power	22	2.00	1.50	.80
1993 Pro Set Power	100	1.00	.70	.40
1993 Pro Set Power Combos	1	3.50	2.75	1.50
1993 Pro Set Power Update Combos	8	8.00	6.00	3.25
1993 Score	14	2.00	1.50	.80
1993 Score Dream Team	2	15.00	11.00	6.00
1993 Score Select	55	13.00	9.75	5.25
1993 Score The Franchise	6	70.00	52.00	28.00
1993 SkyBox Impact	74	2.00	1.50	.80
1993 SkyBox Impact Kelly's Heroes/ Magic's Kingdom	5	10.00	7.50	4.00
1993 SkyBox Premium	64	6.00	4.50	2.50
1993 Topps	120	1.75	1.25	.70
1993 Topps	173	.75	.60	.30
1993 Topps	219	.50	.40	.20
1993 Topps Black Gold	25	9.00	6.75	3.50
1993 Topps Stadium Club	85	5.00	3.75	2.00
1993 Topps Stadium Club	491	2.00	1.50	.80
1993 Upper Deck	73	1.00	.70	.40
1993 Upper Deck	359	2.00	1.50	.80
1993 Upper Deck	421	1.00	.70	.40
1993 Upper Deck	425	1.00	.70	.40
1993 Upper Deck	431	.50	.40	.20
1993 Upper Deck America's Team	7	50.00	37.00	20.00
1993 Upper Deck Dallas Cowboys	8	3.00	2.25	1.25
1993 Upper Deck Future Heroes	39	6.00	4.50	2.50
1993 Upper Deck Pro Bowl	15	35.00	26.00	14.00
1993 Upper Deck SP	72	20.00	15.00	8.00
1993 Upper Deck SP All Pro	7	125.00	94.00	50.00
1994 Bowman	300	3.50	2.75	1.50
1994 Fleer	121	2.00	1.50	.80
1994 Fleer All-Pro	17	7.00	5.25	2.75
1994 Fleer Award Winners	4	3.00	2.25	1.25
1994 Fleer League Leaders	7	5.00	3.75	2.00
1994 Fleer Living Legends	5	50.00	37.00	20.00
1994 Fleer Scoring Machines	18	60.00	45.00	24.00
1994 Fleer Ultra	76	3.50	2.75	1.50
1994 Fleer Ultra Achievement Awards	8	7.00	5.25	2.75
1994 Fleer Ultra Award Winners	3	8.00	6.00	3.25
1994 Fleer Ultra Hot Numbers	13	8.00	6.00	3.25
1994 Fleer Ultra Scoring Power	5	12.00	9.00	4.75
1994 Fleer Ultra Touchdown Kings	7	50.00	37.00	20.00
1994 Fleer Ultra Ultra Stars	8	65.00	49.00	26.00
1994 GameDay	103	3.00	2.25	1.25
1994 GameDay Flashing Stars	4	45.00	34.00	18.00
1994 GameDay Game Breakers	13	8.00	6.00	3.25
1994 Pacific Crown	12	2.25	1.75	.90
1994 Pacific Crown Crystalline Collection	1	35.00	26.00	14.00
1994 Pacific Crown Gems of the Crown	31	25.00	18.50	10.00
1994 Pacific Marquee	31	10.00	7.50	4.00
1994 Pacific Prisms	110	20.00	15.00	8.00
1994 Pinnacle	81	3.50	2.75	1.50
1994 Pinnacle Performers	2	15.00	11.00	6.00
1994 Pinnacle Sportflics Head-to-Head	2	60.00	45.00	24.00
1994 Pinnacle Sportflics	30	6.00	4.50	2.50
1994 Pinnacle Sportflics	177	2.50	2.00	1.00
1994 Pinnacle Team Pinnacle	3	85.00	64.00	34.00
1994 Score	40	2.00	1.50	.80
1994 Score	330	1.00	.70	.40
1994 Score Select	1	4.00	3.00	1.50
1994 Score Select Canton Bound	1	85.00	64.00	34.00
1994 SkyBox Impact	63	2.00	1.50	.80
1994 SkyBox Impact Ultimate Impact	2	20.00	15.00	8.00
1994 SkyBox Premium	41	2.50	2.00	1.00
1994 SkyBox Premium Revolution	5	35.00	26.00	14.00
1994 SkyBox Premium SkyTech Stars	2	18.00	13.50	7.25
1994 Topps	1	2.00	1.50	.80
1994 Topps	118	.75	.60	.30
1994 Topps	547	.50	.40	.20
1994 Topps	611	.80	.60	.30
1994 Topps Finest	1	23.00	17.00	9.25
1994 Topps Finest Inserts	20	50.00	37.00	20.00
1994 Topps Stadium Club	110	2.00	1.50	.80
1994 Topps Stadium Club	300	3.50	2.75	1.50
1994 Topps Stadium Club	516	2.00	1.50	.80
1994 Topps Stadium Club Dynasty and Destiny	1	17.00	12.50	6.75
1994 Topps Stadium Club Ring Leaders	1	50.00	37.00	20.00
1994 Upper Deck	157	3.00	2.25	1.25
1994 Upper Deck Collector's Choice Crash Game	15	24.00	18.00	9.50
1994 Upper Deck Collector's Choice	38	1.00	.70	.40
1994 Upper Deck Collector's Choice	215	2.00	1.50	.80
1994 Upper Deck Hobby Predictor	1	30.00	22.00	12.00
1994 Upper Deck Pro Bowl	10	40.00	30.00	16.00

1994 Upper Deck Retail Predictor	11	12.00	9.00	4.75
1994 Upper Deck SP	122	8.00	6.00	3.25
1994 Upper Deck SP All-Pro	10	25.00	18.50	10.00

Chris Spielman

Set	Card #	MT	NM	EX
1989 Score	167 (R)	1.25	.90	.50
1989 Topps	361 (R)	.30	.25	.12
1990 Fleer	286	.03	.02	.01
1990 Pro Set	103	.03	.02	.01
1990 Pro Set	419	.03	.02	.01
1990 Score	191	.04	.03	.02
1990 Score Young Superstars	19	.15	.11	.06
1990 Score 100 Hottest	17	.10	.08	.04
1990 Topps	353	.04	.03	.02
1991 Bowman	156	.03	.02	.01
1991 Fleer Ultra Update	29	.10	.08	.04
1991 Pacific	145	.04	.03	.02
1991 Pinnacle	270	.10	.08	.04
1991 Pro Set	503	.03	.02	.01
1991 Pro Set Platinum	189	.05	.04	.02
1991 Score	9	.04	.03	.02
1991 Score	341	.06	.05	.02
1991 Topps	412	.04	.03	.02
1991 Topps Stadium Club	298	.30	.25	.12
1991 Upper Deck	264	.05	.04	.02
1992 Bowman	532	.30	.25	.12
1992 Fleer	124	.03	.02	.01
1992 Fleer Team Leaders	4	6.50	5.00	2.50
1992 Fleer Ultra	123	.05	.04	.02
1992 Pacific	94	.05	.04	.02
1992 Pinnacle	19	.05	.04	.02
1992 Pro Set	170	.05	.04	.02
1992 Pro Set Power	54	.05	.04	.02
1992 Pro Set Power Power Combos	6	3.00	2.25	1.25
1992 Score	5	.05	.04	.02
1992 Topps	225	.05	.04	.02
1992 Topps Stadium Club	175	.08	.06	.03
1992 Upper Deck	90	.05	.04	.02
1992 Upper Deck	390	.05	.04	.02
1992 Upper Deck Pro Bowl	10	1.50	1.25	.60
1993 Bowman	278	.15	.11	.06
1993 Fleer	232	.05	.04	.02
1993 GameDay	148	.10	.08	.04
1993 Pacific	102	.05	.04	.02
1993 Pinnacle	7	.10	.08	.04
1993 Pinnacle Men of Autumn	36	.25	.20	.10
1993 Pro Set	143	.05	.04	.02
1993 Pro Set Power	54	.05	.04	.02
1993 Pro Set Power All-Power Defense	23	.25	.20	.10

1993 Score	104	.04	.03	.02
1993 Score Select	51	.10	.08	.04
1993 SkyBox Impact	102	.03	.02	.01
1993 Topps	146	.05	.04	.02
1993 Topps	297	.05	.04	.02
1993 Topps Stadium Club	342	.10	.08	.04
1993 Upper Deck	332	.05	.04	.02
1993 Upper Deck SP	89	.25	.20	.10
1994 Bowman	382	.10	.08	.04
1994 Fleer	162	.08	.06	.03
1994 Fleer Ultra	102	.08	.06	.03
1994 GameDay	139	.10	.08	.04
1994 Pacific Crown	86	.06	.05	.02
1994 Pinnacle	129	.09	.07	.04
1994 Pinnacle Sportflics	90	.15	.11	.06
1994 Score	255	.05	.04	.02
1994 Score Select	71	.10	.08	.04
1994 SkyBox Impact	86	.08	.06	.03
1994 Topps	185	.05	.04	.02
1994 Topps Finest	62	.65	.50	.25
1994 Topps Stadium Club	20	.10	.08	.04
1994 Upper Deck	309	.10	.08	.04
1994 Upper Deck Collector's Choice	92	.05	.04	.02

Ken Stabler

Set	Card #	NM	EX	VG
1973 Topps	487 (R)	50.00	25.00	15.00
1974 Topps	451	15.00	7.50	4.50
1975 Topps	380	10.00	5.00	3.00
1975 Topps	458	4.00	2.00	1.25
1976 Topps	415	6.50	3.25	2.00
1977 Topps	110	4.50	2.25	1.25
1977 Topps	526	.40	.20	.12
1978 Topps	365	3.00	1.50	.90
1979 Topps	520	2.00	1.00	.60
1980 Topps	65	1.50	.70	.45

Set	Card #	MT	NM	EX
1981 Topps	405	1.00	.70	.40
1982 Topps	105	1.00	.70	.40
1983 Topps	118	.60	.45	.25
1989 Pro Set Announcer Inserts	18	.25	.20	.10
1992 Pro Set	350	.05	.04	.02

Values for recent cards and sets are listed in Mint (MT), Near Mint (NM), reflecting the fact that many cards from recent years have been preserved in to condition. Recent cards and sets in less than Excellent condition have little collector interest.

Bart Starr

Set	Card #	NM	EX	VG
1957 Topps	119 (R)	400.00	200.00	120.00
1958 Topps	66	95.00	47.00	28.00
1959 Topps	23	55.00	27.00	16.50
1960 Topps	51	40.00	20.00	12.00
1961 Fleer	88	50.00	25.00	15.00
1961 Topps	39	30.00	15.00	9.00
1962 Topps	63	50.00	25.00	15.00
1963 Topps	86	30.00	15.00	9.00
1964 Philadelphia	79	28.00	14.00	8.50
1965 Philadelphia	81	25.00	12.50	7.50
1966 Philadelphia	88	25.00	12.50	7.50
1967 Philadelphia	82	20.00	10.00	6.00
1968 Topps	1	35.00	17.50	10.50
1969 Topps	215	25.00	12.50	7.50
1969 Topps Four In Ones	(31)	6.00	3.00	1.75
1970 Topps	30	20.00	10.00	6.00
1971 Topps	200	22.00	11.00	6.50

Set	Card #	MT	NM	EX
1990 Pro Set Super Bowl MVPs	1	.30	.25	.12
1990 Pro Set Super Bowl MVPs	2	.30	.25	.12
1992 Topps Stadium Club QB Legends	2	3.75	2.75	1.50
1993 Upper Deck NFL Experience	3	.25	.20	.10

Definitions for grading conditions are located in the Introduction of this price guide.

Roger Staubach

Set	Card #	NM	EX	VG
1972 Topps	4	4.00	2.00	1.25
1972 Topps	122	20.00	10.00	6.00

Set	Card #	NM	EX	VG
1972 Topps	200 (R)	150.00	75.00	45.00
1973 Topps	475	40.00	20.00	12.00
1974 Topps	500	28.00	14.00	8.50
1975 Topps	145	25.00	12.50	7.50
1976 Topps	395	15.00	7.50	4.50
1977 Topps	45	10.00	5.00	3.00
1978 Topps	290	8.00	4.00	2.50
1979 Topps	400	7.00	3.50	2.00

Set	Card #	MT	NM	EX
1990 Pro Set Series II Inserts	6	2.00	2.00	2.00
1990 Pro Set Super Bowl MVPs	6	.50	.40	.20
1990 Pro Set Super Bowl 160	37	.30	.30	.30
1992 Topps Stadium Club QB Legends	5	7.50	5.75	3.00
1993 Upper Deck America's Team	1	12.00	9.00	4.75
1993 Upper Deck NFL Experience	2	.25	.20	.10

Jan Stenerud

Set	Card #	NM	EX	VG
1970 Topps	25 (R)	12.00	6.00	3.50
1971 Topps	61	3.00	1.50	.90
1972 Topps	7	1.50	.70	.45
1972 Topps	61	2.00	1.00	.60
1973 Topps	285	1.50	.70	.45
1974 Topps	355	1.25	.60	.40
1975 Topps	488	1.25	.60	.40
1976 Topps	160	.75	.40	.25
1977 Topps	335	.60	.30	.20
1978 Topps	238	.50	.25	.15
1979 Topps	142	.50	.25	.15
1980 Topps	266	.40	.20	.12

Set	Card #	MT	NM	EX
1981 Topps	387	.20	.15	.08
1982 Topps	366	.25	.20	.10
1982 Topps	367	.10	.08	.04
1983 Topps	85	.10	.08	.04
1984 Topps	6	.10	.08	.04
1984 Topps	275	.25	.20	.10
1985 Topps	98	.20	.15	.08
1991 Pro Set	31	.03	.02	.01
1991 Score	670	.05	.04	.02

Cards before 1981 are priced in Near Mint (NM),
Excellent (EX), and Very Good (VG).
Cards 1981 to present are Mint (MT), Near Mint (NM),
and Excellent (EX).

Dana Stubblefield

Set	Card #	MT	NM	EX
1993 Bowman	3 (R)	1.00	.70	.40
1993 Fleer NFL Prospects	16	1.00	.70	.40
1993 Fleer Ultra	439 (R)	1.00	.70	.40
1993 GameDay	103 (R)	1.00	.70	.40
1993 Pacific	440 (R)	.50	.40	.20
1993 Pinnacle Rookies	19	15.00	11.00	6.00
1993 Pro Set	396 (R)	.50	.40	.20
1993 Pro Set All-Rookie Forecast	18	.65	.50	.25
1993 Pro Set Power Update Impact Rookies	13	1.00	.70	.40
1993 Pro Set Power Update Prospects	44 (R)	.40	.30	.15
1993 Score Select	169 (R)	1.50	1.25	.60
1993 SkyBox Impact	384 (R)	.50	.40	.20
1993 SkyBox Premium	170 (R)	.50	.40	.20
1993 Topps	64 (R)	.50	.40	.20
1993 Topps	436	.25	.20	.10
1993 Topps Stadium Club	508	.50	.40	.20
1993 Upper Deck	477 (R)	.50	.40	.20
1993 Upper Deck San Francisco 49ers	5	1.00	.70	.40
1993 Upper Deck SP	241 (R)	1.75	1.25	.70
1994 Bowman	243	.25	.20	.10
1994 Fleer	423	.25	.20	.10
1994 Fleer Award Winners	5	.50	.40	.20
1994 Fleer Rookie Sensations	19	6.00	4.50	2.50
1994 Fleer Ultra	282	.25	.20	.10
1994 Fleer Ultra Award Winners	4	1.00	.70	.40
1994 Fleer Ultra 2nd Year Standouts	15	2.00	1.50	.80
1994 GameDay	370	.15	.11	.06
1994 GameDay Second-Year Stars	16	1.00	.70	.40
1994 Pacific Crown	42	.20	.15	.08
1994 Pinnacle	83	.20	.15	.08
1994 Pinnacle Sportflics	55	.25	.20	.10
1994 Score	326	.25	.20	.10
1994 Score Select	195	.20	.15	.08
1994 Score Select Future Force	11	8.00	6.00	3.25
1994 Score Sophomore Showcase	16	3.00	2.25	1.25
1994 SkyBox Impact	233	.25	.20	.10
1994 SkyBox Impact Instant Impact	8	1.75	1.25	.70
1994 SkyBox Premium	138	.20	.15	.08
1994 Topps	149	.35	.25	.14
1994 Topps Finest	108	2.50	2.00	1.00
1994 Topps Stadium Club	80	.30	.25	.12
1994 Topps Stadium Club	183	.15	.11	.06
1994 Topps Stadium Club	524	.12	.09	.05
1994 Upper Deck	325	.40	.30	.15
1994 Upper Deck Collector's Choice	90	.20	.15	.08
1994 Upper Deck SP	199	.25	.20	.10

Fran Tarkenton

Set	Card #	NM	EX	VG
1962 Topps	90 (R)	225.00	112.50	67.50
1963 Topps	98	60.00	30.00	18.00
1964 Philadelphia	109	40.00	20.00	12.00
1965 Philadelphia	110	30.00	15.00	9.00
1966 Philadelphia	114	27.00	15.00	9.00
1967 Philadelphia	106	24.00	12.00	7.25
1968 Topps	161	25.00	12.50	7.50
1969 Topps	150	25.00	12.50	7.50
1969 Topps Four In Ones	(16)	6.00	3.00	1.75
1970 Topps	80	20.00	10.00	6.00
1971 Topps	120	20.00	10.00	6.00
1972 Topps	225	19.00	9.50	5.75
1973 Topps	60	15.00	7.50	4.50
1974 Topps	129	10.00	5.00	3.00
1975 Topps	400	8.50	4.25	2.50
1976 Topps	7	3.00	1.50	.90
1976 Topps	500	7.00	3.50	2.00
1977 Topps	400	6.00	3.00	1.75
1977 Topps	454	3.00	1.50	.90
1978 Topps	5	2.00	1.00	.60
1978 Topps	100	4.00	2.00	1.25
1979 Topps	200	4.00	2.00	1.25

Charley Taylor

Set	Card #	NM	EX	VG
1965 Philadelphia	195 (R)	60.00	30.00	18.00
1966 Philadelphia	194	18.00	9.00	5.40
1967 Philadelphia	190	7.50	3.75	2.25
1968 Topps	192	6.00	3.00	1.75
1969 Topps	67	5.50	2.75	1.75
1969 Topps Four In Ones	(53)	2.00	1.00	.60
1970 Topps	145	4.50	2.25	1.25
1971 Topps	26	4.25	2.25	1.25
1972 Topps	334	40.00	20.00	12.00
1973 Topps	236	4.00	2.00	1.25
1974 Topps	510	2.50	1.25	.70
1975 Topps	20	2.25	1.25	.70

1976 Topps	8	1.00	.50	.30
1976 Topps	450	2.00	1.00	.60

Jim Taylor

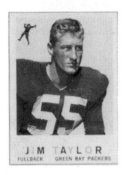

Set	Card #	NM	EX	VG
1959 Topps	155 (R)	17.00	8.50	5.00
1960 Topps	52	8.00	4.00	2.50
1961 Fleer	89	30.00	15.00	9.00
1961 Topps	41	24.00	12.00	7.25
1962 Topps	66	30.00	15.00	9.00
1963 Topps	87	16.00	8.00	4.75
1964 Philadelphia	80	15.00	7.50	4.50
1965 Philadelphia	82	14.00	7.00	4.25
1966 Philadelphia	89	13.00	6.50	4.00
1968 Topps	160	10.00	5.00	3.00

John Taylor

Set	Card #	MT	NM	EX
1989 Pro Set	384 (R)	1.00	.70	.40
1989 Score	238 (R)	3.00	2.25	1.25
1989 Score	291	.60	.45	.25
1989 Topps	13 (R)	1.00	.70	.40
1990 Fleer	14	.20	.15	.08
1990 Pro Set	297	.20	.15	.08
1990 Pro Set	421	.10	.08	.04
1990 Score	9	.20	.15	.08
1990 Score 100 Hottest	91	.20	.15	.08
1990 Topps	10	.20	.15	.08
1990 Topps 1000 Yard Club	24	.25	.20	.10
1991 Bowman	472	.10	.08	.04
1991 Fleer	365	.10	.08	.04
1991 Fleer Ultra	255	.10	.08	.04
1991 Pacific	469	.15	.11	.06
1991 Pinnacle	137	.25	.20	.10
1991 Pro Set	295	.08	.06	.03

1991 Pro Set	333	.03	.02	.01
1991 Pro Set Platinum	107	.10	.08	.04
1991 Score	282	.10	.08	.04
1991 Topps	75	.15	.11	.06
1991 Topps Stadium Club	350	.30	.25	.12
1991 Upper Deck	121	.12	.09	.05
1992 Bowman	99	.75	.60	.30
1992 Bowman	110	.35	.25	.14
1992 Fleer	385	.03	.02	.01
1992 Fleer Ultra	370	.05	.04	.02
1992 GameDay	394	.20	.15	.08
1992 Pacific	283	.05	.04	.02
1992 Pinnacle	130	.05	.04	.02
1992 Pro Set	321	.08	.06	.03
1992 Pro Set Power	82	.10	.08	.04
1992 Score	185	.08	.06	.03
1992 SkyBox Impact	114	.08	.06	.03
1992 SkyBox Primetime	340	.10	.08	.04
1992 Topps	430	.05	.04	.02
1992 Topps Stadium Club	482	.08	.06	.03
1992 Topps 1000-Yard Club	19	.75	.60	.30
1992 Upper Deck	87	.05	.04	.02
1992 Upper Deck	143	.05	.04	.02
1993 Bowman	397	.20	.15	.08
1993 Fleer	38	.10	.08	.04
1993 Fleer Ultra	440	.08	.06	.03
1993 GameDay	389	.10	.08	.04
1993 Pinnacle	202	.10	.08	.04
1993 Pro Set	397	.10	.08	.04
1993 Pro Set Power	82	.15	.11	.06
1993 Score	407	.04	.03	.02
1993 Score Select	120	.10	.08	.04
1993 SkyBox Impact	292	.06	.05	.02
1993 SkyBox Premium	114	.15	.11	.06
1993 Topps	248	.10	.08	.04
1993 Topps Stadium Club	275	.10	.08	.04
1993 Upper Deck	258	.05	.04	.02
1993 Upper Deck San Francisco 49ers	13	.35	.25	.14
1994 Bowman	96	.15	.11	.06
1994 Fleer	424	.10	.08	.04
1994 Fleer Ultra	499	.08	.06	.03
1994 GameDay	371	.10	.08	.04
1994 Pinnacle	176	.09	.07	.04
1994 Score	68	.10	.08	.04
1994 Score Select	78	.10	.08	.04
1994 SkyBox Impact	234	.10	.08	.04
1994 SkyBox Premium	139	.08	.06	.03
1994 Topps	384	.05	.04	.02
1994 Topps Stadium Club	145	.10	.08	.04
1994 Upper Deck	295	.10	.08	.04
1994 Upper Deck Collector's Choice	96	.05	.04	.02

Lawrence Taylor

Set	Card #	MT	NM	EX
1982 Topps	434 (R)	37.00	28.00	15.00
1982 Topps	435	10.00	7.50	4.00

1983 Topps	133	8.00	6.00	3.25
1984 Topps	321	3.00	2.25	1.25
1984 Topps	322	2.00	1.50	.80
1985 Topps	124	1.25	.90	.50
1986 Topps	151	.75	.60	.30
1987 Topps	26	.50	.40	.20
1988 Topps	285	.25	.20	.10
1989 Pro Set	292	.15	.11	.06
1989 Score	192	.50	.40	.20
1989 Score	295	.30	.25	.12
1989 Score	322	.25	.20	.10
1989 Topps	166	.15	.11	.06
1990 Fleer	77	.10	.08	.04
1990 Fleer All-Pro	14	.75	.60	.30
1990 Pro Set	231	.10	.08	.04
1990 Pro Set	422	.10	.08	.04
1990 Score	50	.10	.08	.04
1990 Score	552	.08	.06	.03
1990 Score	571	.08	.06	.03
1990 Score 100 Hottest	25	.30	.25	.12
1990 Topps	52	.10	.08	.04
1991 Bowman	371	.10	.08	.04
1991 Fleer	319	.10	.08	.04
1991 Fleer	398	.08	.06	.03
1991 Fleer All-Pro	15	.40	.30	.15
1991 Fleer Pro Visions	3	.40	.30	.15
1991 Fleer Ultra	224	.10	.08	.04
1991 Pacific	356	.10	.08	.04
1991 Pinnacle	273	.50	.40	.20
1991 Pro Set	336	.08	.06	.03
1991 Pro Set	394	.05	.04	.02
1991 Pro Set	602	.08	.06	.03
1991 Pro Set	718	.03	.02	.01
1991 Pro Set Platinum	81	.10	.08	.04
1991 Pro Set Platinum	148	.10	.08	.04
1991 Score	529	.10	.08	.04
1991 Topps	16	.10	.08	.04
1991 Topps Stadium Club	281	.60	.45	.25
1991 Upper Deck	445	.10	.08	.04
1992 GameDay	56	.20	.15	.08
1992 Pro Set	597	.10	.08	.04
1992 Pro Set Power	56	.15	.11	.06
1992 SkyBox Impact	14	.10	.08	.04
1992 SkyBox Impact	319	.07	.05	.03
1992 SkyBox Impact Major Impact	20	1.00	.70	.40
1992 SkyBox Primetime	200	.20	.15	.08
1992 SkyBox Primetime	209	.10	.08	.04
1992 Topps	756	.05	.04	.02
1992 Topps Stadium Club	610	1.00	.70	.40
1992 Topps Stadium Club	680	1.25	.90	.50
1992 Upper Deck	599	.15	.11	.06
1992 Upper Deck Gold	44	.30	.25	.12
1992 Upper Deck NFL Fanimation	3	2.50	2.00	1.00
1993 Bowman	80	.40	.30	.15
1993 Fleer	477	.10	.08	.04
1993 Fleer Ultra	332	.15	.11	.06
1993 GameDay	54	.15	.11	.06
1993 Pacific	49	.10	.08	.04
1993 Pacific Prisms	72	1.00	.70	.40
1993 Pinnacle	246	.15	.11	.06
1993 Pro Set	309	.10	.08	.04
1993 Pro Set Power	156	.08	.06	.03
1993 Pro Set Power All-Power Defense	24	.50	.40	.20
1993 Score	435	.10	.08	.04
1993 Score Select	65	.50	.40	.20
1993 SkyBox Impact	230	.10	.08	.04
1993 SkyBox Impact Kelly's Heroes/ Magic's Kingdom	9	2.00	1.50	.80
1993 SkyBox Premium	151	.15	.11	.06
1993 Topps	105	.10	.08	.04
1993 Topps Stadium Club	310	.15	.11	.06
1993 Upper Deck	117	.15	.11	.06
1993 Upper Deck NFL Experience	40	.25	.20	.10
1993 Upper Deck SP	189	.50	.40	.20
1994 Topps Finest	193	2.50	2.00	1.00

Vinny Testaverde

Set	Card #	MT	NM	EX
1988 Topps	352 (R)	1.25	.90	.50
1989 Pro Set	419	.30	.25	.12
1989 Score	224	.50	.40	.20
1989 Topps	327	.15	.11	.06
1990 Fleer	356	.10	.08	.04
1990 Pro Set	318	.08	.06	.03
1990 Score	261	.10	.08	.04
1990 Score 100 Hottest	63	.20	.15	.08
1990 Topps	407	.10	.08	.04
1991 Bowman	519	.10	.08	.04
1991 Fleer	380	.10	.08	.04
1991 Fleer Ultra	266	.10	.08	.04
1991 Pacific	513	.08	.06	.03
1991 Pinnacle	93	.15	.11	.06
1991 Pro Set	41	.03	.02	.01
1991 Pro Set	314	.08	.06	.03
1991 Pro Set Platinum	116	.08	.06	.03
1991 Score	398	.04	.03	.02
1991 Topps	491	.10	.08	.04
1991 Topps Stadium Club	24	.30	.25	.12
1991 Upper Deck	261	.10	.08	.04
1992 Bowman	219	.30	.25	.12
1992 Fleer	410	.03	.02	.01
1992 Fleer Ultra	396	.05	.04	.02
1992 GameDay	337	.12	.09	.05
1992 Pacific	308	.05	.04	.02
1992 Pinnacle	165	.05	.04	.02
1992 Pro Set	339	.05	.04	.02
1992 Pro Set Gold MVPs	28	.45	.35	.20
1992 Pro Set Power	14	.05	.04	.02
1992 Score	262	.08	.06	.03
1992 SkyBox Impact	188	.05	.04	.02
1992 SkyBox Primetime	6	.10	.08	.04
1992 Topps	565	.05	.04	.02
1992 Topps Stadium Club	355	.08	.06	.03
1992 Upper Deck	147	.05	.04	.02
1993 Fleer	484	.05	.04	.02
1993 Fleer Ultra	83	.08	.06	.03
1993 GameDay	193	.10	.08	.04
1993 Pinnacle	325	.10	.08	.04
1993 Pro Set	114	.05	.04	.02
1993 Pro Set Power Power Moves	3	.30	.25	.12
1993 Pro Set Power Update Moves	3	.15	.11	.06
1993 Score	262	.07	.05	.03
1993 SkyBox Impact	64	.05	.04	.02
1993 SkyBox Premium	246	.10	.08	.04
1993 Topps	562	.08	.06	.03
1993 Topps Stadium Club	546	.10	.08	.04
1993 Upper Deck	212	.05	.04	.02
1994 Bowman	93	.10	.08	.04
1994 Fleer	104	.10	.08	.04
1994 Fleer Ultra	64	.08	.06	.03
1994 GameDay	88	.10	.00	.04
1994 Pacific Crown	268	.06	.05	.02
1994 Pacific Prisms	113	1.00	.70	.40
1994 Pinnacle	34	.09	.07	.04

Set	Card #	MT	NM	EX
1994 Pinnacle Sportflics	81	.15	.11	.06
1994 Score	194	.08	.06	.03
1994 SkyBox Impact	53	.10	.08	.04
1994 SkyBox Premium	35	.10	.08	.04
1994 Topps	71	.05	.04	.02
1994 Topps Finest	136	1.50	1.25	.60
1994 Topps Stadium Club	75	.10	.08	.04
1994 Upper Deck	306	.10	.08	.04
1994 Upper Deck Collector's Choice	146	.05	.04	.02
1994 Upper Deck SP	62	.20	.15	.08

Derrick Thomas

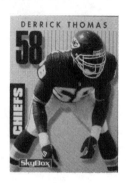

Set	Card #	MT	NM	EX
1989 Pro Set	498 (R)	2.00	1.50	.80
1989 Score	258 (R)	7.50	5.75	3.00
1989 Topps Traded	90 (R)	.75	.60	.30
1990 Fleer	209	.20	.15	.08
1990 Fleer All-Pro	13	1.00	.75	.40
1990 Pro Set	6	.10	.08	.04
1990 Pro Set	373	.06	.05	.02
1990 Pro Set	536	.25	.20	.10
1990 Score	500	.25	.20	.10
1990 Score	553	.20	.15	.08
1990 Score Young Superstars	13	.35	.25	.14
1990 Topps	248	.30	.25	.12
1991 Bowman	221	.25	.20	.10
1991 Bowman	275	.10	.08	.04
1991 Fleer	100	.25	.20	.10
1991 Fleer	400	.08	.06	.03
1991 Fleer All-Pro	13	.40	.30	.15
1991 Fleer Pro Visions	9	.50	.40	.20
1991 Fleer Ultra	72	.25	.20	.10
1991 Fleer Ultra Performances	3	1.00	.70	.40
1991 Pacific	222	.25	.20	.10
1991 Pinnacle	100	.40	.30	.15
1991 Pro Set	19	12.00	9.00	4.75
1991 Pro Set	188	.15	.11	.06
1991 Pro Set	420	.08	.06	.03
1991 Pro Set Platinum	51	.25	.20	.10
1991 Pro Set Platinum	147	.25	.20	.10
1991 Score	5	.25	.20	.10
1991 Score	342	.08	.06	.03
1991 Score	661	.10	.08	.04
1991 Score	666	.10	.08	.04
1991 Topps	3	.12	.09	.05
1991 Topps	12	.10	.08	.04
1991 Topps	143	.30	.25	.12
1991 Topps Stadium Club	355	1.50	1.25	.60
1991 Upper Deck	165	.25	.20	.10
1991 Upper Deck	404	.12	.09	.05
1992 Bowman	418	1.00	.70	.40
1992 Bowman	434A	3.00	2.25	1.25
1992 Fleer	184	.15	.11	.06
1992 Fleer All-Pro	19	.75	.60	.30
1992 Fleer Team Leaders	18	12.00	9.00	4.75
1992 Fleer Ultra	182	.35	.25	.14

Set	Card #	MT	NM	EX
1992 GameDay	134	.35	.25	.14
1992 Pacific	453	.20	.15	.08
1992 Pinnacle	30	.35	.25	.14
1992 Pinnacle Team Pinnacle	2	20.00	15.00	8.00
1992 Pinnacle Team 2000	15	.50	.40	.20
1992 Pro Set	204	.15	.11	.06
1992 Pro Set	395	.10	.08	.04
1992 Pro Set Gold MVPs	7	.50	.40	.20
1992 Pro Set Power	58	.35	.25	.14
1992 Score	20	.10	.08	.04
1992 Score	533	.10	.08	.04
1992 Score Dream Team	13	3.50	2.75	1.50
1992 SkyBox Impact	210	.15	.11	.06
1992 SkyBox Impact	320	.07	.05	.03
1992 SkyBox Impact Major Impact	9	1.00	.70	.40
1992 SkyBox Primetime	58	.35	.25	.14
1992 SkyBox Primetime	284	.25	.20	.10
1992 SkyBox Primetime	307	.20	.15	.08
1992 SkyBox Primetime Poster Cards	10	2.25	1.75	.90
1992 Topps	459	.15	.11	.06
1992 Topps Stadium Club	33	.35	.25	.14
1992 Topps Stadium Club	306	.15	.11	.06
1992 Upper Deck	144	.05	.04	.02
1992 Upper Deck	359	.15	.11	.06
1992 Upper Deck Pro Bowl	9	1.50	1.25	.60
1993 Bowman	410	.50	.40	.20
1993 Fleer	56	.10	.08	.04
1993 Fleer All-Pro	20	2.00	1.50	.80
1993 Fleer Team Leaders	2	3.00	2.25	1.25
1993 Fleer Ultra	209	.25	.20	.10
1993 Fleer Ultra Ultra Stars	7	4.00	3.00	1.50
1993 GameDay	9	.25	.20	.10
1993 Pacific	346	.12	.09	.05
1993 Pacific Prisms	43	1.50	1.25	.60
1993 Pinnacle	45	.35	.25	.14
1993 Pinnacle Men of Autumn	12	.40	.30	.15
1993 Pinnacle Team Pinnacle	10	15.00	11.00	6.00
1993 Pro Set	201	.10	.08	.04
1993 Pro Set College Connections	6	1.50	1.25	.60
1993 Pro Set Power	58	.10	.08	.04
1993 Pro Set Power All-Power Defense	12	.50	.40	.20
1993 Score	149	.10	.08	.04
1993 Score Dream Team	24	1.00	.70	.40
1993 Score Select	40	.50	.40	.20
1993 Score The Franchise	12	6.00	4.50	2.50
1993 SkyBox Impact	142	.15	.11	.06
1993 SkyBox Impact Kelly's Heroes/Magic's Kingdom	8	2.00	1.50	.80
1993 SkyBox Poster Art Cards	9	.75	.60	.30
1993 SkyBox Premium	209	.25	.20	.10
1993 Topps	168	.15	.11	.06
1993 Topps	267	.05	.04	.02
1993 Topps Stadium Club	173	.40	.30	.15
1993 Topps Stadium Club	492	.15	.11	.06
1993 Upper Deck	354	.20	.15	.08
1993 Upper Deck Kansas City Chiefs	10	1.00	.70	.40
1993 Upper Deck SP	125	.25	.20	.10
1993 Upper Deck SP All Pro	15	7.00	5.25	2.75
1993 Upper Deck Team MVP	9	.75	.60	.30
1994 Bowman	305	.10	.08	.04
1994 Fleer	230	.20	.15	.08
1994 Fleer All-Pro	19	.75	.60	.30
1994 Fleer Ultra	148	.25	.20	.10
1994 GameDay	197	.15	.11	.06
1994 Pacific Crown	58	.15	.11	.06
1994 Pacific Prisms	114	1.50	1.25	.60
1994 Pinnacle	32	.20	.15	.08

Set	Card #	MT	NM	EX
1994 Pinnacle Sportflics	80	.35	.25	.14
1994 Score	257	.15	.11	.06
1994 Score Dream Team	15	5.00	3.75	2.00
1994 Score Select	42	.10	.08	.04
1994 SkyBox Impact	125	.15	.11	.06
1994 SkyBox Premium	77	.15	.11	.06
1994 Topps	130	.10	.08	.04
1994 Topps	551	.08	.06	.03
1994 Topps All-Pros	20	4.00	3.00	1.50
1994 Topps Finest	30	2.00	1.50	.80
1994 Topps Stadium Club	224	.10	.08	.04
1994 Topps Stadium Club	324	.15	.11	.06
1994 Topps Stadium Club	441	.15	.11	.06
1994 Upper Deck	313	.20	.15	.08
1994 Upper Deck Collector's Choice	214	.10	.08	.04
1994 Upper Deck Pro Bowl	19	5.00	3.75	2.00
1994 Upper Deck SP	91	.25	.20	.10

Thurman Thomas

Set	Card #	MT	NM	EX
1989 Pro Set	32 (R)	2.75	2.00	1.00
1989 Score	211 (R)	18.00	13.50	7.25
1989 Topps	45 (R)	3.00	2.25	1.25
1990 Fleer	124	.50	.40	.20
1990 Pro Set	10	.25	.20	.10
1990 Pro Set	374	.25	.20	.10
1990 Pro Set	444	.40	.30	.15
1990 Score	110	.40	.30	.15
1990 Score	322	.20	.15	.08
1990 Score Young Superstars	36	.90	.70	.35
1990 Score 100 Hottest	13	.50	.40	.20
1990 Topps	206	.50	.40	.20
1990 Topps 1000 Yard Club	11	.25	.20	.10
1991 Bowman	45	.50	.40	.20
1991 Bowman	281	.25	.20	.10
1991 Fleer	14	.40	.30	.15
1991 Fleer	417	.20	.15	.08
1991 Fleer All-Pro	26	1.00	.75	.40
1991 Fleer Ultra	10	.50	.40	.20
1991 Fleer Ultra Performances	7	2.00	1.50	.80
1991 Pacific	33	.50	.40	.20
1991 Pinnacle	107	1.50	1.25	.60
1991 Pinnacle	363	.40	.30	.15
1991 Pinnacle	384	.50	.40	.20
1991 Pro Set	13	.20	.15	.08
1991 Pro Set	52	.20	.15	.08
1991 Pro Set	86	.35	.25	.14
1991 Pro Set	415	.15	.11	.06
1991 Pro Set Platinum	5	.40	.30	.15
1991 Pro Set Platinum PC	10	1.50	1.25	.60
1991 Score	234	.40	.30	.15
1991 Score	623	.20	.15	.08
1991 Score	664	.20	.15	.08
1991 Score	678	.20	.15	.08
1991 Topps	9	.30	.25	.12
1991 Topps	52	.50	.40	.20
1991 Topps Stadium Club	395	3.00	2.25	1.25
1991 Topps 1000 Yard Club	3	.75	.60	.30
1991 Upper Deck	356	.50	.40	.20
1991 Upper Deck	452	.25	.20	.10
1991 Upper Deck Game Breaker Holograms	2	1.25	.90	.50
1992 Bowman	112	6.00	4.50	2.50
1992 Bowman	410	5.00	3.75	2.00
1992 Fleer	33	.50	.40	.20
1992 Fleer	452	.25	.20	.10
1992 Fleer	476	.20	.15	.08
1992 Fleer All-Pro	8	1.75	1.25	.60
1992 Fleer Ultra	31	.75	.60	.30
1992 Fleer Ultra Award Winners	5	4.00	3.00	1.50
1992 GameDay	416	1.25	.90	.50
1992 Pacific	22	.40	.30	.15
1992 Pacific Prism Inserts	1	2.00	1.50	.80
1992 Pinnacle	22	.75	.60	.30
1992 Pinnacle Team Pinnacle	3	10.00	7.50	4.00
1992 Pro Set	2	.20	.15	.08
1992 Pro Set	11	.20	.15	.08
1992 Pro Set	43	.20	.15	.08
1992 Pro Set	59	.20	.15	.08
1992 Pro Set	69	.20	.15	.08
1992 Pro Set	105	.40	.30	.15
1992 Pro Set	396	.20	.15	.08
1992 Pro Set Gold MVPs	1	1.75	1.25	.70
1992 Pro Set Ground Force	105	10.00	7.50	4.00
1992 Pro Set Power	34	.80	.60	.30
1992 Score	10	.40	.30	.15
1992 SkyBox Impact	225	.40	.30	.15
1992 SkyBox Impact	307	.20	.15	.08
1992 SkyBox Impact Major Impact	10	3.00	2.25	1.25
1992 SkyBox Primetime	34	1.00	.70	.40
1992 SkyBox Primetime	86	.40	.30	.15
1992 SkyBox Primetime	288	.50	.40	.20
1992 SkyBox Primetime Poster Cards	4	5.50	4.25	2.25
1992 Topps	320	.40	.30	.15
1992 Topps Stadium Club	134	.75	.60	.30
1992 Topps 1000-Yard Club	4	2.00	1.50	.80
1992 Upper Deck	145	.50	.40	.20
1992 Upper Deck	309	.25	.20	.10
1992 Upper Deck	353	.25	.20	.10
1992 Upper Deck	512	.25	.20	.10
1992 Upper Deck Pro Bowl	5	8.00	6.00	3.25
1993 Bowman	60	1.50	1.25	.60
1993 Fleer	229	.50	.40	.20
1993 Fleer	245	.25	.20	.10
1993 Fleer Ultra	36	.75	.60	.30
1993 Fleer Ultra League Leaders	10	10.00	7.50	4.00
1993 Fleer Ultra Touchdown Kings	10	2.00	1.50	.80
1993 GameDay	235	1.00	.70	.40
1993 GameDay Game Breakers	12	1.50	1.25	.60
1993 Pacific	207	.45	.35	.20
1993 Pacific Gold Prisms	19	15.00	11.00	6.00
1993 Pacific Prism Inserts	19	10.00	7.50	4.00
1993 Pacific Prisms	8	5.00	3.75	2.00
1993 Pacific Triple Folders	1	1.25	.90	.50
1993 Pacific Triple Folder Superstars	20	1.00	.70	.40
1993 Pinnacle	138	.75	.60	.30
1993 Pinnacle Men of Autumn	2	1.00	.75	.40
1993 Pinnacle Team Pinnacle	2	75.00	60.00	30.00
1993 Pro Set	11	.15	.11	.06
1993 Pro Set	54	.40	.30	.15

1993 Pro Set College Connections	1	4.00	3.00	1.50
1993 Pro Set Power	34	.40	.30	.15
1993 Score	96	.35	.25	.14
1993 Score Select	84	2.00	1.50	.80
1993 Score The Franchise	2	14.00	10.50	5.50
1993 SkyBox Impact	25	.40	.30	.15
1993 SkyBox Impact Kelly's Heroes/ Magic's Kingdom	4	6.00	4.50	2.50
1993 SkyBox Premium	14	.75	.60	.30
1993 SkyBox Thunder and Lightning	1	6.00	4.50	2.50
1993 Topps	308	.50	.40	.20
1993 Topps Black Gold	40	3.00	2.25	1.25
1993 Topps Stadium Club	248	.60	.45	.25
1993 Topps Stadium Club	497	.50	.40	.20
1993 Upper Deck	249	.40	.30	.15
1993 Upper Deck	428	.20	.15	.08
1993 Upper Deck	438	.25	.20	.10
1993 Upper Deck SP	36	3.50	2.75	1.50
1993 Upper Deck SP All Pro	8	20.00	15.00	8.00
1993 Upper Deck Team MVP	3	2.00	1.50	.80
1994 Bowman	172	.40	.30	.15
1994 Fleer	52	.30	.25	.12
1994 Fleer All-Pro	20	1.25	.90	.50
1994 Fleer League Leaders	9	1.00	.70	.40
1994 Fleer Scoring Machines	19	10.00	7.50	4.00
1994 Fleer Ultra	32	.60	.45	.25
1994 Fleer Ultra Achievement Awards	9	.75	.60	.30
1994 Fleer Ultra Hot Numbers	14	2.00	1.50	.80
1994 GameDay	45	.45	.35	.20
1994 GameDay Game Breakers	14	1.00	.70	.40
1994 Pacific Crown	30	.30	.25	.12
1994 Pacific Crown Crystalline Collection	3	10.00	7.50	4.00
1994 Pacific Crown Gems of the Crown	32	8.00	6.00	3.25
1994 Pacific Marquee	33	2.25	1.75	.90
1994 Pacific Prisms	115	2.75	2.00	1.00
1994 Pinnacle	69	.45	.35	.20
1994 Pinnacle Sportflics	5	.85	.60	.35
1994 Pinnacle Team Pinnacle	3	85.00	64.00	34.00
1994 Score	204	.25	.20	.10
1994 Score Dream Team	16	15.00	11.00	6.00
1994 Score Select	66	.50	.40	.20
1994 Score Select Canton Bound	12	12.00	9.00	4.75
1994 SkyBox Impact	30	.35	.25	.14
1994 SkyBox Impact Ultimate Impact	13	2.00	1.50	.80
1994 SkyBox Premium	20	.40	.30	.15
1994 SkyBox Premium Revolution	2	7.00	5.25	2.75
1994 SkyBox Premium SkyTech Stars	22	6.00	4.50	2.50
1994 Topps	201	.40	.30	.15
1994 Topps	315	.15	.11	.06
1994 Topps	317	.10	.08	.04
1994 Topps Finest	151	6.00	4.50	2.50
1994 Topps Finest Inserts	10	12.00	9.00	4.75
1994 Topps Stadium Club	73	.25	.20	.10
1994 Topps Stadium Club	111	.25	.20	.10
1994 Topps Stadium Club	483	.60	.45	.25
1994 Topps Stadium Club Ring Leaders	5	15.00	11.00	6.00
1994 Upper Deck	270	.45	.35	.20
1994 Upper Deck Collector's Choice Crash Game	12	9.00	6.75	3.50
1994 Upper Deck Collector's Choice	227	.35	.25	.14

1994 Upper Deck Hobby Predictor	9	4.00	3.00	1.50
1994 Upper Deck Pro Bowl	14	10.00	7.50	4.00
1994 Upper Deck Retail Predictor	15	7.00	5.25	2.75
1994 Upper Deck SP	22	.25	.20	.10
1994 Upper Deck SP All-Pro	4	10.00	7.50	4.00

Jim Thorpe

JIM THORPE Halfback

Set	Card #	NM	EX	VG
1955 Topps All-Americans	37	300.00	150.00	90.00

Al Toon

AL TOON
WIDE RECEIVER • JETS

Set	Card #	MT	NM	EX
1986 Topps	101 (R)	3.00	2.25	1.25
1987 Topps	131	.50	.40	.20
1987 Topps 1000 Yard Club	12	.25	.20	.10
1988 Topps	216	.05	.04	.02
1988 Topps	305	.20	.15	.08
1988 Topps 1000 Yard Club	9	.10	.08	.04
1989 Pro Set	308	.03	.02	.01
1989 Score	10	.10	.08	.04
1989 Topps	218	.05	.04	.02
1989 Topps	225	.05	.04	.02
1989 Topps 1000 Yard Club	18	.10	.08	.04
1990 Fleer	369	.03	.02	.01
1990 Pro Set	240	.03	.02	.01
1990 Score	346	.04	.03	.02

1990 Topps	463	.04	.03	.02
1991 Bowman	379	.03	.02	.01
1991 Fleer	154	.10	.08	.04
1991 Fleer Ultra	108	.04	.03	.02
1991 Pacific	376	.04	.03	.02
1991 Pinnacle	346	.10	.08	.04
1991 Pinnacle	380	.10	.08	.04
1991 Pinnacle	401	.10	.08	.04
1991 Pro Set	251	.03	.02	.01
1991 Pro Set Platinum	84	.05	.04	.02
1991 Score	350	.04	.03	.02
1991 Topps	476	.04	.03	.02
1991 Topps Stadium Club	193	.30	.25	.12
1991 Upper Deck	233	.05	.04	.02
1992 GameDay	260	.12	.09	.05
1992 Pro Set	606	.05	.04	.02
1992 Pro Set Power	188	.05	.04	.02
1992 SkyBox Impact	153	.05	.04	.02
1992 SkyBox Primetime	83	.10	.08	.04
1992 Topps	730	.05	.04	.02
1992 Topps Stadium Club	634	.60	.45	.25
1992 Upper Deck Gold	38	.10	.08	.04

Cards before 1981 are priced in Near Mint (NM),
Excellent (EX), and Very Good (VG).
Cards 1981 to present are Mint (MT), Near Mint (NM),
and Excellent (EX).

Johnny Unitas

JOHNNY UNITAS
QUARTERBACK BALTIMORE COLTS

Set	Card #	NM	EX	VG
1957 Topps	138 (R)	450.00	225.00	135.00
1958 Topps	22	115.00	57.00	34.00
1959 Topps	1	100.00	50.00	30.00
1960 Topps	1	80.00	40.00	24.00
1961 Fleer	30	70.00	35.00	21.00
1961 Topps	1	95.00	47.50	28.50
1962 Topps	1	110.00	55.00	33.00
1963 Topps	1	95.00	47.00	28.00
1964 Philadelphia	12	40.00	20.00	12.00
1965 Philadelphia	12	40.00	20.00	12.00
1966 Philadelphia	24	30.00	15.00	9.00
1967 Philadelphia	23	30.00	15.00	9.00
1968 Topps	100	25.00	12.50	7.50
1969 Topps	25	25.00	12.50	7.50
1969 Topps Four In Ones	(60)	9.00	4.50	2.75
1970 Topps	180	22.00	11.00	6.50
1971 Topps	1	30.00	15.00	9.00
1972 Topps	165	20.00	10.00	6.00
1972 Topps	251	8.00	4.00	2.50
1973 Topps	455	18.00	9.00	5.50
1974 Topps	150	16.00	8.00	4.75

Set	Card #	MT	NM	EX
1992 Topps Stadium Club QB Legends	3	3.75	2.75	1.50

Gene Upshaw

Set	Card #	NM	EX	VG
1972 Topps	186 (R)	14.00	7.00	4.25
1973 Topps	50	3.50	1.75	1.00
1974 Topps	65	2.00	1.00	.60
1975 Topps	190	1.50	.70	.45
1976 Topps	295	1.00	.50	.30
1977 Topps	415	1.00	.50	.30
1978 Topps	90	.15	.08	.05
1979 Topps	260	.50	.25	.15
1980 Topps	449	.30	.15	.09

Set	Card #	MT	NM	EX
1981 Topps	219	.20	.15	.08

Herschel Walker

Set	Card #	MT	NM	EX
1984 Topps USFL	74 (R)	30.00	22.00	12.00
1985 Topps USFL	86	15.00	11.00	6.00
1985 Topps USFL New Jersey Generals	8	15.00	11.00	6.00
1987 Topps	264 (R)	2.50	2.00	1.00
1988 Topps	259	.15	.11	.06
1988 Topps	261	.25	.20	.10
1988 Topps 1000 Yard Club	15	.75	.60	.30
1989 Pro Set	96	.20	.15	.08
1989 Pro Set	561	.03	.02	.01
1989 Score	34	.45	.35	.20
1989 Score	317	.25	.20	.10
1989 Score	331	.25	.20	.10
1989 Topps	385	.15	.11	.06
1989 Topps Traded	120	.12	.09	.05
1989 Topps 1000 Yard Club	2	.60	.45	.25
1990 Fleer	107	.03	.02	.01
1990 Pro Set	197	.03	.02	.01

1990 Score	34	.04	.03	.02
1990 Score	561	.04	.03	.02
1990 Score 100 Hottest	76	.20	.15	.08
1990 Topps	105	.04	.03	.02
1991 Bowman	314	.08	.06	.03
1991 Fleer	288	.15	.11	.06
1991 Fleer Ultra	202	.08	.06	.03
1991 Pacific	299	.04	.03	.02
1991 Pinnacle	97	.10	.08	.04
1991 Pinnacle	370	.10	.08	.04
1991 Pro Set	44	.03	.02	.01
1991 Pro Set	576	.05	.04	.02
1991 Pro Set Platinum	135	.05	.04	.02
1991 Score	348	.06	.05	.02
1991 Topps	395	.04	.03	.02
1991 Topps Stadium Club	401	.30	.25	.12
1991 Upper Deck	346	.05	.04	.02
1992 Bowman	172	.30	.25	.12
1992 Fleer	253	.03	.02	.01
1992 Pacific	187	.05	.04	.02
1992 Pacific Prism Inserts	10	1.50	1.25	.60
1992 Pinnacle	293	.05	.04	.02
1992 Pinnacle	332	.05	.04	.02
1992 Pro Set	45	.05	.04	.02
1992 Pro Set	241	.05	.04	.02
1992 Pro Set	615	.05	.04	.02
1992 Pro Set Power	134	.05	.04	.02
1992 Score	276	.07	.05	.03
1992 Topps	188	.05	.04	.02
1992 Topps Stadium Club	72	.08	.06	.03
1992 Upper Deck	194	.10	.08	.04
1992 Upper Deck	481	.05	.04	.02
1993 Bowman	308	.20	.15	.08
1993 Fleer Ultra	368	.08	.06	.03
1993 GameDay	142	.10	.08	.04
1993 Pacific	27	.05	.04	.02
1993 Pacific Prisms	79	1.25	.90	.50
1993 Pacific Triple Folders	26	.75	.60	.30
1993 Pro Set	340	.05	.04	.02
1993 Score	248	.06	.05	.02
1993 Topps	460	.07	.05	.03
1993 Topps Black Gold	44	.50	.40	.20
1993 Topps Stadium Club	355	.10	.08	.04
1994 Bowman	167	.10	.08	.04
1994 Fleer	379	.10	.08	.04
1994 Fleer Ultra	249	.08	.06	.03
1994 GameDay	327	.10	.08	.04
1994 Pacific Crown	254	.06	.05	.02
1994 Pacific Crown Crystalline Collection	18	3.50	2.75	1.50
1994 Pacific Crown Gems of the Crown	33	2.50	2.00	1.00
1994 Pacific Prisms	119	1.00	.70	.40
1994 Pinnacle	107	.09	.07	.04
1994 Pinnacle Sportflics	34	.15	.11	.06
1994 Score	187	.05	.04	.02
1994 Score Select	84	.10	.08	.04
1994 SkyBox Impact	208	.06	.05	.02
1994 SkyBox Premium	122	.08	.06	.03
1994 Topps	40	.07	.05	.03
1994 Topps Stadium Club	33	.10	.08	.04
1994 Topps Stadium Club Ring Leaders	12	10.00	7.50	4.00
1994 Upper Deck	262	.10	.08	.04
1994 Upper Deck Collector's Choice	149	.05	.04	.02
1994 Upper Deck SP	134	.20	.15	.08

Values for recent cards and sets are listed in Mint (MT), Near Mint (NM), reflecting the fact that many cards from recent years have been preserved in to condition. Recent cards and sets in less than Excellent condition have little collector interest.

Paul Warfield

Set	Card #	NM	EX	VG
1965 Philadelphia	41 (R)	75.00	37.00	22.00
1967 Philadelphia	46	20.00	10.00	6.00
1968 Topps	49	10.00	5.00	3.00
1970 Topps	135	6.00	3.00	1.75
1971 Topps	261	7.00	3.50	2.00
1972 Topps	167	6.00	3.00	1.75
1972 Topps	271	50.00	25.00	15.00
1973 Topps	511	5.00	2.50	1.50
1974 Topps	128	4.00	2.00	1.25
1976 Topps	317	3.00	1.50	.90
1977 Topps	185	2.00	1.00	.60

Chris Warren

Set	Card #	MT	NM	EX
1991 Bowman	508 (R)	.45	.35	.20
1991 Fleer	194 (R)	.35	.25	.14
1991 Pacific	489 (R)	.45	.35	.20
1991 Pinnacle	233 (R)	1.25	.90	.50
1991 Score	439 (R)	.45	.35	.20
1991 Topps	285 (R)	.30	.25	.12
1991 Upper Deck	513 (R)	.35	.25	.14
1992 Bowman	516	2.50	2.00	1.00
1992 Pacific	623	.25	.20	.10
1992 Pro Set	659	.30	.25	.12
1992 Pro Set Power	142	.50	.40	.20
1992 Score	198	.30	.25	.12
1992 Topps	587	.25	.20	.10
1992 Topps Stadium Club	425	.40	.30	.15
1992 Upper Deck	114	.30	.25	.12
1993 Bowman	307	1.00	.70	.40
1993 Fleer	195	.15	.11	.06
1993 Fleer Ultra	460	.35	.25	.14
1993 GameDay	228	.25	.20	.10
1993 Pacific	389	.25	.20	.10
1993 Pacific Prisms	97	1.50	1.25	.60
1993 Pinnacle	29	.20	.15	.08

Set	Card #	MT	NM	EX
1993 Pinnacle Men of Autumn	53	.30	.25	.12
1993 Pro Set	413	.10	.08	.04
1993 Pro Set Power	42	.15	.11	.06
1993 Score	81	.15	.11	.06
1993 Score Select	26	.85	.60	.35
1993 SkyBox Impact	309	.10	.08	.04
1993 SkyBox Premium	235	.20	.15	.08
1993 Topps	274	.05	.04	.02
1993 Topps	375	.15	.11	.06
1993 Topps Black Gold	21	1.25	.90	.50
1993 Topps Stadium Club	16	.40	.30	.15
1993 Upper Deck	389	.15	.11	.06
1993 Upper Deck SP	251	1.00	.70	.40
1994 Bowman	38	.25	.20	.10
1994 Fleer	444	.20	.15	.08
1994 Fleer Ultra	296	.15	.11	.06
1994 GameDay	387	.10	.08	.04
1994 Pacific Crown	327	.06	.05	.02
1994 Pacific Crown Crystalline Collection	8	2.00	1.50	.80
1994 Pacific Crown Gems of the Crown	34	3.50	2.75	1.50
1994 Pacific Marquee	34	1.25	.90	.50
1994 Pacific Prisms	120	1.00	.70	.40
1994 Pinnacle	122	.15	.11	.06
1994 Pinnacle Sportflics	9	.25	.20	.10
1994 Score	216	.05	.04	.02
1994 Score Select	80	.10	.08	.04
1994 SkyBox Impact	244	.12	.09	.05
1994 SkyBox Premium	147	.15	.11	.06
1994 Topps	303	.05	.04	.02
1994 Topps Finest	59	1.50	1.25	.60
1994 Topps Finest Inserts	2	3.50	2.75	1.50
1994 Topps Stadium Club	129	.15	.11	.06
1994 Upper Deck	146	.15	.11	.06
1994 Upper Deck Collector's Choice	39	.05	.04	.02
1994 Upper Deck Collector's Choice	204	.05	.04	.02
1994 Upper Deck SP	108	.40	.30	.15

Ricky Watters

Set	Card #	MT	NM	EX
1991 Bowman	489 (R)	1.25	.90	.50
1991 Fleer Ultra	297 (R)	1.50	1.25	.60
1991 Pro Set	774 (R)	1.25	.90	.50
1991 Score	575 (R)	1.25	.90	.50
1991 Topps Stadium Club	60 (R)	9.50	7.25	3.75
1991 Upper Deck	9 (R)	1.25	.90	.50
1992 Pro Set	652	.45	.35	.20
1992 Pro Set Power	132	.75	.60	.30
1992 Upper Deck	547	.75	.60	.30
1992 Upper Deck Coach's Report	12	3.50	2.75	1.50
1992 Upper Deck Coach's Report	20	1.50	1.25	.60
1993 Bowman	191	1.00	.70	.40

Set	Card #	MT	NM	EX
1993 Fleer	207	.40	.30	.15
1993 Fleer Ultra	443	.75	.60	.30
1993 Fleer Ultra Ultra Stars	8	6.00	4.50	2.50
1993 GameDay	181	1.00	.70	.40
1993 GameDay Game Breakers	8	2.00	1.50	.80
1993 Pacific	148	.35	.25	.14
1993 Pacific Prisms	92	5.00	3.75	2.00
1993 Pinnacle	11	1.00	.70	.40
1993 Pinnacle Men of Autumn	52	1.00	.75	.40
1993 Pinnacle Team 2001	24	2.00	1.50	.80
1993 Pro Set	398	.35	.25	.14
1993 Pro Set Power	32	.40	.30	.15
1993 Score	3	.40	.30	.15
1993 Score Select	127	1.25	.90	.50
1993 SkyBox Impact	299	.40	.30	.15
1993 SkyBox Premium	168	1.00	.70	.40
1993 Topps	281	.40	.30	.15
1993 Topps Black Gold	17	3.00	2.25	1.25
1993 Topps Stadium Club	103	.75	.60	.30
1993 Topps Stadium Club	244	.50	.40	.20
1993 Upper Deck	77	.25	.20	.10
1993 Upper Deck	342	.30	.25	.12
1993 Upper Deck	434	.25	.20	.10
1993 Upper Deck Future Heroes	42	1.50	1.25	.60
1993 Upper Deck Pro Bowl	18	6.50	5.00	2.50
1993 Upper Deck San Francisco 49ers	19	.75	.60	.30
1993 Upper Deck SP	242	1.25	.90	.50
1994 Bowman	32	.10	.08	.04
1994 Fleer	427	.40	.30	.15
1994 Fleer Pro-Visions	2	.40	.30	.15
1994 Fleer Scoring Machines	20	6.50	5.00	2.50
1994 Fleer Ultra	283	.15	.11	.06
1994 Fleer Ultra Scoring Power	6	2.00	1.50	.80
1994 Fleer Ultra Touchdown Kings	8	9.00	6.75	3.50
1994 GameDay	372	.10	.08	.04
1994 Pacific Crown	44	.20	.15	.08
1994 Pacific Crown Crystalline Collection	12	6.00	4.50	2.50
1994 Pacific Crown Gems of the Crown	35	5.00	3.75	2.00
1994 Pacific Marquee	35	1.25	.90	.50
1994 Pacific Prisms	121	2.00	1.50	.80
1994 Pinnacle	105	.15	.11	.06
1994 Pinnacle Performers	15	2.50	2.00	1.00
1994 Pinnacle Sportflics	24	.40	.30	.15
1994 Score	121	.20	.15	.08
1994 Score Select	126	.15	.11	.06
1994 SkyBox Impact	235	.30	.25	.12
1994 SkyBox Impact Ultimate Impact	8	2.00	1.50	.80
1994 SkyBox Premium	140	.20	.15	.08
1994 SkyBox Premium SkyTech Stars	17	2.00	1.50	.80
1994 Topps	500	.05	.04	.02
1994 Topps Finest	179	6.00	4.50	2.50
1994 Topps Stadium Club	201	.25	.20	.10
1994 Upper Deck	265	.15	.11	.06
1994 Upper Deck Collector's Choice Crash Game	19	8.00	6.00	3.25
1994 Upper Deck Collector's Choice	46	.10	.08	.04
1994 Upper Deck Collector's Choice	234	.10	.08	.04
1994 Upper Deck Pro Bowl	15	10.00	7.50	4.00
1994 Upper Deck Retail Predictor	19	5.00	3.75	2.00
1994 Upper Deck SP	198	.25	.20	.10

Reggie White

Set	Card #	MT	NM	EX
1984 Topps USFL	58 (R)	75.00	56.00	30.00
1985 Topps USFL	75	25.00	18.50	10.00
1986 Topps	275 (R)	9.00	6.75	3.50
1987 Topps	301	2.25	1.75	.90
1988 Topps	241	.60	.45	.25
1989 Pro Set	325	.25	.20	.10
1989 Score	92	1.00	.70	.40
1989 Score	296	.50	.40	.20
1989 Score	321	.50	.40	.20
1989 Topps	108	.25	.20	.10
1990 Fleer	93	.15	.11	.06
1990 Fleer All-Pro	16	.60	.45	.25
1990 Pro Set	252	.15	.11	.06
1990 Pro Set	423	.08	.06	.03
1990 Score	203	.15	.11	.06
1990 Score	574	.04	.03	.02
1990 Score 100 Hottest	56	.25	.20	.10
1990 Topps	86	.15	.11	.06
1991 Bowman	403	.15	.11	.06
1991 Fleer	336	.15	.11	.06
1991 Fleer	397	.08	.06	.03
1991 Fleer Ultra	236	.15	.11	.06
1991 Fleer Ultra Performances	10	.60	.45	.25
1991 Pacific	395	.20	.15	.08
1991 Pinnacle	190	.40	.30	.15
1991 Pinnacle	408	.20	.15	.08
1991 Pro Set	390	.05	.04	.02
1991 Pro Set	620	.10	.08	.04
1991 Pro Set Platinum	91	.15	.11	.06
1991 Score	344	.08	.06	.03
1991 Score	560	.15	.11	.06
1991 Score	655	.08	.06	.03
1991 Topps	212	.15	.11	.06
1991 Topps Stadium Club	74	1.00	.70	.40
1991 Upper Deck	148	.15	.11	.06
1992 Bowman	1	1.00	.70	.40
1992 Bowman	469	2.50	2.00	1.00
1992 Fleer	327	.15	.11	.06
1992 Fleer All-Pro	13	.50	.40	.20
1992 Fleer Team Leaders	10	12.00	9.00	4.75
1992 Fleer Ultra	315	.35	.25	.14
1992 Pacific	239	.15	.11	.06
1992 Pinnacle	1	.25	.20	.10
1992 Pinnacle	351	.25	.20	.10
1992 Pinnacle Team Pinnacle	11	13.00	9.75	5.25
1992 Pro Set	18	.08	.06	.03
1992 Pro Set	287	.15	.11	.06
1992 Pro Set	427	.05	.04	.02
1992 Pro Set Power	92	.30	.25	.12
1992 Score	25	.10	.08	.04
1992 Score	530	.08	.06	.03
1992 Score Dream Team	11	4.00	3.00	1.50
1992 Topps	162	.15	.11	.06
1992 Topps Stadium Club	287	.25	.20	.10
1992 Topps Stadium Club	308	.20	.15	.08
1992 Upper Deck	185	.20	.15	.08
1992 Upper Deck	363	.10	.08	.04
1992 Upper Deck Pro Bowl	7	4.00	3.00	1.50
1993 Bowman	110	.50	.40	.20
1993 Fleer	176	.20	.15	.08
1993 Fleer Ultra	157	.30	.25	.12
1993 Fleer Ultra Ultra Stars	9	6.00	4.50	2.50
1993 GameDay	441	.25	.20	.10
1993 Pacific	413	.10	.08	.04
1993 Pacific Prisms	33	1.50	1.25	.60
1993 Pinnacle	137	.25	.20	.10
1993 Pinnacle Men of Autumn	21	.40	.30	.15
1993 Pinnacle Team Pinnacle	8	15.00	11.00	6.00
1993 Pro Set	158	.15	.11	.06
1993 Pro Set Power Power Moves	8	.60	.45	.25
1993 Pro Set Power Update Moves	8	.35	.25	.14
1993 Score	98	.10	.08	.04
1993 Score	416	.04	.03	.02
1993 Score Dream Team	17	1.00	.70	.40
1993 Score Select	98	.40	.30	.15
1993 SkyBox Impact	110	.10	.08	.04
1993 SkyBox Premium	69	.25	.20	.10
1993 Topps	40	.12	.09	.05
1993 Topps	85	.05	.04	.02
1993 Topps	490	.10	.08	.04
1993 Topps Stadium Club	247	.15	.11	.06
1993 Topps Stadium Club	350	.30	.25	.12
1993 Upper Deck	490	.15	.11	.06
1993 Upper Deck SP	97	.60	.45	.25
1993 Upper Deck SP All Pro	14	10.00	7.50	4.00
1994 Bowman	132	.10	.08	.04
1994 Fleer	180	.15	.11	.06
1994 Fleer All-Pro	22	.75	.60	.30
1994 Fleer Living Legends	6	12.00	9.00	4.75
1994 Fleer Ultra	114	.12	.09	.05
1994 Fleer Ultra Achievement Awards	10	.75	.60	.30
1994 GameDay	155	.10	.08	.04
1994 Pacific Crown	147	.08	.06	.03
1994 Pacific Prisms	123	1.50	1.25	.60
1994 Pinnacle	170	.12	.09	.05
1994 Pinnacle Sportflics Sack Attack	5	.05	.05	.05
1994 Pinnacle Sportflics Head-to-Head	6	35.00	26.00	14.00
1994 Pinnacle Sportflics	106	.25	.20	.10
1994 Pinnacle Team Pinnacle	9	12.00	9.00	4.75
1994 Score	51	.15	.11	.06
1994 Score Select	48	.12	.09	.05
1994 Score Select Canton Bound	7	12.00	9.00	4.75
1994 SkyBox Impact	06	.15	.11	.06
1994 SkyBox Impact Ultimate Impact	11	2.00	1.50	.80
1994 SkyBox Premium	60	.10	.08	.04
1994 SkyBox Premium SkyTech Stars	15	2.00	1.50	.80
1994 Topps	190	.15	.11	.06
1994 Topps	475	.08	.06	.03
1994 Topps All-Pros	14	4.00	3.00	1.50
1994 Topps Finest	92	2.50	2.00	1.00
1994 Topps Stadium Club	480	.12	.09	.05
1994 Topps Stadium Club Dynasty and Destiny	3	5.00	3.75	2.00
1994 Topps Stadium Club Ring Leaders	9	10.00	7.50	4.00
1994 Upper Deck	310	.12	.09	.05
1994 Upper Deck Collector's Choice	237	.12	.09	.05
1994 Upper Deck Pro Bowl	17	5.00	3.75	2.00
1994 Upper Deck SP	165	.30	.25	.12

1994 Upper Deck SP All-Pro	14	5.00	3.75	2.00

Rod Woodson

Kellen Winslow

Set	Card #	MT	NM	EX
1981 Topps	150 (R)	13.00	9.75	5.25
1981 Topps	524	3.00	2.25	1.25
1982 Topps	241	2.00	1.50	.80
1982 Topps	242	1.00	.70	.40
1983 Topps	203	.10	.08	.04
1983 Topps	382	.75	.60	.30
1984 Topps	174	.20	.15	.08
1984 Topps	186	.60	.45	.25
1984 Topps	187	.25	.20	.10
1985 Topps	379	.30	.25	.12
1986 Topps	237	.25	.20	.10
1987 Topps	343	.20	.15	.08
1988 Topps	203	.05	.04	.02
1988 Topps	209	.15	.11	.06

A card number in parentheses ()
indicates the set is unnumbered.

Willie Wood

Set	Card #	NM	EX	VG
1963 Topps	95 (R)	27.00	13.50	8.00
1964 Philadelphia	82	8.00	4.00	2.50
1965 Philadelphia	83	8.00	4.00	2.50
1966 Philadelphia	90	4.50	2.25	1.25
1967 Philadelphia	83	5.00	2.50	1.50
1969 Topps	168	3.50	1.75	1.00
1969 Topps Four In Ones	(65)	1.00	.50	.30
1970 Topps	261	3.00	1.50	.90
1971 Topps	55	2.50	1.25	.70

Set	Card #	MT	NM	EX
1989 Pro Set	354 (R)	1.25	.90	.50
1989 Score	78 (R)	4.00	3.00	1.50
1989 Topps	323 (R)	1.00	.70	.40
1990 Fleer	152	.10	.08	.04
1990 Fleer All-Pro	25	.50	.40	.20
1990 Pro Set	16	.03	.02	.01
1990 Pro Set	377	.03	.02	.01
1990 Pro Set	626	.25	.20	.10
1990 Score	255	.25	.20	.10
1990 Score	577	.04	.03	.02
1990 Score 100 Hottest	98	.25	.20	.10
1990 Topps	179	.15	.11	.06
1991 Bowman	446	.05	.04	.02
1991 Fleer	168	.10	.08	.04
1991 Fleer Ultra	117	.08	.06	.03
1991 Fleer Ultra Performances	8	.60	.45	.25
1991 Pacific	433	.04	.03	.02
1991 Pinnacle	72	.10	.08	.04
1991 Pro Set	278	.05	.04	.02
1991 Pro Set	424	.04	.03	.02
1991 Pro Set Platinum	100	.08	.06	.03
1991 Score	338	.06	.05	.02
1991 Score	547	.06	.05	.02
1991 Score	646	.06	.05	.02
1991 Topps	297	.04	.03	.02
1991 Topps Stadium Club	30	.75	.60	.30
1991 Upper Deck	111	.05	.04	.02
1991 Upper Deck	473	.05	.04	.02
1992 Bowman	117	.60	.45	.25
1992 Fleer	353	.03	.02	.01
1992 Fleer	466	.03	.02	.01
1992 Fleer Team Leaders	22	12.00	9.00	4.75
1992 Fleer Ultra	340	.08	.06	.03
1992 Pacific	260	.05	.04	.02
1992 Pinnacle	217	.05	.04	.02
1992 Pro Set	305	.08	.06	.03
1992 Pro Set	399	.05	.04	.02
1992 Pro Set Gold MVPs	12	.50	.40	.20
1992 Pro Set Power	26	.10	.08	.04
1992 Score	375	.07	.05	.03
1992 Topps	200	.05	.04	.02
1992 Topps Stadium Club	240	.12	.09	.05
1992 Topps Stadium Club	309	.15	.11	.06
1992 Upper Deck Pro Bowl	13	1.50	1.25	.60
1993 Bowman	96	.20	.15	.08
1993 Fleer	179	.05	.04	.02
1993 Fleer All-Pro	24	1.00	.70	.40
1993 Fleer Ultra	405	.08	.06	.03
1993 GameDay	26	.15	.11	.06
1993 Pacific	275	.05	.04	.02
1993 Pinnacle	92	.10	.08	.04
1993 Pinnacle Men of Autumn	50	.40	.30	.15
1993 Pinnacle Team Pinnacle	12	18.00	13.50	7.25
1993 Pro Set	370	.05	.04	.02
1993 Pro Set Power	26	.15	.11	.06

1993 Pro Set Power All-Power Defense	18	.50	.40	.20
1993 Pro Set Power Update Combos	5	1.00	.70	.40
1993 Score	13	.06	.05	.02
1993 Score Dream Team	19	.65	.50	.25
1993 Score Select	48	.10	.08	.04
1993 Score The Franchise	23	5.00	3.75	2.00
1993 SkyBox Impact	275	.05	.04	.02
1993 SkyBox Impact Kelly's Heroes/Magic's Kingdom	10	1.25	.90	.50
1993 SkyBox Premium	212	.10	.08	.04
1993 Topps	520	.07	.05	.03
1993 Topps Black Gold	13	1.00	.70	.40
1993 Topps Stadium Club	112	.10	.08	.04
1993 Upper Deck	327	.05	.04	.02
1993 Upper Deck SP	225	.25	.20	.10
1994 Bowman	290	.15	.11	.06
1994 Fleer	396	.10	.08	.04
1994 Fleer All-Pro	23	.50	.40	.20
1994 Fleer Pro-Visions	9	.25	.20	.10
1994 Fleer Ultra	261	.12	.09	.05
1994 Fleer Ultra Award Winners	5	1.00	.70	.40
1994 Fleer Ultra Ultra Stars	9	10.00	7.50	4.00
1994 GameDay	344	.10	.08	.04
1994 GameDay Game Breakers	15	.75	.60	.30
1994 Pacific Crown	179	.06	.05	.02
1994 Pinnacle	6	.12	.09	.05
1994 Pinnacle Sportflics Head-to-Head	3	35.00	26.00	14.00
1994 Pinnacle Sportflics	56	.15	.11	.06
1994 Score	13	.10	.08	.04
1994 Score Dream Team	17	4.00	3.00	1.50
1994 Score Select	5	.12	.09	.05
1994 SkyBox Impact	213	.10	.08	.04
1994 SkyBox Premium	127	.15	.11	.06
1994 SkyBox Premium SkyTech Stars	11	2.00	1.50	.80
1994 Topps	10	.10	.08	.04
1994 Topps Finest	198	1.50	1.25	.60
1994 Topps Stadium Club	48	.12	.09	.05
1994 Topps Stadium Club	442	.12	.09	.05
1994 Upper Deck	293	.12	.09	.05
1994 Upper Deck Collector's Choice	78	.07	.05	.03
1994 Upper Deck Pro Bowl	16	4.00	3.00	1.50
1994 Upper Deck SP	75	.25	.20	.10

Steve Young

Set	Card #	MT	NM	EX
1984 Topps USFL	52 (R)	175.00	131.25	70.00
1985 Topps USFL	65	80.00	60.00	32.00
1986 Topps	374 (R)	17.00	12.50	6.75
1987 Topps	384	7.00	5.25	2.75

1988 Topps	39	1.25	.90	.50
1989 Pro Set	388	.70	.50	.30
1989 Score	212	3.50	2.75	1.50
1989 Topps Traded	24	.50	.40	.20
1990 Fleer	17	.40	.30	.15
1990 Pro Set	645	.40	.30	.15
1990 Score	145	.50	.40	.20
1991 Bowman	485	.40	.30	.15
1991 Fleer	367	.40	.30	.15
1991 Fleer Ultra	256	.50	.40	.20
1991 Pacific	470	.50	.40	.20
1991 Pinnacle	201	1.25	.90	.50
1991 Pro Set	296	.50	.40	.20
1991 Pro Set Platinum	271	.50	.40	.20
1991 Score	505	.60	.45	.25
1991 Upper Deck	101	.45	.35	.20
1992 Bowman	237	3.75	2.75	1.50
1992 Bowman	246	5.50	4.25	2.25
1992 Fleer	386	.30	.25	.12
1992 Fleer	469	.03	.02	.01
1992 Fleer Ultra	371	.85	.60	.35
1992 GameDay	220	1.25	.90	.50
1992 Pacific	605	.40	.30	.15
1992 Pinnacle	18	.85	.60	.35
1992 Pro Set	5	.15	.11	.06
1992 Pro Set	323	.40	.30	.15
1992 Pro Set Power	108	.50	.40	.20
1992 Score	4	.35	.25	.14
1992 Score	542	.10	.08	.04
1992 SkyBox Impact	38	.40	.30	.15
1992 SkyBox Impact	306	.15	.11	.06
1992 SkyBox Primetime	99	.85	.60	.35
1992 Topps	191	.25	.20	.10
1992 Topps Stadium Club	366	.70	.50	.30
1992 Upper Deck	299	.40	.30	.15
1992 Upper Deck	365	.20	.15	.08
1992 Upper Deck	519	.20	.15	.08
1993 Bowman	270	1.25	.90	.50
1993 Fleer	212	.25	.20	.10
1993 Fleer	240	.15	.11	.06
1993 Fleer	247	.15	.11	.06
1993 Fleer All-Pro	25	3.50	2.75	1.50
1993 Fleer Team Leaders	3	10.00	7.50	4.00
1993 Fleer Ultra	444	.50	.40	.20
1993 Fleer Ultra Award Winners	10	9.00	6.75	3.50
1993 Fleer Ultra Ultra Stars	10	6.00	4.50	2.50
1993 GameDay	8	.50	.40	.20
1993 GameDay Game Breakers	3	1.50	1.25	.60
1993 Pacific	149	.40	.30	.15
1993 Pacific Gold Prisms	20	20.00	15.00	8.00
1993 Pacific Prism Inserts	20	7.50	5.75	3.00
1993 Pacific Prisms	93	4.00	3.00	1.50
1993 Pinnacle	255	.50	.40	.20
1993 Pinnacle Men of Autumn	25	1.00	.75	.40
1993 Pro Set	2	.10	.08	.04
1993 Pro Set	5	.10	.08	.04
1993 Pro Set	399	.25	.20	.10
1993 Pro Set Power	(108)	.35	.25	.14
1993 Pro Set Power Update Combos	2	2.50	2.00	1.00
1993 Score	16	.25	.20	.10
1993 Score	440	.10	.08	.04
1993 Score Dream Team	1	3.00	2.25	1.25
1993 Score Select	1	1.25	.90	.50
1993 Score Select Gridiron Skills	2	40.00	30.00	16.00
1993 Score The Franchise	25	13.00	9.75	5.25
1993 SkyBox Impact	291	.25	.20	.10
1993 SkyBox Poster Art Cards	10	1.25	.90	.50
1993 SkyBox Premium	33	.60	.45	.25
1993 SkyBox Thunder and Lightning	8	12.00	9.00	4.75
1993 Topps	88	.12	.09	.05
1993 Topps	135	.25	.20	.10
1993 Topps	220	.12	.09	.05
1993 Topps Black Gold	23	1.25	.90	.50

1993 Topps Stadium Club	208	.50	.40	.20
1993 Topps Stadium Club	500	.45	.35	.20
1993 Upper Deck	358	.40	.30	.15
1993 Upper Deck	432	.15	.11	.06
1993 Upper Deck Pro Bowl	12	7.50	5.75	3.00
1993 Upper Deck San Francisco 49ers	21	2.00	1.50	.80
1993 Upper Deck San Francisco 49ers	25	1.00	.70	.40
1993 Upper Deck SP	243	1.75	1.25	.70
1993 Upper Deck SP All Pro	1	17.00	12.50	6.75
1993 Upper Deck Team MVP	15	1.50	1.25	.60
1994 Bowman	350	.50	.40	.20
1994 Fleer	429	.75	.60	.30
1994 Fleer All-Pro	24	1.00	.70	.40
1994 Fleer League Leaders	10	1.00	.70	.40
1994 Fleer Ultra	285	.20	.15	.08
1994 Fleer Ultra Hot Numbers	15	2.50	2.00	1.00
1994 Fleer Ultra Touchdown Kings	9	12.00	9.00	4.75
1994 GameDay	374	.25	.20	.10
1994 GameDay Game Breakers	16	1.50	1.25	.60
1994 Pacific Crown	45	.20	.15	.08
1994 Pacific Crown Gems of the Crown	36	4.00	3.00	1.50
1994 Pacific Marquee	36	2.00	1.50	.80
1994 Pacific Prisms	126	1.50	1.25	.60
1994 Pinnacle	22	.15	.11	.06
1994 Pinnacle Performers	6	4.00	3.00	1.50
1994 Pinnacle Sportflics Head-to-Head	7	15.00	11.00	6.00
1994 Pinnacle Sportflics	101	.60	.45	.25
1994 Pinnacle Sportflics	179	.50	.40	.20
1994 Score	56	.15	.11	.06
1994 Score Dream Team	18	13.00	9.75	5.25
1994 Score Select	36	.40	.30	.15
1994 Score Select Canton Bound	8	20.00	15.00	8.00
1994 SkyBox Impact	236	.75	.60	.30
1994 SkyBox Impact Ultimate Impact	7	2.00	1.50	.80
1994 SkyBox Premium	141	.20	.15	.08
1994 SkyBox Premium Revolution	14	6.00	4.50	2.50
1994 SkyBox Premium SkyTech Stars	29	3.00	2.25	1.25
1994 Topps	60	.65	.50	.25
1994 Topps	120	.60	.45	.25
1994 Topps	470	.12	.09	.05
1994 Topps	555	.20	.15	.08
1994 Topps	613	.20	.15	.08
1994 Topps Finest	77	7.50	5.63	3.00
1994 Topps Finest Inserts	28	6.00	4.50	2.50
1994 Topps Stadium Club	109	.15	.11	.06
1994 Topps Stadium Club	295	.30	.25	.12
1994 Topps Stadium Club	374	.20	.15	.08
1994 Topps Stadium Club	511	.15	.11	.06
1994 Topps Stadium Club Ring Leaders	2	15.00	11.00	6.00
1994 Upper Deck	145	.20	.15	.08
1994 Upper Deck Collector's Choice Crash Game	1	11.00	8.25	4.50
1994 Upper Deck Collector's Choice	240	.25	.20	.10
1994 Upper Deck Pro Bowl	11	9.00	6.75	3.50
1994 Upper Deck Retail Predictor	2	10.00	7.50	4.00
1994 Upper Deck SP	197	1.00	.70	.40
1994 Upper Deck SP All-Pro	32	12.50	9.50	5.00
1994 Upper Deck Then And Now	4	10.00	7.50	4.00

BASKETBALL

Kareem Abdul-Jabbar

Set	Card #	NM	EX	VG
1969 Topps	25 (R)	550.00	412.00	220.00
1970 Topps	2	21.00	10.50	6.25
1970 Topps	5	16.00	8.00	4.75
1970 Topps	75	100.00	50.00	30.00
1971 Topps	100	50.00	25.00	15.00
1971 Topps	133	10.00	5.00	3.00
1971 Topps	138	10.00	5.00	3.00
1971 Topps	139	10.00	5.00	3.00
1971 Topps	140	7.50	3.75	2.25
1971 Topps	142	10.00	5.00	3.00
1972 Topps	100	32.00	16.00	9.50
1972 Topps	163	30.00	15.00	9.00
1972 Topps	173	10.00	5.00	3.00
1972 Topps	175	12.00	6.00	3.50
1973 Topps	50	23.00	11.50	7.00
1973 Topps	153	5.00	2.50	1.50
1973 Topps	154	5.00	2.50	1.50
1973 Topps	155	6.00	3.00	1.75
1974 Topps	1	35.00	17.50	10.50
1974 Topps	91	7.50	3.75	2.25
1974 Topps	144	6.00	3.00	1.75
1974 Topps	145	5.00	2.50	1.50
1974 Topps	146	4.00	2.00	1.25
1975 Topps	1	9.00	4.50	2.75
1975 Topps	90	20.00	10.00	6.00
1975 Topps	126	5.00	2.50	1.50
1976 Topps	100	30.00	15.00	9.00
1976 Topps	126	18.00	9.00	5.50
1977 Topps	1	18.00	9.00	5.40
1978 Topps	110	8.00	4.00	2.50
1979 Topps	10	8.00	4.00	2.50
1980 Topps	14	2.50	1.25	.70
1980 Topps	43	2.00	1.00	.60
1980 Topps	44	5.00	2.50	1.50
1980 Topps	50	2.00	1.00	.60
1980 Topps	131	3.00	1.50	.90
1980 Topps	132	5.00	2.50	1.50
1980 Topps	140	6.00	3.00	1.75
1980 Topps	162	2.00	1.00	.60

Set	Card #	MT	NM	EX
1981 Topps	20	5.00	3.75	2.00
1981 Topps	106	2.50	2.00	1.00
1981 Topps	55	1.50	1.25	.60
1983 Star Co.	14	40.00	30.00	16.00
1983 Star Co. All-Star Game	14	10.00	7.50	4.00
1984 Star Co.	173	35.00	26.00	14.00
1984 Star Co.	282	13.00	9.75	5.25
1984 Star Co. All-Star Game	14	10.00	7.50	4.00
1984 Star Co. Awards Banquet	21	10.00	7.50	4.00
1984 Star Co. Court Kings	1	15.00	11.00	6.00
1985 Star Co.	26	45.00	34.00	18.00
1985 Star Co. Lite All-Stars	8	15.00	11.00	6.00
1986 Fleer	1	12.00	9.00	4.75
1986 Star Co. Best of the Old	1	160.00	120.00	64.00
1986 Star Co. Best of the Best	1	25.00	18.50	10.00
1986 Star Co. Court Kings	2	12.00	9.00	4.75
1987 Fleer	1	9.00	6.75	3.50
1988 Fleer	64	4.00	3.00	1.50

Alvan Adams

Set	Card #	NM	EX	VG
1976 Topps	75 (R)	5.00	2.50	1.50
1977 Topps	95	1.00	.50	.30
1978 Topps	77	.75	.40	.25
1979 Topps	52	.20	.10	.06
1980 Topps	68	.75	.40	.25
1980 Topps	156	.25	.13	.08

Set	Card #	MT	NM	EX
1981 Topps	79	.15	.11	.06
1981 Topps	60	.15	.11	.06
1983 Star Co.	110	2.00	1.50	.80
1984 Star Co.	38	2.75	2.00	1.00
1985 Star Co.	35	2.50	2.00	1.00
1985 Star Co. Last 11 R.O.Y.	10	2.50	2.00	1.00
1986 Fleer	2	1.25	.90	.50
1987 Fleer	2	.40	.30	.15

All-Star card: A special card identifying a player as a member of a National League, American League or Major League all-star team. Players shown on all-star cards may or may not be members of their league's official All-Star team. All-star cards can be part of a regular set or issued as an independent set. For several years, Topps has issued two different "glossy" sets of all-star cards on specially-coated stock.

Mark Aguirre

Danny Ainge

Set	Card #	MT	NM	EX
1983 Star Co.	49 (R)	80.00	60.00	32.00
1984 Star Co.	250	6.00	4.50	2.50
1984 Star Co. All-Star Game	15	2.00	1.50	.80
1984 Star Co. Court Kings	3	4.00	3.00	1.50
1985 Star Co.	160	6.00	4.50	2.50
1986 Fleer	3 (R)	5.00	3.75	2.00
1986 Star Co. Court Kings	1	3.00	2.25	1.25
1987 Fleer	3	1.25	.90	.50
1988 Fleer	27	.40	.30	.15
1989 Fleer	44	.20	.15	.08
1989 NBA Hoops	95	.10	.08	.04
1990 Fleer	54	.07	.05	.03
1990 NBA Hoops	101	.07	.05	.03
1990 SkyBox	82	.10	.08	.04
1991 Fleer	57	.05	.04	.02
1991 NBA Hoops	59	.08	.06	.03
1991 SkyBox	78	.08	.06	.03
1991 SkyBox	439	.05	.04	.02
1991 Upper Deck	165	.08	.06	.03
1992 Fleer	62	.08	.06	.03
1992 Fleer Ultra	55	.12	.09	.05
1992 NBA Hoops	62	.07	.05	.03
1992 SkyBox	66	.05	.04	.02
1992 Topps	86	.04	.03	.02
1992 Topps Archives	12	.05	.04	.02
1992 Topps Stadium Club	66	.10	.08	.04
1992 Upper Deck	209	.05	.04	.02
1992 Upper Deck 15000-Point Club	6	2.00	1.50	.80
1993 Fleer	58	.05	.04	.02
1993 Fleer	305	.05	.04	.02
1993 Fleer Ultra	55	.10	.08	.04
1993 Fleer Ultra	265	.10	.08	.04
1993 NBA Hoops	60	.06	.05	.02
1993 NBA Hoops	350	.06	.05	.02
1993 SkyBox	235	.05	.04	.02
1993 Topps	185	.05	.04	.02
1993 Topps	295	.05	.04	.02
1993 Topps Finest	40	.35	.25	.14
1993 Topps Stadium Club	325	.10	.08	.04
1993 Upper Deck	390	.05	.04	.02

Set	Card #	MT	NM	EX
1983 Star Co.	27 (R)	80.00	60.00	32.00
1984 Star Co.	2	20.00	15.00	8.00
1985 Star Co.	96	20.00	15.00	8.00
1986 Fleer	4 (R)	14.00	10.50	5.50
1987 Fleer	4	4.00	3.00	1.50
1988 Fleer	8	1.25	.90	.50
1989 Fleer	133	.40	.30	.15
1989 NBA Hoops	215	.15	.11	.06
1990 Fleer	162	.07	.05	.03
1990 Fleer Update	79	.10	.08	.04
1990 NBA Hoops	253	.15	.11	.06
1990 NBA Hoops	427	.20	.15	.08
1990 SkyBox	242	.10	.08	.04
1990 SkyBox	407	.10	.08	.04
1991 Fleer	167	.07	.05	.03
1991 NBA Hoops	171	.07	.05	.03
1991 SkyBox	233	.08	.06	.03
1991 SkyBox	453	.05	.04	.02
1991 SkyBox	590	.05	.04	.02
1991 Upper Deck	279	.08	.06	.03
1992 Fleer	177	.05	.04	.02
1992 Fleer	410	.05	.04	.02
1992 Fleer Ultra	336	.10	.08	.04
1992 NBA Hoops	188	.08	.06	.03
1992 NBA Hoops	450	.10	.08	.04
1992 SkyBox	199	.08	.06	.03
1992 SkyBox	316	.05	.04	.02
1992 SkyBox	388	.10	.08	.04
1992 Topps	360	.04	.03	.02
1992 Topps Archives	13	.05	.04	.02
1992 Topps Stadium Club	252	.10	.08	.04
1992 Upper Deck	75	.08	.06	.03
1992 Upper Deck	322	.05	.04	.02
1993 Fleer	162	.05	.04	.02
1993 Fleer Jam Session	173	.10	.08	.04
1993 Fleer Ultra	144	.10	.08	.04
1993 NBA Hoops	168	.06	.05	.02
1993 SkyBox	144	.05	.04	.02
1993 Topps	186	.05	.04	.02
1993 Topps Finest	41	.35	.25	.14
1993 Topps Stadium Club	55	.10	.08	.04
1993 Upper Deck	79	.05	.04	.02
1993 Upper Deck	465	.08	.06	.03
1993 Upper Deck	504	.05	.04	.02
1993 Upper Deck SE	100	.10	.08	.04
1994 Fleer	174	.05	.04	.02
1994 Fleer Flair	115	.15	.11	.06
1994 Fleer Jam Session	146	.10	.08	.04
1994 Fleer Ultra	145	.08	.06	.03
1994 NBA Hoops	165	.04	.03	.02
1994 SkyBox	127	.06	.05	.02
1994 Topps	90	.06	.05	.02
1994 Topps Finest	12	.15	.11	.06
1994 Topps Stadium Club	118	.08	.06	.03
1994 Topps Stadium Club	119	.08	.06	.03
1994 Upper Deck Collector's Choice	222	.05	.04	.02

Airbrushing: The touching up of a photo by an artist. Usually done on trading cards to show a player, who has changed teams, in his new uniform.

Autographed card: A card that has actually been signed by the player pictured, as opposed to the facsimile signatures that are sometimes printed on cards as part of the design. The value of an autographed card is generally greater than that same card would be if it were unautographed.

Kenny Anderson

Set	Card #	MT	NM	EX
1991 Fleer	322 (R)	1.00	.70	.40
1991 NBA Hoops	547 (R)	1.00	.70	.40
1991 SkyBox	514 (R)	1.50	1.25	.60
1991 Upper Deck	444 (R)	2.50	2.00	1.00
1991 Upper Deck Rookie Standouts	36R	2.50	2.00	1.00
1992 Fleer	140	.20	.15	.08
1992 Fleer Ultra	114	.50	.40	.20
1992 Fleer Ultra Playmakers	1	1.50	1.25	.60
1992 NBA Hoops	144	.25	.20	.10
1992 SkyBox	151	.40	.30	.15
1992 Topps	95	.15	.11	.06
1992 Topps Archives	140	.30	.25	.12
1992 Topps Stadium Club	69	.50	.40	.20
1992 Upper Deck	127	.35	.25	.14
1992 Upper Deck All-Division Team	5	.75	.60	.30
1993 Fleer	130	.20	.15	.08
1993 Fleer Jam Session	137	.25	.20	.10
1993 Fleer Ultra	118	.25	.20	.10
1993 NBA Hoops	137	.20	.15	.08
1993 NBA Hoops Admiral's Choice	3	.30	.25	.12
1993 SkyBox	120	.20	.15	.08
1993 SkyBox	329	.15	.11	.06
1993 SkyBox Center Stage	7	1.00	.70	.40
1993 SkyBox Thunder and Lightning	4	3.00	2.25	1.25
1993 Topps	222	.15	.11	.06
1993 Topps BlackGold	3	1.00	.70	.40
1993 Topps Finest	94	1.00	.70	.40
1993 Topps Finest	174	1.50	1.25	.60
1993 Topps Stadium Club	2	.15	.11	.06
1993 Topps Stadium Club	330	.20	.15	.08
1993 Upper Deck	2	.25	.20	.10
1993 Upper Deck	243	.10	.08	.04
1993 Upper Deck	448	.15	.11	.06
1993 Upper Deck SE	165	.25	.20	.10
1993 Upper Deck SE East Future All Stars	9	9.00	6.75	3.50
1993 Upper Deck 3-D Basketball	60	.10	.08	.04
1993 Upper Deck 3-D Triple Double	6	1.50	1.25	.60
1994 Fleer	139	.20	.15	.08
1994 Fleer Flair	93	.50	.40	.20
1994 Fleer Jam Session	115	.20	.15	.08
1994 Fleer NBA All-Stars	1	.65	.50	.25
1994 Fleer Team Leaders	6	2.00	1.50	.80
1994 Fleer Ultra	114	.15	.11	.06
1994 NBA Hoops	130	.15	.11	.06
1994 NBA Hoops	224	.08	.06	.03
1994 NBA Hoops Power Ratings	33	1.00	.70	.40
1994 NBA Hoops Supreme Court	28	.75	.60	.30
1994 SkyBox	103	.06	.05	.02
1994 Topps	10	.06	.05	.02
1994 Topps	138	.06	.05	.02
1994 Topps Finest	7	.30	.25	.12
1994 Topps Finest Iron Men	2	4.00	3.00	1.50
1994 Topps Finest Marathon Men	3	2.50	2.00	1.00
1994 Topps Stadium Club Dynasty and Destiny	1B	.80	.60	.30
1994 Topps Stadium Club Rising Stars	1	10.00	7.50	4.00
1994 Topps Super Passers	4	2.25	1.75	.90
1994 Upper Deck	120	.12	.09	.05
1994 Upper Deck Collector's Choice 750 Assists	2	5.00	3.75	2.00
1994 Upper Deck Collector's Choice	193	.10	.08	.04
1994 Upper Deck Collector's Choice	307	.20	.15	.08
1994 Upper Deck Predictors Retail	13	6.00	4.50	2.50

Nick Anderson

Set	Card #	MT	NM	EX
1990 Fleer	132 (R)	.75	.60	.30
1990 Fleer Rookie Sensations	7	6.00	4.50	2.50
1990 NBA Hoops	214 (R)	.90	.70	.35
1990 NBA Hoops	373	.15	.11	.06
1990 SkyBox	199 (R)	1.25	.90	.50
1991 Fleer	143	.15	.11	.06
1991 NBA Hoops	147	.15	.11	.06
1991 SkyBox	200	.15	.11	.06
1991 Upper Deck	228	.10	.08	.04
1991 Upper Deck	477	.15	.11	.06
1992 Fleer	158	.10	.08	.04
1992 Fleer Ultra	128	.12	.09	.05
1992 NBA Hoops	160	.15	.11	.06
1992 SkyBox	169	.15	.11	.06
1992 Topps	142	.10	.08	.04
1992 Topps Archives	115	.15	.11	.06
1992 Topps Stadium Club	35	.15	.11	.06
1992 Upper Deck	161	.15	.11	.06
1993 Fleer	147	.10	.08	.04
1993 Fleer Jam Session	156	.10	.08	.04
1993 Fleer Ultra	133	.10	.08	.04
1993 NBA Hoops	152	.10	.08	.04
1993 NBA Hoops	441	.05	.04	.02
1993 SkyBox	132	.05	.04	.02
1993 SkyBox Dynamic Dunks	1	1.50	1.25	.60
1993 Topps	50	.10	.08	.04
1993 Topps	113	.10	.08	.04
1993 Topps Finest	81	.35	.25	.14

1993 Topps Stadium Club	333	.12	.09	.05
1993 Upper Deck	269	.05	.04	.02
1993 Upper Deck	454	.10	.08	.04
1993 Upper Deck SE	79	.10	.08	.04
1994 Fleer	157	.05	.04	.02
1994 Fleer Flair	105	.15	.11	.06
1994 Fleer Jam Session	132	.12	.09	.05
1994 Fleer Ultra	131	.08	.06	.03
1994 NBA Hoops	148	.04	.03	.02
1994 NBA Hoops Power Ratings	37	.30	.25	.12
1994 SkyBox	116	.06	.05	.02
1994 Topps	155	.06	.05	.02
1994 Topps Finest	107	.20	.15	.08
1994 Topps Finest	111	.20	.15	.08
1994 Topps Stadium Club	58	.08	.06	.03
1994 Upper Deck Collector's Choice	78	.05	.04	.02
1994 Upper Deck Special Edition	65	.20	.15	.08

Nate Archibald

Set	Card #	NM	EX	VG
1971 Topps	29 (R)	27.50	13.50	8.25
1972 Topps	115	8.00	4.00	2.50
1972 Topps	169	4.00	2.00	1.25
1972 Topps	171	10.00	5.00	3.00
1972 Topps	172	10.00	5.00	3.00
1973 Topps	1	8.00	4.00	2.50
1973 Topps	158	3.00	1.50	.90
1974 Topps	170	4.00	2.00	1.25
1975 Topps	15	4.00	2.00	1.25
1975 Topps	124	.75	.40	.25
1976 Topps	20	4.00	2.00	1.25
1976 Topps	129	2.00	1.00	.60
1977 Topps	127	2.50	1.25	.70
1978 Topps	26	1.25	.60	.40
1979 Topps	110	1.00	.50	.30
1980 Topps	4	1.00	.50	.30
1980 Topps	78	.75	.40	.25
1980 Topps	124	1.00	.50	.30
1980 Topps	172	.75	.40	.25

Set	Card #	MT	NM	EX
1981 Topps	3	.60	.45	.25
1981 Topps	100	.40	.30	.15
1981 Topps	45	2.50	2.00	1.00
1983 Star Co.	39	15.00	11.00	6.00

B.J. Armstrong

Set	Card #	MT	NM	EX
1990 Fleer	22 (R)	.65	.50	.25
1990 NBA Hoops	60 (R)	.75	.60	.30
1990 SkyBox	37 (R)	1.00	.70	.40
1991 Fleer	25	.10	.08	.04
1991 NBA Hoops	26	.25	.20	.10
1991 SkyBox	34	.20	.15	.08
1991 SkyBox	435	.12	.09	.05
1991 SkyBox	489	.20	.15	.08
1991 Upper Deck	184	.20	.15	.08
1992 Fleer	28	.10	.08	.04
1992 Fleer Ultra	24	.15	.11	.06
1992 NBA Hoops	27	.08	.06	.03
1992 SkyBox	28	.08	.06	.03
1992 Topps	73	.15	.11	.06
1992 Topps Archives	116	.20	.15	.08
1992 Topps Stadium Club	87	.15	.11	.06
1992 Upper Deck	157	.10	.08	.04
1993 Fleer	25	.05	.04	.02
1993 Fleer	221	.05	.04	.02
1993 Fleer Jam Session	27	.15	.11	.06
1993 Fleer Ultra	26	.15	.11	.06
1993 NBA Hoops	25	.06	.05	.02
1993 SkyBox	42	.12	.09	.05
1993 Topps	174	.10	.08	.04
1993 Topps Finest	62	1.50	1.25	.60
1993 Topps Stadium Club	74	.15	.11	.06
1993 Upper Deck	169	.05	.04	.02
1993 Upper Deck	257	.10	.08	.04
1993 Upper Deck SE	95	.20	.15	.08
1993 Upper Deck SE East Future All Stars	3	6.00	4.50	2.50
1994 Fleer	29	.07	.05	.03
1994 Fleer Flair	20	.15	.11	.06
1994 Fleer Jam Session	25	.10	.08	.04
1994 Fleer NBA All-Stars	2	.35	.25	.14
1994 Fleer Ultra	25	.08	.06	.03
1994 NBA Hoops	23	.04	.03	.02
1994 NBA Hoops	225	.04	.03	.02
1994 NBA Hoops Supreme Court	6	.30	.25	.12
1994 SkyBox	21	.06	.05	.02
1994 Topps	9	.06	.05	.02
1994 Topps Finest	25	.20	.15	.08
1994 Topps Finest Marathon Men	9	.75	.60	.30
1994 Topps Stadium Club	85	.08	.06	.03
1994 Upper Deck	31	.10	.08	.04
1994 Upper Deck Collector's Choice	80	.05	.04	.02
1994 Upper Deck Collector's Choice	210	.05	.04	.02
1994 Upper Deck Special Edition	10	.20	.15	.08

Vin Baker

Set	Card #	MT	NM	EX
1993 Fleer	321 (R)	.90	.70	.35
1993 Fleer Jam Session	120 (R)	1.50	1.25	.60
1993 Fleer Jam Session Rookie Standouts	1	3.50	2.75	1.50
1993 Fleer Lottery Exchange	8	5.00	3.75	2.00
1993 Fleer Ultra	106 (R)	1.75	1.25	.70
1993 Fleer Ultra	282	.60	.45	.25
1993 Fleer Ultra All-Rookies	1	5.00	3.75	2.00
1993 NBA Hoops	363 (R)	1.00	.75	.40
1993 NBA Hoops Draft Redemption	8	6.50	4.90	2.60
1993 NBA Hoops II Magic's All-Rookie Team	8	6.00	4.50	2.50
1993 SkyBox	244 (R)	1.25	.90	.50
1993 SkyBox Draft Picks	8	6.00	4.50	2.50
1993 Topps	306 (R)	.90	.70	.35
1993 Topps Finest	139 (R)	4.00	3.00	1.50
1993 Topps Stadium Club	307 (R)	1.25	.90	.50
1993 Upper Deck	330 (R)	1.25	.90	.50
1993 Upper Deck	490	.35	.25	.14
1993 Upper Deck Rookie Exchange Gold/Silver	8	2.00	1.50	.80
1993 Upper Deck Rookie Standouts	19	7.00	5.25	2.75
1993 Upper Deck SE	69 (R)	1.00	.70	.40
1993 Upper Deck SE East Future All Stars	8	15.00	11.00	6.00
1993 Upper Deck 3-D Basketball	85 (R)	.75	.20	.10
1994 Fleer	123	.35	.25	.14
1994 Fleer Flair	83	1.00	.70	.40
1994 Fleer Flair Hot Numbers	1	2.25	1.75	.90
1994 Fleer Jam Session	104	.45	.35	.20
1994 Fleer Jam Session Second Year Stars	1	1.00	.70	.40
1994 Fleer Rookie Sensations	1	4.00	3.00	1.50
1994 Fleer Team Leaders	5	1.00	.70	.40
1994 Fleer Ultra	102	.50	.40	.20
1994 Fleer Ultra NBA All-Rookie Team	1	12.00	9.00	4.75
1994 Fleer Young Lions	1	1.25	.90	.50
1994 NBA Hoops	116	.25	.20	.10
1994 NBA Hoops	428	.30	.25	.12
1994 NBA Hoops Power Ratings	29	1.00	.70	.40
1994 NBA Hoops Supreme Court	25	1.50	1.25	.60
1994 SkyBox	91	.50	.40	.20
1994 SkyBox Ragin' Rookies	15	2.50	2.00	1.00
1994 Topps	93	.30	.25	.12
1994 Topps Finest	66	1.25	.90	.50
1994 Topps Stadium Club	129	.65	.50	.25
1994 Topps Stadium Club Clear Cut	15	5.00	3.75	2.00
1994 Upper Deck	3	.30	.25	.12
1994 Upper Deck Collector's Choice	42	.25	.20	.10
1994 Upper Deck Collector's Choice	180	.08	.06	.03
1994 Upper Deck Special Edition	51	1.50	1.25	.60

Charles Barkley

Set	Card #	MT	NM	EX
1984 Star Co.	202 (R)	425.00	319.00	170.00
1984 Star Co. Court Kings	41	45.00	34.00	18.00
1985 Star Co.	2	175.00	131.00	70.00
1985 Star Co. All-Rookie Team	3	90.00	67.00	36.00
1986 Fleer	7 (R)	150.00	112.00	60.00
1986 Star Co. Best of the Best	2	125.00	94.00	50.00
1986 Star Co. Court Kings	3	50.00	37.00	20.00
1987 Fleer	9	37.00	28.00	15.00
1988 Fleer	85	9.00	6.75	3.50
1988 Fleer	129	5.00	3.75	2.00
1989 Fleer	113	3.00	2.25	1.25
1989 NBA Hoops	96	.50	.40	.20
1989 NBA Hoops	110	1.00	.70	.40
1990 Fleer	139	.60	.45	.25
1990 Fleer All-Stars	1	1.25	.90	.50
1990 NBA Hoops	1	.50	.40	.20
1990 NBA Hoops	225	.60	.45	.25
1990 NBA Hoops	374	.30	.25	.12
1990 SkyBox	211	.75	.60	.30
1991 Fleer	151	.50	.40	.20
1991 Fleer	213	.25	.20	.10
1991 Fleer	391	.30	.25	.12
1991 Fleer Pro Visions	3	.75	.60	.30
1991 NBA Hoops	156	.40	.30	.15
1991 NBA Hoops	248	.25	.20	.10
1991 NBA Hoops	487	.30	.25	.12
1991 NBA Hoops	531	.25	.20	.10
1991 NBA Hoops	575	1.00	.70	.40
1991 NBA Hoops MVP All-Stars	12	5.00	3.75	2.00
1991 SkyBox	211	.50	.40	.20
1991 SkyBox	316	.30	.25	.12
1991 SkyBox	424	.30	.25	.12
1991 SkyBox	478	.25	.20	.10
1991 SkyBox	530	1.00	.70	.40
1991 Upper Deck	70	.40	.30	.15
1991 Upper Deck	345	.50	.40	.20
1991 Upper Deck	454	.50	.40	.20
1992 Fleer	178	.50	.40	.20
1992 Fleer	265	.25	.20	.10
1992 Fleer	411	.40	.30	.15
1992 Fleer All-Stars	2	10.00	7.50	4.00
1992 Fleer Ultra	206	.40	.30	.15

1992 Fleer Ultra	337	.75	.60	.30
1992 Fleer Ultra All-NBA Team	7	5.00	3.75	2.00
1992 NBA Hoops	170	.50	.40	.20
1992 NBA Hoops	294	.30	.25	.12
1992 NBA Hoops	336	.25	.20	.10
1992 NBA Hoops	451	.75	.60	.30
1992 NBA Hoops Supreme Court	7SC	4.00	3.00	1.50
1992 SkyBox	179	.85	.60	.35
1992 SkyBox	389	.50	.40	.20
1992 SkyBox I Olympic Team	7USA	5.00	3.75	2.00
1992 SkyBox II Thunder and Lightning	3	20.00	15.00	8.00
1992 Topps	107	.20	.15	.08
1992 Topps	270	.35	.25	.14
1992 Topps Archives	44	.75	.60	.30
1992 Topps Beam Team	1	2.00	1.50	1.00
1992 Topps Stadium Club	197	.50	.40	.20
1992 Topps Stadium Club	360	1.00	.70	.40
1992 Topps Stadium Club Beam Team	15	12.00	9.00	4.75
1992 Upper Deck	26	.50	.40	.20
1992 Upper Deck	334	.50	.40	.20
1992 Upper Deck	435	.30	.25	.12
1992 Upper Deck All-Division Team	18	1.50	1.25	.60
1992 Upper Deck All-NBA	10AN	5.00	3.75	2.00
1992 Upper Deck All-Star Weekend	11	1.25	.75	.40
1992 Upper Deck 15000-Point Club	11	10.00	7.50	4.00
1993 Fleer	163	.40	.30	.15
1993 Fleer	229	.25	.20	.10
1993 Fleer All-Stars	13	3.50	2.75	1.50
1993 Fleer Jam Session	174	.80	.60	.30
1993 Fleer Jam Session Gamebreakers	1	1.75	1.25	.70
1993 Fleer Living Legends	1	8.00	6.00	3.25
1993 Fleer NBA Superstars	2	1.50	1.25	.60
1993 Fleer Towers of Power	1	12.00	9.00	4.75
1993 Fleer Ultra	145	.75	.60	.30
1993 Fleer Ultra All-NBA Team	1	6.00	4.50	2.50
1993 Fleer Ultra Famous Nicknames	1	3.00	2.25	1.25
1993 Fleer Ultra Jam City	1	15.00	11.00	6.00
1993 Fleer Ultra NBA Award Winners	2	15.00	11.00	6.00
1993 Fleer Ultra Rebound Kings	1	1.25	.90	.50
1993 Fleer Ultra Scoring Kings	2	20.00	15.00	8.00
1993 NBA Hoops	169	.45	.35	.20
1993 NBA Hoops	269	.25	.20	.10
1993 NBA Hoops	295	.25	.20	.10
1993 NBA Hoops	443	.25	.20	.10
1993 NBA Hoops Face to Face	6	4.00	3.00	1.50
1993 NBA Hoops Supreme Court	1	2.00	1.50	.80
1993 SkyBox	18	.30	.25	.12
1993 SkyBox	145	.50	.40	.20
1993 SkyBox	332	.25	.20	.10
1993 SkyBox Center Stage	3	4.00	3.00	1.50
1993 SkyBox Dynamic Dunks	2	8.00	6.00	3.25
1993 SkyBox Showdown Series	8	1.25	.90	.50
1993 Topps	1	.25	.20	.10
1993 Topps	104	.20	.15	.08
1993 Topps	204	.25	.20	.10
1993 Topps	373	.40	.30	.15
1993 Topps	393	.25	.20	.10
1993 Topps Finest	125	3.50	2.75	1.50
1993 Topps Finest	200	6.00	4.50	2.50
1993 Topps Finest Main Attraction	21	15.00	11.00	6.00
1993 Topps Stadium Club	110	.45	.35	.20
1993 Topps Stadium Club	177	.50	.40	.20
1993 Topps Stadium Club	188	.50	.40	.20
1993 Topps Stadium Club	320	.75	.60	.30
1993 Topps Stadium Club Beam Team	5	10.00	7.50	4.00
1993 Topps Stadium Club Rim Rockers	3	5.00	3.75	2.00
1993 Upper Deck	174	.30	.25	.12
1993 Upper Deck	280	.60	.45	.25
1993 Upper Deck	498	.35	.25	.14
1993 Upper Deck All-NBA	1	2.00	1.50	.80
1993 Upper Deck Jordan's Flight Team	2	12.00	9.00	4.75
1993 Upper Deck Locker Talk	8	4.00	3.00	1.50
1993 Upper Deck SE	91	.75	.60	.30
1993 Upper Deck SE Behind the Glass	4	6.00	4.50	2.50
1993 Upper Deck SE West Future All Stars	10	22.00	16.50	8.75
1993 Upper Deck Team MVP's	21	2.00	1.50	.80
1993 Upper Deck 3-D Basketball	54	.60	.25	.12
1993 Upper Deck 3-D Basketball	90	.65	.50	.25
1993 Upper Deck 3-D Triple Double	1	4.00	3.00	1.50
1994 Fleer	175	.60	.45	.25
1994 Fleer Flair	116	2.25	1.75	.90
1994 Fleer Flair Scoring Power	1	5.00	3.75	2.00
1994 Fleer Jam Session	147	.80	.60	.30
1994 Fleer Jam Session GameBreakers	1	3.00	2.25	1.25
1994 Fleer Jam Session Slam Dunk Heroes	1	12.50	9.50	5.00
1994 Fleer NBA All-Stars	14	1.75	1.25	.70
1994 Fleer Superstars	1	18.00	13.50	7.25
1994 Fleer Team Leaders	7	10.00	7.50	4.00
1994 Fleer Towers of Power	1	5.00	3.75	2.00
1994 Fleer Ultra	146	.65	.50	.25
1994 Fleer Ultra All-NBA Team	6	2.50	2.00	1.00
1994 Fleer Ultra Scoring Kings	1	20.00	15.00	8.00
1994 Fleer Ultra Ultra Power	1	3.00	2.25	1.25
1994 NBA Hoops	166	.50	.40	.20
1994 NBA Hoops	238	.25	.20	.10
1994 NBA Hoops Big Numbers	12	10.00	7.50	4.00
1994 NBA Hoops Power Ratings	41	6.00	4.50	2.50
1994 NBA Hoops Supreme Court	36	3.00	2.25	1.25
1994 SkyBox	128	.60	.45	.25
1994 SkyBox	176	.30	.25	.12
1994 SkyBox Center Stage	8	30.00	22.00	12.00
1994 Topps	109	.30	.25	.12
1994 Topps	195	.30	.25	.12
1994 Topps Finest	34	2.00	1.50	.80
1994 Topps Stadium Club	13	.70	.50	.30
1994 Topps Stadium Club Clear Cut	21	10.00	7.50	4.00
1994 Topps Stadium Club Dynasty and Destiny	10A	3.00	2.25	1.25
1994 Topps Super Scorers	9	4.00	3.00	1.50
1994 Upper Deck	17	.35	.25	.14
1994 Upper Deck	121	.75	.60	.30
1994 Upper Deck Collector's Choice 2,000 Pts	1	7.00	5.25	2.75

Set	Card #	NM	EX	VG
1994 Upper Deck Collector's Choice	186	.35	.25	.14
1994 Upper Deck Collector's Choice	199	.35	.25	.14
1994 Upper Deck Collector's Choice	234	.70	.50	.30
1994 Upper Deck Collector's Choice	392	.40	.30	.15
1994 Upper Deck Predictors Hobby	1	10.00	7.50	4.00
1994 Upper Deck Predictors Retail	9	3.00	2.25	1.25
1994 Upper Deck Predictors Hobby	17	6.00	4.50	2.50

Rick Barry

Set	Card #	NM	EX	VG
1971 Topps	147	3.00	1.50	.90
1971 Topps	149	2.00	1.00	.60
1971 Topps	170 (R)	55.00	27.00	16.50
1972 Topps	44	17.00	8.50	5.10
1972 Topps	242	5.00	2.50	1.50
1972 Topps	244	4.00	2.00	1.25
1972 Topps	250	13.00	6.50	4.00
1972 Topps	259	5.00	2.50	1.50
1973 Topps	90	13.00	6.50	4.00
1973 Topps	156	3.00	1.50	.90
1974 Topps	50	10.00	5.00	3.00
1974 Topps	87	2.00	1.00	.60
1974 Topps	147	.75	.40	.25
1975 Topps	1	9.00	4.50	2.75
1975 Topps	3	4.00	2.00	1.25
1975 Topps	6	3.00	1.50	.90
1975 Topps	100	9.00	4.50	2.75
1975 Topps	122	2.00	1.00	.60
1976 Topps	50	9.00	4.50	2.75
1976 Topps	132	5.00	2.50	1.50
1977 Topps	130	5.00	2.50	1.50
1978 Topps	60	3.00	1.50	.90
1979 Topps	120	2.25	1.25	.70
1980 Topps	28	1.00	.50	.30
1980 Topps	116	1.00	.50	.30

Set	Card #	MT	NM	EX
1985 Star Co. Schick Legends	2	6.00	4.50	2.50

Elgin Baylor

Set	Card #	NM	EX	VG
1961-62 Fleer	3 (R)	350.00	262.00	140.00
1961-62 Fleer	46	95.00	71.00	38.00
1969 Topps	35	60.00	45.00	24.00
1970 Topps	65	38.00	19.00	11.50
1970 Topps	113	15.00	7.50	4.50
1971 Topps	10	25.00	12.50	7.50

Walt Bellamy

Set	Card #	NM	EX	VG
1961-62 Fleer	4 (R)	45.00	34.00	18.00
1969 Topps	95	10.00	7.50	4.00
1970 Topps	18	5.00	2.50	1.50
1971 Topps	116	4.50	2.25	1.25
1972 Topps	97	3.00	1.50	.90
1973 Topps	46	1.50	.70	.45
1974 Topps	65	2.00	1.00	.60
1974 Topps	81	4.50	2.25	1.25

Set	Card #	MT	NM	EX
1985 Star Co. Schick Legends	4	2.00	1.50	.80

Blank-back: Usually used to refer to a card that has no printing on the back because of a manufacturing mistake. Cards that were intentionally issued without printing on the back are also known as blank-backed.

Bowman: A very famous card company that made baseball cards from 1948-55, football cards from 1948-55, and basketball cards in 1948. Bowman was bought by Topps in 1956 and card production ceased. Topps revived the Bowman name in 1989 to date for a set of baseball cards.

Henry Bibby

Set	Card #	NM	EX	VG
1973 Topps	48 (R)	4.50	2.25	1.25
1974 Topps	16	.50	.25	.15
1975 Topps	146	.50	.25	.15
1976 Topps	36	1.00	.50	.30
1977 Topps	2	.25	.13	.08
1978 Topps	65	.25	.13	.08
1979 Topps	3	.20	.10	.06
1980 Topps	10	.25	.13	.08
1980 Topps	150	.25	.13	.08

Set	Card #	MT	NM	EX
1981 Topps	90	.15	.11	.06

Dave Bing

Set	Card #	NM	EX	VG
1969 Topps	55 (R)	40.00	30.00	16.00
1970 Topps	125	10.00	5.00	3.00
1971 Topps	78	7.00	3.50	2.00
1972 Topps	35	6.00	3.00	1.75
1973 Topps	170	4.50	2.25	1.25
1974 Topps	40	4.00	2.00	1.25
1974 Topps	86	1.00	.50	.30
1975 Topps	121	2.00	1.00	.60
1975 Topps	160	2.50	1.25	.70
1976 Topps	76	2.50	1.25	.70
1978 Topps	61	1.50	.70	.45

Set	Card #	MT	NM	EX
1985 Star Co. Schick Legends	5	2.00	1.50	.80

Bid price: The price an investor, dealer, etc., offers to buy cards.

Larry Bird

Set	Card #	NM	EX	VG
1980 Topps	6 (R)	475.00	237.00	142.00
1980 Topps	48	25.00	12.50	7.50
1980 Topps	49	25.00	12.50	7.50
1980 Topps	94	80.00	40.00	24.00
1980 Topps	98	20.00	10.00	6.00
1980 Topps	165	20.00	10.00	6.00

Set	Card #	MT	NM	EX
1981 Topps	4	25.00	18.50	10.00
1981 Topps	101	12.00	9.00	4.75
1981 Topps	45	2.50	2.00	1.00
1983 Star Co.	26	400.00	300.00	160.00
1983 Star Co. All-Star Game	2	30.00	22.00	12.00
1983 Star Co. All-Star Game	29	15.00	11.00	6.00
1984 Star Co.	1	190.00	142.00	76.00
1984 Star Co.	12	95.00	71.00	38.00
1984 Star Co. All-Star Game	2	50.00	37.00	20.00
1984 Star Co. Awards Banquet	8	27.00	20.00	11.00
1984 Star Co. Awards Banquet	10	10.00	7.50	4.00
1984 Star Co. Awards Banquet	15	27.00	20.00	11.00
1984 Star Co. Court Kings	18	30.00	22.00	12.00
1985 Star Co.	95	130.00	97.00	52.00
1985 Star Co. Last 11 R.O.Y.	6	90.00	67.00	36.00
1985 Star Co. Lite All-Stars	2	90.00	67.00	36.00
1986 Fleer	9	45.00	34.00	18.00
1986 Star Co. Best of the Best	3	120.00	90.00	48.00
1986 Star Co. Court Kings	4	55.00	41.00	22.00
1987 Fleer	11	30.00	22.00	12.00
1988 Fleer	9	11.00	8.25	4.50
1988 Fleer	124	4.50	3.50	1.75
1989 Fleer	8	3.50	2.75	1.50
1989 NBA Hoops	150	1.25	.90	.50
1990 Fleer	8	.60	.45	.25
1990 Fleer All-Stars	2	1.25	.90	.50
1990 NBA Hoops	2	.65	.50	.25
1990 NBA Hoops	39	.75	.60	.30
1990 NBA Hoops	356	.25	.20	.10
1990 SkyBox	14	1.00	.70	.40
1991 Fleer	8	.40	.30	.15
1991 Fleer	373	.30	.25	.12
1991 NBA Hoops	9	.50	.40	.20
1991 NBA Hoops	314	.25	.20	.10
1991 NBA Hoops	319	.25	.20	.10
1991 NBA Hoops	451	.25	.20	.10
1991 NBA Hoops	532	.25	.20	.10
1991 NBA Hoops	576	1.50	1.25	.60
1991 SkyBox	12	.75	.60	.30
1991 SkyBox	460	.30	.25	.12
1991 SkyBox	531	1.25	.90	.50
1991 SkyBox	591	.50	.40	.20

Set	Card #	MT	NM	EX
1991 Upper Deck	77	.40	.30	.15
1991 Upper Deck	344	.75	.60	.30
1992 Fleer	11	.85	.60	.35
1992 Fleer	256	.50	.40	.20
1992 NBA Hoops	10	.50	.40	.20
1992 NBA Hoops	322	.20	.15	.08
1992 NBA Hoops	337	.30	.25	.12
1992 SkyBox	10	1.50	1.25	.60
1992 SkyBox I Olympic Team	6USA	6.00	4.50	2.50
1992 Topps	1	.50	.40	.20
1992 Topps	100	.25	.20	.10
1992 Topps Stadium Club	33	1.50	1.25	.60
1992 Topps Stadium Club	194	1.00	.70	.40
1992 Upper Deck	33a	1.25	.90	.50
1992 Upper Deck	507	.40	.30	.15
1993 Fleer Living Legends	2	10.00	7.50	4.00
1993 NBA Hoops	422	.25	.20	.10
1993 SkyBox Showdown Series	12	2.50	2.00	1.00
1993 Topps Finest	2	7.00	5.25	2.75
1992 Upper Deck 15000- Point Club	9	2.00	1.50	.80
1993 Fleer	138	.05	.04	.02
1993 Fleer Jam Session	146	.10	.08	.04
1993 Fleer Ultra	125	.10	.08	.04
1993 NBA Hoops	144	.06	.05	.02
1993 SkyBox	125	.05	.04	.02
1993 Topps	85	.05	.04	.02
1993 Topps Stadium Club	342	.10	.08	.04
1993 Upper Deck	127	.05	.04	.02

Mookie Blaylock

Rolando Blackman

Set	Card #	MT	NM	EX
1983 Star Co.	50 (R)	80.00	60.00	32.00
1984 Star Co.	251	9.00	6.75	3.50
1984 Star Co. Court Kings	27	3.00	2.25	1.25
1985 Star Co.	159	8.00	6.00	3.25
1986 Fleer	11 (R)	6.00	4.50	2.50
1986 Star Co. Court Kings	5	3.00	2.25	1.25
1987 Fleer	12	1.50	1.25	.60
1988 Fleer	28	.75	.60	.30
1989 Fleer	32	.07	.05	.03
1989 NBA Hoops	20	.05	.04	.02
1990 Fleer	38	.03	.02	.01
1990 NBA Hoops	14	.15	.11	.06
1990 NBA Hoops	82	.07	.05	.03
1990 NBA Hoops	360	.05	.04	.02
1990 SkyBox	60	.05	.04	.02
1991 Fleer	43	.07	.05	.03
1991 NBA Hoops	43	.07	.05	.03
1991 NBA Hoops	459	.05	.04	.02
1991 SkyBox	57	.05	.04	.02
1991 Upper Deck	154	.05	.04	.02
1992 Fleer	149	.05	.04	.02
1992 Fleer	393	.06	.05	.02
1992 Fleer Sharpshooters	18	.50	.40	.20
1992 Fleer Ultra	319	.10	.08	.04
1992 NBA Hoops	45	.05	.04	.02
1992 NBA Hoops	433	.05	.04	.02
1992 SkyBox	47	.05	.04	.02
1992 SkyBox	373	.05	.04	.02
1992 Topps	355	.04	.03	.02
1992 Topps Archives	14	.05	.04	.02
1992 Topps Stadium Club	226	.10	.08	.04
1992 Upper Deck	89	.05	.04	.02
1992 Upper Deck	321	.05	.04	.02

Set	Card #	MT	NM	EX
1990 Fleer	117 (R)	.50	.40	.20
1990 NBA Hoops	193 (R)	.50	.40	.20
1990 SkyBox	176 (R)	.90	.70	.35
1991 Fleer	128	.10	.08	.04
1991 NBA Hoops	131	.06	.05	.02
1991 SkyBox	177	.08	.06	.03
1991 Upper Deck	235	.10	.08	.04
1992 Fleer	141	.08	.06	.03
1992 Fleer	301	.05	.04	.02
1992 Fleer Total "D"	13	5.50	4.25	2.25
1992 Fleer Ultra	115	.10	.08	.04
1992 Fleer Ultra	221	.10	.08	.04
1992 NBA Hoops	145	.08	.06	.03
1992 NBA Hoops	351	.05	.04	.02
1992 SkyBox	152	.08	.06	.03
1992 SkyBox	367	.05	.04	.02
1992 Topps	180	.04	.03	.02
1992 Topps	268	.04	.03	.02
1992 Topps Archives	117	.05	.04	.02
1992 Topps Stadium Club	64	.10	.08	.04
1992 Topps Stadium Club	344	.10	.08	.04
1992 Upper Deck	151	.05	.04	.02
1992 Upper Deck	318	.05	.04	.02
1993 Fleer	2	.05	.04	.02
1993 Fleer Jam Session	2	.10	.08	.04
1993 Fleer Ultra	2	.10	.08	.04
1993 NBA Hoops	2	.06	.05	.02
1993 SkyBox	25	.05	.04	.02
1993 Topps	125	.05	.04	.02
1993 Topps Finest	135	.35	.25	.14
1993 Topps Stadium Club	249	.10	.08	.04
1993 Upper Deck	279	.05	.04	.02
1993 Upper Deck	442	.05	.04	.02
1993 Upper Deck SE	87	.20	.15	.08
1994 Fleer	2	.08	.06	.03
1994 Fleer All-Defensive Team	1	.50	.40	.20
1994 Fleer Flair	2	.25	.20	.10
1994 Fleer Jam Session	2	.10	.08	.04
1994 Fleer NBA All-Stars	3	.35	.25	.14
1994 Fleer Team Leaders	1	5.00	3.75	2.00
1994 Fleer Total D	1	1.00	.70	.40
1994 Fleer Triple Threats	1	.50	.40	.20
1994 Fleer Ultra	2	.10	.08	.04
1994 NBA Hoops	2	.04	.03	.02
1994 NBA Hoops	226	.04	.03	.02

1994 NBA Hoops Power Ratings	1	.50	.40	.20
1994 NBA Hoops Supreme Court	1	.30	.25	.12
1994 SkyBox	2	.06	.05	.02
1994 Topps	2	.06	.05	.02
1994 Topps Finest	125	.20	.15	.08
1994 Topps Stadium Club	53	.08	.06	.03
1994 Topps Stadium Club	54	.08	.06	.03
1994 Topps Super Passers	3	1.75	1.25	.70
1994 Topps Super Stealers	3	2.00	1.50	.80
1994 Upper Deck Collector's Choice 750 Assists	3	3.50	2.75	1.50
1994 Upper Deck Collector's Choice	90	.06	.05	.02
1994 Upper Deck Predictors Retail	12	4.00	3.00	1.50
1994 Upper Deck Special Edition	3	.25	.20	.10

1993 Upper Deck	1	.05	.04	.02
1993 Upper Deck	437	.05	.04	.02
1993 Upper Deck Locker Talk	12	1.00	.70	.40
1993 Upper Deck SE	163	.10	.08	.04
1994 Fleer	19	.05	.04	.02
1994 Fleer Jam Session	18	.10	.08	.04
1994 Fleer Ultra	18	.08	.06	.03
1994 NBA Hoops	16	.04	.03	.02
1994 SkyBox	14	.06	.05	.02
1994 Topps	69	.06	.05	.02
1994 Topps Finest	51	.20	.15	.08
1994 Topps Finest	94	.15	.11	.06
1994 Topps Stadium Club	134	.08	.06	.03
1994 Topps Super Passers	2	2.25	1.75	.90
1994 Upper Deck Collector's Choice 750 Assists	4	4.50	3.50	1.75
1994 Upper Deck Collector's Choice	101	.05	.04	.02
1994 Upper Deck Predictors Retail	(15)	4.00	3.00	1.50
1994 Upper Deck Special Edition	7	.20	.15	.08

Muggsy Bogues

Set	Card #	MT	NM	EX
1988 Fleer	13 (R)	4.00	3.00	1.50
1989 NBA Hoops	218	.05	.04	.02
1990 Fleer	16	.03	.02	.01
1990 NBA Hoops	50	.03	.02	.01
1990 SkyBox	26	.05	.04	.02
1991 Fleer	17	.05	.04	.02
1991 NBA Hoops	18	.05	.04	.02
1991 NBA Hoops	505	.05	.04	.02
1991 SkyBox	23	.05	.04	.02
1991 Upper Deck	242	.05	.04	.02
1992 Fleer	20	.05	.04	.02
1992 Fleer Ultra	17	.10	.08	.04
1992 Fleer Ultra Playmakers	2	.50	.40	.20
1992 NBA Hoops	19	.05	.04	.02
1992 SkyBox	19	.05	.04	.02
1992 SkyBox II Thunder and Lightning	5	16.00	12.00	6.50
1992 Topps	176	.04	.03	.02
1992 Topps Archives	89	.05	.04	.02
1992 Topps Stadium Club	71	.10	.08	.04
1992 Upper Deck	222	.05	.04	.02
1993 Fleer	17	.05	.04	.02
1993 Fleer Jam Session	17	.15	.11	.06
1993 Fleer Ultra	16	.10	.08	.04
1993 Fleer Ultra Famous Nicknames	2	.75	.60	.30
1993 NBA Hoops	18	.06	.05	.02
1993 SkyBox	36	.05	.04	.02
1993 Topps	9	.05	.04	.02
1993 Topps Finest	53	.35	.25	.14
1993 Topps Stadium Club	204	.10	.08	.04

Bill Bradley

Set	Card #	NM	EX	VG
1969 Topps	43 (R)	150.00	112.00	60.00
1970 Topps	7	55.00	27.50	16.50
1970 Topps	172	15.00	7.50	4.50
1971 Topps	2	30.00	15.00	9.00
1972 Topps	122	20.00	10.00	6.00
1973 Topps	82	14.00	7.00	4.25
1974 Topps	93	5.00	2.50	1.50
1974 Topps	113	10.00	5.00	3.00
1975 Topps	3	4.00	2.00	1.25
1975 Topps	37	9.50	4.75	2.75
1975 Topps	128	2.50	1.25	.70
1976 Topps	43	14.00	7.00	4.25

Borders: The portion of a card which surrounds the picture. Borders are usually white but are sometimes colored. The condition of a card's borders is one of the vital components in determining a card's grade.

Boxed set: A set of cards, usually consisting of either 33 or 44 cards, issued as a complete set and sold in its own box at a large chain or discount store. Boxed sets are usually made by one of the major manufacturers and contain cards of only the biggest names or hottest rookies.

Fred Brown

Set	Card #	NM	EX	VG
1973 Topps	103 (R)	4.00	2.00	1.25
1974 Topps	97	1.00	.50	.30
1974 Topps	125	1.00	.50	.30
1975 Topps	41	1.50	.70	.45
1976 Topps	15	2.00	1.00	.60
1977 Topps	30	.50	.25	.15
1978 Topps	59	.60	.30	.20
1979 Topps	46	.45	.25	.14
1980 Topps	77	.25	.13	.08
1980 Topps	165	20.00	10.00	6.00

Set	Card #	MT	NM	EX
1981 Topps	43	.15	.11	.06
1983 Star Co.	194	2.00	1.50	.80

> Buy price: The price which a dealer is willing to pay for cards or memorabilia. A dealer's buy price is usually quite a bit lower than that item's catalog or retail price.

Larry Brown

Set	Card #	NM	EX	VG
1971 Topps	152 (R)	25.00	12.50	7.50
1972 Topps	264	3.00	1.50	.90

Set	Card #	MT	NM	EX
1989 NBA Hoops	102	.10	.08	.04
1990 NBA Hoops	328	.03	.02	.01
1990 SkyBox	324	.10	.08	.04
1991 Fleer	183	.05	.04	.02
1991 NBA Hoops	244	.05	.04	.02
1991 SkyBox	401	.05	.04	.02
1992 Fleer	97	.05	.04	.02
1992 NBA Hoops	250	.05	.04	.02
1992 SkyBox	266	.05	.04	.02
1993 NBA Hoops	240	.06	.05	.02
1994 NBA Hoops	284	.04	.03	.02

Quinn Buckner

Set	Card #	NM	EX	VG
1978 Topps	29 (R)	3.00	1.50	.90
1980 Topps	11	.25	.13	.08
1980 Topps	50	2.00	1.00	.60
1980 Topps	138	.25	.13	.08
1980 Topps	144	.25	.13	.08

Set	Card #	MT	NM	EX
1981 Topps	56	.15	.11	.06
1983 Star Co.	28	3.00	2.25	1.25
1984 Star Co.	3	2.75	2.00	1.00
1985 Star Co.	82	2.50	2.00	1.00
1993 NBA Hoops	235	.06	.05	.02

Austin Carr

Set	Card #	NM	EX	VG
1972 Topps	90 (R)	7.00	3.50	2.00
1973 Topps	115	1.50	.70	.45
1974 Topps	60	2.00	1.00	.60
1974 Topps	85	1.00	.50	.30
1975 Topps	105	1.00	.50	.30
1976 Topps	53	2.00	1.00	.60
1977 Topps	32	.75	.40	.25
1978 Topps	9	.25	.13	.08
1979 Topps	76	.20	.10	.06
1980 Topps	14	2.50	1.25	.70
1980 Topps	102	.25	.13	.08

> Caption: The title on a card which identifies or describes the subject pictured, but may also be a line of dialogue. It generally appears under the illustration and/or on the back.

Bill Cartwright

Wilt Chamberlain

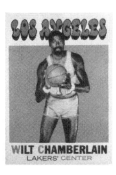

WILT CHAMBERLAIN
LAKERS' CENTER

Set	Card #	NM	EX	VG
1980 Topps	42	.25	.13	.08
1980 Topps	53	.25	.13	.08
1980 Topps	60	3.00	1.50	.90
1980 Topps	68	.75	.40	.25
1980 Topps	94 (R)	80.00	40.00	24.00
1980 Topps	148	3.00	1.50	.90
1980 Topps	166	.75	.40	.25

Set	Card #	MT	NM	EX
1981 Topps	26	.75	.60	.30
1981 Topps	102	.40	.30	.15
1981 Topps	58	2.00	1.50	.80
1983 Star Co.	62	7.00	5.25	2.75
1984 Star Co.	29	5.00	3.75	2.00
1985 Star Co.	167	4.00	3.00	1.50
1987 Fleer	17	2.00	1.50	.80
1989 Fleer	19	.07	.05	.03
1989 NBA Hoops	255	.05	.04	.02
1990 Fleer	23	.03	.02	.01
1990 NBA Hoops	61	.03	.02	.01
1990 SkyBox	38	.05	.04	.02
1991 Fleer	26	.07	.05	.03
1991 NBA Hoops	27	.05	.04	.02
1991 SkyBox	35	.05	.04	.02
1991 Upper Deck	189	.05	.04	.02
1992 Fleer	29	.05	.04	.02
1992 Fleer Ultra	25	.10	.08	.04
1992 NBA Hoops	28	.05	.04	.02
1992 SkyBox	29	.05	.04	.02
1992 Topps	165	.04	.03	.02
1992 Topps Stadium Club	174	.10	.08	.04
1992 Upper Deck	93	.05	.04	.02
1993 Fleer	26	.05	.04	.02
1993 Fleer Jam Session	29	.10	.08	.04
1993 Fleer Ultra	28	.10	.08	.04
1993 NBA Hoops	26	.06	.05	.02
1993 SkyBox	43	.05	.04	.02
1993 Topps	45	.05	.04	.02
1993 Topps Finest	170	.35	.25	.14
1993 Topps Stadium Club	16	.10	.08	.04
1993 Upper Deck	155	.05	.04	.02
1993 Upper Deck SE	62	.10	.08	.04
1994 Fleer	372	.05	.04	.02
1994 Fleer Jam Session	177	.10	.08	.04
1994 NBA Hoops	25	.04	.03	.02
1994 NBA Hoops	373	.04	.03	.02
1994 Upper Deck Collector's Choice	242	.05	.04	.02
1994 Upper Deck Special Edition	11	.20	.15	.08

Set	Card #	NM	EX	VG
1961-62 Fleer	8 (R)	1300.	650.00	390.00
1961-62 Fleer	47	350.00	262.00	140.00
1969 Topps	1	190.00	142.00	76.00
1970 Topps	50	90.00	45.00	27.00
1970 Topps	173	16.00	8.00	4.75
1971 Topps	70	50.00	25.00	15.00
1971 Topps	140	7.50	3.75	2.25
1971 Topps	142	10.00	5.00	3.00
1972 Topps	1	40.00	20.00	12.00
1972 Topps	159	8.00	4.00	2.50
1972 Topps	168	25.00	12.50	7.50
1972 Topps	173	10.00	5.00	3.00
1972 Topps	175	12.00	6.00	3.50
1973 Topps	64	6.00	3.00	1.75
1973 Topps	80	22.00	11.00	6.50
1973 Topps	155	6.00	3.00	1.75
1973 Topps	157	6.00	3.00	1.75
1974 Topps	250	30.00	15.00	9.00

Tom Chambers

Tom Chambers

Set	Card #	MT	NM	EX
1983 Star Co.	195 (R)	30.00	22.00	12.00
1984 Star Co.	113	14.00	10.50	5.50
1984 Star Co. Court Kings	39	5.00	3.75	2.00
1985 Star Co.	66	10.00	7.50	4.00
1986 Fleer	15 (R)	8.00	6.00	3.25
1986 Star Co. Best of the Best	4	10.00	7.50	4.00
1986 Star Co. Court Kings	6	4.00	3.00	1.50
1987 Fleer	19	2.50	2.00	1.00
1988 Fleer	106	.75	.60	.30
1989 Fleer	119	.30	.25	.12
1989 NBA Hoops	170	.15	.11	.06
1989 NBA Hoops	197	.15	.11	.06
1990 Fleer	146	.20	.15	.08

Case: A sealed case containing wax boxes or other product units which card companies sell at wholesale to dealers or retail stores. For instance, a 1990 Topps "wax case" is made up of 20 "wax boxes.

Set	Card #			
1990 Fleer All-Stars	8	.30	.25	.12
1990 NBA Hoops	15	.15	.11	.06
1990 NBA Hoops	234	.15	.11	.06
1990 SkyBox	220	.25	.20	.10
1991 Fleer	158	.10	.08	.04
1991 NBA Hoops	163	.06	.05	.02
1991 NBA Hoops	261	.10	.08	.04
1991 NBA Hoops	489	.10	.08	.04
1991 NBA Hoops	523	.10	.08	.04
1991 NBA Hoops MVP All-Stars	8	1.00	.70	.40
1991 SkyBox	223	.10	.08	.04
1991 Upper Deck	56	.08	.06	.03
1991 Upper Deck	174	.08	.06	.03
1992 Fleer	180	.08	.06	.03
1992 Fleer Ultra	143	.12	.09	.05
1992 NBA Hoops	179	.06	.05	.02
1992 SkyBox	189	.08	.06	.03
1992 Topps	18	.04	.03	.02
1992 Topps	201	.04	.03	.02
1992 Topps Archives	15	.05	.04	.02
1992 Topps Stadium Club	152	.10	.08	.04
1992 Upper Deck	64	.15	.11	.06
1992 Upper Deck	114	.05	.04	.02
1992 Upper Deck	409	.05	.04	.02
1992 Upper Deck 15000-Point Club	12	2.00	1.50	.80
1993 Fleer	165	.05	.04	.02
1993 Fleer	387	.05	.04	.02
1993 Fleer Jam Session	222	.10	.08	.04
1993 Fleer Ultra	348	.10	.08	.04
1993 NBA Hoops	412	.06	.05	.02
1993 SkyBox	286	.05	.04	.02
1993 Topps	220	.05	.04	.02
1993 Topps Finest	20	.35	.25	.14
1993 Topps Stadium Club	338	.10	.08	.04
1993 Upper Deck	410	.05	.04	.02
1993 Upper Deck SE	71	.10	.08	.04
1994 Fleer	220	.05	.04	.02
1994 NBA Hoops	208	.04	.03	.02
1994 Topps	117	.06	.05	.02
1994 Topps Stadium Club	51	.08	.06	.03
1994 Upper Deck Collector's Choice	342	.05	.04	.02

Don Chaney

DON CHANEY

Set	Card #	NM	EX	VG
1970 Topps	47 (R)	9.00	4.50	2.75
1971 Topps	82	3.00	1.50	.90
1972 Topps	131	2.00	1.00	.60
1973 Topps	57	2.00	1.00	.60
1974 Topps	133	1.00	.50	.30
1975 Topps	265	1.50	.70	.45
1977 Topps	27	.30	.15	.09

Set	Card #	MT	NM	EX
1989 NBA Hoops	123	1.00	.70	.40

1990 NBA Hoops	314	.03	.02	.01
1990 NBA Hoops	350	.05	.04	.02
1990 SkyBox	310	.07	.05	.03
1991 Fleer	73	.03	.02	.01
1991 NBA Hoops	230	.05	.04	.02
1991 SkyBox	387	.05	.04	.02
1993 Fleer Flair USA Basketball	1	.20	.15	.08
1993 Fleer Ultra	372	.10	.08	.04
1993 NBA Hoops	237	.06	.05	.02
1994 NBA Hoops	281	.04	.03	.02

Calbert Cheaney

Set	Card #	MT	NM	EX
1993 Fleer	393 (R)	.55	.40	.20
1993 Fleer Jam Session	231 (R)	.85	.60	.35
1993 Fleer Jam Session Rookie Standouts	3	1.50	1.25	.60
1993 Fleer Lottery Exchange	6	1.50	1.25	.60
1993 Fleer Ultra	193 (R)	.90	.70	.35
1993 Fleer Ultra	354	.40	.30	.15
1993 Fleer Ultra All-Rookies	3	3.00	2.25	1.25
1993 NBA Hoops	416 (R)	.65	.50	.25
1993 NBA Hoops Draft Redemption	6	3.00	2.25	1.25
1993 NBA Hoops II Magic's All-Rookie Team	6	3.50	2.75	1.50
1993 SkyBox	191 (R)	.75	.60	.30
1993 SkyBox Draft Picks	6	3.00	2.25	1.25
1993 Topps	158 (R)	.60	.45	.25
1993 Topps	250	.35	.25	.14
1993 Topps Finest	84 (R)	2.00	1.50	.80
1993 Topps Stadium Club	127 (R)	1.00	.70	.40
1993 Topps Stadium Club	329	.60	.45	.25
1993 Topps Stadium Club Beam Team	27	4.00	3.00	1.50
1993 Upper Deck	164 (R)	.65	.50	.25
1993 Upper Deck	354	.30	.25	.12
1993 Upper Deck	487	.45	.35	.20
1993 Upper Deck Rookie Exchange Gold/Silver	6	1.50	1.25	.60
1993 Upper Deck Rookie Standouts	13	3.00	2.25	1.25
1993 Upper Deck SE	40 (R)	.50	.40	.20
1993 Upper Deck SE	182	.30	.25	.12
1993 Upper Deck SE East Future All Stars	15	9.00	6.75	3.50
1993 Upper Deck 3-D Basketball	84 (R)	.50	.20	.10
1994 Fleer	230	.30	.25	.12
1994 Fleer Flair	153	.30	.25	.12
1994 Fleer Jam Session	193	.25	.20	.10
1994 Fleer Rookie Sensations	5	2.75	2.00	1.00

1994 Fleer Ultra	192	.40	.30	.15
1994 NBA Hoops	219	.20	.15	.08
1994 NBA Hoops	426	.25	.20	.10
1994 NBA Hoops Supreme Court	49	.65	.50	.25
1994 SkyBox	171	.35	.25	.14
1994 SkyBox Ragin' Rookies	24	1.00	.70	.40
1994 Topps	125	.15	.11	.06
1994 Topps Stadium Club	164	.35	.25	.14
1994 Upper Deck	40	.35	.25	.14
1994 Upper Deck Col.'s Choice Hobby Blowups	5	1.00	.70	.40
1994 Upper Deck Collector's Choice	40	.08	.06	.03
1994 Upper Deck Special Edition	88	.75	.60	.30

Maurice Cheeks

Set	Card #	NM	EX	VG
1980 Topps	30	.75	.40	.25
1980 Topps	66 (R)	35.00	17.50	10.50
1980 Topps	154	5.00	2.50	1.50
1980 Topps	171	1.00	.50	.30

Set	Card #	MT	NM	EX
1981 Topps	90	1.50	1.25	.60
1981 Topps	59	1.50	1.25	.60
1983 Star Co.	2	12.00	9.00	4.75
1983 Star Co. All-Star Game	3	2.00	1.50	.80
1984 Star Co.	203	5.00	3.75	2.00
1984 Star Co. Court Kings	29	2.50	2.00	1.00
1985 Star Co.	1	4.00	3.00	1.50
1986 Fleer	16	3.00	2.25	1.25
1986 Star Co. Court Kings	7	3.00	2.25	1.25
1987 Fleer	20	1.50	1.25	.60
1988 Fleer	86	.65	.50	.25
1989 Fleer	115	.20	.15	.08
1989 NBA Hoops	65	.25	.20	.10
1989 NBA Hoops	320	.05	.04	.02
1990 Fleer	124	.05	.04	.02
1990 NBA Hoops	202	.05	.04	.02
1990 SkyBox	186	.10	.08	.04
1991 Fleer	135	.07	.05	.03
1991 Fleer	242	.03	.02	.01
1991 NBA Hoops	139	.05	.04	.02
1991 NBA Hoops	320	.05	.04	.02
1991 NBA Hoops	331	.05	.04	.02
1991 NBA Hoops	533	.05	.04	.02
1991 SkyBox	188	.05	.04	.02
1991 SkyBox	615	.05	.04	.02
1991 Upper Deck	281	.05	.04	.02
1992 Fleer Ultra	314	.10	.08	.04
1992 NBA Hoops	2	.05	.04	.02
1992 SkyBox	2	.05	.04	.02

Phil Chenier

Set	Card #	NM	EX	VG
1972 Topps	102 (R)	4.00	2.00	1.25
1973 Topps	113	1.50	.70	.45
1974 Topps	98	1.00	.50	.30
1974 Topps	165	1.00	.50	.30
1975 Topps	190	.50	.25	.15
1976 Topps	27	1.00	.50	.30
1977 Topps	55	.25	.13	.08
1979 Topps	103	.20	.10	.06

Derrick Coleman

Set	Card #	MT	NM	EX
1990 Fleer Update	60 (R)	3.00	2.25	1.25
1990 NBA Hoops	390 (R)	1.50	1.25	.60
1990 SkyBox	362 (R)	2.50	2.00	1.00
1991 Fleer	130	.40	.30	.15
1991 Fleer	388	.20	.15	.08
1991 Fleer Rookie Sensations	3	8.00	6.00	3.25
1991 NBA Hoops	134	.30	.25	.12
1991 NBA Hoops	482	.25	.20	.10
1991 NBA Hoops	519	.20	.15	.08
1991 SkyBox	180	.50	.40	.20
1991 SkyBox	318	.15	.11	.06
1991 SkyBox	502	.25	.20	.10
1991 Upper Deck	35	.25	.20	.10
1991 Upper Deck	88	.25	.20	.10
1991 Upper Deck	332	.60	.45	.25
1991 Upper Deck Holograms	7AW	1.00	.70	.40
1991 Upper Deck Rookie Standouts	10R	3.00	2.25	1.25
1992 Fleer	143	.20	.15	.08
1992 Fleer	296	.15	.11	.06
1992 Fleer Team Leaders	17	20.00	15.00	8.00
1992 Fleer Ultra	117	.40	.30	.15
1992 Fleer Ultra	210	.15	.11	.06
1992 NBA Hoops	147	.20	.15	.08

1992 SkyBox	154	.25	.20	.10
1992 SkyBox	298	.15	.11	.06
1992 Topps	230	.10	.08	.04
1992 Topps Archives	10	.10	.08	.04
1992 Topps Archives	133	.30	.25	.12
1992 Topps Stadium Club	193	.25	.20	.10
1992 Topps Stadium Club	384	.35	.25	.14
1992 Upper Deck	124	.25	.20	.10
1992 Upper Deck	485	.15	.11	.06
1992 Upper Deck	502	.10	.08	.04
1992 Upper Deck All-Division Team	2	.50	.40	.20
1992 Upper Deck Team MVP's	18TM	2.00	1.50	.80
1993 Fleer	133	.20	.15	.08
1993 Fleer Flair USA Basketball	5	.30	.25	.12
1993 Fleer Jam Session	139	.25	.20	.10
1993 Fleer NBA Superstars	3	.50	.40	.20
1993 Fleer Towers of Power	3	4.50	3.50	1.75
1993 Fleer Ultra	119	.35	.25	.14
1993 Fleer Ultra	361	.30	.25	.12
1993 Fleer Ultra All-NBA Team	11	2.50	2.00	1.00
1993 Fleer Ultra Famous Nicknames	3	1.50	1.25	.60
1993 Fleer Ultra Jam City	2	6.00	4.50	2.50
1993 Fleer Ultra Rebound Kings	2	.40	.30	.15
1993 NBA Hoops	140	.25	.20	.10
1993 NBA Hoops	439	.08	.06	.03
1993 NBA Hoops Admiral's Choice	2	.30	.25	.12
1993 SkyBox	122	.25	.20	.10
1993 SkyBox Thunder and Lightning	4	3.00	2.25	1.25
1993 Topps	166	.15	.11	.06
1993 Topps	388	.10	.08	.04
1993 Topps BlackGold	8	1.00	.70	.40
1993 Topps Finest	80	2.00	1.50	.80
1993 Topps Finest	98	1.00	.70	.40
1993 Topps Finest Main Attraction	17	5.00	3.75	2.00
1993 Topps Stadium Club	101	.20	.15	.08
1993 Topps Stadium Club	170	.15	.11	.06
1993 Topps Stadium Club	190	.25	.20	.10
1993 Topps Stadium Club	282	.25	.20	.10
1993 Topps Stadium Club Beam Team	7	4.00	3.00	1.50
1993 Upper Deck	83	.25	.20	.10
1993 Upper Deck	428	.15	.11	.06
1993 Upper Deck All-NBA	12	1.00	.60	.30
1993 Upper Deck Future Heroes	28	1.50	1.25	.60
1993 Upper Deck Jordan's Flight Team	6	5.00	3.75	2.00
1993 Upper Deck Locker Talk	7	1.50	1.25	.60
1993 Upper Deck SE	44	.30	.25	.12
1993 Upper Deck SE East Future All Stars	10	9.00	6.75	3.50
1993 Upper Deck Team MVP's	17	.50	.40	.20
1993 Upper Deck USA Basketball	1	.15	.11	.06
1993 Upper Deck 3-D Basketball	28	.10	.08	.04
1993 Upper Deck 3-D Basketball	75	.10	.08	.04
1993 Upper Deck 3-D Basketball	92	.10	.08	.04
1994 Fleer	142	.25	.20	.10
1994 Fleer Flair	96	.70	.50	.30
1994 Fleer Flair	159	.25	.20	.10
1994 Fleer Jam Session	117	.25	.20	.10
1994 Fleer NBA All-Stars	4	.75	.60	.30
1994 Fleer Pro-Visions	4	.75	.60	.30
1994 Fleer Ultra	117	.35	.25	.14
1994 Fleer Ultra All-NBA Team	11	.75	.60	.30
1994 Fleer Ultra Double Trouble	1	.65	.50	.25
1994 Fleer Ultra Ultra Power	2	1.50	1.25	.60
1994 NBA Hoops	133	.15	.11	.06
1994 NBA Hoops	227	.06	.05	.02
1994 NBA Hoops Power Ratings	34	2.00	1.50	.80
1994 NBA Hoops Supreme Court	29	.75	.60	.30
1994 SkyBox	105	.30	.25	.12
1994 SkyBox Dream Team II Dream Play	7	4.50	3.50	1.75
1994 Topps	12	.06	.05	.02
1994 Topps	103	.10	.08	.04
1994 Topps	176	.15	.11	.06
1994 Topps Finest	50	.65	.50	.25
1994 Topps Finest	101	.50	.40	.20
1994 Topps Stadium Club	23	.40	.30	.15
1994 Topps Stadium Club Clear Cut	17	3.00	2.25	1.25
1994 Topps Stadium Club Dynasty and Destiny	2B	1.00	.70	.40
1994 Topps Super Rebounders	8	1.50	1.25	.60
1994 Upper Deck	21	.15	.11	.06
1994 Upper Deck	171	.20	.15	.08
1994 Upper Deck Col.'s Choice 1,000 Rebounds	1	1.50	1.25	.60
1994 Upper Deck Collector's Choice 2,000 Pts	2	3.00	2.25	1.25
1994 Upper Deck Collector's Choice	44	.25	.20	.10
1994 Upper Deck Collector's Choice	182	.10	.08	.04
1994 Upper Deck Collector's Choice	388	.25	.20	.10
1994 Upper Deck Collector's Choice	406	.20	.15	.08
1994 Upper Deck Special Edition	56	.75	.60	.30

Doug Collins

Set	Card #	NM	EX	VG
1974 Topps	129 (R)	14.00	7.00	4.25
1975 Topps	129	1.00	.50	.30
1975 Topps	148	5.00	2.50	1.50
1976 Topps	38	6.00	3.00	1.75
1977 Topps	65	1.75	.90	.50
1978 Topps	2	1.50	.70	.45
1979 Topps	64	1.00	.50	.30
1980 Topps	32	.25	.13	.08
1980 Topps	148	3.00	1.50	.90

Bob Cousy

Set	Card #	NM	EX	VG
1957 Topps	17 (R)	525.00	262.00	157.00
1961-62 Fleer	10	240.00	180.00	96.00
1961-62 Fleer	49	65.00	49.00	26.00

Set	Card #	MT	NM	EX
1985 Star Co. Schick Legends	7	12.00	9.00	4.75

Dave Cowens

Set	Card #	NM	EX	VG
1971 Topps	47 (R)	50.00	25.00	15.00
1972 Topps	7	15.00	7.50	4.50
1973 Topps	40	6.00	3.00	1.75
1973 Topps	157	6.00	3.00	1.75
1974 Topps	82	4.00	2.00	1.25
1974 Topps	148	3.00	1.50	.90
1974 Topps	155	7.00	3.50	2.00
1975 Topps	117	2.00	1.00	.60
1975 Topps	170	7.00	3.50	2.00
1976 Topps	30	9.00	4.50	2.75
1976 Topps	131	5.00	2.50	1.50
1977 Topps	90	3.00	1.50	.90
1978 Topps	40	2.00	1.00	.60
1979 Topps	5	2.00	1.00	.60
1980 Topps	7	1.00	.50	.30
1980 Topps	95	1.00	.50	.30

Card lot: A "lot" of cards is the same card, such as a 1988 Topps Don Mattingly card, sold in a lot or "grouping" of five, 10, 25, 50, 100 or whatever number of cards. A collector purchasing a "lot" or cards gets the cards at a discounted price, as opposed to buying a single card. Example: a single Mattingly card costs $1, but 100 Mattingly cards cost $75, or 75 cents each.

Terry Cummings

Set	Card #	MT	NM	EX
1983 Star Co.	123 (R)	16.00	12.00	6.50
1983 Star Co. All-Rookies	1		7.00	5.25	2.75
1984 Star Co.	125	8.00	6.00	3.25
1984 Star Co. Court Kings	37	6.00	4.50	2.50
1985 Star Co.	124	7.00	5.25	2.75
1985 Star Co. Last 11 R.O.Y.	3	3.50	2.75	1.50
1986 Fleer	20 (R)	5.00	3.75	2.00
1986 Star Co. Best of the Best	5	10.00	7.50	4.00
1986 Star Co. Court Kings	8	3.00	2.25	1.25
1987 Fleer	23	1.50	1.25	.60
1988 Fleer	74	.50	.40	.20
1989 Fleer	142	.20	.15	.08
1989 NBA Hoops	100	.15	.11	.06
1989 NBA Hoops	256	.10	.08	.04
1989 NBA Hoops	312	.25	.20	.10
1990 Fleer	170	.07	.05	.03
1990 NBA Hoops	266	.07	.05	.03
1990 SkyBox	255	.10	.08	.04
1991 Fleer	184	.07	.05	.03
1991 NBA Hoops	189	.06	.05	.02
1991 NBA Hoops	495	.05	.04	.02
1991 SkyBox	255	.08	.06	.03
1991 Upper Deck	267	.08	.06	.03
1992 Fleer	203	.08	.06	.03
1992 Fleer Ultra	164	.12	.09	.05
1992 NBA Hoops	206	.08	.06	.03
1992 SkyBox	220	.08	.06	.03
1992 Topps	91	.04	.03	.02
1992 Topps	209	.04	.03	.02
1992 Topps Archives	24	.05	.04	.02
1992 Topps Stadium Club	120	.10	.08	.04
1992 Upper Deck	168	.08	.06	.03
1992 Upper Deck 15000-Point Club	14	2.00	1.50	.80
1993 Fleer	189	.05	.04	.02
1993 Fleer Jam Session	203	.10	.08	.04
1993 Fleer Ultra	336	.10	.08	.04
1993 NBA Hoops	197	.06	.05	.02
1993 SkyBox	277	.05	.04	.02
1993 Topps	273	.05	.04	.02
1993 Topps Finest	45	.35	.25	.14
1993 Topps Stadium Club	290	.10	.08	.04
1993 Upper Deck	273	.05	.04	.02
1994 Fleer	203	.05	.04	.02
1994 Fleer Jam Session	169	.10	.08	.04
1994 Fleer Ultra	170	.08	.06	.03
1994 Topps	35	.06	.05	.02
1994 Topps Finest	108	.20	.15	.08
1994 Topps Finest	119	.15	.11	.06
1994 Topps Stadium Club	122	.08	.06	.03
1994 Topps Stadium Club	123	.08	.06	.03
1994 Upper Deck Collector's Choice	65	.05	.04	.02
1994 Upper Deck Special Edition	79	.20	.15	.08

Billy Cunningham

Set	Card #	NM	EX	VG
1969 Topps	40 (R)	50.00	37.00	20.00
1970 Topps	108	10.00	5.00	3.00
1970 Topps	140	15.00	7.50	4.50
1971 Topps	79	8.00	4.00	2.50
1972 Topps	167	2.50	1.25	.70
1972 Topps	215	7.00	3.50	2.00
1973 Topps	200	5.00	2.50	1.50
1974 Topps	221	5.00	2.50	1.50
1974 Topps	235	4.00	2.00	1.25
1975 Topps	20	4.00	2.00	1.25
1975 Topps	129	1.00	.50	.30
1976 Topps	93	5.00	2.50	1.50

Bob Dandridge

Set	Card #	NM	EX	VG
1970 Topps	63 (R)	9.00	4.50	2.75
1971 Topps	59	2.50	1.25	.70
1972 Topps	42	1.00	.50	.30
1973 Topps	33	.70	.35	.20
1974 Topps	126	.50	.25	.15
1975 Topps	17	.50	.25	.15
1976 Topps	81	1.00	.50	.30
1977 Topps	25	.25	.13	.08
1978 Topps	92	.25	.13	.08
1979 Topps	130	.20	.10	.06
1980 Topps	85	.25	.13	.08
1980 Topps	173	.25	.13	.08

Louie Dampier

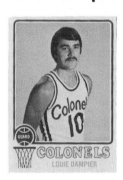

Set	Card #	NM	EX	VG
1971 Topps	224 (R)	7.00	3.50	2.00
1972 Topps	198	3.00	1.50	.90
1972 Topps	261	1.25	.60	.40
1972 Topps	264	3.00	1.50	.90
1973 Topps	183	.70	.35	.20
1973 Topps	236	1.50	.70	.45
1974 Topps	209	.50	.25	.15
1974 Topps	213	.50	.25	.15
1974 Topps	255	.50	.25	.15
1975 Topps	223	1.50	.70	.45
1975 Topps	270	.50	.25	.15
1975 Topps	280	1.25	.60	.40
1978 Topps	51	.25	.13	.08

Dealer: A person who buys, sells and trades baseball cards and other memorabilia for profit. A dealer may be full-time, part-time, own a shop, operate a mail-order business from his home, deal at baseball card shows on weekends or do any combination of the above.

Adrian Dantley

Set	Card #	NM	EX	VG
1977 Topps	56 (R)	11.00	5.50	3.30
1978 Topps	132	3.50	1.75	1.00
1979 Topps	54	1.50	.70	.45
1980 Topps	9	.25	.13	.08
1980 Topps	34	.25	.13	.08
1980 Topps	61	.25	.13	.08
1980 Topps	128	.25	.13	.08
1980 Topps	156	.25	.13	.08
1980 Topps	157	.25	.13	.08

Set	Card #	MT	NM	EX
1981 Topps	40	.75	.60	.30
1981 Topps	65	.15	.11	.06
1983 Star Co.	133	6.00	4.50	2.50
1984 Star Co.	228	7.50	5.75	3.00
1984 Star Co. All-Star Game	16	3.00	2.25	1.25
1984 Star Co. Awards Banquet	4	3.00	2.25	1.25
1984 Star Co. Awards Banquet	13	3.00	2.25	1.25
1984 Star Co. Court Kings	36	5.00	3.75	2.00

Set	Card #			
1985 Star Co.	138	5.00	3.75	2.00
1985 Star Co. Last 11 R.O.Y.	9	5.00	3.75	2.00
1985 Star Co. Lite All-Stars	9	3.00	2.25	1.25
1986 Fleer	21	2.00	1.50	.80
1986 Star Co. Court Kings	9	3.50	2.75	1.50
1987 Fleer	24	1.75	1.25	.70
1988 Fleer	39	.50	.40	.20
1989 Fleer	33	.20	.15	.08
1989 NBA Hoops	125	.15	.11	.06
1990 Fleer	39	.07	.05	.03
1990 NBA Hoops	83	.20	.15	.08
1990 SkyBox	61	.25	.20	.10

Brad Daugherty

Set	Card #	MT	NM	EX
1987 Fleer	25 (R)	8.00	6.00	3.25
1988 Fleer	22	1.25	.90	.50
1989 Fleer	25	.50	.40	.20
1989 Fleer	166	.35	.25	.14
1989 NBA Hoops	48	.15	.11	.06
1989 NBA Hoops	50	.25	.20	.10
1990 Fleer	31	.10	.08	.04
1990 NBA Hoops	73	.10	.08	.04
1990 SkyBox	50	.15	.11	.06
1991 Fleer	34	.10	.08	.04
1991 Fleer	376	.05	.04	.02
1991 NBA Hoops	36	.10	.08	.04
1991 NBA Hoops	249	.10	.08	.04
1991 NBA Hoops	457	.10	.08	.04
1991 NBA Hoops	507	.10	.08	.04
1991 SkyBox	47	.10	.08	.04
1991 Upper Deck	63	.10	.08	.04
1991 Upper Deck	364	.15	.11	.06
1991 Upper Deck	461	.12	.09	.05
1992 Fleer	40	.15	.11	.06
1992 Fleer	257	.08	.06	.03
1992 Fleer All-Stars	3	1.00	.70	.40
1992 Fleer Ultra	35	.10	.08	.04
1992 Fleer Ultra	209	.10	.08	.04
1992 Fleer Ultra All-NBA Team	13	1.00	.70	.40
1992 NBA Hoops	38	.10	.08	.04
1992 NBA Hoops	295	.07	.05	.03
1992 SkyBox	39	.10	.08	.04
1992 SkyBox	286	.08	.06	.03
1992 SkyBox II Thunder and Lightning	6	4.00	3.00	1.50
1992 Topps	116	.04	.03	.02
1992 Topps	352	.04	.03	.02
1992 Topps Archives	6	.10	.08	.04
1992 Topps Archives	78	.10	.08	.04
1992 Topps Stadium Club	245	.15	.11	.06
1992 Upper Deck	247	.10	.08	.04
1992 Upper Deck	427	.08	.06	.03
1992 Upper Deck	498	.10	.08	.04
1992 Upper Deck All-Division Team	6	.50	.40	.20

1992 Upper Deck Team MVP's	6TM	.75	.60	.30
1993 Fleer	35	.10	.08	.04
1993 Fleer All-Stars	1	.75	.60	.30
1993 Fleer Jam Session	37	.15	.11	.06
1993 Fleer Towers of Power	4	2.50	2.00	1.00
1993 Fleer Ultra	36	.10	.08	.04
1993 NBA Hoops	37	.10	.08	.04
1993 NBA Hoops	268	.10	.08	.04
1993 SkyBox	7	.15	.11	.06
1993 SkyBox	50	.15	.11	.06
1993 Topps	349	.10	.08	.04
1993 Topps Finest	100	.35	.25	.14
1993 Topps Finest	193	.35	.25	.14
1993 Topps Stadium Club	7	.15	.11	.06
1993 Topps Stadium Club	317	.15	.11	.06
1993 Upper Deck	60	.10	.08	.04
1993 Upper Deck	181	.10	.08	.04
1993 Upper Deck	241	.05	.04	.02
1993 Upper Deck	433	.10	.08	.04
1993 Upper Deck SE	67	.10	.08	.04
1993 Upper Deck 3-D Basketball	10	.10	.08	.04
1994 Fleer	39	.05	.04	.02
1994 Fleer Flair	27	.20	.15	.08
1994 Fleer Jam Session	34	.10	.08	.04
1994 Fleer Ultra	33	.08	.06	.03
1994 NBA Hoops	33	.04	.03	.02
1994 NBA Hoops Supreme Court	9	.40	.30	.15
1994 SkyBox	29	.06	.05	.02
1994 Topps	110	.06	.05	.02
1994 Topps Finest	20	.15	.11	.06
1994 Topps Stadium Club	11	.08	.06	.03
1994 Upper Deck	114	.10	.08	.04

Walter Davis

Set	Card #	NM	EX	VG
1978 Topps	10 (R)	8.00	4.00	2.50
1979 Topps	80	1.00	.50	.30
1980 Topps	70	.20	.10	.06
1980 Topps	78	.75	.40	.25
1980 Topps	158	.25	.13	.08
1980 Topps	172	.75	.40	.25

Set	Card #	MT	NM	EX
1981 Topps	33	.30	.25	.12
1983 Star Co.	109	6.00	4.50	2.50
1984 Star Co.	39	5.00	3.75	2.00
1984 Star Co. All-Star Game	17	2.50	2.00	1.00
1985 Star Co.	36	2.50	2.00	1.00
1985 Star Co. Last 11 R.O.Y.	8	5.00	3.75	2.00
1986 Fleer	23	3.00	2.25	1.25
1987 Fleer	26	1.75	1.25	.70
1989 Fleer	39	.07	.05	.03
1989 NBA Hoops	61	.05	.04	.02
1990 Fleer	47	.07	.05	.03

1990 NBA Hoops	93	.05	.04	.02
1990 SkyBox	73	.10	.08	.04
1991 Fleer	274	.03	.02	.01
1991 NBA Hoops	173	.05	.04	.02
1991 NBA Hoops	356	.08	.06	.03
1991 NBA Hoops	557	.05	.04	.02
1991 SkyBox	236	.05	.04	.02
1991 SkyBox	623	.05	.04	.02
1991 Upper Deck	380	.05	.04	.02
1991 Upper Deck	422	.08	.06	.03
1992 SkyBox	58	.05	.04	.02

Darryl Dawkins

Set	Card #	NM	EX	VG
1977 Topps	132 (R)	9.00	4.50	2.70
1978 Topps	34	1.50	.70	.45
1979 Topps	105	1.00	.50	.30
1980 Topps	55	.25	.13	.08
1980 Topps	160	.25	.13	.08

Set	Card #	MT	NM	EX
1981 Topps	29	.40	.30	.15
1981 Topps	103	.15	.11	.06
1983 Star Co.	148	6.00	4.50	2.50
1984 Star Co.	88	5.00	3.75	2.00
1985 Star Co.	61	4.00	3.00	1.50
1986 Fleer	24	3.00	2.25	1.25
1986 Star Co. Court Kings	10	3.00	2.25	1.25
1992 Fleer	300	.05	.04	.02

Dave DeBusschere

Set	Card #	NM	EX	VG
1969 Topps	85 (R)	42.00	31.00	17.00

1970 Topps	135	15.00	7.50	4.50
1970 Topps	170	7.00	3.50	2.00
1971 Topps	107	8.00	4.00	2.50
1972 Topps	105	6.00	3.00	1.75
1973 Topps	30	6.00	3.00	1.75
1974 Topps	93	5.00	2.50	1.50

Set	Card #	MT	NM	EX
1985 Star Co. Schick Legends	10	2.00	1.50	.80

Vlade Divac

Set	Card #	MT	NM	EX
1990 Fleer	91 (R)	.30	.25	.12
1990 Fleer Rookie Sensations	9	3.00	2.25	1.25
1990 NBA Hoops	2	1.50	1.25	.60
1990 NBA Hoops	154 (R)	.30	.25	.12
1990 NBA Hoops	384	.05	.04	.02
1990 SkyBox	135 (R)	.40	.30	.15
1991 Fleer	97	.15	.11	.06
1991 NBA Hoops	99	.06	.05	.02
1991 SkyBox	134	.10	.08	.04
1991 SkyBox	335	.10	.08	.04
1991 SkyBox	498	.05	.04	.02
1991 Upper Deck	175	.08	.06	.03
1992 Fleer	107	.05	.04	.02
1992 Fleer Ultra	90	.10	.08	.04
1992 NBA Hoops	108	.05	.04	.02
1992 SkyBox	114	.05	.04	.02
1992 SkyBox	294	.05	.04	.02
1992 Topps	32	.04	.03	.02
1992 Topps Archives	118	.05	.04	.02
1992 Topps Stadium Club	126	.10	.08	.04
1992 Upper Deck	199	.05	.04	.02
1992 Upper Deck Foreign Exchange	2	.60	.45	.25
1993 Fleer	101	.05	.04	.02
1993 Fleer Jam Session	105	.10	.08	.04
1993 Fleer NBA Internationals	2	.75	.50	.25
1993 Fleer Towers of Power	6	2.50	2.00	1.00
1993 Fleer Ultra	94	.10	.08	.04
1993 NBA Hoops	106	.06	.05	.02
1993 SkyBox	98	.05	.04	.02
1993 Topps	14	.05	.04	.02
1993 Topps Finest	120	.35	.25	.14
1993 Topps Finest	197	.35	.25	.14
1993 Topps Stadium Club	50	.10	.08	.04
1993 Upper Deck	16	.05	.04	.02
1993 Upper Deck	457	.08	.06	.03
1993 Upper Deck SE	12	.10	.08	.04
1993 Upper Deck 3-D Basketball	6	.10	.08	.04
1994 Fleer	108	.05	.04	.02
1994 Fleer Flair	73	.15	.11	.06
1994 Fleer Jam Session	92	.10	.08	.04
1994 Fleer Team Leaders	5	1.00	.70	.40
1994 Fleer Ultra	86	.08	.06	.03

	Card #	MT	NM	EX
1994 NBA Hoops	100	.04	.03	.02
1994 NBA Hoops	441	.06	.05	.02
1994 NBA Hoops Power Ratings	25	.30	.25	.12
1994 SkyBox	80	.06	.05	.02
1994 Topps	114	.06	.05	.02
1994 Topps Finest	89	.20	.15	.08
1994 Upper Deck	135	.10	.08	.04
1994 Upper Deck Collector's Choice	312	.08	.06	.03

Clyde Drexler

Set	Card #	MT	NM	EX
1983 Star Co.	100 (R)	200.00	150.00	80.00
1984 Star Co.	165	100.00	75.00	40.00
1984 Star Co. Slam Dunk	3	22.00	16.50	8.75
1985 Star Co.	106	70.00	52.00	28.00
1985 Star Co. Gatorade Slam Dunk	4	30.00	22.00	12.00
1986 Fleer	26 (R)	35.00	26.00	14.00
1987 Fleer	30	9.50	7.25	3.75
1988 Fleer	92	2.25	1.75	.90
1989 Fleer	128	1.00	.70	.40
1989 Fleer	164	1.00	.70	.40
1989 NBA Hoops	69	.25	.20	.10
1989 NBA Hoops	190	.30	.25	.12
1990 Fleer	154	.25	.20	.10
1990 Fleer All-Stars	11	.50	.40	.20
1990 NBA Hoops	16	.20	.15	.08
1990 NBA Hoops	245	.20	.15	.08
1990 NBA Hoops	376	.20	.15	.08
1990 SkyBox	233	.40	.30	.15
1991 Fleer	168	.20	.15	.08
1991 Fleer	393	.15	.11	.06
1991 NBA Hoops	174	.25	.20	.10
1991 NBA Hoops	262	.15	.11	.06
1991 NBA Hoops	491	.20	.15	.08
1991 SkyBox	237	.25	.20	.10
1991 SkyBox	480	.10	.08	.04
1991 SkyBox	579	.15	.11	.06
1991 Upper Deck	357	.25	.20	.10
1991 Upper Deck	463	.20	.15	.08
1992 Fleer	186	.20	.15	.08
1992 Fleer	250	.20	.15	.08
1992 Fleer	270	.15	.11	.06
1992 Fleer All-Stars	13	1.50	1.25	.60
1992 Fleer Sharpshooters	13	1.00	.70	.40
1992 Fleer Team Leaders	22	20.00	15.00	8.00
1992 Fleer Ultra	149	.40	.30	.15
1992 Fleer Ultra All-NBA Team	5	1.25	.90	.50
1992 NBA Hoops	189	.25	.20	.10
1992 NBA Hoops	306	.15	.11	.06
1992 NBA Hoops	338	.20	.15	.08
1992 NBA Hoops Supreme Court	5SC	1.25	.90	.50
1992 SkyBox	201	.25	.20	.10
1992 SkyBox	315	.15	.11	.06
1992 SkyBox I Olympic Team	1USA	1.50	1.25	.60
1992 SkyBox II Thunder and Lightning	2	5.00	3.75	2.00
1992 Topps	102	.15	.11	.06
1992 Topps	212	.10	.08	.04
1992 Topps	354	.20	.15	.08
1992 Topps Archives	33	.30	.25	.12
1992 Topps Beam Team	1	2.00	1.50	1.00
1992 Topps Stadium Club	199	.25	.20	.10
1992 Topps Stadium Club	287	.50	.40	.20
1992 Topps Stadium Club Beam Team	4	5.00	3.75	2.00
1992 Upper Deck	438	.15	.11	.06
1992 Upper Deck	486	.15	.11	.06
1992 Upper Deck	503	.10	.08	.04
1992 Upper Deck All-Division Team	20	.50	.40	.20
1992 Upper Deck All-NBA	2AN	1.50	1.25	.60
1992 Upper Deck Team MVP's	23TM	2.00	1.50	.80
1992 Upper Deck 15000-Point Club	13	3.00	2.25	1.25
1993 Fleer	173	.20	.15	.08
1993 Fleer All-Stars	14	1.00	.70	.40
1993 Fleer Jam Session	184	.20	.15	.08
1993 Fleer NBA Superstars	4	.50	.40	.20
1993 Fleer Ultra	154	.20	.15	.08
1993 Fleer Ultra Famous Nicknames	4	1.50	1.25	.60
1993 Fleer Ultra Jam City	3	6.00	4.50	2.50
1993 NBA Hoops	176	.20	.15	.08
1993 NBA Hoops	270	.12	.09	.05
1993 NBA Hoops Face to Face	4	5.00	3.75	2.00
1993 SkyBox	150	.25	.20	.10
1993 SkyBox	334	.10	.08	.04
1993 SkyBox Showdown Series	11	2.25	1.75	.90
1993 Topps	206	.15	.11	.06
1993 Topps	249	.25	.20	.10
1993 Topps Finest	74	2.00	1.50	.80
1993 Topps Finest	129	1.75	1.25	.70
1993 Topps Finest Main Attraction	22	5.00	3.75	2.00
1993 Topps Stadium Club	117	.20	.15	.08
1993 Topps Stadium Club	354	.15	.11	.06
1993 Upper Deck	90	.20	.15	.08
1993 Upper Deck	238	.15	.11	.06
1993 Upper Deck	473	.15	.11	.06
1993 Upper Deck Jordan's Flight Team	7	5.00	3.75	2.00
1993 Upper Deck SE	10	.25	.20	.10
1993 Upper Deck SE West Future All Stars	11	10.00	7.50,	4.00
1993 Upper Deck Team MVP's	22	.75	.60	.30
1993 Upper Deck 3-D Basketball	68	.10	.08	.04
1993 Upper Deck 3-D Basketball	103	.10	.08	.04
1994 Fleer	183	.25	.20	.10
1994 Fleer Flair	120	.75	.60	.30
1994 Fleer Jam Session	155	.35	.25	.14
1994 Fleer NBA All-Stars	15	.75	.60	.30
1994 Fleer Ultra	155	.15	.11	.06
1994 NBA Hoops	174	.20	.15	.08
1994 NBA Hoops	239	.08	.06	.03
1994 NBA Hoops Power Ratings	43	2.00	1.50	.80
1994 NBA Hoops Supreme Court	39	.75	.60	.30
1994 SkyBox	134	.06	.05	.02
1994 Topps	184	.10	.08	.04
1994 Topps Finest	30	.85	.60	.35
1994 Topps Stadium Club	64	.35	.25	.14
1994 Topps Stadium Club Dynasty and Destiny	8A	1.00	.70	.40

Set	Card #	MT	NM	EX
1994 Upper Deck	35	.15	.11	.06
1994 Upper Deck Collector's Choice	22	.25	.20	.10
1994 Upper Deck Collector's Choice	187	.10	.08	.04

Joe Dumars

Set	Card #	MT	NM	EX
1986 Fleer	27 (R)	30.00	22.00	12.00
1987 Fleer	31	8.00	6.00	3.25
1988 Fleer	40	2.00	1.50	.80
1989 Fleer	45	.60	.45	.25
1989 NBA Hoops	1	.25	.20	.10
1990 Fleer	55	.15	.11	.06
1990 NBA Hoops	3	.15	.11	.06
1990 NBA Hoops	103	.15	.11	.06
1990 NBA Hoops	362	.15	.11	.06
1990 SkyBox	84	.30	.25	.12
1991 Fleer	59	.15	.11	.06
1991 Fleer	379	.05	.04	.02
1991 NBA Hoops	60	.10	.08	.04
1991 NBA Hoops	250	.10	.08	.04
1991 NBA Hoops	463	.10	.08	.04
1991 SkyBox	VI	.75	.50	.20
1991 SkyBox	81	.20	.15	.08
1991 SkyBox	565	.10	.08	.04
1991 Upper Deck	61	.12	.09	.05
1991 Upper Deck	335	.20	.15	.08
1991 Upper Deck	459	.12	.09	.05
1992 Fleer	63	.20	.15	.08
1992 Fleer All-Stars	4	1.25	.90	.50
1992 Fleer Total "D"	4	8.00	6.00	3.25
1992 Fleer Ultra	56	.30	.25	.12
1992 NBA Hoops	64	.10	.08	.04
1992 NBA Hoops	296	.07	.05	.03
1992 SkyBox	69	.25	.20	.10
1992 Topps	111	.04	.03	.02
1992 Topps	347	.10	.08	.04
1992 Topps Archives	63	.15	.11	.06
1992 Topps Stadium Club	386	.20	.15	.08
1992 Upper Deck	268	.10	.08	.04
1992 Upper Deck	428	.10	.08	.04
1992 Upper Deck	500	.10	.08	.04
1993 Fleer	59	.10	.08	.04
1993 Fleer All-Stars	2	1.00	.70	.40
1993 Fleer Flair USA Basketball	6	.20	.15	.08
1993 Fleer Jam Session	60	.10	.08	.04
1993 Fleer NBA Superstars	5	.25	.20	.10
1993 Fleer Ultra	56	.10	.08	.04
1993 Fleer Ultra	362	.08	.06	.03
1993 Fleer Ultra All-Defensive Team	1	10.00	7.50	4.00
1993 Fleer Ultra All-NBA Team	6	1.25	.90	.50
1993 Fleer Ultra Scoring Kings	1	6.50	5.00	2.50
1993 NBA Hoops	61	.10	.08	.04
1993 NBA Hoops	262	.10	.08	.04
1993 SkyBox	66	.15	.11	.06
1993 SkyBox	324	.10	.08	.04
1993 SkyBox Showdown Series	10	.75	.60	.30
1993 Topps	115	.10	.08	.04
1993 Topps	351	.07	.05	.03
1993 Topps Finest	103	.35	.25	.14
1993 Topps Finest	199	.75	.60	.30
1993 Topps Finest Main Attraction	8	4.00	3.00	1.50
1993 Topps Stadium Club	335	.10	.08	.04
1993 Upper Deck	42	.25	.20	.10
1993 Upper Deck All-NBA	10	.75	.50	.25
1993 Upper Deck SE	68	.25	.20	.10
1993 Upper Deck Team MVP's	8	.50	.40	.20
1993 Upper Deck USA Basketball	2	.10	.08	.04
1993 Upper Deck 3-D Basketball	16	.20	.15	.08
1994 Fleer	65	.15	.11	.06
1994 Fleer Flair	45	.50	.40	.20
1994 Fleer Flair	160	.20	.15	.08
1994 Fleer Jam Session	54	.12	.09	.05
1994 Fleer Sharpshooters	2	1.00	.70	.40
1994 Fleer Team Leaders	3	2.00	1.50	.80
1994 Fleer Ultra	56	.08	.06	.03
1994 NBA Hoops	57	.12	.09	.05
1994 NBA Hoops Power Ratings	15	.75	.60	.30
1994 NBA Hoops Supreme Court	14	.60	.45	.25
1994 SkyBox	47	.08	.06	.03
1994 SkyBox Dream Team II Portraits	9	10.00	7.50	4.00
1994 Topps	25	.06	.05	.02
1994 Topps Finest	160	.15	.11	.06
1994 Topps Stadium Club	83	.08	.06	.03
1994 Upper Deck	169	.15	.11	.06
1994 Upper Deck Collector's Choice 2,000 Pts	3	2.00	1.50	.80
1994 Upper Deck Collector's Choice	104	.15	.11	.06
1994 Upper Deck Collector's Choice	173	.10	.08	.04
1994 Upper Deck Special Edition	26	.60	.45	.25

Mike Dunleavy

Set	Card #	MT	NM	EX
1981 Topps	85 (R)	1.50	1.25	.60
1984 Star Co.	128	4.00	3.00	1.50
1990 NBA Hoops	351	.07	.05	.03
1990 NBA Hoops	410	.05	.04	.02
1990 SkyBox	313	.10	.08	.04
1991 Fleer	98	.05	.04	.02
1991 NBA Hoops	233	.05	.04	.02

Set	Card #	MT	NM	EX
1991 SkyBox	390	.05	.04	.02
1992 Fleer	125	.05	.04	.02
1992 NBA Hoops	253	.05	.04	.02
1992 SkyBox	269	.05	.04	.02
1993 NBA Hoops	244	.06	.05	.02
1994 NBA Hoops	287	.04	.03	.02

Sean Elliott

Set	Card #	MT	NM	EX
1990 Fleer	171 (R)	.35	.25	.14
1990 Fleer Rookie Sensations	2	3.50	2.75	1.50
1990 NBA Hoops	267 (R)	.30	.25	.12
1990 SkyBox	256 (R)	.50	.40	.20
1991 Fleer	185	.10	.08	.04
1991 NBA Hoops	190	.15	.11	.06
1991 NBA Hoops	526	.08	.06	.03
1991 SkyBox	256	.15	.11	.06
1991 Upper Deck	287	.15	.11	.06
1992 Fleer	204	.10	.08	.04
1992 Fleer	271	.06	.05	.02
1992 Fleer Ultra	165	.15	.11	.06
1992 NBA Hoops	207	.10	.08	.04
1992 SkyBox	221	.10	.08	.04
1992 Topps	10	.10	.08	.04
1992 Topps Archives	121	.15	.11	.06
1992 Topps Stadium Club	65	.15	.11	.06
1992 Upper Deck	131	.15	.11	.06
1992 Upper Deck	439	.08	.06	.03
1992 Upper Deck	505	.10	.08	.04
1992 Upper Deck All-Division Team	13	.40	.30	.15
1993 Fleer	192	.10	.08	.04
1993 Fleer	281	.05	.04	.02
1993 Fleer All-Stars	15	.75	.60	.30
1993 Fleer Jam Session	61	.10	.08	.04
1993 Fleer Ultra	170	.10	.08	.04
1993 Fleer Ultra	242	.08	.06	.03
1993 NBA Hoops	199	.10	.08	.04
1993 NBA Hoops	271	.06	.05	.02
1993 NBA Hoops	331	.06	.05	.02
1993 SkyBox	164	.05	.04	.02
1993 SkyBox	220	.10	.08	.04
1993 Topps	196	.08	.06	.03
1993 Topps	229	.05	.04	.02
1993 Topps BlackGold	1	.60	.45	.25
1993 Topps Finest	37	.35	.25	.14
1993 Topps Stadium Club	203	.12	.09	.05
1993 Upper Deck	416	.15	.11	.06
1993 Upper Deck Jordan's Flight Team	8	2.50	2.00	1.00
1993 Upper Deck SE	50	.10	.08	.04
1993 Upper Deck 3-D Basketball	65	.10	.08	.04
1994 Fleer	66	.05	.04	.02
1994 Fleer	366	.05	.04	.02
1994 Fleer Flair	134	.15	.11	.06
1994 Fleer Jam Session	171	.10	.08	.04
1994 Fleer Ultra	171	.08	.06	.03
1994 NBA Hoops	58	.04	.03	.02
1994 NBA Hoops	370	.04	.03	.02
1994 SkyBox	48	.06	.05	.02
1994 Topps	180	.06	.05	.02
1994 Topps Finest	82	.15	.11	.06
1994 Upper Deck	53	.10	.08	.04
1994 Upper Deck Collector's Choice	273	.05	.04	.02

LaPhonso Ellis

Set	Card #	MT	NM	EX
1992 Fleer	328 (R)	.70	.50	.30
1992 Fleer Ultra	251 (R)	1.00	.75	.40
1992 Fleer Ultra All-Rookies	1	3.50	2.75	1.50
1992 NBA Hoops	375 (R)	1.25	.90	.50
1992 NBA Hoops Draft Redemption	4D	10.00	7.50	4.00
1992 NBA Hoops II Magic's All-Rookie Team	4	15.00	11.00	6.00
1992 SkyBox	336 (R)	1.50	1.25	.60
1992 SkyBox Draft Picks	5	4.00	3.00	1.60
1992 Topps	319 (R)	.30	.25	.12
1992 Topps Stadium Club	343 (R)	1.25	.90	.50
1992 Upper Deck	4 (R)	.65	.50	.25
1992 Upper Deck	21	.20	.15	.08
1992 Upper Deck	460	.20	.15	.08
1992 Upper Deck Rookie Standouts	4	2.50	2.00	1.00
1993 Fleer	51	.15	.11	.06
1993 Fleer Jam Session	54	.10	.08	.04
1993 Fleer Rookie Sensations	7	3.00	2.25	1.25
1993 Fleer Ultra	50	.15	.11	.06
1993 Fleer Ultra All-Rookie Team	1	1.00	.70	.40
1993 NBA Hoops	53	.12	.09	.05
1993 NBA Hoops Face to Face	5	4.00	3.00	1.50
1993 SkyBox	61	.12	.09	.05
1993 SkyBox	323	.10	.08	.04
1993 SkyBox NBA All-Rookie Team	5	3.00	2.25	1.25
1993 Topps	141	.15	.11	.06
1993 Topps BlackGold	16	.75	.60	.30
1993 Topps Finest	43	1.25	.90	.50
1993 Topps Stadium Club	144	.12	.09	.05
1993 Topps Stadium Club Beam Team	16	3.00	2.25	1.25
1993 Upper Deck	391	.20	.15	.08
1993 Upper Deck All-Rookie	5	3.00	2.25	1.25
1993 Upper Deck Future Heroes	29	1.00	.70	.40
1993 Upper Deck Jordan's Flight Team	9	4.00	3.00	1.50

Set	Card #	NM	EX	VG
1993 Upper Deck SE	74	.20	.15	.08
1993 Upper Deck 3-D Basketball	53	.10	.08	.04
1994 Fleer	57	.08	.06	.03
1994 Fleer Flair	39	.15	.11	.06
1994 Fleer Jam Session	46	.12	.09	.05
1994 Fleer Ultra	48	.08	.06	.03
1994 NBA Hoops	49	.06	.05	.02
1994 NBA Hoops Power Ratings	14	.30	.25	.12
1994 SkyBox	41	.06	.05	.02
1994 Topps	145	.06	.05	.02
1994 Topps Finest	92	.20	.15	.08
1994 Topps Stadium Club	150	.10	.08	.04
1994 Topps Stadium Club Rising Stars	6	3.50	2.75	1.50
1994 Upper Deck	105	.10	.08	.04
1994 Upper Deck Collector's Choice	20	.06	.05	.02
1994 Upper Deck Special Edition	23	.20	.15	.08

Alex English

Set	Card #	NM	EX	VG
1979 Topps	31 (R)	13.00	6.50	4.00
1980 Topps	19	1.50	.70	.45
1980 Topps	107	1.50	.70	.45

Set	Card #	MT	NM	EX
1981 Topps	68	2.00	1.50	.80
1983 Star Co.	186	10.00	7.50	4.00
1983 Star Co. All-Star Game	15	4.00	3.00	1.50
1984 Star Co.	137	7.00	5.25	2.75
1984 Star Co. All-Star Game	18	3.00	2.25	1.25
1984 Star Co. Court Kings	22	5.00	3.75	2.00
1985 Star Co.	50	5.00	3.75	2.00
1986 Fleer	30	3.00	2.25	1.25
1986 Star Co. Court Kings	12	3.50	2.75	1.50
1987 Fleer	34	2.00	1.50	.80
1988 Fleer	34	.50	.40	.20
1989 Fleer	40	.25	.20	.10
1989 NBA Hoops	120	.15	.11	.06
1989 NBA Hoops	133	.05	.04	.02
1990 Fleer	48	.07	.05	.03
1990 NBA Hoops	94	.20	.15	.08
1990 NBA Hoops	407	.20	.15	.08
1990 SkyBox	74	.25	.20	.10
1990 SkyBox	375	.10	.08	.04
1990 Star Co. Court Kings	2	14.00	9.00	3.75
1990 Star Co. Slam	2	15.00	10.00	4.00
1991 NBA Hoops	315	.10	.08	.04

Exclusive: When a company makes an agreement that a distributor is the only one selling the company's cards at the offering price.

Julius Erving

Set	Card #	NM	EX	VG
1972 Topps	195 (R)	300.00	150.00	90.00
1972 Topps	255	65.00	32.00	19.50
1972 Topps	263	20.00	10.00	6.00
1973 Topps	234	7.00	3.50	2.00
1973 Topps	240	75.00	37.00	22.00
1974 Topps	200	55.00	27.00	16.50
1974 Topps	207	7.00	3.50	2.00
1974 Topps	226	8.00	4.00	2.50
1975 Topps	221	6.00	3.00	1.75
1975 Topps	282	6.00	3.00	1.75
1975 Topps	300	50.00	25.00	15.00
1976 Topps	1	55.00	27.00	16.50
1976 Topps	127	25.00	12.50	7.50
1977 Topps	100	22.00	11.00	6.50
1978 Topps	130	12.00	6.00	3.60
1979 Topps	20	14.00	7.00	4.25
1980 Topps	1	6.00	3.00	1.75
1980 Topps	6	475.00	237.00	142.00
1980 Topps	23	2.00	1.00	.60
1980 Topps	51	2.00	1.00	.60
1980 Topps	137	3.00	1.50	.90
1980 Topps	142	3.00	1.50	.90
1980 Topps	146	80.00	40.00	24.00
1980 Topps	176	7.50	3.75	2.25

Set	Card #	MT	NM	EX
1981 Topps	30	7.00	5.25	2.75
1981 Topps	104	4.00	3.00	1.50
1981 Topps	59	1.50	1.25	.60
1983 Star Co.	1	80.00	60.00	32.00
1983 Star Co. All-Star Game	1	8.00	6.00	3.25
1983 Star Co. All-Star Game	4	12.00	9.00	4.75
1983 Star Co. All-Star Game	26	8.00	6.00	3.25
1984 Star Co.	204	38.00	28.00	15.00
1984 Star Co.	281	20.00	15.00	8.00
1984 Star Co. All-Star Game	4	15.00	11.00	6.00
1984 Star Co. Court Kings	4	12.00	9.00	4.75
1984 Star Co. Slam Dunk	4	22.00	16.50	8.75
1985 Star Co.	3	30.00	22.00	12.00
1985 Star Co. Lite All-Stars	3	25.00	18.50	10.00
1986 Fleer	31	16.00	12.00	6.50
1986 Star Co. Best of the Old	2	175.00	131.00	70.00
1986 Star Co. Best of the Best	6	40.00	30.00	16.00
1986 Star Co. Court Kings	13	15.00	11.00	6.00
1987 Fleer	35	10.00	7.50	4.00

Patrick Ewing

Set	Card #	MT	NM	EX
1985 Star Co.	166 (R)	300.00	225.00	120.00
1986 Fleer	32 (R)	85.00	64.00	34.00
1986 Star Co. Best of the New	1	200.00	150.00	80.00
1986 Star Co. Best of the Best	7	95.00	71.00	38.00
1986 Star Co. Court Kings	14	45.00	34.00	18.00
1987 Fleer	37	22.00	16.50	8.75
1988 Fleer	80	6.00	4.50	2.50
1988 Fleer	130	2.50	2.00	1.00
1989 Fleer	100	1.50	1.25	.60
1989 Fleer	167	.60	.45	.25
1989 NBA Hoops	80	.50	.40	.20
1989 NBA Hoops	159	.30	.25	.12
1990 Fleer	125	.30	.25	.12
1990 Fleer All-Stars	12	.75	.60	.30
1990 NBA Hoops	4	.50	.40	.20
1990 NBA Hoops	203	.15	.11	.06
1990 NBA Hoops	372	.15	.11	.06
1990 NBA Hoops	388	.20	.15	.08
1990 SkyBox	187	.50	.40	.20
1990 Star Co. Court Kings	3	22.00	15.00	6.25
1990 Star Co. Slam	3	22.00	15.00	6.25
1991 Fleer	136	.30	.25	.12
1991 Fleer	215	.15	.11	.06
1991 Fleer	389	.15	.11	.06
1991 Fleer Pro Visions	4	.50	.40	.20
1991 NBA Hoops	140	.25	.20	.10
1991 NBA Hoops	251	.20	.15	.08
1991 NBA Hoops	483	.15	.11	.06
1991 NBA Hoops	577	.75	.60	.30
1991 SkyBox	189	.25	.20	.10
1991 SkyBox	476	.15	.11	.06
1991 SkyBox	532	.80	.60	.30
1991 Upper Deck	68	.25	.20	.10
1991 Upper Deck	343	.35	.25	.14
1991 Upper Deck	455	.25	.20	.10
1992 Fleer	150	.30	.25	.12
1992 Fleer	291	.25	.20	.10
1992 Fleer All-Stars	5	6.00	4.50	2.50
1992 Fleer Team Leaders	18	50.00	37.00	20.00
1992 Fleer Total "D"	7	27.00	20.00	11.00
1992 Fleer Ultra	122	.80	.60	.30
1992 Fleer Ultra All-NBA Team	8	3.50	2.75	1.50
1992 NBA Hoops	b	.50	.30	.15
1992 NBA Hoops	g	.75	.50	.20
1992 NBA Hoops	153	.40	.30	.15
1992 NBA Hoops	297	.25	.20	.10
1992 NBA Hoops	333	.25	.20	.10
1992 NBA Hoops	339	.20	.15	.08
1992 NBA Hoops	484	.25	.20	.10
1992 NBA Hoops Supreme Court	4SC	3.00	2.25	1.25
1992 SkyBox	161	.50	.40	.20
1992 SkyBox	299	.30	.25	.12
1992 SkyBox I Olympic Team	8USA	4.00	3.00	1.50
1992 Topps	66	.25	.20	.10
1992 Topps	121	.10	.08	.04
1992 Topps	211	.10	.08	.04
1992 Topps Archives	5	.25	.20	.10
1992 Topps Archives	64	.50	.40	.20
1992 Topps Beam Team	2	1.00	.75	.40
1992 Topps Stadium Club	100	.75	.60	.30
1992 Topps Stadium Club	207	.40	.30	.15
1992 Topps Stadium Club Beam Team	18	10.00	7.50	4.00
1992 Upper Deck	46	.15	.11	.06
1992 Upper Deck	130	.30	.25	.12
1992 Upper Deck	429	.25	.20	.10
1992 Upper Deck All-NBA	8AN	3.00	2.25	1.25
1992 Upper Deck Foreign Exchange	3	4.00	3.00	1.50
1992 Upper Deck Team MVP's	19TM	4.00	3.00	1.50
1993 Fleer	141	.25	.20	.10
1993 Fleer All-Stars	3	2.50	2.00	1.00
1993 Fleer Jam Session	149	.50	.40	.20
1993 Fleer Jam Session Slam Dunk Heroes	1	1.25	.90	.50
1993 Fleer Living Legends	3	5.00	3.75	2.00
1993 Fleer NBA Internationals	3	2.50	1.50	.75
1993 Fleer NBA Superstars	6	1.00	.70	.40
1993 Fleer Towers of Power	7	11.00	8.25	4.50
1993 Fleer Ultra	127	.60	.45	.25
1993 Fleer Ultra All-NBA Team	7	4.00	3.00	1.60
1993 Fleer Ultra Inside Outside	1	1.00	.70	.40
1993 Fleer Ultra Jam City	4	12.00	9.00	4.75
1993 Fleer Ultra Scoring Kings	3	15.00	11.00	6.00
1993 NBA Hoops	146	.35	.25	.14
1993 NBA Hoops	265	.15	.11	.06
1993 NBA Hoops	440	.10	.08	.04
1993 NBA Hoops Face to Face	2	6.00	4.50	2.40
1993 NBA Hoops Supreme Court	3	2.00	1.50	.80
1993 SkyBox	10	.25	.20	.10
1993 SkyBox	126	.50	.40	.20
1993 SkyBox Showdown Series	1	1.50	1.25	.60
1993 SkyBox Showdown Series	2	2.50	2.00	1.00
1993 SkyBox Thunder and Lightning	5	3.00	2.25	1.25
1993 Topps	100	.15	.11	.06
1993 Topps	200	.20	.15	.08
1993 Topps	300	.25	.20	.10
1993 Topps	390	.20	.15	.08
1993 Topps Finest	90	2.00	1.50	.80
1993 Topps Finest	165	4.00	3.00	1.50
1993 Topps Finest Main Attraction	18	12.00	9.00	4.75
1993 Topps Stadium Club	68	.30	.25	.12
1993 Topps Stadium Club	189	.30	.25	.12
1993 Topps Stadium Club	200	.60	.45	.25
1993 Topps Stadium Club Beam Team	3	8.00	6.00	3.25
1993 Upper Deck	244	.15	.11	.06
1993 Upper Deck	256	.45	.35	.20
1993 Upper Deck	471	.20	.15	.08
1993 Upper Deck All-NBA	8	1.25	.75	.40
1993 Upper Deck SE	138	.50	.40	.20
1993 Upper Deck SE Behind the Glass	2	5.00	3.75	2.00
1993 Upper Deck SE East Future All Stars	11	17.00	12.50	6.75
1993 Upper Deck Team MVP's	18	1.25	.90	.50
1993 Upper Deck 3-D Basketball	8	.20	.15	.08
1993 Upper Deck 3-D Basketball	98	.25	.20	.10
1994 Fleer	150	.40	.30	.15

1994 Fleer Career Achievement Awards	1	8.00	6.00	3.25
1994 Fleer Flair	99	1.25	.90	.50
1994 Fleer Flair Center Spotlight	1	10.00	7.50	4.00
1994 Fleer Flair Hot Numbers	3	3.75	2.75	1.50
1994 Fleer Flair Scoring Power	2	3.50	2.75	1.50
1994 Fleer Jam Session	124	.75	.60	.30
1994 Fleer Jam Session GameBreakers	2	1.75	1.25	.70
1994 Fleer NBA All-Stars	5	1.50	1.25	.60
1994 Fleer Superstars	2	12.00	9.00	4.75
1994 Fleer Team Leaders	6	2.00	1.50	.80
1994 Fleer Towers of Power	2	2.00	1.50	.80
1994 Fleer Triple Threats	2	1.50	1.25	.60
1994 Fleer Ultra	125	.60	.45	.25
1994 Fleer Ultra Double Trouble	2	1.50	1.25	.60
1994 Fleer Ultra Scoring Kings	2	15.00	13.50	7.25
1994 NBA Hoops	142	.35	.25	.14
1994 NBA Hoops	228	.20	.15	.08
1994 NBA Hoops Big Numbers	4	8.00	6.00	3.25
1994 NBA Hoops Power Ratings	35	3.50	2.75	1.50
1994 NBA Hoops Supreme Court	30	2.00	1.50	.80
1994 SkyBox	110	.50	.40	.20
1994 SkyBox	184	.25	.20	.10
1994 Topps	1	.12	.09	.05
1994 Topps Finest	33	1.50	1.25	.60
1994 Topps Stadium Club	1	.70	.50	.30
1994 Topps Stadium Club	2	.25	.20	.10
1994 Topps Stadium Club Dynasty and Destiny	6A	1.75	1.25	.70
1994 Topps Super Rebounders	9	2.50	2.00	1.00
1994 Topps Super Scorers	6	2.00	1.50	.80
1994 Topps Super Swatters	7	2.25	1.75	.90
1994 Upper Deck	119	.75	.60	.30
1994 Upper Deck Col.'s Choice 1,000 Rebounds	2	4.00	3.00	1.50
1994 Upper Deck Collector's Choice 2,000 Pts	4	7.00	5.25	2.75
1994 Upper Deck Collector's Choice	183	.25	.20	.10
1994 Upper Deck Collector's Choice	203	.25	.20	.10
1994 Upper Deck Collector's Choice	333	.40	.30	.15
1994 Upper Deck Collector's Choice	389	.35	.25	.14
1994 Upper Deck Collector's Choice	405	.30	.25	.12
1994 Upper Deck Predictors Retail	7	3.00	2.25	1.25
1994 Upper Deck Predictors Hobby	9	3.00	2.25	1.25
1994 Upper Deck Predictors Hobby	16	8.00	6.00	3.25

Error card: A card that contains a mistake, including wrong photos, misspelled words, incorrect statistics, and so forth. Usually error cards have no extra value unless they have been corrected, resulting in a "variation" card.

Chris Ford

Set	Card #	NM	EX	VG
1973 Topps	79 (R)	6.00	3.00	1.75
1974 Topps	112	2.50	1.25	.70
1975 Topps	47	1.50	.70	.45
1976 Topps	29	2.00	1.00	.60
1977 Topps	121	1.00	.50	.30
1978 Topps	15	.75	.40	.25
1979 Topps	124	.60	.30	.20
1980 Topps	67	.25	.13	.08
1980 Topps	97	.25	.13	.08

Set	Card #	MT	NM	EX
1981 Topps	73	.50	.40	.20
1990 NBA Hoops	306	.03	.02	.01
1990 NBA Hoops	347	.10	.08	.04
1990 SkyBox	302	.10	.08	.04
1991 Fleer	10	.03	.02	.01
1991 NBA Hoops	222	.05	.04	.02
1991 NBA Hoops	260	.08	.06	.03
1991 SkyBox	379	.05	.04	.02
1992 Fleer	13	.05	.04	.02
1992 NBA Hoops	240	.05	.04	.02
1992 SkyBox	256	.05	.04	.02
1993 NBA Hoops	231	.06	.05	.02
1994 NBA Hoops	275	.04	.03	.02

Walt Frazier

Set	Card #	NM	EX	VG
1969 Topps	98 (R)	75.00	56.00	30.00
1970 Topps	6	7.00	3.50	2.00
1970 Topps	106	14.00	7.00	4.25
1970 Topps	120	30.00	15.00	9.00
1970 Topps	174	9.00	4.50	2.75
1971 Topps	65	16.00	8.00	4.75
1972 Topps	60	10.00	5.00	3.00
1972 Topps	165	4.00	2.00	1.25
1973 Topps	10	6.00	3.00	1.75
1974 Topps	93	5.00	2.50	1.50

Set	Card #			
1974 Topps	150	6.50	3.25	2.00
1975 Topps	6	3.00	1.50	.90
1975 Topps	55	7.00	3.50	2.00
1975 Topps	128	2.50	1.25	.70
1976 Topps	64	6.00	3.00	1.75
1977 Topps	129	4.00	2.00	1.25
1978 Topps	83	3.00	1.50	.90

Set	Card #	MT	NM	EX
1985 Star Co. Schick Legends	11	4.00	3.00	1.50

> Extended set: A term used to describe a late-season series of cards added on to and numbered after a regular set. Also known as an extended series, update set or traded set.
>
> Food set: A set either inserted in packages of food (hot dogs, cereal, popcorn, potato chips, candy, cookies, etc.) or offered as a send-in offer by a food company. Examples of food sets include Kahn's Wieners, Mother's Cookies, etc.

Lloyd Free

Set	Card #	NM	EX	VG
1976 Topps	143 (R)	8.00	4.00	2.50
1977 Topps	18	.75	.40	.25
1978 Topps	116	.25	.13	.08
1979 Topps	40	.20	.10	.06
1980 Topps	8	3.00	1.50	.90
1980 Topps	59	.25	.13	.08
1980 Topps	61	.25	.13	.08
1980 Topps	62	.25	.13	.08
1980 Topps	89	.25	.13	.08
1980 Topps	121	.50	.25	.15
1980 Topps	134	.25	.13	.08
1980 Topps	156	.25	.13	.08

Set	Card #	MT	NM	EX
1981 Topps	13	.15	.11	.06
1981 Topps	51	.15	.11	.06
1983 Star Co.	228	5.00	3.75	2.00
1984 Star Co.	217	4.50	3.50	1.75
1984 Star Co. Court Kings	8	3.00	2.25	1.25
1985 Star Co.	152	4.00	3.00	1.50
1986 Fleer	35	1.25	.90	.50

George Gervin

Set	Card #	NM	EX	VG
1974 Topps	196 (R)	37.00	18.50	11.10
1974 Topps	227	4.00	2.00	1.25
1975 Topps	233	12.00	6.00	3.50

Set	Card #			
1976 Topps	68	10.00	5.00	3.00
1977 Topps	73	6.00	3.00	1.75
1978 Topps	20	3.00	1.50	.90
1979 Topps	1	3.00	1.50	.90
1980 Topps	58	.25	.13	.08
1980 Topps	70	.20	.10	.06
1980 Topps	73	1.00	.50	.30
1980 Topps	122	.25	.13	.08
1980 Topps	154	5.00	2.50	1.50
1980 Topps	161	1.00	.50	.30

Set	Card #	MT	NM	EX
1981 Topps	37	1.00	.70	.40
1981 Topps	106	.40	.30	.15
1981 Topps	62	.15	.11	.06
1983 Star Co.	241	15.00	11.00	6.00
1983 Star Co. All-Star Game	16	4.00	3.00	1.50
1984 Star Co.	67	15.00	11.00	6.00
1984 Star Co. All-Star Game	19	5.00	3.75	2.00
1984 Star Co. Court Kings	25	5.00	3.75	2.00
1985 Star Co.	121	9.00	6.75	3.50
1985 Star Co. Lite All-Stars	10	9.00	6.75	3.50
1986 Fleer	36	5.00	3.75	2.00
1986 Star Co. Best of the Old	3	70.00	52.00	28.00
1986 Star Co. Court Kings	15	5.00	3.75	2.00

Kendall Gill

Set	Card #	MT	NM	EX
1990 Fleer Update	11 (R)	1.25	.90	.50
1990 NBA Hoops	394 (R)	.75	.60	.30
1990 SkyBox	356 (R)	1.00	.70	.40
1991 Fleer	20	.20	.15	.08
1991 Fleer	232	.10	.08	.04
1991 Fleer Rookie Sensations	4	2.50	2.00	1.00
1991 NBA Hoops	21	.20	.15	.08
1991 NBA Hoops	454	.20	.15	.08
1991 SkyBox	27	.25	.20	.10
1991 SkyBox	321	.15	.11	.06
1991 SkyBox	461	.15	.11	.06
1991 SkyBox	488	.15	.11	.06
1991 Upper Deck	39	.10	.08	.04
1991 Upper Deck	321	.20	.15	.08
1991 Upper Deck Rookie Standouts	3R	1.00	.70	.40
1992 Fleer	24	.10	.08	.04
1992 Fleer	297	.20	.15	.08
1992 Fleer Ultra	20	.30	.25	.12
1992 NBA Hoops	22	.15	.11	.06
1992 SkyBox	22	.15	.11	.06
1992 SkyBox	284	.15	.11	.06
1992 Topps	158	.15	.11	.06
1992 Topps Archives	134	.15	.11	.06
1992 Topps Stadium Club	151	.15	.11	.06
1992 Upper Deck	43	.10	.08	.04

1992 Upper Deck	63	.20	.15	.08
1992 Upper Deck	138	.10	.08	.04
1992 Upper Deck Team MVP's	4TM	1.00	.70	.40
1993 Fleer	20	.15	.11	.06
1993 Fleer	381	.05	.04	.02
1993 Fleer Jam Session	212	.15	.11	.06
1993 Fleer Ultra	176	.10	.08	.04
1993 Fleer Ultra	343	.08	.06	.03
1993 NBA Hoops	21	.15	.11	.06
1993 NBA Hoops	408	.06	.05	.02
1993 SkyBox	38	.15	.11	.06
1993 SkyBox	282	.10	.08	.04
1993 Topps	221	.08	.06	.03
1993 Topps BlackGold	25	.75	.60	.30
1993 Topps Finest	207	.35	.25	.14
1993 Topps Stadium Club	253	.15	.11	.06
1993 Upper Deck	13	.15	.11	.06
1993 Upper Deck	384	.10	.08	.04
1993 Upper Deck Jordan's Flight Team	10	3.00	2.25	1.25
1993 Upper Deck SE	77	.20	.15	.08
1994 Fleer	212	.05	.04	.02
1994 Fleer Flair	139	.15	.11	.06
1994 Fleer Jam Session	178	.10	.08	.04
1994 Fleer Ultra	176	.08	.06	.03
1994 NBA Hoops	98	.04	.03	.02
1994 SkyBox	154	.06	.05	.02
1994 Topps	170	.06	.05	.02
1994 Topps	171	.06	.05	.02
1994 Topps Finest	140	.15	.11	.06
1994 Topps Stadium Club	71	.10	.08	.04
1994 Topps Stadium Club	109	.08	.06	.03
1994 Upper Deck	38	.10	.08	.04
1994 Upper Deck Collector's Choice	13	.05	.04	.02
1994 Upper Deck Special Edition	82	.20	.15	.08

Artis Gilmore

Set	Card #	NM	EX	VG
1972 Topps	180 (R)	33.00	16.50	9.90
1972 Topps	251	6.00	3.00	1.75
1972 Topps	260	4.00	2.00	1.25
1972 Topps	263	20.00	10.00	6.00
1973 Topps	235	1.50	.70	.45
1973 Topps	238	1.50	.70	.45
1973 Topps	250	6.00	3.00	1.75
1974 Topps	180	4.00	2.00	1.25
1974 Topps	211	.50	.25	.15
1974 Topps	224	3.00	1.50	.90
1975 Topps	222	6.00	3.00	1.75
1975 Topps	225	1.50	.70	.45
1975 Topps	250	5.00	2.50	1.50
1975 Topps	280	1.25	.60	.40
1976 Topps	25	6.00	3.00	1.75
1977 Topps	115	2.00	1.00	.60
1978 Topps	73	1.75	.90	.50

1979 Topps	25	1.00	.50	.30
1980 Topps	17	.25	.13	.08
1980 Topps	59	.25	.13	.08
1980 Topps	109	.25	.13	.08
1980 Topps	134	.25	.13	.08

Set	Card #	MT	NM	EX
1981 Topps	7	.50	.40	.20
1981 Topps	107	.40	.30	.15
1981 Topps	46	.15	.11	.06
1983 Star Co.	244	7.00	5.25	2.75
1983 Star Co. All-Star Game	17	3.50	2.75	1.50
1984 Star Co.	64	6.00	4.50	2.50
1984 Star Co. Awards Banquet	14	3.00	2.25	1.25
1984 Star Co. Court Kings	34	4.00	3.00	1.50
1985 Star Co.	145	6.00	4.50	2.50
1986 Fleer	37	4.00	3.00	1.50
1987 Fleer	40	2.00	1.50	.80

Gail Goodrich

Set	Card #	NM	EX	VG
1969 Topps	2 (R)	30.00	22.00	12.00
1970 Topps	93	8.00	4.00	2.50
1971 Topps	121	6.00	3.00	1.75
1972 Topps	50	3.00	1.50	.90
1972 Topps	174	1.25	.60	.40
1973 Topps	55	4.00	2.00	1.25
1974 Topps	90	1.00	.50	.30
1974 Topps	120	2.00	1.00	.60
1975 Topps	110	2.00	1.00	.60
1975 Topps	125	1.00	.50	.30
1976 Topps	125	3.00	1.50	.90
1977 Topps	77	1.00	.50	.30
1978 Topps	95	1.00	.50	.30
1979 Topps	32	.75	.40	.25

Glossy set: A set of glossy cards. Glossy sets can be either small and common (Topps' sendaway all-star sets) or large and scarce. Fleer, Topps, Score and Bowman have made glossy versions of their regular baseball card sets.

Glossy card: A card with a special, extra-shiny finish.

Grading service: A company that charges a fee to grade cards. Most grading services work like this: After a card is graded, it is placed in a tamper-proof plastic holder. A network of member-dealers then agrees to buy that card sight-unseen at that grade. Card grading services are a recent innovation, patterned after similar services in the coin collecting hobby.

Horace Grant

Set	Card #	MT	NM	EX
1988 Fleer	16 (R)	10.00	7.50	4.00
1989 Fleer	20	1.25	.90	.50
1989 NBA Hoops	242	.30	.25	.12
1990 Fleer	24	.10	.08	.04
1990 NBA Hoops	63	.10	.08	.04
1990 SkyBox	39	.10	.08	.04
1991 Fleer	27	.10	.08	.04
1991 NBA Hoops	28	.08	.06	.03
1991 SkyBox	36	.12	.09	.05
1991 SkyBox	566	.10	.08	.04
1991 Upper Deck	181	.12	.09	.05
1992 Fleer	30	.10	.08	.04
1992 Fleer Ultra	26	.12	.09	.05
1992 Fleer Ultra	219	.10	.08	.04
1992 NBA Hoops	29	.10	.08	.04
1992 SkyBox	30	.10	.08	.04
1992 SkyBox	285	.05	.04	.02
1992 Topps	324	.10	.08	.04
1992 Topps Archives	91	.15	.11	.06
1992 Topps Stadium Club	138	.15	.11	.06
1992 Upper Deck	135	.10	.08	.04
1993 Fleer	27	.10	.08	.04
1993 Fleer Jam Session	30	.15	.11	.06
1993 Fleer Towers of Power	8	2.50	2.00	1.00
1993 Fleer Ultra	29	.15	.11	.06
1993 Fleer Ultra All-Defensive Team	6	10.00	7.50	4.00
1993 NBA Hoops	27	.10	.08	.04
1993 SkyBox	19	.15	.11	.06
1993 SkyBox	44	.15	.11	.06
1993 Topps	288	.10	.08	.04
1993 Topps Finest	89	.75	.60	.30
1993 Topps Finest	101	.35	.25	.14
1993 Topps Stadium Club	130	.15	.11	.06
1993 Upper Deck	101	.10	.08	.04
1993 Upper Deck	434	.10	.08	.04
1993 Upper Deck SE	115	.10	.08	.04
1994 Fleer	30	.08	.06	.03
1994 Fleer	337	.05	.04	.02
1994 Fleer All-Defensive Team	6	.50	.40	.20
1994 Fleer Jam Session	134	.15	.11	.06
1994 Fleer NBA All-Stars	6	.35	.25	.14
1994 NBA Hoops	26	.04	.03	.02
1994 NBA Hoops	229	.08	.06	.03
1994 NBA Hoops	355	.04	.03	.02
1994 NBA Hoops	428	.30	.25	.12
1994 NBA Hoops Supreme Court	7	.40	.30	.15
1994 SkyBox	23	.06	.05	.02
1994 Topps	7	.06	.05	.02
1994 Upper Deck	155	.10	.08	.04
1994 Upper Deck Col.'s Choice 1,000 Rebounds	3	.75	.60	.30
1994 Upper Deck Collector's Choice	354	.10	.08	.04

Hal Greer

Set	Card #	NM	EX	VG
1961-62 Fleer	16 (R)	75.00	56.00	30.00
1969 Topps	84	8.00	6.00	3.25
1970 Topps	155	5.00	2.50	1.50
1971 Topps	60	4.50	2.25	1.25
1972 Topps	56	3.00	1.50	.90

Matt Guokas

Set	Card #	NM	EX	VG
1970 Topps	124 (R)	10.00	5.00	3.00
1971 Topps	113	3.00	1.50	.90
1972 Topps	9	2.00	1.00	.60
1973 Topps	18	.70	.35	.20
1974 Topps	117	1.00	.50	.30
1975 Topps	28	1.00	.50	.30

Set	Card #	MT	NM	EX
1989 NBA Hoops	321	.05	.04	.02
1990 NBA Hoops	323	.03	.02	.01
1990 NBA Hoops	352	.05	.04	.02
1990 SkyBox	319	.07	.05	.03
1991 Fleer	145	.03	.02	.01
1991 NBA Hoops	239	.05	.04	.02
1991 SkyBox	396	.05	.04	.02
1992 Fleer	161	.05	.04	.02
1992 NBA Hoops	257	.05	.04	.02
1992 SkyBox	273	.05	.04	.02

> Grade: The state of preservation of a card or piece of memorabilia. An item's value is based in large part on its grade (condition).

Happy Hairston

Set	Card #	NM	EX	VG
1969 Topps	83 (R)	10.00	7.50	4.00
1970 Topps	77	4.00	2.00	1.25
1971 Topps	25	2.00	1.00	.60
1972 Topps	121	1.50	.70	.45
1973 Topps	137	.70	.35	.20
1974 Topps	68	1.00	.50	.30
1974 Topps	90	1.00	.50	.30
1975 Topps	125	1.00	.50	.30
1975 Topps	159	.75	.40	.25

Anfernee Hardaway

Set	Card #	MT	NM	EX
1993 Fleer	343 (R)	2.00	1.50	.80
1993 Fleer First Year Phenoms	2	4.00	3.00	1.60
1993 Fleer Jam Session	159 (R)	3.00	2.25	1.25
1993 Fleer Jam Session Rookie Standouts	4	7.00	5.25	2.75
1993 Fleer Lottery Exchange	3	8.00	6.00	3.20
1993 Fleer Ultra	305 (R)	4.00	3.00	1.50
1993 Fleer Ultra All-Rookies	4	11.00	8.25	4.50
1993 Fleer Ultra Famous Nicknames	5	7.00	5.25	2.75
1993 NBA Hoops	380 (R)	2.50	2.00	1.00
1993 NBA Hoops Draft Redemption	3	17.00	12.50	6.75
1993 NBA Hoops II Magic's All-Rookie Team	3	20.00	15.00	8.00
1993 SkyBox	259 (R)	3.00	2.25	1.25
1993 SkyBox Draft Picks	3	17.00	12.50	6.75
1993 SkyBox Thunder and Lightning	6	20.00	18.50	10.00
1993 Topps	334 (R)	2.25	1.70	.90
1993 Topps BlackGold	19	7.00	5.25	2.75
1993 Topps Finest	189 (R)	12.00	9.00	4.75
1993 Topps Stadium Club	266	1.25	.90	.50
1993 Topps Stadium Club	308 (R)	3.00	2.25	1.25
1993 Topps Stadium Club Beam Team	23	20.00	15.00	8.00
1993 Upper Deck	382 (R)	3.00	2.25	1.25
1993 Upper Deck	484	.95	.70	.40
1993 Upper Deck Rookie Exchange Gold/Silver	3	7.00	5.25	2.75
1993 Upper Deck Rookie Standouts	17	17.00	12.50	6.75
1993 Upper Deck SE	51 (R)	3.00	2.25	1.25
1993 Upper Deck SE	188	1.00	.70	.40
1993 Upper Deck SE East Future All Stars	12	55.00	41.00	22.00
1993 Upper Deck 3-D Basketball	83 (R)	2.00	.60	.30
1994 Fleer	159	1.00	.75	.40
1994 Fleer Flair	106	3.50	2.75	1.50
1994 Fleer Flair Hot Numbers	4	8.00	6.00	3.25
1994 Fleer Jam Session	135	2.25	1.75	.90
1994 Fleer Jam Session Flashing Stars	1	5.00	3.75	2.00
1994 Fleer Jam Session Second Year Stars	2	5.00	3.75	2.00
1994 Fleer Pro-Visions	8	3.00	2.25	1.25
1994 Fleer Rookie Sensations	9	12.00	9.00	4.75
1994 Fleer Ultra	134	1.75	1.25	.70
1994 Fleer Ultra Double Trouble	3	4.50	3.50	1.75
1994 Fleer Ultra NBA All-Rookie Team	2	45.00	34.00	18.00
1994 Fleer Young Lions	2	6.00	4.50	2.50
1994 NBA Hoops	151	.75	.60	.30
1994 NBA Hoops	264	.40	.30	.15
1994 NBA Hoops	423	1.75	1.25	.70
1994 NBA Hoops Big Numbers	8	15.00	11.00	6.00
1994 NBA Hoops Power Ratings	38	8.00	6.00	3.25
1994 NBA Hoops Supreme Court	32	3.50	2.75	1.50
1994 Pacific Draft Prism Gold Sonic Boom	21	1.50	1.50	1.50
1994 Pacific Draft Prism Gold Sonic Boom	69	1.50	1.50	1.50
1994 Pacific Prisms	21	3.00	2.25	1.25
1994 Pacific Prisms	69	2.75	2.00	1.00
1994 SkyBox	117	1.50	1.25	.60
1994 SkyBox Center Stage	3	40.00	30.00	16.00
1994 SkyBox Ragin' Rookies	18	4.25	3.25	1.75
1994 Topps	14	.30	.25	.12
1994 Topps	75	1.00	.70	.40
1994 Topps	76	.50	.40	.20
1994 Topps Finest Iron Men	7	15.00	11.00	6.00
1994 Topps Finest Marathon Men	10	10.00	7.50	4.00
1994 Topps Stadium Club	16	1.75	1.25	.70
1994 Topps Stadium Club	17	.75	.60	.30
1994 Topps Stadium Club Dynasty and Destiny	3B	4.50	3.50	1.75
1994 Topps Stadium Club Rising Stars	10	25.00	18.50	10.00
1994 Topps Super Stealers	6	5.00	3.75	2.00
1994 Upper Deck	2	.50	.40	.20
1994 Upper Deck Collector's Choice	1	1.00	.70	.40
1994 Upper Deck Collector's Choice 750 Assists	6	10.00	7.50	4.00
1994 Upper Deck Predictors Retail	17	10.00	7.50	4.00
1994 Upper Deck Special Edition	63	5.00	3.75	2.00

Tim Hardaway

Set	Card #	MT	NM	EX
1990 Fleer	63 (R)	1.25	.90	.50
1990 Fleer Rookie Sensations	8	15.00	11.00	6.00
1990 NBA Hoops	3	1.50	1.25	.60
1990 NBA Hoops	113 (R)	1.25	.90	.50
1990 SkyBox	95 (R)	1.75	1.25	.70
1991 Fleer	65	.40	.30	.15
1991 Fleer	216	.20	.15	.08
1991 NBA Hoops	67	.35	.25	.14
1991 NBA Hoops	264	.20	.15	.08
1991 NBA Hoops	465	.25	.20	.10
1991 NBA Hoops	511	.25	.20	.10
1991 SkyBox	90	.50	.40	.20
1991 SkyBox	303	.10	.08	.04
1991 SkyBox	413	.12	.09	.05
1991 SkyBox	467	.15	.11	.06
1991 SkyBox	494	.35	.25	.14
1991 Upper Deck	50	.10	.08	.04
1991 Upper Deck	243	.50	.40	.20
1991 Upper Deck	468	.15	.11	.06
1992 Fleer	74	.10	.08	.04
1992 Fleer	251	.25	.20	.10
1992 Fleer All-Stars	14	1.00	.70	.40
1992 Fleer Ultra	64	.35	.25	.14
1992 Fleer Ultra All-NBA Team	9	1.50	1.25	.60
1992 Fleer Ultra Playmakers	3	1.50	1.25	.60
1992 NBA Hoops	74	.12	.09	.05
1992 NBA Hoops	307	.15	.11	.06
1992 SkyBox	79	.15	.11	.06
1992 SkyBox II Thunder and Lightning	9	4.00	3.00	1.50
1992 Topps	119	.10	.08	.04
1992 Topps	188	.10	.08	.04
1992 Topps Archives	123	.15	.11	.06
1992 Topps Beam Team	2	1.00	.75	.40
1992 Topps Stadium Club	211	.40	.30	.15
1992 Topps Stadium Club Beam Team	14	4.50	3.50	1.75
1992 Upper Deck	61	.15	.11	.06
1992 Upper Deck	261	.15	.11	.06
1992 Upper Deck	440	.15	.11	.06
1992 Upper Deck All-Division Team	19	.40	.30	.15
1992 Upper Deck All-NBA	7AN	1.25	.90	.50
1992 Upper Deck Jerry West Selects	15JW	1.50	1.25	.60
1992 Upper Deck Jerry West Selects	20JW	1.50	1.25	.60
1993 Fleer	67	.10	.08	.04
1993 Fleer All-Stars	16	.75	.60	.30
1993 Fleer Flair USA Basketball	7	.25	.20	.10
1993 Fleer Jam Session	69	.15	.11	.06
1993 Fleer Jam Session Gamebreakers	2	.50	.40	.20
1993 Fleer Ultra	65	.10	.08	.04
1993 Fleer Ultra	363	.10	.08	.04
1993 Fleer Ultra All-NBA Team	12	3.50	2.75	1.50
1993 NBA Hoops	69	.12	.09	.05
1993 NBA Hoops	272	.10	.08	.04
1993 NBA Hoops	286	.10	.08	.04
1993 NBA Hoops	431	.08	.06	.03
1993 SkyBox	73	.10	.08	.04
1993 Topps	130	.10	.08	.04
1993 Topps	320	.15	.11	.06
1993 Topps Finest	127	.35	.25	.14
1993 Topps Finest	198	.35	.25	.14
1993 Topps Stadium Club	148	.12	.09	.05
1993 Topps Stadium Club Beam Team	11	3.50	2.75	1.50
1993 Upper Deck	239	.15	.11	.06
1993 Upper Deck	323	.15	.11	.06
1993 Upper Deck	439	.15	.11	.06
1993 Upper Deck	470	.15	.11	.06
1993 Upper Deck All-NBA	14	1.00	.60	.30
1993 Upper Deck USA Basketball	3	.15	.11	.06
1993 Upper Deck 3-D Basketball	47	.10	.08	.04
1993 Upper Deck 3-D Basketball	76	.10	.08	.04
1994 Fleer	72	.07	.05	.03
1994 Fleer Flair	161	.30	.25	.12
1994 Fleer Jam Session	62	.15	.11	.06
1994 Fleer Ultra	60	.12	.09	.05
1994 NBA Hoops	65	.08	.06	.03
1994 NBA Hoops Supreme Court	16	.75	.60	.30
1994 SkyBox	53	.10	.08	.04
1994 SkyBox Dream Team II Dream Play	11	4.00	3.00	1.50
1994 Topps Finest	106	.30	.25	.12
1994 Topps Stadium Club	98	.15	.11	.06
1994 Upper Deck	54	.15	.11	.06
1994 Upper Deck	167	.20	.15	.08
1994 Upper Deck Collector's Choice 750 Assists	7	4.00	3.00	1.50
1994 Upper Deck Collector's Choice	207	.05	.04	.02
1994 Upper Deck Collector's Choice	310	.12	.09	.05
1994 Upper Deck Predictors Retail	16	4.00	3.00	1.50

Derek Harper

Set	Card #	MT	NM	EX
1983 Star Co.	55 (R)	120.00	90.00	48.00
1984 Star Co.	255	15.00	11.00	6.00
1985 Star Co.	163	10.00	7.50	4.00
1986 Fleer	44 (R)	8.00	6.00	3.25
1987 Fleer	48	2.00	1.50	.80
1988 Fleer	30	.85	.60	.35
1989 Fleer	35	.07	.05	.03
1989 NBA Hoops	184	.05	.04	.02

1990 Fleer	42	.03	.02	.01
1990 NBA Hoops	86	.03	.02	.01
1990 SkyBox	64	.05	.04	.02
1991 Fleer	45	.05	.04	.02
1991 Fleer	377	.03	.02	.01
1991 NBA Hoops	46	.05	.04	.02
1991 NBA Hoops	460	.05	.04	.02
1991 NBA Hoops	508	.05	.04	.02
1991 SkyBox	60	.05	.04	.02
1991 Upper Deck	137	.05	.04	.02
1992 Fleer	49	.05	.04	.02
1992 Fleer Ultra	42	.12	.09	.05
1992 NBA Hoops	47	.05	.04	.02
1992 SkyBox	49	.05	.04	.02
1992 SkyBox	287	.05	.04	.02
1992 Topps	93	.04	.03	.02
1992 Topps Archives	36	.05	.04	.02
1992 Topps Stadium Club	6	.10	.08	.04
1992 Upper Deck	98	.05	.04	.02
1992 Upper Deck All-Division Team	15	.25	.20	.10
1992 Upper Deck Team MVP's	7TM	.75	.60	.30
1993 Fleer	44	.05	.04	.02
1993 Fleer Jam Session	46	.10	.08	.04
1993 Fleer Ultra	44	.10	.08	.04
1993 Fleer Ultra	302	.10	.08	.04
1993 NBA Hoops	45	.06	.05	.02
1993 NBA Hoops	428	.06	.05	.02
1993 SkyBox	56	.05	.04	.02
1993 Topps	16	.05	.04	.02
1993 Topps	284	.05	.04	.02
1993 Topps Finest	31	.35	.25	.14
1993 Topps Stadium Club	192	.10	.08	.04
1993 Upper Deck	87	.05	.04	.02
1993 Upper Deck SE	151	.10	.08	.04
1993 Upper Deck 3-D Basketball	48	.10	.08	.04
1994 Fleer	151	.05	.04	.02
1994 Fleer Flair	100	.15	.11	.06
1994 Fleer Jam Session	125	.10	.08	.04
1994 Fleer Ultra	126	.08	.06	.03
1994 NBA Hoops	143	.04	.03	.02
1994 SkyBox	111	.06	.05	.02
1994 Topps	111	.06	.05	.02
1994 Topps Finest	11	.15	.11	.06
1994 Upper Deck Collector's Choice	99	.05	.04	.02
1994 Upper Deck Special Edition	61	.20	.15	.08

Clem Haskins

Set	Card #	NM	EX	VG
1970 Topps	165 (R)	8.00	4.00	2.50
1971 Topps	96	2.00	1.00	.60
1972 Topps	72	2.50	1.25	.70
1973 Topps	59	1.00	.50	.30
1974 Topps	62	1.00	.50	.30

1975 Topps	133	2.00	1.00	.60
1975 Topps	173	.50	.25	.15

John Havlicek

Set	Card #	NM	EX	VG
1969 Topps	20 (R)	175.00	131.00	70.00
1970 Topps	10	70.00	35.00	21.00
1970 Topps	112	30.00	15.00	9.00
1971 Topps	35	35.00	17.50	10.50
1971 Topps	138	10.00	5.00	3.00
1971 Topps	139	10.00	5.00	3.00
1972 Topps	110	27.00	13.50	8.00
1972 Topps	161	14.00	7.00	4.25
1972 Topps	171	10.00	5.00	3.00
1972 Topps	172	10.00	5.00	3.00
1973 Topps	20	15.00	7.50	4.50
1974 Topps	82	4.00	2.00	1.25
1974 Topps	100	10.00	5.00	3.00
1975 Topps	80	9.50	4.75	2.75
1976 Topps	90	15.00	7.50	4.50
1977 Topps	70	7.00	3.50	2.00

Set	Card #	MT	NM	EX
1985 Star Co. Schick Legends	12	8.00	6.00	3.25

Connie Hawkins

Set	Card #	NM	EX	VG
1969 Topps	15 (R)	45.00	34.00	18.00
1970 Topps	109	6.00	3.00	1.75
1970 Topps	130	15.00	7.50	4.50
1971 Topps	105	6.00	3.00	1.75
1972 Topps	30	5.00	2.50	1.50
1973 Topps	43	4.00	2.00	1.25
1974 Topps	104	4.00	2.00	1.25
1975 Topps	195	2.00	1.00	.60

Set	Card #	MT	NM	EX
1985 Star Co. Schick Legends	13	3.00	2.25	1.25

Hersey Hawkins

Set	Card #	MT	NM	EX
1989 Fleer	117 (R)	2.50	2.00	1.00
1989 NBA Hoops	137 (R)	.75	.60	.30
1990 Fleer	143	.15	.11	.06
1990 NBA Hoops	229	.20	.15	.08
1990 SkyBox	216	.20	.15	.08
1991 Fleer	154	.10	.08	.04
1991 NBA Hoops	161	.10	.08	.04
1991 NBA Hoops	252	.10	.08	.04
1991 NBA Hoops	488	.10	.08	.04
1991 NBA Hoops	569	.10	.08	.04
1991 SkyBox	216	.12	.09	.05
1991 SkyBox	505	.10	.08	.04
1991 SkyBox	551	.10	.08	.04
1991 SkyBox	593	.08	.06	.03
1991 Upper Deck	71	.10	.08	.04
1991 Upper Deck	155	.10	.08	.04
1992 Fleer	170	.10	.08	.04
1992 Fleer Sharpshooters	9	.60	.45	.25
1992 Fleer Team Leaders	20	6.00	4.50	2.50
1992 Fleer Ultra	139	.15	.11	.06
1992 NBA Hoops	174	.10	.08	.04
1992 SkyBox	184	.10	.08	.04
1992 SkyBox	301	.05	.04	.02
1992 Topps	260	.04	.03	.02
1992 Topps Archives	104	.05	.04	.02
1992 Topps Stadium Club	26	.10	.08	.04
1992 Upper Deck	187	.10	.08	.04
1993 Fleer	157	.05	.04	.02
1993 Fleer	254	.05	.04	.02
1993 Fleer Jam Session	21	.10	.08	.04
1993 Fleer Ultra	20	.10	.08	.04
1993 Fleer Ultra	215	.10	.08	.04
1993 NBA Hoops	163	.06	.05	.02
1993 NBA Hoops	308	.06	.05	.02
1993 SkyBox	139	.05	.04	.02
1993 SkyBox	203	.05	.04	.02
1993 Topps	276	.05	.04	.02
1993 Topps Finest	149	.35	.25	.14
1993 Topps Stadium Club	25	.10	.08	.04
1993 Topps Stadium Club	102	.10	.08	.04
1993 Topps Stadium Club	259	.10	.08	.04
1993 Upper Deck	389	.05	.04	.02
1993 Upper Deck SE	14	.10	.08	.04
1994 Fleer	24	.05	.04	.02
1994 Fleer Flair	16	.20	.15	.08
1994 Fleer Jam Session	21	.12	.09	.05
1994 Fleer Ultra	21	.08	.06	.03
1994 NBA Hoops	19	.04	.03	.02
1994 SkyBox	18	.06	.05	.02
1994 Topps Finest	109	.20	.15	.08
1994 Topps Finest Marathon Men	7	.65	.50	.25
1994 Upper Deck	88	.10	.08	.04

Elvin Hayes

Set	Card #	NM	EX	VG
1969 Topps	75 (R)	75.00	37.00	22.00
1970 Topps	1	30.00	15.00	9.00
1970 Topps	2	21.00	10.50	6.25
1970 Topps	5	16.00	8.00	4.75
1970 Topps	70	30.00	15.00	9.00
1971 Topps	120	12.00	6.00	3.50
1971 Topps	138	10.00	5.00	3.00
1971 Topps	139	10.00	5.00	3.00
1971 Topps	142	10.00	5.00	3.00
1972 Topps	150	13.00	6.50	4.00
1973 Topps	95	8.00	4.00	2.50
1974 Topps	30	8.00	4.00	2.50
1974 Topps	98	1.00	.50	.30
1974 Topps	148	3.00	1.50	.90
1975 Topps	60	7.00	3.50	2.00
1975 Topps	133	2.00	1.00	.60
1976 Topps	120	6.00	3.00	1.75
1976 Topps	133	4.00	2.00	1.25
1977 Topps	40	4.00	2.00	1.25
1978 Topps	25	3.50	1.75	1.00
1979 Topps	90	3.00	1.50	.90
1980 Topps	4	1.00	.50	.30
1980 Topps	69	.25	.13	.08
1980 Topps	88	.25	.13	.08
1980 Topps	124	1.00	.50	.30
1980 Topps	135	.25	.13	.08
1980 Topps	176	7.50	3.75	2.25

Set	Card #	MT	NM	EX
1981 Topps	42	1.00	.70	.40
1981 Topps	66	.40	.30	.15
1983 Star Co.	76	11.00	8.25	4.50

Gloss: The amount of surface shine on a card. All baseball cards are made with some surface gloss. Cards that keep more of their gloss keep more of their value.

Hand-collated set: A set assembled card-by-card by hand, usually by a collector or dealer putting the set together out of wax, cello or vending boxes.

High numbers: A term usually used to describe the final series in a particular set of cards. High numbers were generally produced in smaller quantities than other series and are, therefore, scarcer and more valuable.

Hologram: The silvery, laser-etched trademark printed as an anti-counterfeiting device on Upper Deck cards. Also, the disc with a team logo inserted into Upper Deck packs.

Hoops: Trade name for the National Basketball Association's set of basketball cards, NBA Hoops.

Walt Hazzard

Set	Card #	NM	EX	VG
1969 Topps	27 (R)	12.00	9.00	4.75
1970 Topps	134	6.00	3.00	1.75
1971 Topps	24	3.00	1.50	.90

Grant Hill

Set	Card #	MT	NM	EX
1994 Fleer	280 (R)	4.50	.04	.02
1994 Fleer First Year Phenoms	1	12.00	9.00	4.75
1994 Fleer Jam Session	55 (R)	8.00	6.00	3.25
1994 NBA Hoops	322 (R)	5.00	3.75	2.00
1994 NBA Hoops	423	1.75	1.25	.70
1994 NBA Hoops Chromium Magic's All-Rookie	3	50.00	37.00	20.00
1994 NBA Hoops Magic's All-Rookie	3	25.00	18.50	10.00
1994 Pacific Draft Prism Gold Sonic Boom	23	10.00	10.00	10.00
1994 Pacific Prisms	23	17.00	12.50	6.75
1994 Topps Stadium Club	181 (R)	6.00	4.50	2.50
1994 Upper Deck	157 (R)	7.00	5.25	2.75
1994 Upper Deck Collector's Choice Rookie	3	15.00	11.00	6.00
1994 Upper Deck Collector's Choice	219 (R)	5.00	3.75	2.00
1994 Upper Deck Collector's Choice	379	2.00	1.50	.80
1994 Upper Deck Collector's Choice	409	2.00	1.50	.80

Jeff Hornacek

Set	Card #	MT	NM	EX
1989 Fleer	121 (R)	2.50	2.00	1.00
1989 NBA Hoops	229 (R)	.50	.40	.20
1990 Fleer	147	.15	.11	.06
1990 NBA Hoops	236	.10	.08	.04
1990 SkyBox	222	.10	.08	.04
1991 Fleer	160	.10	.08	.04
1991 NBA Hoops	164	.08	.06	.03
1991 SkyBox	224	.10	.08	.04
1991 SkyBox	594	.05	.04	.02
1991 Upper Deck	135	.18	.14	.07
1991 Upper Deck	469	.10	.08	.04
1992 Fleer	171	.10	.08	.04
1992 Fleer	405	.05	.04	.02
1992 Fleer All-Stars	15	1.25	.90	.50
1992 Fleer Sharpshooters	3	.50	.40	.20
1992 Fleer Ultra	332	.10	.08	.04
1992 NBA Hoops	180	.08	.06	.03
1992 NBA Hoops	308	.07	.05	.03
1992 NBA Hoops	445	.10	.08	.04
1992 SkyBox	190	.10	.08	.04
1992 SkyBox	384	.10	.08	.04
1992 Topps	112	.04	.03	.02
1992 Topps	343	.04	.03	.02
1992 Topps Archives	82	.05	.04	.02
1992 Topps Beam Team	2	1.00	.75	.40
1992 Topps Stadium Club	323	.10	.08	.04
1992 Topps Stadium Club Beam Team	9	2.00	1.50	.80
1992 Upper Deck	22	.10	.08	.04
1992 Upper Deck	403	.05	.04	.02
1993 Fleer	158	.05	.04	.02
1993 Fleer Jam Session	169	.10	.08	.04
1993 Fleer Ultra	141	.10	.08	.04
1993 NBA Hoops	164	.06	.05	.02
1993 SkyBox	140	.05	.04	.02
1993 SkyBox Thunder and Lightning	7	1.25	1.50	.80
1993 Topps	60	.05	.04	.02
1993 Topps Finest	188	.35	.25	.14
1993 Topps Stadium Club	57	.10	.08	.04
1993 Upper Deck	19	.05	.04	.02
1993 Upper Deck SE	84	.10	.08	.04
1993 Upper Deck 3-D Basketball	51	.10	.08	.04
1994 Fleer	222	.05	.04	.02
1994 Fleer Flair	146	.15	.11	.06
1994 Fleer Jam Session	185	.10	.08	.04
1994 Fleer Ultra	184	.08	.06	.03
1994 NBA Hoops	210	.04	.03	.02
1994 NBA Hoops Power Ratings	51	.30	.25	.12
1994 SkyBox	163	.06	.05	.02
1994 Topps	154	.06	.05	.02
1994 Topps Finest	96	.15	.11	.06
1994 Topps Stadium Club	136	.08	.06	.03
1994 Upper Deck Collector's Choice	14	.05	.04	.02
1994 Upper Deck Special Edition	85	.20	.15	.08

Lou Hudson

Set	Card #	NM	EX	VG
1969 Topps	65 (R)	22.00	16.50	8.75
1970 Topps	3	2.50	1.25	.70
1970 Topps	30	5.00	2.50	1.50
1970 Topps	115	3.00	1.50	.90
1971 Topps	110	3.00	1.50	.90
1972 Topps	130	2.00	1.00	.60
1973 Topps	150	1.00	.50	.30
1974 Topps	81	4.50	2.25	1.25
1974 Topps	130	.50	.25	.15
1975 Topps	25	1.00	.50	.30
1976 Topps	96	1.75	.90	.50
1977 Topps	85	.80	.40	.25
1978 Topps	24	.60	.30	.20
1979 Topps	119	.50	.25	.15

Bobby Hurley

Set	Card #	MT	NM	EX
1993 Fleer	372 (R)	.50	.40	.20
1993 Fleer First Year Phenoms	4	.75	.60	.30
1993 Fleer Jam Session	195 (R)	.65	.50	.25
1993 Fleer Jam Session Rookie Standouts	5	1.25	.90	.50
1993 Fleer Lottery Exchange	7	1.50	1.25	.60
1993 Fleer Ultra	161 (R)	.75	.60	.30
1993 Fleer Ultra	332	.35	.25	.14
1993 Fleer Ultra All-Rookies	6	2.00	1.50	.80
1993 NBA Hoops	401 (R)	.50	.40	.20
1993 NBA Hoops Draft Redemption	7	3.00	2.25	1.25
1993 NBA Hoops II Magic's All-Rookie Team	7	3.50	2.75	1.50
1993 SkyBox	274 (R)	.50	.40	.20
1993 SkyBox Draft Picks	7	3.00	2.25	1.25

Set	Card #			
1993 SkyBox Thunder and Lightning	8	1.25	1.50	.80
1993 Topps	86 (R)	.50	.40	.20
1993 Topps	232	.30	.25	.12
1993 Topps Finest	26 (R)	2.00	1.50	.80
1993 Topps Stadium Club	53 (R)	.75	.60	.30
1993 Topps Stadium Club	213 (R)	.40	.30	.15
1993 Topps Stadium Club	269	.30	.25	.12
1993 Topps Stadium Club Beam Team	20	5.00	3.75	2.00
1993 Upper Deck	314 (R)	.50	.40	.20
1993 Upper Deck	489	.10	.08	.04
1993 Upper Deck Rookie Exchange Gold/Silver	7	1.50	1.25	.60
1993 Upper Deck Rookie Standouts	2	3.00	2.25	1.25
1993 Upper Deck SE	156 (R)	.50	.40	.20
1993 Upper Deck 3-D Basketball	88 (R)	.25	.08	.04
1994 Fleer	193	.20	.15	.08
1994 Fleer Jam Session	162	.20	.15	.08
1994 Fleer Rookie Sensations	12	2.25	1.75	.90
1994 NBA Hoops	184	.10	.08	.04
1994 NBA Hoops	427	.15	.11	.06
1994 NBA Hoops Supreme Court	42	.75	.60	.30
1994 SkyBox	141	.20	.15	.08
1994 SkyBox Ragin' Rookies	21	.75	.60	.30
1994 Topps	44	.15	.11	.06
1994 Topps Stadium Club	112	.08	.06	.03
1994 Upper Deck	77	.10	.08	.04
1994 Upper Deck Col.'s Choice Hobby Blowups	1	.75	.60	.30
1994 Upper Deck Collector's Choice	132	.20	.15	.08
1994 Upper Deck Collector's Choice	418	.05	.04	.02

Dan Issel

Set	Card #	NM	EX	VG
1971 Topps	146	2.00	1.00	.60
1971 Topps	147	3.00	1.50	.90
1971 Topps	200 (R)	50.00	25.00	15.00
1972 Topps	230	16.00	8.00	4.75
1972 Topps	249	6.00	3.00	1.75
1972 Topps	259	5.00	2.50	1.50
1973 Topps	210	6.00	3.00	1.75
1973 Topps	234	7.00	3.50	2.00
1974 Topps	190	5.50	2.75	1.75
1974 Topps	207	7.00	3.50	2.00
1974 Topps	224	3.00	1.50	.90
1975 Topps	260	6.00	3.00	1.75
1976 Topps	94	6.50	3.25	2.00
1977 Topps	41	3.00	1.50	.90
1978 Topps	81	2.00	1.00	.60

1979 Topps	17	1.25	.60	.40
1980 Topps	5	.25	.13	.08
1980 Topps	68	.75	.40	.25
1980 Topps	73	1.00	.50	.30
1980 Topps	120	.25	.13	.08
1980 Topps	125	.25	.13	.08
1980 Topps	166	.75	.40	.25

Set	Card #	MT	NM	EX
1981 Topps	11	1.00	.70	.40
1981 Topps	107	.40	.30	.15
1981 Topps	49	.15	.11	.06
1983 Star Co.	189	13.00	9.75	5.25
1984 Star Co.	142	14.00	10.50	5.50
1984 Star Co.	283	8.00	6.00	3.25
1984 Star Co. Court Kings	28	4.00	3.00	1.50
1992 Fleer	56	.05	.04	.02
1992 NBA Hoops	245	.06	.05	.02
1992 SkyBox	261	.05	.04	.02
1993 NBA Hoops	236	.10	.08	.04
1994 NBA Hoops	280	.08	.06	.03

Jim Jackson

Set	Card #	MT	NM	EX
1992 Upper Deck	33 (R)	7.50	5.65	3.00
1992 Upper Deck	458	1.50	1.25	.60
1993 Fleer	46	.60	.45	.25
1993 Fleer Jam Session	48	.75	.60	.30
1993 Fleer Jam Session 2nd Year Stars	2	2.00	1.50	.80
1993 Fleer Rookie Sensations	11	8.00	6.00	3.25
1993 Fleer Sharpshooters	2	4.00	3.00	1.50
1993 Fleer Ultra	46	.75	.60	.30
1993 Fleer Ultra Inside Outside	2	1.00	.70	.40
1993 NBA Hoops	48	.60	.45	.25
1993 NBA Hoops Face to Face	4	5.00	3.75	2.00
1993 SkyBox	57	.65	.50	.25
1993 SkyBox Thunder and Lightning	1	6.50	6.75	3.50
1993 SkyBox 1992 NBA Draft Picks	4	6.00	4.50	2.50
1993 Topps	38	.50	.40	.20
1993 Topps	150	.25	.20	.10
1993 Topps BlackGold	7	3.00	2.25	1.25
1993 Topps Finest	116	3.00	2.25	1.25
1993 Topps Finest	136	3.00	2.25	1.25
1993 Topps Stadium Club	326	.60	.45	.25
1993 Upper Deck	24	.55	.40	.20
1993 Upper Deck	460	.10	.08	.04
1993 Upper Deck	477	.35	.25	.14
1993 Upper Deck Future Heroes	30	4.00	3.00	1.50
1993 Upper Deck Locker Talk	15	3.50	2.75	1.50
1993 Upper Deck SE	140	.60	.45	.25

1993 Upper Deck SE West Future All Stars	1	20.00	15.00	8.00
1993 Upper Deck Team MVP's	6	1.50	1.25	.60
1993 Upper Deck 3-D Basketball	61	.10	.08	.04
1994 Fleer	49	.20	.15	.08
1994 Fleer Flair	34	1.50	1.25	.60
1994 Fleer Jam Session	40	.40	.30	.15
1994 Fleer Ultra	41	.35	.25	.14
1994 NBA Hoops	43	.25	.20	.10
1994 NBA Hoops Power Ratings	11	4.00	3.00	1.50
1994 NBA Hoops Supreme Court	11	1.75	1.25	.70
1994 SkyBox	36	.30	.25	.12
1994 Topps	153	.25	.20	.10
1994 Topps Finest Iron Men	3	10.00	7.50	4.00
1994 Topps Finest Marathon Men	4	7.50	5.75	3.00
1994 Topps Stadium Club	78	.60	.45	.25
1994 Topps Stadium Club Dynasty and Destiny	4B	2.50	2.00	1.00
1994 Upper Deck	131	.40	.30	.15
1994 Upper Deck Collector's Choice	224	.45	.35	.20
1994 Upper Deck Special Edition	19	2.50	2.00	1.00

Phil Jackson

Set	Card #	NM	EX	VG
1972 Topps	32 (R)	24.00	12.00	7.25
1973 Topps	71	5.00	2.50	1.50
1974 Topps	132	5.00	2.50	1.50
1975 Topps	111	5.00	2.50	1.50
1976 Topps	77	6.00	3.00	1.75

Set	Card #	MT	NM	EX
1989 NBA Hoops	266	.05	.04	.02
1990 NBA Hoops	308	.03	.02	.01
1990 NBA Hoops	348	.05	.04	.02
1990 SkyBox	304	.07	.05	.03
1991 Fleer	28	.03	.02	.01
1991 NBA Hoops	224	.07	.05	.03
1991 SkyBox	381	.07	.05	.03
1992 Fleer	31	.05	.04	.02
1992 NBA Hoops	242	.07	.05	.03
1992 NBA Hoops	305	.05	.04	.02
1992 SkyBox	258	.10	.08	.04
1993 NBA Hoops	233	.06	.05	.02
1994 NBA Hoops	277	.10	.08	.04

Dennis Johnson

Set	Card #	NM	EX	VG
1978 Topps	78 (R)	13.00	6.50	4.00
1979 Topps	6	2.00	1.00	.60
1980 Topps	8	3.00	1.50	.90
1980 Topps	121	.50	.25	.15

Set	Card #	MT	NM	EX
1981 Topps	34	.50	.40	.20
1981 Topps	108	.30	.25	.12
1983 Star Co.	32	15.00	11.00	6.00
1984 Star Co.	6	6.00	4.50	2.50
1985 Star Co.	97	5.00	3.75	2.00
1986 Fleer	50	3.00	2.25	1.25
1987 Fleer	54	1.50	1.25	.60
1988 Fleer	10	.50	.40	.20
1989 Fleer	9	.20	.15	.08
1989 NBA Hoops	121	.05	.04	.02
1990 Fleer	9	.05	.04	.02
1990 NBA Hoops	41	.10	.08	.04
1990 SkyBox	16	.10	.08	.04

Kevin Johnson

Set	Card #	MT	NM	EX
1989 Fleer	123 (R)	6.00	4.50	2.50
1989 NBA Hoops	35 (R)	1.50	1.25	.60
1990 Fleer	149	.25	.20	.10
1990 NBA Hoops	19	.20	.15	.08
1990 NBA Hoops	238	.35	.25	.14
1990 NBA Hoops	375	.15	.11	.06
1990 SkyBox	224	.50	.40	.20
1991 Fleer	161	.15	.11	.06
1991 Fleer	210	.10	.08	.04
1991 Fleer	392	.10	.08	.04
1991 Fleer NBA Schoolyard Sets	4	3.50	2.75	1.50
1991 NBA Hoops	165	.12	.09	.05
1991 NBA Hoops	265	.10	.08	.04
1991 NBA Hoops	302	.10	.08	.04

Set	Card #	MT	NM	EX
1991 NBA Hoops	490	.12	.09	.05
1991 SkyBox	225	.25	.20	.10
1991 SkyBox	479	.15	.11	.06
1991 SkyBox	582	.10	.08	.04
1991 Upper Deck	23	.15	.11	.06
1991 Upper Deck	59	.12	.09	.05
1991 Upper Deck	356	.20	.15	.08
1992 Fleer	181	.15	.11	.06
1992 Fleer	252	.12	.09	.05
1992 Fleer	258	.10	.08	.04
1992 Fleer	282	.10	.08	.04
1992 Fleer Team Leaders	21	12.00	9.00	4.75
1992 Fleer Ultra	144	.15	.11	.06
1992 Fleer Ultra All-NBA Team	15	1.50	1.25	.60
1992 Fleer Ultra Playmakers	5	1.00	.70	.40
1992 NBA Hoops	181	.10	.08	.04
1992 NBA Hoops	326	.15	.11	.06
1992 NBA Hoops	335	.10	.08	.04
1992 SkyBox	191	.15	.11	.06
1992 SkyBox	302	.10	.08	.04
1992 SkyBox II Thunder and Lightning	3	20.00	15.00	8.00
1992 Topps	190	.10	.08	.04
1992 Topps	222	.10	.08	.04
1992 Topps Archives	93	.15	.11	.06
1992 Topps Beam Team	3	2.00	1.50	.80
1992 Topps Stadium Club	216	.15	.11	.06
1992 Topps Stadium Club Beam Team	12	5.00	3.75	2.00
1992 Upper Deck	57	.15	.11	.06
1992 Upper Deck	119	.15	.11	.06
1992 Upper Deck	418	.15	.11	.06
1992 Upper Deck Team MVP's	22TM	1.00	.70	.40
1993 Fleer	167	.15	.11	.06
1993 Fleer Jam Session	178	.20	.15	.08
1993 Fleer Jam Session Gamebreakers	3	.50	.40	.20
1993 Fleer Ultra	147	.20	.15	.08
1993 NBA Hoops	172	.10	.08	.04
1993 SkyBox	20	.12	.09	.05
1993 SkyBox	147	.10	.08	.04
1993 Topps	30	.10	.08	.04
1993 Topps	207	.10	.08	.04
1993 Topps Finest	183	1.25	.90	.50
1993 Topps Stadium Club	15	.25	.20	.10
1993 Upper Deck	7	.15	.11	.06
1993 Upper Deck	472	.15	.11	.06
1993 Upper Deck	502	.15	.11	.06
1993 Upper Deck SE	31	.10	.08	.04
1993 Upper Deck 3-D Basketball	13	.10	.08	.04
1994 Fleer	178	.05	.04	.02
1994 Fleer Flair	118	.50	.40	.20
1994 Fleer Flair	162	.25	.20	.10
1994 Fleer Jam Session	149	.15	.11	.06
1994 Fleer NBA All-Stars	16	.35	.25	.14
1994 Fleer Ultra	150	.15	.11	.06
1994 Fleer Ultra All-NBA Team	7	.75	.60	.30
1994 NBA Hoops	169	.04	.03	.02
1994 NBA Hoops	240	.04	.03	.02
1994 NBA Hoops Power Ratings	42	1.00	.70	.40
1994 NBA Hoops Supreme Court	37	.50	.40	.20
1994 SkyBox	131	.08	.06	.03
1994 SkyBox Dream Team II Dream Play	14	4.00	3.00	1.50
1994 Topps	157	.10	.08	.04
1994 Topps	189	.06	.05	.02
1994 Topps Finest	91	.35	.25	.14
1994 Topps Stadium Club	70	.15	.11	.06
1994 Topps Super Passers	5	1.00	.70	.40
1994 Upper Deck	20	.15	.11	.06
1994 Upper Deck	57	.12	.09	.05
1994 Upper Deck	176	.15	.11	.06

Set	Card #	MT	NM	EX
1994 Upper Deck Collector's Choice	7	.07	.05	.03
1994 Upper Deck Collector's Choice 750 Assists	10	5.00	3.75	2.00
1994 Upper Deck Predictors Retail	14	5.00	3.75	2.00
1994 Upper Deck Special Edition	70	.50	.40	.20

Larry Johnson

Set	Card #	MT	NM	EX
1991 Fleer	255 (R)	2.00	1.50	.80
1991 NBA Hoops	546 (R)	2.00	1.50	.80
1991 SkyBox	513 (R)	4.00	3.00	1.50
1991 Upper Deck	2 (R)	4.50	3.50	1.75
1991 Upper Deck	438	.50	.40	.20
1991 Upper Deck	445	2.25	1.75	.90
1991 Upper Deck	480	1.00	.70	.40
1991 Upper Deck Rookie Standouts	26R	7.00	5.25	2.75
1992 Fleer	25	.75	.60	.30
1992 Fleer	247	.40	.30	.15
1992 Fleer	253	.30	.25	.12
1992 Fleer	259	.30	.25	.12
1992 Fleer	292	.25	.20	.10
1992 Fleer Rookie Sensations	5	30.00	22.00	12.00
1992 Fleer Team Leaders	3	60.00	45.00	24.00
1992 Fleer Ultra	21	1.00	.75	.40
1992 Fleer Ultra NBA Award Winners	3	5.00	3.75	2.00
1992 NBA Hoops	24	.50	.40	.20
1992 SkyBox	25	1.00	.70	.40
1992 SkyBox	319	.50	.40	.20
1992 SkyBox II Thunder and Lightning	5	16.00	12.00	6.50
1992 Topps	283	.40	.30	.15
1992 Topps Archives	11	.30	.25	.12
1992 Topps Archives	144	.75	.60	.30
1992 Topps Stadium Club	192	.75	.60	.30
1992 Topps Stadium Club	213	1.50	1.25	.60
1992 Upper Deck	63	.20	.15	.08
1992 Upper Deck	64	.15	.11	.06
1992 Upper Deck	287	.50	.40	.20
1992 Upper Deck	423	.30	.25	.12
1992 Upper Deck All-Division Team	8	2.00	1.50	.80
1992 Upper Deck All-Rookie	1AR	5.00	3.75	2.00
1992 Upper Deck Holograms	5AW	1.50	1.25	.60
1992 Upper Deck Jerry West Selects	18JW	5.00	3.75	2.00
1993 Fleer	21	.30	.25	.12
1993 Fleer	223	.15	.11	.06
1993 Fleer All-Stars	4	3.00	2.25	1.25
1993 Fleer Flair USA Basketball	8	1.25	.90	.50
1993 Fleer Jam Session	23	.50	.40	.20
1993 Fleer Jam Session Slam Dunk Heroes	2	1.50	1.25	.60
1993 Fleer Towers of Power	10	8.50	6.50	3.50
1993 Fleer Ultra	22	.50	.40	.20
1993 Fleer Ultra	364	.60	.45	.25
1993 Fleer Ultra All-NBA Team	8	3.00	2.25	1.25
1993 Fleer Ultra Famous Nicknames	6	2.00	1.50	.80
1993 Fleer Ultra Inside Outside	3	.75	.60	.30
1993 Fleer Ultra Power in the Key	1	3.00	2.25	1.25
1993 Fleer Ultra Scoring Kings	4	12.00	9.00	4.75
1993 NBA Hoops	22	.30	.25	.12
1993 NBA Hoops	260	.12	.09	.05
1993 NBA Hoops	287	.15	.11	.06
1993 NBA Hoops Face to Face	5	4.00	3.00	1.50
1993 NBA Hoops Supreme Court	5	1.50	1.25	.60
1993 SkyBox	4	.25	.20	.10
1993 SkyBox	39	.50	.40	.25
1993 SkyBox Center Stage	5	3.00	2.25	1.25
1993 SkyBox Showdown Series	8	1.25	.90	.50
1993 Topps	131	.25	.20	.10
1993 Topps	223	.40	.30	.15
1993 Topps	394	.25	.20	.10
1993 Topps BlackGold	9	2.00	1.50	.80
1993 Topps Finest	109	2.00	1.50	.80
1993 Topps Finest	162	3.00	2.25	1.25
1993 Topps Finest Main Attraction	3	10.00	7.50	4.00
1993 Topps Stadium Club	6	.25	.20	.10
1993 Topps Stadium Club	178	.30	.25	.12
1993 Topps Stadium Club	185	.30	.25	.12
1993 Topps Stadium Club	323	.40	.30	.15
1993 Topps Stadium Club Beam Team	15	7.00	5.25	2.75
1993 Upper Deck	194	.15	.11	.06
1993 Upper Deck	365	.40	.30	.15
1993 Upper Deck	435	.25	.20	.10
1993 Upper Deck All-NBA	7	1.50	1.25	.60
1993 Upper Deck Jordan's Flight Team	11	9.00	6.75	3.50
1993 Upper Deck SE	57	.40	.30	.15
1993 Upper Deck SE Behind the Glass	6	4.00	3.00	1.50
1993 Upper Deck USA Basketball	4	.40	.30	.15
1993 Upper Deck 3-D Basketball	30	.30	.25	.12
1993 Upper Deck 3-D Basketball	71	.30	.25	.12
1993 Upper Deck 3-D Basketball	95	.25	.20	.10
1993 Upper Deck 3-D Triple Double	7	3.00	2.25	1.25
1994 Fleer	26	.30	.25	.12
1994 Fleer Flair	17	1.00	.70	.40
1994 Fleer Flair	163	.65	.50	.25
1994 Fleer Jam Session	22	.30	.25	.12
1994 Fleer Jam Session Slam Dunk Heroes	2	6.00	4.50	2.50
1994 Fleer Ultra	22	.40	.30	.15
1994 Fleer Ultra Ultra Power	3	1.50	1.25	.60
1994 Fleer Young Lions	3	2.50	2.00	1.00
1994 NBA Hoops	21	.25	.20	.10
1994 NBA Hoops Power Ratings	5	3.00	2.25	1.25
1994 NBA Hoops Supreme Court	4	1.75	1.25	.70
1994 SkyBox	19	.35	.25	.14
1994 SkyBox Dream Team II Dream Play	2	7.00	5.25	2.75

1994 Topps Stadium Club	113	.20	.15	.08
1994 Upper Deck	90	.50	.40	.20
1994 Upper Deck	180	.30	.25	.12
1994 Upper Deck Collector's Choice	201	.20	.15	.08
1994 Upper Deck Collector's Choice	302	.25	.20	.10
1994 Upper Deck Predictors Hobby	8	3.00	2.25	1.25

Magic Johnson

Set	Card #	NM	EX	VG
1980 Topps	6 (R)	475.00	237.00	142.00
1980 Topps	66	35.00	17.50	10.50
1980 Topps	111	20.00	10.00	6.00
1980 Topps	146	80.00	40.00	24.00

Set	Card #	MT	NM	EX
1981 Topps	21	28.00	21.00	11.00
1981 Topps	109	12.00	9.00	4.75
1983 Star Co.	13	160.00	120.00	64.00
1983 Star Co. All-Star Game	18	25.00	18.50	10.00
1984 Star Co.	172	120.00	90.00	48.00
1984 Star Co. All-Star Game	21	35.00	26.00	14.00
1984 Star Co. Awards Banquet	6	20.00	15.00	8.00
1984 Star Co. Awards Banquet	11	5.00	3.75	2.00
1984 Star Co. Awards Banquet	17	15.00	11.00	6.00
1984 Star Co. Court Kings	15	40.00	30.00	16.00
1985 Star Co.	28	200.00	150.00	80.00
1985 Star Co. Lite All-Stars	11	65.00	49.00	26.00
1986 Fleer	53	32.00	24.00	13.00
1986 Star Co. Best of the Best	8	80.00	60.00	32.00
1986 Star Co. Court Kings	17	45.00	34.00	18.00
1987 Fleer	56	25.00	18.50	10.00
1988 Fleer	67	10.00	7.50	4.00
1988 Fleer	123	4.50	3.50	1.75
1989 Fleer	77	3.00	2.25	1.25
1989 NBA Hoops	166	.40	.30	.15
1989 NBA Hoops	270	1.00	.70	.40
1990 Fleer	93	.60	.45	.25
1990 Fleer All-Stars	4	1.25	.90	.50
1990 NBA Hoops	18	.50	.40	.20
1990 NBA Hoops	157	.75	.60	.30
1990 NBA Hoops	367	.25	.20	.10
1990 NBA Hoops	385	1.00	.70	.40
1990 SkyBox	138	.80	.60	.30
1990 Star Co. Court Kings	4	32.00	20.75	8.25
1990 Star Co. Slam	4	35.00	22.00	9.00
1991 Fleer	100	.50	.40	.20
1991 Fleer Pro Visions	6	.75	.60	.30
1991 NBA Hoops	101	.60	.45	.25
1991 NBA Hoops	266	.25	.20	.10
1991 NBA Hoops	312	.25	.20	.10
1991 NBA Hoops	316	.25	.20	.10
1991 NBA Hoops	321	.25	.20	.10
1991 NBA Hoops	473	.25	.20	.10
1991 NBA Hoops	535	.25	.20	.10
1991 NBA Hoops	578	1.25	.90	.50
1991 NBA Hoops MVP All-Stars	11	5.00	3.75	2.00
1991 SkyBox	V	1.25	.85	.35
1991 SkyBox	137	.75	.60	.30
1991 SkyBox	323	.25	.20	.10
1991 SkyBox	333	1.00	.70	.40
1991 SkyBox	471	.25	.20	.10
1991 SkyBox	533	1.25	.90	.50
1991 Upper Deck	45	.75	.60	.30
1991 Upper Deck	57	.40	.30	.15
1991 Upper Deck	464	.50	.40	.20
1992 NBA Hoops	e	3.00	2.25	1.25
1992 NBA Hoops	309	.25	.20	.10
1992 NBA Hoops	340	.30	.25	.12
1992 NBA Hoops	482	.50	.40	.20
1992 NBA Hoops Supreme Court	10SC	4.00	3.00	1.50
1992 SkyBox	AU2	275.00	200.00	100.00
1992 SkyBox	NNO	15.00	10.00	4.00
1992 SkyBox	310	.35	.25	.14
1992 SkyBox	358	.50	.40	.20
1992 SkyBox I Olympic Team	12USA	4.50	3.50	1.75
1992 Topps	2	.10	.08	.04
1992 Topps	54	.35	.25	.14
1992 Topps	126	.25	.20	.10
1992 Topps Stadium Club	32	1.50	1.25	.60
1992 Upper Deck	32a	1.00	.70	.40
1993 NBA Hoops	422	.25	.20	.10
1993 NBA Hoops Face to Face	8	4.00	3.00	1.50
1993 SkyBox Showdown Series	12	2.50	2.00	1.00

Bobby Jones

Set	Card #	NM	EX	VG
1975 Topps	298 (R)	13.00	6.50	4.00
1976 Topps	144	4.50	2.25	1.25
1977 Topps	118	1.00	.50	.30
1978 Topps	14	1.00	.50	.30
1979 Topps	132	1.00	.50	.30
1980 Topps	67	.25	.13	.08
1980 Topps	74	2.00	1.00	.60
1980 Topps	155	.25	.13	.08
1980 Topps	159	2.00	1.00	.60

Set	Card #	MT	NM	EX
1981 Topps	32	.15	.11	.06
1981 Topps	106	.15	.11	.06
1983 Star Co.	6	10.00	7.50	4.00
1984 Star Co.	207	5.00	3.75	2.00
1985 Star Co.	5	4.00	3.00	1.50

Caldwell Jones

Set	Card #	NM	EX	VG
1974 Topps	187 (R)	5.00	2.50	1.50
1974 Topps	211	.50	.25	.15
1974 Topps	228	1.25	.60	.40
1975 Topps	285	1.25	.60	.40
1975 Topps	305	3.00	1.50	.90
1976 Topps	112	1.50	.70	.45
1977 Topps	34	.25	.13	.08
1978 Topps	103	.25	.13	.08
1979 Topps	33	.20	.10	.06
1980 Topps	17	.25	.13	.08
1980 Topps	64	.25	.13	.08
1980 Topps	109	.25	.13	.08
1980 Topps	141	.25	.13	.08

Set	Card #	MT	NM	EX
1981 Topps	91	.15	.11	.06
1981 Topps	59	1.50	1.25	.60
1983 Star Co.	77	2.00	1.50	.80
1984 Star Co.	108	2.75	2.00	1.00
1989 NBA Hoops	347	.05	.04	.02
1990 NBA Hoops	268	.10	.08	.04
1990 SkyBox	257	.10	.08	.04

Michael Jordan

Set	Card #	MT	NM	EX
1984 Star Co.	101 (R)	2700.	2025.	1080.
1984 Star Co.	195	400.00	300.00	160.00
1984 Star Co.	288	400.00	300.00	160.00
1984 Star Co. Court Kings	26	125.00	95.00	50.00
1985 Star Co.	117	800.00	600.00	320.00
1985 Star Co. All-Rookie Team	2	300.00	225.00	120.00
1985 Star Co. Last 11 R.O.Y.	1	200.00	150.00	80.00
1985 Star Co. Lite All-Stars	4	225.00	169.00	90.00
1986 Fleer	57 (R)	775.00	581.00	310.00

Set	Card #	MT	NM	EX
1986 Star Co. Best of the New	2	950.00	712.00	380.00
1986 Star Co. Best of the Best	9	375.00	281.00	150.00
1986 Star Co. Court Kings	18	180.00	135.00	72.00
1987 Fleer	59	165.00	124.00	66.00
1988 Fleer	17	50.00	37.00	20.00
1988 Fleer	120	16.00	12.00	6.50
1989 Fleer	21	15.00	11.00	6.00
1989 NBA Hoops	21	1.25	.90	.50
1989 NBA Hoops	200	3.00	2.25	1.25
1990 Fleer	26	2.50	2.00	1.00
1990 Fleer All-Stars	5	4.00	3.00	1.50
1990 NBA Hoops	5	2.50	2.00	1.00
1990 NBA Hoops	65	2.75	2.00	1.00
1990 NBA Hoops	358	1.00	.70	.40
1990 NBA Hoops	382	1.00	.70	.40
1990 NBA Hoops	385	1.00	.70	.40
1990 SkyBox	41	3.00	2.25	1.25
1991 Fleer	29	2.00	1.50	.80
1991 Fleer	211	.75	.60	.30
1991 Fleer	220	1.00	.70	.40
1991 Fleer	375	1.00	.70	.40
1991 Fleer Pro Visions	2	3.00	2.25	1.25
1991 NBA Hoops	30	1.50	1.25	.60
1991 NBA Hoops	253	.75	.60	.30
1991 NBA Hoops	306	.60	.45	.25
1991 NBA Hoops	317	.75	.60	.30
1991 NBA Hoops	455	.75	.60	.30
1991 NBA Hoops	536	.75	.60	.30
1991 NBA Hoops	579	4.00	3.00	1.50
1991 NBA Hoops MVP All-Stars	9	25.00	18.50	10.00
1991 NBA Hoops Slam Dunk	4	20.00	15.00	8.00
1991 SkyBox	39	2.50	2.00	1.00
1991 SkyBox	307	1.00	.70	.40
1991 SkyBox	333	1.00	.70	.40
1991 SkyBox	334	.75	.60	.30
1991 SkyBox	408	1.00	.70	.40
1991 SkyBox	462	.75	.60	.30
1991 SkyBox	534	5.00	3.75	2.00
1991 SkyBox	572	1.00	.70	.40
1991 SkyBox	583	1.00	.70	.40
1991 Upper Deck	22	.75	.60	.30
1991 Upper Deck	44	2.50	2.00	1.00
1991 Upper Deck	48	1.00	.70	.40
1991 Upper Deck	69	1.00	.70	.40
1991 Upper Deck	75	1.00	.70	.40
1991 Upper Deck	452	2.00	1.50	.80
1991 Upper Deck Holograms	1AW	5.00	3.75	2.00
1991 Upper Deck Holograms	4AW	5.00	3.75	2.00
1992 Fleer	32	2.00	1.50	.80
1992 Fleer	238	.75	.60	.30
1992 Fleer	246	1.25	.90	.50
1992 Fleer	273	1.00	.70	.40
1992 Fleer All-Stars	6	35.00	26.00	14.00
1992 Fleer Team Leaders	4	275.00	206.00	110.00
1992 Fleer Total "D"	5	135.00	101.00	54.00
1992 Fleer Ultra	27	4.00	3.00	1.50
1992 Fleer Ultra	216	1.25	.90	.50
1992 Fleer Ultra All-NBA Team	4	16.00	12.00	6.50
1992 Fleer Ultra NBA Award Winners	1	22.00	16.50	8.75
1992 NBA Hoops	30	2.00	1.50	.80
1992 NBA Hoops	298	1.25	.90	.50
1992 NBA Hoops	320	.50	.40	.20
1992 NBA Hoops	341	1.00	.70	.40
1992 NBA Hoops Supreme Court	1SC	12.00	9.00	4.75
1992 SkyBox	31	2.50	2.00	1.00
1992 SkyBox	314	2.00	1.50	.80
1992 SkyBox I Olympic Team	11USA	15.00	11.00	6.00
1992 Topps	3	.50	.40	.20
1992 Topps	115	.75	.60	.30
1992 Topps	141	1.25	.90	.50
1992 Topps	205	.75	.60	.30

Set	Card #			
1992 Topps Archives	52	2.00	1.50	.80
1992 Topps Beam Team	3	2.00	1.50	.80
1992 Topps Stadium Club	1	4.50	3.50	1.75
1992 Topps Stadium Club	210	2.00	1.50	.80
1992 Topps Stadium Club Beam Team	1	55.00	41.00	22.00
1992 Upper Deck	23	2.00	1.50	.80
1992 Upper Deck	62	.60	.45	.25
1992 Upper Deck	67	1.00	.70	.40
1992 Upper Deck	425	1.25	.90	.50
1992 Upper Deck	453	1.00	.70	.40
1992 Upper Deck	488	1.00	.70	.40
1992 Upper Deck	506	1.50	1.25	.60
1992 Upper Deck All-Division Team	9	6.00	4.50	2.50
1992 Upper Deck All-NBA	1AN	20.00	15.00	8.00
1992 Upper Deck Holograms	1AW	6.00	4.50	2.50
1992 Upper Deck Holograms	9AW	6.00	4.50	2.50
1992 Upper Deck Jerry West Selects	1JW	10.00	7.50	4.00
1992 Upper Deck Jerry West Selects	4JW	9.00	6.75	3.50
1992 Upper Deck Jerry West Selects	8JW	10.00	7.50	4.00
1992 Upper Deck Jerry West Selects	9JW	10.00	7.50	4.00
1992 Upper Deck Team MVP's	1TM	10.00	7.50	4.00
1992 Upper Deck Team MVP's	5TM	20.00	15.00	8.00
1992 Upper Deck 15000-Point Club	4	40.00	30.00	16.00
1993 Fleer	28	2.50	2.00	1.00
1993 Fleer	224	1.25	.90	.50
1993 Fleer All-Stars	5	15.00	11.00	6.00
1993 Fleer Jam Session	33	3.00	2.25	1.25
1993 Fleer Living Legends	4	30.00	22.00	12.00
1993 Fleer NBA Superstars	7	6.50	5.00	2.50
1993 Fleer Sharpshooters	3	15.00	11.00	6.00
1993 Fleer Ultra	30	3.00	2.25	1.25
1993 Fleer Ultra All-Defensive Team	2	110.00	82.00	44.00
1993 Fleer Ultra All-NBA Team	2	15.00	11.00	6.00
1993 Fleer Ultra Famous Nicknames	7	12.00	9.00	4.75
1993 Fleer Ultra Inside Outside	4	6.50	5.00	2.50
1993 Fleer Ultra Power in the Key	2	35.00	26.00	14.00
1993 Fleer Ultra Scoring Kings	5	80.00	60.00	32.00
1993 NBA Hoops	28	2.25	1.75	.90
1993 NBA Hoops	257	1.00	.70	.40
1993 NBA Hoops	283	.25	.20	.10
1993 NBA Hoops	289	.25	.20	.10
1993 NBA Hoops Face to Face	10	10.00	7.50	4.00
1993 NBA Hoops Supreme Court	11	5.00	3.75	2.00
1993 SkyBox	14	1.00	.70	.40
1993 SkyBox	45	3.00	2.25	1.25
1993 SkyBox Center Stage	1	12.00	9.00	4.75
1993 SkyBox Dynamic Dunks	4	32.00	24.00	13.00
1993 SkyBox Showdown Series	11	2.25	1.75	.90
1993 Topps	23	2.00	1.50	.80
1993 Topps	64	1.00	.70	.40
1993 Topps	101	1.00	.70	.40
1993 Topps	199	1.00	.70	.40
1993 Topps	384	.75	.60	.30
1993 Topps Finest	1	22.00	16.50	8.75
1993 Topps Stadium Club	1	1.50	1.25	.60
1993 Topps Stadium Club	169	3.50	2.75	1.50
1993 Topps Stadium Club	181	1.50	1.25	.60
1993 Topps Stadium Club Beam Team	4	35.00	26.00	14.00
1993 Upper Deck	23	3.00	2.25	1.25
1993 Upper Deck	166	1.00	.70	.40
1993 Upper Deck	171	1.50	1.25	.60
1993 Upper Deck	180	.60	.45	.25
1993 Upper Deck	187	.50	.40	.20
1993 Upper Deck	193	1.25	.90	.50
1993 Upper Deck	198	1.25	.90	.50
1993 Upper Deck	201	1.25	.90	.50
1993 Upper Deck	204	1.25	.90	.50
1993 Upper Deck	237	1.25	.90	.50
1993 Upper Deck	438	1.50	1.25	.60
1993 Upper Deck	466	1.50	1.25	.60
1993 Upper Deck All-NBA	4	5.00	3.00	1.50
1993 Upper Deck All-NBA	15	2.50	1.50	.75
1993 Upper Deck Locker Talk	1	20.00	15.00	8.00
1993 Upper Deck M.J. Mr. June	1	27.00	20.00	11.00
1993 Upper Deck M.J. Mr. June	2	27.00	20.00	11.00
1993 Upper Deck M.J. Mr. June	9	27.00	20.00	11.00
1993 Upper Deck SE Behind the Glass	11	25.00	18.50	10.00
1993 Upper Deck 3-D Basketball	23	2.00	.60	.30
1993 Upper Deck 3-D Basketball	91	1.00	.60	.30
1993 Upper Deck 3-D Triple Double	2	15.00	11.00	6.00
1994 Upper Deck Col.'s Choice Hobby Blowups	3	10.00	7.50	4.00
1994 Upper Deck Collector's Choice	23	2.50	2.00	1.00
1994 Upper Deck Collector's Choice	204	1.25	.90	.50
1994 Upper Deck Collector's Choice	240	2.00	1.50	.80
1994 Upper Deck Collector's Choice	402	1.00	.70	.40
1994 Upper Deck Collector's Choice	420	1.00	.70	.40

Shawn Kemp

Set	Card #	MT	NM	EX
1990 Fleer	178 (R)	2.75	2.00	1.00
1990 NBA Hoops	279 (R)	3.00	2.25	1.25
1990 SkyBox	268 (R)	4.00	3.00	1.50
1991 Fleer	192	.80	.60	.30
1991 Fleer	231	.50	.40	.20
1991 NBA Hoops	200	.75	.60	.30
1991 NBA Hoops	497	.45	.35	.20
1991 NBA Hoops	527	.20	.15	.08
1991 SkyBox	271	1.00	.70	.40
1991 SkyBox	584	.50	.40	.20
1991 Upper Deck	96	.60	.45	.25
1991 Upper Deck	173	1.00	.70	.40

Set	Card #	MT	NM	EX
1991 Upper Deck	481	1.00	.70	.40
1992 Fleer	213	.85	.60	.35
1992 Fleer	266	.35	.25	.14
1992 Fleer Ultra	172	1.25	.90	.50
1992 Fleer Ultra	205	.40	.30	.15
1992 NBA Hoops	216	.75	.60	.30
1992 SkyBox	231	1.50	1.25	.60
1992 SkyBox	306	.65	.50	.25
1992 SkyBox II Thunder and Lightning	7	20.00	15.00	8.00
1992 Topps	267	.40	.30	.15
1992 Topps Archives	136	.60	.45	.25
1992 Topps Beam Team	5	1.50	1.00	.50
1992 Topps Stadium Club	102	1.75	1.25	.70
1992 Topps Stadium Club Beam Team	3	25.00	18.50	10.00
1992 Upper Deck	240	.85	.60	.35
1992 Upper Deck	441	.40	.30	.15
1992 Upper Deck Jerry West Selects	16JW	8.00	6.00	3.25
1993 Fleer	199	.30	.25	.12
1993 Fleer	233	.25	.20	.10
1993 Fleer All-Stars	17	2.50	2.00	1.00
1993 Fleer Flair USA Basketball	9	1.25	.90	.50
1993 Fleer Jam Session	214	.60	.45	.25
1993 Fleer Jam Session Slam Dunk Heroes	3	1.25	.90	.50
1993 Fleer NBA Superstars	8	1.50	1.25	.60
1993 Fleer Towers of Power	11	11.00	8.25	4.50
1993 Fleer Ultra	178	.50	.40	.20
1993 Fleer Ultra	365	.60	.45	.25
1993 Fleer Ultra Jam City	5	12.00	9.00	4.75
1993 Fleer Ultra Rebound Kings	3	1.25	.90	.50
1993 NBA Hoops	207	.40	.30	.15
1993 NBA Hoops	273	.25	.20	.10
1993 NBA Hoops	447	.10	.08	.04
1993 NBA Hoops Admiral's Choice	1	.75	.60	.30
1993 NBA Hoops Face to Face	3	5.00	3.75	2.00
1993 SkyBox	17	.25	.20	.10
1993 SkyBox	169	.50	.40	.20
1993 SkyBox	337	.25	.20	.10
1993 SkyBox Dynamic Dunks	5	7.00	5.25	2.75
1993 SkyBox Showdown Series	7	1.25	.90	.50
1993 Topps	202	.25	.20	.10
1993 Topps	296	.30	.25	.12
1993 Topps Finest	123	3.00	2.25	1.25
1993 Topps Finest	159	5.00	3.75	2.00
1993 Topps Finest Main Attraction	25	12.00	9.00	4.75
1993 Topps Stadium Club	173	.35	.25	.14
1993 Topps Stadium Club	222	.50	.40	.20
1993 Topps Stadium Club	355	.40	.30	.15
1993 Topps Stadium Club Rim Rockers	5	3.50	2.75	1.50
1993 Upper Deck	251	.30	.25	.12
1993 Upper Deck	305	.40	.30	.15
1993 Upper Deck	475	.25	.20	.10
1993 Upper Deck Future Heroes	32	3.00	2.25	1.25
1993 Upper Deck Jordan's Flight Team	12	11.00	8.25	4.50
1993 Upper Deck SE	99	.60	.45	.25
1993 Upper Deck SE Behind the Glass	1	6.00	4.50	2.50
1993 Upper Deck SE West Future All Stars	14	20.00	15.00	8.00
1993 Upper Deck Team MVP's	25	1.50	1.25	.60
1993 Upper Deck USA Basketball	5	.30	.25	.12
1993 Upper Deck 3-D Basketball	40	.25	.20	.10
1993 Upper Deck 3-D Basketball	104	.25	.20	.10
1994 Fleer	213	.35	.25	.14
1994 Fleer Flair	141	2.00	1.50	.80
1994 Fleer Flair	164	1.00	.70	.40
1994 Fleer Flair Hot Numbers	6	5.00	3.75	2.00
1994 Fleer Jam Session	179	1.00	.70	.40
1994 Fleer Jam Session Slam Dunk Heroes	3	10.00	7.50	4.00
1994 Fleer NBA All-Stars	17	1.50	1.25	.60
1994 Fleer Team Leaders	9	3.00	2.25	1.25
1994 Fleer Towers of Power	3	4.00	3.00	1.50
1994 Fleer Triple Threats	3	1.50	1.25	.60
1994 Fleer Ultra	177	.15	.11	.06
1994 Fleer Ultra All-NBA Team	8	1.25	.90	.50
1994 Fleer Ultra Ultra Power	4	2.00	1.50	.80
1994 NBA Hoops	200	.35	.25	.14
1994 NBA Hoops	241	.15	.11	.06
1994 NBA Hoops Power Ratings	49	5.00	3.75	2.00
1994 NBA Hoops Supreme Court	46	2.00	1.50	.80
1994 SkyBox	155	.65	.50	.25
1994 Topps	40	.40	.30	.15
1994 Topps	101	.25	.20	.10
1994 Topps	186	.25	.20	.10
1994 Topps Finest	40	2.50	2.00	1.00
1994 Topps Stadium Club Clear Cut	25	8.00	6.00	3.25
1994 Upper Deck	16	.25	.20	.10
1994 Upper Deck	124	.75	.60	.30
1994 Upper Deck	172	.25	.20	.10
1994 Upper Deck Col.'s Choice Hobby Blowups	2	3.00	2.25	1.25
1994 Upper Deck Col.'s Choice 1,000 Rebounds	4	6.00	4.50	2.50
1994 Upper Deck Collector's Choice	140	.40	.30	.15
1994 Upper Deck Collector's Choice	190	.25	.20	.10
1994 Upper Deck Collector's Choice	206	.20	.15	.08
1994 Upper Deck Collector's Choice	396	.35	.25	.14
1994 Upper Deck Collector's Choice	404	.30	.25	.12
1994 Upper Deck Collector's Choice	417	.35	.25	.14
1994 Upper Deck Predictors Hobby	6	6.00	4.50	2.50

Jason Kidd

Set	Card #	MT	NM	EX
1994 Fleer	268 (R)	2.00	.04	.02

Set	Card #	MT	NM	EX
1994 Fleer First Year Phenoms	2	7.50	5.75	3.00
1994 Fleer Jam Session	41 (R)	4.00	3.00	1.50
1994 Fleer Ultra	43 (R)	3.00	2.25	1.25
1994 NBA Hoops	317 (R)	2.50	2.00	1.00
1994 NBA Hoops	422	.75	.60	.30
1994 NBA Hoops Chromium Magic's All-Rookie	2	35.00	26.00	14.00
1994 NBA Hoops Magic's All-Rookie	2	15.00	11.00	6.00
1994 Pacific Draft Prism Gold Sonic Boom	28	6.00	6.00	6.00
1994 Pacific Prisms	28	10.00	7.50	4.00
1994 SkyBox Draft Picks	2	30.00	22.00	12.00
1994 Topps	37 (R)	1.50	1.25	.60
1994 Topps Stadium Club	172 (R)	3.00	2.25	1.25
1994 Upper Deck	160 (R)	3.50	2.75	1.50
1994 Upper Deck Collector's Choice Rookie	6	6.00	4.50	2.50
1994 Upper Deck Collector's Choice	250 (R)	2.50	2.00	1.00
1994 Upper Deck Collector's Choice	377	.75	.60	.30
1994 Upper Deck Collector's Choice	408	.75	.60	.30

Toni Kukoc

Set	Card #	MT	NM	EX
1993 Fleer	260 (R)	.50	.40	.20
1993 Fleer First Year Phenoms	5	.75	.60	.30
1993 Fleer Ultra	221 (R)	.75	.60	.30
1993 Fleer Ultra All-Rookies	8	3.50	2.75	1.50
1993 Fleer Ultra Famous Nicknames	8	3.00	2.25	1.25
1993 NBA Hoops	313 (R)	.45	.35	.20
1993 NBA Hoops II Magic's All-Rookie Team	10	3.50	2.75	1.50
1993 SkyBox	207 (R)	.50	.40	.20
1993 Topps	316 (R)	.50	.40	.20
1993 Topps Finest	14 (R)	2.00	1.50	.80
1993 Topps Stadium Club	275	.15	.11	.06
1993 Topps Stadium Club	336 (R)	.75	.60	.30
1993 Upper Deck	299 (R)	.50	.40	.20
1993 Upper Deck	496	.10	.08	.04
1993 Upper Deck Rookie Standouts	5	3.50	2.75	1.50
1993 Upper Deck SE	160 (R)	.75	.60	.30
1993 Upper Deck SE	183	.30	.25	.12
1994 Fleer	32	.20	.15	.08
1994 Fleer Flair	22	.75	.60	.30
1994 Fleer Flair Hot Numbers	7	1.00	.70	.40
1994 Fleer Jam Session	28	.20	.15	.08
1994 Fleer Jam Session Second Year Stars	4	.50	.40	.20

Set	Card #	MT	NM	EX
1994 Fleer Pro-Visions	3	.75	.60	.30
1994 Fleer Rookie Sensations	14	2.25	1.75	.90
1994 Fleer Ultra	27	.25	.20	.10
1994 Fleer Ultra NBA All-Rookie Team	8	8.00	6.00	3.25
1994 NBA Hoops	27	.20	.15	.08
1994 NBA Hoops	433	.08	.06	.03
1994 NBA Hoops Power Ratings	7	.60	.45	.25
1994 NBA Hoops Supreme Court	8	.60	.45	.25
1994 SkyBox	24	.15	.11	.06
1994 SkyBox Ragin' Rookies	3	1.00	.70	.40
1994 Topps	98	.15	.11	.06
1994 Topps Stadium Club	18	.25	.20	.10
1994 Upper Deck	9	.12	.09	.05
1994 Upper Deck Collector's Choice	107	.20	.15	.08
1994 Upper Deck Special Edition	12	.65	.50	.25

Christian Laettner

Set	Card #	MT	NM	EX
1992 Fleer	379 (R)	.75	.60	.30
1992 Fleer Ultra	304 (R)	1.00	.70	.40
1992 Fleer Ultra All-Rookies	4	3.00	2.25	1.25
1992 NBA Hoops	342 (R)	1.00	.70	.40
1992 NBA Hoops	421	1.50	1.25	.60
1992 NBA Hoops Draft Redemption	3C	10.00	7.50	4.00
1992 NBA Hoops II Magic's All-Rookie Team	3	20.00	15.00	8.00
1992 SkyBox	369 (R)	1.50	1.25	.60
1992 SkyBox Draft Picks	3	6.00	4.50	2.50
1992 SkyBox I Olympic Team	9USA	4.50	3.50	1.75
1992 Topps	334 (R)	.50	.40	.20
1992 Topps Stadium Club	206	.75	.60	.30
1992 Topps Stadium Club	218 (R)	2.00	1.50	.80
1992 Upper Deck	3 (R)	.75	.60	.30
1992 Upper Deck	472	.30	.25	.12
1992 Upper Deck	494	.40	.30	.15
1992 Upper Deck Rookie Standouts	13	3.00	2.25	1.25
1993 Fleer	123	.20	.15	.08
1993 Fleer Jam Session	131	.15	.11	.06
1993 Fleer Jam Session 2nd Year Stars	3	.75	.60	.30
1993 Fleer NBA Superstars	9	.50	.40	.20
1993 Fleer Rookie Sensations	13	3.00	2.25	1.25
1993 Fleer Towers of Power	12	4.00	3.00	1.50
1993 Fleer Ultra	114	.10	.08	.04

Set	Card #			
1993 Fleer Ultra All-Rookie Team	3	1.00	.70	.40
1993 NBA Hoops	129	.15	.11	.06
1993 NBA Hoops	438	.20	.15	.08
1993 NBA Hoops Face to Face	3	5.00	3.75	2.00
1993 SkyBox	116	.10	.08	.04
1993 SkyBox	328	.12	.09	.05
1993 SkyBox NBA All-Rookie Team	3	3.00	2.25	1.25
1993 Topps	27	.35	.25	.14
1993 Topps	178	.10	.08	.04
1993 Topps BlackGold	11	.60	.45	.25
1993 Topps Finest	111	.35	.25	.14
1993 Topps Finest	130	1.00	.70	.40
1993 Topps Stadium Club	216	.15	.11	.06
1993 Upper Deck	294	.15	.11	.06
1993 Upper Deck	430	.15	.11	.06
1993 Upper Deck All-Rookie	3	3.00	2.25	1.25
1993 Upper Deck Future Heroes	33	1.00	.70	.40
1993 Upper Deck SE	141	.20	.15	.08
1993 Upper Deck Team MVP's	16	.50	.40	.20
1993 Upper Deck 3-D Basketball	14	.15	.11	.06
1994 Fleer	133	.05	.04	.02
1994 Fleer Flair	89	.20	.15	.08
1994 Fleer Jam Session	110	.10	.08	.04
1994 Fleer Ultra	109	.08	.06	.03
1994 NBA Hoops	124	.06	.05	.02
1994 NBA Hoops Power Ratings	31	.40	.30	.15
1994 NBA Hoops Supreme Court	26	.40	.30	.15
1994 SkyBox	99	.08	.06	.03
1994 Topps	65	.06	.05	.02
1994 Topps Finest	80	.15	.11	.06
1994 Topps Stadium Club	81	.08	.06	.03
1994 Topps Stadium Club	112	.08	.06	.03
1994 Topps Stadium Club Clear Cut	16	1.50	1.25	.60
1994 Upper Deck	55	.10	.08	.04
1994 Upper Deck Collector's Choice	66	.05	.04	.02
1994 Upper Deck Special Edition	52	.20	.15	.08

Set	Card #			
1986 Fleer	61	3.00	2.25	1.25
1987 Fleer	61	1.25	.90	.50
1988 Fleer	42	.25	.20	.10
1989 Fleer	48	.25	.20	.10
1989 NBA Hoops	135	.10	.08	.04
1990 Fleer	58	.10	.08	.04
1990 NBA Hoops	108	.10	.08	.04
1990 SkyBox	90	.10	.08	.04
1991 Fleer	62	.10	.08	.04
1991 NBA Hoops	63	.05	.04	.02
1991 SkyBox	85	.05	.04	.02
1991 Upper Deck	167	.05	.04	.02
1992 Fleer	64	.05	.04	.02
1992 Fleer Ultra	57	.10	.08	.04
1992 NBA Hoops	65	.05	.04	.02
1992 SkyBox	70	.05	.04	.02
1992 Topps	29	.04	.03	.02
1992 Topps Stadium Club	25	.10	.08	.04
1992 Upper Deck	223	.05	.04	.02
1993 Fleer	60	.05	.04	.02
1993 Fleer Jam Session	62	.10	.08	.04
1993 Fleer Ultra	57	.10	.08	.04
1993 NBA Hoops	62	.06	.05	.02
1993 NBA Hoops	430	.06	.05	.02
1993 SkyBox	67	.05	.04	.02
1993 Topps	147	.05	.04	.02
1993 Topps Stadium Club	131	.10	.08	.04
1993 Upper Deck	153	.05	.04	.02

Bob Lanier

Set	Card #	NM	EX	VG
1971 Topps	63 (R)	40.00	20.00	12.00
1972 Topps	80	12.00	6.00	3.50
1973 Topps	110	7.00	3.50	2.00
1974 Topps	86	1.00	.50	.30
1974 Topps	131	5.00	2.50	1.50
1975 Topps	30	4.50	2.25	1.25
1975 Topps	121	2.00	1.00	.60
1976 Topps	10	4.00	2.00	1.25
1977 Topps	61	2.00	1.00	.60
1978 Topps	125	1.75	.90	.50
1979 Topps	58	1.00	.50	.30
1980 Topps	46	.60	.30	.20
1980 Topps	82	.75	.40	.25
1980 Topps	104	.75	.40	.25
1980 Topps	127	1.00	.50	.30

Set	Card #	MT	NM	EX
1981 Topps	25	.75	.60	.30
1981 Topps	109	.40	.30	.15
1983 Star Co.	45	22.00	16.50	8.75

Layering: A term used in card grading to describe the separation of the layers of paper that make up the cardboard stock. Layering is a sign of wear that is first noticeable at the corners of the card.

Bill Laimbeer

Set	Card #	MT	NM	EX
1981 Topps	74 (R)	3.50	2.75	1.50
1983 Star Co.	90	7.00	5.25	2.75
1983 Star Co. All-Star Game	6	3.00	2.25	1.25
1984 Star Co.	265	5.00	3.75	2.00
1984 Star Co. All-Star Game	6	1.50	1.25	.60
1985 Star Co.	14	4.00	3.00	1.50

Fat Lever

Set	Card #	MT	NM	EX
1983 Star Co.	102 (R)	6.00	4.50	2.50
1983 Star Co. All-Rookies	5	3.00	2.25	1.25
1984 Star Co.	144	2.75	2.00	1.00
1985 Star Co.	54	4.00	3.00	1.50
1986 Fleer	63 (R)	3.00	2.25	1.25
1987 Fleer	62	1.00	.70	.40
1988 Fleer	35	.50	.40	.20
1989 Fleer	41	.15	.11	.06
1989 NBA Hoops	220	.15	.11	.06
1990 Fleer	50	.07	.05	.03
1990 NBA Hoops	20	.15	.11	.06
1990 NBA Hoops	97	.15	.11	.06
1990 NBA Hoops	408	.15	.11	.06
1990 SkyBox	78	.20	.15	.08
1990 SkyBox	376	.10	.08	.04
1991 Fleer	270	.03	.02	.01
1991 NBA Hoops	47	.05	.04	.02
1991 SkyBox	61	.05	.04	.02
1991 Upper Deck	157	.05	.04	.02
1992 Fleer Ultra	45	.10	.08	.04
1992 NBA Hoops	49	.05	.04	.02
1992 SkyBox	52	.05	.04	.02
1992 Topps	144	.04	.03	.02
1992 Topps	221	.04	.03	.02
1992 Topps Archives	27	.05	.04	.02
1992 Topps Stadium Club	119	.10	.08	.04
1992 Upper Deck	307	.05	.04	.02
1993 Fleer	273	.05	.04	.02
1993 Fleer Ultra	234	.10	.08	.04
1993 NBA Hoops	322	.06	.05	.02
1993 Topps	327	.05	.04	.02
1993 Upper Deck	408	.05	.04	.02
1994 Fleer	52	.05	.04	.02

Bob Love

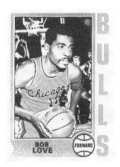

Set	Card #	NM	EX	VG
1969 Topps	78 (R)	30.00	22.00	12.00

Set	Card #	MT	NM	EX
1970 Topps	84	8.00	4.00	2.50
1971 Topps	45	4.50	2.25	1.25
1972 Topps	148	3.00	1.50	.90
1972 Topps	166	1.25	.60	.40
1973 Topps	60	2.00	1.00	.60
1974 Topps	15	1.25	.60	.40
1974 Topps	84	2.00	1.00	.60
1975 Topps	119	2.00	1.00	.60
1975 Topps	140	1.50	.70	.45
1976 Topps	45	2.25	1.25	.70

> Four years ago: Dominique Wilkins' 1986-87 Fleer rookie card (#121) was $27.50 in July 1991.
>
> * * *
>
> Four years ago: Isiah Thomas' 1986-87 Fleer rookie card (#109) was $30 in July 1991.

Clyde Lovellette

Set	Card #	NM	EX	VG
1957 Topps	78 (R)	100.00	50.00	30.00
1961-62 Fleer	29	30.00	22.00	12.00
1961-62 Fleer	58	16.00	12.00	6.50

Jerry Lucas

Set	Card #	NM	EX	VG
1969 Topps	45 (R)	40.00	30.00	16.00
1970 Topps	46	13.00	6.50	4.00
1971 Topps	81	7.00	3.50	2.00
1972 Topps	15	6.00	3.00	1.75
1973 Topps	125	4.50	2.25	1.25

> Limited edition: A term often used by makers of cards and memorabilia to indicate scarcity. A limited edition means just that — production of the item in question will be limited to a certain number. However, that number may be large or small.
>
> Police set: A regional card set made for a police department and given away to kids, usually one card at a time, to promote friendly relations. Police cards often carry a safety or anti-drug message on the back. Baseball, football, basketball and hockey police sets have been made of major league, minor league and college teams. Similar sets issued by fire departments are also generically called "police sets" or "safety sets."

John Lucas

Set	Card #	NM	EX	VG
1977 Topps	58 (R)	11.00	5.50	3.30
1978 Topps	106	2.50	1.25	.70
1979 Topps	127	1.50	.70	.45
1980 Topps	65	.25	.13	.08
1980 Topps	79	.25	.13	.08
1980 Topps	115	.25	.13	.08
1980 Topps	126	.25	.13	.08

Set	Card #	MT	NM	EX
1981 Topps	51	.15	.11	.06
1983 Star Co.	246	7.00	5.25	2.75
1984 Star Co.	242	6.00	4.50	2.50
1985 Star Co.	21	6.00	4.50	2.50
1987 Fleer	66	2.00	1.50	.80
1993 NBA Hoops	253	.06	.05	.02
1994 NBA Hoops	291	.04	.03	.02

Maurice Lucas

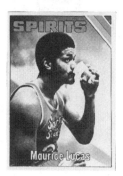

Set	Card #	NM	EX	VG
1975 Topps	302 (R)	13.00	6.50	4.00
1976 Topps	107	3.00	1.50	.90
1977 Topps	80	1.00	.50	.30
1978 Topps	50	1.00	.50	.30
1979 Topps	26	.60	.30	.20
1980 Topps	54	.25	.13	.08
1980 Topps	142	3.00	1.50	.90

Set	Card #	MT	NM	EX
1981 Topps	79	.25	.20	.10
1981 Topps	57	.15	.11	.06
1983 Star Co.	113	2.00	1.50	.90
1983 Star Co. All-Star Game	19	2.50	2.00	1.00
1984 Star Co.	45	2.75	2.00	1.00
1985 Star Co.	30	5.00	3.75	2.00
1986 Fleer	66	1.75	1.25	.70

Dan Majerle

Set	Card #	MT	NM	EX
1989 Fleer	124 (R)	5.00	3.75	2.00
1989 NBA Hoops	183 (R)	1.50	1.25	.60
1990 Fleer	150	.30	.25	.12
1990 NBA Hoops	239	.25	.20	.10
1990 SkyBox	226	.40	.30	.15
1991 Fleer	163	.15	.11	.06
1991 NBA Hoops	167	.10	.08	.04
1991 NBA Hoops	570	.10	.08	.04
1991 SkyBox	228	.20	.15	.08
1991 SkyBox	425	.10	.08	.04
1991 SkyBox	452	.10	.08	.04
1991 SkyBox	552	.10	.08	.04
1991 Upper Deck	172	.15	.11	.06
1991 Upper Deck	475	.08	.06	.03
1992 Fleer	182	.08	.06	.03
1992 Fleer	267	.10	.08	.04
1992 Fleer All-Stars	16	1.00	.70	.40
1992 Fleer Ultra	146	.15	.11	.06
1992 NBA Hoops	184	.10	.08	.04
1992 NBA Hoops	310	.06	.05	.02
1992 SkyBox	194	.10	.08	.04
1992 Topps	122	.10	.08	.04
1992 Topps	326	.15	.11	.06
1992 Topps Archives	105	.20	.15	.08
1992 Topps Stadium Club	184	.15	.11	.06
1992 Upper Deck	177	.15	.11	.06
1992 Upper Deck	395	.15	.11	.06
1992 Upper Deck	442	.10	.08	.04
1993 Fleer	169	.10	.08	.04
1993 Fleer All-Stars	18	.75	.60	.30
1993 Fleer Flair USA Basketball	10	.20	.15	.08
1993 Fleer Jam Session	181	.15	.11	.06
1993 Fleer Jam Session Gamebreakers	4	.40	.30	.15
1993 Fleer Sharpshooters	4	1.00	.70	.40
1993 Fleer Ultra	150	.15	.11	.06
1993 Fleer Ultra	366	.15	.11	.06
1993 Fleer Ultra All-Defensive Team	7	10.00	7.50	4.00
1993 Fleer Ultra Inside Outside	5	.60	.45	.25
1993 NBA Hoops	173	.10	.08	.04
1993 NBA Hoops	274	.10	.08	.04
1993 SkyBox	15	.15	.11	.06
1993 SkyBox	149	.10	.08	.04
1993 Topps	259	.10	.08	.04
1993 Topps Finest	121	.35	.25	.14
1993 Topps Finest	157	.35	.25	.14
1993 Topps Stadium Club	99	.10	.08	.04
1993 Topps Stadium Club	353	.20	.15	.08
1993 Topps Stadium Club Beam Team	14	2.00	1.50	.80
1993 Upper Deck	40	.10	.08	.04
1993 Upper Deck	192	.10	.08	.04
1993 Upper Deck	500	.10	.08	.04
1993 Upper Deck SE	106	.20	.15	.08
1993 Upper Deck USA Basketball	6	.10	.08	.04

1993 Upper Deck 3-D Basketball	42	.15	.11	.06
1994 Fleer	180	.05	.04	.02
1994 Fleer Flair	119	.30	.25	.12
1994 Fleer Flair	165	.20	.15	.08
1994 Fleer Jam Session	152	.15	.11	.06
1994 Fleer Jam Session Flashing Stars	3	.50	.40	.20
1994 Fleer Pro-Visions	9	.40	.30	.15
1994 Fleer Sharpshooters	4	.75	.60	.30
1994 Fleer Ultra	151	.08	.06	.03
1994 NBA Hoops	171	.08	.06	.03
1994 SkyBox	132	.10	.08	.04
1994 SkyBox Dream Team II Portraits	10	8.00	6.00	3.25
1994 Topps	51	.08	.06	.03
1994 Topps Finest	135	.15	.11	.06
1994 Topps Finest Iron Men	6	1.50	1.25	.60
1994 Upper Deck	26	.10	.08	.04
1994 Upper Deck	174	.15	.11	.06
1994 Upper Deck Collector's Choice	69	.05	.04	.02

Karl Malone

KARL MALONE

Set	Card #	MT	NM	EX
1986 Fleer	68 (R)	65.00	49.00	26.00
1987 Fleer	68	15.00	11.00	6.00
1988 Fleer	114	4.00	3.00	1.50
1989 Fleer	155	1.25	.90	.50
1989 Fleer	163	.50	.40	.20
1989 Fleer	165	.40	.30	.15
1989 NBA Hoops	30	.40	.30	.15
1989 NBA Hoops	116	.30	.25	.12
1990 Fleer	188	.25	.20	.10
1990 Fleer All-Stars	7	.90	.70	.35
1990 NBA Hoops	21	.25	.20	.10
1990 NBA Hoops	292	.25	.20	.10
1990 NBA Hoops	380	.15	.11	.06
1990 NBA Hoops	383	.10	.08	.04
1990 SkyBox	282	.40	.30	.15
1991 Fleer	201	.30	.25	.12
1991 Fleer	219	.15	.11	.06
1991 Fleer NBA Schoolyard Sets	5	5.00	3.75	2.00
1991 Fleer Pro Visions	5	.60	.45	.25
1991 NBA Hoops	211	.25	.20	.10
1991 NBA Hoops	267	.15	.11	.06
1991 NBA Hoops	499	.15	.11	.06
1991 NBA Hoops	580	.50	.40	.20
1991 NBA Hoops MVP All-Stars	10	3.00	2.25	1.25
1991 SkyBox	283	.35	.25	.14
1991 SkyBox	430	.15	.11	.06
1991 SkyBox	484	.15	.11	.06
1991 SkyBox	535	.50	.40	.20
1991 Upper Deck	51	.10	.08	.04
1991 Upper Deck	355	.30	.25	.12
1991 Upper Deck	466	.15	.11	.06
1992 Fleer	225	.25	.20	.10
1992 Fleer	268	.15	.11	.06
1992 Fleer All-Stars	17	5.00	3.75	2.00
1992 Fleer Team Leaders	26	30.00	22.00	12.00
1992 Fleer Ultra	182	.60	.45	.25
1992 Fleer Ultra	217	.25	.20	.10
1992 Fleer Ultra All-NBA Team	1	3.00	2.25	1.25
1992 NBA Hoops	227	.20	.15	.08
1992 NBA Hoops	311	.10	.08	.04
1992 NBA Hoops	343	.10	.08	.04
1992 NBA Hoops Supreme Court	6SC	2.50	2.00	1.00
1992 SkyBox	242	.50	.40	.20
1992 SkyBox I Olympic Team	4USA	2.00	1.50	.80
1992 SkyBox II Thunder and Lightning	8	12.00	9.00	4.75
1992 Topps	20	.20	.15	.08
1992 Topps	123	.15	.11	.06
1992 Topps	199	.10	.08	.04
1992 Topps Archives	66	.35	.25	.14
1992 Topps Beam Team	4	1.50	1.00	.50
1992 Topps Stadium Club	13	.60	.45	.25
1992 Topps Stadium Club	205	.30	.25	.12
1992 Topps Stadium Club Beam Team	17	8.00	6.00	3.25
1992 Upper Deck	44	.15	.11	.06
1992 Upper Deck	66	.15	.11	.06
1992 Upper Deck	112	.25	.20	.10
1992 Upper Deck	434	.15	.11	.06
1992 Upper Deck	489	.15	.11	.06
1992 Upper Deck	508	.15	.11	.06
1992 Upper Deck All-Division Team	12	1.00	.70	.40
1992 Upper Deck All-NBA	4AN	2.00	1.50	.80
1992 Upper Deck 15000-Point Club	16	4.00	3.00	1.50
1993 Fleer	211	.25	.20	.10
1993 Fleer All-Stars	19	2.00	1.50	.80
1993 Fleer Jam Session	227	.35	.25	.14
1993 Fleer Jam Session Slam Dunk Heroes	4	1.00	.70	.40
1993 Fleer NBA Superstars	10	.90	.70	.35
1993 Fleer Towers of Power	13	6.00	4.50	2.50
1993 Fleer Ultra	189	.40	.30	.15
1993 Fleer Ultra All-NBA Team	3	2.50	2.00	1.00
1993 Fleer Ultra Famous Nicknames	9	1.50	1.25	.60
1993 Fleer Ultra Power in the Key	3	3.00	2.25	1.25
1993 Fleer Ultra Rebound Kings	4	.75	.60	.30
1993 Fleer Ultra Scoring Kings	6	10.00	7.50	4.00
1993 NBA Hoops	218	.25	.20	.10
1993 NBA Hoops	275	.15	.11	.06
1993 NBA Hoops	283	.25	.20	.10
1993 NBA Hoops	448	.10	.08	.04
1993 NBA Hoops Face to Face	7	5.00	3.75	2.00
1993 NBA Hoops Supreme Court	6	1.00	.70	.40
1993 SkyBox	178	.30	.25	.12
1993 SkyBox	319	.12	.09	.05
1993 SkyBox Showdown Series	7	1.25	.90	.50
1993 Topps	119	.15	.11	.06
1993 Topps	279	.20	.15	.08
1993 Topps	389	.15	.11	.06
1993 Topps Finest	112	2.00	1.50	.80
1993 Topps Finest	215	3.00	2.25	1.25
1993 Topps Finest Main Attraction	26	8.00	6.00	3.25
1993 Topps Stadium Club	125	.40	.30	.15
1993 Topps Stadium Club	174	.25	.20	.10
1993 Topps Stadium Club	186	.30	.25	.12

1993 Topps Stadium Club Beam Team	9	6.00	4.50	2.50
1993 Upper Deck	249	.20	.15	.08
1993 Upper Deck	274	.30	.25	.12
1993 Upper Deck	422	.20	.15	.08
1993 Upper Deck All-NBA	2	1.25	.75	.40
1993 Upper Deck Jordan's Flight Team	13	6.00	4.50	2.50
1993 Upper Deck Locker Talk	11	2.00	1.50	.80
1993 Upper Deck SE	152	.45	.35	.20
1993 Upper Deck SE West Future All Stars	15	12.00	9.00	4.75
1993 Upper Deck 3-D Basketball	1	.25	.20	.10
1993 Upper Deck 3-D Basketball	94	.30	.25	.12
1994 Fleer	224	.30	.25	.12
1994 Fleer Career Achievement Awards	2	6.00	4.50	2.50
1994 Fleer Flair	148	1.50	1.25	.60
1994 Fleer Flair Scoring Power	3	3.00	2.25	1.25
1994 Fleer Jam Session	187	.40	.30	.15
1994 Fleer Jam Session GameBreakers	3	1.25	.90	.50
1994 Fleer NBA All-Stars	18	1.25	.90	.50
1994 Fleer Towers of Power	4	2.00	1.50	.80
1994 Fleer Triple Threats	4	1.00	.70	.40
1994 Fleer Ultra	186	.50	.40	.20
1994 Fleer Ultra All-NBA Team	1	1.00	.70	.40
1994 Fleer Ultra Scoring Kings	3	12.00	11.00	6.00
1994 Fleer Ultra Ultra Power	5	1.50	1.25	.60
1994 NBA Hoops	211	.25	.20	.10
1994 NBA Hoops	242	.10	.08	.04
1994 NBA Hoops Power Ratings	52	3.00	2.25	1.25
1994 NBA Hoops Supreme Court	48	1.50	1.25	.60
1994 SkyBox	165	.45	.35	.20
1994 SkyBox	182	.20	.15	.08
1994 Topps	185	.10	.08	.04
1994 Topps Finest Iron Men	5	8.00	6.00	3.25
1994 Topps Finest Marathon Men	14	5.00	3.75	2.00
1994 Topps Stadium Club	161	.60	.45	.25
1994 Topps Stadium Club	162	.20	.15	.08
1994 Topps Stadium Club Clear Cut	26	5.00	3.75	2.00
1994 Topps Stadium Club Dynasty and Destiny	2A	1.50	1.25	.60
1994 Topps Super Rebounders	7	1.75	1.25	.70
1994 Topps Super Scorers	5	2.00	1.50	.80
1994 Upper Deck	12	.20	.15	.08
1994 Upper Deck Col.'s Choice 1,000 Rebounds	5	3.50	2.75	1.50
1994 Upper Deck Collector's Choice 2,000 Pts	5	5.00	3.75	2.00
1994 Upper Deck Collector's Choice	32	.30	.25	.12
1994 Upper Deck Collector's Choice	191	.15	.11	.06
1994 Upper Deck Collector's Choice	397	.15	.11	.06
1994 Upper Deck Predictors Retail	6	6.00	4.50	2.50
1994 Upper Deck Special Edition	86	1.50	1.25	.60

Moses Malone

Set	Card #	NM	EX	VG
1975 Topps	222	6.00	3.00	1.75
1975 Topps	254 (R)	65.00	32.00	19.50
1975 Topps	286	6.00	3.00	1.75
1976 Topps	101	30.00	15.00	9.00
1977 Topps	124	10.00	5.00	3.00
1978 Topps	38	6.50	3.25	2.00
1979 Topps	100	6.00	3.00	1.75
1980 Topps	2	1.50	.70	.45
1980 Topps	45	3.00	1.50	.90
1980 Topps	71	1.00	.50	.30
1980 Topps	74	2.00	1.00	.60
1980 Topps	90	1.00	.50	.30
1980 Topps	107	1.50	.70	.45
1980 Topps	114	4.00	2.00	1.25
1980 Topps	159	2.00	1.00	.60

Set	Card #	MT	NM	EX
1981 Topps	14	1.75	1.25	.70
1981 Topps	110	1.50	1.25	.60
1981 Topps	52	.60	.45	.25
1983 Star Co.	7	30.00	22.00	12.00
1983 Star Co. All-Star Game	7	5.00	3.75	2.00
1984 Star Co.	201	12.00	9.00	4.75
1984 Star Co.	285	8.00	6.00	3.25
1984 Star Co. Awards Banquet	20	4.00	3.00	1.50
1984 Star Co. Court Kings	17	8.00	6.00	3.25
1985 Star Co.	6	10.00	7.50	4.00
1985 Star Co. Lite All-Stars	5	8.00	6.00	3.25
1986 Fleer	69	4.00	3.00	1.50
1986 Star Co. Best of the Best	10	12.00	9.00	4.75
1986 Star Co. Court Kings	21	5.00	3.75	2.00
1987 Fleer	69	2.00	1.50	.80
1988 Fleer	118	.75	.60	.30
1989 Fleer	4	.40	.30	.15
1989 NBA Hoops	84	.10	.08	.04
1989 NBA Hoops	290	.15	.11	.06
1990 Fleer	3	.10	.08	.04
1990 NBA Hoops	31	.12	.09	.05
1990 SkyBox	6	.10	.08	.04
1991 Fleer	315	.10	.08	.04
1991 NBA Hoops	2	.10	.08	.04
1991 NBA Hoops	315	.10	.08	.04
1991 NBA Hoops	318	.10	.08	.04
1991 NBA Hoops	323	.05	.04	.02
1991 NBA Hoops	394	.10	.08	.04
1991 NBA Hoops	537	.10	.08	.04
1991 SkyBox	4	.10	.08	.04
1991 SkyBox	574	.08	.06	.03
1991 SkyBox	634	.10	.08	.04
1991 Upper Deck	47	.10	.08	.04
1991 Upper Deck	402	.10	.08	.04
1992 Fleer	127	.08	.06	.03
1992 Fleer Ultra	106	.15	.11	.06
1992 NBA Hoops	130	.10	.08	.04
1992 SkyBox	137	.10	.08	.04

Set	Card #			
1992 SkyBox	296	.08	.06	.03
1992 Topps	74	.08	.06	.03
1992 Topps	208	.04	.03	.02
1992 Topps Stadium Club	106	.10	.08	.04
1992 Upper Deck	301	.10	.08	.04
1992 Upper Deck 15000-Point Club	10	2.00	1.50	.80
1993 Fleer	353	.05	.04	.02
1993 Fleer Jam Session	170	.10	.08	.04
1993 Fleer Ultra	315	.08	.06	.03
1993 NBA Hoops	34	.10	.08	.04
1993 NBA Hoops	389	.06	.05	.02
1993 SkyBox	265	.05	.04	.02
1993 Topps	381	.06	.05	.02
1993 Topps Stadium Club	211	.10	.08	.04
1993 Upper Deck	372	.05	.04	.02
1993 Upper Deck SE	120	.10	.08	.04
1994 Fleer	170	.05	.04	.02
1994 Fleer	368	.05	.04	.02
1994 Upper Deck Collector's Choice	2	.05	.04	.02
1994 Upper Deck Collector's Choice	281	.05	.04	.02

Danny Manning

Set	Card #	MT	NM	EX
1989 Fleer	71 (R)	6.00	4.50	2.50
1989 NBA Hoops	40 (R)	2.00	1.50	.80
1990 Fleer	87	.20	.15	.08
1990 NBA Hoops	147	.35	.25	.14
1990 NBA Hoops	366	.05	.04	.02
1990 SkyBox	129	.35	.25	.14
1991 Fleer	92	.15	.11	.06
1991 NBA Hoops	94	.15	.11	.06
1991 NBA Hoops	571	.10	.08	.04
1991 SkyBox	127	.25	.20	.10
1991 SkyBox	553	.15	.11	.06
1991 Upper Deck	164	.25	.20	.10
1992 Fleer	101	.15	.11	.06
1992 Fleer Team Leaders	12	17.00	12.50	6.75
1992 Fleer Ultra	85	.25	.20	.10
1992 NBA Hoops	101	.10	.08	.04
1992 SkyBox	107	.25	.20	.10
1992 Topps	189	.15	.11	.06
1992 Topps Archives	8	.10	.08	.04
1992 Topps Archives	106	.25	.20	.10
1992 Topps Stadium Club	179	.25	.20	.10
1992 Upper Deck	271	.10	.08	.04
1992 Upper Deck	443	.08	.06	.03
1992 Upper Deck Jerry West Selects	17JW	1.00	.70	.40
1993 Fleer	93	.10	.08	.04
1993 Fleer All-Stars	20	.75	.60	.30
1993 Fleer Jam Session	98	.10	.08	.04
1993 Fleer NBA Superstars	11	.50	.40	.20
1993 Fleer Towers of Power	14	2.50	2.00	1.00
1993 Fleer Ultra	88	.10	.08	.04

Set	Card #			
1993 NBA Hoops	96	.10	.08	.04
1993 NBA Hoops	276	.06	.05	.02
1993 NBA Hoops	434	.05	.04	.02
1993 SkyBox	92	.15	.11	.06
1993 Topps	354	.08	.06	.03
1993 Topps Finest	124	.35	.25	.14
1993 Topps Finest	148	1.50	1.25	.60
1993 Topps Finest Main Attraction	12	4.00	3.00	1.50
1993 Topps Stadium Club	233	.15	.11	.06
1993 Topps Stadium Club Beam Team	26	2.00	1.50	.80
1993 Upper Deck	247	.05	.04	.02
1993 Upper Deck	342	.15	.11	.06
1993 Upper Deck SE	82	.20	.15	.08
1993 Upper Deck SE West Future All Stars	7	8.00	6.00	3.25
1993 Upper Deck Team MVP's	12	.75	.60	.30
1993 Upper Deck 3-D Basketball	21	.25	.20	.10
1994 Fleer	8	.10	.08	.04
1994 Fleer	349	.08	.04	.02
1994 Fleer Jam Session	153	.20	.15	.08
1994 Fleer NBA All-Stars	19	.35	.25	.14
1994 NBA Hoops	6	.10	.08	.04
1994 NBA Hoops	243	.06	.05	.02
1994 NBA Hoops	363	.12	.09	.05
1994 NBA Hoops Supreme Court	2	.30	.25	.12
1994 SkyBox	6	.15	.11	.06
1994 Topps	188	.06	.05	.02
1994 Upper Deck Collector's Choice	166	.08	.06	.03
1994 Upper Deck Collector's Choice	315	.10	.08	.04

Pete Maravich

Set	Card #	NM	EX	VG
1970 Topps	123 (R)	185.00	92.00	55.00
1971 Topps	55	42.50	21.00	12.50
1972 Topps	5	35.00	17.50	10.50
1973 Topps	130	22.00	11.00	6.50
1974 Topps	10	20.00	10.00	6.00
1974 Topps	144	6.00	3.00	1.75
1974 Topps	145	5.00	2.50	1.50
1975 Topps	75	12.00	6.00	3.50
1975 Topps	127	3.00	1.50	.90
1976 Topps	60	25.00	12.50	7.50
1976 Topps	130	14.00	7.00	4.25
1977 Topps	20	7.50	3.75	2.25
1978 Topps	80	6.00	3.00	1.75
1979 Topps	60	6.00	3.00	1.75
1980 Topps	8	3.00	1.50	.90
1980 Topps	96	1.50	.70	.45

Set	Card #	MT	NM	EX
1985 Star Co. Schick Legends	18	20.00	15.00	8.00

Sarunas Marciulionis

Set	Card #	MT	NM	EX
1990 Fleer	65 (R)	.15	.11	.06
1990 NBA Hoops	115 (R)	.20	.15	.08
1990 NBA Hoops	384	.05	.04	.02
1990 SkyBox	97 (R)	.10	.08	.04
1991 Fleer	68	.10	.08	.04
1991 NBA Hoops	71	.12	.09	.05
1991 SkyBox	95	.15	.11	.06
1991 Upper Deck	354	.15	.11	.06
1992 Fleer	76	.05	.04	.02
1992 Fleer Ultra	66	.12	.09	.05
1992 NBA Hoops	77	.07	.05	.03
1992 SkyBox	82	.05	.04	.02
1992 Topps	357	.04	.03	.02
1992 Topps Archives	124	.05	.04	.02
1992 Topps Stadium Club	181	.10	.08	.04
1992 Upper Deck	249	.05	.04	.02
1992 Upper Deck Foreign Exchange	4	.50	.40	.20
1993 Fleer	70	.05	.04	.02
1993 Fleer Jam Session	71	.10	.08	.04
1993 Fleer NBA Internationals	6	.50	.30	.15
1993 Fleer Ultra	67	.10	.08	.04
1993 NBA Hoops	72	.06	.05	.02
1993 SkyBox	75	.05	.04	.02
1993 Topps	368	.05	.04	.02
1993 Topps Finest	12	.35	.25	.14
1993 Topps Stadium Club	72	.10	.08	.04
1993 Upper Deck	95	.05	.04	.02
1994 Fleer	375	.05	.04	.02
1994 NBA Hoops	67	.04	.03	.02
1994 NBA Hoops	374	.04	.03	.02
1994 NBA Hoops	449	.04	.03	.02
1994 Upper Deck Collector's Choice	357	.05	.04	.02

Major set: A large, nationally-distributed set produced by a major card manufacturer, such as Topps, Fleer, Donruss, Score, Sportflics or Upper Deck.

Megalot: A card investor's term referring to a very large (normally 1,000 or more) group of cards of one player, purchased as an investment.

Memorabilia: Usually used in card collecting to refer to items other than cards which mark or commemorate a player and his career, a team or an event.

Mylar: Trade name for a type of inert plastic used to make supplies for the protection of cards and memorabilia.

Jamal Mashburn

Set	Card #	MT	NM	EX
1993 Fleer	274 (R)	1.75	1.25	.70
1993 Fleer First Year Phenoms	6	3.50	2.75	1.50
1993 Fleer Jam Session	49 (R)	2.50	2.00	1.00
1993 Fleer Jam Session Rookie Standouts	6	4.00	3.00	1.50
1993 Fleer Lottery Exchange	4	6.00	4.50	2.50
1993 Fleer Towers of Power	15	13.00	9.75	5.25
1993 Fleer Ultra	235 (R)	2.75	2.05	1.10
1993 Fleer Ultra All-Rookies	9	8.00	6.00	3.25
1993 NBA Hoops	323 (R)	1.50	1.25	.60
1993 NBA Hoops Draft Redemption	4	10.00	7.50	4.00
1993 NBA Hoops II Magic's All-Rookie Team	4	10.00	7.50	4.00
1993 SkyBox	215 (R)	2.25	1.70	.90
1993 SkyBox Draft Picks	4	10.00	7.50	4.00
1993 SkyBox Thunder and Lightning	1	6.50	6.75	3.50
1993 Topps	312 (R)	1.50	1.25	.60
1993 Topps BlackGold	24	4.00	3.00	1.50
1993 Topps Finest	22 (R)	6.00	4.50	2.50
1993 Topps Finest	110	2.00	1.50	.80
1993 Topps Finest Main Attraction	6	14.00	10.50	5.50
1993 Topps Stadium Club	220 (R)	2.50	2.00	1.00
1993 Topps Stadium Club	265	1.00	.70	.40
1993 Topps Stadium Club Beam Team	22	15.00	11.00	6.00
1993 Upper Deck	352 (R)	2.00	1.50	.80
1993 Upper Deck	486	.75	.60	.30
1993 Upper Deck Rookie Exchange Gold/Silver	4	4.50	3.50	1.75
1993 Upper Deck Rookie Standouts	9	10.00	7.50	4.00
1993 Upper Deck SE	167 (R)	1.50	1.25	.60
1993 Upper Deck SE	194	.50	.40	.20
1993 Upper Deck SE West Future All Stars	2	30.00	22.00	12.00
1993 Upper Deck 3-D Basketball	82 (R)	1.50	.30	.15
1994 Fleer	53	.60	.45	.25
1994 Fleer Flair	35	2.00	1.50	.80
1994 Fleer Flair Hot Numbers	8	6.00	4.50	2.50
1994 Fleer Jam Session	42	.75	.60	.30
1994 Fleer Jam Session Second Year Stars	5	2.50	2.00	1.00
1994 Fleer Jam Session Slam Dunk Heroes	4	12.50	9.50	5.00
1994 Fleer Pro-Visions	1	2.00	1.50	.80
1994 Fleer Rookie Sensations	16	9.00	6.75	3.50

1994 Fleer Team Leaders	2	2.50	2.00	1.00
1994 Fleer Ultra	44	1.25	.90	.50
1994 Fleer Ultra Double Trouble	4	2.00	1.50	.80
1994 Fleer Ultra NBA All-Rookie Team	3	30.00	22.00	12.00
1994 NBA Hoops	46	.50	.40	.20
1994 NBA Hoops	424	1.00	.70	.40
1994 NBA Hoops Big Numbers	2	9.00	6.75	3.50
1994 NBA Hoops Power Ratings	12	2.50	2.00	1.00
1994 NBA Hoops Supreme Court	12	2.00	1.50	.80
1994 Pacific Draft Prism Gold Sonic Boom	31	.80	.80	.80
1994 Pacific Draft Prism Gold Sonic Boom	70	.80	.80	.80
1994 Pacific Prisms	31	2.25	1.75	.90
1994 Pacific Prisms	70	2.00	1.50	.80
1994 SkyBox	38	1.00	.70	.40
1994 SkyBox Ragin' Rookies	5	3.50	2.75	1.50
1994 Topps	70	.40	.30	.15
1994 Topps Finest	4	.75	.60	.30
1994 Topps Finest	60	2.25	1.75	.90
1994 Topps Stadium Club	125	1.25	.90	.50
1994 Topps Stadium Club Clear Cut	6	10.00	7.50	4.00
1994 Topps Stadium Club Dynasty and Destiny	5B	2.50	2.00	1.00
1994 Topps Stadium Club Rising Stars	3	20.00	15.00	8.00
1994 Upper Deck	4	.50	.40	.20
1994 Upper Deck Collector's Choice	157	.60	.45	.25
1994 Upper Deck Collector's Choice	171	.50	.40	.20
1994 Upper Deck Special Edition	16	3.00	2.25	1.25

Key cards: The most important cards in a set.

Cedric Maxwell

Set	Card #	NM	EX	VG
1978 Topps	128 (R)	2.50	1.25	.70
1979 Topps	23	.40	.20	.12
1980 Topps	27	.25	.13	.08
1980 Topps	117	.25	.13	.08

Set	Card #	MT	NM	EX
1981 Topps	5	.25	.20	.10
1981 Topps	107	.15	.11	.06
1983 Star Co.	33	15.00	11.00	6.00
1984 Star Co.	8	2.75	2.00	1.00
1985 Star Co.	91	4.00	3.00	1.50
1986 Fleer	70	1.25	.90	.50
1987 Fleer	70	.40	.30	.15

Bob McAdoo

BOB McADOO

Set	Card #	NM	EX	VG
1973 Topps	135 (R)	20.00	10.00	6.00
1974 Topps	80	7.00	3.50	2.00
1974 Topps	83	1.25	.60	.40
1974 Topps	144	6.00	3.00	1.75
1974 Topps	145	5.00	2.50	1.50
1974 Topps	146	4.00	2.00	1.25
1974 Topps	148	3.00	1.50	.90
1975 Topps	1	9.00	4.50	2.75
1975 Topps	10	6.00	3.00	1.75
1976 Topps	140	6.00	3.00	1.75
1977 Topps	45	1.00	.50	.30
1978 Topps	5	1.25	.60	.40
1979 Topps	75	1.00	.50	.30
1980 Topps	88	.25	.13	.08
1980 Topps	99	.25	.13	.08

Set	Card #	MT	NM	EX
1983 Star Co.	18	15.00	11.00	6.00
1984 Star Co.	178	6.00	4.50	2.50

Xavier McDaniel

Set	Card #	MT	NM	EX
1986 Fleer	72 (R)	7.00	5.25	2.75
1987 Fleer	73	2.50	2.00	1.00
1988 Fleer	108	.75	.60	.30
1989 Fleer	148	.25	.20	.10
1989 NBA Hoops	70	.15	.11	.06
1990 Fleer	179	.10	.08	.04
1990 Fleer Update	77	.15	.11	.06
1990 NBA Hoops	280	.07	.05	.03
1990 NBA Hoops	379	.05	.04	.02
1990 SkyBox	269	.10	.08	.04
1991 Fleer	164	.10	.08	.04
1991 Fleer	328	.03	.02	.01
1991 NBA Hoops	168	.05	.04	.02
1991 NBA Hoops	403	.05	.04	.02
1991 SkyBox	229	.05	.04	.02

1991 SkyBox	585	.05	.04	.02
1991 SkyBox	638	.05	.04	.02
1991 Upper Deck	151	.05	.04	.02
1991 Upper Deck	495	.05	.04	.02
1992 Fleer	153	.05	.04	.02
1992 Fleer	307	.05	.04	.02
1992 Fleer Ultra	229	.10	.08	.04
1992 NBA Hoops	156	.05	.04	.02
1992 NBA Hoops	357	.10	.08	.04
1992 SkyBox	165	.05	.04	.02
1992 SkyBox	330	.05	.04	.02
1992 Topps	293	.04	.03	.02
1992 Topps Archives	69	.05	.04	.02
1992 Topps Stadium Club	256	.10	.08	.04
1992 Upper Deck	269	.05	.04	.02
1992 Upper Deck	336	.05	.04	.02
1993 Fleer	15	.05	.04	.02
1993 Fleer Ultra	14	.10	.08	.04
1993 NBA Hoops	15	.06	.05	.02
1993 SkyBox	34	.05	.04	.02
1993 Topps	313	.05	.04	.02
1993 Topps Finest	61	.35	.25	.14
1993 Topps Stadium Club	60	.10	.08	.04
1993 Topps Stadium Club	137	.10	.08	.04
1993 Upper Deck	18	.05	.04	.02
1993 Upper Deck SE	117	.10	.08	.04
1993 Upper Deck 3-D Basketball	50	.10	.08	.04
1994 Fleer	15	.07	.05	.03
1994 Fleer Flair	11	.15	.11	.06
1994 Fleer Jam Session	13	.12	.09	.05
1994 Fleer Ultra	13	.08	.06	.03
1994 NBA Hoops	12	.04	.03	.02
1994 SkyBox	12	.06	.05	.02
1994 Topps	46	.06	.05	.02
1994 Topps Finest	84	.15	.11	.06
1994 Topps Stadium Club	157	.08	.06	.03
1994 Topps Stadium Club	158	.08	.06	.03
1994 Upper Deck Collector's Choice	131	.05	.04	.02
1994 Upper Deck Special Edition	5	.20	.15	.08

George McGinnis

Set	Card #	NM	EX	VG
1972 Topps	183 (R)	15.00	7.50	4.50
1972 Topps	243	3.00	1.50	.90
1973 Topps	180	4.00	2.00	1.25
1973 Topps	234	7.00	3.50	2.00
1974 Topps	207	7.00	3.50	2.00
1974 Topps	211	.50	.25	.15
1974 Topps	220	3.00	1.50	.90
1974 Topps	223	1.00	.50	.30
1975 Topps	184	2.00	1.00	.60
1975 Topps	221	6.00	3.00	1.75
1975 Topps	226	1.50	.70	.45
1975 Topps	279	1.25	.60	.40
1976 Topps	70	3.00	1.50	.90
1976 Topps	128	1.25	.60	.40

1977 Topps	50	.75	.40	.25
1978 Topps	90	.50	.25	.15
1979 Topps	125	1.00	.50	.30
1980 Topps	39	.25	.13	.08
1980 Topps	127	1.00	.50	.30

Set	Card #	MT	NM	EX
1981 Topps	92	.30	.25	.12

Kevin McHale

Set	Card #	MT	NM	EX
1981 Topps	75 (R)	19.00	14.00	7.50
1983 Star Co.	34	65.00	49.00	26.00
1984 Star Co.	9	18.00	13.50	7.25
1984 Star Co. All-Star Game	7	10.00	7.50	4.00
1984 Star Co. Awards Banquet	5	7.00	5.25	2.75
1984 Star Co. Court Kings	42	6.00	4.50	2.50
1985 Star Co.	98	13.00	9.75	5.25
1986 Fleer	73	4.00	3.00	1.50
1986 Star Co. Court Kings	22	8.00	6.00	3.25
1987 Fleer	74	4.00	3.00	1.50
1988 Fleer	11	1.00	.70	.40
1989 Fleer	11	.40	.30	.15
1989 NBA Hoops	156	.05	.04	.02
1989 NBA Hoops	280	.20	.15	.08
1990 Fleer	12	.10	.08	.04
1990 NBA Hoops	6	.75	.60	.30
1990 NBA Hoops	44	.12	.09	.05
1990 SkyBox	19	.20	.15	.08
1991 Fleer	13	.10	.08	.04
1991 Fleer NBA Schoolyard Sets	3	.65	.50	.25
1991 NBA Hoops	14	.10	.08	.04
1991 NBA Hoops	255	.10	.08	.04
1991 NBA Hoops	504	.05	.04	.02
1991 SkyBox	17	.10	.08	.04
1991 SkyBox	433	.10	.08	.04
1991 Upper Deck	62	.08	.06	.03
1991 Upper Deck	225	.10	.08	.04
1992 Fleer	17	.12	.09	.05
1992 Fleer Ultra	14	.15	.11	.06
1992 NBA Hoops	16	.10	.08	.04
1992 SkyBox	16	.10	.08	.04
1992 Topps	57	.10	.08	.04
1992 Topps	213	.04	.03	.02
1992 Topps Stadium Club	147	.10	.08	.04
1992 Upper Deck	183	.10	.08	.04
1992 Upper Deck 15000-Point Club	2	2.00	1.50	.80

Mini: Small-size cards, sometimes miniature reproductions of regular cards (1975 Topps mini) and sometimes independent issues (1986-89 Topps Mini League Leaders).

George Mikan

Set	Card #	NM	EX	VG
1948 Bowman	69 (R)	4500.	2250.	1350.

Reggie Miller

Set	Card #	MT	NM	EX
1988 Fleer	57 (R)	20.00	15.00	8.00
1989 Fleer	65	2.00	1.50	.80
1989 NBA Hoops	29	.50	.40	.20
1990 Fleer	78	.25	.20	.10
1990 NBA Hoops	7	.15	.11	.06
1990 NBA Hoops	135	.20	.15	.08
1990 NBA Hoops	365	.07	.05	.03
1990 SkyBox	117	.20	.15	.08
1991 Fleer	83	.15	.11	.06
1991 Fleer	226	.07	.05	.03
1991 NBA Hoops	84	.15	.11	.06
1991 NBA Hoops	303	.10	.08	.04
1991 NBA Hoops	469	.08	.06	.03
1991 SkyBox	114	.25	.20	.10
1991 SkyBox	596	.05	.04	.02
1991 Upper Deck	256	.25	.20	.10
1992 Fleer	91	.20	.15	.08
1992 Fleer Sharpshooters	1	1.00	.50	.30
1992 Fleer Team Leaders	11	17.00	12.50	6.75
1992 Fleer Ultra	78	.35	.25	.14
1992 NBA Hoops	92	.25	.20	.10
1992 SkyBox	97	.30	.25	.12
1992 SkyBox	292	.10	.08	.04
1992 Topps	193	.15	.11	.06
1992 Topps	215	.04	.03	.02
1992 Topps Archives	67	.15	.11	.06
1992 Topps Beam Team	1	2.00	1.50	1.00
1992 Topps Stadium Club	357	.40	.30	.15
1992 Topps Stadium Club Beam Team	7	6.00	4.50	2.50
1992 Upper Deck	123	.25	.20	.10
1992 Upper Deck Team MVP's	12TM	.75	.60	.30
1993 Fleer	85	.25	.20	.10
1993 Fleer Flair USA Basketball	11	1.00	.70	.40
1993 Fleer Jam Session	89	.25	.20	.10
1993 Fleer NBA Superstars	12	.50	.40	.20
1993 Fleer Ultra	81	.35	.25	.14
1993 NBA Hoops	87	.10	.08	.04
1993 SkyBox	85	.25	.20	.10
1993 SkyBox Showdown Series	10	.75	.60	.30
1993 Topps	57	.10	.08	.04
1993 Topps	133	.10	.08	.04
1993 Topps	187	.10	.08	.04
1993 Topps Finest	11	2.00	1.50	.80
1993 Topps Finest	106	.35	.25	.14
1993 Topps Finest Main Attraction	11	5.00	3.75	2.00
1993 Topps Stadium Club	306	.35	.25	.14
1993 Topps Stadium Club Beam Team	6	4.00	3.00	1.50
1993 Upper Deck	309	.20	.15	.08
1993 Upper Deck SE	53	.35	.25	.14
1993 Upper Deck Team MVP's	11	.50	.40	.20
1993 Upper Deck USA Basketball	7	.20	.15	.08
1993 Upper Deck 3-D Basketball	5	.15	.11	.06
1994 Fleer	92	.25	.20	.10
1994 Fleer Flair	62	1.00	.70	.40
1994 Fleer Flair	166	.25	.20	.10
1994 Fleer Flair Hot Numbers	9	3.00	2.25	1.25
1994 Fleer Jam Session	80	.25	.20	.10
1994 Fleer Jam Session Flashing Stars	4	1.50	1.25	.60
1994 Fleer Sharpshooters	5	2.50	2.00	1.00
1994 Fleer Team Leaders	4	7.00	5.25	2.75
1994 Fleer Triple Threats	5	1.00	.70	.40
1994 Fleer Ultra	76	.25	.20	.10
1994 Fleer Ultra Double Trouble	5	1.75	1.25	.70
1994 NBA Hoops	86	.15	.11	.06
1994 NBA Hoops Power Ratings	22	1.50	1.25	.60
1994 NBA Hoops Supreme Court	20	1.00	.70	.40
1994 SkyBox	68	.15	.11	.06
1994 SkyBox	183	.15	.11	.06
1994 SkyBox Dream Team II Dream Play	13	6.00	4.50	2.50
1994 SkyBox Dream Team II Portraits	13	18.00	13.50	7.25
1994 Topps	146	.10	.08	.04
1994 Topps Finest	155	.50	.40	.20
1994 Topps Stadium Club	144	.25	.20	.10
1994 Topps Stadium Club Clear Cut	11	4.00	3.00	1.50
1994 Upper Deck	126	.30	.25	.12
1994 Upper Deck	175	.20	.15	.08
1994 Upper Deck Collector's Choice 2,000 Pts	6	3.00	2.25	1.25
1994 Upper Deck Collector's Choice	31	.25	.20	.10
1994 Upper Deck Collector's Choice	176	.15	.11	.06
1994 Upper Deck Collector's Choice	382	.15	.11	.06

Minor leaguer: A card depicting a player from the minor leagues. Minor league sets are a fast-growing segment of the hobby.

Miscut: A card that has been cut incorrectly from a press sheet during the manufacturing process and decreases in value as a result.

Harold Miner

Set	Card #	MT	NM	EX
1992 Fleer	369 (R)	.50	.40	.20
1992 Fleer Ultra	293 (R)	.50	.40	.20
1992 Fleer Ultra All-Rookies	5	2.00	1.50	.80
1992 NBA Hoops	413 (R)	.75	.60	.30
1992 NBA Hoops II Magic's All-Rookie Team	10	9.00	6.75	3.50
1992 SkyBox	360 (R)	.75	.60	.30
1992 SkyBox Draft Picks	12	2.00	1.50	.80
1992 Topps	278 (R)	.30	.25	.12
1992 Topps Stadium Club	317 (R)	.75	.60	.30
1992 Upper Deck	8 (R)	.40	.30	.15
1992 Upper Deck	446	.10	.08	.04
1992 Upper Deck	469	.10	.08	.04
1992 Upper Deck Rookie Standouts	9	1.50	1.25	.60
1993 Fleer	108	.10	.08	.04
1993 Fleer Jam Session	113	.15	.11	.06
1993 Fleer Jam Session 2nd Year Stars	5	.75	.60	.30
1993 Fleer Rookie Sensations	16	2.00	1.50	.80
1993 Fleer Ultra	100	.12	.09	.05
1993 Fleer Ultra Famous Nicknames	10	.75	.60	.30
1993 Fleer Ultra Jam City	6	2.00	1.50	.80
1993 NBA Hoops	113	.12	.09	.05
1993 NBA Hoops Face to Face	10	10.00	7.50	4.00
1993 SkyBox	103	.10	.08	.04
1993 SkyBox Thunder and Lightning	2	1.25	1.50	.80
1993 Topps	175	.10	.08	.04
1993 Topps	246	.12	.09	.05
1993 Topps Finest	218	.35	.25	.14
1993 Topps Stadium Club	86	.12	.09	.05
1993 Topps Stadium Club Rim Rockers	2	1.00	.70	.40
1993 Upper Deck	21	.15	.11	.06
1993 Upper Deck Jordan's Flight Team	14	2.50	2.00	1.00
1993 Upper Deck Locker Talk	5	.75	.60	.30
1993 Upper Deck SE	129	.20	.15	.08
1993 Upper Deck SE East Future All Stars	7	6.00	4.50	2.50
1993 Upper Deck 3-D Basketball	105	.25	.20	.10
1994 Fleer	117	.05	.04	.02
1994 Fleer Flair	79	.15	.11	.06
1994 Fleer Jam Session	99	.10	.08	.04
1994 Fleer Ultra	96	.08	.06	.03
1994 NBA Hoops	110	.04	.03	.02
1994 NBA Hoops Supreme Court	23	.30	.25	.12
1994 SkyBox	85	.06	.05	.02
1994 Topps	123	.06	.05	.02
1994 Topps	124	.06	.05	.02
1994 Upper Deck	95	.10	.08	.04
1994 Upper Deck Collector's Choice	88	.07	.05	.03
1994 Upper Deck Collector's Choice	209	.05	.04	.02
1994 Upper Deck Special Edition	46	.20	.15	.08

Sidney Moncrief

Set	Card #	NM	EX	VG
1980 Topps	52	4.00	2.00	1.25
1980 Topps	140	6.00	3.00	1.75

Set	Card #	MT	NM	EX
1981 Topps	99	1.50	1.25	.60
1983 Star Co.	38	16.00	12.00	6.50
1983 Star Co. All-Star Game	8	2.00	1.50	.80
1984 Star Co.	135	6.00	4.50	2.50
1984 Star Co. All-Star Game	8	2.00	1.50	.80
1984 Star Co. Awards Banquet	7	3.00	2.25	1.25
1984 Star Co. Court Kings	7	3.50	2.75	1.50
1985 Star Co.	128	6.00	4.50	2.50
1986 Fleer	75	4.00	3.00	1.50
1986 Star Co. Court Kings	23	3.00	2.25	1.25
1987 Fleer	76	2.00	1.50	.80
1989 NBA Hoops	275	.30	.25	.12
1990 NBA Hoops	402	.15	.11	.06
1990 SkyBox	367	.10	.08	.04
1991 NBA Hoops	3	.06	.05	.02
1991 SkyBox	6	.06	.05	.02
1991 Upper Deck	240	.05	.04	.02

Earl Monroe

Set	Card #	NM	EX	VG
1969 Topps	80 (R)	40.00	30.00	16.00

1970 Topps	20	13.00	6.50	4.00
1971 Topps	130	10.00	5.00	3.00
1972 Topps	73	7.00	3.50	2.00
1972 Topps	154	3.00	1.50	.90
1973 Topps	142	5.00	2.50	1.50
1974 Topps	25	6.00	3.00	1.75
1975 Topps	73	6.00	3.00	1.75
1976 Topps	98	4.50	2.25	1.25
1977 Topps	6	3.00	1.50	.90
1978 Topps	45	3.00	1.50	.90
1979 Topps	8	2.00	1.00	.60
1980 Topps	63	1.00	.50	.30
1980 Topps	151	1.00	.50	.30

Set	Card #	MT	NM	EX
1985 Star Co. Schick Legends	19	3.00	2.25	1.25

Chris Mullin

Eric Montross

Set	Card #	MT	NM	EX
1994 Fleer	249 (R)	.50	.40	.20
1994 Fleer First Year Phenoms	4	1.25	.90	.50
1994 Fleer Jam Session	14 (R)	1.00	.70	.40
1994 Fleer Ultra	14 (R)	.65	.50	.25
1994 NBA Hoops	308 (R)	.50	.40	.20
1994 NBA Hoops	429	.25	.20	.10
1994 Pacific Prisms	38	3.50	2.75	1.50
1994 SkyBox Draft Picks	9	8.00	6.00	3.25
1994 Topps	136 (R)	.60	.45	.25
1994 Topps Stadium Club	179 (R)	.70	.50	.30
1994 Upper Deck	162 (R)	.75	.60	.30
1994 Upper Deck Collector's Choice Rookie	8	2.00	1.50	.80
1994 Upper Deck Collector's Choice	370 (R)	.85	.60	.35
1994 Upper Deck Collector's Choice	373	.20	.15	.08
1994 Upper Deck Collector's Choice	414	.20	.15	.08

Multi-player card: A card picturing more than one player. Multi-player cards often show rookies or stars.

Nine-pocket sheet: The most common type of plastic sheet. A nine-pocket sheet is about the size of a sheet of typing paper and is designed to fit into a standard three-ring binder. The sheet has nine pockets to hold most normal-sized modern cards.

Set	Card #	MT	NM	EX
1986 Fleer	77 (R)	30.00	22.00	12.00
1987 Fleer	77	8.50	6.50	3.50
1988 Fleer	48	3.00	2.25	1.25
1989 Fleer	55	.75	.60	.30
1989 NBA Hoops	90	.25	.20	.10
1989 NBA Hoops	230	.15	.11	.06
1990 Fleer	66	.20	.15	.08
1990 NBA Hoops	22	.20	.15	.08
1990 NBA Hoops	116	.10	.08	.04
1990 NBA Hoops	363	.10	.08	.04
1990 SkyBox	98	.30	.25	.12
1991 Fleer	69	.15	.11	.06
1991 Fleer	218	.10	.08	.04
1991 Fleer	380	.12	.09	.05
1991 Fleer NBA Schoolyard Sets	1	2.00	1.50	.80
1991 NBA Hoops	72	.15	.11	.06
1991 NBA Hoops	268	.15	.11	.06
1991 NBA Hoops	466	.20	.15	.08
1991 NBA Hoops	581	.50	.40	.20
1991 SkyBox	96	.15	.11	.06
1991 SkyBox	301	.10	.08	.04
1991 SkyBox	303	.10	.08	.04
1991 SkyBox	467	.15	.11	.06
1991 SkyBox	536	.50	.40	.20
1991 SkyBox	597	.15	.11	.06
1991 Upper Deck	60	.15	.11	.06
1991 Upper Deck	245	.25	.20	.10
1991 Upper Deck	465	.20	.15	.08
1992 Fleer	77	.15	.11	.06
1992 Fleer	245	.12	.09	.05
1992 Fleer All-Stars	18	1.50	1.25	.60
1992 Fleer Sharpshooters	17	.75	.60	.30
1992 Fleer Team Leaders	9	15.00	11.00	6.00
1992 Fleer Ultra	67	.25	.20	.10
1992 Fleer Ultra All-NBA Team	2	1.00	.70	.40
1992 NBA Hoops	78	.15	.11	.06
1992 NBA Hoops	312	.10	.08	.04
1992 NBA Hoops	344	.10	.08	.04
1992 NBA Hoops Supreme Court	9SC	1.25	.90	.50
1992 SkyBox	83	.25	.20	.10
1992 SkyBox	290	.10	.08	.04
1992 SkyBox I Olympic Team	2USA	1.50	1.25	.60
1992 Topps	120	.10	.08	.04
1992 Topps	298	.15	.11	.06
1992 Topps Archives	68	.25	.20	.10
1992 Topps Beam Team	7	4.00	3.00	1.60
1992 Topps Stadium Club	11	.40	.30	.15
1992 Topps Stadium Club	202	.25	.20	.10
1992 Topps Stadium Club Beam Team	6	5.00	3.75	2.00
1992 Upper Deck	207	.25	.20	.10
1992 Upper Deck All-Division Team	17	.75	.60	.30
1992 Upper Deck All-NBA	5AN	1.50	1.25	.60

Set	Card #			
1992 Upper Deck Team MVP's	10TM	1.00	.70	.40
1993 Fleer	71	.15	.11	.06
1993 Fleer Jam Session	72	.25	.20	.10
1993 Fleer NBA Superstars	14	.50	.40	.20
1993 Fleer Ultra	68	.20	.15	.08
1993 NBA Hoops	73	.15	.11	.06
1993 NBA Hoops Face to Face	11	3.00	2.25	1.25
1993 SkyBox	76	.20	.15	.08
1993 SkyBox	325	.10	.08	.04
1993 Topps	191	.15	.11	.06
1993 Topps	209	.15	.11	.06
1993 Topps Finest	122	1.00	.70	.40
1993 Topps Finest	176	1.00	.70	.40
1993 Topps Stadium Club	289	.25	.20	.10
1993 Upper Deck	92	.20	.15	.08
1993 Upper Deck	242	.10	.08	.04
1993 Upper Deck SE	61	.25	.20	.10
1993 Upper Deck Team MVP's	9	.75	.60	.30
1993 Upper Deck 3-D Basketball	62	.10	.08	.04
1993 Upper Deck 3-D Basketball	78	.10	.08	.04
1994 Fleer	75	.20	.15	.08
1994 Fleer Jam Session	63	.30	.25	.12
1994 Fleer Ultra	61	.15	.11	.06
1994 NBA Hoops	68	.12	.09	.05
1994 NBA Hoops Power Ratings	18	.75	.60	.30
1994 NBA Hoops Supreme Court	17	.75	.60	.30
1994 Topps	122	.08	.06	.03
1994 Topps Finest	1	.25	.20	.10
1994 Topps Stadium Club	69	.25	.20	.10
1994 Topps Stadium Club	105	.12	.09	.05
1994 Topps Stadium Club Clear Cut	9	2.00	1.50	.80
1994 Upper Deck Collector's Choice	17	.20	.15	.08
1994 Upper Deck Special Edition	27	.60	.45	.25

Calvin Murphy

Set	Card #	NM	EX	VG
1970 Topps	137 (R)	40.00	20.00	12.00
1971 Topps	58	6.00	3.00	1.75
1972 Topps	31	4.00	2.00	1.25
1972 Topps	174	1.25	.60	.40
1973 Topps	13	3.50	1.75	1.00
1973 Topps	156	3.00	1.50	.90
1974 Topps	88	1.00	.50	.30
1974 Topps	149	.50	.25	.15
1974 Topps	152	3.50	1.75	1.00
1975 Topps	3	4.00	2.00	1.25
1975 Topps	123	.75	.40	.25
1975 Topps	180	2.50	1.25	.70

1976 Topps	44	2.50	1.25	.70
1977 Topps	105	1.00	.50	.30
1978 Topps	13	1.25	.60	.40
1979 Topps	81	.75	.40	.25
1980 Topps	30	.75	.40	.25
1980 Topps	75	.25	.13	.08
1980 Topps	105	.25	.13	.08
1980 Topps	118	.25	.13	.08

Set	Card #	MT	NM	EX
1981 Topps	15	.30	.25	.12

Dikembe Mutombo

Set	Card #	MT	NM	EX
1991 Fleer	277 (R)	1.00	.70	.40
1991 Fleer	378	.50	.40	.20
1991 NBA Hoops	549 (R)	1.00	.70	.40
1991 SkyBox	411	.10	.08	.04
1991 SkyBox	516 (R)	2.00	1.50	.80
1991 Upper Deck	3 (R)	1.75	1.25	.70
1991 Upper Deck	446	.65	.50	.25
1991 Upper Deck	471	.40	.30	.15
1991 Upper Deck Rookie Standouts	29R	2.25	1.75	.90
1992 Fleer	60	.25	.20	.10
1992 Fleer	286	.08	.06	.03
1992 Fleer All-Stars	19	1.00	.70	.40
1992 Fleer Rookie Sensations	7	13.00	9.75	5.25
1992 Fleer Team Leaders	7	20.00	15.00	8.00
1992 Fleer Total "D"	12	12.00	9.00	4.75
1992 Fleer Ultra	53	.45	.35	.20
1992 Fleer Ultra	202	.20	.15	.08
1992 Fleer Ultra Rejectors	2	1.25	.90	.50
1992 NBA Hoops	60	.20	.15	.08
1992 NBA Hoops	313	.10	.08	.04
1992 SkyBox	64	.25	.20	.10
1992 Topps	110	.10	.08	.04
1992 Topps	281	.20	.15	.08
1992 Topps Archives	146	.30	.25	.12
1992 Topps Stadium Club	196	.25	.20	.10
1992 Topps Stadium Club	273	.50	.40	.20
1992 Upper Deck	255	.20	.15	.08
1992 Upper Deck	499	.10	.08	.04
1992 Upper Deck	509	.10	.08	.04
1992 Upper Deck All-Rookie	2AR	2.00	1.50	.80
1992 Upper Deck Foreign Exchange	5	2.00	1.50	.80
1992 Upper Deck Jerry West Selects	12JW	1.00	.70	.40
1992 Upper Deck Jerry West Selects	13JW	1.00	.70	.40
1992 Upper Deck Team MVP's	8TM	2.00	1.50	.80
1993 Fleer	54	.10	.08	.04
1993 Fleer Jam Session	56	.15	.11	.06
1993 Fleer NBA Internationals	7	1.00	.60	.30

Set	Card #			
1993 Fleer Towers of Power	18	4.50	3.50	1.75
1993 Fleer Ultra	52	.10	.08	.04
1993 Fleer Ultra Rebound Kings	6	.40	.30	.15
1993 NBA Hoops	56	.10	.08	.04
1993 SkyBox	63	.15	.11	.06
1993 SkyBox Showdown Series	4	1.25	.90	.50
1993 SkyBox Showdown Series	6	1.00	.70	.40
1993 Topps	262	.08	.06	.03
1993 Topps BlackGold	12	.60	.45	.25
1993 Topps Finest	119	.35	.25	.14
1993 Topps Finest	164	2.00	1.50	.80
1993 Topps Stadium Club	56	.15	.11	.06
1993 Topps Stadium Club	63	.10	.08	.04
1993 Topps Stadium Club	109	.10	.08	.04
1993 Upper Deck	55	.30	.25	.12
1993 Upper Deck	246	.05	.04	.02
1993 Upper Deck	431	.10	.08	.04
1993 Upper Deck SE	150	.10	.08	.04
1993 Upper Deck SE Behind the Glass	3	1.25	.90	.50
1993 Upper Deck SE West Future All Stars	3	8.00	6.00	3.25
1993 Upper Deck 3-D Basketball	64	.10	.08	.04
1993 Upper Deck 3-D Basketball	107	.10	.08	.04
1993 Upper Deck 3-D Triple Double	8	.75	.60	.30
1994 Fleer	58	.20	.15	.08
1994 Fleer Flair	40	.70	.50	.30
1994 Fleer Flair Hot Numbers	10	1.50	1.25	.60
1994 Fleer Jam Session	47	.15	.11	.06
1994 Fleer Jam Session Slam Dunk Heroes	5	4.00	3.00	1.50
1994 Fleer NBA League Leaders	4	1.25	.90	.50
1994 Fleer Team Leaders	3	2.00	1.50	.80
1994 Fleer Total D	3	2.50	2.00	1.00
1994 Fleer Towers of Power	6	1.00	.70	.40
1994 Fleer Ultra	49	.15	.11	.06
1994 Fleer Ultra Ultra Power	6	1.25	.90	.50
1994 NBA Hoops	50	.12	.09	.05
1994 NBA Hoops Predators	2	3.00	2.25	1.25
1994 NBA Hoops Supreme Court	13	1.00	.70	.40
1994 Pacific Prisms	41	1.25	.90	.50
1994 Pacific Prisms	72	1.25	.90	.50
1994 SkyBox	42	.08	.06	.03
1994 Topps	50	.08	.06	.03
1994 Topps	105	.08	.06	.03
1994 Topps Finest Marathon Men	18	3.00	2.25	1.25
1994 Topps Stadium Club	65	.12	.09	.05
1994 Topps Stadium Club Clear Cut	7	3.00	2.25	1.25
1994 Topps Stadium Club Rising Stars	9	7.50	5.75	3.00
1994 Topps Super Rebounders	5	3.00	2.25	1.25
1994 Topps Super Swatters	1	4.00	3.00	1.50
1994 Upper Deck	132	.12	.09	.05
1994 Upper Deck Col.'s Choice 1,000 Rebounds	7	3.00	2.25	1.25
1994 Upper Deck Collector's Choice	55	.20	.15	.08
1994 Upper Deck Collector's Choice	172	.10	.08	.04
1994 Upper Deck Predictors Hobby	12	10.00	7.50	4.00

Larry Nance

Set	Card #	MT	NM	EX
1983 Star Co.	115 (R)	35.00	26.00	14.00
1984 Star Co.	47	13.00	9.75	5.25
1984 Star Co. Awards Banquet	9	4.00	3.00	1.50
1984 Star Co. Court Kings	19	5.00	3.75	2.00
1984 Star Co. Slam Dunk	7	12.00	9.00	4.75
1984 Star Co. Slam Dunk	11	10.00	7.50	4.00
1985 Star Co.	34	15.00	11.00	6.00
1986 Fleer	78 (R)	9.00	6.75	3.50
1986 Star Co. Court Kings	24	8.00	6.00	3.25
1987 Fleer	78	3.00	2.25	1.25
1988 Fleer	24	1.00	.70	.40
1989 Fleer	28	.30	.25	.12
1989 Fleer	166	.35	.25	.14
1989 NBA Hoops	25	.15	.11	.06
1989 NBA Hoops	217	.05	.04	.02
1990 Fleer	35	.05	.04	.02
1990 Fleer	78	.03	.02	.01
1990 SkyBox	55	.05	.04	.02
1991 Fleer	37	.07	.05	.03
1991 NBA Hoops	39	.06	.05	.02
1991 NBA Hoops	458	.10	.08	.04
1991 NBA Hoops Slam Dunk	1	.75	.60	.30
1991 SkyBox	52	.08	.06	.03
1991 Upper Deck	223	.07	.05	.03
1992 Fleer	42	.10	.08	.04
1992 Fleer	276	.05	.04	.02
1992 Fleer Total "D"	9	5.50	4.25	2.25
1992 Fleer Ultra	37	.12	.09	.05
1992 NBA Hoops	42	.08	.06	.03
1992 SkyBox	43	.08	.06	.03
1992 Topps	163	.04	.03	.02
1992 Topps Archives	18	.05	.04	.02
1992 Topps Stadium Club	298	.10	.08	.04
1992 Upper Deck	281	.08	.06	.03
1992 Upper Deck	430	.05	.04	.02
1992 Upper Deck 15000-Point Club	18	2.00	1.50	.80
1993 Fleer	38	.05	.04	.02
1993 Fleer All-Stars	6	.50	.40	.20
1993 Fleer Jam Session	41	.10	.08	.04
1993 Fleer Ultra	39	.10	.08	.04
1993 Fleer Ultra All-Defensive Team	8	10.00	7.50	4.00
1993 NBA Hoops	40	.06	.05	.02
1993 NBA Hoops	266	.06	.05	.02
1993 NBA Hoops	427	.06	.05	.02
1993 SkyBox	51	.05	.04	.02
1993 Topps	74	.05	.04	.02
1993 Topps Finest	51	.35	.25	.14
1993 Topps Stadium Club	17	.10	.08	.04
1993 Topps Stadium Club	62	.10	.08	.04
1993 Upper Deck	281	.05	.04	.02
1993 Upper Deck 3-D Basketball	39	.10	.08	.04
1994 Fleer	42	.05	.04	.02
1994 NBA Hoops	36	.04	.03	.02

Don Nelson

Set	Card #	NM	EX	VG
1969 Topps	82 (R)	35.00	26.00	14.00
1970 Topps	86	18.00	9.00	5.40
1971 Topps	114	7.00	5.25	2.75
1972 Topps	92	6.50	3.25	2.00
1973 Topps	78	4.00	2.00	1.25
1974 Topps	46	3.00	1.50	.90
1975 Topps	44	3.00	1.50	.90

Set	Card #	MT	NM	EX
1985 Star Co. Coaches	7	3.00	2.25	1.25
1989 NBA Hoops	273	.05	.04	.02
1990 NBA Hoops	313	.03	.02	.01
1990 NBA Hoops	345	.10	.08	.04
1990 SkyBox	309	.10	.08	.04
1991 Fleer	70	.03	.02	.01
1991 NBA Hoops	229	.05	.04	.02
1991 SkyBox	386	.05	.04	.02
1992 Fleer	78	.05	.04	.02
1992 NBA Hoops	247	.05	.04	.02
1992 NBA Hoops	319	.10	.08	.04
1992 SkyBox	263	.05	.04	.02
1993 Fleer Flair USA Basketball	4	.40	.30	.15
1993 Fleer Ultra	372	.10	.08	.04
1993 NBA Hoops	238	.06	.05	.02
1994 NBA Hoops	282	.04	.03	.02

Norm Nixon

Set	Card #	NM	EX	VG
1978 Topps	63 (R)	4.00	2.00	1.25
1979 Topps	97	.50	.25	.15
1980 Topps	47	.25	.13	.08
1980 Topps	55	.25	.13	.08
1980 Topps	135	.25	.13	.08
1980 Topps	160	.25	.13	.08

Set	Card #	MT	NM	EX
1981 Topps	22	.25	.20	.10
1981 Topps	55	1.50	1.25	.60
1983 Star Co.	129	4.00	3.00	1.50
1984 Star Co.	20	2.75	2.00	1.00
1986 Fleer	80	1.25	.90	.50

Shaquille O'Neal

Set	Card #	MT	NM	EX
1992 Fleer	298	2.50	2.00	1.00
1992 Fleer	401 (R)	8.00	6.00	3.20
1992 Fleer Ultra	328 (R)	10.00	7.50	4.00
1992 Fleer Ultra All-Rookies	7	20.00	15.00	8.00
1992 Fleer Ultra Rejectors	4	19.00	14.00	7.50
1992 NBA Hoops	442 (R)	12.00	9.00	4.75
1992 NBA Hoops Draft Redemption	1A	75.00	56.00	30.00
1992 NBA Hoops II Magic's All-Rookie Team	1	120.00	90.00	48.00
1992 SkyBox	382 (R)	12.00	9.00	4.75
1992 SkyBox Draft Picks	1	35.00	26.00	14.00
1992 Topps	362 (R)	4.00	3.00	1.50
1992 Topps Beam Team	7	4.00	3.00	1.60
1992 Topps Stadium Club	201	4.50	3.50	1.75
1992 Topps Stadium Club	247 (R)	14.00	10.50	5.50
1992 Topps Stadium Club Beam Team	21	100.00	75.00	40.00
1992 Upper Deck	1 (R)	13.00	9.75	5.25
1992 Upper Deck	424	2.50	2.00	1.00
1992 Upper Deck	474	4.00	3.00	1.50
1992 Upper Deck All-Division Team	1	10.00	7.50	4.00
1992 Upper Deck Rookie Standouts	15	16.00	12.00	6.50
1993 Fleer	149	2.25	1.70	.90
1993 Fleer	231	1.00	.70	.40
1993 Fleer All-Stars	7	10.00	7.50	4.00
1993 Fleer Flair USA Basketball	13	4.00	3.00	1.50
1993 Fleer Jam Session	160	3.25	2.45	1.30
1993 Fleer Jam Session Slam Dunk Heroes	7	3.00	2.25	1.25
1993 Fleer Jam Session 2nd Year Stars	7	4.00	3.00	1.50
1993 Fleer NBA Superstars	16	5.00	3.75	2.00
1993 Fleer Rookie Sensations	18	25.00	18.50	10.00
1993 Fleer Towers of Power	21	30.00	22.00	12.00
1993 Fleer Ultra	135	3.50	2.75	1.50
1993 Fleer Ultra All-Rookie Team	5	12.00	9.00	4.75
1993 Fleer Ultra Famous Nicknames	13	9.00	6.75	3.50
1993 Fleer Ultra Jam City	7	45.00	34.00	18.00

Card	#			
1993 Fleer Ultra NBA Award Winners	4	45.00	34.00	18.00
1993 Fleer Ultra Power in the Key	7	20.00	15.00	8.00
1993 Fleer Ultra Rebound Kings	9	5.00	3.75	2.00
1993 Fleer Ultra Scoring Kings	8	50.00	37.00	20.00
1993 NBA Hoops	155	2.00	1.50	.80
1993 NBA Hoops	264	1.00	.70	.40
1993 NBA Hoops	284	.30	.25	.12
1993 NBA Hoops	290	.35	.25	.14
1993 NBA Hoops Admiral's Choice	4	3.00	2.25	1.25
1993 NBA Hoops Face to Face	1	10.00	7.50	4.00
1993 NBA Hoops Supreme Court	4	4.00	3.00	1.50
1993 SkyBox	133	2.75	2.05	1.10
1993 SkyBox	331	1.50	1.25	.60
1993 SkyBox Center Stage	2	10.00	7.50	4.00
1993 SkyBox NBA All-Rookie Team	1	20.00	15.00	8.00
1993 SkyBox Showdown Series	2	2.50	2.00	1.00
1993 SkyBox Showdown Series	3	3.00	2.25	1.25
1993 SkyBox Thunder and Lightning	6	20.00	18.50	10.00
1993 Topps	3	.90	.70	.35
1993 Topps	134	.85	.60	.35
1993 Topps	152	1.00	.70	.40
1993 Topps	181	2.00	1.50	.80
1993 Topps	386	1.00	.70	.40
1993 Topps BlackGold	18	9.00	6.75	3.50
1993 Topps Finest	3	17.00	12.50	6.75
1993 Topps Finest	99	10.00	7.50	4.00
1993 Topps Finest Main Attraction	19	40.00	30.00	16.00
1993 Topps Stadium Club	100	3.50	2.75	1.50
1993 Topps Stadium Club	175	1.75	1.25	.70
1993 Topps Stadium Club	358	1.50	1.25	.60
1993 Topps Stadium Club Beam Team	1	23.00	17.00	9.25
1993 Topps Stadium Club Rim Rockers	1	12.00	9.00	4.75
1993 Upper Deck	177	1.00	.70	.40
1993 Upper Deck	228	.50	.40	.20
1993 Upper Deck	300	2.75	2.05	1.10
1993 Upper Deck	469	1.00	.70	.40
1993 Upper Deck All-Rookie	1	24.00	18.00	9.50
1993 Upper Deck Future Heroes	35	10.00	7.50	4.00
1993 Upper Deck Jordan's Flight Team	16	32.00	24.00	13.00
1993 Upper Deck Locker Talk	3	15.00	11.00	6.00
1993 Upper Deck SE	32	2.50	2.00	1.00
1993 Upper Deck SE Behind the Glass	14	20.00	15.00	8.00
1993 Upper Deck SE East Future All Stars	13	70.00	52.00	28.00
1993 Upper Deck Team MVP's	19	5.00	3.75	2.00
1993 Upper Deck USA Basketball	9	1.50	1.25	.60
1993 Upper Deck 3-D Basketball	32	1.75	.60	.30
1993 Upper Deck 3-D Basketball	79	1.00	.70	.40
1993 Upper Deck 3-D Basketball	102	.75	.60	.30
1994 Fleer	160	2.00	1.50	.80
1994 Fleer Flair	107	5.50	4.25	2.25
1994 Fleer Flair	168	2.50	2.00	1.00
1994 Fleer Flair Center Spotlight	4	50.00	37.00	20.00
1994 Fleer Flair Hot Numbers	12	13.00	9.75	5.25
1994 Fleer Flair Scoring Power	5	12.00	9.00	4.75
1994 Fleer Jam Session	136	3.50	2.75	1.50
1994 Fleer Jam Session GameBreakers	6	7.50	5.75	3.00
1994 Fleer Jam Session Slam Dunk Heroes	7	35.00	26.00	14.00
1994 Fleer NBA All-Stars	9	5.00	3.75	2.00
1994 Fleer NBA League Leaders	5	7.50	5.75	3.00
1994 Fleer Team Leaders	7	10.00	7.50	4.00
1994 Fleer Towers of Power	8	12.00	9.00	4.75
1994 Fleer Triple Threats	7	4.50	3.50	1.75
1994 Fleer Ultra	135	2.00	1.50	.80
1994 Fleer Ultra All-NBA Team	12	5.00	3.75	2.00
1994 Fleer Ultra Scoring Kings	5	45.00	34.00	18.00
1994 Fleer Ultra Ultra Power	8	8.00	6.00	3.20
1994 Fleer Young Lions	5	10.00	7.50	4.00
1994 NBA Hoops	152	1.50	1.25	.60
1994 NBA Hoops	231	.65	.50	.25
1994 NBA Hoops Big Numbers	5	25.00	18.50	10.00
1994 NBA Hoops Predators	3	12.00	9.00	4.75
1994 NBA Hoops Supreme Court	33	7.00	5.25	2.75
1994 SkyBox	118	2.25	1.75	.90
1994 SkyBox Center Stage	2	60.00	45.00	24.00
1994 SkyBox Dream Team II Dream Play	12	45.00	34.00	18.00
1994 Topps	13	.50	.40	.20
1994 Topps	100	.75	.60	.30
1994 Topps Finest	32	6.00	4.50	2.50
1994 Topps Stadium Club	32	2.25	1.75	.90
1994 Topps Stadium Club Dynasty and Destiny	7B	7.00	5.25	2.75
1994 Topps Stadium Club Rising Stars	5	45.00	34.00	18.00
1994 Topps Super Rebounders	2	8.00	6.00	3.25
1994 Topps Super Scorers	2	10.00	7.50	4.00
1994 Topps Super Swatters	6	6.00	4.50	2.50
1994 Upper Deck	23	1.00	.70	.40
1994 Upper Deck	100	2.50	2.00	1.00
1994 Upper Deck	178	1.50	1.25	.60
1994 Upper Deck Col.'s Choice 1,000 Rebounds	8	15.00	11.00	6.00
1994 Upper Deck Collector's Choice 2,000 Pts	7	18.00	13.50	7.25
1994 Upper Deck Collector's Choice	184	1.25	.90	.50
1994 Upper Deck Collector's Choice	197	1.25	.90	.50
1994 Upper Deck Collector's Choice	205	1.00	.70	.40
1994 Upper Deck Collector's Choice	232	1.50	1.25	.60
1994 Upper Deck Collector's Choice	390	1.25	.90	.50
1994 Upper Deck Collector's Choice	400	.75	.60	.30
1994 Upper Deck Predictors Retail	2	15.00	11.00	6.00
1994 Upper Deck Predictors Hobby	3	20.00	15.00	8.00
1994 Upper Deck Predictors Hobby	15	20.00	15.00	8.00

Charles Oakley

Set	Card #	MT	NM	EX
1986 Fleer	81 (R)	15.00	11.00	6.00
1987 Fleer	79	3.00	2.25	1.25
1988 Fleer	18	.25	.20	.10
1989 Fleer	103	.07	.05	.03
1989 NBA Hoops	213	.05	.04	.02
1990 Fleer	128	.03	.02	.01
1990 NBA Hoops	207	.05	.04	.02
1990 SkyBox	191	.10	.08	.04
1991 Fleer	138	.03	.02	.01
1991 NBA Hoops	142	.05	.04	.02
1991 NBA Hoops	484	.05	.04	.02
1991 SkyBox	192	.05	.04	.02
1991 SkyBox	476	.15	.11	.06
1991 SkyBox	605	.05	.04	.02
1991 Upper Deck	258	.05	.04	.02
1992 Fleer	154	.05	.04	.02
1992 Fleer Ultra	124	.10	.08	.04
1992 NBA Hoops	157	.05	.04	.02
1992 SkyBox	166	.05	.04	.02
1992 Topps	127	.04	.03	.02
1992 Topps Archives	70	.05	.04	.02
1992 Topps Stadium Club	55	.10	.08	.04
1992 Upper Deck	302	.05	.04	.02
1993 Fleer	143	.05	.04	.02
1993 Fleer Jam Session	151	.10	.08	.04
1993 Fleer Ultra	129	.10	.08	.04
1993 Fleer Ultra Rebound Kings	7	.30	.25	.12
1993 NBA Hoops	148	.06	.05	.02
1993 SkyBox	128	.05	.04	.02
1993 Topps	25	.05	.04	.02
1993 Topps Finest	144	.35	.25	.14
1993 Topps Stadium Club	225	.10	.08	.04
1993 Upper Deck	28	.05	.04	.02
1993 Upper Deck	426	.05	.04	.02
1993 Upper Deck SE	72	.10	.08	.04
1994 Fleer	153	.05	.04	.02
1994 Fleer All-Defensive Team	2	.50	.40	.20
1994 Fleer Flair	102	.15	.11	.06
1994 Fleer Jam Session	127	.10	.08	.04
1994 Fleer NBA All-Stars	8	.35	.25	.14
1994 Fleer Total D	4	1.25	.90	.50
1994 Fleer Ultra	128	.08	.06	.03
1994 Fleer Ultra Ultra Power	7	.75	.60	.30
1994 NBA Hoops	145	.04	.03	.02
1994 NBA Hoops	232	.25	.20	.10
1994 SkyBox	113	.06	.05	.02
1994 SkyBox	177	.06	.05	.02
1994 Topps	3	.06	.05	.02
1994 Topps Finest Marathon Men	15	.75	.60	.30
1994 Topps Stadium Club	127	.08	.06	.03
1994 Topps Stadium Club Clear Cut	18	1.50	1.25	.60
1994 Topps Super Rebounders	6	1.00	.70	.40
1994 Upper Deck Col.'s Choice 1,000 Rebounds	10	.75	.60	.30
1994 Upper Deck Collector's Choice	97	.05	.04	.02

Hakeem Olajuwon

Set	Card #	MT	NM	EX
1984 Star Co.	237 (R)	500.00	375.00	200.00
1984 Star Co. Court Kings	47	30.00	22.00	12.00
1985 Star Co.	18	200.00	150.00	80.00
1985 Star Co. All-Rookie Team	1	125.00	94.00	50.00
1986 Fleer	82 (R)	160.00	120.00	64.00
1986 Star Co. Best of the New	3	325.00	244.00	130.00
1986 Star Co. Best of the Best	11	140.00	105.00	56.00
1986 Star Co. Court Kings	25	75.00	56.00	30.00
1987 Fleer	80	40.00	30.00	16.00
1988 Fleer	53	10.00	7.50	4.00
1988 Fleer	126	3.50	2.75	1.50
1989 Fleer	61	4.00	3.00	1.50
1989 Fleer	164	1.00	.70	.40
1989 NBA Hoops	178	.60	.45	.25
1989 NBA Hoops	180	1.00	.70	.40
1990 Fleer	73	.80	.60	.30
1990 Fleer All-Stars	3	1.25	.90	.50
1990 NBA Hoops	23	.60	.45	.25
1990 NBA Hoops	127	.80	.60	.30
1990 NBA Hoops	364	.40	.30	.15
1990 SkyBox	110	.75	.60	.30
1991 Fleer	77	.60	.45	.25
1991 Fleer	214	.35	.25	.14
1991 Fleer	223	.35	.25	.14
1991 Fleer	381	.30	.25	.12
1991 NBA Hoops	78	.50	.40	.20
1991 NBA Hoops	304	.25	.20	.10
1991 NBA Hoops	467	.40	.30	.15
1991 SkyBox	105	.80	.60	.30
1991 SkyBox	311	.50	.40	.20
1991 SkyBox	324	.50	.40	.20
1991 SkyBox	414	.30	.25	.12
1991 SkyBox	568	.30	.25	.12
1991 Upper Deck	254	.80	.60	.30
1991 Upper Deck	472	.25	.20	.10
1991 Upper Deck Holograms	8AW	1.25	.90	.50
1992 Fleer	84	.85	.60	.35
1992 Fleer	294	.50	.40	.20
1992 Fleer All-Stars	20	12.00	9.00	4.75
1992 Fleer Team Leaders	10	90.00	67.00	36.00
1992 Fleer Total "D"	14	50.00	37.00	20.00
1992 Fleer Ultra	72	1.50	1.25	.60
1992 Fleer Ultra	204	.50	.40	.20
1992 Fleer Ultra Rejectors	3	4.00	3.00	1.50
1992 NBA Hoops	85	.70	.50	.30
1992 NBA Hoops	314	.50	.40	.20
1992 SkyBox	90	1.00	.70	.40

Set	#			
1992 Topps	105	.30	.25	.12
1992 Topps	214	.15	.11	.06
1992 Topps	337	.50	.40	.20
1992 Topps Archives	4	.45	.35	.20
1992 Topps Archives	54	.75	.60	.30
1992 Topps Beam Team	5	1.50	1.00	.50
1992 Topps Stadium Club	220	1.75	1.25	.70
1992 Topps Stadium Club Beam Team	16	20.00	15.00	8.00
1992 Upper Deck	136	.85	.60	.35
1992 Upper Deck	444	.40	.30	.15
1992 Upper Deck	501	.30	.25	.12
1992 Upper Deck Foreign Exchange	6	8.00	6.00	3.25
1992 Upper Deck Team MVP's	11TM	6.00	4.50	2.50
1992 Upper Deck 15000-Point Club	20	12.00	9.00	4.75
1993 Fleer	79	.60	.45	.25
1993 Fleer	225	.45	.35	.20
1993 Fleer	230	.35	.25	.14
1993 Fleer	235	.30	.25	.12
1993 Fleer All-Stars	21	4.00	3.00	1.50
1993 Fleer Jam Session	83	1.00	.70	.40
1993 Fleer Jam Session Slam Dunk Heroes	6	2.00	1.50	.80
1993 Fleer Living Legends	5	12.00	9.00	4.75
1993 Fleer NBA Superstars	15	2.00	1.50	.80
1993 Fleer Towers of Power	20	15.00	11.00	6.00
1993 Fleer Ultra	76	1.25	.90	.50
1993 Fleer Ultra All-Defensive Team	3	45.00	34.00	18.00
1993 Fleer Ultra All-NBA Team	4	6.00	4.50	2.50
1993 Fleer Ultra Famous Nicknames	12	4.00	3.00	1.50
1993 Fleer Ultra Inside Outside	6	2.00	1.50	.80
1993 Fleer Ultra NBA Award Winners	3	20.00	15.00	8.00
1993 Fleer Ultra Power in the Key	6	15.00	11.00	6.00
1993 Fleer Ultra Rebound Kings	8	2.00	1.50	.80
1993 NBA Hoops	81	.70	.50	.30
1993 NBA Hoops	277	.35	.25	.14
1993 NBA Hoops	290	.35	.25	.14
1993 NBA Hoops	432	.10	.08	.04
1993 NBA Hoops Supreme Court	9	3.00	2.25	1.25
1993 SkyBox	6	.45	.35	.20
1993 SkyBox	81	.75	.60	.30
1993 SkyBox Center Stage	6	5.00	3.75	2.00
1993 SkyBox Dynamic Dunks	8	10.00	7.50	4.00
1993 SkyBox Showdown Series	4	1.25	.90	.50
1993 SkyBox Showdown Series	5	1.50	1.25	.60
1993 Topps	2	.45	.35	.20
1993 Topps	116	.45	.35	.20
1993 Topps	205	.50	.40	.20
1993 Topps	266	.60	.45	.25
1993 Topps	385	.45	.35	.20
1993 Topps Finest	76	7.00	5.25	2.75
1993 Topps Finest	115	4.50	3.50	1.75
1993 Topps Finest Main Attraction	10	20.00	15.00	8.00
1993 Topps Stadium Club	64	.50	.40	.20
1993 Topps Stadium Club	89	1.00	.70	.40
1993 Topps Stadium Club	348	.75	.60	.30
1993 Topps Stadium Club Beam Team	12	11.00	8.25	4.50
1993 Upper Deck	170	.40	.30	.15
1993 Upper Deck	176	.50	.40	.20
1993 Upper Deck	287	1.00	.70	.40
1993 Upper Deck	425	.50	.40	.20
1993 Upper Deck All-NBA	3	2.00	1.50	.80
1993 Upper Deck SE	78	1.50	1.25	.60
1993 Upper Deck SE Behind the Glass	5	8.00	6.00	3.25
1993 Upper Deck SE West Future All Stars	6	30.00	22.00	12.00
1993 Upper Deck Team MVP's	10	2.00	1.50	.80
1993 Upper Deck 3-D Basketball	24	.30	.25	.12
1994 Fleer	85	.85	.60	.35
1994 Fleer All-Defensive Team	3	3.50	2.75	1.50
1994 Fleer Career Achievement Awards	3	15.00	11.00	6.00
1994 Fleer Flair	57	3.00	2.25	1.25
1994 Fleer Flair Center Spotlight	3	30.00	22.00	12.00
1994 Fleer Flair Hot Numbers	11	8.00	6.00	3.25
1994 Fleer Flair Scoring Power	4	8.00	6.00	3.25
1994 Fleer Jam Session	73	1.00	.70	.40
1994 Fleer Jam Session GameBreakers	5	4.00	3.00	1.50
1994 Fleer Jam Session Slam Dunk Heroes	6	15.00	11.00	6.00
1994 Fleer NBA All-Stars	20	3.00	2.25	1.25
1994 Fleer NBA Award Winners	3	4.00	3.00	1.50
1994 Fleer Superstars	3	25.00	18.50	10.00
1994 Fleer Team Leaders	4	7.00	5.25	2.75
1994 Fleer Total D	5	10.00	7.50	4.00
1994 Fleer Towers of Power	7	7.50	5.75	3.00
1994 Fleer Triple Threats	6	2.00	1.50	.80
1994 Fleer Ultra	69	1.00	.70	.40
1994 Fleer Ultra All-NBA Team	2	3.50	2.75	1.50
1994 Fleer Ultra NBA Award Winners	3	4.00	3.00	1.50
1994 Fleer Ultra Scoring Kings	4	25.00	18.50	10.00
1994 NBA Hoops	78	.65	.50	.25
1994 NBA Hoops	244	.35	.25	.14
1994 NBA Hoops	260	.35	.25	.14
1994 NBA Hoops	261	.35	.25	.14
1994 NBA Hoops Big Numbers	3	15.00	11.00	6.00
1994 NBA Hoops Power Ratings	20	8.00	6.00	3.25
1994 NBA Hoops Supreme Court	19	3.50	2.75	1.50
1994 SkyBox	62	.90	.70	.35
1994 SkyBox	178	.40	.30	.15
1994 SkyBox Center Stage	1	35.00	26.00	14.00
1994 Topps	102	.40	.30	.15
1994 Topps	187	.35	.25	.14
1994 Topps Finest Iron Men	10	20.00	15.00	8.00
1994 Topps Stadium Club	79	1.00	.70	.40
1994 Topps Stadium Club Clear Cut	10	12.00	9.00	4.75
1994 Topps Stadium Club Dynasty and Destiny	7A	4.00	3.00	1.50
1994 Topps Super Rebounders	4	4.00	3.00	1.50
1994 Topps Super Scorers	3	5.00	3.75	2.00
1994 Topps Super Swatters	2	3.50	2.75	1.50
1994 Upper Deck	13	.50	.40	.20
1994 Upper Deck Col.'s Choice 1,000 Rebounds	9	10.00	7.50	4.00
1994 Upper Deck Collector's Choice 2,000 Pts	8	12.00	9.00	4.75

1994 Upper Deck Collector's Choice	34	.85	.60	.35
1994 Upper Deck Collector's Choice	175	.50	.40	.20
1994 Upper Deck Collector's Choice	381	.60	.45	.25
1994 Upper Deck Collector's Choice	399	.50	.40	.20
1994 Upper Deck Predictors Hobby	2	12.00	9.00	4.75
1994 Upper Deck Predictors Retail	3	10.00	7.50	4.00
1994 Upper Deck Predictors Hobby	11	12.00	9.00	4.75
1994 Upper Deck Special Edition	33	4.50	3.50	1.75

1994 NBA Hoops Power Ratings	28	.50	.40	.20
1994 SkyBox	55	.06	.05	.02
1994 Topps	59	.06	.05	.02
1994 Topps Finest	70	.20	.15	.08
1994 Upper Deck Collector's Choice	345	.08	.06	.03
1994 Upper Deck Special Edition	28	.20	.15	.08

Billy Owens

Set	Card #	MT	NM	EX
1991 Fleer	288 (R)	.40	.30	.15
1991 NBA Hoops	548 (R)	.50	.40	.20
1991 SkyBox	515 (R)	.75	.60	.30
1991 Upper Deck	438	.50	.40	.20
1991 Upper Deck	442 (R)	1.00	.70	.40
1991 Upper Deck Rookie Standouts	33R	1.50	1.25	.60
1992 Fleer	79	.10	.08	.04
1992 Fleer Rookie Sensations	8	6.00	4.50	2.50
1992 Fleer Ultra	68	.20	.15	.08
1992 NBA Hoops	79	.12	.09	.05
1992 SkyBox	84	.15	.11	.06
1992 SkyBox II Thunder and Lightning	9	4.00	3.00	1.50
1992 Topps	129	.10	.08	.04
1992 Topps Archives	147	.20	.15	.08
1992 Topps Stadium Club	195	.15	.11	.06
1992 Topps Stadium Club	236	.10	.08	.04
1992 Upper Deck	229	.15	.11	.06
1992 Upper Deck All-Rookie	3AR	1.00	.75	.40
1993 Fleer	72	.10	.08	.04
1993 Fleer Jam Session	73	.15	.11	.06
1993 Fleer Ultra	69	.15	.11	.06
1993 NBA Hoops	74	.15	.11	.06
1993 SkyBox	77	.20	.15	.08
1993 Topps	138	.10	.08	.04
1993 Topps BlackGold	6	.75	.60	.30
1993 Topps Finest	65	.35	.25	.14
1993 Topps Stadium Club	198	.10	.08	.04
1993 Upper Deck	291	.15	.11	.06
1993 Upper Deck SE	175	.20	.15	.08
1994 Fleer	76	.08	.06	.03
1994 Fleer	313	.05	.04	.02
1994 Fleer Flair	51	.25	.20	.10
1994 Fleer Jam Session	64	.15	.11	.06
1994 Fleer Ultra	62	.08	.06	.03
1994 NBA Hoops	69	.04	.03	.02
1994 NBA Hoops	343	.06	.05	.02

Robert Parish

Set	Card #	NM	EX	VG
1977 Topps	111 (R)	43.00	21.50	12.90
1978 Topps	86	7.00	3.50	2.10
1979 Topps	93	6.00	3.00	1.75
1980 Topps	2	1.50	.70	.45
1980 Topps	22	1.00	.50	.30
1980 Topps	26	3.00	1.50	.90
1980 Topps	114	4.00	2.00	1.25
1980 Topps	131	3.00	1.50	.90
1980 Topps	147	1.00	.50	.30

Set	Card #	MT	NM	EX
1981 Topps	6	3.00	2.25	1.25
1981 Topps	108	2.00	1.50	.80
1983 Star Co.	35	65.00	49.00	26.00
1983 Star Co. All-Star Game	9	6.00	4.50	2.50
1984 Star Co.	10	18.00	13.50	7.25
1984 Star Co. All-Star Game	9	8.00	6.00	3.25
1984 Star Co. Court Kings	31	8.00	6.00	3.25
1985 Star Co.	99	13.00	9.75	5.25
1986 Fleer	84	4.00	3.00	1.50
1986 Star Co. Court Kings	26	7.00	5.25	2.75
1987 Fleer	81	3.00	2.25	1.25
1988 Fleer	12	1.00	.70	.40
1989 Fleer	12	.40	.30	.15
1989 NBA Hoops	185	.15	.11	.06
1990 Fleer	13	.15	.11	.06
1990 NBA Hoops	8	.15	.11	.06
1990 NBA Hoops	45	.15	.11	.06
1990 SkyBox	20	.10	.08	.04
1991 Fleer	14	.10	.08	.04
1991 NBA Hoops	15	.20	.15	.08
1991 NBA Hoops	256	.10	.08	.04
1991 NBA Hoops	305	.10	.08	.04
1991 NBA Hoops	324	.05	.04	.02
1991 NBA Hoops	452	.08	.06	.03
1991 SkyBox	18	.10	.08	.04
1991 SkyBox	460	.30	.25	.12
1991 SkyBox	575	.05	.04	.02
1991 Upper Deck	72	.08	.06	.03
1991 Upper Deck	163	.10	.08	.04
1992 Fleer	18	.10	.08	.04
1992 Fleer	287	.08	.06	.03
1992 Fleer Ultra	15	.10	.08	.04
1992 Fleer Ultra	214	.12	.09	.05
1992 NBA Hoops	17	.10	.08	.04

1992 SkyBox	17	.10	.08	.04
1992 Topps	146	.10	.08	.04
1992 Topps Stadium Club	63	.15	.11	.06
1992 Upper Deck	179	.10	.08	.04
1992 Upper Deck 15000-Point Club	3	2.00	1.50	.80
1993 Fleer	16	.10	.08	.04
1993 Fleer Jam Session	16	.15	.11	.06
1993 Fleer Towers of Power	22	2.50	2.00	1.00
1993 Fleer Ultra	15	.10	.08	.04
1993 NBA Hoops	16	.10	.08	.04
1993 NBA Hoops	424	.05	.04	.02
1993 SkyBox	35	.05	.04	.02
1993 Topps	142	.08	.06	.03
1993 Topps Finest	39	.35	.25	.14
1993 Topps Stadium Club	20	.15	.11	.06
1993 Upper Deck	284	.05	.04	.02
1993 Upper Deck SE	30	.20	.15	.08
1993 Upper Deck Team MVP's	2	.50	.40	.20
1993 Upper Deck 3-D Basketball	11	.10	.08	.04
1994 Fleer	16	.06	.05	.02
1994 Fleer	256	.05	.04	.02
1994 Fleer Career Achievement Awards	4	3.00	2.25	1.25
1994 Fleer Jam Session	24	.12	.09	.05
1994 Fleer Superstars	4	4.00	3.00	1.50
1994 Fleer Ultra	24	.08	.06	.03
1994 NBA Hoops	13	.04	.03	.02
1994 NBA Hoops	312	.06	.05	.02
1994 Upper Deck Collector's Choice	100	.05	.04	.02
1994 Upper Deck Collector's Choice	167	.05	.04	.02
1994 Upper Deck Collector's Choice	248	.05	.04	.02

John Paxson

Set	Card #	MT	NM	EX
1983 Star Co.	250 (R)	20.00	15.00	8.00
1984 Star Co.	73	8.00	6.00	3.25
1987 Fleer	83 (R)	5.00	3.75	2.00
1989 Fleer	22	.30	.25	.12
1989 NBA Hoops	89	.05	.04	.02
1990 Fleer	28	.03	.02	.01
1990 NBA Hoops	67	.03	.02	.01
1990 SkyBox	44	.05	.04	.02
1991 Fleer	31	.07	.05	.03
1991 NBA Hoops	33	.05	.04	.02
1991 SkyBox	42	.05	.04	.02
1991 SkyBox	336	.10	.08	.04
1991 SkyBox	598	.05	.04	.02
1991 Upper Deck	117	.05	.04	.02
1992 Fleer	35	.08	.06	.03
1992 Fleer Ultra	29	.10	.08	.04
1992 NBA Hoops	32	.05	.04	.02

1992 SkyBox	33	.05	.04	.02
1992 Topps	24	.04	.03	.02
1992 Topps Archives	39	.05	.04	.02
1992 Topps Stadium Club	127	.10	.08	.04
1992 Upper Deck	137	.05	.04	.02
1993 Fleer	30	.05	.04	.02
1993 Fleer Jam Session	32	.10	.08	.04
1993 Fleer Ultra	32	.10	.08	.04
1993 NBA Hoops	30	.06	.05	.02
1993 SkyBox	21	.05	.04	.02
1993 SkyBox	46	.05	.04	.02
1993 Topps	377	.06	.05	.02
1993 Topps Finest	38	.35	.25	.14
1993 Topps Stadium Club	92	.10	.08	.04
1993 Upper Deck	69	.05	.04	.02
1993 Upper Deck	206	.05	.04	.02
1994 Topps	158	.06	.05	.02

Gary Payton

Set	Card #	MT	NM	EX
1990 Fleer Update	92 (R)	2.50	2.00	1.00
1990 NBA Hoops	391 (R)	1.25	.90	.50
1990 SkyBox	365 (R)	1.50	1.25	.60
1991 Fleer	194	.15	.11	.06
1991 Fleer Rookie Sensations	7	.75	.60	.30
1991 Fleer Rookie Sensations	9	3.00	2.25	1.25
1991 NBA Hoops	202	.35	.25	.14
1991 SkyBox	274	.35	.25	.14
1991 SkyBox	510	.20	.15	.08
1991 Upper Deck	153	.30	.25	.12
1991 Upper Deck Rookie Standouts	1R	1.75	1.25	.70
1992 Fleer	216	.12	.09	.05
1992 Fleer Ultra	175	.12	.09	.05
1992 NBA Hoops	219	.10	.08	.04
1992 SkyBox	234	.10	.08	.04
1992 SkyBox II Thunder and Lightning	7	20.00	15.00	8.00
1992 Topps	184	.10	.08	.04
1992 Topps Archives	137	.15	.11	.06
1992 Topps Stadium Club	124	.12	.09	.05
1992 Upper Deck	158	.10	.08	.04
1992 Upper Deck European	97	.25	.20	.10
1993 Fleer	202	.15	.11	.06
1993 Fleer Jam Session	217	.15	.11	.06
1993 Fleer Ultra	181	.10	.08	.04
1993 NBA Hoops	210	.10	.08	.04
1993 SkyBox	172	.15	.11	.06
1993 Topps	155	.05	.04	.02
1993 Topps BlackGold	10	.65	.50	.25
1993 Topps Finest	140	.35	.25	.14
1993 Topps Stadium Club	196	.15	.11	.06
1993 Upper Deck	295	.10	.08	.04
1993 Upper Deck	441	.10	.08	.04
1993 Upper Deck SE	131	.20	.15	.08
1994 Fleer	215	.08	.06	.03

1994 Fleer All-Defensive Team	4	.50	.40	.20
1994 Fleer Flair	143	.30	.25	.12
1994 Fleer Jam Session	181	.20	.15	.08
1994 Fleer NBA All-Stars	21	.35	.25	.14
1994 Fleer Pro-Visions	7	.40	.30	.15
1994 Fleer Total D	6	1.75	1.25	.70
1994 Fleer Ultra	179	.08	.06	.03
1994 Fleer Ultra All-NBA Team	13	.50	.40	.20
1994 NBA Hoops	203	.06	.05	.02
1994 NBA Hoops	245	.04	.03	.02
1994 NBA Hoops Power Ratings	50	1.25	.90	.50
1994 NBA Hoops Supreme Court	45	.30	.25	.12
1994 SkyBox	157	.08	.06	.03
1994 Topps	192	.08	.06	.03
1994 Topps Finest Marathon Men	2	2.00	1.50	.80
1994 Topps Stadium Club	117	.10	.08	.04
1994 Topps Super Stealers	7	1.50	1.25	.60
1994 Upper Deck	25	.10	.08	.04
1994 Upper Deck	82	.10	.08	.04
1994 Upper Deck Collector's Choice	220	.10	.08	.04

1993 Fleer Ultra	115	.10	.08	.04
1993 NBA Hoops	132	.06	.05	.02
1993 SkyBox	117	.05	.04	.02
1993 Topps	345	.05	.04	.02
1993 Topps Finest	55	.35	.25	.14
1993 Topps Stadium Club	40	.10	.08	.04
1993 Upper Deck	5	.05	.04	.02
1993 Upper Deck Locker Talk	10	1.00	.70	.40
1993 Upper Deck SE	103	.10	.08	.04
1993 Upper Deck 3-D Basketball	2	.10	.08	.04
1994 Fleer	134	.05	.04	.02
1994 Fleer	370	.05	.04	.02
1994 Fleer Jam Session	173	.10	.08	.04
1994 NBA Hoops	125	.04	.03	.02
1994 NBA Hoops	372	.04	.03	.02
1994 NBA Hoops Power Ratings	48	.30	.25	.12
1994 Upper Deck Collector's Choice	362	.05	.04	.02

Chuck Person

Set	Card #	MT	NM	EX
1987 Fleer	85 (R)	4.50	3.50	1.75
1988 Fleer	58	.75	.60	.30
1989 Fleer	66	.20	.15	.08
1989 NBA Hoops	45	.15	.11	.06
1990 Fleer	79	.07	.05	.03
1990 NBA Hoops	136	.07	.05	.03
1990 SkyBox	119	.10	.08	.04
1991 Fleer	84	.15	.11	.06
1991 Fleer	382	.03	.02	.01
1991 NBA Hoops	85	.05	.04	.02
1991 NBA Hoops	513	.05	.04	.02
1991 SkyBox	115	.08	.06	.03
1991 SkyBox	570	.05	.04	.02
1991 Upper Deck	253	.05	.04	.02
1992 Fleer	92	.10	.08	.04
1992 Fleer	381	.05	.04	.02
1992 Fleer Sharpshooters	10	.50	.40	.20
1992 Fleer Ultra	307	.10	.08	.04
1992 NBA Hoops	93	.08	.06	.03
1992 NBA Hoops	423	.08	.06	.03
1992 SkyBox	98	.05	.04	.02
1992 SkyBox	370	.10	.08	.04
1992 Topps	327	.04	.03	.02
1992 Topps Archives	84	.05	.04	.02
1992 Topps Stadium Club	364	.10	.08	.04
1992 Upper Deck	125	.05	.04	.02
1992 Upper Deck	345	.05	.04	.02
1993 Fleer	125	.05	.04	.02
1993 Fleer Jam Session	133	.10	.08	.04

Drazen Petrovic

Set	Card #	MT	NM	EX
1990 Fleer Update	81 (R)	1.00	.70	.40
1990 NBA Hoops	248 (R)	.40	.30	.15
1990 SkyBox	237 (R)	.75	.60	.30
1991 Fleer	134	.10	.08	.04
1991 NBA Hoops	137	.10	.08	.04
1991 SkyBox	186	.10	.08	.04
1991 SkyBox	599	.10	.08	.04
1991 Upper Deck	315	.12	.09	.05
1992 Fleer	147	.10	.08	.04
1992 Fleer Sharpshooters	4	.50	.60	.30
1992 Fleer Ultra	120	.15	.11	.06
1992 NBA Hoops	151	.10	.08	.04
1992 NBA Hoops	332	.08	.06	.03
1992 SkyBox	159	.10	.08	.04
1992 Topps	234	.04	.03	.02
1992 Topps Archives	125	.20	.15	.08
1992 Topps Stadium Club	10	.15	.11	.06
1992 Upper Deck	122	.10	.08	.04
1992 Upper Deck	502	.10	.08	.04
1992 Upper Deck Foreign Exchange	7	.75	.60	.30

Panel: A strip of two or more uncut cards. Some card sets are issued in panels.

Perez-Steele: Usually used as a term to refer to an ongoing set of Hall of Fame postcards issued by the Perez-Steele Galleries of Fort Washington, Pa. The company has made a number of artistic card sets, including the Celebration and Greatest Moments sets. Popular with autograph collectors.

Bob Pettit

Set	Card #	NM	EX	VG
1957 Topps	24 (R)	200.00	100.00	60.00
1961-62 Fleer	34	70.00	52.00	28.00
1961-62 Fleer	59	35.00	26.00	14.00

Set	Card #	MT	NM	EX
1985 Star Co. Schick Legends	20	5.00	3.75	2.00

Ricky Pierce

Set	Card #	MT	NM	EX
1983 Star Co.	130 (R)	30.00	22.00	12.00
1985 Star Co.	129	10.00	7.50	4.00
1986 Fleer	87 (R)	9.00	6.75	3.50
1987 Fleer	87	2.00	1.50	.80
1989 Fleer	88	.30	.25	.12
1989 NBA Hoops	212	.05	.04	.02
1990 Fleer	106	.07	.05	.03
1990 NBA Hoops	179	.07	.05	.03
1990 SkyBox	162	.05	.04	.02
1991 Fleer	195	.05	.04	.02
1991 Fleer	396	.03	.02	.01
1991 NBA Hoops	203	.07	.05	.03
1991 NBA Hoops	257	.10	.08	.04
1991 NBA Hoops	498	.05	.04	.02
1991 SkyBox	269	.08	.06	.03
1991 SkyBox	456	.05	.04	.02
1991 SkyBox	600	.05	.04	.02
1991 Upper Deck	67	.06	.05	.02
1991 Upper Deck	156	.05	.04	.02
1992 Fleer	217	.08	.06	.03
1992 Fleer Team Leaders	25	6.00	4.50	2.50
1992 Fleer Ultra	176	.15	.11	.06
1992 NBA Hoops	220	.06	.05	.02
1992 SkyBox	235	.05	.04	.02
1992 Topps	85	.04	.03	.02
1992 Topps Archives	28	.05	.04	.02
1992 Topps Stadium Club	148	.10	.08	.04

	Card #	NM	EX	VG
1992 Upper Deck	273	.08	.06	.03
1992 Upper Deck Team MVP's	26TM	.75	.60	.30
1993 Fleer	204	.05	.04	.02
1993 Fleer Jam Session	219	.10	.08	.04
1993 Fleer Ultra	183	.10	.08	.04
1993 NBA Hoops	212	.06	.05	.02
1993 SkyBox	11	.15	.11	.06
1993 SkyBox	174	.05	.04	.02
1993 Topps	93	.05	.04	.02
1993 Topps Finest	5	.35	.25	.14
1993 Topps Stadium Club	278	.10	.08	.04
1993 Upper Deck	76	.05	.04	.02
1993 Upper Deck SE	49	.10	.08	.04
1993 Upper Deck 3-D Basketball	15	.10	.08	.04
1994 Fleer	217	.05	.04	.02
1994 Fleer	287	.05	.04	.02
1994 Fleer Jam Session	65	.12	.09	.05
1994 NBA Hoops	205	.04	.03	.02
1994 NBA Hoops	326	.04	.03	.02
1994 SkyBox	159	.06	.05	.02
1994 Upper Deck Collector's Choice	236	.08	.06	.03

Scottie Pippen

Set	Card #	MT	NM	EX
1988 Fleer	20 (R)	43.00	32.00	17.00
1989 Fleer	23	5.00	3.75	2.00
1989 NBA Hoops	244	1.50	1.25	.60
1990 Fleer	30	.50	.40	.20
1990 NBA Hoops	9	.50	.40	.20
1990 NBA Hoops	69	.40	.30	.15
1990 SkyBox	46	.60	.45	.25
1991 Fleer	33	.30	.25	.12
1991 NBA Hoops	34	.35	.25	.14
1991 NBA Hoops	456	.25	.20	.10
1991 NBA Hoops	506	.15	.11	.06
1991 NBA Hoops	582	.50	.40	.20
1991 SkyBox	44	.40	.30	.15
1991 SkyBox	462	.75	.60	.30
1991 SkyBox	537	.75	.60	.30
1991 SkyBox	586	.25	.20	.10
1991 SkyBox	606	.15	.11	.06
1991 Upper Deck	125	.50	.40	.20
1991 Upper Deck	453	.25	.20	.10
1992 Fleer	36	.30	.25	.12
1992 Fleer	254	.25	.20	.10
1992 Fleer	260	.20	.15	.08
1992 Fleer	299	.15	.11	.06
1992 Fleer All-Stars	8	6.00	4.50	2.50
1992 Fleer Total "D"	3	25.00	18.50	10.00
1992 Fleer Ultra	31	.75	.60	.30
1992 Fleer Ultra	213	.25	.20	.10
1992 Fleer Ultra All-NBA Team	6	4.00	3.00	1.50
1992 Fleer Ultra Scottie Pippen	1	1.00	.70	.40

1992 Fleer Ultra Scottie Pippen	2	1.00	.70	.40
1992 Fleer Ultra Scottie Pippen	3	1.00	.70	.40
1992 Fleer Ultra Scottie Pippen	4	1.00	.70	.40
1992 Fleer Ultra Scottie Pippen	5	1.00	.70	.40
1992 Fleer Ultra Scottie Pippen	6	1.00	.70	.40
1992 Fleer Ultra Scottie Pippen	7	1.00	.70	.40
1992 Fleer Ultra Scottie Pippen	8	1.00	.70	.40
1992 Fleer Ultra Scottie Pippen	9	1.00	.70	.40
1992 Fleer Ultra Scottie Pippen	10	1.00	.70	.40
1992 Fleer Ultra Scottie Pippen	11	1.00	.70	.40
1992 Fleer Ultra Scottie Pippen	12	1.00	.70	.40
1992 NBA Hoops	34	.45	.35	.20
1992 NBA Hoops	300	.15	.11	.06
1992 NBA Hoops	345	.25	.20	.10
1992 NBA Hoops Supreme Court	2SC	3.00	2.25	1.25
1992 SkyBox	35	.50	.40	.20
1992 SkyBox	317	.30	.25	.12
1992 SkyBox I Olympic Team	5USA	3.00	2.25	1.25
1992 Topps	103	.15	.11	.06
1992 Topps	389	.25	.20	.10
1992 Topps Archives	97	.45	.35	.20
1992 Topps Beam Team	6	1.00	.60	.30
1992 Topps Stadium Club	198	.50	.40	.20
1992 Topps Stadium Club	367	.80	.60	.30
1992 Topps Stadium Club Beam Team	5	10.00	7.50	4.00
1992 Upper Deck	37	.20	.15	.08
1992 Upper Deck	62	.60	.45	.25
1992 Upper Deck	133	.40	.30	.15
1992 Upper Deck	422	.25	.20	.10
1992 Upper Deck All-NBA	9AN	3.00	2.25	1.25
1993 Fleer	32	.35	.25	.14
1993 Fleer All-Stars	8	2.00	1.50	.80
1993 Fleer Jam Session	34	.60	.45	.25
1993 Fleer Jam Session Gamebreakers	5	1.25	.90	.50
1993 Fleer Ultra	34	.50	.40	.20
1993 Fleer Ultra All-Defensive Team	4	25.00	18.50	10.00
1993 Fleer Ultra All-NBA Team	13	4.00	3.00	1.60
1993 Fleer Ultra Inside Outside	7	.90	.70	.35
1993 NBA Hoops	32	.25	.20	.10
1993 NBA Hoops	259	.15	.11	.06
1993 NBA Hoops	293	.15	.11	.06
1993 NBA Hoops	426	.10	.08	.04
1993 NBA Hoops Face to Face	9	4.00	3.00	1.50
1993 NBA Hoops Supreme Court	10	1.50	1.25	.60
1993 SkyBox	16	.25	.20	.10
1993 SkyBox	47	.35	.25	.14
1993 SkyBox	321	.12	.09	.05
1993 SkyBox Showdown Series	9	1.25	.90	.50
1993 Topps	92	.25	.20	.10
1993 Topps	117	.15	.11	.06
1993 Topps	391	.15	.11	.06
1993 Topps Finest	105	2.00	1.50	.80
1993 Topps Finest	208	4.00	3.00	1.50
1993 Topps Finest Main Attraction	4	12.00	9.00	4.75
1993 Topps Stadium Club	61	.30	.25	.12
1993 Topps Stadium Club	103	.30	.25	.12
1993 Topps Stadium Club	184	.30	.25	.12
1993 Topps Stadium Club	300	.50	.40	.20
1993 Topps Stadium Club Beam Team	18	9.00	6.75	3.50
1993 Upper Deck	199	.20	.15	.08
1993 Upper Deck	310	.40	.30	.15
1993 Upper Deck	449	.25	.20	.10
1993 Upper Deck All-NBA	11	1.25	.75	.40
1993 Upper Deck Jordan's Flight Team	17	8.00	6.00	3.25
1993 Upper Deck SE	1	.20	.15	.08
1993 Upper Deck SE Behind the Glass	10	5.00	3.75	2.00
1993 Upper Deck SE East Future All Stars	4	15.00	11.00	6.00
1993 Upper Deck Team MVP's	4	1.50	1.25	.60
1993 Upper Deck 3-D Basketball	63	.25	.20	.10
1993 Upper Deck 3-D Basketball	93	.40	.30	.15
1993 Upper Deck 3-D Triple Double	3	3.00	2.25	1.25
1994 Fleer	35	.40	.30	.15
1994 Fleer All-Defensive Team	5	2.00	1.50	.80
1994 Fleer Career Achievement Awards	5	8.00	6.00	3.25
1994 Fleer Flair	24	1.25	.90	.50
1994 Fleer Flair Hot Numbers	13	4.00	3.00	1.50
1994 Fleer Flair Scoring Power	6	3.50	2.75	1.50
1994 Fleer Jam Session	31	.30	.25	.12
1994 Fleer Jam Session GameBreakers	7	1.50	1.25	.60
1994 Fleer NBA All-Stars	10	1.50	1.25	.60
1994 Fleer Superstars	5	10.00	7.50	4.00
1994 Fleer Team Leaders	2	2.50	2.00	1.00
1994 Fleer Total D	7	5.00	3.75	2.00
1994 Fleer Triple Threats	8	1.00	.70	.40
1994 Fleer Ultra	31	.50	.40	.20
1994 Fleer Ultra All-NBA Team	3	1.50	1.25	.60
1994 Fleer Ultra Double Trouble	7	1.50	1.25	.60
1994 Fleer Ultra Scoring Kings	6	15.00	11.00	6.00
1994 NBA Hoops	30	.30	.25	.12
1994 NBA Hoops	233	.20	.15	.08
1994 NBA Hoops Big Numbers	9	6.00	4.50	2.50
1994 NBA Hoops Power Ratings	8	2.50	2.00	1.00
1994 SkyBox	26	.45	.35	.20
1994 SkyBox	180	.15	.11	.06
1994 SkyBox Center Stage	5	12.00	9.00	4.75
1994 Topps	11	.15	.11	.06
1994 Topps	29	.25	.20	.10
1994 Topps Finest	75	1.50	1.25	.60
1994 Topps Stadium Club	33	.55	.40	.20
1994 Topps Stadium Club Clear Cut	4	7.00	5.25	2.75
1994 Topps Stadium Club Dynasty and Destiny	9A	2.00	1.50	.80
1994 Topps Super Scorers	8	1.75	1.25	.70
1994 Topps Super Stealers	2	3.00	2.25	1.25
1994 Upper Deck	11	.30	.25	.12
1994 Upper Deck	127	.60	.45	.25
1994 Upper Deck Collector's Choice 2,000 Pts	9	6.00	4.50	2.40
1994 Upper Deck Collector's Choice	33	.40	.30	.15
1994 Upper Deck Collector's Choice	169	.20	.15	.08
1994 Upper Deck Collector's Choice	375	.15	.11	.06
1994 Upper Deck Predictors Hobby	4	6.00	4.50	2.50

1994 Upper Deck Predictors Retail	4	4.00	3.00	1.50

Terry Porter

Mark Price

Set	Card #	MT	NM	EX
1987 Fleer	89 (R)	6.00	4.50	2.50
1988 Fleer	96	1.25	.90	.50
1989 Fleer	131	.25	.20	.10
1989 NBA Hoops	105	.15	.11	.06
1990 Fleer	158	.15	.11	.06
1990 NBA Hoops	249	.20	.15	.08
1990 SkyBox	238	.10	.08	.04
1991 Fleer	171	.15	.11	.06
1991 NBA Hoops	177	.10	.08	.04
1991 NBA Hoops	269	.10	.08	.04
1991 NBA Hoops	492	.08	.06	.03
1991 NBA Hoops	524	.10	.08	.04
1991 SkyBox	240	.10	.08	.04
1991 SkyBox	480	.10	.08	.04
1991 SkyBox	607	.12	.09	.05
1991 Upper Deck	54	.10	.08	.04
1991 Upper Deck	351	.12	.09	.05
1992 Fleer	190	.12	.09	.05
1992 Fleer Sharpshooters	6	.50	.40	.20
1992 Fleer Ultra	153	.15	.11	.06
1992 Fleer Ultra Playmakers	7	.50	.40	.20
1992 NBA Hoops	193	.08	.06	.03
1992 SkyBox	205	.10	.08	.04
1992 Topps	51	.04	.03	.02
1992 Topps Archives	71	.10	.08	.04
1992 Topps Stadium Club	108	.10	.08	.04
1992 Upper Deck	109	.10	.08	.04
1992 Upper Deck	445	.08	.06	.03
1993 Fleer	177	.05	.04	.02
1993 Fleer All-Stars	22	.50	.40	.20
1993 Fleer Jam Session	188	.10	.08	.04
1993 Fleer Ultra	156	.10	.08	.04
1993 NBA Hoops	182	.06	.05	.02
1993 NBA Hoops	278	.06	.05	.02
1993 SkyBox	153	.05	.04	.02
1993 Topps	145	.05	.04	.02
1993 Topps Stadium Club	219	.10	.08	.04
1993 Upper Deck	105	.05	.04	.02
1993 Upper Deck SE	24	.10	.08	.04
1993 Upper Deck 3-D Basketball	41	.10	.08	.04
1994 Fleer	187	.05	.04	.02
1994 Fleer Jam Session	158	.12	.09	.05
1994 Fleer Ultra	159	.08	.06	.03
1994 NBA Hoops	178	.04	.03	.02
1994 SkyBox	137	.06	.05	.02
1994 Topps Finest	41	.15	.11	.06
1994 Topps Stadium Club	82	.08	.06	.03
1994 Upper Deck	133	.10	.08	.04
1994 Upper Deck Collector's Choice	230	.05	.04	.02

Set	Card #	MT	NM	EX
1988 Fleer	25 (R)	12.00	9.00	4.75
1989 Fleer	29	1.25	.90	.50
1989 Fleer	166	.35	.25	.14
1989 NBA Hoops	28	.05	.04	.02
1989 NBA Hoops	160	.30	.25	.12
1990 Fleer	36	.10	.08	.04
1990 NBA Hoops	79	.10	.08	.04
1990 NBA Hoops	359	.05	.04	.02
1990 SkyBox	56	.25	.20	.10
1991 Fleer	38	.10	.08	.04
1991 NBA Hoops	40	.10	.08	.04
1991 SkyBox	53	.10	.08	.04
1991 SkyBox	601	.10	.08	.04
1991 Upper Deck	239	.10	.08	.04
1991 Upper Deck	460	.10	.08	.04
1992 Fleer	43	.10	.08	.04
1992 Fleer	242	.10	.08	.04
1992 Fleer All-Stars	9	1.00	.70	.40
1992 Fleer Sharpshooters	7	.50	.40	.20
1992 Fleer Team Leaders	5	10.00	7.50	4.00
1992 Fleer Ultra	38	.10	.08	.04
1992 Fleer Ultra All-NBA Team	14	1.50	1.25	.60
1992 Fleer Ultra Playmakers	6	.75	.60	.30
1992 NBA Hoops	43	.10	.08	.04
1992 NBA Hoops	301	.07	.05	.03
1992 SkyBox	44	.10	.08	.04
1992 SkyBox II Thunder and Lightning	6	4.00	3.00	1.50
1992 Topps	113	.10	.08	.04
1992 Topps	218	.10	.08	.04
1992 Topps	379	.10	.08	.04
1992 Topps Archives	85	.10	.08	.04
1992 Topps Beam Team	5	1.50	1.00	.50
1992 Topps Stadium Club	12	.30	.25	.12
1992 Topps Stadium Club Beam Team	13	3.00	2.25	1.25
1992 Upper Deck	234	.15	.11	.06
1992 Upper Deck	431	.10	.08	.04
1992 Upper Deck	498	.10	.08	.04
1992 Upper Deck All-Division Team	10	.40	.30	.15
1993 Fleer	39	.10	.08	.04
1993 Fleer	226	.10	.08	.04
1993 Fleer All-Stars	9	1.00	.70	.40
1993 Fleer Flair USA Basketball	14	.20	.15	.08
1993 Fleer Jam Session	42	.15	.11	.06
1993 Fleer Jam Session Gamebreakers	6	.40	.30	.15
1993 Fleer NBA Superstars	17	.25	.20	.10
1993 Fleer Sharpshooters	5	1.00	.70	.40
1993 Fleer Ultra	40	.15	.11	.06
1993 Fleer Ultra	368	.10	.08	.04
1993 Fleer Ultra All-NBA Team	5	2.50	2.00	1.00
1993 NBA Hoops	41	.10	.08	.04

1993 NBA Hoops	263	.10	.08	.04
1993 NBA Hoops	287	.15	.11	.06
1993 SkyBox	52	.15	.11	.06
1993 SkyBox	322	.05	.04	.02
1993 Topps	118	.10	.08	.04
1993 Topps	203	.10	.08	.04
1993 Topps	294	.10	.08	.04
1993 Topps Finest	107	.35	.25	.14
1993 Topps Finest	205	.35	.25	.14
1993 Topps Finest Main Attraction	5	3.50	2.75	1.50
1993 Topps Stadium Club	340	.15	.11	.06
1993 Topps Stadium Club Beam Team	2	2.00	1.50	.80
1993 Upper Deck	173	.12	.09	.05
1993 Upper Deck	278	.15	.11	.06
1993 Upper Deck	451	.10	.08	.04
1993 Upper Deck All-NBA	5	.75	.50	.25
1993 Upper Deck SE	149	.20	.15	.08
1993 Upper Deck SE	198	.20	.15	.08
1993 Upper Deck SE East Future All Stars	5	6.00	4.50	2.50
1993 Upper Deck Team MVP's	5	.75	.60	.30
1993 Upper Deck USA Basketball	10	.10	.08	.04
1993 Upper Deck 3-D Basketball	35	.10	.08	.04
1994 Fleer	44	.06	.05	.02
1994 Fleer Flair	30	.15	.11	.06
1994 Fleer Flair	169	.15	.11	.06
1994 Fleer Jam Session	37	.10	.08	.04
1994 Fleer NBA All-Stars	11	.35	.25	.14
1994 Fleer Sharpshooters	6	.50	.40	.20
1994 Fleer Team Leaders	2	2.50	2.00	1.00
1994 Fleer Ultra	37	.08	.06	.03
1994 Fleer Ultra All-NBA Team	14	.50	.40	.20
1994 NBA Hoops	38	.04	.03	.02
1994 NBA Hoops	234	.04	.03	.02
1994 NBA Hoops	434	.04	.03	.02
1994 NBA Hoops Power Ratings	10	.50	.40	.20
1994 NBA Hoops Supreme Court	10	.40	.30	.15
1994 SkyBox	33	.10	.08	.04
1994 SkyBox Dream Team II Portraits	4	8.00	6.00	3.25
1994 Topps	4	.06	.05	.02
1994 Topps	196	.06	.05	.02
1994 Topps	198	.06	.05	.02
1994 Topps Stadium Club	124	.08	.06	.03
1994 Topps Stadium Club Dynasty and Destiny	1A	.65	.50	.25
1994 Topps Super Passers	9	1.00	.70	.40
1994 Upper Deck	24	.12	.09	.05
1994 Upper Deck	170	.15	.11	.06
1994 Upper Deck Collector's Choice 750 Assists	12	2.00	1.50	.80
1994 Upper Deck Collector's Choice	25	.05	.04	.02
1994 Upper Deck Collector's Choice	170	.05	.04	.02
1994 Upper Deck Collector's Choice	195	.05	.04	.02
1994 Upper Deck Collector's Choice	376	.10	.08	.04
1994 Upper Deck Special Edition	13	.35	.25	.14

Rack pack: A cellophane-wrapped pack of cards, usually having three compartments, designed to be hung from a peg in a retail store. Rack packs vary in the number of cards in each pack; also, some rack packs consist of nothing but cello-wrapped wax packs.

Willis Reed

Set	Card #	NM	EX	VG
1969 Topps	60 (R)	50.00	37.00	20.00
1970 Topps	110	10.00	5.00	3.00
1970 Topps	150	18.00	9.00	5.50
1970 Topps	168	7.00	3.50	2.00
1971 Topps	30	9.00	4.50	2.75
1972 Topps	129	9.00	4.50	2.75
1973 Topps	66	3.00	1.50	.90
1973 Topps	105	6.00	3.00	1.75

Set	Card #	MT	NM	EX
1989 NBA Hoops	92	.25	.20	.10

Glen Rice

Set	Card #	MT	NM	EX
1990 Fleer	101 (R)	1.00	.70	.40
1990 Fleer Rookie Sensations	3	10.00	7.50	4.00
1990 NBA Hoops	168 (R)	.80	.60	.30
1990 SkyBox	150 (R)	1.00	.70	.40
1991 Fleer	111	.15	.11	.06
1991 Fleer	385	.15	.11	.06
1991 NBA Hoops	113	.15	.11	.06
1991 SkyBox	151	.25	.20	.10
1991 SkyBox	472	.10	.08	.04
1991 Upper Deck	147	.25	.20	.10
1992 Fleer	120	.15	.11	.06
1992 Fleer Sharpshooters	5	.50	.40	.20
1992 Fleer Team Leaders	14	10.00	7.50	4.00
1992 Fleer Ultra	101	.10	.08	.04
1992 NBA Hoops	121	.15	.11	.06
1992 SkyBox	128	.15	.11	.06
1992 SkyBox	295	.10	.08	.04
1992 Topps	77	.15	.11	.06
1992 Topps Archives	127	.20	.15	.08
1992 Topps Beam Team	7	4.00	3.00	1.60
1992 Topps Stadium Club	180	.15	.11	.06
1992 Topps Stadium Club	203	.20	.15	.08

Set	Card #	MT	NM	EX
1992 Topps Stadium Club Beam Team	8	2.00	1.50	.80
1992 Upper Deck	126	.15	.11	.06
1992 Upper Deck All-Division Team	3	.40	.30	.15
1992 Upper Deck Jerry West Selects	11JW	1.00	.70	.40
1993 Fleer	109	.10	.08	.04
1993 Fleer Jam Session	114	.15	.11	.06
1993 Fleer Sharpshooters	6	1.00	.70	.40
1993 Fleer Ultra	101	.10	.08	.04
1993 NBA Hoops	114	.10	.08	.04
1993 SkyBox	104	.15	.11	.06
1993 SkyBox	327	.05	.04	.02
1993 Topps	337	.08	.06	.03
1993 Topps BlackGold	5	.75	.60	.30
1993 Topps Finest	15	1.50	1.25	.60
1993 Topps Stadium Club	47	.10	.08	.04
1993 Upper Deck	154	.10	.08	.04
1993 Upper Deck	480	.10	.08	.04
1993 Upper Deck SE	148	.20	.15	.08
1993 Upper Deck Team MVP's	14	.50	.40	.20
1993 Upper Deck 3-D Basketball	12	.15	.11	.06
1994 Fleer	118	.07	.05	.03
1994 Fleer Jam Session	100	.10	.08	.04
1994 Fleer Sharpshooters	7	1.00	.70	.40
1994 Fleer Team Leaders	5	1.00	.70	.40
1994 Fleer Ultra	97	.10	.08	.04
1994 NBA Hoops	111	.08	.06	.03
1994 NBA Hoops Power Ratings	27	.65	.50	.25
1994 SkyBox	86	.10	.08	.04
1994 Topps	56	.08	.06	.03
1994 Topps	57	.06	.05	.02
1994 Topps Finest	102	.25	.20	.10
1994 Topps Finest	147	.40	.30	.15
1994 Topps Stadium Club	80	.20	.15	.08
1994 Topps Stadium Club	111	.08	.06	.03
1994 Upper Deck Collector's Choice 2,000 Pts	10	2.00	1.50	.80
1994 Upper Deck Collector's Choice	41	.06	.05	.02
1994 Upper Deck Special Edition	47	.35	.25	.14

Pooh Richardson

Set	Card #	MT	NM	EX
1990 Fleer	116 (R)	.25	.20	.10
1990 Fleer Rookie Sensations	6	2.00	1.50	.80
1990 NBA Hoops	4	1.50	1.25	.60
1990 NBA Hoops	190 (R)	.15	.11	.06
1990 NBA Hoops	370	.10	.08	.04
1990 SkyBox	173 (R)	.30	.25	.12
1991 Fleer	125	.10	.08	.04
1991 NBA Hoops	129	.08	.06	.03

Set	Card #	MT	NM	EX
1991 NBA Hoops	480	.10	.08	.04
1991 SkyBox	173	.18	.14	.07
1991 SkyBox	501	.05	.04	.02
1991 Upper Deck	246	.15	.11	.06
1992 Fleer	136	.06	.05	.02
1992 Fleer	352	.06	.05	.02
1992 Fleer Ultra	276	.10	.08	.04
1992 NBA Hoops	140	.08	.06	.03
1992 NBA Hoops	398	.08	.06	.03
1992 SkyBox	147	.08	.06	.03
1992 SkyBox	348	.10	.08	.04
1992 Topps	280	.04	.03	.02
1992 Topps Archives	128	.05	.04	.02
1992 Topps Stadium Club	318	.10	.08	.04
1992 Upper Deck	134	.08	.06	.03
1992 Upper Deck	328	.05	.04	.02
1992 Upper Deck Team MVP's	17TM	.75	.60	.30
1993 Fleer	87	.05	.04	.02
1993 Fleer Jam Session	91	.10	.08	.04
1993 Fleer Ultra	83	.10	.08	.04
1993 NBA Hoops	89	.06	.05	.02
1993 SkyBox	86	.05	.04	.02
1993 Topps	110	.05	.04	.02
1993 Topps Finest	33	.35	.25	.14
1993 Topps Stadium Club	106	.10	.08	.04
1993 Topps Stadium Club	142	.10	.08	.04
1993 Upper Deck	260	.05	.04	.02
1993 Upper Deck SE	64	.10	.08	.04
1993 Upper Deck 3-D Basketball	46	.10	.08	.04
1994 Fleer	93	.05	.04	.02
1994 Fleer	303	.05	.04	.02
1994 Fleer Jam Session	85	.10	.08	.04
1994 NBA Hoops	336	.04	.03	.02
1994 NBA Hoops Power Ratings	23	.30	.25	.12
1994 SkyBox	69	.06	.05	.02
1994 Upper Deck Collector's Choice	215	.05	.04	.02

Mitch Richmond

Set	Card #	MT	NM	EX
1989 Fleer	56 (R)	5.00	3.75	2.00
1989 NBA Hoops	260 (R)	1.25	.90	.50
1990 Fleer	67	.15	.11	.06
1990 NBA Hoops	118	.15	.11	.06
1990 SkyBox	100	.25	.20	.10
1991 Fleer	71	.15	.11	.06
1991 Fleer	350	.10	.08	.04
1991 NBA Hoops	73	.10	.08	.04
1991 NBA Hoops	429	.10	.08	.04
1991 NBA Hoops	573	.08	.06	.03
1991 SkyBox	98	.12	.09	.05
1991 SkyBox	303	.10	.08	.04
1991 SkyBox	555	.08	.06	.03
1991 SkyBox	644	.10	.08	.04
1991 Upper Deck	265	.15	.11	.06

1991 Upper Deck	490	.20	.15	.08
1992 Fleer	196	.10	.08	.04
1992 Fleer Sharpshooters	14	.50	.40	.20
1992 Fleer Team Leaders	23	10.00	7.50	4.00
1992 Fleer Ultra	158	.12	.09	.05
1992 NBA Hoops	200	.08	.06	.03
1992 SkyBox	214	.08	.06	.03
1992 Topps	25	.15	.11	.06
1992 Topps Archives	109	.05	.04	.02
1992 Topps Stadium Club	253	.10	.08	.04
1992 Upper Deck	162	.08	.06	.03
1992 Upper Deck Team MVP's	24TM	.75	.60	.30
1993 Fleer	183	.05	.04	.02
1993 Fleer Jam Session	196	.15	.11	.06
1993 Fleer NBA Superstars	18	.25	.20	.10
1993 Fleer Sharpshooters	7	1.00	.70	.40
1993 Fleer Ultra	162	.10	.08	.04
1993 NBA Hoops	190	.06	.05	.02
1993 SkyBox	157	.15	.11	.06
1993 SkyBox	335	.05	.04	.02
1993 Topps	280	.05	.04	.02
1993 Topps Finest	126	.35	.25	.14
1993 Topps Finest	179	.35	.25	.14
1993 Topps Finest Main Attraction	23	3.50	2.75	1.50
1993 Topps Stadium Club	54	.10	.08	.04
1993 Upper Deck	64	.05	.04	.02
1993 Upper Deck	461	.10	.08	.04
1993 Upper Deck SE	86	.10	.08	.04
1993 Upper Deck SE West Future All Stars	12	6.00	4.50	2.50
1993 Upper Deck Team MVP's	23	.50	.40	.20
1993 Upper Deck 3-D Basketball	27	.10	.08	.04
1994 Fleer	195	.08	.06	.03
1994 Fleer Flair	128	.25	.20	.10
1994 Fleer Flair Scoring Power	7	1.00	.70	.40
1994 Fleer Jam Session	164	.15	.11	.06
1994 Fleer Jam Session Flashing Stars	5	.50	.40	.20
1994 Fleer Sharpshooters	8	1.50	1.25	.60
1994 Fleer Team Leaders	8	3.00	2.25	1.25
1994 Fleer Ultra	166	.10	.08	.04
1994 Fleer Ultra All-NBA Team	9	.50	.40	.20
1994 Fleer Ultra Scoring Kings	7	5.00	7.50	4.00
1994 NBA Hoops	186	.08	.06	.03
1994 NBA Hoops	246	.04	.03	.02
1994 NBA Hoops Power Ratings	45	.75	.60	.30
1994 NBA Hoops Supreme Court	41	.40	.30	.15
1994 SkyBox	143	.08	.06	.03
1994 Topps	116	.06	.05	.02
1994 Topps	183	.06	.05	.02
1994 Topps Finest	22	.25	.20	.10
1994 Topps Stadium Club	178	.10	.08	.04
1994 Topps Stadium Club Clear Cut	23	2.00	1.50	.80
1994 Topps Stadium Club Dynasty and Destiny	4A	.50	.40	.20
1994 Topps Super Scorers	7	1.00	.70	.40
1994 Upper Deck	19	.15	.11	.06
1994 Upper Deck Collector's Choice 2,000 Pts	11	2.00	1.50	.80
1994 Upper Deck Collector's Choice	102	.05	.04	.02
1994 Upper Deck Collector's Choice	188	.06	.05	.02
1994 Upper Deck Predictors Retail	8	4.00	3.00	1.50
1994 Upper Deck Special Edition	75	.30	.25	.12

Isaiah Rider

Rider emerges in Minnesota, opens eyes in rookie year

Set	Card #	MT	NM	EX
1993 Fleer	329 (R)	1.00	.75	.40
1993 Fleer First Year Phenoms	8	2.00	1.50	.80
1993 Fleer Lottery Exchange	5	5.00	3.75	2.00
1993 Fleer Ultra	292 (R)	2.00	1.50	.80
1993 Fleer Ultra All-Rookies	12	5.00	3.75	2.00
1993 NBA Hoops	367 (R)	1.25	.90	.50
1993 NBA Hoops Draft Redemption	5	8.00	6.00	3.25
1993 NBA Hoops II Magic's All-Rookie Team	5	8.00	6.00	3.25
1993 SkyBox	251 (R)	1.00	.75	.40
1993 SkyBox Draft Picks	5	8.00	6.00	3.25
1993 SkyBox Thunder and Lightning	3	6.00	4.50	2.50
1993 Topps	322 (R)	1.00	.70	.40
1993 Topps BlackGold	14	3.00	2.25	1.25
1993 Topps Finest	79 (R)	5.00	3.75	2.00
1993 Topps Finest Main Attraction	16	14.00	10.50	5.50
1993 Topps Stadium Club	234 (R)	1.50	1.25	.60
1993 Topps Stadium Club	270	.50	.40	.20
1993 Topps Stadium Club Beam Team	24	9.00	6.75	3.50
1993 Upper Deck	361 (R)	1.00	.70	.40
1993 Upper Deck	488	.50	.40	.20
1993 Upper Deck Rookie Exchange Gold/ Silver	5	4.00	3.00	1.50
1993 Upper Deck Rookie Standouts	3	8.00	6.00	3.25
1993 Upper Deck SE	170 (R)	1.25	.90	.50
1993 Upper Deck SE	191	.50	.40	.20
1993 Upper Deck SE	197	.50	.40	.20
1993 Upper Deck SE West Future All Stars	9	20.00	15.00	8.00
1993 Upper Deck 3-D Basketball	86 (R)	1.00	.15	.08
1994 Fleer	135	.60	.45	.25
1994 Fleer Flair	90	1.50	1.25	.60
1994 Fleer Flair Hot Numbers	14	2.50	2.00	1.00
1994 Fleer Jam Session	112	.40	.30	.15
1994 Fleer Jam Session Flashing Stars	6	2.00	1.50	.80
1994 Fleer Jam Session Second Year Stars	7	1.75	1.25	.70
1994 Fleer Rookie Sensations	20	5.00	3.75	2.00
1994 Fleer Team Leaders	6	2.00	1.50	.80
1994 Fleer Ultra	110	.80	.60	.30
1994 Fleer Ultra NBA All-Rookie Team	4	20.00	15.00	8.00
1994 NBA Hoops	126	.30	.25	.12
1994 NBA Hoops	425	.65	.50	.25

1994 NBA Hoops Big Numbers	10	6.00	4.50	2.50
1994 NBA Hoops Power Ratings	32	1.25	.90	.50
1994 NBA Hoops Supreme Court	27	1.75	1.25	.70
1994 Pacific Prisms	49	1.00	.70	.40
1994 SkyBox	100	.60	.45	.25
1994 SkyBox Ragin' Rookies	16	3.00	2.25	1.25
1994 Topps	15	.15	.11	.06
1994 Topps	115	.35	.25	.14
1994 Topps Finest	141	1.75	1.25	.70
1994 Topps Stadium Club	56	.75	.60	.30
1994 Topps Stadium Club	57	.25	.20	.10
1994 Topps Stadium Club Dynasty and Destiny	8B	2.00	1.50	.80
1994 Topps Stadium Club Rising Stars	8	8.00	6.00	3.25
1994 Upper Deck	5	.30	.25	.12
1994 Upper Deck Collector's Choice	134	.60	.45	.25
1994 Upper Deck Collector's Choice	181	.30	.25	.12
1994 Upper Deck Special Edition	53	2.00	1.50	.80

Pat Riley

Set	Card #	NM	EX	VG
1970 Topps	13 (R)	60.00	30.00	18.00
1972 Topps	144	14.00	7.00	4.25
1973 Topps	21	11.00	5.50	3.25
1974 Topps	31	7.50	3.75	2.25
1975 Topps	71	8.00	4.00	2.50

Set	Card #	MT	NM	EX
1985 Star Co. Coaches	9	5.00	3.75	2.00
1985 Star Co. Lite All-Stars	13	10.00	7.50	4.00
1989 NBA Hoops	108	.05	.04	.02
1990 NBA Hoops	317	.15	.11	.06
1991 Fleer	139	.05	.04	.02
1991 NBA Hoops	238	.07	.05	.03
1991 SkyBox	395	.07	.05	.03
1992 Fleer	155	.05	.04	.02
1992 NBA Hoops	256	.06	.05	.02
1992 SkyBox	272	.07	.05	.03
1993 NBA Hoops	247	.10	.08	.04
1994 NBA Hoops	289	.10	.08	.04

Rare: Difficult to obtain and limited in number. See "Scarce."

Rated Rookie (RR): A Donruss subset featuring young players the company thinks are the top rookie players from a particular year (1984-present).

Doc Rivers

Set	Card #	MT	NM	EX
1983 Star Co.	271 (R)	17.00	12.50	6.75
1984 Star Co.	84	9.00	6.75	3.50
1985 Star Co.	47	7.00	5.25	2.75
1986 Fleer	91 (R)	3.00	2.25	1.25
1987 Fleer	92	1.00	.70	.40
1988 Fleer	3	.50	.40	.20
1989 Fleer	5	.10	.08	.04
1989 NBA Hoops	252	.05	.04	.02
1990 Fleer Update	3	.05	.04	.02
1990 NBA Hoops	32	.07	.05	.03
1990 SkyBox	7	.05	.04	.02
1991 Fleer	298	.05	.04	.02
1991 NBA Hoops	4	.06	.05	.02
1991 NBA Hoops	380	.06	.05	.02
1991 SkyBox	7	.05	.04	.02
1991 SkyBox	631	.05	.04	.02
1991 Upper Deck	46	.05	.04	.02
1991 Upper Deck	420	.08	.06	.03
1992 Fleer	103	.05	.04	.02
1992 Fleer	283	.05	.04	.02
1992 Fleer	396	.05	.04	.02
1992 Fleer Ultra	125	.10	.08	.04
1992 Fleer Ultra	322	.10	.08	.04
1992 NBA Hoops	104	.05	.04	.02
1992 NBA Hoops	437	.05	.04	.02
1992 SkyBox	110	.05	.04	.02
1992 SkyBox	377	.05	.04	.02
1992 Topps	217	.04	.03	.02
1992 Topps	290	.04	.03	.02
1992 Topps Archives	40	.05	.04	.02
1992 Topps Stadium Club	241	.10	.08	.04
1992 Upper Deck	101	.05	.04	.02
1992 Upper Deck	413	.05	.04	.02
1993 Fleer	144	.05	.04	.02
1993 Fleer Jam Session	152	.10	.08	.04
1993 Fleer Ultra	130	.10	.08	.04
1993 NBA Hoops	149	.06	.05	.02
1993 SkyBox	129	.05	.04	.02
1993 Topps	210	.05	.04	.02
1993 Topps Stadium Club	81	.10	.08	.04
1993 Upper Deck	36	.05	.04	.02
1993 Upper Deck	443	.05	.04	.02
1993 Upper Deck SE	102	.10	.08	.04
1994 Fleer	154	.05	.04	.02
1994 Fleer Jam Session	128	.10	.08	.04
1994 Fleer Ultra	129	.08	.06	.03
1994 Topps	60	.06	.05	.02
1994 Upper Deck Collector's Choice	290	.05	.04	.02
1994 Upper Deck Special Edition	60	.20	.15	.08

Regional set: A card set limited in distribution to one geographical area. Regional sets often depict players from one team.

Oscar Robertson

Set	Card #	NM	EX	VG
1961-62 Fleer	36 (R)	500.00	375.00	200.00
1961-62 Fleer	61	150.00	112.00	60.00
1969 Topps	50	70.00	52.00	28.00
1970 Topps	100	35.00	17.50	10.50
1970 Topps	114	25.00	12.50	7.50
1971 Topps	1	50.00	25.00	15.00
1971 Topps	136	6.00	3.00	1.75
1971 Topps	141	1.50	.70	.45
1971 Topps	143	6.00	3.00	1.75
1972 Topps	25	20.00	10.00	6.00
1973 Topps	70	20.00	10.00	6.00
1974 Topps	55	13.00	6.50	4.00
1974 Topps	91	7.50	3.75	2.25

Set	Card #	MT	NM	EX
1985 Star Co. Schick Legends	21	12.00	9.00	4.75

David Robinson

Set	Card #	MT	NM	EX
1989 NBA Hoops	138 (R)	25.00	18.50	10.00
1989 NBA Hoops	310	4.00	3.00	1.50
1990 Fleer	172 (R)	1.25	.90	.50
1990 Fleer All-Stars	10	2.50	2.00	1.00
1990 Fleer Rookie Sensations	1	30.00	22.00	12.00
1990 NBA Hoops	1	1.50	1.25	.60
1990 NBA Hoops	24	1.00	.70	.40
1990 NBA Hoops	270	1.00	.70	.40
1990 NBA Hoops	378	.60	.45	.25
1990 SkyBox	260	1.50	1.25	.60
1990 Star Co. Court Kings	5	42.00	26.00	10.50
1990 Star Co. Slam	7	45.00	30.00	12.00
1991 Fleer	187	.40	.30	.15
1991 Fleer	225	.25	.20	.10
1991 Fleer	395	.25	.20	.10
1991 Fleer Pro Visions	1	1.25	.90	.50

Set	Card #	MT	NM	EX
1991 NBA Hoops	194	.60	.45	.25
1991 NBA Hoops	270	.25	.20	.10
1991 NBA Hoops	309	.25	.20	.10
1991 NBA Hoops	311	.25	.20	.10
1991 NBA Hoops	327	.30	.25	.12
1991 NBA Hoops	496	.30	.25	.12
1991 NBA Hoops	583	1.00	.70	.40
1991 SkyBox	261	.65	.50	.25
1991 SkyBox	311	.50	.40	.20
1991 SkyBox	428	.30	.25	.12
1991 SkyBox	509	.40	.30	.15
1991 SkyBox	538	1.25	.90	.50
1991 Upper Deck	58	.40	.30	.15
1991 Upper Deck	94	.40	.30	.15
1991 Upper Deck	324	.75	.60	.30
1991 Upper Deck	467	.35	.25	.14
1991 Upper Deck Holograms	6AW	1.25	.90	.50
1992 Fleer	207	.50	.40	.20
1992 Fleer	244	.30	.25	.12
1992 Fleer	248	.25	.20	.10
1992 Fleer	288	.20	.15	.08
1992 Fleer All-Stars	21	9.00	6.75	3.50
1992 Fleer Team Leaders	24	65.00	49.00	26.00
1992 Fleer Total "D"	1	35.00	26.00	14.00
1992 Fleer Ultra	167	1.00	.70	.40
1992 Fleer Ultra	201	.25	.20	.10
1992 Fleer Ultra All-NBA Team	3	5.00	3.75	2.00
1992 Fleer Ultra NBA Award Winners	2	6.00	4.50	2.40
1992 Fleer Ultra Rejectors	5	3.00	2.25	1.25
1992 NBA Hoops	209	.60	.45	.25
1992 NBA Hoops	315	.25	.20	.10
1992 NBA Hoops	323	.20	.15	.08
1992 NBA Hoops	334	.25	.20	.10
1992 NBA Hoops	346	.25	.20	.10
1992 NBA Hoops	481	.35	.25	.14
1992 NBA Hoops Supreme Court	3SC	5.00	3.75	2.00
1992 SkyBox	NNO	15.00	10.00	4.00
1992 SkyBox	224	.75	.60	.30
1992 SkyBox	305	.30	.25	.12
1992 Topps	4	.15	.11	.06
1992 Topps	106	.15	.11	.06
1992 Topps	277	.25	.20	.10
1992 Topps Archives	7	.25	.20	.10
1992 Topps Archives	130	.50	.40	.20
1992 Topps Beam Team	6	1.00	.60	.30
1992 Topps Stadium Club	191	.60	.45	.25
1992 Topps Stadium Club	361	1.00	.70	.40
1992 Topps Stadium Club Beam Team	20	15.00	11.00	6.00
1992 Upper Deck	82	.40	.30	.15
1992 Upper Deck	436	.20	.15	.08
1992 Upper Deck	496	.20	.15	.08
1992 Upper Deck All-Division Team	11	1.25	.90	.50
1992 Upper Deck All-NBA	3AN	4.00	3.00	1.50
1992 Upper Deck Holograms	6AW	1.75	1.25	.70
1992 Upper Deck Holograms	7AW	1.75	1.25	.70
1992 Upper Deck Jerry West Selects	3JW	4.00	3.00	1.50
1992 Upper Deck Team MVP's	25TM	5.00	3.75	2.00
1993 Fleer	196	.40	.30	.15
1993 Fleer All-Stars	23	4.00	3.00	1.60
1993 Fleer Jam Session	209	.75	.60	.30
1993 Fleer Jam Session Slam Dunk Heroes	8	1.25	.90	.50
1993 Fleer NBA Superstars	19	1.75	1.25	.70
1993 Fleer Towers of Power	25	12.00	9.00	4.75
1993 Fleer Ultra	174	.75	.60	.30
1993 Fleer Ultra All-Defensive Team	9	30.00	22.00	12.00
1993 Fleer Ultra All-NBA Team	14	4.00	3.00	1.60

1993 Fleer Ultra Famous Nicknames	14	3.50	2.75	1.50
1993 Fleer Ultra Jam City	8	14.00	10.50	5.50
1993 Fleer Ultra Scoring Kings	9	20.00	15.00	8.00
1993 NBA Hoops	203	.50	.40	.20
1993 NBA Hoops	279	.25	.20	.10
1993 NBA Hoops	446	.08	.06	.03
1993 NBA Hoops David Robinson Commemorative	1	2.00	1.50	.80
1993 NBA Hoops David's Best	1	1.00	.75	.40
1993 NBA Hoops David's Best	2	1.00	.75	.40
1993 NBA Hoops David's Best	3	1.00	.75	.40
1993 NBA Hoops David's Best	4	1.00	.75	.40
1993 NBA Hoops David's Best	5	1.00	.75	.40
1993 NBA Hoops Face to Face	1	10.00	7.50	4.00
1993 NBA Hoops Supreme Court	2	2.00	1.50	.80
1993 SkyBox	9	.20	.15	.08
1993 SkyBox	168	.60	.45	.25
1993 SkyBox	336	.25	.20	.10
1993 SkyBox Showdown Series	5	1.50	1.25	.60
1993 SkyBox Showdown Series	6	1.00	.70	.40
1993 SkyBox Thunder and Lightning	9	2.00	2.75	1.50
1993 Topps	52	.25	.20	.10
1993 Topps	228	.40	.30	.15
1993 Topps	387	.25	.20	.10
1993 Topps Finest	21	6.00	4.50	2.50
1993 Topps Finest	118	4.00	3.00	1.50
1993 Topps Finest Main Attraction	24	15.00	11.00	6.00
1993 Topps Stadium Club	10	.50	.40	.20
1993 Topps Stadium Club	172	.40	.30	.15
1993 Topps Stadium Club	328	.75	.60	.30
1993 Topps Stadium Club	356	.35	.25	.14
1993 Topps Stadium Club Beam Team	13	10.00	7.50	4.00
1993 Upper Deck	50	.50	.40	.20
1993 Upper Deck	183	.10	.08	.04
1993 Upper Deck	248	.30	.25	.12
1993 Upper Deck	464	.20	.15	.08
1993 Upper Deck	474	.30	.25	.12
1993 Upper Deck All-NBA	13	1.50	1.00	.60
1993 Upper Deck Locker Talk	9	4.00	3.00	1.50
1993 Upper Deck SE	177	.75	.60	.30
1993 Upper Deck SE West Future All Stars	13	25.00	18.50	10.00
1993 Upper Deck Team MVP's	24	1.25	.90	.50
1993 Upper Deck 3-D Basketball	70	.60	.30	.15
1993 Upper Deck 3-D Basketball	97	.25	.20	.10
1994 Fleer	208	.60	.45	.25
1994 Fleer All-Defensive Team	8	2.50	2.00	1.00
1994 Fleer Flair	137	2.50	2.00	1.00
1994 Fleer Flair Center Spotlight	5	20.00	15.00	8.00
1994 Fleer Flair Hot Numbers	15	6.50	5.00	2.50
1994 Fleer Flair Scoring Power	8	5.00	3.75	2.00
1994 Fleer Jam Session	175	1.00	.70	.40
1994 Fleer Jam Session GameBreakers	8	3.00	2.25	1.25
1994 Fleer NBA All-Stars	24	1.75	1.25	.70
1994 Fleer NBA League Leaders	6	3.00	2.25	1.25
1994 Fleer Team Leaders	8	3.00	2.25	1.25

1994 Fleer Total D	8	7.50	5.75	3.00
1994 Fleer Towers of Power	9	4.00	3.00	1.50
1994 Fleer Triple Threats	9	1.75	1.25	.70
1994 Fleer Ultra	174	.70	.50	.30
1994 Fleer Ultra All-NBA Team	10	1.50	1.25	.60
1994 Fleer Ultra Double Trouble	8	2.50	2.00	1.00
1994 Fleer Ultra Scoring Kings	8	20.00	15.00	8.00
1994 NBA Hoops	196	.55	.40	.20
1994 NBA Hoops	248	.30	.25	.12
1994 NBA Hoops Big Numbers	1	10.00	7.50	4.00
1994 NBA Hoops Predators	5	8.00	6.00	3.25
1994 NBA Hoops Supreme Court	43	3.00	2.25	1.25
1994 SkyBox	152	.75	.60	.30
1994 SkyBox Center Stage	6	20.00	15.00	8.00
1994 Topps	108	.25	.20	.10
1994 Topps	194	.25	.20	.10
1994 Topps Finest Iron Men	8	12.00	9.00	4.75
1994 Topps Stadium Club	160	.90	.70	.35
1994 Topps Stadium Club Clear Cut	24	9.00	6.75	3.50
1994 Topps Super Scorers	1	7.00	5.25	2.75
1994 Topps Super Swatters	3	3.00	2.25	1.25
1994 Upper Deck	18	.40	.30	.15
1994 Upper Deck	96	.85	.60	.35
1994 Upper Deck Col.'s Choice 1,000 Rebounds	12	8.00	6.00	3.25
1994 Upper Deck Collector's Choice 2,000 Pts	12	10.00	7.50	4.00
1994 Upper Deck Collector's Choice	50	.50	.40	.20
1994 Upper Deck Collector's Choice	189	.35	.25	.14
1994 Upper Deck Collector's Choice	395	.60	.45	.25
1994 Upper Deck Collector's Choice	403	.35	.25	.14
1994 Upper Deck Predictors Retail	1	10.00	7.50	4.00
1994 Upper Deck Predictors Hobby	5	12.00	9.00	4.75
1994 Upper Deck Predictors Hobby	18	12.00	9.00	4.75

Glenn Robinson

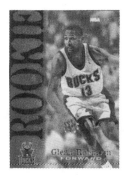

Set	Card #	MT	NM	EX
1994 Fleer	320 (R)	4.00	3.00	1.50

Set	Card #	MT	NM	EX
1994 Fleer First Year Phenoms	8	10.00	7.50	4.00
1994 NBA Hoops	349 (R)	4.50	3.50	1.75
1994 NBA Hoops	421	1.25	.90	.50
1994 NBA Hoops Chromium Magic's All-Rookie	1	45.00	34.00	18.00
1994 NBA Hoops Magic's All-Rookie	1	20.00	15.00	8.00
1994 Pacific Prisms	50	12.00	9.00	4.75
1994 Upper Deck Collector's Choice Rookie	11	13.00	9.75	5.25
1994 Upper Deck Collector's Choice	266 (R)	3.50	2.75	1.50
1994 Upper Deck Collector's Choice	386	1.25	.90	.50
1994 Upper Deck Collector's Choice	407	1.00	.70	.40

Dennis Rodman

Set	Card #	MT	NM	EX
1988 Fleer	43 (R)	8.50	6.00	3.25
1989 Fleer	49	.75	.60	.30
1989 NBA Hoops	211	.20	.15	.08
1990 Fleer	59	.20	.15	.08
1990 NBA Hoops	10	.15	.11	.06
1990 NBA Hoops	109	.12	.09	.05
1990 SkyBox	91	.10	.08	.04
1991 Fleer	63	.10	.08	.04
1991 NBA Hoops	64	.10	.08	.04
1991 SkyBox	86	.10	.08	.04
1991 SkyBox	608	.08	.06	.03
1991 Upper Deck	185	.08	.06	.03
1991 Upper Deck	457	.10	.08	.04
1991 Upper Deck Holograms	9AW	.60	.45	.25
1992 Fleer	66	.08	.06	.03
1992 Fleer	239	.08	.06	.03
1992 Fleer	261	.08	.06	.03
1992 Fleer	289	.05	.04	.02
1992 Fleer All-Stars	10	1.25	.90	.50
1992 Fleer Total "D"	2	5.50	4.25	2.25
1992 Fleer Ultra	58	.15	.11	.06
1992 Fleer Ultra All-NBA Team	11	1.00	.70	.40
1992 NBA Hoops	66	.08	.06	.03
1992 NBA Hoops	302	.05	.04	.02
1992 SkyBox	71	.08	.06	.03
1992 Topps	117	.10	.08	.04
1992 Topps	137	.04	.03	.02
1992 Topps Archives	86	.15	.11	.06
1992 Topps Beam Team	3	2.00	1.50	.80
1992 Topps Stadium Club	314	.10	.08	.04
1992 Topps Stadium Club Beam Team	19	2.50	2.00	1.00
1992 Upper Deck	242	.10	.08	.04
1992 Upper Deck Holograms	3AW	.60	.45	.25
1992 Upper Deck Jerry West Selects	2JW	.75	.60	.30
1993 Fleer	64	.05	.04	.02
1993 Fleer	227	.05	.04	.02
1993 Fleer	378	.05	.04	.02
1993 Fleer Jam Session	210	.15	.11	.06
1993 Fleer Towers of Power	26	2.50	2.00	1.00
1993 Fleer Ultra	61	.10	.08	.04
1993 Fleer Ultra	340	.10	.08	.04
1993 Fleer Ultra All-Defensive Team	5	10.00	7.50	4.00
1993 Fleer Ultra Rebound Kings	10	.40	.30	.15
1993 NBA Hoops	66	.10	.08	.04
1993 NBA Hoops	284	.30	.25	.12
1993 NBA Hoops	405	.06	.05	.02
1993 SkyBox	70	.10	.08	.04
1993 SkyBox	280	.10	.08	.04
1993 SkyBox Thunder and Lightning	9	2.00	2.75	1.50
1993 Topps	77	.10	.08	.04
1993 Topps	324	.08	.06	.03
1993 Topps Finest	113	.35	.25	.14
1993 Topps Finest	173	.35	.25	.14
1993 Topps Stadium Club	183	.25	.20	.10
1993 Topps Stadium Club	305	.10	.08	.04
1993 Upper Deck	167	.05	.04	.02
1993 Upper Deck	396	.15	.11	.06
1993 Upper Deck	421	.15	.11	.06
1993 Upper Deck SE	63	.10	.08	.04
1993 Upper Deck 3-D Basketball	43	.10	.08	.04
1994 Fleer	209	.05	.04	.02
1994 Fleer All-Defensive Team	9	.50	.40	.20
1994 Fleer Flair	138	.15	.11	.06
1994 Fleer Jam Session	176	.10	.08	.04
1994 Fleer NBA League Leaders	7	.50	.40	.20
1994 Fleer Pro-Visions	6	.40	.30	.15
1994 Fleer Ultra	175	.08	.06	.03
1994 Fleer Ultra Ultra Power	9	.75	.60	.30
1994 NBA Hoops	197	.04	.03	.02
1994 NBA Hoops	448	.04	.03	.02
1994 NBA Hoops Predators	6	1.00	.70	.40
1994 NBA Hoops Supreme Court	44	.30	.25	.12
1994 SkyBox	153	.06	.05	.02
1994 Topps	54	.06	.05	.02
1994 Topps	107	.06	.05	.02
1994 Topps Finest	134	.20	.15	.08
1994 Topps Stadium Club	72	.10	.08	.04
1994 Topps Stadium Club	73	.08	.06	.03
1994 Topps Super Rebounders	1	3.00	2.25	1.25
1994 Upper Deck Col.'s Choice 1,000 Rebounds	13	3.00	2.25	1.25
1994 Upper Deck Collector's Choice	10	.05	.04	.02
1994 Upper Deck Collector's Choice	202	.05	.04	.02
1994 Upper Deck Predictors Hobby	14	6.00	4.50	2.50
1994 Upper Deck Special Edition	81	.20	.15	.08

Record Breaker card: A special Topps card found in a regular issue set which commemorates a record-breaking performance by a player from the previous season.

Reprint: A reproduction of a previously-issued sports card or set. Generally produced to satisfy collector demand, they usually — but not always — are labeled "reprint" and have little collector value.

Bill Russell

Set	Card #	NM	EX	VG
1957 Topps	77 (R)	2000.	1000.	600.00
1961-62 Fleer	38	500.00	375.00	200.00
1961-62 Fleer	62	200.00	150.00	80.00

Dolph Schayes

Set	Card #	NM	EX	VG
1957 Topps	13 (R)	125.00	62.00	37.00
1961-62 Fleer	39	32.50	24.00	13.00
1961-62 Fleer	63	16.00	12.00	6.50

Detlef Schrempf

Set	Card #	MT	NM	EX
1987 Fleer	97 (R)	13.00	9.75	5.25
1989 Fleer	67	1.50	1.25	.60
1989 NBA Hoops	282	.05	.04	.02

1990 Fleer	81	.10	.08	.04
1990 NBA Hoops	138	.10	.08	.04
1990 SkyBox	121	.10	.08	.04
1991 Fleer	85	.10	.08	.04
1991 NBA Hoops	87	.10	.08	.04
1991 NBA Hoops	470	.06	.05	.02
1991 SkyBox	117	.10	.08	.04
1991 SkyBox	415	.05	.04	.02
1991 SkyBox	442	.10	.08	.04
1991 Upper Deck	260	.08	.06	.03
1991 Upper Deck Holograms	5AW	.60	.45	.25
1992 Fleer	93	.10	.08	.04
1992 Fleer	249	.08	.06	.03
1992 Fleer Ultra	79	.15	.11	.06
1992 Fleer Ultra NBA Award Winners	4	2.00	1.50	.80
1992 NBA Hoops	94	.08	.06	.03
1992 SkyBox	99	.05	.04	.02
1992 Topps	64	.04	.03	.02
1992 Topps Archives	73	.05	.04	.02
1992 Topps Stadium Club	141	.10	.08	.04
1992 Upper Deck	169	.08	.06	.03
1992 Upper Deck	432	.08	.06	.03
1992 Upper Deck Foreign Exchange	8	.50	.40	.20
1992 Upper Deck Holograms	4AW	.60	.45	.25
1992 Upper Deck Jerry West Selects	6JW	.75	.60	.30
1993 Fleer	88	.05	.04	.02
1993 Fleer	386	.05	.04	.02
1993 Fleer All-Stars	10	.50	.40	.20
1993 Fleer Jam Session	92	.10	.08	.04
1993 Fleer NBA Internationals	9	.60	.30	.15
1993 Fleer Ultra	84	.10	.08	.04
1993 Fleer Ultra	346	.10	.08	.04
1993 NBA Hoops	90	.06	.05	.02
1993 NBA Hoops	267	.06	.05	.02
1993 NBA Hoops	411	.06	.05	.02
1993 SkyBox	87	.05	.04	.02
1993 SkyBox	284	.10	.08	.04
1993 Topps	132	.08	.06	.03
1993 Topps	268	.05	.04	.02
1993 Topps Finest	28	.35	.25	.14
1993 Topps Finest	128	.35	.25	.14
1993 Topps Stadium Club	5	.10	.08	.04
1993 Topps Stadium Club	22	.10	.08	.04
1993 Topps Stadium Club	297	.15	.11	.06
1993 Upper Deck	104	.05	.04	.02
1993 Upper Deck	362	.05	.04	.02
1993 Upper Deck SE	3	.10	.08	.04
1993 Upper Deck 3-D Triple Double	4	.75	.60	.30
1994 Fleer	218	.07	.05	.03
1994 Fleer Jam Session	183	.10	.08	.04
1994 Fleer Ultra	181	.08	.06	.03
1994 NBA Hoops	206	.08	.06	.03
1994 SkyBox	160	.08	.06	.03
1994 Topps	112	.06	.05	.02
1994 Topps Finest	118	.20	.15	.08
1994 Topps Stadium Club	48	.10	.08	.04
1994 Upper Deck Collector's Choice	111	.05	.04	.02
1994 Upper Deck Special Edition	84	.20	.15	.08

Rookie card: A player's first card issued by a major card producer in its regular annual set. It may or may not be issued during the player's actual rookie season. A rookie card is often a player's most valuable card.

Scarce: Not easily obtainable.

Scuff: A rub or abrasion on a card which removes a portion of its gloss or printing. Scuffed cards are worth less than non-scuffed cards.

Dennis Scott

Set	Card #	MT	NM	EX
1990 Fleer Update	68 (R)	.65	.50	.25
1990 NBA Hoops	393 (R)	.30	.25	.12
1990 SkyBox	363 (R)	.50	.40	.20
1991 Fleer	147	.15	.11	.06
1991 Fleer Rookie Sensations	2	1.50	1.25	.60
1991 NBA Hoops	151	.15	.11	.06
1991 NBA Hoops	485	.12	.09	.05
1991 SkyBox	205	.15	.11	.06
1991 SkyBox	320	.10	.08	.04
1991 SkyBox	504	.15	.11	.06
1991 SkyBox	602	.10	.08	.04
1991 Upper Deck	38	.10	.08	.04
1991 Upper Deck	257	.15	.11	.06
1991 Upper Deck Rookie Standouts	2R	.30	.25	.12
1992 Fleer	163	.10	.08	.04
1992 Fleer Ultra	132	.12	.09	.05
1992 NBA Hoops	164	.10	.08	.04
1992 SkyBox	173	.15	.11	.06
1992 Topps	192	.10	.08	.04
1992 Topps Archives	138	.10	.08	.04
1992 Topps Stadium Club	155	.10	.08	.04
1992 Upper Deck	141	.10	.08	.04
1993 Fleer	151	.05	.04	.02
1993 Fleer Jam Session	162	.10	.08	.04
1993 Fleer Ultra	136	.10	.08	.04
1993 NBA Hoops	157	.10	.08	.04
1993 SkyBox	135	.05	.04	.02
1993 Topps	383	.05	.04	.02
1993 Topps BlackGold	2	.60	.45	.25
1993 Topps Finest	138	.35	.25	.14
1993 Topps Stadium Club	135	.10	.08	.04
1993 Upper Deck	43	.05	.04	.02
1993 Upper Deck SE	15	.10	.08	.04
1993 Upper Deck 3-D Basketball	69	.10	.08	.04
1994 Fleer	162	.05	.04	.02
1994 Fleer Flair	108	.15	.11	.06
1994 Fleer Jam Session	137	.10	.08	.04
1994 Fleer Sharpshooters	9	.50	.40	.20
1994 Fleer Ultra	136	.08	.06	.03
1994 NBA Hoops	154	.04	.03	.02
1994 SkyBox	120	.06	.05	.02
1994 Topps	133	.06	.05	.02
1994 Topps Finest	148	.20	.15	.08
1994 Topps Stadium Club Clear Cut	19	1.00	.70	.40
1994 Upper Deck Collector's Choice	81	.05	.04	.02
1994 Upper Deck Special Edition	64	.20	.15	.08

Second-year card: The second card of a player issued in the major sets. Usually, a second-year card is the most expensive card of a player, next to the rookie card.

Jack Sikma

Set	Card #	NM	EX	VG
1978 Topps	117 (R)	8.00	4.00	2.50
1979 Topps	66	1.25	.60	.40
1980 Topps	48	25.00	12.50	7.50
1980 Topps	72	.20	.10	.06
1980 Topps	98	20.00	10.00	6.00
1980 Topps	153	.25	.13	.08

Set	Card #	MT	NM	EX
1981 Topps	39	.50	.40	.20
1981 Topps	110	.40	.30	.15
1981 Topps	64	.40	.30	.15
1983 Star Co.	193	7.00	5.25	2.75
1983 Star Co. All-Star Game	21	2.50	2.00	1.00
1984 Star Co.	120	5.00	3.75	2.00
1984 Star Co. All-Star Game	24	1.50	1.25	.60
1984 Star Co. Court Kings	21	2.50	2.00	1.00
1985 Star Co.	69	5.00	3.75	2.00
1986 Fleer	102	3.00	2.25	1.25
1987 Fleer	100	1.75	1.25	.70
1988 Fleer	76	.50	.40	.20
1989 Fleer	91	.20	.15	.08
1989 NBA Hoops	66	.05	.04	.02
1990 Fleer	110	.05	.04	.02
1990 NBA Hoops	183	.07	.05	.03
1990 SkyBox	166	.05	.04	.02
1991 Fleer	120	.07	.05	.03
1991 NBA Hoops	122	.05	.04	.02
1991 SkyBox	165	.05	.04	.02
1991 Upper Deck	370	.05	.04	.02

Lionel Simmons

Set	Card #	MT	NM	EX
1990 Fleer Update	87 (R)	.75	.60	.30
1990 NBA Hoops	396 (R)	.40	.30	.15

Set	Card #			
1990 SkyBox	364 (R)	.60	.45	.25
1991 Fleer	179	.15	.11	.06
1991 Fleer	394	.05	.04	.02
1991 Fleer Rookie Sensations	1	1.50	1.25	.60
1991 Fleer Rookie Sensations	5	.75	.60	.30
1991 NBA Hoops	185	.15	.11	.06
1991 NBA Hoops	493	.15	.11	.06
1991 NBA Hoops	525	.12	.09	.05
1991 SkyBox	250	.12	.09	.05
1991 SkyBox	319	.10	.08	.04
1991 SkyBox	508	.10	.08	.04
1991 Upper Deck	36	.15	.11	.06
1991 Upper Deck	375	.20	.15	.08
1992 Fleer	198	.15	.11	.06
1992 Fleer Ultra	159	.12	.09	.05
1992 NBA Hoops	201	.15	.11	.06
1992 SkyBox	215	.12	.09	.05
1992 Topps	22	.04	.03	.02
1992 Topps Archives	139	.10	.08	.04
1992 Topps Stadium Club	128	.10	.08	.04
1992 Upper Deck	243	.12	.09	.05
1993 Fleer	184	.10	.08	.04
1993 Fleer Jam Session	197	.15	.11	.06
1993 Fleer Ultra	163	.10	.08	.04
1993 NBA Hoops	191	.10	.08	.04
1993 NBA Hoops	445	.06	.05	.02
1993 SkyBox	158	.15	.11	.06
1993 Topps	184	.05	.04	.02
1993 Topps Finest	68	.35	.25	.14
1993 Topps Stadium Club	28	.10	.08	.04
1993 Upper Deck	99	.05	.04	.02
1993 Upper Deck SE	118	.10	.08	.04
1994 Fleer	196	.05	.04	.02
1994 Fleer Flair	129	.15	.11	.06
1994 Fleer Jam Session	165	.10	.08	.04
1994 Fleer Ultra	167	.08	.06	.03
1994 NBA Hoops	187	.04	.03	.02
1994 SkyBox	144	.06	.05	.02
1994 Topps	134	.06	.05	.02
1994 Topps Finest	127	.15	.11	.06
1994 Topps Stadium Club	37	.08	.06	.03
1994 Upper Deck Special Edition	77	.20	.15	.08

Set	Card #			
1991 NBA Hoops	521	.05	.04	.02
1991 SkyBox	206	.05	.04	.02
1991 SkyBox	310	.05	.04	.02
1991 Upper Deck	226	.05	.04	.02
1992 Fleer	164	.05	.04	.02
1992 Fleer Team Leaders	19	6.00	4.50	2.50
1992 Fleer Ultra	133	.10	.08	.04
1992 Fleer Ultra Playmakers	8	.50	.40	.20
1992 NBA Hoops	165	.05	.04	.02
1992 SkyBox	174	.05	.04	.02
1992 SkyBox	300	.05	.04	.02
1992 Topps	42	.04	.03	.02
1992 Topps	224	.04	.03	.02
1992 Topps Archives	88	.05	.04	.02
1992 Topps Stadium Club	160	.10	.08	.04
1992 Upper Deck	149	.05	.04	.02
1992 Upper Deck Team MVP's	20TM	.75	.60	.30
1993 Fleer	152	.05	.04	.02
1993 Fleer Jam Session	163	.10	.08	.04
1993 Fleer Ultra	137	.10	.08	.04
1993 NBA Hoops	158	.06	.05	.02
1993 SkyBox	136	.05	.04	.02
1993 Topps	267	.05	.04	.02
1993 Topps Finest	58	.35	.25	.14
1993 Topps Stadium Club	104	.10	.08	.04
1993 Topps Stadium Club	237	.10	.08	.04
1993 Upper Deck	17	.05	.04	.02
1993 Upper Deck SE	126	.10	.08	.04
1993 Upper Deck 3-D Basketball	25	.10	.08	.04
1994 Fleer	163	.05	.04	.02
1994 Fleer	384	.05	.04	.02
1994 Fleer Jam Session	197	.10	.08	.04
1994 Fleer Ultra	197	.08	.06	.03
1994 NBA Hoops	155	.04	.03	.02
1994 NBA Hoops	380	.04	.03	.02
1994 SkyBox	121	.06	.05	.02
1994 Topps Stadium Club	110	.08	.06	.03
1994 Upper Deck Collector's Choice	237	.05	.04	.02

Scott Skiles

Set	Card #	MT	NM	EX
1989 Fleer	110 (R)	1.00	.70	.40
1989 NBA Hoops	249 (R)	1.00	.70	.40
1989 NBA Hoops	318	.40	.30	.15
1990 NBA Hoops	220	.03	.02	.01
1990 SkyBox	205	.05	.04	.02
1991 Fleer	148	.03	.02	.01
1991 Fleer	390	.03	.02	.01
1991 NBA Hoops	152	.05	.04	.02
1991 NBA Hoops	486	.05	.04	.02

Jerry Sloan

Set	Card #	NM	EX	VG
1970 Topps	148 (R)	12.00	6.00	3.50
1971 Topps	87	4.50	2.25	1.25
1972 Topps	11	3.00	1.50	.90
1973 Topps	83	2.00	1.00	.60
1974 Topps	51	1.50	.70	.45
1975 Topps	9	1.00	.50	.30
1976 Topps	123	3.00	1.50	.90

Set	Card #	MT	NM	EX
1989 NBA Hoops	267	.05	.04	.02
1990 NBA Hoops	330	.03	.02	.01
1990 NBA Hoops	354	.05	.04	.02
1990 SkyBox	326	.07	.05	.03

Set	Card #	MT	NM	EX
1991 Fleer	202	.03	.02	.01
1991 NBA Hoops	246	.05	.04	.02
1991 SkyBox	403	.05	.04	.02
1992 Fleer	226	.05	.04	.02
1992 NBA Hoops	264	.05	.04	.02
1992 SkyBox	280	.05	.04	.02
1993 NBA Hoops	255	.06	.05	.02
1994 NBA Hoops	295	.04	.03	.02

Kenny Smith

Set	Card #	MT	NM	EX
1988 Fleer	100 (R)	4.00	3.00	1.50
1989 Fleer	138	.25	.20	.10
1989 NBA Hoops	232	.15	.11	.06
1990 Fleer	4	.07	.05	.03
1990 Fleer Update	36	.10	.08	.04
1990 NBA Hoops	33	.15	.11	.06
1990 NBA Hoops	414	.10	.08	.04
1990 SkyBox	8	.10	.08	.04
1990 SkyBox	385	.10	.08	.04
1991 Fleer	78	.07	.05	.03
1991 Fleer	230	.07	.05	.03
1991 NBA Hoops	79	.05	.04	.02
1991 SkyBox	106	.05	.04	.02
1991 SkyBox	587	.05	.04	.02
1991 Upper Deck	276	.05	.04	.02
1992 Fleer	85	.05	.04	.02
1992 Fleer Ultra	73	.12	.09	.05
1992 NBA Hoops	86	.05	.04	.02
1992 SkyBox	91	.05	.04	.02
1992 SkyBox	291	.05	.04	.02
1992 Topps	170	.04	.03	.02
1992 Topps Archives	99	.05	.04	.02
1992 Topps Stadium Club	166	.10	.08	.04
1992 Upper Deck	176	.05	.04	.02
1993 Fleer	80	.05	.04	.02
1993 Fleer Jam Session	84	.10	.08	.04
1993 Fleer Ultra	77	.10	.08	.04
1993 NBA Hoops	82	.06	.05	.02
1993 SkyBox	82	.05	.04	.02
1993 Topps	382	.06	.05	.02
1993 Topps Finest	209	.35	.25	.14
1993 Topps Stadium Club	132	.10	.08	.04
1993 Upper Deck	47	.05	.04	.02
1993 Upper Deck	444	.05	.04	.02
1993 Upper Deck SE	22	.10	.08	.04
1994 Fleer	86	.05	.04	.02
1994 Fleer Flair	58	.15	.11	.06
1994 Fleer Jam Session	74	.10	.08	.04
1994 Fleer Ultra	70	.08	.06	.03
1994 NBA Hoops	79	.04	.03	.02
1994 SkyBox	63	.06	.05	.02
1994 Topps	132	.06	.05	.02
1994 Topps Finest	9	.20	.15	.08
1994 Upper Deck	102	.10	.08	.04
1994 Upper Deck Collector's Choice	275	.05	.04	.02

Steve Smith

Set	Card #	MT	NM	EX
1991 Fleer	309 (R)	.75	.60	.30
1991 NBA Hoops	550 (R)	.65	.50	.25
1991 SkyBox	517 (R)	1.00	.70	.40
1991 Upper Deck	4 (R)	1.25	.90	.50
1991 Upper Deck	447	.75	.60	.30
1991 Upper Deck Rookie Standouts	32R	2.00	1.50	.80
1992 Fleer	123	.25	.20	.10
1992 Fleer Rookie Sensations	11	7.00	5.25	2.75
1992 Fleer Ultra	104	.30	.25	.12
1992 NBA Hoops	124	.25	.20	.10
1992 SkyBox	131	.30	.25	.12
1992 Topps	147	.15	.11	.06
1992 Topps Archives	148	.20	.15	.08
1992 Topps Stadium Club	79	.25	.20	.10
1992 Upper Deck	110	.20	.15	.08
1992 Upper Deck All-Rookie	4AR	1.50	1.25	.60
1993 Fleer	113	.15	.11	.06
1993 Fleer Flair USA Basketball	15	.20	.15	.08
1993 Fleer Jam Session	118	.15	.11	.06
1993 Fleer Ultra	104	.15	.11	.06
1993 Fleer Ultra	369	.15	.11	.06
1993 NBA Hoops	118	.15	.11	.06
1993 SkyBox	107	.10	.08	.04
1993 Topps	10	.10	.08	.04
1993 Topps BlackGold	15	.60	.45	.25
1993 Topps Finest	70	1.50	1.25	.60
1993 Topps Finest	97	.35	.25	.14
1993 Topps Finest Main Attraction	14	3.50	2.75	1.50
1993 Topps Stadium Club	3	.10	.08	.04
1993 Topps Stadium Club	287	.15	.11	.06
1993 Upper Deck	296	.12	.09	.05
1993 Upper Deck SE	35	.20	.15	.08
1993 Upper Deck USA Basketball	11	.10	.08	.04
1994 Fleer	245	.08	.04	.02
1994 Fleer Flair	82	.20	.15	.08
1994 Fleer Flair	170	.15	.11	.06
1994 Fleer Jam Session	103	.10	.08	.04
1994 Fleer Ultra	101	.08	.06	.03
1994 NBA Hoops	305	.08	.06	.03
1994 NBA Hoops Supreme Court	24	.30	.25	.12
1994 SkyBox	90	.06	.05	.02
1994 Topps	83	.06	.05	.02
1994 Topps Stadium Club	128	.08	.06	.03
1994 Topps Stadium Club Clear Cut	14	1.50	1.25	.60
1994 Upper Deck	37	.10	.08	.04
1994 Upper Deck	173	.12	.09	.05
1994 Upper Deck Collector's Choice	3	.07	.05	.03
1994 Upper Deck Collector's Choice	179	.07	.05	.03

1994 Upper Deck Collector's Choice	279	.08	.06	.03
1994 Upper Deck Special Edition	48	.20	.15	.08

Latrell Sprewell

Set	Card #	MT	NM	EX
1992 Fleer	343 (R)	2.00	1.50	.80
1992 Fleer Ultra	266 (R)	3.00	2.25	1.25
1992 Fleer Ultra All-Rookies	8	10.00	7.50	4.00
1992 NBA Hoops	389 (R)	4.00	3.00	1.50
1992 SkyBox	342 (R)	4.00	3.00	1.50
1992 SkyBox Draft Picks	24	10.00	7.50	4.00
1992 Topps	392 (R)	1.00	.70	.40
1992 Topps Stadium Club	320 (R)	5.00	3.75	2.00
1992 Upper Deck	386 (R)	3.50	2.75	1.50
1992 Upper Deck	463	1.00	.70	.40
1992 Upper Deck Rookie Standouts	5	8.00	6.00	3.25
1993 Fleer	73	.50	.40	.20
1993 Fleer Jam Session	74	.75	.60	.30
1993 Fleer Rookie Sensations	21	8.00	6.00	3.20
1993 Fleer Sharpshooters	8	4.00	3.00	1.50
1993 Fleer Ultra	70	.85	.60	.35
1993 Fleer Ultra Inside Outside	8	1.25	.90	.50
1993 NBA Hoops	75	.50	.40	.20
1993 SkyBox	78	.75	.60	.30
1993 Topps	153	.25	.20	.10
1993 Topps	340	.50	.40	.20
1993 Topps Finest	30	5.00	3.75	2.00
1993 Topps Stadium Club	294	.75	.60	.30
1993 Upper Deck	63	.50	.40	.20
1993 Upper Deck	452	.25	.20	.10
1993 Upper Deck All-Rookie	8	8.00	6.00	3.25
1993 Upper Deck Locker Talk	13	4.00	3.00	1.50
1993 Upper Deck SE	21	.65	.50	.25
1993 Upper Deck SE West Future All Stars	4	22.00	16.50	8.75
1993 Upper Deck 3-D Basketball	3	.25	.20	.10
1994 Fleer	77	.30	.25	.12
1994 Fleer All-Defensive Team	10	2.00	1.50	.80
1994 Fleer Flair	52	2.00	1.50	.80
1994 Fleer Flair Hot Numbers	16	4.50	3.50	1.75
1994 Fleer Flair Scoring Power	9	4.00	3.00	1.50
1994 Fleer Jam Session	66	.40	.30	.15
1994 Fleer Jam Session Flashing Stars	7	3.50	2.75	1.50
1994 Fleer NBA All-Stars	25	1.25	.90	.50
1994 Fleer Sharpshooters	10	5.00	3.75	2.00

1994 Fleer Team Leaders	3	2.00	1.50	.80
1994 Fleer Total D	9	5.00	3.75	2.00
1994 Fleer Triple Threats	10	1.00	.70	.40
1994 Fleer Ultra	63	.75	.60	.30
1994 Fleer Ultra All-NBA Team	4	2.00	1.50	.80
1994 Fleer Ultra Double Trouble	9	1.75	1.25	.70
1994 Fleer Ultra Scoring Kings	9	15.00	13.50	7.25
1994 NBA Hoops	70	.30	.25	.12
1994 NBA Hoops	249	.20	.15	.08
1994 NBA Hoops	435	.20	.15	.08
1994 NBA Hoops Big Numbers	6	6.00	4.50	2.50
1994 NBA Hoops Power Ratings	17	4.00	3.00	1.50
1994 SkyBox	56	.70	.50	.30
1994 SkyBox Center Stage	7	12.00	9.00	4.75
1994 Topps	191	.20	.15	.08
1994 Topps Finest Iron Men	9	6.00	4.50	2.50
1994 Topps Finest Marathon Men	1	4.00	3.00	1.50
1994 Topps Stadium Club	45	.80	.60	.30
1994 Topps Stadium Club Dynasty and Destiny	9B	2.50	2.00	1.00
1994 Topps Stadium Club Rising Stars	2	12.00	9.00	4.75
1994 Topps Super Stealers	9	3.50	2.75	1.50
1994 Upper Deck	15	.30	.25	.12
1994 Upper Deck	144	.85	.60	.35
1994 Upper Deck Collector's Choice 2,000 Pts	13	5.00	3.75	2.00
1994 Upper Deck Collector's Choice	15	.40	.30	.15
1994 Upper Deck Collector's Choice	198	.20	.15	.08
1994 Upper Deck Collector's Choice	380	.15	.11	.06
1994 Upper Deck Special Edition	29	2.25	1.75	.90

John Starks

Set	Card #	MT	NM	EX
1991 Fleer	330 (R)	.50	.40	.20
1991 NBA Hoops	406 (R)	.50	.40	.20
1991 SkyBox	194 (R)	1.00	.70	.40
1991 SkyBox	503	.30	.25	.12
1991 Upper Deck	219 (R)	1.75	1.25	.70
1991 Upper Deck	482	.40	.30	.15
1992 Fleer	156	.10	.08	.04
1992 Fleer Ultra	127	.15	.11	.06
1992 NBA Hoops	158	.20	.15	.08
1992 SkyBox	167	.10	.08	.04
1992 Topps	44	.10	.08	.04

Set	Card #	MT	NM	EX
1992 Topps Stadium Club	140	.15	.11	.06
1992 Upper Deck	282	.15	.11	.06
1992 Upper Deck	492	.15	.11	.06
1993 Fleer	146	.15	.11	.06
1993 Fleer Jam Session	154	.20	.15	.08
1993 Fleer Jam Session Gamebreakers	7	.40	.30	.15
1993 Fleer Sharpshooters	9	1.00	.70	.40
1993 Fleer Ultra	132	.15	.11	.06
1993 Fleer Ultra All-Defensive Team	10	10.00	7.50	4.00
1993 Fleer Ultra Inside Outside	9	.60	.45	.25
1993 NBA Hoops	151	.15	.11	.06
1993 SkyBox	13	.20	.15	.08
1993 SkyBox	131	.12	.09	.05
1993 SkyBox	330	.05	.04	.02
1993 SkyBox Center Stage	4	1.00	.70	.40
1993 SkyBox Thunder and Lightning	5	3.00	2.25	1.25
1993 Topps	61	.10	.08	.04
1993 Topps	208	.08	.06	.03
1993 Topps Finest	95	.35	.25	.14
1993 Topps Finest	194	.35	.25	.14
1993 Topps Stadium Club	116	.10	.08	.04
1993 Topps Stadium Club	350	.15	.11	.06
1993 Upper Deck	51	.15	.11	.06
1993 Upper Deck Locker Talk	14	.75	.60	.30
1993 Upper Deck SE	83	.10	.08	.04
1993 Upper Deck SE Behind the Glass	8	2.50	2.00	1.00
1993 Upper Deck 3-D Basketball	20	.10	.08	.04
1994 Fleer	156	.05	.04	.02
1994 Fleer Flair	104	.15	.11	.06
1994 Fleer Flair Hot Numbers	17	1.00	.70	.40
1994 Fleer Jam Session	130	.10	.08	.04
1994 Fleer NBA All-Stars	12	.35	.25	.14
1994 Fleer Pro-Visions	2	.40	.30	.15
1994 Fleer Ultra	130	.08	.06	.03
1994 NBA Hoops	147	.04	.03	.02
1994 NBA Hoops	235	.04	.03	.02
1994 NBA Hoops	443	.06	.05	.02
1994 NBA Hoops Power Ratings	36	.30	.25	.12
1994 NBA Hoops Supreme Court	31	.30	.25	.12
1994 SkyBox	115	.06	.05	.02
1994 Topps	5	.06	.05	.02
1994 Topps	30	.06	.05	.02
1994 Upper Deck Collector's Choice	303	.08	.06	.03
1994 Upper Deck Special Edition	62	.20	.15	.08
1985 Star Co.	144	75.00	56.00	30.00
1985 Star Co. All-Rookie Team	8	35.00	26.00	14.00
1986 Star Co. Best of the Best	12	50.00	37.00	20.00
1988 Fleer	115 (R)	22.00	16.50	8.75
1988 Fleer	127	3.50	2.75	1.50
1989 Fleer	156	1.75	1.25	.70
1989 Fleer	163	.50	.40	.20
1989 NBA Hoops	140	.40	.30	.15
1989 NBA Hoops	297	.25	.20	.10
1990 Fleer	189	.20	.15	.08
1990 Fleer All-Stars	9	.40	.30	.15
1990 NBA Hoops	25	.20	.15	.08
1990 NBA Hoops	294	.15	.11	.06
1990 SkyBox	284	.25	.20	.10
1990 Star Co. Court Kings	6	22.00	15.00	6.25
1990 Star Co. Slam	8	25.00	17.00	7.00
1991 Fleer	203	.15	.11	.06
1991 Fleer	217	.10	.08	.04
1991 Fleer	221	.10	.08	.04
1991 Fleer	397	.10	.08	.04
1991 NBA Hoops	212	.15	.11	.06
1991 NBA Hoops	271	.10	.08	.04
1991 NBA Hoops	500	.12	.09	.05
1991 NBA Hoops	528	.15	.11	.06
1991 NBA Hoops	584	.50	.40	.20
1991 SkyBox	285	.15	.11	.06
1991 SkyBox	306	.10	.08	.04
1991 SkyBox	484	.15	.11	.06
1991 SkyBox	539	.40	.30	.15
1991 Upper Deck	52	.15	.11	.06
1991 Upper Deck	136	.25	.20	.10
1991 Upper Deck	470	.12	.09	.05
1991 Upper Deck Holograms	3AW	1.00	.70	.40
1992 Fleer	227	.25	.20	.10
1992 Fleer	240	.10	.08	.04
1992 Fleer All-Stars	22	1.25	.90	.50
1992 Fleer Sharpshooters	11	1.25	.90	.50
1992 Fleer Total "D"	6	10.00	7.50	4.00
1992 Fleer Ultra	183	.50	.40	.20
1992 Fleer Ultra All-NBA Team	10	1.50	1.25	.60
1992 Fleer Ultra Playmakers	9	1.50	1.25	.60
1992 NBA Hoops	d	3.00	2.00	.75
1992 NBA Hoops	229	.25	.20	.10
1992 NBA Hoops	316	.10	.08	.04
1992 NBA Hoops	347	.10	.08	.04
1992 NBA Hoops	483	.20	.15	.08
1992 NBA Hoops Supreme Court	8SC	1.25	.90	.50
1992 SkyBox	244	.30	.25	.12
1992 SkyBox	307	.10	.08	.04
1992 SkyBox I Olympic Team	3USA	1.50	1.25	.60
1992 SkyBox II Thunder and Lightning	8	12.00	9.00	4.75
1992 Topps	101	.10	.08	.04
1992 Topps	223	.15	.11	.06
1992 Topps	301	.20	.15	.08
1992 Topps Archives	57	.15	.11	.06
1992 Topps Beam Team	4	1.50	1.00	.50
1992 Topps Stadium Club	200	.25	.20	.10
1992 Topps Stadium Club	265	.40	.30	.15
1992 Topps Stadium Club Beam Team	11	5.00	3.75	2.00
1992 Upper Deck	66	.15	.11	.06
1992 Upper Deck	116	.20	.15	.08
1992 Upper Deck	437	.12	.09	.05
1992 Upper Deck All-Division Team	14	.75	.60	.30
1992 Upper Deck All-NBA	6AN	1.50	1.25	.60
1992 Upper Deck Holograms	2AW	.60	.45	.25
1992 Upper Deck Holograms	8AW	.60	.45	.25
1992 Upper Deck Team MVP's	27TM	1.50	1.25	.60
1993 Fleer	212	.15	.11	.06

John Stockton

Set	Card #	MT	NM	EX
1984 Star Co.	235 (R)	185.00	139.00	74.00

Rod Strickland

1993 Fleer	228	.10	.08	.04
1993 Fleer	236	.10	.08	.04
1993 Fleer All-Stars	24	1.00	.70	.40
1993 Fleer Jam Session	228	.25	.20	.10
1993 Fleer Ultra	190	.20	.15	.08
1993 Fleer Ultra All-NBA Team	9	2.50	2.00	1.00
1993 NBA Hoops	219	.15	.11	.06
1993 NBA Hoops	280	.10	.08	.04
1993 NBA Hoops	286	.10	.08	.04
1993 NBA Hoops	289	.25	.20	.10
1993 NBA Hoops Supreme Court	8	1.00	.70	.40
1993 SkyBox	179	.20	.15	.08
1993 SkyBox	338	.10	.08	.04
1993 Topps	102	.10	.08	.04
1993 Topps	201	.15	.11	.06
1993 Topps	356	.15	.11	.06
1993 Topps Finest	117	1.00	.70	.40
1993 Topps Finest	219	2.00	1.50	.80
1993 Topps Stadium Club	313	.20	.15	.08
1993 Topps Stadium Club Beam Team	19	5.00	3.75	2.00
1993 Upper Deck	12	.25	.20	.10
1993 Upper Deck	168	.15	.11	.06
1993 Upper Deck	445	.10	.08	.04
1993 Upper Deck	478	.10	.08	.04
1993 Upper Deck All-NBA	9	1.00	.60	.30
1993 Upper Deck SE	90	.30	.25	.12
1993 Upper Deck Team MVP's	26	.50	.40	.20
1993 Upper Deck 3-D Basketball	18	.20	.15	.08
1994 Fleer	227	.25	.20	.10
1994 Fleer Flair	151	.60	.45	.25
1994 Fleer Flair Hot Numbers	18	2.50	2.00	1.00
1994 Fleer Jam Session	190	.20	.15	.08
1994 Fleer NBA All-Stars	26	.75	.60	.30
1994 Fleer NBA League Leaders	8	1.25	.90	.50
1994 Fleer Team Leaders	9	3.00	2.25	1.25
1994 Fleer Total D	10	3.50	2.75	1.50
1994 Fleer Ultra	189	.15	.11	.06
1994 Fleer Ultra All-NBA Team	5	.50	.40	.20
1994 Fleer Ultra Double Trouble	10	.65	.50	.25
1994 NBA Hoops	214	.15	.11	.06
1994 NBA Hoops	250	.08	.06	.03
1994 NBA Hoops Predators	8	2.00	1.50	.80
1994 NBA Hoops Supreme Court	47	1.00	.70	.40
1994 SkyBox	168	.20	.15	.08
1994 Topps	53	.08	.06	.03
1994 Topps	190	.08	.06	.03
1994 Topps Finest	150	.15	.11	.06
1994 Topps Stadium Club	75	.12	.09	.05
1994 Topps Stadium Club	76	.10	.08	.04
1994 Topps Stadium Club Dynasty and Destiny	3A	1.00	.70	.40
1994 Topps Super Passers	1	3.00	2.25	1.25
1994 Topps Super Stealers	4	1.75	1.25	.70
1994 Upper Deck	14	.15	.11	.06
1994 Upper Deck	87	.12	.09	.05
1994 Upper Deck Collector's Choice 750 Assists	13	10.00	7.50	4.00
1994 Upper Deck Collector's Choice	196	.10	.08	.04
1994 Upper Deck Collector's Choice	208	.05	.04	.02
1994 Upper Deck Collector's Choice	212	.10	.08	.04
1994 Upper Deck Predictors Retail	11	12.00	9.00	4.75
1994 Upper Deck Predictors Hobby	19	3.00	2.25	1.25

Set	Card #	MT	NM	EX
1989 Fleer	104 (R)	3.00	2.25	1.25
1989 NBA Hoops	8 (R)	.50	.40	.20
1990 Fleer	173	.10	.08	.04
1990 NBA Hoops	271	.03	.02	.01
1990 SkyBox	261	.10	.08	.04
1991 Fleer	188	.07	.05	.03
1991 NBA Hoops	196	.07	.05	.03
1991 SkyBox	263	.05	.04	.02
1991 Upper Deck	214	.05	.04	.02
1992 Fleer	192	.05	.04	.02
1992 Fleer	420	.06	.05	.02
1992 Fleer Ultra	346	.10	.08	.04
1992 NBA Hoops	210	.05	.04	.02
1992 NBA Hoops	458	.05	.04	.02
1992 SkyBox	225	.05	.04	.02
1992 SkyBox	394	.10	.08	.04
1992 Topps	330	.04	.03	.02
1992 Topps Archives	113	.05	.04	.02
1992 Topps Stadium Club	234	.10	.08	.04
1992 Upper Deck	74	.05	.04	.02
1992 Upper Deck	384	.05	.04	.02
1993 Fleer	179	.05	.04	.02
1993 Fleer Jam Session	191	.10	.08	.04
1993 Fleer Ultra	158	.10	.08	.04
1993 NBA Hoops	184	.06	.05	.02
1993 SkyBox	155	.05	.04	.02
1993 Topps	84	.05	.04	.02
1993 Topps Finest	195	.35	.25	.14
1993 Topps Stadium Club	105	.10	.08	.04
1993 Topps Stadium Club	165	.10	.08	.04
1993 Upper Deck	73	.05	.04	.02
1993 Upper Deck	455	.06	.05	.02
1993 Upper Deck SE	70	.10	.08	.04
1994 Fleer	190	.05	.04	.02
1994 Fleer Flair	124	.20	.15	.08
1994 Fleer Jam Session	160	.20	.15	.08
1994 Fleer Team Leaders	8	3.00	2.25	1.25
1994 Fleer Ultra	162	.10	.08	.04
1994 NBA Hoops	181	.04	.03	.02
1994 SkyBox	40	.06	.05	.02
1994 Topps Finest	8	.25	.20	.10
1994 Topps Finest	165	.15	.11	.06
1994 Topps Finest Marathon Men	6	1.50	1.25	.60
1994 Topps Stadium Club	43	.08	.06	.03
1994 Topps Super Passers	6	1.75	1.25	.70
1994 Upper Deck Collector's Choice 750 Assists	14	3.00	2.25	1.25
1994 Upper Deck Collector's Choice	151	.05	.04	.02
1994 Upper Deck Predictors Retail	18	5.00	3.75	2.00
1994 Upper Deck Special Edition	73	.25	.20	.10

Reggie Theus

Set	Card #	NM	EX	VG
1979 Topps	44 (R)	3.00	1.50	.90
1980 Topps	31	.25	.13	.08
1980 Topps	84	.25	.13	.08
1980 Topps	85	.25	.13	.08
1980 Topps	129	.25	.13	.08
1980 Topps	143	.25	.13	.08
1980 Topps	168	.25	.13	.08

Set	Card #	MT	NM	EX
1981 Topps	69	.15	.11	.06
1981 Topps	46	.15	.11	.06
1983 Star Co.	225	4.00	3.00	1.50
1983 Star Co. All-Star Game	10	2.50	2.00	1.00
1984 Star Co.	270	4.00	3.00	1.50
1984 Star Co. Court Kings	16	2.50	2.00	1.00
1985 Star Co.	74	4.00	3.00	1.50
1986 Fleer	108	3.00	2.25	1.25
1987 Fleer	105	1.50	1.25	.60
1988 Fleer	98	.20	.15	.08
1989 Fleer	111	.07	.05	.03
1989 NBA Hoops	165	.15	.11	.06
1989 NBA Hoops	302	.05	.04	.02
1990 Fleer	136	.05	.04	.02
1990 Fleer Update	62	.05	.04	.02
1990 NBA Hoops	222	.10	.08	.04
1990 NBA Hoops	420	.05	.04	.02
1990 SkyBox	207	.10	.08	.04
1990 SkyBox	399	.07	.05	.03
1991 NBA Hoops	138	.05	.04	.02
1991 SkyBox	187	.05	.04	.02
1991 SkyBox	325	.05	.04	.02
1991 Upper Deck	264	.05	.04	.02

Isiah Thomas

Set	Card #	MT	NM	EX
1983 Star Co.	94 (R)	150.00	112.00	60.00

Set	Card #			
1983 Star Co. All-Star Game	11	18.00	13.50	7.25
1984 Star Co.	261	45.00	34.00	18.00
1984 Star Co.	287	20.00	15.00	8.00
1984 Star Co. All-Star Game	1	6.00	4.50	2.50
1984 Star Co. All-Star Game	11	15.00	11.00	6.00
1984 Star Co. Awards Banquet	12	7.00	5.25	2.75
1984 Star Co. Court Kings	30	10.00	7.50	4.00
1985 Star Co.	10	35.00	26.00	14.00
1985 Star Co. Lite All-Stars	6	15.00	11.00	6.00
1986 Fleer	109 (R)	33.00	25.00	13.00
1986 Star Co. Best of the Best	13	30.00	22.00	12.00
1986 Star Co. Court Kings	28	13.00	9.75	5.25
1987 Fleer	106	8.00	6.00	3.25
1988 Fleer	45	2.75	2.00	1.00
1989 Fleer	50	.75	.60	.30
1989 NBA Hoops	177	.20	.15	.08
1989 NBA Hoops	250	.20	.15	.08
1990 Fleer	61	.20	.15	.08
1990 Fleer All-Stars	6	.40	.30	.15
1990 NBA Hoops	11	.15	.11	.06
1990 NBA Hoops	111	.20	.15	.08
1990 NBA Hoops	389	.20	.15	.08
1990 SkyBox	93	.25	.20	.10
1990 Star Co. Court Kings	7	18.00	12.00	5.00
1991 Fleer	64	.15	.11	.06
1991 Fleer NBA Schoolyard Sets	2	2.00	1.50	.80
1991 NBA Hoops	66	.12	.09	.05
1991 NBA Hoops	464	.10	.08	.04
1991 NBA Hoops	510	.12	.09	.05
1991 NBA Hoops MVP All-Stars	7	1.00	.70	.40
1991 SkyBox	88	.15	.11	.06
1991 SkyBox	412	.10	.08	.04
1991 Upper Deck	333	.20	.15	.08
1991 Upper Deck	451	.12	.09	.05
1992 Fleer	69	.20	.15	.08
1992 Fleer	255	.10	.08	.04
1992 Fleer All-Stars	11	1.25	.90	.50
1992 Fleer Team Leaders	8	15.00	11.00	6.00
1992 Fleer Ultra	59	.25	.20	.10
1992 Fleer Ultra Playmakers	10	1.25	.90	.50
1992 NBA Hoops	68	.10	.08	.04
1992 NBA Hoops	303	.07	.05	.03
1992 SkyBox	73	.25	.20	.10
1992 SkyBox	289	.10	.08	.04
1992 Topps	118	.10	.08	.04
1992 Topps	219	.10	.08	.04
1992 Topps	331	.12	.09	.05
1992 Topps Archives	20	.15	.11	.06
1992 Topps Stadium Club	50	.25	.20	.10
1992 Topps Stadium Club	204	.20	.15	.08
1992 Upper Deck	263	.10	.08	.04
1992 Upper Deck	426	.10	.08	.04
1992 Upper Deck	500	.10	.08	.04
1992 Upper Deck Team MVP's	9TM	.75	.60	.30
1992 Upper Deck 15000-Point Club	5	2.50	2.00	1.00
1993 Fleer	65	.10	.08	.04
1993 Fleer All-Stars	11	1.00	.70	.40
1993 Fleer Flair USA Basketball	16	.20	.15	.08
1993 Fleer Jam Session	66	.30	.25	.12
1993 Fleer Ultra	62	.20	.15	.08
1993 Fleer Ultra	370	.20	.15	.08
1993 NBA Hoops	67	.10	.08	.04
1993 NBA Hoops	258	.10	.08	.04
1993 SkyBox	71	.15	.11	.06
1993 Topps	311	.08	.06	.03
1993 Topps Finest	87	1.50	1.25	.60
1993 Topps Stadium Club	149	.15	.11	.06
1993 Upper Deck	245	.10	.08	.04
1993 Upper Deck	264	.15	.11	.06

1993 Upper Deck	450	.15	.11	.06
1993 Upper Deck SE	20	.25	.20	.10
1993 Upper Deck SE East Future All Stars	6	8.00	6.00	3.25
1993 Upper Deck USA Basketball	12	.10	.08	.04
1993 Upper Deck 3-D Basketball	44	.10	.08	.04
1993 Upper Deck 3-D Basketball	77	.10	.08	.04
1994 Fleer Flair	171	.15	.11	.06
1994 SkyBox Dream Team II Dream Play	8	5.00	3.75	2.00
1994 Upper Deck	168	.15	.11	.06
1994 Upper Deck Collector's Choice	12	.20	.15	.08

David Thompson

DAVID THOMPSON

Set	Card #	NM	EX	VG
1976 Topps	110 (R)	30.00	15.00	9.00
1977 Topps	60	2.50	1.25	.70
1978 Topps	100	2.00	1.00	.60
1979 Topps	50	2.00	1.00	.60
1980 Topps	44	5.00	2.50	1.50
1980 Topps	108	.25	.13	.08

Set	Card #	MT	NM	EX
1981 Topps	12	.40	.30	.15
1981 Topps	49	.15	.11	.06
1983 Star Co. All-Star Game	22	2.00	1.50	.80

Nate Thurmond

Set	Card #	NM	EX	VG
1969 Topps	10 (R)	35.00	26.00	14.00
1970 Topps	90	9.00	4.50	2.75
1970 Topps	111	3.00	1.50	.90
1971 Topps	131	6.00	3.00	1.75
1972 Topps	28	5.00	2.50	1.50
1973 Topps	5	4.00	2.00	1.25
1974 Topps	87	2.00	1.00	.60
1974 Topps	105	3.00	1.50	.90
1975 Topps	85	2.00	1.00	.60
1975 Topps	119	2.00	1.00	.60

Set	Card #	MT	NM	EX
1985 Star Co. Schick Legends	22	1.00	.70	.40

Wayman Tisdale

Set	Card #	MT	NM	EX
1986 Fleer	113 (R)	5.50	4.25	2.25
1987 Fleer	111	1.50	1.25	.60
1988 Fleer	60	.65	.50	.25
1989 Fleer	139	.20	.15	.08
1989 NBA Hoops	225	.20	.15	.08
1990 Fleer	167	.07	.05	.03
1990 NBA Hoops	262	.07	.05	.03
1990 NBA Hoops	377	.05	.04	.02
1990 SkyBox	251	.10	.08	.04
1991 Fleer	181	.07	.05	.03
1991 NBA Hoops	187	.06	.05	.02
1991 NBA Hoops	494	.05	.04	.02
1991 NBA Hoops	563	.05	.04	.02
1991 SkyBox	252	.08	.06	.03
1991 SkyBox	562	.05	.04	.02
1991 Upper Deck	372	.08	.06	.03
1992 Fleer	199	.08	.06	.03
1992 Fleer Ultra	160	.10	.08	.04
1992 NBA Hoops	202	.07	.05	.03
1992 SkyBox	216	.08	.06	.03
1992 Topps	282	.04	.03	.02
1992 Topps Archives	74	.05	.04	.02
1992 Topps Stadium Club	242	.10	.08	.04
1992 Upper Deck	265	.08	.06	.03
1993 Fleer	185	.05	.04	.02
1993 Fleer Jam Session	198	.10	.08	.04
1993 Fleer Towers of Power	28	2.50	2.00	1.00
1993 Fleer Ultra	164	.10	.08	.04
1993 NBA Hoops	192	.06	.05	.02
1993 SkyBox	159	.05	.04	.02
1993 Topps	254	.05	.04	.02
1993 Topps Finest	155	.35	.25	.14
1993 Topps Stadium Club	83	.10	.08	.04
1993 Upper Deck	307	.05	.04	.02
1993 Upper Deck SE	81	.10	.08	.04
1994 Fleer	197	.05	.04	.02
1994 Fleer	355	.05	.04	.02
1994 Fleer Jam Session	154	.10	.08	.04
1994 NBA Hoops	188	.04	.03	.02
1994 NBA Hoops	365	.04	.03	.02
1994 SkyBox	145	.06	.05	.02
1994 Topps Stadium Club	132	.08	.06	.03
1994 Topps Stadium Club	133	.08	.06	.03
1994 Upper Deck Collector's Choice	329	.05	.04	.02

Rudy Tomjanovich

Set	Card #	NM	EX	VG
1971 Topps	91 (R)	25.00	12.50	7.50
1972 Topps	103	8.00	4.00	2.50
1973 Topps	145	8.00	4.00	2.50
1974 Topps	28	6.00	3.00	1.75
1974 Topps	88	1.00	.50	.30
1974 Topps	146	4.00	2.00	1.25
1975 Topps	70	7.00	3.50	2.00
1975 Topps	123	.75	.40	.25
1976 Topps	66	10.00	5.00	3.00
1977 Topps	15	2.00	1.00	.60
1978 Topps	58	1.00	.50	.30
1979 Topps	41	1.00	.50	.30
1980 Topps	32	.25	.13	.08
1980 Topps	120	.25	.13	.08

Set	Card #	MT	NM	EX
1992 Fleer	87	.05	.04	.02
1992 NBA Hoops	248	.05	.04	.02
1992 SkyBox	264	.05	.04	.02
1993 NBA Hoops	239	.06	.05	.02
1994 NBA Hoops	283	.10	.08	.04

Wes Unseld

Set	Card #	NM	EX	VG
1969 Topps	56 (R)	42.00	31.00	17.00
1970 Topps	72	11.00	5.50	3.25
1971 Topps	95	6.00	3.00	1.75
1972 Topps	21	5.00	2.50	1.50
1973 Topps	176	5.00	2.50	1.50
1974 Topps	121	4.00	2.00	1.25
1975 Topps	115	4.00	2.00	1.25
1975 Topps	133	2.00	1.00	.60
1976 Topps	5	4.00	2.00	1.25
1977 Topps	75	1.50	.70	.45
1978 Topps	7	2.00	1.00	.60
1979 Topps	65	.75	.40	.25

1980 Topps	31	.25	.13	.08
1980 Topps	87	.25	.13	.08
1980 Topps	143	.25	.13	.08
1980 Topps	175	.25	.13	.08

Set	Card #	MT	NM	EX
1989 NBA Hoops	53	.05	.04	.02
1990 NBA Hoops	331	.05	.04	.02
1990 NBA Hoops	344	.10	.08	.04
1990 SkyBox	327	.10	.08	.04
1991 Fleer	209	.05	.04	.02
1991 NBA Hoops	247	.05	.04	.02
1991 SkyBox	404	.07	.05	.03
1992 Fleer	236	.05	.04	.02
1992 NBA Hoops	265	.05	.04	.02
1992 SkyBox	281	.05	.04	.02
1993 NBA Hoops	256	.06	.05	.02

Nick Van Exel

Set	Card #	MT	NM	EX
1993 Fleer	316 (R)	.60	.45	.25
1993 Fleer First Year Phenoms	9	.75	.60	.30
1993 Fleer Ultra	278 (R)	.75	.60	.30
1993 Fleer Ultra All-Rookies	14	4.00	3.00	1.50
1993 NBA Hoops	356 (R)	.40	.30	.15
1993 SkyBox	241 (R)	.65	.50	.25
1993 Topps	302 (R)	.35	.25	.14
1993 Topps Finest	50 (R)	2.00	1.50	.80
1993 Topps Stadium Club	273	.15	.11	.06
1993 Topps Stadium Club	281 (R)	.50	.40	.20
1993 Topps Stadium Club Beam Team	17	5.00	3.75	2.00
1993 Upper Deck	162 (R)	.50	.40	.20
1993 Upper Deck	373 (R)	.25	.20	.10
1993 Upper Deck Rookie Standouts	15	3.00	2.25	1.25
1993 Upper Deck SE	134 (R)	.50	.40	.20
1993 Upper Deck SE	189	.40	.30	.15
1993 Upper Deck SE West Future All Stars	8	10.00	7.50	4.00
1994 Fleer	113	.20	.15	.08
1994 Fleer Flair	76	.70	.50	.30
1994 Fleer Flair Hot Numbers	19	1.75	1.25	.70
1994 Fleer Jam Session	96	.35	.25	.14
1994 Fleer Rookie Sensations	24	2.00	1.50	.80
1994 Fleer Ultra	91	.25	.20	.10
1994 Fleer Ultra NBA All-Rookie Team	10	8.00	6.00	3.25
1994 NBA Hoops	105	.15	.11	.06
1994 NBA Hoops	442	.08	.06	.03
1994 NBA Hoops Power Ratings	26	.50	.40	.20
1994 NBA Hoops Supreme Court	22	.65	.50	.25

1994 SkyBox	84	.25	.20	.10
1994 SkyBox Ragin' Rookies	13	1.50	1.25	.60
1994 Upper Deck	7	.15	.11	.06
1994 Upper Deck Collector's Choice	178	.10	.08	.04
1994 Upper Deck Special Edition	42	.65	.50	.25

Norm Van Lier

Set	Card #	NM	EX	VG
1970 Topps	97 (R)	15.00	7.50	4.50
1971 Topps	19	4.00	2.00	1.25
1971 Topps	143	6.00	3.00	1.75
1972 Topps	111	2.00	1.00	.60
1973 Topps	31	1.00	.50	.30
1974 Topps	84	2.00	1.00	.60
1974 Topps	140	1.00	.50	.30
1975 Topps	119	2.00	1.00	.60
1975 Topps	155	1.00	.50	.30
1976 Topps	108	1.00	.50	.30
1977 Topps	4	.25	.13	.08
1978 Topps	102	.25	.13	.08

Chet Walker

Set	Card #	NM	EX	VG
1969 Topps	91 (R)	15.00	11.00	6.00
1970 Topps	4	9.00	4.50	2.75
1970 Topps	60	5.00	2.50	1.50
1971 Topps	66	2.50	1.25	.70
1971 Topps	141	1.50	.70	.45
1972 Topps	152	3.00	1.50	.90
1973 Topps	45	1.75	.90	.50
1974 Topps	84	2.00	1.00	.60
1974 Topps	171	1.00	.50	.30
1975 Topps	119	2.00	1.00	.60

Traded set: An auxiliary set of cards issued toward the end of the season to reflect trades that were made after the printing of the regular set. Sometimes called "Update" sets, they also usually feature rookies not included in the regular set. The first stand-alone traded set was a baseball traded set issued by Topps in 1981.

Trimmed card: A card that has been cut down from its original size, greatly reducing its value.

Uncut sheet: A full press sheet of cards that has never been cut into individual cards.

Bill Walton

Set	Card #	NM	EX	VG
1974 Topps	39 (R)	65.00	32.00	19.50
1975 Topps	77	25.00	12.50	7.50
1976 Topps	57	25.00	12.50	7.50
1977 Topps	120	10.00	5.00	3.00
1978 Topps	1	12.00	6.00	3.50
1979 Topps	45	6.00	3.00	1.75
1980 Topps	46	.60	.30	.20
1980 Topps	127	1.00	.50	.30

Set	Card #	MT	NM	EX
1983 Star Co.	121	20.00	15.00	8.00
1984 Star Co.	22	20.00	15.00	8.00
1984 Star Co. Court Kings	9	6.00	4.50	2.50
1985 Star Co.	101	15.00	11.00	6.00
1986 Fleer	119	8.00	6.00	3.25
1986 Star Co. Best of the Old	4	85.00	64.00	34.00

Clarence Weatherspoon

Set	Card #	MT	NM	EX
1992 Fleer	409 (R)	1.00	.70	.40
1992 Fleer Ultra	335 (R)	1.50	1.25	.60
1992 Fleer Ultra All-Rookies	9	3.50	2.75	1.50
1992 NBA Hoops	449 (R)	1.50	1.25	.60
1992 NBA Hoops Draft Redemption	8H	10.00	7.50	4.00
1992 NBA Hoops II Magic's All-Rookie Team	8	20.00	15.00	8.00
1992 SkyBox	387 (R)	1.50	1.25	.60
1992 SkyBox Draft Picks	9	5.00	3.75	2.00
1992 Topps	294 (R)	.50	.40	.20
1992 Topps Stadium Club	346 (R)	1.75	1.25	.70
1992 Upper Deck	5 (R)	1.00	.70	.40
1992 Upper Deck	452	.40	.30	.15
1992 Upper Deck	475	.50	.40	.20

1992 Upper Deck Rookie Standouts	16	3.00	2.25	1.25
1993 Fleer	161	.15	.11	.06
1993 Fleer Jam Session	172	.15	.11	.06
1993 Fleer Rookie Sensations	23	3.00	2.25	1.25
1993 Fleer Ultra	143	.25	.20	.10
1993 NBA Hoops	167	.20	.15	.08
1993 NBA Hoops	442	.08	.06	.03
1993 NBA Hoops Face to Face	6	4.00	3.00	1.50
1993 SkyBox	143	.15	.11	.06
1993 Topps	164	.10	.08	.04
1993 Topps	179	.15	.11	.06
1993 Topps Finest	77	1.00	.70	.40
1993 Topps Finest	91	1.50	1.25	.60
1993 Topps Stadium Club	66	.15	.11	.06
1993 Topps Stadium Club	95	.25	.20	.10
1993 Topps Stadium Club	187	.30	.25	.12
1993 Upper Deck	30	.20	.15	.08
1993 Upper Deck	427	.20	.15	.08
1993 Upper Deck All-Rookie	9	4.00	3.00	1.50
1993 Upper Deck Jordan's Flight Team	18	4.00	3.00	1.50
1993 Upper Deck Locker Talk	6	1.50	1.25	.60
1993 Upper Deck SE	110	.20	.15	.08
1993 Upper Deck Team MVP's	20	.50	.40	.20
1993 Upper Deck 3-D Basketball	66	.20	.15	.08
1993 Upper Deck 3-D Basketball	99	.25	.20	.10
1994 Fleer	172	.07	.05	.03
1994 Fleer Flair	114	.25	.20	.10
1994 Fleer Jam Session	144	.15	.11	.06
1994 Fleer Team Leaders	7	10.00	7.50	4.00
1994 Fleer Ultra	143	.12	.09	.05
1994 NBA Hoops Power Ratings	40	.65	.50	.25
1994 NBA Hoops Supreme Court	35	.50	.40	.20
1994 SkyBox	126	.06	.05	.02
1994 Topps	27	.08	.06	.03
1994 Topps Finest Iron Men	4	1.50	1.25	.60
1994 Topps Finest Marathon Men	13	1.25	.90	.50
1994 Topps Stadium Club	163	.08	.06	.03
1994 Topps Stadium Club Clear Cut	20	2.00	1.50	.80
1994 Upper Deck Collector's Choice	35	.07	.05	.03
1994 Upper Deck Collector's Choice	185	.08	.06	.03
1994 Upper Deck Special Edition	67	.30	.25	.12

Want list: A collector's or dealer's list of items he is wishing to buy. Often, a collector will send a dealer a "want list," and the dealer will try to locate the items on the list.

Wax box: A retail box of wax packs. There are usually 36 wax packs in a wax box.

Wax case: A wholesale case of wax boxes. There are usually 20 wax boxes in a wax case. Often the term is shortened to "wax."

Wax pack: The basic unit of retail baseball card packaging. A specific number of baseball cards, packaged with a premium (bubble gum, puzzle pieces, logo stickers and so forth) in a wax-coated wrapper.

Spud Webb

Set	Card #	MT	NM	EX
1986 Fleer	120 (R)	9.00	6.75	3.50
1988 Fleer	4	.75	.60	.30
1989 Fleer	6	.20	.15	.08
1989 NBA Hoops	115	.25	.20	.10
1990 Fleer	5	.10	.08	.04
1990 NBA Hoops	35	.10	.08	.04
1990 SkyBox	10	.10	.08	.04
1991 Fleer	4	.10	.08	.04
1991 Fleer	352	.03	.02	.01
1991 NBA Hoops	6	.05	.04	.02
1991 NBA Hoops	431	.05	.04	.02
1991 NBA Hoops Slam Dunk	3	.75	.60	.30
1991 SkyBox	9	.05	.04	.02
1991 SkyBox	646	.05	.04	.02
1991 Upper Deck	251	.05	.04	.02
1991 Upper Deck	419	.05	.04	.02
1992 Fleer	200	.08	.06	.03
1992 Fleer	278	.05	.04	.02
1992 Fleer Ultra	161	.10	.08	.04
1992 NBA Hoops	203	.05	.04	.02
1992 SkyBox	217	.05	.04	.02
1992 SkyBox	304	.05	.04	.02
1992 Topps	63	.04	.03	.02
1992 Topps Archives	75	.05	.04	.02
1992 Topps Stadium Club	72	.10	.08	.04
1992 Upper Deck	96	.05	.04	.02
1993 Fleer	186	.05	.04	.02
1993 Fleer Jam Session	199	.10	.08	.04
1993 Fleer Ultra	165	.10	.08	.04
1993 NBA Hoops	193	.06	.05	.02
1993 SkyBox	160	.05	.04	.02
1993 Topps	169	.05	.04	.02
1993 Topps Finest	57	.35	.25	.14
1993 Topps Stadium Club	122	.10	.08	.04
1993 Upper Deck	286	.05	.04	.02
1993 Upper Deck Jordan's Flight Team	19	3.00	2.25	1.25
1993 Upper Deck SE	25	.10	.08	.04
1993 Upper Deck 3-D Basketball	45	.10	.08	.04
1994 Fleer	198	.05	.04	.02
1994 Fleer Flair	130	.15	.11	.06
1994 Fleer Jam Session	166	.10	.08	.04
1994 NBA Hoops	189	.04	.03	.02
1994 NBA Hoops	446	.04	.03	.02
1994 SkyBox	146	.06	.05	.02
1994 Topps	85	.06	.05	.02
1994 Topps Finest	146	.15	.11	.06
1994 Topps Stadium Club	95	.08	.06	.03
1994 Upper Deck	128	.10	.08	.04
1994 Upper Deck Collector's Choice	89	.05	.04	.02

Chris Webber

Set	Card #	MT	NM	EX
1993 Fleer	292 (R)	3.00	2.25	1.25
1993 Fleer First Year Phenoms	10	5.00	3.75	2.00
1993 Fleer Jam Session	75 (R)	4.50	3.50	1.75
1993 Fleer Jam Session Rookie Standouts	8	8.00	6.00	3.20
1993 Fleer Lottery Exchange	1	10.00	7.50	4.00
1993 Fleer Towers of Power	29	30.00	22.00	12.00
1993 Fleer Ultra	252 (R)	4.50	3.50	1.75
1993 Fleer Ultra All-Rookies	15	13.00	9.75	5.25
1993 Fleer Ultra Power in the Key	9	20.00	15.00	8.00
1993 NBA Hoops	341 (R)	3.00	2.25	1.25
1993 NBA Hoops Admiral's Choice	5	3.00	2.25	1.25
1993 NBA Hoops Draft Redemption	1	20.00	15.00	8.00
1993 NBA Hoops II Magic's All-Rookie Team	1	25.00	18.50	10.00
1993 SkyBox	227 (R)	3.50	2.75	1.50
1993 SkyBox Draft Picks	1	22.00	16.50	8.75
1993 Topps	224 (R)	3.00	2.25	1.25
1993 Topps BlackGold	23	8.00	6.00	3.25
1993 Topps Finest	212 (R)	17.00	12.50	6.75
1993 Topps Finest Main Attraction	9	40.00	30.00	16.00
1993 Topps Stadium Club	224 (R)	4.50	3.50	1.75
1993 Topps Stadium Club	268	1.50	1.25	.60
1993 Topps Stadium Club	352	1.50	1.25	.60
1993 Topps Stadium Club Beam Team	21	25.00	18.50	10.00
1993 Upper Deck	311 (R)	3.50	2.75	1.50
1993 Upper Deck	483	1.00	.70	.40
1993 Upper Deck Rookie Exchange Gold/Silver	1	8.00	6.00	3.25
1993 Upper Deck Rookie Standouts	1	20.00	15.00	8.00
1993 Upper Deck SE	4 (R)	4.00	3.00	1.50
1993 Upper Deck SE	186	1.50	1.25	.60
1993 Upper Deck SE Behind the Glass	7	20.00	15.00	8.00
1993 Upper Deck SE West Future All Stars	5	70.00	52.00	28.00
1993 Upper Deck 3-D Basketball	72	1.00	.40	.20
1993 Upper Deck 3-D Basketball	81 (R)	2.50	1.25	.60
1993 Upper Deck 3-D Basketball	106	1.00	1.25	.60
1994 Fleer	78	1.25	.90	.50
1994 Fleer	387	.65	.04	.02
1994 Fleer Flair	53	4.00	3.00	1.50
1994 Fleer Flair Center Spotlight	6	35.00	26.00	14.00
1994 Fleer Flair Hot Numbers	20	10.00	7.50	4.00
1994 Fleer Jam Session	67	2.75	2.00	1.00
1994 Fleer Jam Session Second Year Stars	8	4.00	3.00	1.50
1994 Fleer Jam Session Slam Dunk Heroes	8	20.00	15.00	8.00
1994 Fleer NBA Award Winners	4	6.00	4.50	2.50
1994 Fleer Pro-Visions	5	3.50	2.75	1.50
1994 Fleer Rookie Sensations	25	15.00	11.00	6.00
1994 Fleer Towers of Power	10	8.00	6.00	3.25
1994 Fleer Ultra	64	2.00	1.50	.80
1994 Fleer Ultra NBA All-Rookie Team	5	50.00	37.00	20.00
1994 Fleer Ultra NBA Award Winners	4	6.00	4.50	2.50
1994 Fleer Ultra Ultra Power	10	6.00	4.50	2.50
1994 Fleer Young Lions	6	6.00	4.50	2.50
1994 NBA Hoops	71	1.00	.70	.40
1994 NBA Hoops	259	.40	.30	.15
1994 NBA Hoops	382	1.00	.70	.40
1994 NBA Hoops	421	1.25	.90	.50
1994 NBA Hoops Big Numbers	7	20.00	15.00	8.00
1994 SkyBox	57	2.00	1.50	.80
1994 SkyBox Center Stage	4	45.00	34.00	18.00
1994 SkyBox Ragin' Rookies	9	5.00	3.75	2.00
1994 Topps	47	1.25	.90	.50
1994 Topps	48	.65	.50	.25
1994 Topps	106	.40	.30	.15
1994 Topps Finest	104	2.00	1.50	.80
1994 Topps Finest	120	4.00	3.00	1.50
1994 Topps Stadium Club	9	2.00	1.50	.80
1994 Topps Stadium Club	10	1.00	.70	.40
1994 Topps Stadium Club Dynasty and Destiny	10B	6.00	4.50	2.50
1994 Topps Stadium Club Rising Stars	7	30.00	22.00	12.00
1994 Topps Super Swatters	9	4.00	3.00	1.50
1994 Upper Deck	1	.75	.60	.30
1994 Upper Deck Collector's Choice	4	1.25	.90	.50
1994 Upper Deck Collector's Choice 2,000 Pts	14	14.00	10.50	5.50
1994 Upper Deck Collector's Choice	174	.75	.60	.30
1994 Upper Deck Collector's Choice	200	.75	.60	.30
1994 Upper Deck Predictors Retail	5	3.00	2.25	1.25
1994 Upper Deck Special Edition	30	6.00	4.50	2.50

Jerry West

Set	Card #	NM	EX	VG
1961-62 Fleer	43 (R)	700.00	525.00	280.00
1961-62 Fleer	66	250.00	187.00	100.00
1969 Topps	90	100.00	75.00	40.00
1970 Topps	1	30.00	15.00	9.00
1970 Topps	107	28.00	14.00	8.50
1970 Topps	160	55.00	27.00	16.50
1970 Topps	171	15.00	7.50	4.50
1971 Topps	50	40.00	20.00	12.00
1971 Topps	143	6.00	3.00	1.75
1972 Topps	75	26.00	13.00	7.75
1972 Topps	158	7.00	3.50	2.00
1972 Topps	164	16.00	8.00	4.75
1972 Topps	176	6.00	3.00	1.75
1973 Topps	100	22.00	11.00	6.50
1974 Topps	176	20.00	10.00	6.00

Set	Card #	MT	NM	EX
1991 Upper Deck Jerry West Heroes	1	1.00	.70	.40
1991 Upper Deck Jerry West Heroes	2	1.00	.70	.40
1991 Upper Deck Jerry West Heroes	3	1.00	.70	.40
1991 Upper Deck Jerry West Heroes	4	1.00	.70	.40
1991 Upper Deck Jerry West Heroes	5	1.00	.70	.40
1991 Upper Deck Jerry West Heroes	6	1.00	.70	.40
1991 Upper Deck Jerry West Heroes	7	1.00	.70	.40
1991 Upper Deck Jerry West Heroes	8	1.00	.70	.40

Paul Westphal

Set	Card #	NM	EX	VG
1973 Topps	126 (R)	25.00	12.50	7.50
1974 Topps	64	10.00	5.00	3.00
1975 Topps	186	6.00	3.00	1.75

Set	Card #	NM	EX	VG
1976 Topps	55	9.00	4.50	2.75
1977 Topps	10	3.00	1.50	.90
1978 Topps	120	2.00	1.00	.60
1979 Topps	30	1.00	.50	.30
1980 Topps	7	1.00	.50	.30
1980 Topps	21	.25	.13	.08
1980 Topps	38	.25	.13	.08
1980 Topps	83	.25	.13	.08
1980 Topps	95	1.00	.50	.30
1980 Topps	123	.25	.13	.08
1980 Topps	133	2.00	1.00	.60
1980 Topps	149	.25	.13	.08

Set	Card #	MT	NM	EX
1981 Topps	101	.30	.25	.12
1983 Star Co.	120	10.00	7.50	4.00
1992 Fleer	184	.05	.04	.02
1992 NBA Hoops	259	.05	.04	.02
1992 SkyBox	275	.05	.04	.02
1993 NBA Hoops	250	.06	.05	.02
1994 NBA Hoops	292	.04	.03	.02

Jo Jo White

Set	Card #	NM	EX	VG
1970 Topps	143 (R)	20.00	10.00	6.00
1971 Topps	69	5.00	2.50	1.50
1972 Topps	45	4.00	2.00	1.25
1973 Topps	168	2.00	1.00	.60
1974 Topps	27	2.00	1.00	.60
1974 Topps	82	4.00	2.00	1.25
1975 Topps	117	2.00	1.00	.60
1975 Topps	135	2.00	1.00	.60
1976 Topps	115	1.50	.70	.45
1977 Topps	35	1.00	.50	.30
1978 Topps	85	.75	.40	.25
1979 Topps	11	.50	.25	.15

Sidney Wicks

Set	Card #	NM	EX	VG
1972 Topps	20 (R)	10.00	5.00	3.00

1973 Topps	160	2.50	1.25	.70
1974 Topps	96	1.00	.50	.30
1974 Topps	175	2.00	1.00	.60
1975 Topps	40	1.50	.70	.45
1975 Topps	131	1.00	.50	.30
1976 Topps	31	2.00	1.00	.60
1977 Topps	52	.60	.30	.20
1978 Topps	109	.60	.30	.20
1979 Topps	16	.50	.25	.15

Len Wilkens

Set	Card #	NM	EX	VG
1961-62 Fleer	44 (R)	125.00	94.00	50.00
1969 Topps	44	30.00	22.00	12.00
1970 Topps	6	7.00	3.50	2.00
1970 Topps	80	18.00	9.00	5.50
1971 Topps	80	10.00	5.00	3.00
1972 Topps	81	6.00	3.00	1.75
1972 Topps	176	6.00	3.00	1.75
1973 Topps	158	3.00	1.50	.90
1973 Topps	165	4.00	2.00	1.25
1974 Topps	85	1.00	.50	.30
1974 Topps	149	.50	.25	.15

Set	Card #	MT	NM	EX
1985 Star Co. Coaches	10	3.00	2.25	1.25
1989 NBA Hoops	216	.15	.11	.06
1990 NBA Hoops	309	.05	.04	.02
1990 NBA Hoops	349	.10	.08	.04
1990 SkyBox	305	.10	.08	.04
1991 Fleer	41	.05	.04	.02
1991 NBA Hoops	225	.05	.04	.02
1991 NBA Hoops	586	.08	.06	.03
1991 SkyBox	382	.07	.05	.03
1991 SkyBox	543	.20	.15	.08
1992 Fleer	45	.05	.04	.02
1992 NBA Hoops	243	.05	.04	.02
1992 SkyBox	259	.05	.04	.02
1993 NBA Hoops	230	.10	.08	.04
1994 NBA Hoops	274	.04	.03	.02

Variation: A card that exists in two different forms within the same set. A "variation" frequently occurs when an error card has been corrected. Some variations are worth more than others, based on the quantity of each variation produced.

Vending case: A wholesale package containing nothing but cards, originally intended to be used to fill card-vending machines. Most often a vending case contains 24 boxes of 500 cards each.

Jamaal Wilkes

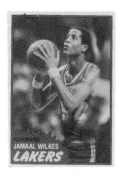

Set	Card #	NM	EX	VG
1975 Topps	50 (R)	15.00	7.50	4.50
1976 Topps	16	4.00	2.00	1.25
1977 Topps	33	1.00	.50	.30
1978 Topps	3	1.00	.50	.30
1979 Topps	35	.50	.25	.15
1980 Topps	7	1.00	.50	.30
1980 Topps	123	.25	.13	.08

Set	Card #	MT	NM	EX
1981 Topps	23	.35	.25	.14
1983 Star Co.	24	8.00	6.00	3.25
1983 Star Co. All-Star Game	24	2.00	1.50	.80
1984 Star Co.	183	4.00	3.00	1.50
1985 Star Co.	94	5.00	3.75	2.00
1985 Star Co. Last 11 R.O.Y.	11	4.00	3.00	1.50

Dominique Wilkins

Set	Card #	MT	NM	EX
1983 Star Co.	263 (R)	375.00	281.00	150.00
1983 Star Co. All-Rookies	8	55.00	41.00	22.00
1984 Star Co.	76	130.00	97.00	52.00
1984 Star Co. Court Kings	12	12.00	9.00	4.75
1984 Star Co. Slam Dunk	9	45.00	34.00	18.00
1985 Star Co.	42	100.00	75.00	40.00
1986 Fleer	121 (R)	75.00	56.00	30.00
1986 Star Co. Best of the Best	14	85.00	64.00	34.00
1986 Star Co. Court Kings	32	40.00	30.00	16.00
1987 Fleer	118	20.00	15.00	8.00
1988 Fleer	5	5.00	3.75	2.00
1988 Fleer	125	3.00	2.25	1.25
1989 Fleer	7	1.50	1.25	.60
1989 Fleer	165	.40	.30	.15
1989 NBA Hoops	130	.40	.30	.15
1989 NBA Hoops	234	.25	.20	.10

Card	#			
1990 Fleer	6	.25	.20	.10
1990 NBA Hoops	12	.30	.25	.12
1990 NBA Hoops	36	.35	.25	.14
1990 NBA Hoops	355	.15	.11	.06
1990 SkyBox	11	.30	.25	.12
1990 Star Co. Court Kings	8	16.00	11.00	4.50
1990 Star Co. Slam	9	20.00	14.00	6.00
1991 Fleer	6	.30	.25	.12
1991 Fleer	212	.15	.11	.06
1991 Fleer	372	.15	.11	.06
1991 NBA Hoops	7	.20	.15	.08
1991 NBA Hoops	259	.20	.15	.08
1991 NBA Hoops	449	.15	.11	.06
1991 NBA Hoops Slam Dunk	2	3.00	2.25	1.25
1991 SkyBox	10	.35	.25	.14
1991 SkyBox	326	.15	.11	.06
1991 SkyBox	459	.10	.08	.04
1991 SkyBox	588	.10	.08	.04
1991 Upper Deck	66	.20	.15	.08
1991 Upper Deck	255	.35	.25	.14
1992 Fleer	8	.30	.25	.12
1992 Fleer	279	.20	.15	.08
1992 Fleer Team Leaders	1	35.00	26.00	14.00
1992 Fleer Ultra	6	.75	.60	.30
1992 NBA Hoops	8	.30	.25	.12
1992 SkyBox	8	.50	.40	.20
1992 SkyBox	282	.30	.25	.12
1992 Topps	35	.25	.20	.10
1992 Topps	125	.10	.08	.04
1992 Topps	200	.15	.11	.06
1992 Topps Archives	30	.50	.40	.20
1992 Topps Beam Team	4	1.50	1.00	.50
1992 Topps Stadium Club	208	.40	.30	.15
1992 Topps Stadium Club	260	.75	.60	.30
1992 Topps Stadium Club Beam Team	2	10.00	7.50	4.00
1992 Upper Deck	148	.30	.25	.12
1992 Upper Deck	400	.30	.25	.12
1992 Upper Deck	433	.15	.11	.06
1992 Upper Deck	454	.20	.15	.08
1992 Upper Deck All-Division Team	7	1.00	.70	.40
1992 Upper Deck Foreign Exchange	10	4.00	3.00	1.50
1992 Upper Deck Team MVP's	2TM	3.00	2.25	1.25
1992 Upper Deck 15000-Point Club	1	5.00	3.75	2.00
1993 Fleer	7	.25	.20	.10
1993 Fleer	237	.20	.15	.08
1993 Fleer All-Stars	12	2.00	1.50	.80
1993 Fleer Flair USA Basketball	17	1.00	.70	.40
1993 Fleer Jam Session	8	.35	.25	.14
1993 Fleer Jam Session Gamebreakers	8	1.25	.90	.50
1993 Fleer Living Legends	6	5.00	3.75	2.00
1993 Fleer NBA Internationals	12	2.00	1.50	.80
1993 Fleer NBA Superstars	20	1.00	.70	.40
1993 Fleer Sharpshooters	10	3.00	2.25	1.25
1993 Fleer Towers of Power	30	8.00	6.00	3.25
1993 Fleer Ultra	7	.30	.25	.12
1993 Fleer Ultra	371	.50	.40	.20
1993 Fleer Ultra All-NBA Team	10	4.00	3.00	1.50
1993 Fleer Ultra Famous Nicknames	15	2.00	1.50	.80
1993 Fleer Ultra Jam City	9	10.00	7.50	4.00
1993 Fleer Ultra Scoring Kings	10	12.00	9.00	4.75
1993 NBA Hoops	7	.25	.20	.10
1993 NBA Hoops	261	.15	.11	.06
1993 NBA Hoops	423	.10	.08	.04
1993 NBA Hoops Face to Face	12	4.00	3.00	1.50
1993 SkyBox	28	.25	.20	.10

Card	#			
1993 SkyBox Dynamic Dunks	9	5.00	3.75	2.00
1993 SkyBox Showdown Series	9	1.25	.90	.50
1993 Topps	103	.15	.11	.06
1993 Topps	292	.25	.20	.10
1993 Topps	392	.15	.11	.06
1993 Topps Finest	102	2.00	1.50	.80
1993 Topps Finest	163	3.00	2.25	1.25
1993 Topps Finest Main Attraction	1	10.00	7.50	4.00
1993 Topps Stadium Club	65	.30	.25	.12
1993 Topps Stadium Club	129	.40	.30	.15
1993 Topps Stadium Club	182	.30	.25	.12
1993 Topps Stadium Club Beam Team	8	7.00	5.25	2.75
1993 Topps Stadium Club Rim Rockers	4	3.50	2.75	1.50
1993 Upper Deck	240	.20	.15	.08
1993 Upper Deck	290	.25	.20	.10
1993 Upper Deck	467	.20	.15	.08
1993 Upper Deck All-NBA	6	1.50	1.00	.50
1993 Upper Deck Jordan's Flight Team	20	7.00	5.25	2.75
1993 Upper Deck SE	155	.50	.40	.20
1993 Upper Deck SE East Future All Stars	1	13.00	9.75	5.25
1993 Upper Deck Team MVP's	1	1.00	.70	.40
1993 Upper Deck 3-D Basketball	4	.25	.20	.10
1993 Upper Deck 3-D Basketball	89	.40	.30	.15
1994 Fleer	105	.30	.25	.12
1994 Fleer	252	.30	.04	.02
1994 Fleer Career Achievement Awards	6	8.00	6.00	3.25
1994 Fleer Flair	172	.15	.11	.06
1994 Fleer Flair Scoring Power	10	2.00	1.50	.80
1994 Fleer Jam Session	16	.35	.25	.14
1994 Fleer Jam Session Flashing Stars	8	2.00	1.50	.80
1994 Fleer NBA All-Stars	13	1.25	.90	.50
1994 Fleer Superstars	6	15.00	11.00	6.00
1994 Fleer Team Leaders	1	5.00	3.75	2.00
1994 Fleer Ultra	16	.15	.11	.06
1994 Fleer Ultra All-NBA Team	15	1.00	.70	.40
1994 Fleer Ultra Scoring Kings	10	5.00	7.50	4.00
1994 NBA Hoops	97	.25	.20	.10
1994 NBA Hoops	236	.08	.06	.03
1994 NBA Hoops	309	.30	.25	.12
1994 NBA Hoops Power Ratings	4	2.50	2.00	1.00
1994 NBA Hoops Supreme Court	21	1.50	1.25	.60
1994 SkyBox	77	.40	.30	.15
1994 SkyBox Dream Team II Dream Play	6	10.00	7.50	4.00
1994 Topps	6	.06	.05	.02
1994 Topps Super Scorers	4	1.75	1.25	.70
1994 Upper Deck	22	.15	.11	.06
1994 Upper Deck	146	.50	.40	.20
1994 Upper Deck	177	.20	.15	.08
1994 Upper Deck Collector's Choice 2,000 Pts	15	5.00	3.75	2.00

Walt Williams

Kevin Willis

Set	Card #	MT	NM	EX
1992 Fleer	424 (R)	.60	.45	.25
1992 Fleer Ultra	352 (R)	.65	.50	.25
1992 Fleer Ultra All-Rookies	10	2.00	1.50	.80
1992 NBA Hoops	463 (R)	1.00	.75	.40
1992 NBA Hoops Draft Redemption	6F	5.00	3.75	2.00
1992 NBA Hoops II Magic's All-Rookie Team	6	9.00	6.75	3.50
1992 SkyBox	396 (R)	1.00	.75	.40
1992 SkyBox Draft Picks	7	2.50	2.00	1.00
1992 Topps	302 (R)	.35	.25	.14
1992 Topps Stadium Club	293 (R)	1.00	.75	.40
1992 Upper Deck	330 (R)	.50	.40	.20
1992 Upper Deck	479	.30	.25	.12
1992 Upper Deck Rookie Standouts	18	1.50	1.25	.60
1993 Fleer	187	.15	.11	.06
1993 Fleer Jam Session	200	.15	.11	.06
1993 Fleer Jam Session 2nd Year Stars	8	.60	.45	.25
1993 Fleer Rookie Sensations	24	2.00	1.50	.80
1993 Fleer Ultra	166	.15	.11	.06
1993 Fleer Ultra Inside Outside	10	.60	.45	.25
1993 NBA Hoops	194	.10	.08	.04
1993 NBA Hoops Face to Face	8	4.00	3.00	1.50
1993 SkyBox	161	.15	.11	.06
1993 SkyBox Thunder and Lightning	8	1.25	1.50	.80
1993 Topps	98	.10	.08	.04
1993 Topps	154	.10	.08	.04
1993 Topps Finest	210	.35	.25	.14
1993 Topps Stadium Club	331	.15	.11	.06
1993 Upper Deck	282	.15	.11	.06
1993 Upper Deck All-Rookie	6	1.00	.70	.40
1993 Upper Deck Future Heroes	36	.75	.60	.30
1993 Upper Deck SE	172	.10	.08	.04
1993 Upper Deck 3-D Basketball	33	.10	.08	.04
1994 Fleer	199	.05	.04	.02
1994 Fleer Flair	131	.20	.15	.08
1994 Fleer Jam Session	167	.15	.11	.06
1994 Fleer Ultra	168	.08	.06	.03
1994 NBA Hoops	190	.06	.05	.02
1994 SkyBox	147	.06	.05	.02
1994 Topps	168	.06	.05	.02
1994 Topps Finest	62	.15	.11	.06
1994 Topps Stadium Club	88	.08	.06	.03
1994 Upper Deck Collector's Choice	137	.07	.05	.03
1994 Upper Deck Special Edition	76	.20	.15	.08

Set	Card #	MT	NM	EX
1985 Star Co.	48 (R)	42.00	31.00	17.00
1985 Star Co. All-Rookie Team	9	20.00	15.00	8.00
1986 Fleer	126 (R)	13.00	9.75	5.25
1987 Fleer	124	3.00	2.25	1.25
1988 Fleer	6	1.50	1.25	.60
1989 NBA Hoops	98	.15	.11	.06
1990 Fleer	7	.03	.02	.01
1990 NBA Hoops	37	.03	.02	.01
1990 SkyBox	12	.05	.04	.02
1991 Fleer	7	.03	.02	.01
1991 NBA Hoops	8	.05	.04	.02
1991 NBA Hoops	450	.08	.06	.03
1991 SkyBox	11	.05	.04	.02
1991 SkyBox	326	.15	.11	.06
1991 Upper Deck	278	.10	.08	.04
1991 Upper Deck	462	.08	.06	.03
1992 Fleer	9	.08	.06	.03
1992 Fleer All-Stars	12	1.00	.70	.40
1992 Fleer Ultra	7	.15	.11	.06
1992 Fleer Ultra All-NBA Team	12	1.00	.70	.40
1992 NBA Hoops	9	.05	.04	.02
1992 NBA Hoops	304	.05	.04	.02
1992 SkyBox	9	.08	.06	.03
1992 Topps	109	.04	.03	.02
1992 Topps	266	.04	.03	.02
1992 Topps Archives	59	.05	.04	.02
1992 Topps Stadium Club	5	.10	.08	.04
1992 Upper Deck	144	.08	.06	.03
1992 Upper Deck	397	.05	.04	.02
1993 Fleer	8	.05	.04	.02
1993 Fleer Jam Session	9	.10	.08	.04
1993 Fleer Ultra	8	.10	.08	.04
1993 NBA Hoops	8	.06	.05	.02
1993 SkyBox	29	.05	.04	.02
1993 Topps	81	.05	.04	.02
1993 Topps Finest	78	.35	.25	.14
1993 Topps Stadium Club	69	.10	.08	.04
1993 Topps Stadium Club	332	.10	.08	.04
1993 Upper Deck	117	.05	.04	.02
1993 Upper Deck	424	.06	.05	.02
1993 Upper Deck SE	29	.10	.08	.04
1993 Upper Deck SE Behind the Glass	9	3.00	2.25	1.25
1994 Fleer	9	.08	.06	.03
1994 Fleer	315	.05	.04	.02
1994 Fleer Jam Session	6	.15	.11	.06
1994 Fleer Ultra	7	.12	.09	.05
1994 NBA Hoops	7	.04	.03	.02
1994 NBA Hoops	345	.06	.05	.02
1994 SkyBox	7	.10	.08	.04
1994 Topps	41	.08	.06	.03
1994 Topps	42	.06	.05	.02
1994 Topps Finest	97	.15	.11	.06
1994 Topps Finest	103	.20	.15	.08
1994 Topps Stadium Club	110	.08	.06	.03
1994 Topps Stadium Club	145	.08	.06	.03

		MT	NM	EX
1994 Topps Super Rebounders	3	1.00	.70	.40
1994 Upper Deck	61	.10	.08	.04
1994 Upper Deck Col.'s Choice 1,000 Rebounds	15	1.00	.70	.40
1994 Upper Deck Special Edition	2	.25	.20	.10

James Worthy

Set	Card #	MT	NM	EX
1983 Star Co.	25 (R)	65.00	49.00	26.00
1983 Star Co. All-Rookies	10	10.00	7.50	4.00
1984 Star Co.	184	25.00	18.50	10.00
1984 Star Co. Court Kings	49	10.00	7.50	4.00
1985 Star Co.	33	25.00	18.50	10.00
1986 Fleer	131 (R)	16.00	12.00	6.50
1986 Star Co. Best of the Best	15	15.00	11.00	6.00
1986 Star Co. Court Kings	33	8.00	6.00	3.25
1987 Fleer	130	4.00	3.00	1.50
1988 Fleer	70	1.00	.70	.40
1989 Fleer	80	.40	.30	.15
1989 NBA Hoops	210	.15	.11	.06
1989 NBA Hoops	219	.12	.09	.05
1990 Fleer	97	.10	.08	.04
1990 NBA Hoops	26	.15	.11	.06
1990 NBA Hoops	163	.10	.08	.04
1990 SkyBox	143	.10	.08	.04
1990 Star Co. Court Kings	10	16.00	11.00	4.50
1991 Fleer	104	.10	.08	.04
1991 Fleer	384	.05	.04	.02
1991 NBA Hoops	106	.10	.08	.04
1991 NBA Hoops	272	.10	.08	.04
1991 NBA Hoops	474	.10	.08	.04
1991 NBA Hoops	515	.10	.08	.04
1991 SkyBox	V	1.25	.85	.35
1991 SkyBox	143	.10	.08	.04
1991 SkyBox	471	.25	.20	.10
1991 Upper Deck	49	.12	.09	.05
1991 Upper Deck	146	.12	.09	.05
1991 Upper Deck	473	.12	.09	.05
1992 Fleer	114	.10	.08	.04
1992 Fleer	274	.10	.08	.04
1992 Fleer All-Stars	24	1.25	.90	.50
1992 Fleer Team Leaders	13	10.00	7.50	4.00
1992 Fleer Ultra	96	.10	.08	.04
1992 NBA Hoops	115	.10	.08	.04
1992 NBA Hoops	318	.10	.08	.04
1992 SkyBox	121	.10	.08	.04
1992 Topps	108	.04	.03	.02
1992 Topps	255	.10	.08	.04
1992 Topps Archives	2	.10	.08	.04
1992 Topps Archives	31	.10	.08	.04
1992 Topps Stadium Club	327	.20	.15	.08
1992 Upper Deck	156	.10	.08	.04
1992 Upper Deck Team MVP's	14TM	.60	.45	.25
1992 Upper Deck 15000-Point Club	8	2.00	1.50	.80
1993 Fleer	105	.10	.08	.04
1993 Fleer Jam Session	110	.15	.11	.06
1993 Fleer Ultra	97	.10	.08	.04
1993 NBA Hoops	110	.10	.08	.04
1993 NBA Hoops	435	.05	.04	.02
1993 SkyBox	101	.15	.11	.06
1993 Topps	88	.08	.06	.03
1993 Topps Finest	181	.35	.25	.14
1993 Topps Stadium Club	91	.10	.08	.04
1993 Upper Deck	142	.10	.08	.04
1993 Upper Deck	250	.05	.04	.02
1993 Upper Deck	457	.08	.06	.03
1993 Upper Deck SE	42	.20	.15	.08
1993 Upper Deck Team MVP's	13	.50	.40	.20
1993 Upper Deck 3-D Basketball	17	.10	.08	.04
1994 Fleer	114	.05	.04	.02
1994 Fleer Flair	77	.15	.11	.06
1994 Fleer Jam Session	97	.10	.08	.04
1994 Fleer Ultra	92	.08	.06	.03
1994 NBA Hoops	106	.04	.03	.02
1994 Topps	64	.06	.05	.02
1994 Topps Finest	42	.15	.11	.06
1994 Topps Stadium Club	114	.10	.08	.04
1994 Topps Stadium Club	146	.08	.06	.03
1994 Topps Stadium Club	147	.08	.06	.03
1994 Topps Stadium Club Dynasty and Destiny	5A	.65	.50	.25
1994 Upper Deck Collector's Choice	142	.05	.04	.02
1994 Upper Deck Special Edition	43	.20	.15	.08

HOCKEY

Tony Amonte

Set	Card #	MT	NM	EX
1991 O-Pee-Chee Premier	11 (R)	.50	.40	.20
1991 O-Pee-Chee/Topps	26 (R)	.30	.25	.12
1991 Parkhurst	114 (R)	.75	.60	.30
1991 Parkhurst	443	.20	.15	.08
1991 Pinnacle	301 (R)	.75	.60	.30
1991 Pinnacle	390	.25	.20	.10
1991 Pro Set	550 (R)	.50	.40	.20
1991 Pro Set Platinum	262 (R)	.50	.40	.20
1991 Score American	398 (R)	.40	.30	.15
1991 Score Canadian	288 (R)	.40	.30	.15
1991 Upper Deck	450 (R)	.50	.40	.20
1992 Bowman	389	.70	.50	.30
1992 Fleer Ultra	133	.30	.25	.12
1992 Fleer Ultra Rookies	1	3.00	2.25	1.25
1992 O-Pee-Chee	155	.25	.20	.10
1992 O-Pee-Chee	255	.10	.08	.04
1992 O-Pee-Chee 25th Anniversary Series	24	.25	.20	.10
1992 Parkhurst	107	.05	.04	.02
1992 Parkhurst	235	.05	.04	.02
1992 Pinnacle	55	.25	.20	.10
1992 Pinnacle Team 2000	4	.75	.60	.30
1992 Pro Set	118	.20	.15	.08
1992 Pro Set Rookie Goal Leaders	1	3.00	2.25	1.25
1992 Score	389	.25	.20	.10
1992 Score	415	.10	.08	.04
1992 Score	506	.05	.04	.02
1992 Topps	6	.20	.15	.08
1992 Topps	229	.40	.30	.15
1992 Topps Stadium Club	32	.20	.15	.08
1992 Topps Stadium Club	250	.15	.11	.06
1992 Upper Deck	138	.30	.25	.12
1992 Upper Deck	359	.20	.15	.08
1992 Upper Deck	635	.10	.08	.04
1992 Upper Deck All-Rookie Team	1	4.50	3.00	1.50
1993 Donruss	217	.10	.08	.04
1993 Donruss	411	.20	.15	.08
1993 Fleer PowerPlay	156	.20	.15	.08
1993 Fleer Ultra	202	.20	.15	.08
1993 Leaf	17	.30	.25	.12
1993 Parkhurst	132	.20	.15	.08
1993 Pinnacle	6	.15	.11	.06
1993 Pinnacle Team 2001	19	.50	.40	.20
1993 Score	215	.15	.11	.06
1993 Topps Premier	70	.10	.08	.04
1993 Topps Stadium Club	226	.20	.15	.08
1993 Topps Stadium Club	458	.10	.08	.04
1993 Upper Deck	64	.25	.20	.10
1993 Upper Deck SP Inserts	97	.35	.25	.14
1994 Donruss	107	.08	.06	.03
1994 Leaf	2	.15	.11	.06
1994 O-Pee-Chee Premier	5	.05	.04	.02
1994 Parkhurst Vintage Parkhurst	56	.20	.15	.08
1994 Pinnacle	16	.10	.08	.04
1994 Pinnacle Artist's Proofs	16	6.00	4.50	2.50
1994 Pinnacle Rink Collection	16	3.50	2.75	1.50
1994 Score	92	.05	.04	.02
1994 Score Hockey Gold Line	92	.25	.20	.10
1994 Topps Premier	5	.05	.04	.02
1994 Upper Deck	4	.10	.08	.04
1994 Upper Deck Electric Ice	4	3.50	2.75	1.50

Glenn Anderson

Set	Card #	MT	NM	EX
1981 O-Pee-Chee	108 (R)	20.00	15.00	8.00
1982 O-Pee-Chee	100	5.00	3.75	2.00
1983 O-Pee-Chee	24	2.00	1.50	.80
1984 O-Pee-Chee	238	1.00	.70	.40
1985 O-Pee-Chee	168	1.00	.70	.40
1986 O-Pee-Chee	80	1.00	.70	.40
1986 Topps	80	.60	.45	.25
1987 O-Pee-Chee	199	.50	.40	.20
1988 O-Pee-Chee	189	.50	.40	.20
1988 Topps	189	.20	.15	.08
1989 O-Pee-Chee	226	.07	.05	.03
1990 Bowman	195	.04	.03	.02
1990 O-Pee-Chee	145	.05	.04	.02
1990 Pro Set	81	.07	.05	.03
1990 Score	114	.05	.04	.02
1990 Score Hockey's 100 Hottest Rising Stars	54	.10	.08	.04
1990 Topps	145	.03	.02	.01
1990 Upper Deck	284	.08	.06	.03
1991 Bowman	116	.05	.04	.02
1991 O-Pee-Chee Premier	10	.05	.04	.02
1991 O-Pee-Chee/Topps	124	.12	.09	.05
1991 Parkhurst	177	.05	.04	.02
1991 Pinnacle	12	.08	.06	.03
1991 Pro Set	75	.05	.04	.02
1991 Score American	47	.05	.04	.02
1991 Score Canadian	47	.05	.04	.02

Set	Card #	MT	NM	EX
1991 Score Canadian	611	.05	.04	.02
1991 Score Traded	61	.05	.04	.02
1991 Topps Stadium Club	116	.08	.06	.03
1991 Upper Deck	250	.05	.04	.02
1992 Bowman	104	.25	.20	.10
1992 Fleer Ultra	207	.06	.05	.02
1992 O-Pee-Chee	134	.05	.04	.02
1992 Parkhurst	178	.05	.04	.02
1992 Pinnacle	355	.06	.05	.02
1992 Pro Set	185	.05	.04	.02
1992 Score	241	.05	.04	.02
1992 Topps	162	.06	.05	.02
1992 Topps Stadium Club	124	.05	.04	.02
1993 Donruss	340	.10	.08	.04
1993 Donruss	460	.10	.08	.04
1993 Fleer PowerPlay	237	.10	.08	.04
1993 Fleer Ultra	9	.07	.05	.03
1993 Leaf	41	.10	.08	.04
1993 Parkhurst	201	.10	.08	.04
1993 Pinnacle	398	.08	.06	.03
1993 Score	180	.05	.04	.02
1993 Score	449	.05	.04	.02
1993 Topps Premier	104	.05	.04	.02
1993 Topps Stadium Club	168	.05	.04	.02
1994 Donruss	254	.08	.06	.03
1994 Fleer Ultra	135	.08	.06	.03
1994 Leaf	14	.10	.08	.04
1994 O-Pee-Chee Premier	270	.05	.04	.02
1994 Topps Premier	270	.05	.04	.02

Dave Andreychuk

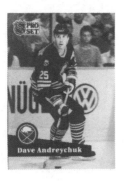

Dave Andreychuk

Set	Card #	MT	NM	EX
1984 O-Pee-Chee	17 (R)	25.00	18.50	10.00
1984 O-Pee-Chee	353	3.00	2.25	1.25
1984 Topps	13 (R)	6.00	4.50	2.50
1985 O-Pee-Chee	143	10.00	7.50	4.00
1985 Topps	143	6.00	4.50	2.50
1986 O-Pee-Chee	16	6.00	4.50	2.50
1986 Topps	16	4.00	3.00	1.50
1987 O-Pee-Chee	3	3.00	2.25	1.25
1987 Topps	3	1.25	.90	.50
1988 O-Pee-Chee	163	1.00	.70	.40
1988 Topps	163	.30	.25	.12
1989 O-Pee-Chee	105	.07	.05	.03
1989 O-Pee-Chee	106	.07	.05	.03
1989 Topps	106	.15	.11	.06
1990 Bowman	246	.04	.03	.02
1990 O-Pee-Chee	169	.05	.04	.02
1990 Pro Set	17	.25	.20	.10
1990 Pro Set	363	.05	.04	.02
1990 Score	189	.05	.04	.02
1990 Score Hockey's 100 Hottest Rising Stars	87	.10	.08	.04
1990 Topps	169	.03	.02	.01
1990 Upper Deck	41	.30	.25	.12
1991 Bowman	22	.05	.04	.02
1991 O-Pee-Chee/Topps	38	.05	.04	.02
1991 Parkhurst	17	.25	.20	.10
1991 Parkhurst	437	.05	.04	.02
1991 Pinnacle	122	.25	.20	.10
1991 Pro Set	23	.05	.04	.02
1991 Pro Set Platinum	8	.05	.04	.02
1991 Score American	277	.05	.04	.02
1991 Score Canadian	497	.05	.04	.02
1991 Upper Deck	124	.10	.08	.04
1992 Bowman	44	.60	.45	.25
1992 Fleer Ultra	12	.06	.05	.02
1992 O-Pee-Chee	141	.05	.04	.02
1992 Parkhurst	10	.05	.04	.02
1992 Parkhurst	409	.10	.08	.04
1992 Pinnacle	58	.06	.05	.02
1992 Pro Set	15	.05	.04	.02
1992 Pro Set	249	.05	.04	.02
1992 Score	204	.05	.04	.02
1992 Topps	164	.06	.05	.02
1992 Topps Stadium Club	132	.05	.04	.02
1992 Upper Deck	269	.05	.04	.02
1993 Donruss	342	.10	.08	.04
1993 Fleer PowerPlay	238	.35	.25	.14
1993 Fleer PowerPlay Slapshot Artists	1	.75	.60	.30
1993 Fleer Ultra	57	.07	.05	.03
1993 Fleer Ultra Red Light Specials	1	1.00	.70	.40
1993 Leaf	63	.10	.08	.04
1993 Leaf Gold All-Stars	4	6.00	4.50	2.50
1993 Parkhurst	200	.12	.09	.05
1993 Pinnacle	42	.15	.11	.06
1993 Pinnacle Nifty 50	11	14.00	10.50	5.50
1993 Score	343	.05	.04	.02
1993 Score	481	.05	.04	.02
1993 Score Canadian Dynamic Duos	1	20.00	15.00	8.00
1993 Topps Premier	235	.05	.04	.02
1993 Topps Stadium Club	23	.05	.04	.02
1993 Upper Deck	86	.05	.04	.02
1993 Upper Deck SP Inserts	155	.30	.25	.12
1994 Donruss	323	.08	.06	.03
1994 Fleer Flair	177	.25	.20	.10
1994 Fleer Ultra	211	.08	.06	.03
1994 Fleer Ultra Ultra Power	1	7.00	5.25	2.75
1994 Leaf	72	.10	.08	.04
1994 O-Pee-Chee Premier	38	.05	.04	.02
1994 Parkhurst	303	.06	.05	.02
1994 Parkhurst Vintage Parkhurst	89	.20	.15	.08
1994 Pinnacle	5	.10	.08	.04
1994 Pinnacle Artist's Proofs	5	5.00	3.75	2.00
1994 Pinnacle Rink Collection	5	3.00	2.25	1.25
1994 Score Dream Team	11	5.00	3.75	2.00
1994 Score 90-Plus Club	10	5.00	3.75	2.00
1994 Topps Premier	38	.05	.04	.02
1994 Topps Premier Finest Inserts	4	4.50	3.50	1.75
1994 Topps Stadium Club	58	.08	.06	.03
1994 Topps Stadium Club	140	.05	.04	.02
1994 Upper Deck Scoring Predictor	6	4.00	3.00	1.50
1994 Upper Deck SP	77	.30	.25	.12

Ask price: The price a dealer, investor or collector offers to sell his cards for.

Big cards: The trade name for Topps' oversized, glossy-finish card issues produced from 1988-1990. The cards are reminiscent of Topps cards from the 1950s.

Blister pack: A blister pack is a method of card packaging in which cards are packaged in hard plastic on a cardboard backing, with three or four pockets of cards. Issued by Donruss (1987-present).

Jason Arnott

Set	Card #	MT	NM	EX
1993 Donruss	120 (R)	2.50	2.00	1.00
1993 Donruss Rated Rookies	12	10.00	7.50	4.00
1993 Donruss Special Print	H	14.00	10.50	5.50
1993 Fleer PowerPlay	337	3.00	2.25	1.25
1993 Fleer PowerPlay Rookie Standouts	1	5.00	3.75	2.00
1993 Fleer Ultra	312 (R)	2.50	2.00	1.00
1993 Fleer Ultra Wave of the Future	1	6.00	4.50	2.50
1993 Leaf	382 (R)	2.00	1.50	.80
1993 Leaf Freshman Phenoms	7	8.00	6.00	3.25
1993 Parkhurst	261 (R)	2.00	1.50	.80
1993 Parkhurst Calder Candidates	6CC	20.00	15.00	8.00
1993 Parkhurst East-West Stars	8W	20.00	15.00	8.00
1993 Pinnacle	441 (R)	2.00	1.50	.80
1993 Pinnacle Super Rookies	7	15.00	11.00	6.00
1993 Score	594 (R)	1.50	1.25	.60
1993 Score Canadian Dynamic Duos	7	20.00	15.00	8.00
1993 Topps Stadium Club	345 (R)	2.50	2.00	1.00
1993 Upper Deck	423 (R)	2.50	2.00	1.00
1993 Upper Deck Silver Skates Dye-Cut Retail	9R	15.00	11.00	6.00
1993 Upper Deck SP Inserts	48	6.00	4.50	2.50
1994 Donruss	25	.80	.60	.30
1994 Donruss Elite Series	1	35.00	26.00	14.00
1994 Fleer Flair	56	1.75	1.25	.70
1994 Fleer Flair Center Spotlight	1	7.50	5.75	3.00
1994 Fleer Ultra	68	.55	.40	.20
1994 Fleer Ultra Ultra All-Rookies	1	25.00	18.50	10.00
1994 Fleer Ultra Ultra Power	2	20.00	15.00	8.00
1994 Leaf	133	.75	.60	.30
1994 Leaf Gold Rookies	2	9.00	6.75	3.50
1994 Leaf Gold Stars	10	32.00	24.00	13.00
1994 Leaf Limited	8	10.00	7.50	4.00
1994 O-Pee-Chee Premier	193	.40	.30	.15
1994 O-Pee-Chee Premier Finest Inserts	10	14.00	10.50	5.50
1994 Parkhurst	271	1.00	.70	.40
1994 Parkhurst Crash the Game	8	7.50	5.75	3.50
1994 Parkhurst Vintage Parkhurst	84	1.25	.90	.50
1994 Pinnacle	124	1.00	.70	.40
1994 Pinnacle Artist's Proofs	124	50.00	37.00	20.00
1994 Pinnacle Northern Lights	14	20.00	15.00	8.00
1994 Pinnacle Rink Collection	124	20.00	15.00	8.00
1994 Score	254	.75	.60	.30
1994 Score Franchise	8	22.00	16.50	8.75
1994 Score Hockey Gold Line	254	4.00	3.00	1.50
1994 Topps Premier	193	.40	.30	.15
1994 Topps Stadium Club	7	.75	.60	.30
1994 Topps Stadium Club	115	.25	.20	.10
1994 Upper Deck Be-A-Player	19	.10	.10	.10
1994 Upper Deck Ice Gallery	2	10.00	7.50	4.00
1994 Upper Deck SP	26	3.50	2.75	1.50

Andy Bathgate

Set	Card #	NM	EX	VG
1953 Parkhurst	56 (R)	115.00	57.00	34.00
1954 Topps	11	90.00	45.00	27.00
1957 Topps	60	35.00	17.50	10.50
1958 Topps	21	30.00	15.00	9.00
1959 Topps	34	25.00	12.50	7.50
1960 Topps	45	20.00	10.00	6.00
1961 Topps	22	22.00	11.00	6.50
1961 Topps	53	20.00	10.00	6.00
1962 Topps	52	15.00	7.50	4.50
1963 Topps	52	25.00	18.50	10.00
1964 Topps	86	45.00	22.00	13.50
1965 Topps	48	10.00	5.00	3.00
1966 Topps	44	10.00	5.00	3.00
1968 O-Pee-Chee	104	4.00	2.00	1.25
1968 Topps	104	4.50	2.25	1.25
1970 O-Pee-Chee	207	2.50	1.25	.70

Don Beaupre

Set	Card #	MT	NM	EX
1981 O-Pee-Chee	159 (R)	6.00	4.50	2.50
1981 Topps	103 (R)	3.00	2.25	1.25
1982 O-Pee-Chee	163	1.00	.70	.40

1983 O-Pee-Chee	166	.15	.11	.06
1984 O-Pee-Chee	94	.15	.11	.06
1984 Topps	70	.05	.04	.02
1985 O-Pee-Chee	142	.25	.20	.10
1985 Topps	142	.15	.11	.06
1986 O-Pee-Chee	89	.15	.11	.06
1986 Topps	89	.10	.08	.04
1987 O-Pee-Chee	132	.12	.09	.05
1987 Topps	132	.08	.06	.03
1988 O-Pee-Chee	42	.15	.11	.06
1988 Topps	42	.07	.05	.03
1990 Bowman	72	.04	.03	.02
1990 O-Pee-Chee	253	.05	.04	.02
1990 Pro Set	307	.05	.04	.02
1990 Score	215	.05	.04	.02
1990 Topps	253	.03	.02	.01
1990 Upper Deck	217	.08	.06	.03
1991 Bowman	304	.05	.04	.02
1991 O-Pee-Chee/Topps	505	.05	.04	.02
1991 Parkhurst	416	.05	.04	.02
1991 Pinnacle	148	.08	.06	.03
1991 Pro Set	257	.05	.04	.02
1991 Pro Set	601	.05	.04	.02
1991 Pro Set Platinum	139	.05	.04	.02
1991 Score American	185	.05	.04	.02
1991 Score Canadian	185	.05	.04	.02
1991 Topps Stadium Club	246	.08	.06	.03
1991 Upper Deck	197	.05	.04	.02
1992 Bowman	222	16.00	12.00	6.50
1992 Bowman	297	.25	.20	.10
1992 Fleer Ultra	229	.06	.05	.02
1992 O-Pee-Chee	28	.05	.04	.02
1992 Parkhurst	197	.05	.04	.02
1992 Pinnacle	48	.06	.05	.02
1992 Pinnacle	268	.40	.30	.15
1992 Pro Set	206	.05	.04	.02
1992 Score	320	.05	.04	.02
1992 Topps	195	.06	.05	.02
1992 Topps Stadium Club	270	.05	.04	.02
1992 Upper Deck	310	.05	.04	.02
1993 Fleer PowerPlay	463	.08	.06	.03
1993 Fleer Ultra	28	.07	.05	.03
1993 Parkhurst	225	.10	.08	.04
1993 Pinnacle	292	.08	.06	.03
1993 Score	58	.05	.04	.02
1993 Topps Premier	304	.06	.05	.02
1993 Topps Stadium Club	71	.05	.04	.02
1993 Upper Deck	123	.05	.04	.02

Ed Belfour

Ed Belfour

Set	Card #	MT	NM	EX
1990 Bowman	7 (R)	1.50	1.25	.60
1990 Pro Set	598 (R)	.75	.60	.30
1990 Score Traded	103 (R)	2.25	1.75	.90
1990 Upper Deck	55 (R)	2.50	2.00	1.00
1991 Bowman	390	.45	.35	.20
1991 O-Pee-Chee Premier	19	.40	.30	.15
1991 O-Pee-Chee/Topps	4	.15	.11	.06
1991 O-Pee-Chee/Topps	20	.25	.20	.10
1991 O-Pee-Chee/Topps	263	.15	.11	.06

1991 O-Pee-Chee/Topps	271	.05	.04	.02
1991 O-Pee-Chee/Topps	288	.35	.25	.14
1991 O-Pee-Chee/Topps	425	.05	.04	.02
1991 O-Pee-Chee/Topps	518	.15	.11	.06
1991 O-Pee-Chee/Topps	519	.15	.11	.06
1991 Parkhurst	30	.75	.60	.30
1991 Parkhurst	218	.05	.04	.02
1991 Pinnacle	127	.90	.70	.35
1991 Pinnacle	388	.30	.25	.12
1991 Pinnacle	400	.25	.20	.10
1991 Pro Set	43	.20	.15	.08
1991 Pro Set	321	.10	.08	.04
1991 Pro Set	600	.10	.08	.04
1991 Pro Set Platinum	26	.25	.20	.10
1991 Score American	290	.25	.20	.10
1991 Score American	348	.10	.08	.04
1991 Score American	410	.10	.08	.04
1991 Score American	411	.10	.08	.04
1991 Score American	430	.10	.08	.04
1991 Score American	431	.10	.08	.04
1991 Score American	433	.10	.08	.04
1991 Score Canadian	300	.10	.08	.04
1991 Score Canadian	301	.10	.08	.04
1991 Score Canadian	320	.10	.08	.04
1991 Score Canadian	321	.10	.08	.04
1991 Score Canadian	323	.10	.08	.04
1991 Score Canadian	378	.10	.08	.04
1991 Score Canadian	510	.20	.15	.08
1991 Score Hot Card	9	1.50	1.25	.60
1991 Topps Stadium Club	333	1.00	.70	.40
1991 Upper Deck	39	.15	.11	.06
1991 Upper Deck	164	.60	.45	.25
1991 Upper Deck	625	.15	.11	.06
1991 Upper Deck Collector Cards	2	1.00	.75	.40
1991 Upper Deck Collector Cards	4	1.00	.75	.40
1991 Upper Deck Collector Cards	7	1.00	.75	.40
1992 Bowman	90	1.00	.70	.40
1992 Bowman	199	5.00	3.75	2.00
1992 Fleer Ultra	32	.40	.30	.15
1992 Fleer Ultra All-Stars	9	4.00	3.00	1.50
1992 O-Pee-Chee	81	.25	.20	.10
1992 Parkhurst	28	.40	.30	.15
1992 Parkhurst	461	.20	.15	.08
1992 Pinnacle	118	.40	.30	.15
1992 Pinnacle	265	2.50	2.00	1.00
1992 Pinnacle Team Pinnacle	1	20.00	15.00	8.00
1992 Pro Set	33	.25	.20	.10
1992 Score	178	.25	.20	.10
1992 Topps	22	.20	.15	.08
1992 Topps Stadium Club	243	.25	.20	.10
1992 Topps Stadium Club	333	.40	.30	.15
1992 Upper Deck	203	.30	.25	.12
1993 Donruss	64	.30	.25	.12
1993 Fleer PowerPlay	46	.30	.25	.12
1993 Fleer PowerPlay Netminders	2	7.00	5.25	2.75
1993 Fleer Ultra	22	.25	.20	.10
1993 Fleer Ultra All-Stars	10	4.50	3.50	1.75
1993 Fleer Ultra Award Winners	1	5.00	3.50	2.25
1993 Leaf	62	.25	.20	.10
1993 Leaf	175	.15	.11	.06
1993 Leaf Gold All-Stars	10	9.00	6.75	3.50
1993 Leaf Painted Warriors	6	6.00	4.50	2.50
1993 OPC Premier Black Gold	16	10.00	7.50	4.00
1993 Parkhurst	44	.25	.20	.10
1993 Pinnacle	224	.20	.15	.08
1993 Pinnacle	227	.20	.15	.08
1993 Pinnacle	255	.10	.08	.04
1993 Pinnacle All-Stars	42	.35	.25	.14
1993 Pinnacle Team Pinnacle	1	70.00	52.00	28.00
1993 Score	70	.20	.15	.08
1993 Score	485	.05	.04	.02
1993 Topps Premier	60	.15	.11	.06

Set	Card #	MT	NM	EX
1993 Topps Premier	95	.10	.08	.04
1993 Topps Premier Black Gold	14	3.50	2.75	1.50
1993 Topps Stadium Club	99	.25	.20	.10
1993 Topps Stadium Club	144	.15	.11	.06
1993 Topps Stadium Club	150	.15	.11	.06
1993 Topps Stadium Club All-Stars	1	20.00	15.00	8.00
1993 Upper Deck	147	.20	.15	.08
1993 Upper Deck Award Winners	3	4.00	3.00	1.50
1993 Upper Deck SP Inserts	27	.75	.60	.30
1994 Donruss	275	.25	.20	.10
1994 Donruss Ice Masters	1	2.75	2.00	1.00
1994 Donruss Masked Marvels	1	5.00	3.75	2.00
1994 Fleer Flair	31	.75	.60	.30
1994 Fleer Ultra	39	.15	.11	.06
1994 Leaf	296	.20	.15	.08
1994 Leaf Gold Stars	7	40.00	30.00	16.00
1994 Parkhurst	41	.15	.11	.06
1994 Pinnacle	42	.30	.25	.12
1994 Pinnacle Artist's Proofs	42	15.00	11.00	6.00
1994 Pinnacle Goaltending Greats	4	10.00	7.50	4.00
1994 Pinnacle Rink Collection	42	8.00	6.00	3.25
1994 Score	149	.20	.15	.08
1994 Score Hockey Gold Line	149	1.50	1.25	.60
1994 Topps Stadium Club	155	.35	.25	.14
1994 Topps Stadium Club	180	.20	.15	.08
1994 Upper Deck SP	15	.75	.60	.30

Brian Bellows

Set	Card #	MT	NM	EX
1983 O-Pee-Chee	165	2.50	2.00	1.00
1983 O-Pee-Chee	167 (R)	8.00	6.00	3.25
1984 O-Pee-Chee	95	2.00	1.50	.80
1984 O-Pee-Chee	359	.40	.30	.15
1984 Topps	71	1.00	.70	.40
1985 O-Pee-Chee	50	2.00	1.50	.80
1985 Topps	50	1.25	.90	.50
1986 O-Pee-Chee	75	1.25	.90	.50
1986 Topps	75	.75	.60	.30
1987 O-Pee-Chee	94	.60	.45	.25
1987 Topps	94	.20	.15	.08
1988 O-Pee-Chee	95	.25	.20	.10
1988 Topps	95	.25	.20	.10
1989 O-Pee-Chee	177	.20	.15	.08
1989 Topps	177	.20	.15	.08
1990 Bowman	182	.07	.05	.03
1990 O-Pee-Chee	70	.07	.05	.03
1990 O-Pee-Chee	200	.05	.04	.02
1990 O-Pee-Chee Premier	3	.15	.11	.06
1990 Pro Set	130	.50	.40	.20
1990 Score	7	.15	.11	.06
1990 Score	322	.05	.04	.02
1990 Score Hockey's 100 Hottest Rising Stars	3	.10	.08	.04
1990 Topps	70	.07	.05	.03
1990 Topps	200	.07	.05	.03
1990 Upper Deck	126	.30	.25	.12
1990 Upper Deck	308	.07	.05	.03
1991 Bowman	129	.05	.04	.02
1991 O-Pee-Chee/Topps	110	.05	.04	.02
1991 Parkhurst	79	.05	.04	.02
1991 Pinnacle	129	.08	.06	.03
1991 Pro Set	109	.05	.04	.02
1991 Pro Set Platinum	59	.05	.04	.02
1991 Score American	160	.05	.04	.02
1991 Score Canadian	160	.05	.04	.02
1991 Topps Stadium Club	87	.08	.06	.03
1991 Upper Deck	236	.05	.04	.02
1992 Bowman	200	20.00	15.00	8.00
1992 Bowman	260	.25	.20	.10
1992 Fleer Ultra	100	.06	.05	.02
1992 Fleer Ultra	324	.06	.05	.02
1992 O-Pee-Chee	384	.05	.04	.02
1992 O-Pee-Chee Premier	75	.05	.04	.02
1992 Parkhurst	87	.05	.04	.02
1992 Pinnacle	325	.06	.05	.02
1992 Topps	240	.06	.05	.02
1992 Topps Stadium Club	293	.05	.04	.02
1992 Upper Deck	172	.05	.04	.02
1992 Upper Deck	471	.05	.04	.02
1992 Upper Deck	636	.10	.08	.04
1992 Upper Deck Gordie Howe Selects	1	4.00	3.00	1.50
1993 Donruss	170	.10	.08	.04
1993 Fleer PowerPlay	124	.10	.08	.04
1993 Fleer Ultra	4	.07	.05	.03
1993 Leaf	76	.10	.08	.04
1993 Parkhurst	371	.10	.08	.04
1993 Pinnacle	22	.10	.08	.04
1993 Score	4	.05	.04	.02
1993 Score Canadian Dynamic Duos	6	8.50	6.50	3.50
1993 Topps Premier	202	.05	.04	.02
1993 Topps Stadium Club	156	.05	.04	.02
1993 Upper Deck	390	.05	.04	.02
1993 Upper Deck SP Inserts	76	.30	.25	.12
1994 Donruss	203	.08	.06	.03
1994 Fleer Flair	84	.25	.20	.10
1994 Fleer Ultra	105	.08	.06	.03
1994 Leaf	301	.10	.08	.04
1994 O-Pee-Chee Premier	219	.05	.04	.02
1994 Parkhurst	112	.06	.05	.02
1994 Score	73	.05	.04	.02
1994 Score Hockey Gold Line	73	.25	.20	.10
1994 Topps Premier	219	.05	.04	.02

Rob Blake

Set	Card #	MT	NM	EX
1990 Bowman	142 (R)	.50	.40	.20
1990 O-Pee-Chee Premier	6 (R)	2.00	1.50	.80

1990 Pro Set	611	.45	.35	.20
1990 Score	421 (R)	.50	.40	.20
1990 Upper Deck	45 (R)	1.50	1.25	.60
1991 Bowman	182	.15	.11	.06
1991 O-Pee-Chee Premier	44	.15	.11	.06
1991 O-Pee-Chee/Topps	6	.15	.11	.06
1991 O-Pee-Chee/Topps	112	.15	.11	.06
1991 Parkhurst	293	.05	.04	.02
1991 Pinnacle	201	.30	.25	.12
1991 Pinnacle	382	.20	.15	.08
1991 Pro Set	92	.15	.11	.06
1991 Pro Set Platinum	51	.15	.11	.06
1991 Pro Set Platinum PC	8	1.25	.90	.50
1991 Score American	27	.15	.11	.06
1991 Score American	349	.10	.08	.04
1991 Score Canadian	27	.15	.11	.06
1991 Score Canadian	379	.10	.08	.04
1991 Topps Stadium Club	348	.40	.30	.15
1991 Upper Deck	43	.15	.11	.06
1991 Upper Deck	148	.30	.25	.12
1992 Bowman	367	.75	.60	.30
1992 Fleer Ultra	79	.10	.08	.04
1992 O-Pee-Chee	243	.05	.04	.02
1992 Parkhurst	302	.20	.15	.08
1992 Pinnacle	32	.10	.08	.04
1992 Pinnacle Team 2000	16	1.25	.90	.50
1992 Pro Set	67	.10	.08	.04
1992 Score	177	.05	.04	.02
1992 Topps	211	.15	.11	.06
1992 Topps Stadium Club	23	.10	.08	.04
1992 Upper Deck	140	.05	.04	.02
1993 Donruss	158	.10	.08	.04
1993 Fleer PowerPlay	113	.20	.15	.08
1993 Fleer Ultra	24	.07	.05	.03
1993 Leaf	172	.10	.08	.04
1993 Parkhurst	94	.15	.11	.06
1993 Pinnacle	46	.10	.08	.04
1993 Score	236	.05	.04	.02
1993 Topps Premier	56	.10	.08	.04
1993 Topps Stadium Club	246	.15	.11	.06
1993 Upper Deck	317	.06	.05	.02
1993 Upper Deck SP Inserts	68	.30	.25	.12
1994 Fleer Flair	77	.25	.20	.10
1994 Fleer Ultra	96	.10	.08	.04
1994 Leaf	12	.10	.08	.04
1994 Parkhurst	105	.06	.05	.02
1994 Parkhurst Vintage Parkhurst	85	.20	.15	.08
1994 Pinnacle	9	.10	.08	.04
1994 Pinnacle Artist's Proofs	9	6.00	4.50	2.50
1994 Pinnacle Boomers	10	6.00	4.50	2.50
1994 Pinnacle Rink Collection	9	3.50	2.75	1.50
1994 Pinnacle Team Pinnacle	4	20.00	15.00	8.00
1994 Score	47	.05	.04	.02
1994 Score Hockey Gold Line	47	.50	.40	.20
1994 Topps Stadium Club	135	.10	.08	.04
1994 Upper Deck SP	35	.30	.25	.12

Mike Bossy

Set	Card #	NM	EX	VG
1978 O-Pee-Chee	1	8.00	4.00	2.50
1978 O-Pee-Chee	63	3.50	1.75	1.00
1978 O-Pee-Chee	67	3.00	1.50	.90
1978 O-Pee-Chee	115 (R)	45.00	22.00	13.50
1978 Topps	1	5.00	2.50	1.50
1978 Topps	63	2.00	1.00	.60
1978 Topps	67	2.00	1.00	.60
1978 Topps	115 (R)	27.00	13.50	8.00
1979 O-Pee-Chee	1	4.00	2.00	1.25
1979 O-Pee-Chee	5	3.00	1.50	.90
1979 O-Pee-Chee	7	3.00	1.50	.90
1979 O-Pee-Chee	161	3.00	1.50	.90
1979 O-Pee-Chee	230	15.00	7.50	4.50
1979 Topps	1	2.50	1.25	.70
1979 Topps	5	1.50	.70	.45
1979 Topps	7	2.00	1.00	.60
1979 Topps	161	2.00	1.00	.60
1979 Topps	230	10.00	5.00	3.00
1980 O-Pee-Chee	25	8.00	4.00	2.50
1980 O-Pee-Chee	204	2.00	1.00	.60
1980 Topps	25	5.00	2.50	1.50
1980 Topps	204	1.25	.60	.40

Set	Card #	MT	NM	EX
1981 O-Pee-Chee	198	4.00	3.00	1.50
1981 O-Pee-Chee	208	1.25	.90	.50
1981 O-Pee-Chee	219	.75	.60	.30
1981 O-Pee-Chee	382	1.00	.70	.40
1981 O-Pee-Chee	386	1.00	.70	.40
1981 O-Pee-Chee	388	1.00	.70	.40
1981 O-Pee-Chee	390	1.00	.70	.40
1981 Topps	4	2.00	1.50	.80
1981 Topps	57	.40	.30	.15
1981 Topps	125	1.00	.70	.40
1982 O-Pee-Chee	2	.75	.60	.30
1982 O-Pee-Chee	197	.50	.40	.20
1982 O-Pee-Chee	199	2.00	1.50	.80
1983 O-Pee-Chee	1	.75	.60	.30
1983 O-Pee-Chee	3	1.50	1.25	.60
1983 O-Pee-Chee	205	.60	.45	.25
1983 O-Pee-Chee	210	.60	.45	.25
1984 O-Pee-Chee	122	1.50	1.25	.60
1984 O-Pee-Chee	209	.75	.60	.30
1984 O-Pee-Chee	362	.50	.40	.20
1984 O-Pee-Chee	376	.60	.45	.25
1984 Topps	91	.75	.60	.30
1984 Topps	155	.20	.15	.08
1985 O-Pee-Chee	130	1.00	.70	.40
1985 Topps	130	1.00	.70	.40
1986 O-Pee-Chee	90	.75	.60	.30
1986 Topps	90	.60	.45	.25
1987 O-Pee-Chee	105	.75	.60	.30
1987 Topps	105	.50	.40	.20
1990 Pro Set	650	.20	.15	.08
1992 O-Pee-Chee	391	.25	.20	.10
1992 O-Pee-Chee 25th Anniversary Series	11	.30	.25	.12
1992 Pinnacle	245	.25	.20	.10

Ray Bourque

Set	Card #	NM	EX	VG
1980 O-Pee-Chee	140 (R)	130.00	65.00	39.00
1980 Topps	2	6.00	3.00	1.75
1980 Topps	140 (R)	70.00	35.00	21.00

Set	Card #	MT	NM	EX
1981 O-Pee-Chee	1	30.00	22.00	12.00
1981 O-Pee-Chee	17	7.50	5.75	3.00
1981 Topps	5	4.00	3.00	1.50
1981 Topps	126	2.00	1.50	.80
1982 O-Pee-Chee	24	3.00	2.25	1.25
1983 O-Pee-Chee	45	7.00	5.25	2.75
1984 O-Pee-Chee	1	5.00	3.75	2.00
1984 O-Pee-Chee	211	1.50	1.25	.60
1984 Topps	1	1.50	1.25	.60
1984 Topps	157	.50	.40	.20
1985 O-Pee-Chee	40	4.00	3.00	1.50
1985 Topps	40	2.00	1.50	.80
1986 O-Pee-Chee	1	2.50	2.00	1.00
1986 Topps	1	2.00	1.50	.80
1987 O-Pee-Chee	87	2.00	1.50	.80
1987 O-Pee-Chee Hockey Leaders	4	.75	.60	.30
1987 Topps	87	1.00	.70	.40
1988 O-Pee-Chee	73	1.00	.70	.40
1988 O-Pee-Chee NHL Stars	3	.75	.60	.30
1988 Topps	73	.60	.45	.25
1989 O-Pee-Chee	110	.75	.60	.30
1989 O-Pee-Chee Future Stars	33	.40	.30	.15
1989 Topps	110	.40	.30	.15
1990 Bowman	31	.15	.11	.06
1990 O-Pee-Chee	43	.20	.15	.08
1990 O-Pee-Chee	196	.15	.11	.06
1990 O-Pee-Chee Premier	9	.50	.40	.20
1990 Pro Set	1	1.75	1.25	.70
1990 Pro Set	357	.10	.08	.04
1990 Pro Set	384	.10	.08	.04
1990 Score	200	.30	.25	.12
1990 Score	313	.15	.11	.06
1990 Score	363	.15	.11	.06
1990 Score Hockey's 100 Hottest Rising Stars	35	.10	.08	.04
1990 Topps	43	.30	.25	.12
1990 Topps	196	.15	.11	.06
1990 Upper Deck	64	.50	.40	.20
1990 Upper Deck	204	.15	.11	.06
1990 Upper Deck	320	.15	.11	.06
1990 Upper Deck	489	.25	.20	.10
1991 Bowman	356	.15	.11	.06
1991 O-Pee-Chee Premier	119	.15	.11	.06
1991 O-Pee-Chee/Topps	66	..12	.09	.05
1991 O-Pee-Chee/Topps	261	.12	.09	.05
1991 O-Pee-Chee/Topps	517	.05	.04	.02
1991 Parkhurst	9	.25	.20	.10
1991 Parkhurst	221	.05	.04	.02
1991 Parkhurst	469	3.00	2.25	1.25
1991 Parkhurst	472	3.00	2.25	1.25
1991 Pinnacle	15	.25	.20	.10
1991 Pinnacle	368	.08	.06	.03
1991 Pinnacle B	2	45.00	34.00	18.00
1991 Pro Set	9	.10	.08	.04
1991 Pro Set	296	.10	.08	.04
1991 Pro Set	322	.10	.08	.04
1991 Pro Set	567	.10	.08	.04
1991 Pro Set Platinum	2	.10	.08	.04
1991 Pro Set Platinum	278	.05	.04	.02
1991 Score American	50	.10	.08	.04
1991 Score American	344	.10	.08	.04
1991 Score American	415	.10	.08	.04
1991 Score American	429	.10	.08	.04
1991 Score Canadian	50	.10	.08	.04
1991 Score Canadian	319	.10	.08	.04
1991 Score Canadian	331	.10	.08	.04
1991 Score Canadian	374	.10	.08	.04
1991 Topps Stadium Club	233	.40	.30	.15
1991 Topps Stadium Club Charter Member Set	3	2.00	1.00	1.00
1991 Upper Deck	255	.20	.15	.08
1991 Upper Deck	633	.10	.08	.04
1991 Upper Deck Collector Cards	5	1.00	.75	.40
1992 Bowman	3	.80	.60	.30
1992 Bowman	223	4.00	3.00	1.50
1992 Fleer Ultra	2	.20	.15	.08
1992 Fleer Ultra All-Stars	2	2.25	1.75	.90
1992 Fleer Ultra Award Winners	8	2.50	2.00	1.00
1992 O-Pee-Chee	126	.10	.08	.04
1992 Parkhurst	1	.25	.20	.10
1992 Parkhurst	464	.08	.06	.03
1992 Pinnacle	2	.20	.15	.08
1992 Pinnacle Team Pinnacle	2	15.00	11.00	6.00
1992 Pro Set	4	.10	.08	.04
1992 Pro Set	261	.05	.04	.02
1992 Score	100	.20	.15	.08
1992 Score	419	.05	.04	.02
1992 Score	447	.05	.04	.02
1992 Score	490	.08	.06	.03
1992 Score	520	.05	.04	.02
1992 Topps	262	.06	.05	.02
1992 Topps Stadium Club	249	.15	.11	.06
1992 Topps Stadium Club	267	.25	.20	.10
1992 Upper Deck	265	.20	.15	.08
1992 Upper Deck	626	.10	.08	.04
1993 Donruss	24	.20	.15	.08
1993 Fleer PowerPlay	16	.20	.15	.08
1993 Fleer PowerPlay Slapshot Artists	2	1.00	.70	.40
1993 Fleer Ultra	1	.20	.15	.08
1993 Fleer Ultra All-Stars	2	4.50	3.50	1.75
1993 Leaf	215	.20	.15	.08
1993 Leaf Gold All-Stars	7	6.00	4.50	2.50
1993 OPC Premier Black Gold	21	8.00	6.00	3.25
1993 Parkhurst	14	.15	.11	.06
1993 Pinnacle	250	.25	.20	.10
1993 Pinnacle All-Stars	21	.25	.20	.10
1993 Pinnacle All-Stars	48	3.50	2.75	1.50
1993 Pinnacle Hockey Captains	2	5.00	3.75	2.00
1993 Pinnacle Team Pinnacle	8	27.00	20.00	11.00
1993 Score	29	.10	.08	.04
1993 Score Dream Team	7	6.00	4.50	2.50
1993 Score Franchise	1	6.00	4.50	2.50
1993 Topps Premier	93	.10	.08	.04
1993 Topps Premier	350	.15	.11	.06
1993 Topps Premier	383	.10	.08	.04
1993 Topps Premier Black Gold	15	2.50	2.00	1.00
1993 Topps Stadium Club	160	.15	.11	.06
1993 Topps Stadium Club All-Stars	2	5.00	3.75	2.00
1993 Upper Deck	116	.10	.08	.04
1993 Upper Deck Next in Line	4	5.00	3.75	2.00

Set	Card #	NM	EX	VG
1993 Upper Deck SP Inserts	7	.70	.50	.30
1994 Donruss	68	.20	.15	.08
1994 Fleer Flair	8	.35	.25	.14
1994 Fleer Ultra	10	.12	.09	.05
1994 Fleer Ultra All-Stars	1	.40	.30	.15
1994 Fleer Ultra NHL Award Winners	1	1.00	.70	.40
1994 Leaf	77	.20	.15	.08
1994 Leaf Gold Stars	6	28.00	21.00	11.00
1994 O-Pee-Chee Premier	36	.10	.08	.04
1994 Parkhurst	13	.20	.15	.08
1994 Parkhurst	304	.10	.08	.04
1994 Parkhurst Crash the Game	2	5.00	3.75	2.00
1994 Pinnacle	190	.30	.25	.12
1994 Pinnacle Artist's Proofs	190	20.00	15.00	8.00
1994 Pinnacle Boomers	7	7.00	5.25	2.75
1994 Pinnacle Rink Collection	190	10.00	7.50	4.00
1994 Pinnacle Team Pinnacle	3	20.00	15.00	8.00
1994 Score	180	.15	.11	.06
1994 Score Dream Team	3	6.00	4.50	2.50
1994 Score Hockey Gold Line	180	1.00	.70	.40
1994 Score 90-Plus Club	21	6.00	4.50	2.50
1994 Topps Premier	36	.10	.08	.04
1994 Topps Stadium Club	77	.15	.11	.06
1994 Topps Stadium Club	267	.10	.08	.04
1994 Topps Stadium Club Finest	8	5.00	3.75	2.00
1994 Upper Deck Scoring Predictor	14	6.00	4.50	2.50
1994 Upper Deck SP	4	.75	.60	.30

Johnny Bower

Set	Card #	NM	EX	VG
1954 Parkhurst	65 (R)	250.00	125.00	75.00
1958 Parkhurst	46	85.00	42.00	25.00
1959 Parkhurst	25	20.00	10.00	6.00
1959 Parkhurst	32	50.00	25.00	15.00
1960 Parkhurst	3	40.00	20.00	12.00
1961 Parkhurst	3	30.00	15.00	9.00
1961 Parkhurst	16	18.00	9.00	5.50
1962 Parkhurst	16	20.00	10.00	6.00
1963 Parkhurst	5	25.00	12.50	7.50
1963 Parkhurst	65	25.00	12.50	7.50
1964 Topps	40	40.00	20.00	12.00
1965 Topps	77	10.00	5.00	3.00
1966 Topps	12	15.00	7.50	4.50
1967 Topps	76	15.00	7.50	4.50
1968 O-Pee-Chee	122	7.00	3.50	2.00
1968 Topps	122	6.00	3.00	1.75
1969 O-Pee-Chee	187	5.00	2.50	1.50

Set	Card #	MT	NM	EX
1993 Parkhurst Parkie Reprints	65	18.00	13.50	7.25

Scotty Bowman

Set	Card #	NM	EX	VG
1974 O-Pee-Chee	261 (R)	18.00	9.00	5.50
1974 Topps	261 (R)	9.00	4.50	2.70

Four years ago: Mario Lemieux's 1995-86 O-Pee-Chee rookie card (#9) was $125 in July 1991.

* * *

Four years ago: Steve Yzerman's 1984-85 O-Pee-Chee rookie card (#67) was $40 in July 1991.

* * *

Four years ago: Guy Lafleur's 1971-72 O-Pee-Chee rookie card (#148) was $150 in July 1991.

* * *

Four years ago: Jari Kurri's 1981-82 O-Pee-Chee rookie card (#107) was $17.50 in July 1991.

Pavel Bure

Set	Card #	MT	NM	EX
1990 Upper Deck	526 (R)	20.00	15.00	8.00
1991 O-Pee-Chee Premier	67	2.00	1.50	.80
1991 Parkhurst	404	2.00	1.50	.80
1991 Parkhurst	446	.60	.45	.25
1991 Parkhurst	462	15.00	11.00	6.00
1991 Pinnacle	315	3.00	2.25	1.25
1991 Pro Set	564 (R)	1.75	1.25	.70
1991 Pro Set Platinum	272	2.00	1.50	.80
1991 Score Traded	49	3.00	2.25	1.25
1991 Upper Deck	54	3.00	2.25	1.25
1991 Upper Deck	555	2.00	1.50	.80
1991 Upper Deck	647	1.00	.70	.40
1992 Bowman	154	11.00	8.25	4.50
1992 Fleer Ultra	219	2.50	2.00	1.00
1992 Fleer Ultra Award Winners	9	8.00	6.00	3.25
1992 Fleer Ultra Imports	2	15.00	11.00	6.00
1992 Fleer Ultra Rookies	3	8.00	6.00	3.25
1992 O-Pee-Chee	25	1.00	.70	.40
1992 O-Pee-Chee	324	.40	.30	.15
1992 O-Pee-Chee Premier Star Performers	10	3.00	2.25	1.25
1992 O-Pee-Chee 25th Anniversary Series	25	.25	.20	.10
1992 Parkhurst	188	2.50	2.00	1.00
1992 Parkhurst	234	1.00	.70	.40
1992 Parkhurst	460	1.00	.70	.40
1992 Parkhurst	506	4.00	3.00	1.50
1992 Pinnacle	110	3.50	2.75	1.50
1992 Pinnacle Team Pinnacle	4	20.00	15.00	8.00

Set	Card #	MT	NM	EX
1992 Pinnacle Team 2000	8	8.00	6.00	3.25
1992 Pro Set	192	1.75	1.25	.70
1992 Pro Set Award Winners	3	15.00	11.00	6.00
1992 Pro Set Gold Team Leaders	13	13.00	9.75	5.25
1992 Pro Set Rookie Goal Leaders	2	15.00	11.00	6.00
1992 Score	14	1.00	.70	.40
1992 Score	504	.60	.45	.25
1992 Score	523	.60	.45	.25
1992 Topps	8	.60	.45	.25
1992 Topps	353	1.50	1.25	.60
1992 Topps Stadium Club	246	1.75	1.25	.70
1992 Topps Stadium Club	489	2.50	2.00	1.00
1992 Upper Deck	156	1.25	.90	.50
1992 Upper Deck	362	.75	.60	.30
1992 Upper Deck	431	1.00	.70	.40
1992 Upper Deck Euro Stars	2	10.00	7.50	4.00
1992 Upper Deck Euro-Rookie Team	1	10.00	7.50	4.00
1992 Upper Deck World Junior Grads	5	15.00	11.00	6.00
1993 Donruss	351	2.00	1.50	.80
1993 Donruss Ice Kings	8	7.00	5.25	2.75
1993 Fleer PowerPlay	248	1.75	1.25	.70
1993 Fleer PowerPlay Global Greats	1	6.00	4.50	2.50
1993 Fleer PowerPlay Point Leaders	1	4.00	3.00	1.50
1993 Fleer Ultra	37	1.25	.90	.50
1993 Fleer Ultra All-Stars	17	10.00	7.50	4.00
1993 Fleer Ultra Red Light Specials	2	7.00	5.25	2.75
1993 Fleer Ultra Speed Merchants	1	42.00	31.00	17.00
1993 Leaf	10	1.25	.90	.50
1993 Leaf Gold All-Stars	8	13.00	9.75	5.25
1993 OPC Premier Black Gold	7	20.00	15.00	8.00
1993 Parkhurst	211	1.25	.90	.50
1993 Parkhurst East-West Stars	2W	35.00	26.00	14.00
1993 Parkhurst US Canada Gold-Foiled	7	30.00	22.00	12.00
1993 Pinnacle	320	1.00	.70	.40
1993 Pinnacle All-Stars	31	1.00	.70	.40
1993 Pinnacle Nifty 50	6	35.00	26.00	14.00
1993 Pinnacle Team Pinnacle	10	37.00	28.00	15.00
1993 Pinnacle Team 2001	3	8.00	6.00	3.25
1993 Score	333	.75	.60	.30
1993 Score Dream Team	19	30.00	22.00	12.00
1993 Score Franchise	22	32.00	24.00	13.00
1993 Score International Stars	1	6.00	4.50	2.50
1993 Topps Premier	260	1.00	.70	.40
1993 Topps Premier	440	.50	.40	.20
1993 Topps Stadium Club	480	1.25	.90	.50
1993 Topps Stadium Club All-Stars	6	15.00	11.00	6.00
1993 Upper Deck	35	1.00	.70	.40
1993 Upper Deck	307	.50	.40	.20
1993 Upper Deck Future Heroes	30	25.00	18.50	10.00
1993 Upper Deck NHL's Best	5	26.00	19.50	10.50
1993 Upper Deck Silver Skates Dye-Cut Hobby	2H	25.00	18.50	10.00
1993 Upper Deck SP Inserts	162	10.00	7.50	4.00
1994 Donruss	19	1.25	.90	.50
1994 Donruss Elite Series	3	50.00	37.00	20.00
1994 Fleer Flair	189	3.50	2.75	1.50
1994 Fleer Flair Hot Numbers	1	40.00	30.00	16.00
1994 Fleer Flair Scoring Power	1	12.00	9.00	4.75
1994 Fleer Ultra	222	1.50	1.25	.60
1994 Fleer Ultra All-Stars	7	3.00	2.25	1.25
1994 Fleer Ultra Scoring Kings	1	6.00	4.50	2.50
1994 Leaf	10	1.25	.90	.50
1994 Leaf Fire On Ice	3	15.00	11.00	6.00
1994 Leaf Gold Stars	4	70.00	52.00	28.00
1994 O-Pee-Chee Go to Guys	5	28.00	28.00	28.00
1994 O-Pee-Chee Premier	39	.75	.60	.30
1994 O-Pee-Chee Premier	151	.25	.20	.10
1994 Parkhurst	297	.90	.70	.35
1994 Parkhurst Crash the Game	24	15.00	11.00	6.00
1994 Parkhurst Vintage Parkhurst	18	5.00	3.75	2.00
1994 Pinnacle	140	2.00	1.50	.80
1994 Pinnacle Artist's Proofs	140	150.00	112.00	60.00
1994 Pinnacle Boomers	13	30.00	22.00	12.00
1994 Pinnacle Hockey MVP's	(2)	100.00	75.00	40.00
1994 Pinnacle Northern Lights	17	40.00	30.00	16.00
1994 Pinnacle Rink Collection	140	60.00	45.00	24.00
1994 Pinnacle Team Pinnacle	12	70.00	52.00	28.00
1994 Score	190	.75	.60	.30
1994 Score Dream Team	24	25.00	18.50	10.00
1994 Score Franchise	24	60.00	45.00	24.00
1994 Score Hockey Gold Line	190	7.00	5.25	2.75
1994 Score 90-Plus Club	5	17.00	12.50	6.75
1994 Topps Premier	39	.75	.60	.30
1994 Topps Premier	151	.25	.20	.10
1994 Topps Premier Finest Inserts	1	25.00	18.50	10.00
1994 Topps Stadium Club	10	1.25	.90	.50
1994 Topps Stadium Club Dynasty and Destiny	3	17.00	12.50	6.75
1994 Topps Stadium Club Finest	5	15.00	11.00	6.00
1994 Upper Deck	227	.85	.60	.35
1994 Upper Deck Award Predictor	2	16.00	12.00	6.50
1994 Upper Deck Electric Ice	227	35.00	26.00	14.00
1994 Upper Deck Scoring Predictor	1	17.00	12.50	6.75
1994 Upper Deck Scoring Predictor	25	18.00	13.50	7.25

Guy Carbonneau

Set	Card #	MT	NM	EX
1983 O-Pee-Chee	185 (R)	6.00	4.50	2.50
1984 O-Pee-Chee	257	2.00	1.50	.80
1985 O-Pee-Chee	233	1.00	.70	.40
1986 O-Pee-Chee	176	.50	.40	.20
1986 Topps	176	.20	.15	.08

1987 O-Pee-Chee	232	.12	.09	.05
1988 O-Pee-Chee	203	.15	.11	.06
1989 O-Pee-Chee	53	.07	.05	.03
1989 Topps	53	.05	.04	.02
1990 Bowman	44	.04	.03	.02
1990 O-Pee-Chee	93	.05	.04	.02
1990 Pro Set	146	.05	.04	.02
1990 Score	91	.05	.04	.02
1990 Score Hockey's 100 Hottest Rising Stars	43	.10	.08	.04
1990 Topps	93	.03	.02	.01
1990 Upper Deck	188	.08	.06	.03
1991 Bowman	338	.05	.04	.02
1991 O-Pee-Chee/Topps	54	.12	.09	.05
1991 Parkhurst	92	.05	.04	.02
1991 Parkhurst	466	2.00	1.50	.80
1991 Pinnacle	130	.08	.06	.03
1991 Pinnacle	374	.08	.06	.03
1991 Pro Set	130A	.05	.04	.02
1991 Pro Set	130B	.05	.04	.02
1991 Pro Set	345	.05	.04	.02
1991 Pro Set	576	.05	.04	.02
1991 Pro Set Platinum	63	.05	.04	.02
1991 Score American	19	.05	.04	.02
1991 Score Canadian	19	.05	.04	.02
1991 Topps Stadium Club	41	.08	.06	.03
1991 Upper Deck	265	.05	.04	.02
1992 Bowman	38	.25	.20	.10
1992 Fleer Ultra	102	.06	.05	.02
1992 Fleer Ultra Award Winners	3	2.50	2.00	1.00
1992 O-Pee-Chee	206	.05	.04	.02
1992 Parkhurst	485	.25	.20	.10
1992 Parkhurst	508	.25	.20	.10
1992 Pinnacle	43	.06	.05	.02
1992 Pro Set	88	.05	.04	.02
1992 Pro Set Award Winners	5	2.00	1.50	.80
1992 Score	269	.05	.04	.02
1992 Score	524	.05	.04	.02
1992 Topps	125	.06	.05	.02
1992 Topps Stadium Club	260	.05	.04	.02
1992 Topps Stadium Club	289	.05	.04	.02
1992 Upper Deck	260	.05	.04	.02
1992 Upper Deck	439	.05	.04	.02
1993 Donruss	450	.15	.11	.06
1993 Fleer PowerPlay	126	.10	.08	.04
1993 Fleer Ultra	350	.07	.05	.03
1993 Parkhurst	372	.10	.08	.04
1993 Pinnacle	280	.12	.09	.05
1993 Pinnacle Hockey Captains	12	5.00	3.75	2.00
1993 Score	51	.05	.04	.02
1993 Topps Premier	250	.05	.04	.02
1993 Topps Stadium Club	1	.05	.04	.02
1994 Leaf	23	.10	.08	.04
1994 Score	46	.05	.04	.02
1994 Score Hockey Gold Line	46	.25	.20	.10
1994 Topps Stadium Club	174	.05	.04	.02
1994 Upper Deck	122	.10	.08	.04
1994 Upper Deck Electric Ice	122	3.50	2.75	1.50

> Card stock: The paper or cardboard that baseball cards are printed on.
>
> Cello box: A retail display box of cello packs, usually, but not always, containing 24 packs.
>
> Cello pack: A cellophane-wrapped pack of cards. A cello pack usually contains more cards than a wax pack. Depending on how the cards are packaged, the top and bottom card of a cello pack may or may not be easily visible through the cellophane. Many collectors will pay a premium for a cello pack with a card of a star player or hot rookie showing on the top or bottom.

Jon Casey

Set	Card #	MT	NM	EX
1989 O-Pee-Chee	48 (R)	.65	.50	.25
1989 Topps	48 (R)	.75	.60	.30
1990 Bowman	183	.15	.11	.06
1990 O-Pee-Chee	269	.15	.11	.06
1990 Pro Set	133	.05	.04	.02
1990 Score	182	.12	.09	.05
1990 Score Hockey's 100 Hottest Rising Stars	80	.10	.08	.04
1990 Topps	269	.15	.11	.06
1990 Upper Deck	385	.08	.06	.03
1991 Bowman	119	.05	.04	.02
1991 O-Pee-Chee Premier	112	.05	.04	.02
1991 O-Pee-Chee/Topps	237	.05	.04	.02
1991 Parkhurst	77	.05	.04	.02
1991 Pinnacle	144	.08	.06	.03
1991 Pro Set	111	.05	.04	.02
1991 Pro Set Platinum	56	.05	.04	.02
1991 Score American	191	.05	.04	.02
1991 Score Canadian	191	.05	.04	.02
1991 Topps Stadium Club	138	.10	.08	.04
1991 Upper Deck	205	.05	.04	.02
1992 Bowman	269	.25	.20	.10
1992 Fleer Ultra	90	.06	.05	.02
1992 O-Pee-Chee	16	.05	.04	.02
1992 O-Pee-Chee Premier Star Performers	7	.15	.11	.06
1992 Parkhurst	73	.05	.04	.02
1992 Pinnacle	42	.06	.05	.02
1992 Pro Set	82	.05	.04	.02
1992 Score	249	.05	.04	.02
1992 Topps	379	.06	.05	.02
1992 Topps Stadium Club	198	.05	.04	.02
1992 Upper Deck	190	.05	.04	.02
1993 Donruss	16	.10	.08	.04
1993 Fleer PowerPlay	17	.10	.08	.04
1993 Fleer Ultra	91	.07	.05	.03
1993 Fleer Ultra	266	.07	.05	.03
1993 Leaf	322	.10	.08	.04
1993 Parkhurst	12	.10	.08	.04
1993 Parkhurst	281	.10	.08	.04
1993 Pinnacle	357	.08	.06	.03
1993 Pinnacle All-Stars	41	.20	.15	.08
1993 Pinnacle All-Stars	49	2.50	2.00	1.00
1993 Score	193	.05	.04	.02
1993 Score	526	.05	.04	.02
1993 Topps Premier	437	.05	.04	.02
1993 Topps Stadium Club	303	.10	.08	.04
1993 Topps Stadium Club	456	.05	.04	.02
1993 Upper Deck	507	.05	.04	.02
1993 Upper Deck SP Inserts	8	.30	.25	.12
1994 O-Pee-Chee Premier	229	.05	.04	.02
1994 Parkhurst Vintage Parkhurst	55	.20	.15	.08
1994 Score	111	.05	.04	.02
1994 Score Hockey Gold Line	111	.35	.25	.14
1994 Topps Premier	229	.05	.04	.02
1994 Topps Stadium Club	184	.05	.04	.02

| 1994 Upper Deck | 206 | .10 | .08 | .04 |
| 1994 Upper Deck Electric Ice | 206 | 3.50 | 2.75 | 1.50 |

Gerry Cheevers

Set	Card #	NM	EX	VG
1965 Topps	31 (R)	120.00	60.00	36.00
1967 Topps	99	40.00	20.00	12.00
1968 O-Pee-Chee	140	20.00	10.00	6.00
1968 Topps	1	18.00	9.00	5.50
1969 O-Pee-Chee	22	16.00	8.00	4.75
1969 Topps	22	10.00	5.00	3.00
1970 O-Pee-Chee	1	20.00	10.00	6.00
1970 Topps	1	15.00	7.50	4.50
1971 O-Pee-Chee	54	9.00	4.50	2.75
1971 Topps	4	7.00	3.50	2.00
1971 Topps	54	4.50	2.25	1.25
1972 O-Pee-Chee	340	28.00	14.00	8.50
1974 O-Pee-Chee WHA	30	12.00	6.00	3.50
1975 O-Pee-Chee WHA	20	14.00	7.00	4.25
1975 O-Pee-Chee WHA	67	8.00	4.00	2.40
1976 O-Pee-Chee	120	3.00	1.50	.90
1976 Topps	120	2.50	1.25	.70
1977 O-Pee-Chee	260	2.00	1.00	.60
1977 Topps	260	1.50	.70	.45
1978 O-Pee-Chee	140	1.50	.70	.45
1978 Topps	140	1.00	.50	.30
1979 O-Pee-Chee	85	1.00	.50	.30
1979 Topps	85	1.00	.50	.30
1980 O-Pee-Chee	168	1.00	.50	.30
1980 Topps	168	1.00	.50	.30

Set	Card #	MT	NM	EX
1992 O-Pee-Chee	343	.25	.20	.10
1992 O-Pee-Chee 25th Anniversary Series	5	.25	.20	.10

Chris Chelios

Set	Card #	MT	NM	EX
1984 O-Pee-Chee	259 (R)	15.00	11.00	6.00

Set	Card #	NM	EX	VG
1985 O-Pee-Chee	51	5.00	3.75	2.00
1985 Topps	51	3.50	2.75	1.50
1986 O-Pee-Chee	171	3.00	2.25	1.25
1986 Topps	171	1.50	1.25	.60
1987 O-Pee-Chee	106	1.25	.90	.50
1987 Topps	106	.75	.60	.30
1988 O-Pee-Chee	49	.50	.40	.20
1988 Topps	49	.30	.25	.12
1989 O-Pee-Chee	174	.25	.20	.10
1989 O-Pee-Chee	323	.10	.08	.04
1989 O-Pee-Chee Future Stars	26	.25	.20	.10
1989 Topps	174	.25	.20	.10
1990 Bowman	42	.15	.11	.06
1990 O-Pee-Chee	29	.10	.08	.04
1990 O-Pee-Chee Premier	13	.25	.20	.10
1990 Pro Set	147	.20	.15	.08
1990 Pro Set	368	.10	.08	.04
1990 Pro Set	427	.15	.11	.06
1990 Score	15	.10	.08	.04
1990 Score Hockey's 100 Hottest Rising Stars	9	.10	.08	.04
1990 Score Traded	4	.30	.25	.12
1990 Topps	29	.10	.08	.04
1990 Upper Deck	174	.20	.15	.08
1990 Upper Deck	422	.25	.20	.10
1990 Upper Deck	491	.20	.15	.08
1991 Bowman	398	.05	.04	.02
1991 O-Pee-Chee Premier	17	.05	.04	.02
1991 O-Pee-Chee/Topps	233	.05	.04	.02
1991 O-Pee-Chee/Topps	268	.05	.04	.02
1991 Parkhurst	32	.05	.04	.02
1991 Pinnacle	58	.08	.06	.03
1991 Pinnacle B	9	30.00	22.00	12.00
1991 Pro Set	48	.10	.08	.04
1991 Pro Set	278	.10	.08	.04
1991 Pro Set Platinum	25	.10	.08	.04
1991 Score American	235	.05	.04	.02
1991 Score Canadian	455	.05	.04	.02
1991 Topps Stadium Club	6	.08	.06	.03
1991 Upper Deck	37	.15	.11	.06
1991 Upper Deck	354	.10	.08	.04
1992 Bowman	43	.60	.45	.25
1992 Bowman	201	3.00	2.25	1.25
1992 Fleer Ultra	34	.06	.05	.02
1992 Fleer Ultra All-Stars	7	2.25	1.75	.90
1992 Parkhurst	29	.05	.04	.02
1992 Parkhurst	457	.05	.04	.02
1992 Parkhurst Cherry Picks	16	9.00	6.75	3.50
1992 Pinnacle	109	.06	.05	.02
1992 Pinnacle Team Pinnacle	2	15.00	11.00	6.00
1992 Pro Set	34	.10	.08	.04
1992 Score	2	.05	.04	.02
1992 Score	497	.10	.08	.04
1992 Score USA Greats	2	4.00	3.00	1.50
1992 Topps	98	.06	.05	.02
1992 Topps Stadium Club	87	.05	.04	.02
1992 Upper Deck	159	.05	.04	.02
1992 Upper Deck	629	.10	.08	.04
1992 Upper Deck World Junior Grads	3	3.50	2.75	1.50
1993 Donruss	65	.12	.09	.05
1993 Donruss Ice Kings	5	2.50	2.00	1.00
1993 Fleer PowerPlay	47	.10	.08	.04
1993 Fleer Ultra	40	.07	.05	.03
1993 Fleer Ultra All-Stars	14	2.50	2.00	1.00
1993 Fleer Ultra Award Winners	2	3.00	2.25	1.25
1993 Leaf	51	.10	.08	.04
1993 Leaf Gold All-Stars	2	6.00	4.50	2.50
1993 Parkhurst	45	.12	.09	.05
1993 Pinnacle	181	.10	.08	.04
1993 Pinnacle	223	.10	.08	.04
1993 Pinnacle	233	.10	.08	.04
1993 Pinnacle All-Stars	26	.20	.15	.08
1993 Pinnacle Team Pinnacle	2	25.00	18.50	10.00
1993 Score	101	.05	.04	.02
1993 Score Dream Team	3	4.00	3.00	1.50

		MT	NM	EX
1993 Topps Premier	94	.10	.08	.04
1993 Topps Premier	237	.05	.04	.02
1993 Topps Stadium Club	147	.15	.11	.06
1993 Topps Stadium Club	420	.05	.04	.02
1993 Topps Stadium Club	459	.05	.04	.02
1993 Upper Deck	129	.05	.04	.02
1993 Upper Deck Award Winners	5	2.50	2.00	1.00
1993 Upper Deck Gretzky's Great Ones	2	1.75	1.25	.70
1993 Upper Deck SP Inserts	28	.30	.25	.12
1994 Donruss	118	.08	.06	.03
1994 Fleer Flair	32	.30	.25	.12
1994 Fleer Ultra	40	.10	.08	.04
1994 Fleer Ultra All-Stars	8	.40	.30	.15
1994 Leaf	7	.15	.11	.06
1994 Parkhurst	45	.06	.05	.02
1994 Pinnacle	94	.10	.08	.04
1994 Pinnacle Artist's Proofs	94	8.00	6.00	3.25
1994 Pinnacle Boomers	4	6.00	4.50	2.50
1994 Pinnacle Rink Collection	94	4.00	3.00	1.50
1994 Pinnacle Team Pinnacle	3	20.00	15.00	8.00
1994 Score	189	.05	.04	.02
1994 Score Check-It	17	7.50	5.75	3.00
1994 Score Dream Team	8	5.00	3.75	2.00
1994 Score Hockey Gold Line	189	.40	.30	.15
1994 Topps Stadium Club	70	.05	.04	.02
1994 Topps Stadium Club Dynasty and Destiny	5	5.00	3.75	2.00
1994 Upper Deck	26	.10	.08	.04
1994 Upper Deck Award Predictor	7	4.00	3.00	1.50
1994 Upper Deck Electric Ice	26	6.00	4.50	2.50
1994 Upper Deck SP	16	.30	.25	.12

Dino Ciccarelli

Set	Card #	MT	NM	EX
1981 O-Pee-Chee	161 (R)	20.00	15.00	8.00
1981 Topps	105 (R)	12.00	9.00	4.75
1982 O-Pee-Chee	162	.20	.15	.08
1982 O-Pee-Chee	165	4.00	3.00	1.50
1983 O-Pee-Chee	164	.30	.25	.12
1983 O-Pee-Chee	170	2.50	2.00	1.00
1984 O-Pee-Chee	97	1.00	.70	.40
1984 Topps	73	.50	.40	.20
1985 O-Pee-Chee	13	1.00	.70	.40
1985 Topps	13	.75	.60	.30
1986 O-Pee-Chee	138	.60	.45	.25
1986 Topps	138	.30	.25	.12
1987 O-Pee-Chee	81	.25	.20	.10
1987 Topps	81	.20	.15	.08

		MT	NM	EX
1988 O-Pee-Chee	175	.15	.11	.06
1988 Topps	175	.20	.15	.08
1989 O-Pee-Chee	41	.15	.11	.06
1989 Topps	41	.05	.04	.02
1990 Bowman	69	.04	.03	.02
1990 O-Pee-Chee	100	.05	.04	.02
1990 O-Pee-Chee Premier	14	.15	.11	.06
1990 Pro Set	308	.07	.05	.03
1990 Score	230	.07	.05	.03
1990 Score Hockey's 100 Hottest Rising Stars	94	.10	.08	.04
1990 Topps	100	.07	.05	.03
1990 Upper Deck	76	.08	.06	.03
1991 Bowman	302	.10	.08	.04
1991 O-Pee-Chee/Topps	429	.05	.04	.02
1991 Parkhurst	193	.05	.04	.02
1991 Pinnacle	128	.08	.06	.03
1991 Pro Set	258	.05	.04	.02
1991 Pro Set Platinum	131	.05	.04	.02
1991 Score American	128	.05	.04	.02
1991 Score Canadian	128	.05	.04	.02
1991 Topps Stadium Club	118	.08	.06	.03
1991 Upper Deck	276	.05	.04	.02
1992 Bowman	176	.25	.20	.10
1992 Fleer Ultra	47	.06	.05	.02
1992 Fleer Ultra	283	.06	.05	.02
1992 O-Pee-Chee	249	.05	.04	.02
1992 Parkhurst	45	.05	.04	.02
1992 Topps	318	.06	.05	.02
1992 Topps Stadium Club	399	.05	.04	.02
1992 Upper Deck	461	.05	.04	.02
1993 Donruss	98	.10	.08	.04
1993 Fleer PowerPlay	69	.10	.08	.04
1993 Fleer Ultra	32	.07	.05	.03
1993 Leaf	18	.10	.08	.04
1993 Parkhurst Cherry's Playoff Heroes	5D	12.50	9.50	5.00
1993 Pinnacle	127	.10	.08	.04
1993 Score	214	.05	.04	.02
1993 Topps Premier	49	.05	.04	.02
1993 Topps Stadium Club	294	.05	.04	.02
1993 Upper Deck	136	.05	.04	.02
1994 Donruss	86	.08	.06	.03
1994 Fleer Flair	46	.25	.20	.10
1994 Fleer Ultra	58	.10	.08	.04
1994 Leaf	44	.10	.08	.04
1994 O-Pee-Chee Premier	541	.04	.04	.04
1994 Parkhurst	65	.06	.05	.02
1994 Pinnacle	241	.10	.08	.04
1994 Pinnacle Artist's Proofs	241	6.00	4.50	2.50
1994 Pinnacle Rink Collection	241	3.50	2.75	1.50
1994 Score	19	.05	.04	.02
1994 Score	243	.05	.04	.02
1994 Score	246	.05	.04	.02
1994 Score Hockey Gold Line	19	.25	.20	.10
1994 Score Hockey Gold Line	243	.25	.20	.10
1994 Score Hockey Gold Line	246	.25	.20	.10
1994 Topps Stadium Club	191	.05	.04	.02
1994 Upper Deck	5	.10	.08	.04
1994 Upper Deck Electric Ice	5	3.50	2.75	1.50

Cello case: A wholesale unit of cello boxes, usually, but not always, containing 16 boxes.

Checklist: A list of every card in a particular set, usually with a space allowing the collector to check whether he has the card. A checklist can appear on a card, in a book or elsewhere. As a rule of thumb, checklists on cards are worth more if they're left unchecked.

Bobby Clarke

Paul Coffey

Set	Card #	NM	EX	VG
1970 O-Pee-Chee	195 (R)	130.00	65.00	39.00
1971 O-Pee-Chee	114	45.00	22.00	13.50
1971 Topps	114	30.00	15.00	9.00
1972 O-Pee-Chee	14	30.00	15.00	9.00
1972 O-Pee-Chee Team Canada	5	15.00	7.50	4.50
1972 Topps	90	15.00	7.50	4.50
1973 O-Pee-Chee	50	20.00	10.00	6.00
1973 Topps	2	5.00	2.50	1.50
1973 Topps	3	5.00	2.50	1.50
1973 Topps	50	10.00	5.00	3.00
1974 O-Pee-Chee	3	6.00	3.00	1.75
1974 O-Pee-Chee	135	5.00	2.50	1.50
1974 O-Pee-Chee	154	1.00	.50	.30
1974 O-Pee-Chee	260	12.00	6.00	3.50
1974 Topps	3	3.50	1.75	1.00
1974 Topps	135	4.00	2.00	1.25
1974 Topps	154	2.50	1.25	.70
1974 Topps	260	7.50	3.75	2.25
1975 O-Pee-Chee	209	6.00	3.00	1.75
1975 O-Pee-Chee	250	10.00	5.00	3.00
1975 O-Pee-Chee	286	4.00	2.00	1.25
1975 O-Pee-Chee	325	2.00	1.00	.60
1975 Topps	209	5.50	2.75	1.75
1975 Topps	250	6.00	3.00	1.75
1975 Topps	286	4.00	2.00	1.25
1975 Topps	325	2.00	1.00	.60
1976 O-Pee-Chee	2	3.00	1.50	.90
1976 O-Pee-Chee	3	3.00	1.50	.90
1976 O-Pee-Chee	70	7.00	3.50	2.00
1976 O-Pee-Chee	215	3.00	1.50	.90
1976 O-Pee-Chee	391	1.50	.70	.45
1976 Topps	2	2.00	1.00	.60
1976 Topps	3	2.00	1.00	.60
1976 Topps	70	4.00	2.00	1.25
1976 Topps	215	2.50	1.25	.70
1977 O-Pee-Chee	115	5.00	2.50	1.50
1977 Topps	115	3.50	1.75	1.00
1978 O-Pee-Chee	215	3.00	1.50	.90
1978 Topps	215	2.00	1.00	.60
1979 O-Pee-Chee	125	2.00	1.00	.60
1979 Topps	125	1.50	.70	.45
1980 O-Pee-Chee	55	1.50	.70	.45
1980 Topps	55	1.00	.50	.30

Set	Card #	MT	NM	EX
1981 O-Pee-Chee	240	1.00	.70	.40
1981 Topps	103	.60	.45	.25
1982 O-Pee-Chee	248	1.00	.70	.40
1983 O-Pee-Chee	262	.75	.60	.30
1990 Pro Set	651	.20	.15	.08
1990 Pro Set	657	.20	.15	.08
1990 Upper Deck	509	.25	.20	.10
1992 O-Pee-Chee	43	.30	.25	.12
1992 Parkhurst	468	.25	.20	.10

Set	Card #	MT	NM	EX
1981 O-Pee-Chee	111 (R)	75.00	56.00	30.00
1982 O-Pee-Chee	101	18.00	13.50	7.25
1982 O-Pee-Chee	102	6.00	4.50	2.50
1983 O-Pee-Chee	25	10.00	7.50	4.00
1984 O-Pee-Chee	217	1.50	1.25	.60
1984 O-Pee-Chee	239	4.00	3.00	1.50
1984 Topps	50	2.50	2.00	1.00
1984 Topps	163	.50	.40	.20
1985 O-Pee-Chee	85	3.00	2.25	1.25
1985 Topps	85	2.50	2.00	1.00
1986 O-Pee-Chee	137	3.00	2.25	1.25
1986 Topps	137	1.00	.70	.40
1987 O-Pee-Chee	99	1.75	1.25	.70
1987 Topps	99	1.00	.70	.40
1988 O-Pee-Chee	179	1.00	.70	.40
1988 Topps	179	.75	.60	.30
1989 O-Pee-Chee	95	.75	.60	.30
1989 Topps	95	.40	.30	.15
1990 Bowman	211	.15	.11	.06
1990 O-Pee-Chee	116	.15	.11	.06
1990 O-Pee-Chee	202	.10	.08	.04
1990 O-Pee-Chee Premier	16	.50	.40	.20
1990 Pro Set	231	.30	.25	.12
1990 Pro Set	361	.10	.08	.04
1990 Score	6	.20	.15	.08
1990 Score	319	.10	.08	.04
1990 Score	332	.10	.08	.04
1990 Score Hockey's 100 Hottest Rising Stars	65	.10	.08	.04
1990 Topps	116	.20	.15	.08
1990 Topps	202	.10	.08	.04
1990 Upper Deck	124	.35	.25	.14
1990 Upper Deck	498	.25	.20	.10
1991 Bowman	81	.15	.11	.06
1991 O-Pee-Chee Premier	79	.15	.11	.06
1991 O-Pee-Chee/Topps	183	.12	.09	.05
1991 O-Pee-Chee/Topps	504	.05	.04	.02
1991 Parkhurst	140	.10	.08	.04
1991 Parkhurst	212	.05	.04	.02
1991 Parkhurst	225	.05	.04	.02
1991 Parkhurst	297	.05	.04	.02
1991 Pinnacle	186	.25	.20	.10
1991 Pinnacle	377	.15	.11	.06
1991 Pro Set	190	.10	.08	.04
1991 Pro Set	312	.05	.04	.02
1991 Pro Set Platinum	94	.10	.08	.04
1991 Pro Set Platinum PC	12	1.50	1.25	.60
1991 Score American	115	.10	.08	.04
1991 Score American	372	.10	.08	.04
1991 Score Canadian	115	.10	.08	.04
1991 Score Canadian	262	.10	.08	.04
1991 Topps Stadium Club	212	.35	.25	.14
1991 Upper Deck	11	.10	.08	.04
1991 Upper Deck	177	.20	.15	.08
1991 Upper Deck	615	.10	.08	.04
1992 Bowman	181	.50	.40	.20
1992 Bowman	226	17.00	12.50	6.75
1992 Fleer Ultra	80	.15	.11	.06

Ding: Slight damage to the corner or edge of a card.

1992 Fleer Ultra All-Stars	1	2.25	1.75	.90
1992 O-Pee-Chee	5	.20	.15	.08
1992 O-Pee-Chee	187	.30	.25	.12
1992 O-Pee-Chee	318	.05	.04	.02
1992 O-Pee-Chee Premier Star Performers	4	.30	.25	.12
1992 O-Pee-Chee 25th Anniversary Series	14	.25	.20	.10
1992 Parkhurst	63	.05	.04	.02
1992 Parkhurst	276	.15	.11	.06
1992 Parkhurst	458	.10	.08	.04
1992 Pinnacle	50	.10	.08	.04
1992 Pinnacle Team Pinnacle	3	15.00	11.00	6.00
1992 Pro Set	71	.10	.08	.04
1992 Score	265	.05	.04	.02
1992 Score	441	.05	.04	.02
1992 Topps	5	.06	.05	.02
1992 Topps	182	.06	.05	.02
1992 Topps Stadium Club	169	.20	.15	.08
1992 Upper Deck	116	.05	.04	.02
1993 Donruss	99	.20	.15	.08
1993 Fleer PowerPlay	70	.15	.11	.06
1993 Fleer Ultra	71	.07	.05	.03
1993 Leaf	67	.10	.08	.04
1993 Leaf Gold All-Stars	7	6.00	4.50	2.50
1993 Parkhurst	56	.12	.09	.05
1993 Parkhurst Cherry's Playoff Heroes	8D	15.00	11.00	6.00
1993 Pinnacle	80	.20	.15	.08
1993 Pinnacle All-Stars	43	.20	.15	.08
1993 Pinnacle Team Pinnacle	8	27.00	20.00	11.00
1993 Score	106	.05	.04	.02
1993 Score Dream Team	8	6.00	4.50	2.50
1993 Topps Premier	145	.10	.08	.04
1993 Topps Premier Black Gold	6	2.50	2.00	1.00
1993 Topps Stadium Club	450	.15	.11	.06
1993 Topps Stadium Club All-Stars	2	5.00	3.75	2.00
1993 Topps Stadium Club Finest	4	6.00	4.50	2.50
1993 Upper Deck	315	.08	.06	.03
1993 Upper Deck Gretzky's Great Ones	6	1.75	1.25	.70
1993 Upper Deck SP Inserts	42	.50	.40	.20
1994 Donruss	54	.20	.15	.08
1994 Fleer Flair	47	.40	.30	.15
1994 Fleer Ultra	59	.05	.04	.02
1994 Fleer Ultra All-Stars	9	.40	.30	.15
1994 Leaf	168	.15	.11	.06
1994 Leaf Fire On Ice	8	4.50	3.50	1.75
1994 O-Pee-Chee Premier	15	.10	.08	.04
1994 Parkhurst	63	.06	.05	.02
1994 Pinnacle Team Pinnacle	5	20.00	15.00	8.00
1994 Score Dream Team	6	5.00	3.75	2.00
1994 Topps Premier	15	.10	.08	.04
1994 Upper Deck	24	.25	.20	.10
1994 Upper Deck Electric Ice	24	8.00	6.00	3.25
1994 Upper Deck SP	22	.60	.45	.25

Centering: The positioning of a card picture between its borders. A well-centered card has even borders, an important factor in grading a card.

Chipping. A card-grading term referring to a condition in which a portion of a card's dark-colored border is worn away. Chipping is a real problem, for instance, with 1953 and 1971 Topps cards, and more recent issues with colored borders.

Collation: The act of putting cards in order, usually numerical order.

Shayne Corson

Shayne Corson

Set	Card #	MT	NM	EX
1989 O-Pee-Chee	248	.75	.60	.30
1990 Bowman	41	.04	.03	.02
1990 O-Pee-Chee	58	.05	.04	.02
1990 Pro Set	148	.07	.05	.03
1990 Pro Set	369	.05	.04	.02
1990 Score	213	.07	.05	.03
1990 Score Hockey's 100 Hottest Rising Stars	91	.10	.08	.04
1990 Topps	58	.07	.05	.03
1990 Upper Deck	280	.08	.06	.03
1991 Bowman	328	.05	.04	.02
1991 O-Pee-Chee Premier	161	.05	.04	.02
1991 O-Pee-Chee/Topps	157	.05	.04	.02
1991 Parkhurst	86	.05	.04	.02
1991 Pinnacle	102	.08	.06	.03
1991 Pro Set	413	.05	.04	.02
1991 Score American	65	.05	.04	.02
1991 Score Canadian	65	.05	.04	.02
1991 Topps Stadium Club	5	.08	.06	.03
1991 Upper Deck	282	.05	.04	.02
1991 Upper Deck	505	.05	.04	.02
1992 Bowman	82	.25	.20	.10
1992 Fleer Ultra	57	.06	.05	.02
1992 Fleer Ultra	292	.06	.05	.02
1992 O-Pee-Chee	231	.05	.04	.02
1992 Parkhurst	53	.05	.04	.02
1992 Pinnacle	323	.06	.05	.02
1992 Pro Set	89	.05	.04	.02
1992 Score	158	.05	.04	.02
1992 Topps	201	.06	.05	.02
1992 Topps Stadium Club	221	.05	.04	.02
1992 Upper Deck	330	.05	.04	.02
1992 Upper Deck	541	.05	.04	.02
1993 Donruss	114	.10	.08	.04
1993 Fleer PowerPlay	79	.10	.08	.04
1993 Fleer Ultra	51	.07	.05	.03
1993 Leaf	46	.10	.08	.04
1993 Parkhurst	338	.15	.11	.06
1993 Pinnacle	249	.12	.09	.05
1993 Score	108	.05	.04	.02
1993 Score Canadian Dynamic Duos	7	20.00	15.00	8.00
1993 Topps Premier	38	.05	.04	.02
1993 Topps Stadium Club	40	.05	.04	.02
1993 Upper Deck	132	.05	.04	.02
1993 Upper Deck SP Inserts	49	.30	.25	.12
1994 Donruss	221	.08	.06	.03
1994 Fleer Flair	57	.25	.20	.10
1994 Leaf	164	.15	.11	.06
1994 O-Pee-Chee Premier	210	.05	.04	.02
1994 Parkhurst	75	.06	.05	.02
1994 Parkhurst Vintage Parkhurst	3	.20	.15	.08
1994 Pinnacle	44	.10	.08	.04
1994 Pinnacle Artist's Proofs	44	5.00	3.75	2.00
1994 Pinnacle Rink Collection	44	3.00	2.25	1.25

Set	Card #	NM	EX	VG
1994 Score	174	.05	.04	.02
1994 Score Hockey Gold Line	174	.25	.20	.10
1994 Topps Premier	210	.05	.04	.02

Yvan Cournoyer

Set	Card #	NM	EX	VG
1965 Topps	76 (R)	100.00	50.00	30.00
1966 Topps	72	45.00	22.00	13.50
1967 Topps	70	25.00	12.50	7.50
1968 O-Pee-Chee	62	15.00	7.50	4.50
1968 Topps	62	10.00	5.00	3.00
1969 O-Pee-Chee	6	9.00	4.50	2.75
1969 O-Pee-Chee	221	3.00	1.50	.90
1969 Topps	6	6.50	3.25	2.00
1970 O-Pee-Chee	50	8.00	4.00	2.50
1970 Topps	50	5.00	2.50	1.50
1971 O-Pee-Chee	15	6.00	3.00	1.75
1971 O-Pee-Chee	260	2.00	1.00	.60
1971 Topps	15	4.00	2.00	1.25
1972 O-Pee-Chee	29	5.00	2.50	1.50
1972 O-Pee-Chee	44	1.50	.70	.45
1972 O-Pee-Chee Team Canada	6	10.00	5.00	3.00
1972 Topps	10	3.50	1.75	1.00
1972 Topps	131	3.00	1.50	.90
1973 O-Pee-Chee	157	4.00	2.00	1.25
1973 Topps	115	3.00	1.50	.90
1974 O-Pee-Chee	124	1.00	.50	.30
1974 O-Pee-Chee	140	2.50	1.25	.70
1974 Topps	124	2.50	1.25	.70
1974 Topps	140	2.00	1.00	.60
1975 O-Pee-Chee	70	3.00	1.50	.90
1975 Topps	70	2.00	1.00	.60
1976 O-Pee-Chee	30	2.50	1.25	.70
1976 Topps	30	1.50	.70	.45
1977 O-Pee-Chee	230	1.50	.70	.45
1977 Topps	230	1.50	.70	.45
1978 O-Pee-Chee	60	1.00	.50	.30
1978 Topps	60	1.25	.60	.40

Collectible: Something worth collecting. Baseball cards, programs, pennants, uniforms, and autographs are all examples of collectibles.

Collector issue: A set of cards produced primarily to be sold to collectors and not issued as a premium to be given away or sold with a commercial product. Collector issues fall into two categories: authorized (meaning the issue was made with the approval of professional sports and the players' association) or unauthorized (meaning the issue was made without approval).

Combination card: A single card which depicts two or more players, but is not a team card.

Russ Courtnall

Set	Card #	MT	NM	EX
1986 O-Pee-Chee	174 (R)	7.00	5.25	2.75
1986 Topps	174 (R)	4.00	3.00	1.50
1987 O-Pee-Chee	62	1.50	1.25	.60
1987 Topps	62	.75	.60	.30
1988 O-Pee-Chee	183	.50	.40	.20
1988 Topps	183	.30	.25	.12
1989 O-Pee-Chee	239	.07	.05	.03
1990 Bowman	47	.04	.03	.02
1990 O-Pee-Chee	124	.05	.04	.02
1990 Pro Set	149	.05	.04	.02
1990 Score	148	.05	.04	.02
1990 Topps	124	.06	.05	.02
1990 Upper Deck	259	.08	.06	.03
1991 Bowman	346	.05	.04	.02
1991 O-Pee-Chee Premier	58	.05	.04	.02
1991 O-Pee-Chee/Topps	119	.05	.04	.02
1991 Parkhurst	308	.05	.04	.02
1991 Pinnacle	254	.08	.06	.03
1991 Pro Set	126	.05	.04	.02
1991 Pro Set Platinum	62	.05	.04	.02
1991 Score American	42	.05	.04	.02
1991 Score American	380	.05	.04	.02
1991 Score Canadian	42	.05	.04	.02
1991 Score Canadian	270	.05	.04	.02
1991 Topps Stadium Club	43	.08	.06	.03
1991 Upper Deck	168	.10	.08	.04
1992 Bowman	45	.25	.20	.10
1992 Fleer Ultra	91	.06	.05	.02
1992 Fleer Ultra	316	.06	.05	.02
1992 O-Pee-Chee	284	.05	.04	.02
1992 O-Pee-Chee Premier	20	.05	.04	.02
1992 Pinnacle	337	.06	.05	.02
1992 Score	4	.05	.04	.02
1992 Topps	276	.06	.05	.02
1992 Topps Stadium Club	152	.05	.04	.02
1992 Upper Deck	39	.05	.04	.02
1992 Upper Deck	94	.05	.04	.02
1992 Upper Deck	441	.05	.04	.02
1993 Donruss	80	.10	.08	.04
1993 Fleer PowerPlay	58	.10	.08	.04
1993 Fleer Ultra	50	.07	.05	.03
1993 Fleer Ultra Speed Merchants	2	6.00	4.50	2.50
1993 Leaf	65	.10	.08	.04
1993 Parkhurst	53	.10	.08	.04
1993 Pinnacle	268	.08	.06	.03
1993 Score	130	.05	.04	.02
1993 Topps Premier	153	.05	.04	.02
1993 Topps Stadium Club	55	.05	.04	.02
1993 Upper Deck	32	.05	.04	.02
1993 Upper Deck SP Inserts	36	.30	.25	.12
1994 Donruss	167	.08	.06	.03
1994 Fleer Flair	40	.25	.20	.10
1994 Leaf	126	.10	.08	.04
1994 Parkhurst	52	.06	.05	.02
1994 Pinnacle	133	.10	.08	.04
1994 Pinnacle Artist's Proofs	133	5.00	3.75	2.00

Set	Card #	MT	NM	EX
1994 Pinnacle Rink Collection	133	3.00	2.25	1.25
1994 Score	43	.05	.04	.02
1994 Score Hockey Gold Line	43	.25	.20	.10
1994 Topps Stadium Club	170	.05	.04	.02
1994 Upper Deck	31	.10	.08	.04
1994 Upper Deck Electric Ice	31	3.50	2.75	1.50
1994 Upper Deck SP	19	.30	.25	.12

Alexandre Daigle

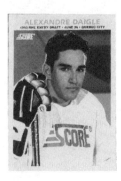

Set	Card #	MT	NM	EX
1992 Upper Deck	587 (R)	3.50	2.75	1.50
1993 Donruss	237	1.00	.70	.40
1993 Donruss Elite	2	40.00	30.00	16.00
1993 Donruss Rated Rookies	1	5.00	3.75	2.00
1993 Donruss Special Print	P	8.00	7.50	4.00
1993 Fleer PowerPlay	396	.75	.60	.30
1993 Fleer PowerPlay Rookie Standouts	3	4.00	3.00	1.50
1993 Fleer Ultra	380	1.00	.70	.40
1993 Fleer Ultra Wave of the Future	3	4.00	3.00	1.50
1993 Leaf	311	1.00	.70	.40
1993 Leaf Freshman Phenoms	1	5.00	3.75	2.00
1993 Leaf Studio Signature	9	5.00	3.75	2.00
1993 Parkhurst	244	.75	.60	.30
1993 Parkhurst Calder Candidates	1CC	10.00	7.50	4.00
1993 Parkhurst Cherry's Playoff Heroes	11D	20.00	15.00	8.00
1993 Parkhurst East-West Stars	3E	14.00	10.50	5.50
1993 Parkhurst First Overall	1	12.00	9.00	4.75
1993 Pinnacle	236	.75	.60	.30
1993 Pinnacle Super Rookies	1	6.00	4.50	2.50
1993 Score	496	9.00	6.75	3.50
1993 Score	587	.50	.40	.20
1993 Topps Finest Hockey Card Series Roster	1	10.00	7.50	4.00
1993 Topps Premier	405	.75	.60	.30
1993 Topps Stadium Club	300	.75	.60	.30
1993 Upper Deck	170	.75	.60	.30
1993 Upper Deck	250	.75	.60	.30
1993 Upper Deck Program of Excellence	15E	12.00	9.00	4.75
1993 Upper Deck Silver Skates Dye-Cut Retail	3R	10.00	7.50	4.00

Set	Card #	MT	NM	EX
1993 Upper Deck SP Inserts	107	1.50	1.25	.60
1994 Donruss	211	.40	.30	.15
1994 Fleer Flair	120	1.00	.70	.40
1994 Fleer Flair Scoring Power	2	5.00	3.75	2.00
1994 Fleer Ultra	146	.30	.25	.12
1994 Fleer Ultra Ultra All-Rookies	3	13.00	9.75	5.25
1994 Leaf	119	.50	.40	.20
1994 Leaf Gold Rookies	5	6.00	4.50	2.50
1994 O-Pee-Chee Premier	140	.25	.20	.10
1994 O-Pee-Chee Premier	195	.25	.20	.10
1994 O-Pee-Chee Premier Finest Inserts	7	9.00	6.75	3.50
1994 Parkhurst	285	.35	.25	.14
1994 Parkhurst Vintage Parkhurst	42	.60	.45	.25
1994 Pinnacle	2	.50	.40	.20
1994 Pinnacle Artist's Proofs	2	18.00	13.50	7.25
1994 Pinnacle Northern Lights	6	10.00	7.50	4.00
1994 Pinnacle Rink Collection	2	9.00	6.75	3.50
1994 Score	248	.30	.25	.12
1994 Score Dream Team	21	7.00	5.25	2.75
1994 Score Franchise	16	13.00	9.75	5.25
1994 Score Hockey Gold Line	248	1.00	.70	.40
1994 Topps Premier	140	.25	.20	.10
1994 Topps Premier	195	.25	.20	.10
1994 Topps Stadium Club	110	.25	.20	.10
1994 Upper Deck	87	.50	.40	.20
1994 Upper Deck Electric Ice	87	12.00	9.00	4.75
1994 Upper Deck Ice Gallery	10	7.00	5.25	2.75
1994 Upper Deck SP	54	1.00	.70	.40

Vincent Damphousse

Set	Card #	MT	NM	EX
1987 O-Pee-Chee	243 (R)	15.00	11.00	6.00
1988 O-Pee-Chee	207	4.00	3.00	1.50
1989 O-Pee-Chee	272	.15	.11	.06
1990 Bowman	163	.15	.11	.06
1990 O-Pee-Chee	121	.07	.05	.03
1990 O-Pee-Chee Premier	21	.50	.40	.20
1990 Pro Set	278	.07	.05	.03
1990 Score	95	.10	.08	.04
1990 Score Hockey's 100 Hottest Rising Stars	47	.10	.08	.04
1990 Topps	121	.07	.05	.03
1990 Upper Deck	224	.25	.20	.10
1990 Upper Deck	484	.08	.06	.03
1991 Bowman	170	.05	.04	.02
1991 O-Pee-Chee Premier	104	.05	.04	.02

Set	Card #	NM	EX	VG
1991 O-Pee-Chee/Topps	299	.05	.04	.02
1991 Parkhurst	48	.05	.04	.02
1991 Pinnacle	91	.08	.06	.03
1991 Pro Set	224	.05	.04	.02
1991 Pro Set	293	.05	.04	.02
1991 Pro Set	381	.08	.06	.03
1991 Pro Set Platinum	35	.05	.04	.02
1991 Score American	300	.05	.04	.02
1991 Score American	338	.05	.04	.02
1991 Score Canadian	368	.05	.04	.02
1991 Score Canadian	609	.05	.04	.02
1991 Score Traded	59	.05	.04	.02
1991 Topps Stadium Club	146	.08	.06	.03
1991 Topps Team Scoring Leaders	9	.10	.05	.05
1991 Upper Deck	136	.05	.04	.02
1991 Upper Deck	535	.05	.04	.02
1992 Bowman	203	3.00	2.25	1.25
1992 Bowman	329	.50	.40	.20
1992 Fleer Ultra	103	.06	.05	.02
1992 O-Pee-Chee	192	.05	.04	.02
1992 O-Pee-Chee Premier	3	.05	.04	.02
1992 Parkhurst	86	.05	.04	.02
1992 Parkhurst	496	.25	.20	.10
1992 Pinnacle	261	.06	.05	.02
1992 Pinnacle	349	.06	.05	.02
1992 Pro Set Gold Team Leaders	5	1.00	.70	.40
1992 Score	170	.05	.04	.02
1992 Topps	55	.06	.05	.02
1992 Topps Stadium Club	191	.05	.04	.02
1992 Upper Deck	307	.05	.04	.02
1992 Upper Deck	476	.05	.04	.02
1993 Donruss	172	.10	.08	.04
1993 Fleer PowerPlay	127	.10	.08	.04
1993 Fleer Ultra	79	.07	.05	.03
1993 Leaf	4	.10	.08	.04
1993 OPC Premier Black Gold	2	9.00	6.75	3.50
1993 Parkhurst	104	.10	.08	.04
1993 Pinnacle	85	.10	.08	.04
1993 Pinnacle	232	.10	.08	.04
1993 Pinnacle Team Pinnacle	10	37.00	28.00	15.00
1993 Score	244	.05	.04	.02
1993 Topps Premier	233	.05	.04	.02
1993 Topps Stadium Club	240	.05	.04	.02
1993 Upper Deck	295	.10	.08	.04
1993 Upper Deck	380	.05	.04	.02
1993 Upper Deck Hat Tricks	8	.60	.45	.25
1993 Upper Deck SP Inserts	77	.30	.25	.12
1994 Donruss	226	.08	.06	.03
1994 Fleer Flair	87	.25	.20	.10
1994 Fleer Ultra	107	.08	.06	.03
1994 Leaf	69	.10	.08	.04
1994 O-Pee-Chee Premier	65	.05	.04	.02
1994 Parkhurst	115	.06	.05	.02
1994 Parkhurst Vintage Parkhurst	23	.20	.15	.08
1994 Pinnacle	4	.10	.08	.04
1994 Pinnacle Artist's Proofs	4	5.00	3.75	2.00
1994 Pinnacle Northern Lights	3	5.50	4.25	2.25
1994 Pinnacle Rink Collection	4	3.00	2.25	1.25
1994 Score	165	.05	.04	.02
1994 Score Hockey Gold Line	165	.25	.20	.10
1994 Score 90-Plus Club	20	5.00	3.75	2.00
1994 Topps Premier	65	.05	.04	.02
1994 Topps Premier Finest Inserts	22	4.50	3.50	1.75
1994 Upper Deck SP	39	.30	.25	.12

Alex Delvecchio

Set	Card #	NM	EX	VG
1951 Parkhurst	63 (R)	225.00	112.00	67.00
1952 Parkhurst	53	120.00	60.00	36.00
1953 Parkhurst	47	60.00	30.00	18.00
1954 Parkhurst	36	50.00	25.00	15.00
1954 Parkhurst	90	25.00	12.50	7.50
1954 Topps	39	125.00	62.00	37.00
1957 Topps	34	40.00	20.00	12.00
1958 Topps	52	30.00	15.00	9.00
1959 Topps	8	25.00	12.50	7.50
1960 Parkhurst	36	30.00	15.00	9.00
1961 Parkhurst	25	25.00	12.50	7.50
1961 Parkhurst	32	10.00	5.00	3.00
1962 Parkhurst	32	22.00	11.00	6.50
1963 Parkhurst	50	25.00	12.50	7.50
1964 Topps	95	65.00	32.00	19.50
1965 Topps	47	20.00	10.00	6.00
1966 Topps	102	15.00	7.50	4.50
1967 Topps	51	14.00	7.00	4.25
1968 O-Pee-Chee	28	9.00	4.50	2.75
1968 Topps	28	6.00	3.00	1.75
1969 O-Pee-Chee	157	6.00	3.00	1.75
1969 O-Pee-Chee	206	3.00	1.50	.90
1969 Topps	64	5.00	2.50	1.50
1970 O-Pee-Chee	157	6.00	3.00	1.75
1971 O-Pee-Chee	37	5.00	2.50	1.50
1971 Topps	37	3.50	1.75	1.00
1972 O-Pee-Chee	26	1.50	.70	.45
1972 Topps	141	3.50	1.75	1.00
1973 O-Pee-Chee	1	5.00	2.50	1.50
1973 Topps	141	2.00	1.00	.60
1974 O-Pee-Chee	222	2.00	1.00	.60
1974 Topps	222	.35	.20	.11

Set	Card #	MT	NM	EX
1990 Pro Set	652	.20	.15	.08
1990 Pro Set	658	.20	.15	.08
1992 Parkhurst Parkie Reprints	19	25.00	12.50	6.00

Diamond King: A Donruss card featuring the artwork produced by Perez-Steele Galleries.

Die-cut card: A baseball card in which the player's outline has been partially separated from the background, enabling the card to be folded into a "stand-up" figure. Die-cut cards that have never been folded are worth more to collectors.

Disc set: A set of disc-shaped cards, usually showing head-and-shoulder shots of players.

Donruss: A baseball-card manufacturer. Donruss began printing baseball cards in 1981.

Decollation: The act of putting cards in random order, usually for packaging.

Marcel Dionne

Set	Card #	NM	EX	VG
1971 O-Pee-Chee	133 (R)	125.00	62.00	37.00
1972 O-Pee-Chee	8	30.00	15.00	9.00
1972 Topps	18	15.00	7.50	4.50
1973 O-Pee-Chee	17	18.00	9.00	5.50
1973 Topps	17	12.00	6.00	3.50
1974 O-Pee-Chee	72	12.00	6.00	3.50
1974 O-Pee-Chee	84	1.00	.50	.30
1974 Topps	72	8.00	4.00	2.50
1974 Topps	84	2.00	1.00	.60
1975 O-Pee-Chee	140	10.00	5.00	3.00
1975 O-Pee-Chee	210	7.50	3.75	2.25
1975 O-Pee-Chee	318	.50	.25	.15
1975 Topps	140	7.00	3.50	2.00
1975 Topps	210	6.50	3.25	2.00
1975 Topps	318	2.00	1.00	.60
1976 O-Pee-Chee	91	8.00	4.00	2.50
1976 O-Pee-Chee	386	1.00	.50	.30
1976 Topps	91	5.00	2.50	1.50
1977 O-Pee-Chee	1	2.50	1.25	.70
1977 O-Pee-Chee	2	2.00	1.00	.60
1977 O-Pee-Chee	3	2.00	1.00	.60
1977 O-Pee-Chee	240	5.00	2.50	1.50
1977 Topps	1	2.00	1.00	.60
1977 Topps	2	1.50	.70	.45
1977 Topps	3	2.00	1.00	.60
1977 Topps	240	4.00	2.00	1.25
1978 O-Pee-Chee	120	4.00	2.00	1.25
1978 Topps	120	3.00	1.50	.90
1979 O-Pee-Chee	1	4.00	2.00	1.25
1979 O-Pee-Chee	2	3.00	1.50	.90
1979 O-Pee-Chee	3	3.00	1.50	.90
1979 O-Pee-Chee	5	3.00	1.50	.90
1979 O-Pee-Chee	160	3.00	1.50	.90
1979 Topps	1	2.50	1.25	.70
1979 Topps	2	2.00	1.00	.60
1979 Topps	3	2.00	1.00	.60
1979 Topps	5	1.50	.70	.45
1979 Topps	160	2.50	1.25	.70
1980 O-Pee-Chee	20	2.00	1.00	.60
1980 O-Pee-Chee	81	1.00	.50	.30
1980 O-Pee-Chee	162	15.00	7.50	4.50
1980 O-Pee-Chee	163	15.00	7.50	4.50
1980 O-Pee-Chee	165	.50	.25	.15
1980 Topps	20	1.50	.70	.45
1980 Topps	81	.75	.40	.25
1980 Topps	162	10.00	5.00	3.00
1980 Topps	163	10.00	5.00	3.00
1980 Topps	165	1.00	.50	.30

Set	Card #	MT	NM	EX
1981 O-Pee-Chee	141	2.00	1.50	.80
1981 O-Pee-Chee	150	.75	.60	.30
1981 O-Pee-Chee	156	.60	.45	.25
1981 O-Pee-Chee	391	3.00	2.25	1.25
1981 Topps	9	.75	.60	.30
1981 Topps	54	.25	.20	.10
1981 Topps	125	.75	.60	.30
1982 O-Pee-Chee	149	.50	.40	.20
1982 O-Pee-Chee	152	1.00	.70	.40
1982 O-Pee-Chee	153	.50	.40	.20
1983 O-Pee-Chee	150	.30	.25	.12
1983 O-Pee-Chee	151	.30	.25	.12
1983 O-Pee-Chee	152	.75	.60	.30
1983 O-Pee-Chee	211	.15	.11	.06
1984 O-Pee-Chee	82	.50	.40	.20
1984 Topps	64	.25	.20	.10
1985 O-Pee-Chee	90	.60	.45	.25
1985 Topps	90	.90	.70	.35
1986 O-Pee-Chee	30	.90	.70	.35
1986 Topps	30	.40	.30	.15
1987 O-Pee-Chee	129	.25	.20	.10
1987 Topps	129	.25	.20	.10
1988 O-Pee-Chee	13	.40	.30	.15
1988 Topps	13	.20	.15	.08
1990 Pro Set	653	.25	.20	.10
1991 Upper Deck	636	.05	.04	.02
1992 O-Pee-Chee 25th Anniversary Series	4	.25	.20	.10

Ken Dryden

Set	Card #	NM	EX	VG
1971 O-Pee-Chee	45 (R)	300.00	150.00	90.00
1971 Topps	45 (R)	100.00	50.00	30.00
1972 O-Pee-Chee	145	45.00	22.00	13.50
1972 O-Pee-Chee	247	25.00	12.50	7.50
1972 O-Pee-Chee Team Canada	7	25.00	12.50	7.50
1972 Topps	127	10.00	5.00	3.00
1972 Topps	160	30.00	15.00	9.00
1973 O-Pee-Chee	136	10.00	5.00	3.00
1973 Topps	4	5.00	2.50	1.50
1973 Topps	10	33.00	16.50	10.00
1974 O-Pee-Chee	155	20.00	10.00	6.00
1974 Topps	155	15.00	7.50	4.50
1975 O-Pee-Chee	35	20.00	10.00	6.00
1975 O-Pee-Chee	213	5.00	2.50	1.50
1975 Topps	35	12.00	6.00	3.50
1975 Topps	213	5.00	2.50	1.50
1976 O-Pee-Chee	6	1.50	.70	.45
1976 O-Pee-Chee	200	15.00	7.50	4.50
1976 Topps	6	2.00	1.00	.60
1976 Topps	200	10.00	5.00	3.00
1977 O-Pee-Chee	6	1.50	.70	.45
1977 O-Pee-Chee	8	3.00	1.50	.90
1977 O-Pee-Chee	100	10.00	5.00	3.00
1977 Topps	6	.40	.20	.12
1977 Topps	8	1.75	.90	.50
1977 Topps	100	7.00	3.50	2.00
1978 O-Pee-Chee	50	7.00	3.50	2.00
1978 O-Pee-Chee	68	2.00	1.00	.60
1978 O-Pee-Chee	70	3.00	1.50	.90
1978 O-Pee-Chee	330	3.00	1.50	.90
1978 Topps	50	5.00	2.50	1.50
1978 Topps	68	1.50	.70	.45
1978 Topps	70	2.50	1.25	.70
1979 O-Pee-Chee	6	2.50	1.25	.70
1979 O-Pee-Chee	8	3.00	1.50	.90
1979 O-Pee-Chee	150	6.00	3.00	1.75

1979 Topps	6	1.50	.70	.45
1979 Topps	8	1.50	.70	.45
1979 Topps	150	4.00	2.00	1.25

Phil Esposito

Set	Card #	NM	EX	VG
1965 Topps	116 (R)	400.00	200.00	120.00
1966 Topps	63	125.00	62.00	37.00
1967 Topps	32	75.00	37.00	22.00
1968 O-Pee-Chee	7	40.00	20.00	12.00
1968 O-Pee-Chee	208	24.00	12.00	7.25
1968 Topps	7	30.00	15.00	9.00
1969 O-Pee-Chee	30	30.00	15.00	9.00
1969 O-Pee-Chee	205	20.00	10.00	6.00
1969 O-Pee-Chee	214	22.00	11.00	6.50
1969 Topps	30	22.00	11.00	6.50
1970 O-Pee-Chee	11	25.00	12.50	7.50
1970 O-Pee-Chee	233	20.00	10.00	6.00
1970 O-Pee-Chee	237	15.00	7.50	4.50
1970 Topps	11	18.00	9.00	5.50
1971 O-Pee-Chee	20	20.00	10.00	6.00
1971 O-Pee-Chee	247	10.00	5.00	3.00
1971 O-Pee-Chee	253	10.00	5.00	3.00
1971 Topps	1	15.00	7.50	4.50
1971 Topps	2	15.00	7.50	4.50
1971 Topps	3	15.00	7.50	4.50
1971 Topps	20	14.00	7.00	4.25
1972 O-Pee-Chee	76	8.00	4.00	2.50
1972 O-Pee-Chee	111	15.00	7.50	4.50
1972 O-Pee-Chee	230	10.00	5.00	3.00
1972 O-Pee-Chee	272	17.00	8.50	5.00
1972 O-Pee-Chee	280	25.00	12.50	7.50
1972 O-Pee-Chee	283	25.00	12.50	7.50
1972 O-Pee-Chee Team Canada	9	25.00	12.50	7.50
1972 Topps	124	6.00	3.00	1.75
1972 Topps	150	9.00	4.50	2.75
1973 O-Pee-Chee	120	10.00	5.00	3.00
1973 O-Pee-Chee	133	4.00	2.00	1.25
1973 O-Pee-Chee	134	6.00	3.00	1.75
1973 O-Pee-Chee	135	6.00	3.00	1.75
1973 O-Pee-Chee	138	4.00	2.00	1.25
1973 Topps	1	5.00	2.50	1.50
1973 Topps	2	5.00	2.50	1.50
1973 Topps	3	5.00	2.50	1.50
1973 Topps	6	3.00	1.50	.90
1973 Topps	120	7.00	3.50	2.00
1974 O-Pee-Chee	1	5.00	2.50	1.50
1974 O-Pee-Chee	3	6.00	3.00	1.75
1974 O-Pee-Chee	28	9.00	4.50	2.75
1974 O-Pee-Chee	129	4.00	2.00	1.25
1974 O-Pee-Chee	200	8.00	4.00	2.50
1974 O-Pee-Chee	244	4.00	2.00	1.25
1974 O-Pee-Chee	246	4.00	2.00	1.25
1974 Topps	1	3.00	1.50	.90
1974 Topps	3	3.50	1.75	1.00
1974 Topps	28	8.00	4.00	2.50
1974 Topps	129	3.00	1.50	.90
1974 Topps	200	4.00	2.00	1.25
1974 Topps	244	4.00	2.00	1.25
1974 Topps	246	4.00	2.00	1.25
1975 O-Pee-Chee	200	7.00	3.50	2.00
1975 O-Pee-Chee	208	4.50	2.25	1.25
1975 O-Pee-Chee	210	7.50	3.75	2.25
1975 O-Pee-Chee	212	2.50	1.25	.70
1975 O-Pee-Chee	292	3.50	1.75	1.00
1975 O-Pee-Chee	314	8.00	4.00	2.50
1975 Topps	200	3.00	1.50	.90
1975 Topps	208	3.50	1.75	1.00
1975 Topps	210	6.50	3.25	2.00
1975 Topps	212	2.00	1.00	.60
1975 Topps	292	2.00	1.00	.60
1975 Topps	314	6.00	3.00	1.75
1976 O-Pee-Chee	245	4.50	2.25	1.25
1976 O-Pee-Chee	390	1.50	.70	.45
1976 Topps	5	2.50	1.25	.70
1976 Topps	245	2.50	1.25	.70
1977 O-Pee-Chee	5	1.00	.50	.30
1977 O-Pee-Chee	55	4.00	2.00	1.25
1977 Topps	5	.40	.20	.12
1977 Topps	55	2.75	1.50	.80
1978 O-Pee-Chee	2	1.50	.70	.45
1978 O-Pee-Chee	67	3.00	1.50	.90
1978 O-Pee-Chee	100	4.00	2.00	1.25
1978 Topps	2	1.00	.50	.30
1978 Topps	67	2.00	1.00	.60
1978 Topps	100	2.50	1.25	.70
1979 O-Pee-Chee	220	3.00	1.50	.90
1979 Topps	220	2.50	1.25	.70
1980 O-Pee-Chee	100	2.00	1.00	.60
1980 O-Pee-Chee	149	.75	.40	.25
1980 Topps	100	1.50	.70	.45
1980 Topps	149	.40	.20	.12

Set	Card #	MT	NM	EX
1990 Pro Set	403	.25	.20	.10
1990 Upper Deck	510	.25	.20	.10
1991 Pro Set	594	.05	.04	.02
1992 O-Pee-Chee	283	.25	.20	.10
1992 O-Pee-Chee 25th Anniversary Series	10	.30	.25	.12

Tony Esposito

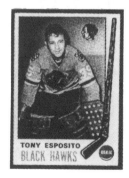

Set	Card #	NM	EX	VG
1969 O-Pee-Chee	138 (R)	135.00	67.00	40.00
1970 O-Pee-Chee	153	50.00	25.00	15.00
1970 O-Pee-Chee	234	20.00	10.00	6.00
1970 O-Pee-Chee	247	20.00	10.00	6.00
1970 O-Pee-Chee	250	20.00	10.00	6.00
1971 O-Pee-Chee	110	35.00	17.50	10.50
1971 Topps	4	7.00	3.50	2.00
1971 Topps	5	6.50	3.25	2.00
1971 Topps	6	10.00	5.00	3.00
1971 Topps	110	20.00	10.00	6.00
1972 O-Pee-Chee	137	20.00	10.00	6.00
1972 O-Pee-Chee	196	8.00	4.00	2.50

		MT	NM	EX
1972 O-Pee-Chee	226	10.00	5.00	3.00
1972 O-Pee-Chee	286	10.00	5.00	3.00
1972 O-Pee-Chee Team Canada	10	15.00	7.50	4.50
1972 Topps	20	12.00	6.00	3.50
1972 Topps	121	4.00	2.00	1.25
1973 O-Pee-Chee	90	10.00	5.00	3.00
1973 O-Pee-Chee	136	10.00	5.00	3.00
1973 Topps	4	5.00	2.50	1.50
1973 Topps	90	6.00	3.00	1.75
1974 O-Pee-Chee	170	8.00	4.00	2.50
1974 Topps	170	4.00	2.00	1.25
1975 O-Pee-Chee	240	5.00	2.50	1.50
1975 Topps	240	3.50	1.75	1.00
1976 O-Pee-Chee	100	3.00	1.50	.90
1976 Topps	100	2.50	1.25	.70
1977 O-Pee-Chee	170	2.00	1.00	.60
1977 Topps	170	2.00	1.00	.60
1978 O-Pee-Chee	70	3.00	1.50	.90
1978 O-Pee-Chee	250	2.00	1.00	.60
1978 Topps	70	2.50	1.25	.70
1978 Topps	250	1.50	.70	.45
1979 O-Pee-Chee	8	3.00	1.50	.90
1979 O-Pee-Chee	80	2.00	1.00	.60
1979 Topps	8	1.50	.70	.45
1979 Topps	80	1.75	.90	.50
1980 O-Pee-Chee	86	.75	.40	.25
1980 O-Pee-Chee	150	1.00	.50	.30
1980 O-Pee-Chee	168	1.00	.50	.30
1980 Topps	86	.75	.40	.25
1980 Topps	150	1.00	.50	.30
1980 Topps	168	1.00	.50	.30

Set	Card #	MT	NM	EX
1981 O-Pee-Chee	54	1.00	.70	.40
1981 O-Pee-Chee	67	.30	.25	.12
1981 Topps	11	.60	.45	.25
1981 Topps	126	.75	.60	.30
1982 O-Pee-Chee	64	.75	.60	.30
1983 O-Pee-Chee	99	.60	.45	.25
1990 Pro Set	659	.25	.20	.10
1992 O-Pee-Chee	194	.40	.30	.15
1992 O-Pee-Chee 25th Anniversary Series	2	.40	.30	.15

Pat Falloon

Set	Card #	MT	NM	EX
1990 Upper Deck	469 (R)	1.00	.70	.40
1991 O-Pee-Chee Premier	56 (R)	.40	.30	.15
1991 Parkhurst	160 (R)	.50	.40	.20
1991 Pinnacle	329	.75	.60	.30
1991 Pro Set	558	.50	.40	.20
1991 Pro Set Platinum	271	.50	.40	.20
1991 Score Canadian	640	.50	.40	.20
1991 Score Traded	90	.50	.40	.20
1991 Upper Deck	593	.50	.40	.20
1992 Bowman	361	.50	.40	.20
1992 Fleer Ultra	194	.25	.20	.10
1992 Fleer Ultra Rookies	6	4.50	3.50	1.75
1992 O-Pee-Chee	227	.25	.20	.10

1992 O-Pee-Chee Premier Star Performers	12	.25	.20	.10
1992 Parkhurst	161	.05	.04	.02
1992 Parkhurst	233	.05	.04	.02
1992 Pinnacle	9	.30	.25	.12
1992 Pinnacle	238	.25	.20	.10
1992 Pinnacle Team 2000	26	2.00	1.50	.80
1992 Pro Set	166	.25	.20	.10
1992 Pro Set Gold Team Leaders	10	2.00	1.50	.80
1992 Pro Set Rookie Goal Leaders	4	4.00	3.00	1.50
1992 Score	125	.25	.20	.10
1992 Score	436	.20	.15	.08
1992 Topps	7	.20	.15	.08
1992 Topps	418	.35	.25	.14
1992 Topps Stadium Club	56	.20	.15	.08
1992 Topps Stadium Club	259	.25	.20	.10
1992 Upper Deck	286	.20	.15	.08
1992 Upper Deck	355	.20	.15	.08
1992 Upper Deck	386	.25	.20	.10
1992 Upper Deck World Junior Grads	13	5.00	3.75	2.00
1993 Donruss	308	.15	.11	.06
1993 Donruss Special Print	T	4.00	3.00	1.50
1993 Fleer PowerPlay	218	.15	.11	.06
1993 Fleer Ultra	56	.25	.20	.10
1993 Leaf	49	.25	.20	.10
1993 Leaf Studio Signature	2	3.50	2.75	1.50
1993 Parkhurst	183	.20	.15	.08
1993 Pinnacle	20	.15	.11	.06
1993 Pinnacle Team 2001	26	.50	.40	.20
1993 Score	133	.20	.15	.08
1993 Score Franchise	19	6.00	4.50	2.50
1993 Topps Premier	259	.25	.20	.10
1993 Topps Stadium Club	224	.15	.11	.06
1993 Upper Deck	39	.20	.15	.08
1993 Upper Deck Future Heroes	29	5.00	3.75	2.00
1993 Upper Deck SP Inserts	141	.50	.40	.20
1994 Donruss	83	.08	.06	.03
1994 Fleer Flair	163	.30	.25	.12
1994 Leaf	95	.10	.08	.04
1994 Parkhurst Vintage Parkhurst	70	.20	.15	.08
1994 Pinnacle	173	.10	.08	.04
1994 Pinnacle Artist's Proofs	173	5.00	3.75	2.00
1994 Pinnacle Rink Collection	173	3.00	2.25	1.25
1994 Score	152	.05	.04	.02
1994 Score Hockey Gold Line	152	.25	.20	.10
1994 Topps Stadium Club	62	.08	.06	.03

Bernie Federko

Set	Card #	NM	EX	VG
1978 O-Pee-Chee	143 (R)	14.00	7.00	4.20

Set	Card #	MT	NM	EX
1978 Topps	143 (R)	8.00	4.00	2.50
1979 O-Pee-Chee	215	4.00	2.00	1.25
1979 Topps	215	3.00	1.50	.90
1980 O-Pee-Chee	71	.35	.20	.11
1980 O-Pee-Chee	136	2.50	1.25	.70
1980 Topps	71	.25	.13	.08
1980 Topps	136	1.50	.70	.45

Set	Card #	MT	NM	EX
1981 O-Pee-Chee	288	1.25	.90	.50
1981 O-Pee-Chee	300	.50	.40	.20
1981 O-Pee-Chee	304	.30	.25	.12
1981 Topps	127	.50	.40	.20
1981 Topps	62	.20	.15	.08
1982 O-Pee-Chee	302	.20	.15	.08
1982 O-Pee-Chee	303	.20	.15	.08
1983 O-Pee-Chee	315	.15	.11	.06
1984 O-Pee-Chee	184	.35	.25	.14
1984 O-Pee-Chee	367	.30	.25	.12
1984 Topps	131	.35	.25	.14
1985 O-Pee-Chee	104	.25	.20	.10
1985 Topps	104	.15	.11	.06
1986 O-Pee-Chee	105	.15	.11	.06
1988 O-Pee-Chee	81	.15	.11	.06
1988 Topps	81	.07	.05	.03
1989 O-Pee-Chee	107	.07	.05	.03
1989 Topps	107	.05	.04	.02
1990 Bowman	238	.04	.03	.02
1990 O-Pee-Chee	191	.05	.04	.02
1990 Pro Set	70	.05	.04	.02
1990 Score	252	.05	.04	.02
1990 Topps	191	.03	.02	.01
1990 Upper Deck	58	.08	.06	.03
1991 Pro Set	597	.05	.04	.02

Sergei Fedorov

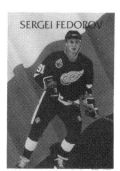

Set	Card #	MT	NM	EX
1990 O-Pee-Chee Central Red Army	19	5.00	3.75	2.00
1990 O-Pee-Chee Premier	30 (R)	18.00	13.50	7.25
1990 Pro Set	604 (R)	1.00	.70	.40
1990 Score Traded	20 (R)	3.50	2.75	1.50
1990 Upper Deck	525 (R)	12.00	9.00	4.75
1991 Bowman	50	.80	.60	.30
1991 O-Pee-Chee Premier	68	1.50	1.25	.60
1991 O-Pee-Chee Premier	173	.50	.40	.20
1991 O-Pee-Chee/Topps	8	.30	.25	.12
1991 O-Pee-Chee/Topps	401	.50	.40	.20
1991 Parkhurst	38	1.50	1.25	.60
1991 Pinnacle	157	2.00	1.50	.80
1991 Pro Set	53	.65	.50	.25
1991 Pro Set Platinum	30	.75	.60	.30
1991 Pro Set Platinum	277	.15	.11	.06
1991 Pro Set Platinum PC	7	4.00	3.00	1.50
1991 Score American	250	.75	.60	.30
1991 Score American	352	.25	.20	.10
1991 Score American	408	.20	.15	.08
1991 Score Canadian	298	.20	.15	.08
1991 Score Canadian	382	.20	.15	.08
1991 Score Canadian	470	.50	.40	.20
1991 Score Hot Card	4	6.00	4.50	2.50
1991 Topps Stadium Club	316	3.50	2.75	1.50
1991 Upper Deck	6	.60	.45	.25
1991 Upper Deck	40	.25	.20	.10
1991 Upper Deck	144	1.25	.90	.50
1991 Upper Deck	631	.20	.15	.08
1991 Upper Deck Euro-Stars	9	3.00	2.00	1.00
1992 Bowman	205	55.00	41.00	22.00
1992 Bowman	416	6.00	4.50	2.50
1992 Fleer Ultra	48	1.50	1.25	.60
1992 Fleer Ultra Imports	3	10.00	7.50	4.00
1992 O-Pee-Chee	195	.80	.60	.30
1992 O-Pee-Chee Premier Star Performers	20	1.50	1.25	.60
1992 Parkhurst	39	1.00	.70	.40
1992 Parkhurst	219	.50	.40	.20
1992 Pro Set	40	1.00	.70	.40
1992 Score	252	.75	.60	.30
1992 Topps	252	.60	.45	.25
1992 Topps Stadium Club	244	1.00	.70	.40
1992 Topps Stadium Club	300	1.00	.70	.40
1992 Upper Deck	157	.75	.60	.30
1992 Upper Deck	632	.25	.20	.10
1992 Upper Deck Euro Stars	1	5.50	4.00	2.25
1992 Upper Deck World Junior Grads	16	12.00	9.00	4.75
1993 Donruss	101	1.25	.90	.50
1993 Donruss Elite	2	55.00	41.00	22.00
1993 Fleer PowerPlay	72	1.25	.90	.50
1993 Fleer PowerPlay Gamebreakers	1	3.00	2.25	1.25
1993 Fleer PowerPlay Global Greats	2	3.00	2.25	1.25
1993 Fleer PowerPlay Slapshot Artists	3	6.00	4.50	2.50
1993 Fleer Ultra	121	1.00	.70	.40
1993 Fleer Ultra Speed Merchants	3	32.00	24.00	13.00
1993 Parkhurst	58	1.00	.70	.40
1993 Parkhurst East-West Stars	10W	25.00	18.50	10.00
1993 Pinnacle	54	1.00	.70	.40
1993 Pinnacle Team 2001	24	6.00	4.50	2.50
1993 Score	250	.50	.40	.20
1993 Score International Stars	3	3.00	2.25	1.25
1993 Score U.S. Dynamic Duos	9	20.00	15.00	8.00
1993 Topps Premier	318	.50	.40	.20
1993 Topps Premier	441	.40	.30	.15
1993 Topps Stadium Club	45	1.00	.70	.40
1993 Upper Deck	171	.75	.60	.30
1993 Upper Deck SP Inserts	44	4.00	3.00	1.50
1994 Donruss	173	.75	.60	.30
1994 Donruss Elite Series	4	35.00	26.00	14.00
1994 Donruss Ice Masters	2	5.00	3.75	2.00
1994 Fleer Flair	48	1.75	1.25	.70
1994 Fleer Flair	213	.60	.45	.25
1994 Fleer Flair	214	.60	.45	.25
1994 Fleer Flair	215	.60	.45	.25
1994 Fleer Flair	216	.60	.45	.25
1994 Fleer Flair	217	.60	.45	.25
1994 Fleer Flair	218	.60	.45	.25
1994 Fleer Flair	219	.60	.45	.25
1994 Fleer Flair	220	.60	.45	.25
1994 Fleer Flair	221	.60	.45	.25
1994 Fleer Flair	222	.60	.45	.25
1994 Fleer Flair Center Spotlight	2	7.50	5.75	3.00
1994 Fleer Flair Scoring Power	3	8.00	6.00	3.25
1994 Fleer Ultra	60	.60	.45	.25
1994 Fleer Ultra NHL Award Winners	3	4.00	3.00	1.50
1994 Fleer Ultra Scoring Kings	2	4.00	3.00	1.50
1994 Leaf	155	.75	.60	.30

		MT	NM	EX
1994 Leaf Fire On Ice	1	12.00	9.00	4.75
1994 Leaf Gold Stars	1	100.00	75.00	40.00
1994 Leaf Limited	7	13.00	9.75	5.25
1994 O-Pee-Chee Go to Guys	9	5.25	5.25	5.25
1994 O-Pee-Chee Premier	40	.40	.30	.15
1994 Parkhurst	305	.30	.25	.12
1994 Parkhurst Crash the Game	7	9.00	6.75	3.50
1994 Parkhurst Vintage Parkhurst	39	3.00	2.25	1.25
1994 Pinnacle	150	1.00	.70	.40
1994 Pinnacle Artist's Proofs	150	75.00	56.00	30.00
1994 Pinnacle Rink Collection	150	30.00	22.00	12.00
1994 Pinnacle Team Pinnacle	8	80.00	60.00	32.00
1994 Score Dream Team	12	14.00	10.50	5.50
1994 Score Franchise	7	35.00	26.00	14.00
1994 Score 90-Plus Club	2	15.00	11.00	6.00
1994 Topps Premier	40	.40	.30	.15
1994 Topps Premier Finest Inserts	3	14.00	10.50	5.50
1994 Topps Stadium Club	250	.60	.45	.25
1994 Topps Stadium Club	268	.30	.25	.12
1994 Topps Stadium Club Finest	6	12.00	9.00	4.75
1994 Upper Deck	37	1.00	.70	.40
1994 Upper Deck Award Predictor	6	12.00	9.00	4.75
1994 Upper Deck Electric Ice	37	35.00	26.00	14.00
1994 Upper Deck Scoring Predictor	4	14.00	10.50	5.50
1994 Upper Deck Scoring Predictor	23	12.00	9.00	4.75

Theoren Fleury

Set	Card #	MT	NM	EX
1989 O-Pee-Chee	232 (R)	3.00	2.25	1.25
1990 Bowman	102	.25	.20	.10
1990 O-Pee-Chee	386	.60	.45	.25
1990 Pro Set	33	.70	.50	.30
1990 Score	226	.30	.25	.12
1990 Topps	386	.30	.25	.12
1990 Upper Deck	47	.50	.40	.20
1990 Upper Deck	478	.35	.25	.14
1991 Bowman	249	.05	.04	.02
1991 Bowman	270	.15	.11	.06
1991 O-Pee-Chee Premier	92	.05	.04	.02
1991 O-Pee-Chee/Topps	282	.35	.25	.14
1991 O-Pee-Chee/Topps	322	.05	.04	.02
1991 Parkhurst	22	.25	.20	.10
1991 Pinnacle	190	.25	.20	.10
1991 Pinnacle	358	.15	.11	.06
1991 Pro Set	28	.10	.08	.04
1991 Pro Set	274	.05	.04	.02
1991 Pro Set Platinum	16	.10	.08	.04
1991 Score American	226	.10	.08	.04
1991 Score American	407	.10	.08	.04
1991 Score Canadian	226	.10	.08	.04
1991 Score Canadian	297	.10	.08	.04
1991 Score Hot Card	7	1.50	1.25	.60
1991 Topps Stadium Club	355	.40	.30	.15
1991 Upper Deck	245	.20	.15	.08
1991 Upper Deck	506	.15	.11	.06
1991 Upper Deck	630	.10	.08	.04
1992 Bowman	206	2.50	2.00	1.00
1992 Bowman	355	.60	.45	.25
1992 Fleer Ultra	21	.15	.11	.06
1992 O-Pee-Chee	99	.05	.04	.02
1992 Parkhurst	19	.05	.04	.02
1992 Pinnacle	125	.20	.15	.08
1992 Pro Set	23	.10	.08	.04
1992 Score	280	.20	.15	.08
1992 Topps	220	.06	.05	.02
1992 Topps Stadium Club	2	.20	.15	.08
1992 Upper Deck	285	.10	.08	.04
1993 Donruss	46	.20	.15	.08
1993 Donruss Special Print	D	4.00	3.00	1.50
1993 Fleer PowerPlay	36	.20	.15	.08
1993 Fleer Ultra	41	.07	.05	.03
1993 Leaf	154	.10	.08	.04
1993 OPC Premier Black Gold	13	8.00	6.00	3.25
1993 Parkhurst	28	.12	.09	.05
1993 Pinnacle	79	.20	.15	.08
1993 Score	191	.05	.04	.02
1993 Score	441	.10	.08	.04
1993 Topps Premier	100	.10	.08	.04
1993 Topps Stadium Club	390	.20	.15	.08
1993 Upper Deck	3	.05	.04	.02
1993 Upper Deck	229	.10	.08	.04
1993 Upper Deck	288	.10	.08	.04
1993 Upper Deck Gretzky's Great Ones	7	1.75	1.25	.70
1993 Upper Deck SP Inserts	21	.35	.25	.14
1994 Donruss	99	.08	.06	.03
1994 Fleer Flair	24	.30	.25	.12
1994 Fleer Ultra	29	.30	.25	.12
1994 Leaf	55	.12	.09	.05
1994 Parkhurst Vintage Parkhurst	20	.20	.15	.08
1994 Pinnacle	38	.10	.08	.04
1994 Pinnacle Artist's Proofs	38	7.00	5.25	2.75
1994 Pinnacle Northern Lights	15	5.50	4.25	2.25
1994 Pinnacle Rink Collection	38	4.00	3.00	1.50
1994 Score	69	.05	.04	.02
1994 Score Check-It	15	7.50	5.75	3.00
1994 Score Franchise	4	8.00	6.00	3.25
1994 Score Hockey Gold Line	69	.40	.30	.15
1994 Topps Premier Finest Inserts	19	4.50	3.50	1.75
1994 Topps Stadium Club	25	.10	.08	.04
1994 Upper Deck SP	11	.30	.25	.12

Facsimile autograph: A reproduced autograph. Facsimile autographs are often found on sports cards as part of the card's design.

Factory set: A complete set of cards collated and packaged by the card company. A factory set may or may not be packaged in a special box. Usually factory sets are sealed or have sealed inner packs as an added security measure. Factory sets with intact seals or inner packs command a slight premium over hand-collated sets.

Grant Fuhr

Set	Card #	MT	NM	EX
1982 O-Pee-Chee	105 (R)	20.00	15.00	8.00
1983 O-Pee-Chee	27	6.00	4.50	2.50
1984 O-Pee-Chee	241	4.00	3.00	1.50
1985 O-Pee-Chee	207	3.00	2.25	1.25
1986 O-Pee-Chee	56	1.75	1.25	.70
1986 Topps	56	1.00	.70	.40
1987 O-Pee-Chee	178	1.00	.70	.40
1987 Topps	178	.50	.40	.20
1988 O-Pee-Chee	59	.60	.45	.25
1988 Topps	59	.30	.25	.12
1989 O-Pee-Chee	192	.75	.60	.30
1989 Topps	192	.15	.11	.06
1990 Bowman	189	.15	.11	.06
1990 O-Pee-Chee	321	.10	.08	.04
1990 Pro Set	82	.25	.20	.10
1990 Score	275	.12	.09	.05
1990 Topps	321	.10	.08	.04
1990 Upper Deck	264	.25	.20	.10
1991 Bowman	111	.05	.04	.02
1991 O-Pee-Chee Premier	100	.05	.04	.02
1991 O-Pee-Chee/Topps	84	.05	.04	.02
1991 Parkhurst	175	.05	.04	.02
1991 Pinnacle	168	.08	.06	.03
1991 Pro Set	78	.10	.08	.04
1991 Pro Set	494	.05	.04	.02
1991 Pro Set Platinum	117	.05	.04	.02
1991 Score American	114	.10	.08	.04
1991 Score Canadian	114	.05	.04	.02
1991 Score Canadian	608	.05	.04	.02
1991 Score Traded	58	.05	.04	.02
1991 Topps Stadium Club	258	.15	.11	.06
1991 Upper Deck	264	.20	.15	.08
1991 Upper Deck	553	.15	.11	.06
1992 Bowman	114	.25	.20	.10
1992 Fleer Ultra	210	.06	.05	.02
1992 O-Pee-Chee	31	.05	.04	.02
1992 O-Pee-Chee	119	.25	.20	.10
1992 O-Pee-Chee 25th Anniversary Series	15	.25	.20	.10
1992 Parkhurst	182	.05	.04	.02
1992 Parkhurst	250	.08	.06	.03
1992 Parkhurst	497	.25	.20	.10
1992 Pinnacle	267	.40	.30	.15
1992 Pinnacle	301	.06	.05	.02
1992 Pro Set	183	.05	.04	.02
1992 Score	20	.05	.04	.02
1992 Score	437	.05	.04	.02
1992 Topps	350	.06	.05	.02
1992 Topps Stadium Club	412	.05	.04	.02
1992 Upper Deck	271	.05	.04	.02
1993 Donruss	34	.10	.08	.04
1993 Fleer PowerPlay	27	.10	.08	.04
1993 Fleer PowerPlay Netminders	3	2.50	2.00	1.00
1993 Fleer Ultra	103	.07	.05	.03
1993 Leaf	66	.10	.08	.04
1993 Leaf Painted Warriors	5	4.00	3.00	1.50
1993 Parkhurst	22	.10	.08	.04
1993 Parkhurst Cherry's Playoff Heroes	7D	12.50	9.50	5.00
1993 Pinnacle	65	.10	.08	.04
1993 Pinnacle Masks	1	25.00	18.50	10.00
1993 Score	75	.05	.04	.02
1993 Topps Premier	218	.05	.04	.02
1993 Topps Stadium Club	260	.05	.04	.02
1993 Upper Deck	163	.05	.04	.02
1993 Upper Deck Gretzky's Great Ones	10	1.75	1.25	.70
1993 Upper Deck SP Inserts	15	.30	.25	.12
1994 Donruss	212	.08	.06	.03
1994 Leaf	78	.15	.11	.06
1994 O-Pee-Chee Premier	80	.10	.08	.04
1994 Topps Premier	80	.10	.08	.04

Bob Gainey

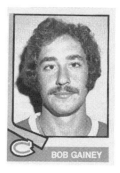

Set	Card #	NM	EX	VG
1974 O-Pee-Chee	388 (R)	20.00	10.00	6.00
1975 O-Pee-Chee	278	7.00	3.50	2.00
1975 Topps	278	4.00	2.00	1.25
1976 O-Pee-Chee	44	4.00	2.00	1.25
1976 O-Pee-Chee	217	.45	.25	.14
1976 Topps	44	2.00	1.00	.60
1976 Topps	217	.20	.10	.06
1977 O-Pee-Chee	129	2.00	1.00	.60
1977 Topps	129	1.00	.50	.30
1978 O-Pee-Chee	76	1.75	.90	.50
1978 Topps	76	1.00	.50	.30
1979 O-Pee-Chee	170	.75	.40	.25
1979 Topps	170	.40	.20	.12
1980 O-Pee-Chee	58	.35	.20	.11
1980 Topps	58	.40	.20	.12

Set	Card #	MT	NM	EX
1981 O-Pee-Chee	176	.50	.40	.20
1981 O-Pee-Chee	194	.30	.25	.12
1981 Topps	13	.20	.15	.08
1982 O-Pee-Chee	181	.20	.15	.08
1983 O-Pee-Chee	187	.15	.11	.06
1985 O-Pee-Chee	169	.25	.20	.10
1986 O-Pee-Chee	96	.15	.11	.06
1986 Topps	96	.25	.20	.10
1987 O-Pee-Chee	228	.12	.09	.05
1988 O-Pee-Chee	216	.15	.11	.06
1990 Pro Set	668	.07	.05	.03

First card: The first card of a player in a national set. A first card may or may not be a player's rookie card; for instance, if a player appeared in a Fleer set one year and a Score set the next, the Fleer card would be that player's rookie card and his first Fleer card, while the Score card would be his first Score card but not his rookie card.

Mike Gartner

Set	Card #	NM	EX	VG
1980 O-Pee-Chee	49	6.00	3.00	1.75
1980 O-Pee-Chee	195 (R)	80.00	40.00	24.00
1980 Topps	49	4.00	2.00	1.25
1980 Topps	195 (R)	40.00	20.00	12.00

Set	Card #	MT	NM	EX
1981 O-Pee-Chee	347	20.00	15.00	8.00
1981 Topps	117	5.00	3.75	2.00
1982 O-Pee-Chee	363	9.00	6.75	3.50
1983 O-Pee-Chee		364	1.00	.70 .40
1983 O-Pee-Chee	369	5.00	3.75	2.00
1984 O-Pee-Chee	197	2.00	1.50	.80
1984 O-Pee-Chee	370	.50	.40	.20
1984 Topps	143	1.50	1.25	.60
1985 O-Pee-Chee	46	3.00	2.25	1.25
1985 Topps	46	2.00	1.50	.80
1986 O-Pee-Chee	59	1.00	.70	.40
1986 Topps	59	.60	.45	.25
1987 O-Pee-Chee	168	.60	.45	.25
1987 Topps	168	.50	.40	.20
1988 O-Pee-Chee	50	.40	.30	.15
1988 Topps	50	.10	.08	.04
1989 O-Pee-Chee	30	.15	.11	.06
1989 Topps	30	.20	.15	.08
1990 O-Pee-Chee	373	.15	.11	.06
1990 O-Pee-Chee Premier	36	.50	.40	.20
1990 Pro Set	196	.07	.05	.03
1990 Pro Set	351	.05	.04	.02
1990 Score	130	.07	.05	.03
1990 Score	333	.10	.08	.04
1990 Score Hockey's 100 Hottest Rising Stars	60	.10	.08	.04
1990 Topps	373	.07	.05	.03
1990 Upper Deck	277	.15	.11	.06
1991 Bowman	74	.05	.04	.02
1991 O-Pee-Chee Premier	164	.10	.08	.04
1991 O-Pee-Chee/Topps	46	.12	.09	.05
1991 Parkhurst	122	.05	.04	.02
1991 Parkhurst	430	.05	.04	.02
1991 Pinnacle	202	.20	.15	.08
1991 Pro Set	167	.10	.08	.04
1991 Pro Set	604	.05	.04	.02
1991 Pro Set Platinum	84	.10	.08	.04
1991 Pro Set Platinum PC	11	1.50	1.25	.60
1991 Score American	135	.10	.08	.04
1991 Score Canadian	135	.10	.08	.04
1991 Topps Stadium Club	51	.15	.11	.06
1991 Upper Deck	247	.15	.11	.06
1992 Bowman	146	.50	.40	.20
1992 Fleer Ultra	135	.06	.05	.02
1992 O-Pee-Chee	245	.05	.04	.02
1992 O-Pee-Chee	300	.05	.04	.02
1992 Parkhurst	108	.05	.04	.02
1992 Pinnacle	94	.06	.05	.02
1992 Pro Set	113	.05	.04	.02
1992 Pro Set	256	.05	.04	.02
1992 Score	50	.05	.04	.02
1992 Score	443	.05	.04	.02
1992 Topps	264	.06	.05	.02

Set	Card #	NM	EX	VG
1992 Topps	404	.06	.05	.02
1992 Topps Stadium Club	311	.05	.04	.02
1992 Upper Deck	126	.05	.04	.02
1993 Donruss	218	.12	.09	.05
1993 Donruss	494	.15	.11	.06
1993 Fleer PowerPlay	157	.10	.08	.04
1993 Fleer Ultra	25	.07	.05	.03
1993 Fleer Ultra Red Light Specials	3	1.00	.70	.40
1993 Fleer Ultra Speed Merchants	4	6.00	4.50	2.50
1993 Leaf	213	.10	.08	.04
1993 Parkhurst	400	.15	.11	.06
1993 Pinnacle	27	.10	.08	.04
1993 Pinnacle	241	.08	.06	.03
1993 Pinnacle All-Stars	8	.20	.15	.08
1993 Pinnacle All-Stars	46	2.50	2.00	1.00
1993 Score	2	.05	.04	.02
1993 Score	447	.05	.04	.02
1993 Topps Premier	375	.08	.06	.03
1993 Topps Premier	384	.10	.08	.04
1993 Topps Stadium Club	110	.05	.04	.02
1993 Topps Stadium Club All-Stars	22	12.00	9.00	4.75
1993 Topps Stadium Club Finest	6	3.50	2.75	1.50
1993 Upper Deck	205	.10	.08	.04
1993 Upper Deck SP Inserts	98	.30	.25	.12
1994 Donruss	111	.08	.06	.03
1994 Fleer Flair	180	.25	.20	.10
1994 Fleer Ultra	214	.08	.06	.03
1994 Leaf	135	.15	.11	.06
1994 Leaf Fire On Ice	11	4.50	3.50	1.75
1994 O-Pee-Chee Premier	253	.08	.06	.03
1994 Parkhurst	228	.06	.05	.02
1994 Pinnacle	31	.10	.08	.04
1994 Pinnacle Artist's Proofs	31	8.00	6.00	3.25
1994 Pinnacle Rink Collection	31	4.00	3.00	1.50
1994 Score	112	.05	.04	.02
1994 Score	242	.05	.04	.02
1994 Score Hockey Gold Line	112	.50	.40	.20
1994 Score Hockey Gold Line	242	.50	.40	.20
1994 Topps Premier	253	.08	.06	.03
1994 Upper Deck	32	.10	.08	.04
1994 Upper Deck	230	.10	.08	.04
1994 Upper Deck Electric Ice	32	6.00	4.50	2.50
1994 Upper Deck Electric Ice	230	5.00	3.75	2.00
1994 Upper Deck SP	78	.30	.25	.12

Bernie Geoffrion

Set	Card #	NM	EX	VG
1951 Parkhurst	14 (R)	400.00	200.00	120.00

1952 Parkhurst	3	200.00	100.00	60.00
1953 Parkhurst	29	120.00	60.00	36.00
1954 Parkhurst	8	90.00	45.00	27.00
1954 Parkhurst	100	125.00	62.00	37.00
1955 Parkhurst	43	100.00	50.00	30.00
1955 Parkhurst	70	50.00	25.00	15.00
1957 Parkhurst	2	90.00	45.00	27.00
1957 Parkhurst	24	25.00	12.50	7.50
1958 Parkhurst	28	75.00	37.00	22.00
1959 Parkhurst	33	60.00	30.00	18.00
1960 Parkhurst	46	60.00	30.00	18.00
1961 Parkhurst	35	50.00	25.00	15.00
1961 Parkhurst	48	10.00	5.00	3.00
1961 Parkhurst	53	45.00	22.00	13.50
1962 Parkhurst	48	45.00	22.00	13.50
1962 Parkhurst	53	40.00	20.00	12.00
1963 Parkhurst	29	40.00	20.00	12.00
1963 Parkhurst	88	45.00	22.00	13.50
1966 Topps	85	30.00	15.00	9.00
1967 Topps	29	22.00	11.00	6.50
1974 O-Pee-Chee	147	3.00	1.50	.90
1974 Topps	147	1.50	.70	.45

Set	Card #	MT	NM	EX
1993 Parkhurst Parkie Reprints	44	18.00	13.50	7.25

Doug Gilmour

Set	Card #	MT	NM	EX
1984 O-Pee-Chee	185 (R)	55.00	41.00	22.00
1985 O-Pee-Chee	76	25.00	18.50	10.00
1985 Topps	76	15.00	11.00	6.00
1986 O-Pee-Chee	93	12.00	9.00	4.75
1986 Topps	93	6.50	5.00	2.50
1987 O-Pee-Chee	175	7.00	5.25	2.75
1987 O-Pee-Chee Hockey Leaders	11	1.50	1.25	.60
1987 Topps	175	4.50	3.50	1.75
1988 O-Pee-Chee	56	4.00	3.00	1.50
1988 Topps	56	2.00	1.50	.80
1989 O-Pee-Chee	74	.50	.40	.20
1989 Topps	74	.75	.60	.30
1990 Bowman	96	.25	.20	.10
1990 O-Pee-Chee	136	.05	.04	.02
1990 Pro Set	34	.05	.04	.02
1990 Score	155	.25	.20	.10
1990 Score Hockey's 100 Hottest Rising Stars	69	.10	.08	.04
1990 Topps	136	.25	.20	.10
1990 Upper Deck	271	.75	.60	.30
1991 Bowman	255	.25	.20	.10
1991 O-Pee-Chee/Topps	208	.20	.15	.08
1991 Parkhurst	26	.25	.20	.10
1991 Parkhurst	396	.50	.40	.20
1991 Parkhurst Promo Cards	(1)	80.00	60.00	32.00
1991 Pinnacle	92	.75	.60	.30
1991 Pro Set	34	.25	.20	.10
1991 Pro Set Platinum	234	.25	.20	.10

1991 Score American	218	.25	.20	.10
1991 Score Canadian	218	.25	.20	.10
1991 Topps Stadium Club	96	1.00	.70	.40
1991 Upper Deck	188	.30	.25	.12
1991 Upper Deck	558	.40	.30	.15
1992 Bowman	83	2.50	2.00	1.00
1992 Fleer Ultra	211	.35	.25	.14
1992 O-Pee-Chee	177	.25	.20	.10
1992 O-Pee-Chee Premier Star Performers	8	.60	.45	.25
1992 Parkhurst	183	.05	.04	.02
1992 Parkhurst	502	1.00	.70	.40
1992 Parkhurst Cherry Picks	1	20.00	15.00	8.00
1992 Pinnacle	233	.25	.20	.10
1992 Pinnacle	279	.25	.20	.10
1992 Pro Set	184	.25	.20	.10
1992 Pro Set Gold Team Leaders	11	5.00	3.75	2.00
1992 Score	40	.05	.04	.02
1992 Topps	122	.15	.11	.06
1992 Topps Stadium Club	359	.50	.40	.20
1992 Upper Deck	215	.35	.25	.14
1992 Upper Deck	639	.35	.25	.14
1993 Donruss	341	.50	.40	.20
1993 Donruss Elite	7	50.00	37.00	20.00
1993 Fleer PowerPlay	244	.40	.30	.15
1993 Fleer PowerPlay Gamebreakers	2	2.00	1.50	.80
1993 Fleer PowerPlay Point Leaders	2	2.00	1.50	.80
1993 Fleer Ultra	110	.40	.30	.15
1993 Fleer Ultra All-Stars	16	5.00	3.75	2.00
1993 Fleer Ultra Award Winners	3	6.00	4.50	2.40
1993 Fleer Ultra Premier Pivots	1	2.50	2.00	1.00
1993 Leaf	93	.40	.30	.15
1993 Leaf Gold All-Stars	6	20.00	15.00	8.00
1993 Leaf Studio Signature	1	6.00	4.50	2.50
1993 OPC Premier Black Gold	11	16.00	12.00	6.50
1993 Parkhurst	469	.45	.35	.20
1993 Parkhurst Cherry's Playoff Heroes	9D	30.00	22.00	12.00
1993 Parkhurst East-West Stars	4W	12.00	9.00	4.75
1993 Parkhurst US Canada Gold-Foiled	10	15.00	11.00	6.00
1993 Pinnacle	100	.40	.30	.15
1993 Pinnacle	226	.20	.15	.08
1993 Pinnacle All-Stars	44	.50	.40	.20
1993 Score	66	.25	.20	.10
1993 Score Canadian Dynamic Duos	1	20.00	15.00	8.00
1993 Score Franchise	21	12.00	9.00	4.75
1993 Topps Premier	390	.15	.11	.06
1993 Topps Stadium Club	140	.35	.25	.14
1993 Topps Stadium Club	149	.15	.11	.06
1993 Topps Stadium Club All-Stars	17	12.00	9.00	4.75
1993 Upper Deck	306	.15	.11	.06
1993 Upper Deck	382	.25	.20	.10
1993 Upper Deck Award Winners	6	5.00	3.75	2.00
1993 Upper Deck Next in Line	5	8.00	6.00	3.25
1993 Upper Deck Silver Skates Dye-Cut Retail	7R	10.00	7.50	4.00
1993 Upper Deck SP Inserts	158	1.00	.70	.40
1994 Donruss	8	.35	.25	.14
1994 Donruss Ice Masters	3	3.50	2.75	1.50
1994 Fleer Flair	181	1.00	.70	.40
1994 Fleer Flair Center Spotlight	3	5.00	3.75	2.00
1994 Fleer Ultra	216	.40	.30	.15
1994 Fleer Ultra Scoring Kings	3	2.50	2.00	1.00
1994 Leaf	99	.40	.30	.15

Set	Card #			
1994 Leaf Fire On Ice	5	9.00	6.75	3.50
1994 Leaf Gold Stars	2	40.00	30.00	16.00
1994 O-Pee-Chee Premier	225	.20	.15	.08
1994 Parkhurst	313	.15	.11	.06
1994 Parkhurst Crash the Game	23	8.00	6.00	3.25
1994 Parkhurst Vintage Parkhurst	80	1.00	.70	.40
1994 Pinnacle	135	.50	.40	.20
1994 Pinnacle Artist's Proofs	135	50.00	37.00	20.00
1994 Pinnacle Northern Lights	8	15.00	11.00	6.00
1994 Pinnacle Rink Collection	135	20.00	15.00	8.00
1994 Pinnacle Team Pinnacle	10	50.00	37.00	20.00
1994 Score	185	.25	.20	.10
1994 Score Dream Team	13	10.00	7.50	4.00
1994 Score Franchise	23	20.00	15.00	8.00
1994 Score Hockey Gold Line	185	1.50	1.25	.60
1994 Score 90-Plus Club	4	11.00	8.25	4.50
1994 Topps Premier	225	.20	.15	.08
1994 Upper Deck	138	.50	.40	.20
1994 Upper Deck Award Predictor	3	7.00	5.25	2.75
1994 Upper Deck Electric Ice	138	25.00	18.50	10.00
1994 Upper Deck Scoring Predictor	11	10.00	7.50	4.00
1994 Upper Deck Scoring Predictor	27	9.00	6.75	3.50

Michel Goulet

Set	Card #	NM	EX	VG
1980 O-Pee-Chee	67 (R)	25.00	12.50	7.50
1980 Topps	67 (R)	15.00	7.50	4.50

Set	Card #	MT	NM	EX
1981 O-Pee-Chee	275	7.00	5.25	2.75
1982 O-Pee-Chee	284	3.50	2.75	1.50
1983 O-Pee-Chee	287	.50	.40	.20
1983 O-Pee-Chee	288	.50	.40	.20
1983 O-Pee-Chee	292	1.50	1.25	.60
1984 O-Pee-Chee	207	.35	.25	.14
1984 O-Pee-Chee	280	1.00	.70	.40
1984 O-Pee-Chee	366	.40	.30	.15
1984 O-Pee-Chee	384	.40	.30	.15
1984 O-Pee-Chee	391	.30	.25	.12
1984 Topps	129	.40	.30	.15
1984 Topps	153	.20	.15	.08
1985 O-Pee-Chee	150	1.00	.70	.40
1985 Topps	150	.20	.15	.08
1986 O-Pee-Chee	92	.50	.40	.20
1986 Topps	92	.25	.20	.10
1987 O-Pee-Chee	77	.30	.25	.12
1987 Topps	77	.20	.15	.08
1988 O-Pee-Chee	54	.15	.11	.06
1988 Topps	54	.10	.08	.04

1989 O-Pee-Chee	57	.07	.05	.03
1989 Topps	57	.15	.11	.06
1990 Pro Set	430	.10	.08	.04
1990 Score	221	.07	.05	.03
1990 Topps	329	.07	.05	.03
1990 Upper Deck	133	.10	.08	.04
1991 Bowman	392	.05	.04	.02
1991 O-Pee-Chee/Topps	336	.05	.04	.02
1991 Parkhurst	36	.05	.04	.02
1991 Parkhurst	215	.05	.04	.02
1991 Parkhurst	428	.05	.04	.02
1991 Pinnacle	109	.08	.06	.03
1991 Pro Set	50	.10	.08	.04
1991 Pro Set Platinum	166	.05	.04	.02
1991 Pro Set Platinum PC	15	1.25	.90	.50
1991 Score American	201	.05	.04	.02
1991 Score American	375	.05	.04	.02
1991 Score Canadian	201	.05	.04	.02
1991 Score Canadian	265	.05	.04	.02
1991 Topps Stadium Club	66	.10	.08	.04
1991 Upper Deck	374	.10	.08	.04
1992 Bowman	310	.25	.20	.10
1992 Fleer Ultra	35	.06	.05	.02
1992 O-Pee-Chee	358	.05	.04	.02
1992 Parkhurst	272	.05	.04	.02
1992 Pinnacle	22	.06	.05	.02
1992 Pro Set	32	.05	.04	.02
1992 Score	222	.05	.04	.02
1992 Score	444	.05	.04	.02
1992 Topps	255	.06	.05	.02
1992 Topps	347	.06	.05	.02
1992 Topps Stadium Club	69	.05	.04	.02
1992 Upper Deck	113	.05	.04	.02
1993 Donruss	71	.10	.08	.04
1993 Fleer PowerPlay	49	.10	.08	.04
1993 Fleer Ultra	289	.07	.05	.03
1993 Leaf	373	.10	.08	.04
1993 Parkhurst	313	.10	.08	.04
1993 Pinnacle	399	.08	.06	.03
1993 Score	153	.05	.04	.02
1993 Topps Premier	386	.05	.04	.02
1993 Topps Stadium Club	12	.05	.04	.02

Adam Graves

Set	Card #	MT	NM	EX
1990 O-Pee-Chee	480 (R)	1.25	.90	.50
1990 Pro Set	84 (R)	.50	.40	.20
1990 Score	163 (R)	.80	.60	.30
1990 Upper Deck	344 (R)	2.50	2.00	1.00
1991 Bowman	97	.05	.04	.02
1991 O-Pee-Chee Premier	28	.05	.04	.02
1991 O-Pee-Chee/Topps	167	.05	.04	.02
1991 Parkhurst	339	.50	.40	.20
1991 Pinnacle	16	.80	.60	.30
1991 Pro Set	67	.05	.04	.02
1991 Pro Set	443	.05	.04	.02
1991 Pro Set Platinum	207	.05	.04	.02
1991 Score American	358	.05	.04	.02
1991 Score Canadian	235	.05	.04	.02

Wayne Gretzky

1991 Score Canadian	594	.05	.04	.02
1991 Score Traded	44	.05	.04	.02
1991 Topps Stadium Club	332	.75	.60	.30
1991 Upper Deck	268	.05	.04	.02
1991 Upper Deck	574	.50	.40	.20
1992 Bowman	373	1.75	1.25	.70
1992 Fleer Ultra	136	.06	.05	.02
1992 O-Pee-Chee	158	.05	.04	.02
1992 Parkhurst	346	.05	.04	.02
1992 Pinnacle	108	.50	.40	.20
1992 Pro Set	115	.05	.04	.02
1992 Score	71	.05	.04	.02
1992 Topps	329	.06	.05	.02
1992 Topps Stadium Club	150	.05	.04	.02
1992 Upper Deck	388	.05	.04	.02
1993 Donruss	219	.35	.25	.14
1993 Fleer PowerPlay	158	.10	.08	.04
1993 Fleer Ultra	43	.07	.05	.03
1993 Leaf	130	.10	.08	.04
1993 Parkhurst	134	.10	.08	.04
1993 Pinnacle	99	.10	.08	.04
1993 Score	35	.05	.04	.02
1993 Score U.S. Dynamic Duos	5	15.00	11.00	6.00
1993 Topps Premier	106	.05	.04	.02
1993 Topps Stadium Club	270	.05	.04	.02
1993 Upper Deck	128	.05	.04	.02
1993 Upper Deck Hat Tricks	1	.60	.45	.25
1993 Upper Deck SP Inserts	99	.30	.25	.12
1994 Donruss	43	.25	.20	.10
1994 Fleer Flair	111	.35	.25	.14
1994 Fleer Ultra	137	.08	.06	.03
1994 Fleer Ultra NHL Award Winners	4	1.00	.70	.40
1994 Fleer Ultra Ultra Power	4	9.00	6.75	3.50
1994 Leaf	255	.10	.08	.04
1994 O-Pee-Chee Premier	128	.10	.08	.04
1994 Parkhurst	147	.25	.20	.10
1994 Parkhurst	307	.10	.08	.04
1994 Parkhurst Crash the Game	15	6.00	4.50	2.50
1994 Pinnacle	62	.35	.25	.14
1994 Pinnacle Artist's Proofs	62	10.00	7.50	4.00
1994 Pinnacle Rink Collection	62	5.00	3.75	2.00
1994 Pinnacle Team Pinnacle	6	25.00	18.50	10.00
1994 Score	164	.15	.11	.06
1994 Score Check-It	9	9.00	6.75	3.50
1994 Score Dream Team	9	5.00	3.75	2.00
1994 Score Hockey Gold Line	164	.25	.20	.10
1994 Topps Premier	128	.10	.08	.04
1994 Topps Premier Finest Inserts	7	6.00	4.50	2.50
1994 Topps Stadium Club	9	.05	.04	.02
1994 Topps Stadium Club	265	.05	.04	.02
1994 Upper Deck	10	.25	.20	.10
1994 Upper Deck Electric Ice	10	6.00	4.50	2.50
1994 Upper Deck Ice Gallery	7	4.00	3.00	1.50
1994 Upper Deck Scoring Predictor	5	4.00	3.00	1.50

Foil: Foil-embossed stamp on a card.

Foil pack: A pack of baseball cards packaged in a tamper-proof, shiny foil. Upper Deck packages its cards in foil packs.

Full sheet: A full press sheet of cards that has never been cut; sometimes referred to as an "uncut" sheet. The number of cards on a sheet varies with the printing process, but most often contains 132 cards.

Set	Card #	NM	EX	VG
1979 O-Pee-Chee	18 (R)	750.00	375.00	225.00
1979 Topps	18 (R)	400.00	212.00	127.00
1980 O-Pee-Chee	3	35.00	17.50	10.50
1980 O-Pee-Chee	87	50.00	25.00	15.00
1980 O-Pee-Chee	162	15.00	7.50	4.50
1980 O-Pee-Chee	163	15.00	7.50	4.50
1980 O-Pee-Chee	182	20.00	10.00	6.00
1980 O-Pee-Chee	250	150.00	75.00	45.00
1980 Topps	3	20.00	10.00	6.00
1980 Topps	87	25.00	12.50	7.50
1980 Topps	162	10.00	5.00	3.00
1980 Topps	163	10.00	5.00	3.00
1980 Topps	182	15.00	7.50	4.50
1980 Topps	250	100.00	50.00	30.00

Set	Card #	MT	NM	EX
1981 O-Pee-Chee	106	55.00	41.00	22.00
1981 O-Pee-Chee	125	25.00	18.50	10.00
1981 O-Pee-Chee	126	12.00	9.00	4.75
1981 O-Pee-Chee	383	10.00	7.50	4.00
1981 O-Pee-Chee	384	10.00	7.50	4.00
1981 O-Pee-Chee	392	10.00	7.50	4.00
1981 Topps	16	12.00	9.00	4.75
1981 Topps	52	3.50	2.75	1.50
1982 O-Pee-Chee	1	10.00	7.50	4.00
1982 O-Pee-Chee	99	7.00	5.25	2.75
1982 O-Pee-Chee	106	40.00	30.00	16.00
1982 O-Pee-Chee	107	15.00	11.00	6.00
1982 O-Pee-Chee	235	6.00	4.50	2.50
1982 O-Pee-Chee	237	6.00	4.50	2.50
1982 O-Pee-Chee	240	6.00	4.50	2.50
1982 O-Pee-Chee	242	6.00	4.50	2.50
1982 O-Pee-Chee	243	6.00	4.50	2.50
1982 Post Cereal		2.50	2.50	2.50
1983 O-Pee-Chee	22	6.00	4.50	2.50
1983 O-Pee-Chee	23	20.00	15.00	8.00
1983 O-Pee-Chee	29	30.00	22.00	12.00
1983 O-Pee-Chee	203	6.00	4.50	2.50
1983 O-Pee-Chee	204	6.00	4.50	2.50
1983 O-Pee-Chee	212	6.00	4.50	2.50
1983 O-Pee-Chee	215	6.00	4.50	2.50
1983 O-Pee-Chee	216	6.00	4.50	2.50
1983 O-Pee-Chee	217	6.00	4.50	2.50
1984 O-Pee-Chee	208	5.00	3.75	2.00
1984 O-Pee-Chee	243	20.00	15.00	8.00
1984 O-Pee-Chee	357	5.00	3.75	2.00
1984 O-Pee-Chee	373	5.00	3.75	2.00
1984 O-Pee-Chee	374	5.00	3.75	2.00
1984 O-Pee-Chee	380	5.00	3.75	2.00
1984 O-Pee-Chee	381	5.00	3.75	2.00
1984 O-Pee-Chee	382	5.00	3.75	2.00
1984 O-Pee-Chee	383	5.00	3.75	2.00
1984 O-Pee-Chee	388	5.00	3.75	2.00
1984 Topps	51	10.00	7.50	4.00
1984 Topps	154	3.00	2.25	1.25
1985 O-Pee-Chee	120	25.00	18.50	10.00
1985 O-Pee-Chee	257	6.00	4.50	2.50
1985 O-Pee-Chee	258	6.00	4.50	2.50
1985 O-Pee-Chee	259	6.00	4.50	2.50

Set	#			
1985 Topps	120	19.00	14.00	7.50
1986 O-Pee-Chee	3	20.00	15.00	8.00
1986 O-Pee-Chee	259	5.00	3.75	2.00
1986 O-Pee-Chee	260	5.00	3.75	2.00
1986 Topps	3	15.00	11.00	6.00
1987 O-Pee-Chee	53	20.00	15.00	8.00
1987 Topps	53	15.00	11.00	6.00
1988 O-Pee-Chee	120	17.00	12.50	6.75
1988 Topps	120	35.00	26.00	14.00
1989 O-Pee-Chee	156	1.50	1.25	.60
1989 O-Pee-Chee	320	.75	.60	.30
1989 O-Pee-Chee	325	.75	.60	.30
1989 O-Pee-Chee Future Stars	30	1.75	1.25	.70
1989 Topps	156	3.50	2.75	1.50
1990 Bowman	143	1.25	.90	.50
1990 O-Pee-Chee	1	.30	.25	.12
1990 O-Pee-Chee	2	.25	.20	.10
1990 O-Pee-Chee	3	.25	.20	.10
1990 O-Pee-Chee	120	1.25	.90	.50
1990 O-Pee-Chee	199	.50	.40	.20
1990 O-Pee-Chee Premier	38	6.00	4.50	2.50
1990 Pro Set	118	1.00	.70	.40
1990 Pro Set	340	.50	.40	.20
1990 Pro Set	388	.50	.40	.20
1990 Pro Set	394	.50	.40	.20
1990 Pro Set	703	.60	.45	.25
1990 Score	1	1.00	.70	.40
1990 Score	321	.40	.30	.15
1990 Score	336	.30	.25	.12
1990 Score	338	.30	.25	.12
1990 Score	347	.25	.20	.10
1990 Score	352	.30	.25	.12
1990 Score	353	.30	.25	.12
1990 Score	361	.30	.25	.12
1990 Score Hockey's 100 Hottest Rising Stars	1	.10	.08	.04
1990 Score Traded	110	1.00	.70	.40
1990 Topps	1	.25	.20	.10
1990 Topps	2	.25	.20	.10
1990 Topps	3	.25	.20	.10
1990 Topps	120	1.25	.90	.50
1990 Topps	199	.25	.20	.10
1990 Topps Team Scoring Leaders	12	.15	.08	.08
1990 Upper Deck	54	2.00	1.50	.80
1990 Upper Deck	205	.60	.45	.25
1990 Upper Deck	476	.75	.60	.30
1990 Upper Deck	545	1.00	.70	.40
1990 Upper Deck Hockey Superstars	(1)	2.00	1.50	.80
1990 Upper Deck Hockey Superstars	(2)	2.00	1.50	.80
1990 Upper Deck Hockey Superstars	(3)	2.00	1.50	.80
1991 Bowman	173	.45	.35	.20
1991 Bowman	176	1.00	.70	.40
1991 O-Pee-Chee Premier	3	1.00	.70	.40
1991 O-Pee-Chee/Topps	201	.35	.25	.14
1991 O-Pee-Chee/Topps	224	.20	.15	.08
1991 O-Pee-Chee/Topps	257	.20	.15	.08
1991 O-Pee-Chee/Topps	258	.20	.15	.08
1991 O-Pee-Chee/Topps	321	1.25	.90	.50
1991 O-Pee-Chee/Topps	520	.40	.30	.15
1991 O-Pee-Chee/Topps	522	.40	.30	.15
1991 O-Pee-Chee/Topps	524	.40	.30	.15
1991 Parkhurst	73	1.50	1.25	.60
1991 Parkhurst	207	.50	.40	.20
1991 Parkhurst	222	.60	.45	.25
1991 Parkhurst	429	.50	.40	.20
1991 Parkhurst	433	.60	.45	.25
1991 Parkhurst	465	15.00	11.00	6.00
1991 Pinnacle	100	2.00	1.50	.80
1991 Pinnacle B	11	110.00	82.00	44.00
1991 Pro Set	101	1.00	.70	.40
1991 Pro Set	285	.25	.20	.10
1991 Pro Set	324	.25	.20	.10
1991 Pro Set	574	.25	.20	.10
1991 Pro Set Platinum	52	1.25	.90	.50
1991 Pro Set Platinum PC	4	6.00	4.50	2.50
1991 Pro Set Platinum PC	14	6.00	4.50	2.50
1991 Score American	100	1.00	.70	.40
1991 Score American	346	.25	.20	.10
1991 Score American	405	.25	.20	.10
1991 Score American	406	.25	.20	.10
1991 Score American	413	.25	.20	.10
1991 Score American	422	.25	.20	.10
1991 Score American	427	.25	.20	.10
1991 Score American	434	.25	.20	.10
1991 Score Canadian	100	1.00	.70	.40
1991 Score Canadian	295	.25	.20	.10
1991 Score Canadian	296	.25	.20	.10
1991 Score Canadian	303	.25	.20	.10
1991 Score Canadian	312	.25	.20	.10
1991 Score Canadian	317	.25	.20	.10
1991 Score Canadian	324	.25	.20	.10
1991 Score Canadian	376	.25	.20	.10
1991 Score Hot Card	2	10.00	7.50	4.00
1991 Topps Stadium Club	1	3.00	2.25	1.25
1991 Upper Deck	13	.75	.60	.30
1991 Upper Deck	38	.75	.60	.30
1991 Upper Deck	437	1.00	.70	.40
1991 Upper Deck	621	.50	.40	.20
1991 Upper Deck Collector Cards	1	2.00	1.50	.80
1991 Upper Deck Collector Cards	6	2.00	1.50	.80
1992 Bowman	1	8.00	6.00	3.25
1992 Bowman	207	17.00	12.50	6.75
1992 Fleer Ultra	83	1.50	1.25	.60
1992 Fleer Ultra All-Stars	10	9.00	6.75	3.50
1992 Fleer Ultra Award Winners	6	8.00	6.00	3.25
1992 O-Pee-Chee	15	1.00	.70	.40
1992 O-Pee-Chee	220	3.00	2.25	1.25
1992 O-Pee-Chee 25th Anniversary Series	12	.60	.45	.25
1992 Parkhurst	65	1.50	1.25	.60
1992 Parkhurst	509	3.50	2.75	1.50
1992 Pinnacle	200	1.50	1.25	.60
1992 Pinnacle	249	.65	.50	.25
1992 Pinnacle Team Pinnacle	5	45.00	34.00	18.00
1992 Pro Set	66	2.00	1.50	.80
1992 Pro Set	246	.80	.60	.30
1992 Pro Set Gold Team Leaders	6	15.00	11.00	6.00
1992 Score	1	1.00	.70	.40
1992 Score	412	.30	.25	.12
1992 Score	426	.30	.25	.12
1992 Score	525	.30	.25	.12
1992 Topps	1	1.00	.70	.40
1992 Topps	123	.30	.25	.12
1992 Topps Stadium Club	18	1.75	1.25	.70
1992 Topps Stadium Club	256	1.25	.90	.50
1992 Upper Deck	25	1.25	.90	.50
1992 Upper Deck	33	.50	.40	.20
1992 Upper Deck	37	.50	.40	.20
1992 Upper Deck	435	.25	.20	.10
1992 Upper Deck	621	.75	.60	.30
1992 Upper Deck All-World Team	1	10.00	7.50	4.00
1992 Upper Deck Gordie Howe Selects	5	20.00	15.00	8.00
1992 Upper Deck World Junior Grads	10	20.00	15.00	8.00
1993 Donruss	152	2.00	1.50	.80
1993 Donruss Elite	10	120.00	90.00	48.00
1993 Donruss Ice Kings	4	8.00	6.00	3.25
1993 Donruss Special Print	K	24.00	18.00	9.50
1993 Fleer PowerPlay	116	3.00	2.25	1.25
1993 Fleer PowerPlay Gamebreakers	3	5.50	4.25	2.25
1993 Fleer PowerPlay Point Leaders	3	5.00	3.75	2.00
1993 Fleer Ultra	114	1.50	1.25	.60
1993 Fleer Ultra All-Stars	15	12.00	9.00	4.75
1993 Fleer Ultra Premier Pivots	2	8.00	6.00	3.20
1993 Fleer Ultra Scoring Kings	2	12.00	9.00	4.75

Set	Card #	NM	EX	VG
1993 Leaf	304	2.00	1.50	.80
1993 Leaf Gold All-Stars	6	20.00	15.00	8.00
1993 Leaf Studio Signature	4	12.00	9.00	4.75
1993 OPC Premier Black Gold	1	35.00	26.00	14.00
1993 Parkhurst	99	2.00	1.50	.80
1993 Parkhurst Cherry's Playoff Heroes	1D	90.00	67.00	36.00
1993 Parkhurst US Canada Gold-Foiled	1	40.00	30.00	16.00
1993 Pinnacle	237	1.00	.70	.40
1993 Pinnacle	400	1.75	1.25	.70
1993 Pinnacle	512	10.00	7.50	4.00
1993 Pinnacle All-Stars	45	1.50	1.25	.60
1993 Pinnacle Hockey Captains	11	40.00	30.00	16.00
1993 Pinnacle Team Pinnacle	5	120.00	90.00	48.00
1993 Score	300	1.00	.70	.40
1993 Score	662	2.00	1.50	.80
1993 Score Dream Team	11	40.00	30.00	16.00
1993 Score Franchise	9	35.00	26.00	14.00
1993 Score U.S. Dynamic Duos	7	40.00	30.00	16.00
1993 Topps Premier	330	1.00	.70	.40
1993 Topps Premier	380	.75	.60	.30
1993 Topps Premier Black Gold	7	9.00	6.75	3.50
1993 Topps Stadium Club	200	1.50	1.25	.60
1993 Topps Stadium Club All-Stars	23	50.00	37.00	20.00
1993 Topps Stadium Club Finest	1	15.00	11.00	6.00
1993 Upper Deck	99	1.50	1.25	.60
1993 Upper Deck Next in Line	1	12.00	9.00	4.75
1993 Upper Deck NHL's Best	9	42.00	31.00	17.00
1993 Upper Deck Silver Skates Dye-Cut Retail	1R	30.00	22.00	12.00
1993 Upper Deck SP Inserts	70	12.00	9.00	4.75
1994 Donruss	127	2.00	1.50	.80
1994 Donruss Elite Series	5	75.00	56.00	30.00
1994 Donruss Ice Masters	4	10.00	7.50	4.00
1994 Fleer Flair	79	4.50	3.50	1.75
1994 Fleer Flair Center Spotlight	4	16.00	12.00	6.50
1994 Fleer Flair Hot Numbers	2	50.00	37.00	20.00
1994 Fleer Ultra All-Stars	10	3.50	2.75	1.50
1994 Fleer Ultra NHL Award Winners	5	6.00	4.50	2.50
1994 Fleer Ultra Scoring Kings	4	8.00	6.00	3.25
1994 Leaf Fire On Ice	4	22.00	16.50	8.75
1994 Leaf Gold Stars	1	100.00	75.00	40.00
1994 Leaf Limited	11	22.00	16.50	8.75
1994 O-Pee-Chee Premier	130	.75	.60	.30
1994 O-Pee-Chee Premier	150	.25	.20	.10
1994 O-Pee-Chee Premier	154	.25	.20	.10
1994 Parkhurst	103	1.75	1.25	.70
1994 Parkhurst	306	.85	.60	.35
1994 Parkhurst Crash the Game	11	22.00	16.50	8.75
1994 Parkhurst Crash the Game	28	17.00	12.50	6.75
1994 Pinnacle	200	3.00	2.25	1.25
1994 Pinnacle Artist's Proofs	200	250.00	187.00	100.00
1994 Pinnacle Rink Collection	200	100.00	75.00	40.00
1994 Pinnacle Team Pinnacle	9	100.00	75.00	40.00
1994 Score	241	.55	.40	.20
1994 Score Dream Team	14	28.00	21.00	11.00
1994 Score Franchise	11	75.00	56.00	30.00
1994 Score Hockey Gold Line	241	10.00	7.50	4.00
1994 Score 90-Plus Club	1	25.00	18.50	10.00
1994 Topps Premier	130	.75	.60	.30
1994 Topps Premier	150	.25	.20	.10
1994 Topps Premier	154	.25	.20	.10
1994 Topps Stadium Club	99	1.50	1.25	.60
1994 Topps Stadium Club	270	.75	.60	.30
1994 Topps Stadium Club Finest	4	20.00	15.00	8.00
1994 Upper Deck	1	2.50	2.00	1.00
1994 Upper Deck	226	1.50	1.25	.60
1994 Upper Deck	228	1.25	.90	.50
1994 Upper Deck Award Predictor	1	24.00	18.00	9.50
1994 Upper Deck Electric Ice	1	100.00	75.00	40.00
1994 Upper Deck Electric Ice	228	50.00	37.00	20.00
1994 Upper Deck Ice Gallery	15	25.00	18.50	10.00
1994 Upper Deck Scoring Predictor	19	24.00	18.00	9.50
1994 Upper Deck Scoring Predictor	21	24.00	18.00	9.50
1994 Upper Deck SP	36	15.00	11.00	6.00

Glenn Hall

Set	Card #	NM	EX	VG
1957 Topps	20 (R)	275.00	137.00	82.00
1958 Topps	13	130.00	65.00	39.00
1959 Topps	32	80.00	40.00	24.00
1960 Topps	25	65.00	32.00	19.50
1961 Topps	22	22.00	11.00	6.50
1961 Topps	32	50.00	25.00	15.00
1962 Topps	24	45.00	22.00	13.50
1963 Topps	23	35.00	17.50	10.50
1964 Topps	12	50.00	25.00	15.00
1964 Topps	110	115.00	57.00	34.00
1965 Topps	55	25.00	12.50	7.50
1966 Topps	54	25.00	12.50	7.50
1966 Topps	126	15.00	7.50	4.50
1967 Topps	129	20.00	10.00	6.00
1968 O-Pee-Chee	111	15.00	7.50	4.50
1968 O-Pee-Chee	215	8.00	4.00	2.50
1968 Topps	111	10.00	5.00	3.00
1969 O-Pee-Chee	12	9.00	4.50	2.75
1969 O-Pee-Chee	207	30.00	15.00	9.00
1969 O-Pee-Chee	211	7.00	3.50	2.00
1969 Topps	12	7.50	3.75	2.25
1970 O-Pee-Chee	210	8.00	4.00	2.50

In-action card: A card showing a ballplayer in action, as opposed to posed.

Insert: A collectible included inside a regular pack of baseball cards to boost sales. Inserts have included posters, baseball player stamps, coins, stickers, comic books, special cards, and tattoos.

Doug Harvey

Doug Harvey – Montreal
First Team All-Star

Set	Card #	NM	EX	VG
1951 Parkhurst	10 (R)	350.00	175.00	105.00
1952 Parkhurst	14	150.00	75.00	45.00
1953 Parkhurst	26	90.00	45.00	27.00
1954 Parkhurst	14	70.00	35.00	21.00
1954 Parkhurst	95	25.00	12.50	7.50
1954 Parkhurst	98	80.00	40.00	24.00
1955 Parkhurst	45	80.00	40.00	24.00
1957 Parkhurst	1	80.00	40.00	24.00
1958 Parkhurst	49	40.00	20.00	12.00
1959 Parkhurst	8	35.00	17.50	10.50
1960 Parkhurst	48	40.00	20.00	12.00
1961 Topps	45	30.00	15.00	9.00
1963 Topps	47	20.00	15.00	8.00
1968 O-Pee-Chee	1	25.00	12.50	7.50

Set	Card #	MT	NM	EX
1993 Parkhurst Parkie Reprints	39	18.00	13.50	7.25
1993 Parkhurst Parkie Reprints	61	15.00	11.00	6.00

Dominik Hasek

Set	Card #	MT	NM	EX
1991 Parkhurst	263 (R)	4.00	3.00	1.50
1991 Parkhurst	449	.75	.60	.30
1991 Pro Set	529 (R)	1.00	.70	.40
1991 Pro Set Platinum	252 (R)	1.00	.70	.40
1991 Score American	316 (R)	1.25	.90	.50
1991 Score Canadian	346 (R)	1.00	.70	.40
1991 Upper Deck	335 (R)	2.50	2.00	1.00
1991 Upper Deck Euro-Stars	14	.60	.40	.20
1992 Bowman	428	5.00	3.75	2.00
1992 O-Pee-Chee	301	.50	.40	.20
1992 Score	373	.40	.30	.15
1992 Topps	136	.06	.05	.02
1992 Topps Stadium Club	107	.50	.40	.20
1992 Upper Deck	92	.50	.40	.20
1992 Upper Deck	366	.05	.04	.02
1992 Upper Deck	506	.50	.40	.20
1992 Upper Deck All-Rookie Team	6	8.00	6.00	3.25
1992 Upper Deck Euro Stars	3	4.00	3.00	1.50
1992 Upper Deck Euro-Rookie Team	3	5.00	3.75	2.00
1993 Fleer PowerPlay	297	.08	.06	.03
1993 Fleer Ultra	274	.10	.08	.04
1993 Leaf	256	.12	.09	.05
1993 Pinnacle	403	.08	.06	.03
1993 Score	281	.05	.04	.02
1993 Topps Premier	320	.07	.05	.03
1993 Topps Premier	463	.08	.06	.03
1993 Topps Stadium Club	178	.05	.04	.02
1993 Upper Deck	387	.06	.05	.02
1994 Donruss	94	.30	.25	.12
1994 Donruss Masked Marvels	3	6.00	4.50	2.50
1994 Fleer Flair	17	.50	.40	.20
1994 Fleer Flair Hot Numbers	3	10.00	7.50	4.00
1994 Fleer Ultra	22	.40	.30	.15
1994 Fleer Ultra NHL Award Winners	6	3.00	2.25	1.25
1994 Fleer Ultra Premier Pad Men	1	13.00	9.75	5.25
1994 Leaf	120	.25	.20	.10
1994 Leaf Gold Stars	8	40.00	30.00	16.00
1994 Leaf Limited	3	7.00	5.25	2.75
1994 O-Pee-Chee Premier	35	.15	.11	.06
1994 O-Pee-Chee Premier	80	.10	.08	.04
1994 O-Pee-Chee Premier	152	.10	.08	.04
1994 O-Pee-Chee Premier	156	.10	.08	.04
1994 Parkhurst	24	.06	.05	.02
1994 Parkhurst Vintage Parkhurst	1	.85	.60	.35
1994 Pinnacle	175	.10	.08	.04
1994 Pinnacle Artist's Proofs	175	24.00	18.00	9.50
1994 Pinnacle Goaltending Greats	1	8.00	6.00	3.25
1994 Pinnacle Hockey MVP's	(1)	50.00	37.00	20.00
1994 Pinnacle Rink Collection	175	12.00	9.00	4.75
1994 Score	78	.05	.04	.02
1994 Score Hockey Gold Line	78	1.75	1.25	.70
1994 Topps Premier	35	.15	.11	.06
1994 Topps Premier	80	.10	.08	.04
1994 Topps Premier	152	.10	.08	.04
1994 Topps Premier	156	.10	.08	.04
1994 Topps Stadium Club	125	.30	.25	.12
1994 Topps Stadium Club	179	.10	.08	.04
1994 Topps Stadium Club	269	.15	.11	.06
1994 Upper Deck	233	.25	.20	.10
1994 Upper Deck Electric Ice	233	8.00	6.00	3.25
1994 Upper Deck SP	8	.80	.60	.30

Last card: The final card issued of a ballplayer (or the final card of any particular set).

Layering: A term used in card grading to describe the separation of the layers of paper that make up the cardboard stock. Layering is a sign of wear that is first noticeable at the corners of the card.

Leaf: Donruss' parent firm. Donruss has issued baseball cards in Canada under the Leaf name from 1985-93.

Dale Hawerchuk

Set	Card #	MT	NM	EX
1982 O-Pee-Chee	3	5.00	3.75	2.00
1982 O-Pee-Chee	374	3.00	2.25	1.25
1982 O-Pee-Chee	380 (R)	18.00	13.50	7.25
1982 O-Pee-Chee	381	4.00	3.00	1.50
1983 O-Pee-Chee	377	1.00	.70	.40
1983 O-Pee-Chee	385	5.00	3.75	2.00
1984 O-Pee-Chee	339	3.00	2.25	1.25
1984 O-Pee-Chee	393	.75	.60	.30
1984 Topps	152	1.00	.70	.40
1985 O-Pee-Chee	109	3.00	2.25	1.25
1985 Topps	109	1.50	1.25	.60
1986 O-Pee-Chee	74	1.25	.90	.50
1986 Topps	74	.75	.60	.30
1987 O-Pee-Chee	149	1.00	.70	.40
1987 Topps	149	.75	.60	.30
1988 O-Pee-Chee	65	.50	.40	.20
1988 Topps	65	.40	.30	.15
1989 O-Pee-Chee	122	.75	.60	.30
1989 Topps	122	.20	.15	.08
1990 Bowman	129	.07	.05	.03
1990 O-Pee-Chee	141	.10	.08	.04
1990 O-Pee-Chee Premier	40	.25	.20	.10
1990 Pro Set	330	.10	.08	.04
1990 Pro Set	415	.07	.05	.03
1990 Score	50	.12	.09	.05
1990 Score Hockey's 100 Hottest Rising Stars	22	.10	.08	.04
1990 Score Traded	2	.10	.08	.04
1990 Topps	141	.12	.09	.05
1990 Upper Deck	53	.20	.15	.08
1990 Upper Deck	443	.08	.06	.03
1991 Bowman	31	.05	.04	.02
1991 O-Pee-Chee Premier	1	.10	.08	.04
1991 O-Pee-Chee/Topps	65	.12	.09	.05
1991 Parkhurst	18	.08	.06	.03
1991 Parkhurst	216	.05	.04	.02
1991 Pinnacle	80	.08	.06	.03
1991 Pro Set	24	.05	.04	.02
1991 Pro Set Platinum	11	.05	.04	.02
1991 Score American	259	.05	.04	.02
1991 Score American	376	.05	.04	.02
1991 Score Canadian	266	.05	.04	.02
1991 Score Canadian	479	.10	.08	.04
1991 Topps Stadium Club	312	.15	.11	.06
1991 Upper Deck	12	.10	.08	.04
1991 Upper Deck	126	.10	.08	.04
1992 Bowman	308	.25	.20	.10
1992 Fleer Ultra	15	.06	.05	.02
1992 O-Pee-Chee	212	.05	.04	.02
1992 Parkhurst	11	.05	.04	.02
1992 Pinnacle	316	.06	.05	.02
1992 Pro Set	12	.05	.04	.02
1992 Score	272	.05	.04	.02
1992 Topps	296	.06	.05	.02
1992 Topps Stadium Club	419	.05	.04	.02
1992 Upper Deck	302	.05	.04	.02
1993 Donruss	35	.12	.09	.05
1993 Fleer PowerPlay	29	.10	.08	.04
1993 Fleer Ultra	149	.07	.05	.03
1993 Leaf	71	.10	.08	.04
1993 Parkhurst	23	.10	.08	.04
1993 Pinnacle	260	.12	.09	.05
1993 Score	159	.05	.04	.02
1993 Topps Finest Hockey Card Series Roster	11	4.00	3.00	1.50
1993 Topps Premier	7	.05	.04	.02
1993 Topps Stadium Club	220	.05	.04	.02
1993 Upper Deck	411	.05	.04	.02
1993 Upper Deck SP Inserts	16	.30	.25	.12
1994 Donruss	44	.08	.06	.03
1994 Fleer Flair	18	.25	.20	.10
1994 Fleer Ultra	23	.10	.08	.04
1994 Leaf	313	.10	.08	.04
1994 Parkhurst	29	.06	.05	.02
1994 Pinnacle	43	.10	.08	.04
1994 Pinnacle Artist's Proofs	43	6.00	4.50	2.50
1994 Pinnacle Rink Collection	43	4.00	3.00	1.50
1994 Score	192	.05	.04	.02
1994 Score Hockey Gold Line	192	.35	.25	.14
1994 Topps Stadium Club	248	.10	.08	.04
1994 Upper Deck	102	.10	.08	.04
1994 Upper Deck Electric Ice	102	3.50	2.75	1.50
1994 Upper Deck SP	9	.30	.25	.12

Ron Hextall

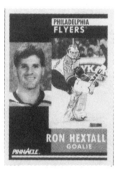

Set	Card #	MT	NM	EX
1987 O-Pee-Chee	169 (R)	6.00	4.50	2.50
1987 Topps	169 (R)	4.00	3.00	1.50
1988 O-Pee-Chee	34	1.25	.90	.50
1988 Topps	34	.75	.60	.30
1989 O-Pee-Chee	155	.35	.25	.14
1989 Topps	155	.35	.25	.14
1990 Bowman	105	.07	.05	.03
1990 O-Pee-Chee	243	.10	.08	.04
1990 O-Pee-Chee Premier	41	.30	.25	.12
1990 Pro Set	216	.15	.11	.06
1990 Score	25	.07	.05	.03
1990 Score Hockey's 100 Hottest Rising Stars	14	.10	.08	.04
1990 Topps	243	.10	.08	.04
1990 Upper Deck	227	.15	.11	.06
1991 Bowman	234	.05	.04	.02
1991 O-Pee-Chee Premier	38	.05	.04	.02
1991 O-Pee-Chee/Topps	470	.05	.04	.02
1991 Parkhurst	126	.05	.04	.02
1991 Pinnacle	118	.08	.06	.03
1991 Pro Set	176	.05	.04	.02
1991 Pro Set Platinum	87	.05	.04	.02
1991 Score American	239	.05	.04	.02
1991 Score Canadian	459	.05	.04	.02
1991 Topps Stadium Club	173	.08	.06	.03

1992 Bowman	195	.25	.20	.10
1992 Fleer Ultra	174	.06	.05	.02
1992 Fleer Ultra	385	.06	.05	.02
1992 O-Pee-Chee	84	.05	.04	.02
1992 O-Pee-Chee Premier	57	.05	.04	.02
1992 Parkhurst	144	.05	.04	.02
1992 Parkhurst Cherry Picks	20	6.00	4.50	2.50
1992 Pinnacle	340	.06	.05	.02
1992 Pro Set	129	.05	.04	.02
1992 Topps	40	.06	.05	.02
1992 Topps Stadium Club	288	.05	.04	.02
1992 Upper Deck	532	.05	.04	.02
1993 Donruss	196	.10	.08	.04
1993 Fleer PowerPlay	147	.10	.08	.04
1993 Fleer Ultra	366	.07	.05	.03
1993 Leaf	341	.10	.08	.04
1993 Parkhurst	118	.10	.08	.04
1993 Pinnacle	376	.08	.06	.03
1993 Pinnacle Masks	8	30.00	22.00	12.00
1993 Score	152	.05	.04	.02
1993 Score	544	.08	.06	.03
1993 Topps Premier	468	.05	.04	.02
1993 Topps Stadium Club	433	.05	.04	.02
1993 Upper Deck	434	.06	.05	.02
1994 Donruss	147	.08	.06	.03
1994 Fleer Flair	127	.25	.20	.10
1994 Fleer Ultra	127	.10	.08	.04
1994 Leaf	50	.10	.08	.04
1994 Parkhurst	136	.06	.05	.02
1994 Pinnacle Hockey Masks	6	45.00	34.00	18.00
1994 Score	140	.05	.04	.02
1994 Score Hockey Gold Line	140	.25	.20	.10
1994 Topps Stadium Club	51	.05	.04	.02
1994 Topps Stadium Club	182	.05	.04	.02
1994 Upper Deck	170	.10	.08	.04
1994 Upper Deck Electric Ice	170	3.50	2.75	1.50

Phil Housley

Set	Card #	MT	NM	EX
1983 O-Pee-Chee	65 (R)	10.00	7.50	4.00
1984 O-Pee-Chee	23	2.50	2.00	1.00
1984 Topps	18	2.00	1.50	.80
1985 Topps	63	2.00	1.50	.80
1986 O-Pee-Chee	154	1.00	.70	.40
1986 Topps	154	.60	.45	.25
1987 O-Pee-Chee	33	.60	.45	.25
1987 Topps	33	.25	.20	.10
1988 O-Pee-Chee	119	.25	.20	.10
1988 Topps	119	.20	.15	.08
1989 O-Pee-Chee	59	.07	.05	.03
1989 Topps	59	.15	.11	.06
1990 Bowman	239	.04	.03	.02
1990 O-Pee-Chee	89	.05	.04	.02
1990 O-Pee-Chee Premier	45	.15	.11	.06

1990 Pro Set	21	.07	.05	.03
1990 Pro Set	364	.05	.04	.02
1990 Pro Set	562	.05	.04	.02
1990 Score	145	.05	.04	.02
1990 Score Hockey's 100 Hottest Rising Stars	63	.10	.08	.04
1990 Score Traded	3	.07	.05	.03
1990 Topps	89	.03	.02	.01
1990 Upper Deck	22	.08	.06	.03
1990 Upper Deck	435	.08	.06	.03
1991 Bowman	197	.05	.04	.02
1991 O-Pee-Chee Premier	50	.05	.04	.02
1991 O-Pee-Chee/Topps	395	.05	.04	.02
1991 Parkhurst	205	.05	.04	.02
1991 Pinnacle	4	.08	.06	.03
1991 Pro Set	267	.05	.04	.02
1991 Pro Set	295	.05	.04	.02
1991 Pro Set Platinum	137	.05	.04	.02
1991 Score American	271	.10	.08	.04
1991 Score Canadian	491	.10	.08	.04
1991 Topps Stadium Club	65	.10	.08	.04
1991 Upper Deck	106	.05	.04	.02
1991 Upper Deck	624	.10	.08	.04
1992 Bowman	20	.25	.20	.10
1992 Bowman	208	2.00	1.50	.80
1992 Fleer Ultra	241	.06	.05	.02
1992 O-Pee-Chee	298	.05	.04	.02
1992 O-Pee-Chee Premier Star Performers	16	.15	.11	.06
1992 Parkhurst	208	.05	.04	.02
1992 Pinnacle	70	.06	.05	.02
1992 Pro Set	212	.05	.04	.02
1992 Pro Set Gold Team Leaders	14	1.00	.70	.40
1992 Score	299	.05	.04	.02
1992 Score	440	.05	.04	.02
1992 Topps	268	.06	.05	.02
1992 Topps	456	.06	.05	.02
1992 Topps Stadium Club	14	.05	.04	.02
1992 Upper Deck	276	.05	.04	.02
1992 Upper Deck	628	.10	.08	.04
1993 Donruss	294	.10	.08	.04
1993 Fleer PowerPlay	271	.10	.08	.04
1993 Fleer PowerPlay	427	.08	.06	.03
1993 Fleer Ultra	100	.07	.05	.03
1993 Fleer Ultra	409	.07	.05	.03
1993 Fleer Ultra All-Stars	18	2.50	2.00	1.00
1993 Leaf	61	.10	.08	.04
1993 OPC Premier Black Gold	4	9.00	6.75	3.50
1993 Parkhurst	174	.10	.08	.04
1993 Pinnacle	351	.10	.08	.04
1993 Pinnacle All-Stars	25	.20	.15	.08
1993 Pinnacle Team Pinnacle	9	22.00	16.50	8.75
1993 Score	232	.05	.04	.02
1993 Score	482	.05	.04	.02
1993 Score	520	.10	.08	.04
1993 Topps Premier	36	.05	.04	.02
1993 Topps Premier	503	.05	.04	.02
1993 Topps Premier Black Gold	19	2.00	1.50	.80
1993 Topps Stadium Club	104	.05	.04	.02
1993 Upper Deck	525	.05	.04	.02
1993 Upper Deck SP Inserts	136	.30	.25	.12
1994 Parkhurst	197	.06	.05	.02
1994 Upper Deck	169	.10	.08	.04
1994 Upper Deck Electric Ice	169	5.00	3.75	2.00

Limited edition: A term often used by makers of cards and memorabilia to indicate scarcity. A limited edition means just that — production of the item in question will be limited to a certain number. However, that number may be large or small.

Gordie Howe

Bobby Hull

Set	Card #	NM	EX	VG
1951 Parkhurst	66 (R)	3000.	1500.	900.00
1952 Parkhurst	88	1400.	700.00	420.00
1953 Parkhurst	50	800.00	400.00	240.00
1954 Parkhurst	41	700.00	350.00	210.00
1954 Parkhurst	92	90.00	45.00	27.00
1954 Topps	8	2200.	1100.	660.00
1957 Topps	42	600.00	300.00	180.00
1958 Topps	8	525.00	262.00	157.00
1959 Topps	48	90.00	45.00	27.00
1959 Topps	63	450.00	225.00	135.00
1960 Parkhurst	20	400.00	200.00	120.00
1961 Parkhurst	20	8.00	4.00	2.50
1961 Parkhurst	30	10.00	5.00	3.00
1961 Parkhurst	31	100.00	50.00	30.00
1962 Parkhurst	30	300.00	150.00	90.00
1962 Parkhurst	31	300.00	150.00	90.00
1963 Parkhurst	55	350.00	175.00	105.00
1964 Topps	89	500.00	250.00	150.00
1965 Topps	108	175.00	87.50	52.50
1965 Topps	122	350.00	175.00	105.00
1966 Topps	109	200.00	100.00	60.00
1966 Topps	121	110.00	55.00	33.00
1967 Topps	43	160.00	80.00	48.00
1967 Topps	131	100.00	50.00	30.00
1968 O-Pee-Chee	29	110.00	55.00	33.00
1968 O-Pee-Chee	203	60.00	30.00	18.00
1968 Topps	29	75.00	37.00	22.00
1969 O-Pee-Chee	61	80.00	40.00	24.00
1969 O-Pee-Chee	193	170.00	85.00	51.00
1969 O-Pee-Chee	215	50.00	25.00	15.00
1969 Topps	61	60.00	30.00	18.00
1970 O-Pee-Chee	29	70.00	35.00	21.00
1970 O-Pee-Chee	238	45.00	22.00	13.50
1970 Topps	29	50.00	25.00	15.00
1971 O-Pee-Chee	262	80.00	40.00	24.00
1971 Topps	70	55.00	27.00	16.50
1975 O-Pee-Chee WHA	66	30.00	15.00	9.00
1975 O-Pee-Chee WHA	100	50.00	25.00	15.00
1976 O-Pee-Chee WHA	50	35.00	17.50	10.50
1976 O-Pee-Chee WHA	72	25.00	12.50	7.50
1977 O-Pee-Chee WHA	1	35.00	17.50	10.50
1979 O-Pee-Chee	175	30.00	15.00	9.00
1979 Topps	175	20.00	10.00	6.00

Set	Card #	MT	NM	EX
1990 Pro Set	654	.35	.25	.14
1990 Pro Set	660	.35	.25	.14
1991 Pro Set	344	.10	.08	.04
1993 Parkhurst Cherry's Playoff Heroes	17D	35.00	26.00	14.00
1993 Parkhurst Parkie Reprints	33	30.00	22.00	12.00
1993 Parkhurst Parkie Reprints	42	30.00	22.00	12.00
1993 Parkhurst Parkie Reprints	51	30.00	22.00	12.00
1993 Parkhurst Parkie Reprints	60	30.00	22.00	12.00

Set	Card #	NM	EX	VG
1958 Topps	66 (R)	3000.	1500.	900.00
1959 Topps	47	600.00	300.00	180.00
1960 Topps	58	400.00	200.00	120.00
1961 Topps	29	350.00	175.00	105.00
1962 Topps	33	300.00	150.00	90.00
1963 Topps	33	220.00	165.00	88.00
1964 Topps	20	275.00	137.00	82.00
1964 Topps	107	190.00	95.00	57.00
1965 Topps	59	175.00	87.00	52.00
1966 Topps	64	75.00	37.00	22.00
1966 Topps	112	150.00	75.00	45.00
1966 Topps	125	80.00	40.00	24.00
1967 Topps	113	120.00	60.00	36.00
1967 Topps	124	70.00	35.00	21.00
1968 O-Pee-Chee	16	90.00	45.00	27.00
1968 O-Pee-Chee	204	50.00	25.00	15.00
1968 Topps	16	60.00	30.00	18.00
1969 O-Pee-Chee	70	75.00	37.00	22.00
1969 O-Pee-Chee	216	35.00	17.50	10.50
1969 Topps	70	45.00	22.00	13.50
1970 O-Pee-Chee	15	50.00	25.00	15.00
1970 O-Pee-Chee	235	30.00	15.00	9.00
1970 Topps	15	35.00	17.50	10.50
1971 O-Pee-Chee	50	40.00	20.00	12.00
1971 O-Pee-Chee	261	30.00	15.00	9.00
1971 Topps	1	15.00	7.50	4.50
1971 Topps	50	25.00	12.50	7.50
1972 O-Pee-Chee	228	25.00	12.50	7.50
1972 O-Pee-Chee	272	17.00	8.50	5.00
1972 O-Pee-Chee	336	55.00	27.00	16.50
1972 Topps	126	16.00	8.00	4.75
1974 O-Pee-Chee WHA	50	35.00	17.50	10.50
1975 O-Pee-Chee WHA	1	60.00	30.00	18.00
1975 O-Pee-Chee WHA	65	25.00	12.50	7.50
1976 O-Pee-Chee WHA	3	7.00	3.50	2.00
1976 O-Pee-Chee WHA	5	5.00	2.50	1.50
1976 O-Pee-Chee WHA	65	20.00	10.00	6.00
1976 O-Pee-Chee WHA	100	30.00	15.00	9.00
1977 O-Pee-Chee WHA	50	20.00	10.00	6.00
1979 O-Pee-Chee	185	25.00	12.50	7.50
1979 Topps	185	15.00	7.50	4.50

Fleer: A manufacturer of football, basketball and baseball cards. Fleer made baseball cards from 1959-63 and again from 1981 to the present.

Fleer Update (FU): A 132-card post-season set from Fleer which includes players traded to other teams during the season, and rookies (1984-present). Sold exclusively through hobby dealers in its own separate box.

Goudey: A famous maker of baseball cards. The Goudey Gum Co. of Boston made baseball cards and non-sport cards from 1933-39.

Brett Hull

Set	Card #	MT	NM	EX
1988 O-Pee-Chee	66 (R)	60.00	45.00	24.00
1988 O-Pee-Chee Future Stars	9	4.00	3.00	1.50
1988 Topps	66 (R)	35.00	26.00	14.00
1989 O-Pee-Chee	186	3.00	2.25	1.25
1989 Topps	186	4.00	3.00	1.50
1990 Bowman	24	.75	.60	.30
1990 O-Pee-Chee	4	.20	.15	.08
1990 O-Pee-Chee	77	.90	.70	.35
1990 O-Pee-Chee	195	.50	.40	.20
1990 O-Pee-Chee Premier	47	3.50	2.75	1.50
1990 Pro Set	1	1.75	1.25	.70
1990 Pro Set	263	.60	.45	.25
1990 Pro Set	342	.50	.40	.20
1990 Pro Set	378	.30	.25	.12
1990 Pro Set	395	.50	.40	.20
1990 Score	300	.85	.60	.35
1990 Score	317	.30	.25	.12
1990 Score	346	.20	.15	.08
1990 Score	351	.20	.15	.08
1990 Score	366	.05	.04	.02
1990 Score Hockey's 100 Hottest Rising Stars	100	.10	.08	.04
1990 Topps	4	.20	.15	.08
1990 Topps	77	.60	.45	.25
1990 Topps	195	.25	.20	.10
1990 Upper Deck	154	1.50	1.25	.60
1990 Upper Deck	203	.30	.25	.12
1990 Upper Deck	474	.50	.40	.20
1990 Upper Deck	546	.50	.40	.20
1990 Upper Deck Hockey Superstars	(4)	1.25	.90	.50
1991 Bowman	367	.25	.20	.10
1991 Bowman	375	.75	.60	.30
1991 O-Pee-Chee Premier	49	.75	.60	.30
1991 O-Pee-Chee/Topps	190	.20	.15	.08
1991 O-Pee-Chee/Topps	259	.20	.15	.08
1991 O-Pee-Chee/Topps	303	.50	.40	.20
1991 O-Pee-Chee/Topps	403	.20	.15	.08
1991 O-Pee-Chee/Topps	516	.15	.11	.06
1991 Parkhurst	157	.90	.70	.35
1991 Parkhurst	219	.05	.04	.02
1991 Parkhurst	432	.20	.15	.08
1991 Parkhurst	474	6.00	4.50	2.50
1991 Pinnacle	200	1.25	.90	.50
1991 Pinnacle	356	.40	.30	.15
1991 Pinnacle	376	.25	.20	.10
1991 Pinnacle B	12	75.00	56.00	30.00
1991 Pro Set	215	.60	.45	.25
1991 Pro Set	290	.20	.15	.08
1991 Pro Set	320	.20	.15	.08
1991 Pro Set	326	.15	.11	.06
1991 Pro Set Platinum	109	.40	.30	.15
1991 Pro Set Platinum	282	.25	.20	.10
1991 Pro Set Platinum PC	5	4.00	3.00	1.50
1991 Score American	1	.50	.40	.20
1991 Score American	337	.20	.15	.08
1991 Score American	347	.15	.11	.06
1991 Score American	371	.20	.15	.08
1991 Score American	404	.15	.11	.06
1991 Score American	412	.20	.15	.08
1991 Score American	428	.15	.11	.06
1991 Score Canadian	1	.50	.40	.20
1991 Score Canadian	261	.15	.11	.06
1991 Score Canadian	294	.15	.11	.06
1991 Score Canadian	302	.15	.11	.06
1991 Score Canadian	318	.15	.11	.06
1991 Score Canadian	367	.15	.11	.06
1991 Score Canadian	377	.15	.11	.06
1991 Score Hot Card	3	4.00	3.00	1.50
1991 Topps Stadium Club	67	2.00	1.50	.80
1991 Upper Deck	33	.40	.30	.15
1991 Upper Deck	464	1.00	.70	.40
1991 Upper Deck	622	.20	.15	.08
1991 Upper Deck Collector Cards	3	1.25	.90	.50
1992 Bowman	186	4.50	3.50	1.75
1992 Bowman	209	9.00	6.75	3.50
1992 Fleer Ultra	186	1.00	.70	.40
1992 Fleer Ultra All-Stars	12	4.50	3.50	1.75
1992 O-Pee-Chee	87	.50	.40	.20
1992 O-Pee-Chee	124	.75	.60	.30
1992 O-Pee-Chee Premier Star Performers	21	1.00	.70	.40
1992 O-Pee-Chee 25th Anniversary Series	21	.35	.25	.14
1992 Parkhurst	153	.80	.60	.30
1992 Parkhurst	459	.30	.25	.12
1992 Pinnacle	100	1.25	.90	.50
1992 Pinnacle	257	.25	.20	.10
1992 Pinnacle Team Pinnacle	6	25.00	18.50	10.00
1992 Pro Set	156	.75	.60	.30
1992 Pro Set	245	.15	.11	.06
1992 Pro Set Gold Team Leaders	8	5.00	3.75	2.00
1992 Score	350	.50	.40	.20
1992 Score	411	.25	.20	.10
1992 Score	435	.20	.15	.08
1992 Score	442	.20	.15	.08
1992 Score	500	.25	.20	.10
1992 Topps	2	.50	.15	.20
1992 Topps	260	.20	.15	.08
1992 Topps	340	.20	.15	.08
1992 Topps Stadium Club	1	.75	.60	.30
1992 Topps Stadium Club	258	.75	.60	.30
1992 Upper Deck	29	.80	.60	.30
1992 Upper Deck	620	.25	.20	.10
1992 Upper Deck All-World Team	2	6.00	4.50	2.50
1992 Upper Deck Gordie Howe Selects	7	7.00	5.25	2.75
1993 Donruss	286	1.00	.70	.40
1993 Donruss Elite	5	50.00	37.00	20.00
1993 Donruss Special Print	U	7.00	5.25	2.75
1993 Fleer PowerPlay	211	.75	.60	.30
1993 Fleer PowerPlay Point Leaders	4	.90	.70	.35
1993 Fleer PowerPlay Slapshot Artists	4	3.00	2.25	1.25
1993 Fleer Ultra	117	.60	.45	.25
1993 Fleer Ultra Red Light Specials	4	4.00	3.00	1.50
1993 Fleer Ultra Scoring Kings	3	8.00	6.00	3.25
1993 Leaf	255	.75	.60	.30
1993 Leaf Gold All-Stars	3	9.00	6.75	3.50
1993 Leaf Studio Signature	8	7.00	5.25	2.75
1993 OPC Premier Black Gold	22	15.00	11.00	6.00
1993 Parkhurst	180	.75	.60	.30
1993 Parkhurst East-West Stars	7W	12.00	9.00	4.50
1993 Parkhurst US Canada Gold-Foiled	4	15.00	11.00	6.00
1993 Pinnacle	200	.75	.60	.30
1993 Pinnacle All-Stars	34	.75	.60	.30

Set		MT	NM	EX
1993 Pinnacle Hockey Captains	20	12.00	9.00	4.75
1993 Pinnacle Nifty 50	10	24.00	18.00	9.50
1993 Pinnacle Team Pinnacle	6	40.00	30.00	16.00
1993 Score	335	.35	.25	.14
1993 Score Dream Team	18	13.00	9.75	5.25
1993 Score Franchise	18	12.00	9.00	4.75
1993 Score U.S. Dynamic Duos	4	16.00	12.00	6.50
1993 Topps Premier	425	.35	.25	.14
1993 Topps Premier Black Gold	21	5.00	3.75	2.00
1993 Topps Stadium Club	65	.75	.60	.30
1993 Topps Stadium Club All-Stars	4	13.00	9.75	5.25
1993 Topps Stadium Club Finest	3	10.00	7.50	4.00
1993 Upper Deck	160	.50	.40	.20
1993 Upper Deck	232	.25	.20	.10
1993 Upper Deck Gretzky's Great Ones	3	3.00	2.25	1.25
1993 Upper Deck Next in Line	2	6.00	4.50	2.50
1993 Upper Deck NHL's Best	3	12.00	9.00	4.75
1993 Upper Deck Silver Skates Dye-Cut Retail	5R	10.00	7.50	4.00
1993 Upper Deck SP Inserts	137	3.00	2.25	1.25
1994 Fleer Flair	153	1.75	1.25	.70
1994 Fleer Flair Hot Numbers	4	18.00	13.50	7.25
1994 Fleer Ultra	183	.50	.40	.20
1994 Fleer Ultra All-Stars	11	1.50	1.25	.60
1994 Leaf	16	.35	.25	.14
1994 Leaf Gold Stars	4	70.00	52.00	28.00
1994 Parkhurst	309	.20	.15	.08
1994 Parkhurst Crash the Game	20	7.50	5.75	3.50
1994 Parkhurst Vintage Parkhurst	35	2.00	1.50	.80
1994 Pinnacle Boomers	9	12.00	9.00	4.75
1994 Pinnacle Team Pinnacle	11	30.00	22.00	12.00
1994 Score	100	.35	.25	.14
1994 Score Dream Team	22	10.00	7.50	4.00
1994 Score Franchise	20	16.00	12.00	6.50
1994 Score Hockey Gold Line	100	2.50	2.00	1.00
1994 Score 90-Plus Club	11	10.00	7.50	4.00
1994 Topps Premier Finest Inserts	2	10.00	7.50	4.00
1994 Topps Stadium Club	100	.50	.40	.20
1994 Topps Stadium Club Dynasty and Destiny	3	17.00	12.50	6.75
1994 Topps Stadium Club Finest	2	9.00	6.75	3.50
1994 Upper Deck	229	.40	.30	.15
1994 Upper Deck Electric Ice	229	12.00	9.00	4.75
1994 Upper Deck Scoring Predictor	2	9.00	6.75	3.50
1994 Upper Deck SP	66	4.00	3.00	1.50

Common card: A card picturing a "common" or ordinary player _ that is, not a star or superstar. "Commons" are the lowest-priced cards in a given series or set.

Counterfeit card: A phony card made to look like a real card. Counterfeit cards have no collector value.

Legitimate issue: A licensed card set issued as a premium with a commercial product to increase sales; not a collector issue.

Al Iafrate

Set	Card #	MT	NM	EX
1985 O-Pee-Chee	210	18.00	13.50	7.25
1986 O-Pee-Chee	26	5.00	3.75	2.00
1986 Topps	26 (FC)	3.00	2.25	1.25
1987 O-Pee-Chee	238	2.00	1.50	.80
1988 O-Pee-Chee	71	.70	.50	.30
1988 Topps	71	.20	.15	.08
1989 O-Pee-Chee	79	.07	.05	.03
1989 Topps	79	.20	.15	.08
1990 Bowman	153	.04	.03	.02
1990 O-Pee-Chee	91	.05	.04	.02
1990 O-Pee-Chee Premier	48	.50	.40	.20
1990 Pro Set	281	.05	.04	.02
1990 Pro Set	354	.05	.04	.02
1990 Score	195	.10	.08	.04
1990 Score	334	.10	.08	.04
1990 Score Hockey's 100 Hottest Rising Stars	85	.10	.08	.04
1990 Topps	91	.03	.02	.01
1990 Upper Deck	157	.15	.11	.06
1990 Upper Deck	539	.10	.08	.04
1991 Bowman	300	.05	.04	.02
1991 O-Pee-Chee/Topps	148	.05	.04	.02
1991 Parkhurst	194	.05	.04	.02
1991 Pinnacle	207	.20	.15	.08
1991 Pro Set	250	.05	.04	.02
1991 Pro Set Platinum	130	.05	.04	.02
1991 Score American	209	.10	.08	.04
1991 Score Canadian	209	.05	.04	.02
1991 Topps Stadium Club	372	.20	.15	.08
1991 Upper Deck	318	.15	.11	.06
1992 Bowman	251	.40	.30	.15
1992 Fleer Ultra	233	.06	.05	.02
1992 O-Pee-Chee	341	.05	.04	.02
1992 Parkhurst	203	.05	.04	.02
1992 Pinnacle	66	.06	.05	.02
1992 Pro Set	205	.05	.04	.02
1992 Score	11	.05	.04	.02
1992 Topps	133	.06	.05	.02
1992 Topps Stadium Club	302	.05	.04	.02
1992 Upper Deck	54	.05	.04	.02
1993 Donruss	371	.10	.08	.04
1993 Donruss	402	.10	.08	.04
1993 Donruss Special Print	Y	4.00	3.00	1.50
1993 Fleer PowerPlay	263	.10	.08	.04
1993 Fleer PowerPlay Slapshot Artists	5	.75	.60	.30
1993 Fleer Ultra	11	.07	.05	.03
1993 Fleer Ultra All-Stars	8	2.50	2.00	1.00
1993 Fleer Ultra Speed Merchants	5	6.00	4.50	2.50
1993 Leaf	141	.10	.08	.04
1993 Parkhurst	217	.10	.08	.04
1993 Pinnacle	189	.10	.08	.04
1993 Pinnacle All-Stars	19	.20	.15	.08
1993 Pinnacle All-Stars	47	2.50	2.00	1.00
1993 Pinnacle Team Pinnacle	9	22.00	16.50	8.75
1993 Score	188	.05	.04	.02

1993 Score Dream Team	9	4.00	3.00	1.50
1993 Topps Premier	45	.05	.04	.02
1993 Topps Premier	174	.05	.04	.02
1993 Topps Stadium Club	80	.05	.04	.02
1993 Topps Stadium Club	455	.05	.04	.02
1993 Upper Deck	183	.05	.04	.02
1993 Upper Deck SP Inserts	170	.30	.25	.12
1994 Donruss	205	.08	.06	.03
1994 Fleer Flair	10	.25	.20	.10
1994 Leaf	212	.10	.08	.04
1994 O-Pee-Chee Premier	20	.08	.06	.03
1994 Parkhurst	15	.06	.05	.02
1994 Pinnacle	39	.10	.08	.04
1994 Pinnacle Artist's Proofs	39	5.00	3.75	2.00
1994 Pinnacle Boomers	1	6.00	4.50	2.50
1994 Pinnacle Rink Collection	39	3.00	2.25	1.25
1994 Score	168	.05	.04	.02
1994 Score Hockey Gold Line	168	.40	.30	.15
1994 Topps Premier	20	.08	.06	.03
1994 Topps Stadium Club	202	.05	.04	.02
1994 Upper Deck	82	.10	.08	.04
1994 Upper Deck Electric Ice	82	3.50	2.75	1.50

Jaromir Jagr

Set	Card #	MT	NM	EX
1990 O-Pee-Chee Premier	50 (R)	14.00	10.50	5.50
1990 Pro Set	632 (R)	2.50	2.00	1.00
1990 Score	428 (R)	1.00	.70	.40
1990 Score Traded	70	2.00	1.50	.80
1990 Upper Deck	356 (R)	4.00	3.00	1.50
1991 Bowman	95	.50	.40	.20
1991 O-Pee-Chee Premier	24	1.00	.70	.40
1991 O-Pee-Chee/Topps	9	.25	.20	.10
1991 O-Pee-Chee/Topps	40	.50	.40	.20
1991 Parkhurst	132	1.25	.90	.50
1991 Pinnacle	53	1.50	1.25	.60
1991 Pro Set	183	.50	.40	.20
1991 Pro Set Platinum	92	.50	.40	.20
1991 Score American	98	.50	.40	.20
1991 Score American	351	.25	.20	.10
1991 Score Canadian	98	.40	.30	.15
1991 Score Canadian	381	.20	.15	.08
1991 Score Hot Card	8	3.00	2.25	1.25
1991 Topps Stadium Club	343	2.00	1.50	.80
1991 Upper Deck	20	.50	.40	.20
1991 Upper Deck	42	.25	.20	.10
1991 Upper Deck	256	1.00	.70	.40
1991 Upper Deck	617	.25	.20	.10
1991 Upper Deck Euro-Stars	6	2.50	1.50	.75
1992 Bowman	231	9.00	6.75	3.50
1992 Bowman	302	4.00	3.00	1.50
1992 Fleer Ultra	164	1.00	.70	.40
1992 Fleer Ultra All-Stars	6	4.00	3.00	1.50
1992 Fleer Ultra Imports	6	7.00	5.25	2.75
1992 O-Pee-Chee	102	.50	.40	.20
1992 Parkhurst	135	.75	.60	.30
1992 Parkhurst	220	.05	.04	.02
1992 Parkhurst	465	.30	.25	.12
1992 Pinnacle	275	1.00	.70	.40
1992 Pinnacle Team Pinnacle	6	25.00	18.50	10.00
1992 Pinnacle Team 2000	15	3.00	2.25	1.25
1992 Pro Set	141	.75	.60	.30
1992 Score	113	.50	.40	.20
1992 Score	494	.25	.20	.10
1992 Topps	24	.60	.45	.25
1992 Topps Stadium Club	498	1.00	.70	.40
1992 Upper Deck	28	.70	.50	.30
1992 Upper Deck	622	.25	.20	.10
1992 Upper Deck All-World Team	3	6.00	4.50	2.50
1992 Upper Deck Euro Stars	14	4.50	3.00	1.50
1992 Upper Deck World Junior Grads	6	8.00	6.00	3.25
1993 Donruss	270	.75	.60	.30
1993 Donruss Ice Kings	3	2.50	2.00	1.00
1993 Fleer PowerPlay	189	.60	.45	.25
1993 Fleer PowerPlay Global Greats	3	1.50	1.25	.60
1993 Fleer PowerPlay Point Leaders	5	.90	.70	.35
1993 Fleer Ultra	65	.65	.50	.25
1993 Fleer Ultra Red Light Specials	5	3.50	2.75	1.50
1993 Leaf	346	.75	.60	.30
1993 OPC Premier Black Gold	19	15.00	11.00	6.00
1993 Parkhurst	154	.50	.40	.20
1993 Pinnacle	195	.75	.60	.30
1993 Pinnacle All-Stars	20	.50	.40	.20
1993 Pinnacle Team Pinnacle	6	40.00	30.00	16.00
1993 Pinnacle Team 2001	12	2.00	1.50	.80
1993 Score	50	.40	.30	.15
1993 Score International Stars	9	2.50	2.00	1.00
1993 Topps Premier	105	.40	.30	.15
1993 Topps Premier	325	.25	.20	.10
1993 Topps Stadium Club	98	.50	.40	.20
1993 Topps Stadium Club All-Stars	4	13.00	9.75	5.25
1993 Upper Deck	139	.60	.45	.25
1993 Upper Deck Future Heroes	33	10.00	7.50	4.00
1993 Upper Deck Silver Skates Dye-Cut Retail	8R	10.00	7.50	4.00
1993 Upper Deck SP Inserts	121	2.00	1.50	.80
1994 Donruss	159	.50	.40	.20
1994 Fleer Ultra	164	.25	.20	.10
1994 Leaf	151	.50	.40	.20
1994 Parkhurst	174	.30	.25	.12
1994 Parkhurst	314	.25	.20	.10
1994 Pinnacle	98	.65	.50	.25
1994 Pinnacle Artist's Proofs	98	40.00	30.00	16.00
1994 Pinnacle Rink Collection	98	20.00	15.00	8.00
1994 Pinnacle Team Pinnacle	11	30.00	22.00	12.00
1994 Score	135	.30	.25	.12
1994 Score Hockey Gold Line	135	2.50	2.00	1.00
1994 Score 90-Plus Club	9	7.00	5.25	2.75
1994 Topps Premier	460	2.75	2.75	2.75
1994 Topps Stadium Club	68	.35	.25	.14
1994 Upper Deck	93	.60	.45	.25
1994 Upper Deck Electric Ice	93	25.00	18.50	10.00
1994 Upper Deck Scoring Predictor	18	8.00	6.00	3.25
1994 Upper Deck Scoring Predictor	29	8.00	6.00	3.25
1994 Upper Deck SP	60	2.00	1.50	.80

Craig Janney

Set	Card #	MT	NM	EX
1988 O-Pee-Chee Future Stars	10	1.25	.90	.50
1989 O-Pee-Chee	190 (R)	1.50	1.25	.60
1989 O-Pee-Chee Future Stars	2	.65	.50	.25
1989 Topps	190 (R)	3.00	2.25	1.25
1990 Bowman	33	.15	.11	.06
1990 O-Pee-Chee	212	.20	.15	.08
1990 Pro Set	8	.30	.25	.12
1990 Score	118	.20	.15	.08
1990 Score Hockey's 100 Hottest Rising Stars	58	.10	.08	.04
1990 Topps	212	.20	.15	.08
1990 Upper Deck	234	.35	.25	.14
1991 Bowman	355	.15	.11	.06
1991 O-Pee-Chee Premier	93	.10	.08	.04
1991 O-Pee-Chee/Topps	41	.12	.09	.05
1991 Parkhurst	4	.20	.15	.08
1991 Parkhurst	378	.05	.04	.02
1991 Pinnacle	57	.25	.20	.10
1991 Pro Set	2	.10	.08	.04
1991 Pro Set Platinum	3	.10	.08	.04
1991 Score American	253	.10	.08	.04
1991 Score Canadian	473	.10	.08	.04
1991 Topps Stadium Club	147	.25	.20	.10
1991 Upper Deck	128	.25	.20	.10
1991 Upper Deck	512	.05	.04	.02
1992 Bowman	14	.60	.45	.25
1992 Fleer Ultra	187	.15	.11	.06
1992 O-Pee-Chee	325	.05	.04	.02
1992 Parkhurst	154	.05	.04	.02
1992 Pinnacle	196	.10	.08	.04
1992 Pro Set	157	.05	.04	.02
1992 Score	285	.05	.04	.02
1992 Score USA Greats	11	5.00	3.75	2.00
1992 Topps	134	.06	.05	.02
1992 Topps Stadium Club	41	.20	.15	.08
1992 Upper Deck	125	.10	.08	.04
1993 Donruss	295	.10	.08	.04
1993 Fleer PowerPlay	212	.10	.08	.04
1993 Fleer Ultra	134	.10	.08	.04
1993 Leaf	181	.15	.11	.06
1993 Parkhurst	443	.10	.08	.04
1993 Pinnacle	130	.10	.08	.04
1993 Score	186	.05	.04	.02
1993 Score U.S. Dynamic Duos	4	16.00	12.00	6.50
1993 Topps Premier	120	.05	.04	.02
1993 Topps Stadium Club	335	.05	.04	.02
1993 Upper Deck	225	.10	.08	.04
1993 Upper Deck	303	.10	.08	.04
1993 Upper Deck	323	.05	.04	.02
1993 Upper Deck SP Inserts	138	.30	.25	.12
1994 Donruss	28	.08	.06	.03
1994 Fleer Flair	154	.35	.25	.14
1994 Leaf	52	.10	.08	.04
1994 O-Pee-Chee Premier	60	.05	.04	.02
1994 Parkhurst	200	.06	.05	.02
1994 Pinnacle	84	.10	.08	.04
1994 Pinnacle Artist's Proofs	84	7.00	5.25	2.75
1994 Pinnacle Rink Collection	84	4.00	3.00	1.50
1994 Score	127	.05	.04	.02
1994 Score Hockey Gold Line	127	.40	.30	.15
1994 Topps Premier	60	.05	.04	.02
1994 Upper Deck	18	.10	.08	.04
1994 Upper Deck Electric Ice	18	5.00	3.75	2.00
1994 Upper Deck Scoring Predictor	16	4.00	3.00	1.50
1994 Upper Deck SP	67	.30	.25	.12

Curtis Joseph

Set	Card #	MT	NM	EX
1990 O-Pee-Chee	171 (R)	1.00	.70	.40
1990 O-Pee-Chee Premier	51 (R)	6.00	4.50	2.50
1990 Pro Set	638	.65	.50	.25
1990 Score	151 (R)	.75	.60	.30
1990 Topps	171 (R)	.80	.60	.30
1990 Upper Deck	175 (R)	2.00	1.50	.80
1991 O-Pee-Chee Premier	165	.25	.20	.10
1991 O-Pee-Chee/Topps	417	.15	.11	.06
1991 Parkhurst	152	.05	.04	.02
1991 Pinnacle	105	.50	.40	.20
1991 Pro Set	473	.20	.15	.08
1991 Pro Set Platinum	225	.20	.15	.08
1991 Score American	296	.15	.11	.06
1991 Score Canadian	516	.20	.15	.08
1991 Upper Deck	139	.50	.40	.20
1992 Bowman	368	1.25	.90	.50
1992 Fleer Ultra	188	.06	.05	.02
1992 O-Pee-Chee	339	.05	.04	.02
1992 Parkhurst	155	.05	.04	.02
1992 Parkhurst	503	.75	.60	.30
1992 Pinnacle	54	.06	.05	.02
1992 Pinnacle	264	2.50	2.00	1.00
1992 Pro Set	164	.05	.04	.02
1992 Score	262	.05	.04	.02
1992 Topps	237	.15	.11	.06
1992 Upper Deck	186	.05	.04	.02
1993 Donruss	296	.10	.08	.04
1993 Fleer PowerPlay	213	.10	.08	.04
1993 Fleer PowerPlay Gamebreakers	4	1.50	1.25	.60
1993 Fleer PowerPlay Netminders	4	7.00	5.25	2.75
1993 Fleer Ultra	172	.10	.08	.04
1993 Leaf	2	.20	.15	.08
1993 Leaf Painted Warriors	2	5.00	3.75	2.00
1993 Parkhurst	175	.15	.11	.06
1993 Pinnacle	15	.20	.15	.08
1993 Score	116	.05	.04	.02
1993 Topps Premier	222	.05	.04	.02
1993 Topps Premier	272	.08	.06	.03

		MT	NM	EX
1993 Topps Premier Black Gold	18	2.50	2.00	1.00
1993 Topps Stadium Club	162	.15	.11	.06
1993 Upper Deck	157	.10	.08	.04
1993 Upper Deck SP Inserts	139	.30	.25	.12
1994 Donruss	287	.25	.20	.10
1994 Donruss Masked Marvels	5	6.00	4.50	2.50
1994 Fleer Flair	156	.75	.60	.30
1994 Fleer Ultra	184	.35	.25	.14
1994 Fleer Ultra Premier Pad Men	3	13.00	9.75	5.25
1994 Leaf	208	.15	.11	.06
1994 Leaf Gold Stars	7	40.00	30.00	16.00
1994 Parkhurst	199	.06	.05	.02
1994 Parkhurst Vintage Parkhurst	17	.50	.40	.20
1994 Pinnacle	6	.35	.25	.14
1994 Pinnacle Artist's Proofs	6	25.00	18.50	10.00
1994 Pinnacle Goaltending Greats	13	8.00	6.00	3.25
1994 Pinnacle Hockey Masks	10	55.00	41.00	22.00
1994 Pinnacle Rink Collection	6	12.00	9.00	4.75
1994 Pinnacle Team Pinnacle	2	25.00	18.50	10.00
1994 Score	181	.15	.11	.06
1994 Score Hockey Gold Line	181	1.50	1.25	.60
1994 Topps Stadium Club	142	.15	.11	.06
1994 Upper Deck	91	.30	.25	.12
1994 Upper Deck Electric Ice	91	10.00	7.50	4.00
1994 Upper Deck SP	68	.85	.60	.35

Joe Juneau

Set	Card #	MT	NM	EX
1991 Parkhurst	234 (R)	4.00	3.00	1.50
1992 Bowman	292	3.00	2.25	1.25
1992 Fleer Ultra	4	2.00	1.50	.80
1992 O-Pee-Chee	189	.75	.60	.30
1992 O-Pee-Chee Premier	101	1.50	1.25	.60
1992 Parkhurst	2	1.00	.75	.40
1992 Pinnacle	221	1.50	1.25	.60
1992 Pinnacle Team 2000	19	3.00	2.25	1.25
1992 Pro Set	219	1.25	.90	.50
1992 Score	453	1.25	.90	.50
1992 Score Canadian Olympic Heroes	2	30.00	22.00	12.00
1992 Topps	365	1.00	.70	.40
1992 Topps Stadium Club	297	1.00	.70	.40
1992 Upper Deck	354	.75	.60	.30
1992 Upper Deck	399	1.00	.70	.40
1992 Upper Deck Calder Candidates	9	9.00	6.75	3.50

		MT	NM	EX
1992 Upper Deck Gordie Howe Selects	11	8.00	6.00	3.25
1992 Upper Deck Holograms	1	4.00	3.00	1.60
1993 Donruss	26	1.00	.70	.40
1993 Donruss	504	.75	.60	.30
1993 Fleer PowerPlay	19	.75	.60	.30
1993 Fleer PowerPlay Point Leaders	6	1.25	.90	.50
1993 Fleer PowerPlay Second-Year Stars	2	2.00	1.50	.80
1993 Fleer Ultra	49	1.00	.70	.40
1993 Leaf	218	.75	.60	.30
1993 Leaf Gold Rookies	2	5.00	3.75	2.00
1993 Parkhurst	241	.50	.40	.20
1993 Parkhurst	280	.65	.50	.25
1993 Pinnacle	5	.60	.45	.25
1993 Pinnacle Team 2001	4	2.00	1.50	.80
1993 Score	330	.65	.50	.25
1993 Topps Premier	125	.25	.20	.10
1993 Topps Premier	299	.50	.40	.20
1993 Topps Premier Black Gold	12	5.00	3.75	2.00
1993 Topps Stadium Club	202	.65	.50	.25
1993 Upper Deck	282	.40	.30	.15
1993 Upper Deck	343	.60	.45	.25
1993 Upper Deck Future Heroes	35	10.00	7.50	4.00
1993 Upper Deck NHL's Best	10	10.00	7.50	4.00
1993 Upper Deck SP Inserts	9	1.50	1.25	.60
1994 Donruss	258	.35	.25	.14
1994 Fleer Flair	200	.40	.30	.15
1994 Leaf	62	.20	.15	.08
1994 Leaf Fire On Ice	7	6.00	4.50	2.50
1994 O-Pee-Chee Premier	100	.15	.11	.06
1994 Parkhurst	253	.06	.05	.02
1994 Parkhurst Crash the Game	25	5.00	3.75	2.00
1994 Pinnacle	7	.50	.40	.20
1994 Pinnacle Artist's Proofs	7	15.00	11.00	6.00
1994 Pinnacle Rink Collection	7	7.50	5.75	3.00
1994 Score	124	.30	.25	.12
1994 Score Franchise	25	10.00 ·	7.50	4.00
1994 Score Hockey Gold Line	124	.60	.45	.25
1994 Topps Premier	100	.15	.11	.06
1994 Upper Deck	88	.40	.30	.15
1994 Upper Deck Electric Ice	88	12.00	9.00	4.75
1994 Upper Deck Scoring Predictor	15	4.00	3.00	1.50

Jari Kurri

Set	Card #	MT	NM	EX
1981 O-Pee-Chee	107 (R)	45.00	34.00	18.00

1981 Topps	18 (R)	6.00	4.50	2.50
1982 O-Pee-Chee	111	8.00	6.00	3.25
1983 O-Pee-Chee	34	5.00	3.75	2.00
1984 O-Pee-Chee	215	.75	.60	.30
1984 O-Pee-Chee	249	3.00	2.25	1.25
1984 Topps	52	1.00	.70	.40
1984 Topps	161	.40	.30	.15
1985 O-Pee-Chee	155	3.00	2.25	1.25
1985 O-Pee-Chee	261	.75	.60	.30
1985 Topps	155	1.50	1.25	.60
1986 O-Pee-Chee	108	1.50	1.25	.60
1986 Topps	108	1.25	.90	.50
1987 O-Pee-Chee	148	1.00	.70	.40
1987 Topps	148	.60	.45	.25
1988 O-Pee-Chee	147	.50	.40	.20
1988 Topps	147	.30	.25	.12
1989 O-Pee-Chee	43	.50	.40	.20
1989 Topps	43	.15	.11	.06
1990 Bowman	191	.10	.08	.04
1990 O-Pee-Chee	5	.07	.05	.03
1990 O-Pee-Chee	108	.10	.08	.04
1990 Pro Set	87	.20	.15	.08
1990 Pro Set	348	.05	.04	.02
1990 Score	158	.12	.09	.05
1990 Score	348	.10	.08	.04
1990 Topps	5	.07	.05	.03
1990 Topps	108	.12	.09	.05
1990 Upper Deck	146	.20	.15	.08
1991 O-Pee-Chee Premier	111	.10	.08	.04
1991 O-Pee-Chee/Topps	295	.05	.04	.02
1991 Parkhurst	72	.05	.04	.02
1991 Parkhurst	210	.05	.04	.02
1991 Parkhurst	223	.05	.04	.02
1991 Pinnacle	48	.20	.15	.08
1991 Pro Set	93	.05	.04	.02
1991 Pro Set Platinum	48	.05	.04	.02
1991 Score Canadian	600	.10	.08	.04
1991 Score Traded	50	.05	.04	.02
1991 Upper Deck	24	.15	.11	.06
1991 Upper Deck	366	.10	.08	.04
1992 Bowman	94	.25	.20	.10
1992 Fleer Ultra	85	.06	.05	.02
1992 Fleer Ultra Imports	11	3.00	2.25	1.25
1992 O-Pee-Chee	205	.05	.04	.02
1992 Parkhurst	67	.05	.04	.02
1992 Parkhurst	445	.05	.04	.02
1992 Pinnacle	60	.06	.05	.02
1992 Pinnacle	243	.06	.05	.02
1992 Pro Set	68	.10	.08	.04
1992 Score	398	.05	.04	.02
1992 Topps	51	.06	.05	.02
1992 Topps Stadium Club	138	.05	.04	.02
1992 Upper Deck	218	.05	.04	.02
1992 Upper Deck World Junior Grads	4	3.50	2.75	1.50
1993 Donruss	151	.10	.08	.04
1993 Fleer PowerPlay	118	.10	.08	.04
1993 Fleer PowerPlay Global Greats	4	.50	.40	.20
1993 Fleer Ultra	165	.07	.05	.03
1993 Leaf	240	.12	.09	.05
1993 Parkhurst	365	.12	.09	.05
1993 Pinnacle	75	.10	.08	.04
1993 Pinnacle All-Stars	35	.20	.15	.08
1993 Score	100	.05	.04	.02
1993 Score	446	.10	.08	.04
1993 Score International Stars	7	.50	.40	.20
1993 Score U.S. Dynamic Duos	7	40.00	30.00	16.00
1993 Topps Premier	206	.05	.04	.02
1993 Topps Stadium Club	400	.05	.04	.02
1993 Topps Stadium Club All-Stars	12	9.00	6.75	3.50
1993 Upper Deck	332	.05	.04	.02
1994 Donruss	93	.08	.06	.03
1994 Fleer Flair	81	.25	.20	.10
1994 Fleer Ultra	100	.10	.08	.04
1994 Leaf	104	.15	.11	.06
1994 O-Pee-Chee Premier	25	.08	.06	.03
1994 Parkhurst	104	.06	.05	.02

1994 Pinnacle	35	.10	.08	.04
1994 Pinnacle Artist's Proofs	35	7.00	5.25	2.75
1994 Pinnacle Rink Collection	35	3.50	2.75	1.50
1994 Score	114	.05	.04	.02
1994 Score Hockey Gold Line	114	.35	.25	.14
1994 Topps Premier	25	.08	.06	.03
1994 Upper Deck SP	37	.30	.25	.12

Scott Lachance

Set	Card #	MT	NM	EX
1991 Parkhurst	326 (R)	.40	.30	.15
1991 Upper Deck	692 (R)	.50	.40	.20
1992 Bowman	438	.40	.30	.15
1992 Fleer Ultra	130	.20	.15	.08
1992 O-Pee-Chee	390	.25	.20	.10
1992 O-Pee-Chee Premier	79	.10	.08	.04
1992 Parkhurst	105	.05	.04	.02
1992 Pinnacle	223	.30	.25	.12
1992 Pinnacle	244	.25	.20	.10
1992 Pinnacle Team 2000	6	1.25	.90	.50
1992 Pro Set	234	.10	.08	.04
1992 Score	449	.05	.04	.02
1992 Topps	366	.35	.25	.14
1992 Topps Stadium Club	201	.25	.20	.10
1992 Upper Deck	360	.10	.08	.04
1992 Upper Deck	409	.10	.08	.04
1992 Upper Deck	571	.10	.08	.04
1992 Upper Deck Calder Candidates	16	4.00	3.00	1.50
1992 Upper Deck Holograms	4	3.00	2.00	1.00
1993 Donruss	206	.10	.08	.04
1993 Fleer PowerPlay	152	.10	.08	.04
1993 Fleer Ultra	369	.15	.11	.06
1993 Leaf	139	.10	.08	.04
1993 Parkhurst	120	.20	.15	.08
1993 Pinnacle	62	.10	.08	.04
1993 Pinnacle Team 2001	21	.50	.40	.20
1993 Score	103	.10	.08	.04
1993 Topps Premier	257	.05	.04	.02
1993 Topps Stadium Club	465	.05	.04	.02
1993 Upper Deck	320	.08	.06	.03
1993 Upper Deck SP Inserts	92	.30	.25	.12
1994 Donruss	41	.08	.06	.03
1994 O-Pee-Chee Premier	66	.05	.04	.02
1994 Parkhurst	140	.06	.05	.02
1994 Pinnacle	193	.10	.08	.04
1994 Pinnacle Artist's Proofs	193	5.00	3.75	2.00
1994 Pinnacle Rink Collection	193	3.00	2.25	1.25
1994 Score	195	.05	.04	.02
1994 Score Hockey Gold Line	195	.25	.20	.10
1994 Topps Premier	66	.05	.04	.02

Guy Lafleur

Set	Card #	NM	EX	VG
1971 O-Pee-Chee	148 (R)	200.00	100.00	60.00
1972 O-Pee-Chee	59	50.00	25.00	15.00
1972 Topps	79	22.00	11.00	6.50
1973 O-Pee-Chee	72	25.00	12.50	7.50
1973 Topps	72	15.00	7.50	4.50
1974 O-Pee-Chee	232	20.00	10.00	6.00
1974 Topps	232	13.00	6.50	3.90
1975 O-Pee-Chee	126	15.00	7.50	4.50
1975 O-Pee-Chee	208	4.50	2.25	1.25
1975 O-Pee-Chee	290	5.00	2.50	1.50
1975 O-Pee-Chee	322	3.00	1.50	.90
1975 Topps	126	10.00	5.00	3.00
1975 Topps	208	3.50	1.75	1.00
1975 Topps	290	3.00	1.50	.90
1975 Topps	322	2.00	1.00	.60
1976 O-Pee-Chee	1	3.00	1.50	.90
1976 O-Pee-Chee	2	3.00	1.50	.90
1976 O-Pee-Chee	3	3.00	1.50	.90
1976 O-Pee-Chee	5	*3.00	1.50	.90
1976 O-Pee-Chee	163	12.00	6.00	3.50
1976 O-Pee-Chee	388	2.00	1.00	.60
1976 Topps	1	2.00	1.00	.60
1976 Topps	2	2.00	1.00	.60
1976 Topps	3	2.00	1.00	.60
1976 Topps	5	2.50	1.25	.70
1976 Topps	163	8.00	4.00	2.50
1977 O-Pee-Chee	1	2.50	1.25	.70
1977 O-Pee-Chee	2	2.00	1.00	.60
1977 O-Pee-Chee	3	2.00	1.00	.60
1977 O-Pee-Chee	7	1.50	.70	.45
1977 O-Pee-Chee	200	9.00	4.50	2.75
1977 O-Pee-Chee	214	2.50	1.25	.70
1977 O-Pee-Chee	216	2.50	1.25	.70
1977 O-Pee-Chee	218	2.50	1.25	.70
1977 Topps	1	2.00	1.00	.60
1977 Topps	2	1.50	.70	.45
1977 Topps	3	2.00	1.00	.60
1977 Topps	7	1.50	.70	.45
1977 Topps	200	5.00	2.50	1.50
1977 Topps	214	2.00	1.00	.60
1977 Topps	216	2.00	1.00	.60
1977 Topps	218	1.75	.90	.50
1978 O-Pee-Chee	3	1.25	.60	.40
1978 O-Pee-Chee	63	3.50	1.75	1.00
1978 O-Pee-Chee	64	2.00	1.00	.60
1978 O-Pee-Chee	65	3.00	1.50	.90
1978 O-Pee-Chee	69	1.50	.70	.45
1978 O-Pee-Chee	90	6.00	3.00	1.75
1978 O-Pee-Chee	326	2.50	1.25	.70
1978 Topps	3	1.00	.50	.30
1978 Topps	63	2.00	1.00	.60
1978 Topps	64	1.50	.70	.45
1978 Topps	65	1.50	.70	.45
1978 Topps	69	1.50	.70	.45
1978 Topps	90	4.00	2.00	1.25
1979 O-Pee-Chee	1	4.00	2.00	1.25
1979 O-Pee-Chee	2	3.00	1.50	.90
1979 O-Pee-Chee	3	3.00	1.50	.90
1979 O-Pee-Chee	7	3.00	1.50	.90
1979 O-Pee-Chee	200	5.00	2.50	1.50
1979 Topps	1	2.50	1.25	.70
1979 Topps	2	2.00	1.00	.60
1979 Topps	3	2.00	1.00	.60
1979 Topps	7	2.00	1.00	.60
1979 Topps	200	3.50	1.75	1.00
1980 O-Pee-Chee	10	4.00	2.00	1.25
1980 O-Pee-Chee	82	1.50	.70	.45
1980 O-Pee-Chee	162	15.00	7.50	4.50
1980 O-Pee-Chee	163	15.00	7.50	4.50
1980 O-Pee-Chee	216	1.00	.50	.30
1980 Topps	10	2.50	1.25	.70
1980 Topps	82	1.00	.50	.30
1980 Topps	162	10.00	5.00	3.00
1980 Topps	163	10.00	5.00	3.00
1980 Topps	216	1.50	.70	.45

Set	Card #	MT	NM	EX
1981 O-Pee-Chee	177	3.00	2.25	1.25
1981 O-Pee-Chee	195	1.00	.70	.40
1981 O-Pee-Chee	19	1.00	.70	.40
1982 O-Pee-Chee	186	1.75	1.25	.70
1982 O-Pee-Chee	187	.75	.60	.30
1983 O-Pee-Chee	183	.40	.30	.15
1983 O-Pee-Chee	189	1.50	1.25	.70
1984 O-Pee-Chee	264	1.50	1.25	.60
1984 O-Pee-Chee	360	.50	.40	.20
1984 Topps	81	.75	.60	.30
1989 O-Pee-Chee	189	.75	.60	.30
1989 Topps	189	.30	.25	.12
1990 O-Pee-Chee	142	.20	.15	.08
1990 O-Pee-Chee Premier	55	.20	.15	.08
1990 Pro Set	250	.20	.15	.08
1990 Score	290	.07	.05	.03
1990 Score Hockey's 100 Hottest Rising Stars	96	.10	.08	.04
1990 Topps	142	.20	.15	.08
1990 Upper Deck	162	.08	.06	.03
1991 O-Pee-Chee/Topps	1	.12	.09	.05
1991 O-Pee-Chee/Topps	2	.12	.09	.05
1991 O-Pee-Chee/Topps	3	.12	.09	.05
1991 Pro Set	317	.05	.04	.02
1991 Upper Deck	219	.05	.04	.02
1991 Upper Deck	638	.05	.04	.02

Rod Langway

Set	Card #	NM	EX	VG
1980 O-Pee-Chee	344 (R)	10.00	5.00	3.00

Set	Card #	MT	NM	EX
1981 O-Pee-Chee	186	2.50	2.00	1.00
1982 O-Pee-Chee	368	1.00	.70	.40
1983 O-Pee-Chee	207	.15	.11	.06
1983 O-Pee-Chee	365	.15	.11	.06
1983 O-Pee-Chee	374	.50	.40	.20
1984 O-Pee-Chee	202	.75	.60	.30
1984 O-Pee-Chee	210	.15	.11	.06
1984 O-Pee-Chee	377	.20	.15	.08

Set	Card #	MT	NM	EX
1984 Topps	147	.20	.15	.08
1984 Topps	156	.15	.11	.06
1985 O-Pee-Chee	8	.25	.20	.10
1985 Topps	8	.15	.11	.06
1986 O-Pee-Chee	164	.15	.11	.06
1986 Topps	164	.25	.20	.10
1987 O-Pee-Chee	108	.12	.09	.05
1987 Topps	108	.12	.09	.05
1988 O-Pee-Chee	192	.15	.11	.06
1988 Topps	192	.07	.05	.03
1989 O-Pee-Chee	55	.07	.05	.03
1989 Topps	55	.05	.04	.02
1990 O-Pee-Chee	353	.05	.04	.02
1990 Pro Set	314	.05	.04	.02
1990 Score	20	.05	.04	.02
1990 Score Hockey's 100 Hottest Rising Stars	11	.10	.08	.04
1990 Topps	353	.03	.02	.01
1990 Upper Deck	57	.10	.08	.04
1990 Upper Deck	309	.07	.05	.03
1991 O-Pee-Chee/Topps	105	.05	.04	.02
1991 Pinnacle	195	.08	.06	.03
1991 Pro Set	259	.05	.04	.02
1991 Pro Set	587	.05	.04	.02
1991 Score American	228	.05	.04	.02
1991 Score Canadian	228	.05	.04	.02
1991 Topps Stadium Club	225	.08	.06	.03
1991 Upper Deck	314	.05	.04	.02
1992 Bowman	279	.25	.20	.10
1992 O-Pee-Chee	347	.05	.04	.02
1992 Pinnacle	131	.06	.05	.02
1992 Score	143	.05	.04	.02
1992 Topps	46	.06	.05	.02
1992 Topps Stadium Club	215	.05	.04	.02
1993 Score	145	.05	.04	.02

Pat LaFontaine

Set	Card #	MT	NM	EX
1984 O-Pee-Chee	129 (R)	45.00	34.00	18.00
1984 O-Pee-Chee	392	5.00	3.75	2.00
1984 Topps	96 (R)	10.00	7.50	4.00
1985 Topps	137	12.00	9.00	4.75
1986 O-Pee-Chee	2	9.00	6.75	3.50
1986 Topps	2	3.50	2.75	1.50
1987 O-Pee-Chee	173	5.50	4.25	2.25
1987 Topps	173	2.50	2.00	1.00
1988 O-Pee-Chee	123	2.00	1.50	.80
1988 Topps	123	1.00	.70	.40
1989 O-Pee-Chee	60	.75	.60	.30
1989 Topps	60	.50	.40	.20
1990 Bowman	123	.30	.25	.12
1990 O-Pee-Chee	184	.15	.11	.06
1990 O-Pee-Chee Premier	56	1.50	1.25	.60
1990 Pro Set	186	.20	.15	.08
1990 Pro Set	372	.10	.08	.04
1990 Score	250	.40	.30	.15
1990 Score Hockey's 100 Hottest Rising Stars	95	.10	.08	.04
1990 Topps	184	.40	.30	.15
1990 Upper Deck	246	.75	.60	.30
1990 Upper Deck	306	.15	.11	.06
1990 Upper Deck	479	.25	.20	.10
1991 Bowman	222	.25	.20	.10
1991 O-Pee-Chee Premier	64	.25	.20	.10
1991 O-Pee-Chee/Topps	80	.25	.20	.10
1991 Parkhurst	16	.35	.25	.14
1991 Pinnacle	25	.50	.40	.20
1991 Pro Set	149	.25	.20	.10
1991 Pro Set	308	.10	.08	.04
1991 Pro Set	358	.25	.20	.10
1991 Pro Set Platinum	157	.20	.15	.08
1991 Score American	260	.20	.15	.08
1991 Score American	332	.15	.11	.06
1991 Score Canadian	362	.10	.08	.04
1991 Score Canadian	480	.20	.15	.08
1991 Score Traded	100	.25	.15	.08
1991 Topps Stadium Club	123	.75	.60	.30
1991 Upper Deck	253	.40	.30	.15
1991 Upper Deck	556	.40	.30	.15
1992 Bowman	142	1.50	1.25	.60
1992 Fleer Ultra	16	.30	.25	.12
1992 O-Pee-Chee	285	.20	.15	.08
1992 O-Pee-Chee Premier Star Performers	17	.40	.30	.15
1992 Parkhurst	12	.30	.25	.12
1992 Pinnacle	7	.35	.25	.14
1992 Pinnacle	254	.20	.15	.08
1992 Pro Set	13	.15	.11	.06
1992 Score	6	.20	.15	.08
1992 Score	420	.15	.11	.06
1992 Score Sharpshooters	8	2.50	1.25	.60
1992 Score USA Greats	1	6.00	4.50	2.50
1992 Topps	345	.20	.15	.08
1992 Topps Stadium Club	95	.40	.30	.15
1992 Upper Deck	165	.25	.20	.10
1992 Upper Deck Gordie Howe Selects	3	6.00	4.50	2.50
1993 Donruss	37	.30	.25	.12
1993 Donruss Ice Kings	2	2.50	2.00	1.00
1993 Fleer PowerPlay	31	.35	.25	.14
1993 Fleer PowerPlay Point Leaders	7	.75	.60	.30
1993 Fleer Ultra	219	.25	.20	.10
1993 Fleer Ultra All-Stars	4	6.00	4.50	2.50
1993 Fleer Ultra Premier Pivots	3	2.50	2.00	1.00
1993 Fleer Ultra Scoring Kings	1	6.00	4.50	2.50
1993 Fleer Ultra Speed Merchants	6	6.00	4.50	2.50
1993 Leaf	12	.40	.30	.15
1993 Leaf Gold All-Stars	1	14.00	10.50	5.50
1993 Leaf Studio Signature	3	6.00	4.50	2.50
1993 OPC Premier Black Gold	14	10.00	7.50	4.00
1993 Parkhurst	289	.25	.20	.10
1993 Parkhurst East-West Stars	8E	12.00	9.00	4.75
1993 Pinnacle	300	.35	.25	.14
1993 Pinnacle All-Stars	11	.35	.25	.14
1993 Pinnacle Hockey Captains	3	7.50	5.75	3.00
1993 Pinnacle Nifty 50	12	14.00	10.50	5.50
1993 Score	345	.20	.15	.08
1993 Score Dream Team	13	9.00	6.75	3.50
1993 Score Franchise	2	9.00	6.75	3.50
1993 Score U.S. Dynamic Duos	2	12.00	9.00	4.75
1993 Topps Premier	171	.15	.11	.06
1993 Topps Premier	490	.10	.08	.04
1993 Topps Premier Black Gold	24	3.50	2.75	1.50
1993 Topps Stadium Club	20	.30	.25	.12
1993 Topps Stadium Club	460	.25	.20	.10
1993 Topps Stadium Club All-Stars	5	11.00	8.25	4.50
1993 Upper Deck	137	.25	.20	.10
1993 Upper Deck	221	.20	.15	.08

Set	Card #	MT	NM	EX
1993 Upper Deck	287	.10	.08	.04
1993 Upper Deck Hat Tricks	10	1.00	.70	.40
1993 Upper Deck SP Inserts	17	.65	.50	.25
1994 Donruss	300	.20	.15	.08
1994 Fleer Flair	19	.40	.30	.15
1994 Fleer Flair Center Spotlight	5	4.00	3.00	1.50
1994 Fleer Ultra	24	.15	.11	.06
1994 Leaf	278	.20	.15	.08
1994 O-Pee-Chee Premier	180	.25	.20	.10
1994 Parkhurst	310	.10	.08	.04
1994 Parkhurst Crash the Game	3	5.00	3.75	2.00
1994 Parkhurst Vintage Parkhurst	73	.50	.40	.20
1994 Score	2	.15	.11	.06
1994 Score Franchise	3	10.00	7.50	4.00
1994 Score Hockey Gold Line	2	1.00	.70	.40
1994 Topps Premier	180	.25	.20	.10
1994 Upper Deck	17	.20	.15	.08
1994 Upper Deck Electric Ice	17	10.00	7.50	4.00
1994 Upper Deck Ice Gallery	14	7.00	5.25	2.75
1994 Upper Deck Scoring Predictor	17	4.00	3.00	1.50
1994 Upper Deck Scoring Predictor	22	4.00	3.00	1.50

Brian Leetch

Set	Card #	MT	NM	EX
1988 O-Pee-Chee Future Stars	12	2.50	2.00	1.00
1989 O-Pee-Chee	136 (R)	5.00	3.75	2.00
1989 O-Pee-Chee	321	.60	.45	.25
1989 O-Pee-Chee	326	.50	.40	.20
1989 O-Pee-Chee Future Stars	11	1.75	1.25	.70
1989 Topps	136 (R)	10.00	7.50	4.00
1990 Bowman	215a	.50	.40	.20
1990 Bowman	215b	.30	.25	.12
1990 O-Pee-Chee	221	.50	.40	.20
1990 O-Pee-Chee Premier	61	2.00	1.50	.80
1990 Pro Set	201	.40	.30	.15
1990 Pro Set	373	.15	.11	.06
1990 Score	225	.50	.40	.20
1990 Score Hockey's 100 Hottest Rising Stars	93	.10	.08	.04
1990 Topps	221	.60	.45	.25
1990 Upper Deck	253	1.00	.70	.40
1990 Upper Deck	315	.20	.15	.08
1990 Upper Deck	485	.20	.15	.08
1991 Bowman	75	.40	.30	.15
1991 O-Pee-Chee Premier	57	.20	.15	.08
1991 O-Pee-Chee/Topps	108	.35	.25	.14
1991 O-Pee-Chee/Topps	269	.05	.04	.02
1991 Parkhurst	119	.50	.40	.20
1991 Parkhurst	438	.05	.04	.02
1991 Parkhurst	464	5.00	3.75	2.00
1991 Parkhurst	471	5.00	3.75	2.00
1991 Pinnacle	136	.75	.60	.30
1991 Pinnacle B	3	40.00	30.00	16.00
1991 Pro Set	159	.25	.20	.10
1991 Pro Set	309	.10	.08	.04
1991 Pro Set Platinum	79	.15	.11	.06
1991 Pro Set Platinum	284	.10	.08	.04
1991 Score American	5	.20	.15	.08
1991 Score American	333	.10	.08	.04
1991 Score American	343	.10	.08	.04
1991 Score Canadian	5	.20	.15	.08
1991 Score Canadian	363	.10	.08	.04
1991 Score Canadian	373	.10	.08	.04
1991 Topps Stadium Club	201	1.00	.70	.40
1991 Upper Deck	35	.20	.15	.08
1991 Upper Deck	153	.75	.60	.30
1991 Upper Deck	612	.10	.08	.04
1992 Bowman	149	1.75	1.25	.70
1992 Bowman	232	20.00	15.00	8.00
1992 Fleer Ultra	138	.30	.25	.12
1992 Fleer Ultra Award Winners	2	3.50	2.75	1.50
1992 O-Pee-Chee	378	.25	.20	.10
1992 Parkhurst	110	.05	.04	.02
1992 Parkhurst	467	.15	.11	.06
1992 Pinnacle	15	.40	.30	.15
1992 Pinnacle Team Pinnacle	3	15.00	11.00	6.00
1992 Pro Set	112	.20	.15	.08
1992 Pro Set Award Winners	4	5.00	3.75	2.00
1992 Score	375	.20	.15	.08
1992 Score	416	.10	.08	.04
1992 Score	491	.05	.04	.02
1992 Score	522	.05	.04	.02
1992 Score USA Greats	8	7.00	5.25	2.75
1992 Topps	261	.06	.05	.02
1992 Topps	293	.20	.15	.08
1992 Topps Stadium Club	73	.25	.20	.10
1992 Topps Stadium Club	248	.15	.11	.06
1992 Upper Deck	284	.20	.15	.08
1992 Upper Deck	434	.20	.15	.08
1992 Upper Deck	640	.10	.08	.04
1992 Upper Deck World Junior Grads	15	7.00	5.25	2.75
1993 Donruss	221	.40	.30	.15
1993 Fleer PowerPlay	160	.25	.20	.10
1993 Fleer PowerPlay Slapshot Artists	6	1.00	.70	.40
1993 Fleer Ultra	132	.40	.30	.15
1993 Leaf	70	.25	.20	.10
1993 Parkhurst	131	.20	.15	.08
1993 Pinnacle	275	.35	.25	.14
1993 Pinnacle Team Pinnacle	2	25.00	18.50	10.00
1993 Score	235	.15	.11	.06
1993 Score Dream Team	6	12.00	9.00	4.75
1993 Score Franchise	13	12.00	9.00	4.75
1993 Topps Premier	25	.15	.11	.06
1993 Topps Premier	505	.07	.05	.03
1993 Topps Stadium Club	88	.20	.15	.08
1993 Upper Deck	348	.05	.04	.02
1993 Upper Deck Next in Line	4	5.00	3.75	2.00
1993 Upper Deck SP Inserts	102	1.00	.70	.40
1994 Donruss	152	.20	.15	.08
1994 Fleer Flair	114	.40	.30	.15
1994 Fleer Flair Scoring Power	5	3.50	2.75	1.50
1994 Fleer Ultra	139	.12	.09	.05
1994 Fleer Ultra All-Stars	2	.40	.30	.15
1994 Fleer Ultra NHL Award Winners	7	1.00	.70	.40
1994 Leaf Gold Stars	6	28.00	21.00	11.00
1994 O-Pee-Chee Premier	37	.15	.11	.06
1994 Parkhurst	151	.20	.15	.08

Set	Card #			
1994 Parkhurst Vintage Parkhurst	15	.50	.40	.20
1994 Pinnacle	155	.30	.25	.12
1994 Pinnacle Artist's Proofs	155	15.00	11.00	6.00
1994 Pinnacle Rink Collection	155	7.00	5.25	2.75
1994 Pinnacle Team Pinnacle	4	20.00	15.00	8.00
1994 Score	184	.15	.11	.06
1994 Score Dream Team	4	7.00	5.25	2.75
1994 Score Hockey Gold Line	184	1.00	.70	.40
1994 Topps Premier	37	.15	.11	.06
1994 Topps Stadium Club	55	.10	.08	.04
1994 Topps Stadium Club	150	.20	.15	.08
1994 Topps Stadium Club Finest	7	5.00	3.75	2.00
1994 Upper Deck	231	.10	.08	.04
1994 Upper Deck Award Predictor	11	4.00	3.00	1.50
1994 Upper Deck Electric Ice	231	3.50	2.75	1.50
1994 Upper Deck Scoring Predictor	13	6.00	4.50	2.50
1994 Upper Deck SP	50	.60	.45	.25

Mario Lemieux

MARIO LEMIEUX   C

Set	Card #	MT	NM	EX
1985 O-Pee-Chee	9 (R)	350.00	262.00	140.00
1985 O-Pee-Chee	262	40.00	30.00	16.00
1985 Topps	9 (R)	160.00	120.00	65.00
1986 O-Pee-Chee	122	70.00	52.00	28.00
1986 Topps	122	40.00	30.00	16.00
1987 O-Pee-Chee	15	35.00	26.00	14.00
1987 Topps	15	25.00	18.50	10.00
1988 O-Pee-Chee	1	8.00	6.00	3.25
1988 Topps	1	5.00	3.75	2.00
1989 O-Pee-Chee	1	1.00	.70	.40
1989 O-Pee-Chee	319	.50	.40	.20
1989 O-Pee-Chee	327	.40	.30	.15
1989 Topps	1	2.00	1.50	.80
1990 Bowman	204	1.00	.70	.40
1990 O-Pee-Chee	175	1.00	.70	.40
1990 O-Pee-Chee Premier	63	4.00	3.00	1.50
1990 Pro Set	236	1.00	.70	.40
1990 Pro Set	362	.25	.20	.10
1990 Score	2	1.00	.70	.40
1990 Score	337	.30	.25	.12
1990 Score Hockey's 100 Hottest Rising Stars	34	.10	.08	.04
1990 Topps	175	1.00	.70	.40
1990 Upper Deck	59	.50	.40	.20
1990 Upper Deck	144	1.50	1.25	.60
1991 Bowman	87	.75	.60	.30
1991 Bowman	425	.40	.30	.15
1991 O-Pee-Chee Premier	114	1.00	.70	.40
1991 O-Pee-Chee/Topps	153	.80	.60	.30
1991 O-Pee-Chee/Topps	523	.25	.20	.10
1991 Parkhurst	137	1.50	1.25	.60
1991 Parkhurst	467	10.00	7.50	4.00
1991 Pinnacle	1	1.50	1.25	.60
1991 Pinnacle	380	.50	.40	.20
1991 Pinnacle B	5	90.00	67.00	36.00
1991 Pro Set	194	1.00	.70	.40
1991 Pro Set	318	.25	.20	.10
1991 Pro Set	581	.25	.20	.10
1991 Pro Set Platinum	91	.70	.50	.30
1991 Score American	200	.75	.60	.30
1991 Score American	335	.25	.20	.10
1991 Score American	426	.25	.20	.10
1991 Score Canadian	200	.75	.60	.30
1991 Score Canadian	316	.25	.20	.10
1991 Score Canadian	365	.25	.20	.10
1991 Score Hot Card	5	6.00	4.50	2.50
1991 Topps Stadium Club	174	2.50	2.00	1.00
1991 Upper Deck	156	1.00	.70	.40
1991 Upper Deck	611	.40	.30	.15
1991 Upper Deck Collector Cards	9	1.50	1.25	.60
1992 Bowman	189	5.50	4.25	2.25
1992 Bowman	233	14.00	10.50	5.50
1992 Bowman	440	12.00	9.00	4.75
1992 Fleer Ultra	165	1.00	.70	.40
1992 Fleer Ultra All-Stars	4	7.00	5.25	2.75
1992 Fleer Ultra Award Winners	5	8.00	6.00	3.25
1992 O-Pee-Chee	138	.75	.60	.30
1992 O-Pee-Chee	240	.30	.25	.12
1992 O-Pee-Chee	292	2.00	1.50	.80
1992 O-Pee-Chee Premier Star Performers	22	2.50	2.00	1.00
1992 O-Pee-Chee 25th Anniversary Series	18	.60	.45	.25
1992 Parkhurst	136	1.25	.90	.50
1992 Parkhurst	462	.75	.60	.30
1992 Parkhurst	498	2.00	1.50	.80
1992 Pinnacle	300	1.25	.90	.50
1992 Pro Set	1	.60	.45	.25
1992 Pro Set	139	1.50	1.25	.60
1992 Score	390	.75	.60	.30
1992 Score	413	.30	.25	.12
1992 Score	433	.30	.25	.12
1992 Score	448	.30	.25	.12
1992 Score	519	.30	.25	.12
1992 Topps	212	.75	.60	.30
1992 Topps	265	.40	.30	.15
1992 Topps	504	.30	.25	.12
1992 Topps Stadium Club	94	1.25	.90	.50
1992 Topps Stadium Club	251	1.25	.90	.50
1992 Upper Deck	26	1.00	.70	.40
1992 Upper Deck	433	.25	.20	.10
1992 Upper Deck	436	.25	.20	.10
1992 Upper Deck Gordie Howe Selects	9	15.00	11.00	6.00
1992 Upper Deck World Junior Grads	11	15.00	11.00	6.00
1993 Donruss	262	1.25	.90	.50
1993 Donruss Elite	1	80.00	60.00	32.00
1993 Donruss Ice Kings	7	6.00	4.50	2.50
1993 Donruss Special Print	R	16.00	12.00	6.50
1993 Fleer PowerPlay	190	1.50	1.25	.60
1993 Fleer PowerPlay Gamebreakers	5	4.50	3.50	1.75
1993 Fleer PowerPlay Point Leaders	8	4.00	3.00	1.50
1993 Fleer Ultra	116	1.50	1.25	.60
1993 Fleer Ultra Award Winners	4	9.00	6.75	3.50
1993 Fleer Ultra Premier Pivots	4	4.00	3.00	1.50
1993 Fleer Ultra Red Light Specials	6	6.00	4.50	2.50
1993 Fleer Ultra Scoring Kings	4	8.00	6.00	3.25
1993 Leaf	1	1.50	1.25	.60
1993 Leaf	210	.40	.30	.15
1993 Leaf Gold All-Stars	1	14.00	10.50	5.50

1993 Leaf Hat Trick Artists	4	6.00	4.50	2.50
1993 Leaf Mario Lemieux	1	3.00	2.25	1.25
1993 Leaf Mario Lemieux	2	3.00	2.25	1.25
1993 Leaf Mario Lemieux	3	3.00	2.25	1.25
1993 Leaf Mario Lemieux	4	3.00	2.25	1.25
1993 Leaf Mario Lemieux	5	3.00	2.25	1.25
1993 Leaf Mario Lemieux	6	3.00	2.25	1.25
1993 Leaf Mario Lemieux	7	3.00	2.25	1.25
1993 Leaf Mario Lemieux	8	3.00	2.25	1.25
1993 Leaf Mario Lemieux	9	3.00	2.25	1.25
1993 Leaf Mario Lemieux	10	3.00	2.25	1.25
1993 OPC Premier Black Gold	18	30.00	22.00	12.00
1993 Parkhurst	425	1.00	.70	.40
1993 Parkhurst Cherry's Playoff Heroes	2D	60.00	45.00	24.00
1993 Parkhurst East-West Stars	2E	28.00	21.00	11.00
1993 Parkhurst First Overall	10	30.00	22.00	12.00
1993 Parkhurst US Canada Gold-Foiled	2	30.00	22.00	12.00
1993 Pinnacle	221	.50	.40	.20
1993 Pinnacle	230	.50	.40	.20
1993 Pinnacle	310	1.00	.70	.40
1993 Pinnacle Hockey Captains	18	20.00	15.00	8.00
1993 Pinnacle Nifty 50	4	30.00	22.00	12.00
1993 Pinnacle Team Pinnacle	5	120.00	90.00	48.00
1993 Score	350	.75	.60	.30
1993 Score	479	.20	.15	.08
1993 Score	480	.20	.15	.08
1993 Score Canadian Dynamic Duos	8	30.00	22.00	12.00
1993 Score Dream Team	10	30.00	22.00	12.00
1993 Score Franchise	16	30.00	22.00	12.00
1993 Topps Finest Hockey Card Series Roster	10	12.00	9.00	4.75
1993 Topps Premier	37	.25	.20	.10
1993 Topps Premier	91	.25	.20	.10
1993 Topps Premier	185	.25	.20	.10
1993 Topps Premier	220	.75	.60	.30
1993 Topps Premier Black Gold	9	8.00	6.00	3.25
1993 Topps Stadium Club	143	.40	.30	.15
1993 Topps Stadium Club	146	.35	.25	.14
1993 Topps Stadium Club	148	.35	.25	.14
1993 Topps Stadium Club	310	.75	.60	.30
1993 Topps Stadium Club All-Stars	23	50.00	37.00	20.00
1993 Topps Stadium Club Finest	10	12.00	9.00	4.75
1993 Upper Deck	301	.40	.30	.15
1993 Upper Deck	407	.60	.45	.25
1993 Upper Deck Award Winners	1	7.00	5.25	2.75
1993 Upper Deck Gretzky's Great Ones	4	6.00	4.50	2.50
1993 Upper Deck NHL's Best	7	25.00	18.50	10.00
1993 Upper Deck Program of Excellence	13E	25.00	18.50	10.00
1993 Upper Deck Silver Skates Dye-Cut Hobby	1H	25.00	18.50	10.00
1993 Upper Deck SP Inserts	122	6.00	4.50	2.50
1994 Donruss	5	1.00	.70	.40
1994 Donruss Elite Series	6	40.00	30.00	16.00
1994 Donruss Ice Masters	5	6.00	4.50	2.50
1994 Fleer Flair	135	2.50	2.00	1.00
1994 Fleer Flair Center Spotlight	6	8.00	6.00	3.25
1994 Fleer Flair Hot Numbers	5	25.00	18.50	10.00
1994 Fleer Ultra	165	1.00	.70	.40
1994 Fleer Ultra Scoring Kings	5	3.00	2.25	1.25
1994 Leaf	1	.75	.60	.30
1994 Leaf Fire On Ice	9	12.00	9.00	4.75
1994 Leaf Limited	18	13.00	9.75	5.25
1994 O-Pee-Chee Premier	250	.50	.40	.20
1994 Parkhurst	296	.60	.45	.25
1994 Parkhurst Crash the Game	18	10.00	7.50	4.00
1994 Parkhurst Vintage Parkhurst	6	3.50	2.75	1.50
1994 Pinnacle	170	1.00	.70	.40
1994 Pinnacle Artist's Proofs	170	100.00	75.00	40.00
1994 Pinnacle Rink Collection	170	40.00	30.00	16.00
1994 Pinnacle Team Pinnacle	10	50.00	37.00	20.00
1994 Score Dream Team	15	15.00	11.00	6.00
1994 Score Franchise	18	45.00	34.00	18.00
1994 Topps Premier	250	.50	.40	.20
1994 Topps Stadium Club	60	.50	.40	.20
1994 Topps Stadium Club Finest	1	12.00	9.00	4.75
1994 Upper Deck	22	1.00	.70	.40
1994 Upper Deck Electric Ice	22	45.00	34.00	18.00
1994 Upper Deck SP	61	6.00	4.50	2.50

Trevor Linden

Set	Card #	MT	NM	EX
1989 O-Pee-Chee	89 (R)	2.00	1.50	.80
1989 O-Pee-Chee Future Stars	19	1.25	.90	.50
1989 Topps	89 (R)	3.50	2.75	1.50
1990 Bowman	61	.25	.20	.10
1990 O-Pee-Chee	225	.25	.20	.10
1990 Pro Set	299	.20	.15	.08
1990 Score	32	.30	.25	.12
1990 Score Hockey's 100 Hottest Rising Stars	16	.10	.08	.04
1990 Topps	225	.25	.20	.10
1990 Upper Deck	256	.80	.60	.30
1990 Upper Deck	480	.25	.20	.10
1991 Bowman	327	.15	.11	.06
1991 O-Pee-Chee Premier	77	.30	.25	.12
1991 O-Pee-Chee/Topps	364	.15	.11	.06
1991 Parkhurst	179	.05	.04	.02
1991 Pinnacle	2	.25	.20	.10
1991 Pro Set	236	.15	.11	.06
1991 Pro Set	294	.05	.04	.02
1991 Pro Set	586	.05	.04	.02
1991 Pro Set Platinum	124	.10	.08	.04
1991 Score American	8	.15	.11	.06
1991 Score American	339	.05	.04	.02
1991 Score Canadian	8	.10	.08	.04
1991 Score Canadian	369	.05	.04	.02
1991 Score Kellogg's	20	1.00	.70	.40
1991 Topps Stadium Club	84	.50	.40	.20

Set	Card #	MT	NM	EX
1991 Upper Deck	174	.25	.20	.10
1991 Upper Deck	628	.10	.08	.04
1992 Bowman	210	15.00	11.00	6.00
1992 Bowman	261	.60	.45	.25
1992 Fleer Ultra	222	.25	.20	.10
1992 O-Pee-Chee	120	.15	.11	.06
1992 Parkhurst	190	.05	.04	.02
1992 Pinnacle	47	.20	.15	.08
1992 Pinnacle Team 2000	24	1.50	1.25	.60
1992 Pro Set	197	.10	.08	.04
1992 Pro Set Gold Team Leaders	12	2.00	1.50	.80
1992 Score	305	.15	.11	.06
1992 Score	438	.05	.04	.02
1992 Topps	499	.06	.05	.02
1992 Topps Stadium Club	80	.20	.15	.08
1992 Upper Deck	38	.05	.04	.02
1992 Upper Deck	158	.20	.15	.08
1992 Upper Deck World Junior Grads	14	7.00	5.25	2.75
1993 Donruss	354	.15	.11	.06
1993 Fleer PowerPlay	251	.10	.08	.04
1993 Fleer Ultra	109	.10	.08	.04
1993 Leaf	193	.10	.08	.04
1993 Parkhurst	215	.15	.11	.06
1993 Pinnacle	43	.10	.08	.04
1993 Pinnacle Hockey Captains	24	6.00	4.50	2.50
1993 Pinnacle Team 2001	16	.50	.40	.20
1993 Score	117	.10	.08	.04
1993 Topps Premier	225	.05	.04	.02
1993 Topps Stadium Club	357	.12	.09	.05
1993 Upper Deck	383	.06	.05	.02
1993 Upper Deck SP Inserts	164	.30	.25	.12
1994 Donruss	181	.08	.06	.03
1994 Fleer Flair	191	.25	.20	.10
1994 Fleer Ultra	226	.10	.08	.04
1994 O-Pee-Chee Premier	75	.05	.04	.02
1994 Parkhurst	241	.06	.05	.02
1994 Pinnacle	8	.10	.08	.04
1994 Pinnacle Artist's Proofs	8	7.00	5.25	2.75
1994 Pinnacle Northern Lights	18	5.50	4.25	2.25
1994 Pinnacle Rink Collection	8	4.00	3.00	1.50
1994 Topps Premier	75	.05	.04	.02
1994 Upper Deck SP	83	.30	.25	.12

Eric Lindros

Set	Card #	MT	NM	EX
1990 Score	440 (R)	8.00	6.00	3.25
1990 Score	440a (R)	15.00	11.00	6.00
1990 Score	442	2.00	1.50	.80
1990 Score	443	2.00	1.50	.80
1990 Score	444	2.00	1.50	.80
1990 Score	445	2.00	1.50	.80

Set	Card #	MT	NM	EX
1990 Score Traded	88	12.00	9.00	4.75
1990 Upper Deck	473	5.00	3.75	2.00
1991 Pinnacle	365	7.50	5.25	2.75
1991 Score American	354	1.00	.70	.40
1991 Score American	355	1.00	.70	.40
1991 Score American	356	1.00	.70	.40
1991 Score Canadian	329	1.25	.90	.50
1991 Score Canadian	330	1.25	.90	.50
1991 Score Canadian	384	1.25	.90	.50
1991 Score Canadian	385	1.25	.90	.50
1991 Score Hot Card	1	15.00	11.00	6.00
1991 Score Traded	88	3.00	2.00	1.00
1991 Upper Deck	9	6.00	4.50	2.50
1992 Bowman	442	25.00	18.50	10.00
1992 Fleer Ultra	157	5.00	3.75	2.00
1992 O-Pee-Chee Premier	102	4.00	3.00	1.50
1992 O-Pee-Chee Premier Top Rookies	1	7.50	5.00	2.50
1992 Parkhurst	128	5.50	4.25	2.25
1992 Parkhurst Cherry Picks	6	45.00	34.00	18.00
1992 Pinnacle	88	6.00	4.50	2.50
1992 Pinnacle	236	1.50	1.25	.60
1992 Pinnacle Team Pinnacle	5	45.00	34.00	18.00
1992 Pinnacle Team 2000	1	8.50	6.50	3.50
1992 Pro Set	236	5.00	3.75	2.00
1992 Score	432	1.75	1.25	.70
1992 Score	550	4.00	3.00	1.50
1992 Score Canadian Olympic Heroes	1	50.00	37.00	20.00
1992 Topps	529	4.00	3.00	1.50
1992 Topps Stadium Club	501	4.50	3.50	1.75
1992 Upper Deck	88	5.00	3.75	2.00
1992 Upper Deck	470	3.50	2.75	1.50
1992 Upper Deck Calder Candidates	6	20.00	15.00	8.00
1992 Upper Deck Gordie Howe Selects	14	20.00	15.00	8.00
1992 Upper Deck World Junior Grads	12	20.00	15.00	8.00
1993 Donruss	242	4.00	3.00	1.50
1993 Donruss Elite	4	100.00	75.00	40.00
1993 Donruss Ice Kings	9	7.00	5.25	2.75
1993 Donruss Special Print	Q	25.00	18.50	10.00
1993 Fleer PowerPlay	183	3.50	2.75	1.50
1993 Fleer PowerPlay Gamebreakers	6	6.00	4.50	2.50
1993 Fleer PowerPlay Second-Year Stars	5	5.00	3.75	2.00
1993 Fleer Ultra	161	3.00	2.25	1.25
1993 Fleer Ultra	249	.30	.25	.12
1993 Fleer Ultra Premier Pivots	5	7.00	5.25	2.75
1993 Leaf	233	2.50	2.00	1.00
1993 Leaf Gold Rookies	3	15.00	11.00	6.00
1993 Leaf Hat Trick Artists	7	8.00	6.00	3.25
1993 Leaf Studio Signature	10	12.00	9.00	4.75
1993 OPC Premier Black Gold	12	40.00	30.00	16.00
1993 Parkhurst	236	1.50	1.25	.60
1993 Parkhurst	416	3.00	2.25	1.25
1993 Parkhurst Cherry's Playoff Heroes	15D	80.00	60.00	32.00
1993 Parkhurst East-West Stars	1E	45.00	34.00	18.00
1993 Parkhurst First Overall	3	40.00	30.00	16.00
1993 Parkhurst US Canada Gold-Foiled	3	35.00	26.00	14.00
1993 Pinnacle	1	3.00	2.25	1.25
1993 Pinnacle Team Pinnacle	11	70.00	52.00	28.00
1993 Pinnacle Team 2001	1	10.00	7.50	4.00
1993 Score	1	1.75	1.25	.70
1993 Score Dream Team	12	35.00	26.00	14.00
1993 Score Franchise	15	30.00	22.00	12.00

1993 Score U.S. Dynamic Duos	1	45.00	34.00	18.00
1993 Topps Finest Hockey Card Series Roster	3	15.00	11.00	6.00
1993 Topps Premier	121	.75	.60	.30
1993 Topps Premier	310	1.50	1.25	.60
1993 Topps Premier Black Gold	13	10.00	7.50	4.00
1993 Topps Stadium Club	10	2.00	1.50	.80
1993 Upper Deck	30	1.50	1.25	.60
1993 Upper Deck	280	1.00	.70	.40
1993 Upper Deck Future Heroes	31	40.00	30.00	16.00
1993 Upper Deck NHL's Best	8	42.00	31.00	17.00
1993 Upper Deck Program of Excellence	12E	40.00	30.00	16.00
1993 Upper Deck Silver Skates Dye-Cut Hobby	3H	35.00	26.00	14.00
1993 Upper Deck SP Inserts	116	10.00	7.50	4.00
1994 Donruss	137	1.50	1.25	.60
1994 Donruss Elite Series	7	65.00	49.00	26.00
1994 Donruss Ice Masters	6	7.00	5.25	2.75
1994 Fleer Flair	129	4.00	3.00	1.50
1994 Fleer Flair Center Spotlight	7	14.00	10.50	5.50
1994 Fleer Flair Scoring Power	6	14.00	10.50	5.50
1994 Fleer Ultra All-Stars	3	3.00	2.25	1.25
1994 Fleer Ultra Scoring Kings	6	7.00	5.25	2.75
1994 Fleer Ultra Ultra Power	5	25.00	18.50	10.00
1994 Leaf Fire On Ice	6	18.00	13.50	7.25
1994 Leaf Limited	17	20.00	15.00	8.00
1994 O-Pee-Chee Premier	241	1.00	.75	.40
1994 Parkhurst	301	1.75	1.25	.70
1994 Parkhurst Crash the Game	17	20.00	15.00	8.00
1994 Parkhurst Vintage Parkhurst	69	6.00	4.50	2.50
1994 Pinnacle	1	2.50	2.00	1.00
1994 Pinnacle Artist's Proofs	1	100.00	75.00	40.00
1994 Pinnacle Boomers	16	30.00	22.00	12.00
1994 Pinnacle Rink Collection	1	45.00	34.00	18.00
1994 Pinnacle Team Pinnacle	8	80.00	60.00	32.00
1994 Score	1	1.25	.90	.50
1994 Score Check-It	1	60.00	45.00	24.00
1994 Score Dream Team	19	25.00	18.50	10.00
1994 Score Franchise	17	65.00	49.00	26.00
1994 Score Hockey Gold Line	1	8.00	6.00	3.25
1994 Score 90-Plus Club	12	25.00	18.50	10.00
1994 Topps Premier	241	.75	.60	.30
1994 Topps Premier Finest Inserts	12	20.00	15.00	8.00
1994 Topps Stadium Club	88	1.50	1.25	.60
1994 Topps Stadium Club	203	1.00	.75	.40
1994 Topps Stadium Club Dynasty and Destiny	2	20.00	15.00	8.00
1994 Upper Deck	98	2.00	1.50	.80
1994 Upper Deck Award Predictor	8	20.00	15.00	8.00
1994 Upper Deck Electric Ice	98	75.00	56.00	30.00
1994 Upper Deck Scoring Predictor	9	18.00	13.50	7.25
1994 Upper Deck Scoring Predictor	28	18.00	13.50	7.25

Obverse: The front of the card displaying the picture.

Al MacInnis

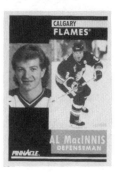

Set	Card #	MT	NM	EX
1985 O-Pee-Chee	237 (R)	40.00	30.00	16.00
1986 O-Pee-Chee	173	10.00	7.50	4.00
1986 Topps	173 (FC)	6.00	4.50	2.50
1987 O-Pee-Chee	72	4.00	3.00	1.50
1987 Topps	72	2.50	2.00	1.00
1988 O-Pee-Chee	231	3.00	2.25	1.25
1989 O-Pee-Chee	49	.25	.20	.10
1989 O-Pee-Chee Future Stars	27	.25	.20	.10
1989 Topps	49	.25	.20	.10
1990 Bowman	93	.07	.05	.03
1990 O-Pee-Chee	127	.10	.08	.04
1990 O-Pee-Chee	197	.05	.04	.02
1990 O-Pee-Chee Premier	65	.30	.25	.12
1990 Pro Set	35	.07	.05	.03
1990 Pro Set	337	.12	.09	.05
1990 Score	5	.15	.11	.06
1990 Score	314	.07	.05	.03
1990 Score	335	.05	.04	.02
1990 Score Hockey's 100 Hottest Rising Stars	36	.10	.08	.04
1990 Topps	127	.10	.08	.04
1990 Topps	197	.03	.02	.01
1990 Upper Deck	143	.25	.20	.10
1990 Upper Deck	319	.07	.05	.03
1990 Upper Deck	497	.08	.06	.03
1991 Bowman	262	.05	.04	.02
1991 O-Pee-Chee Premier	81	.05	.04	.02
1991 O-Pee-Chee/Topps	262	.05	.04	.02
1991 O-Pee-Chee/Topps	491	.05	.04	.02
1991 Parkhurst	28	.05	.04	.02
1991 Pinnacle	220	.20	.15	.08
1991 Pinnacle	399	.20	.15	.08
1991 Pinnacle B	8	30.00	22.00	12.00
1991 Pro Set	33	.05	.04	.02
1991 Pro Set	275	.05	.04	.02
1991 Pro Set Platinum	19	.05	.04	.02
1991 Pro Set Platinum	276	.05	.04	.02
1991 Score American	2	.05	.04	.02
1991 Score American	417	.05	.04	.02
1991 Score Canadian	2	.05	.04	.02
1991 Score Canadian	299	.10	.08	.04
1991 Score Canadian	333	.05	.04	.02
1991 Score Kellogg's	16	1.00	.70	.40
1991 Topps Stadium Club	79	.10	.08	.04
1991 Upper Deck	8	.05	.04	.02
1991 Upper Deck	243	.10	.08	.04
1991 Upper Deck	632	.10	.08	.04
1992 Bowman	51	.25	.20	.10
1992 Bowman	211	2.00	1.50	.80
1992 Fleer Ultra	23	.06	.05	.02
1992 Fleer Ultra All-Stars	8	2.25	1.75	.90
1992 O-Pee-Chee	330	.05	.04	.02
1992 Parkhurst	20	.05	.04	.02
1992 Pinnacle	83	.06	.05	.02
1992 Pro Set	22	.05	.04	.02
1992 Score	302	.05	.04	.02
1992 Score	421	.05	.04	.02

Set		NM	EX	VG
1992 Score	496	.05	.04	.02
1992 Topps	452	.06	.05	.02
1992 Topps Stadium Club	128	.05	.04	.02
1992 Upper Deck	257	.05	.04	.02
1993 Donruss	47	.10	.08	.04
1993 Fleer PowerPlay	38	.10	.08	.04
1993 Fleer PowerPlay Slapshot Artists	7	.75	.60	.30
1993 Fleer Ultra	113	.07	.05	.03
1993 Leaf	180	.10	.08	.04
1993 Parkhurst	36	.10	.08	.04
1993 Parkhurst Cherry's Playoff Heroes	3D	12.50	9.50	5.00
1993 Pinnacle	155	.10	.08	.04
1993 Pinnacle Team Pinnacle	3	25.00	18.50	10.00
1993 Score	121	.05	.04	.02
1993 Score Dream Team	4	4.00	3.00	1.50
1993 Score Franchise	3	4.00	3.00	1.50
1993 Topps Premier	276	.05	.04	.02
1993 Topps Stadium Club	105	.05	.04	.02
1993 Upper Deck	412	.05	.04	.02
1993 Upper Deck SP Inserts	22	.30	.25	.12
1994 Fleer Flair	157	.30	.25	.12
1994 Fleer Ultra	185	.08	.06	.03
1994 O-Pee-Chee Premier	110	.05	.04	.02
1994 O-Pee-Chee Premier	127	.05	.04	.02
1994 Parkhurst	35	.06	.05	.02
1994 Pinnacle Boomers	3	6.00	4.50	2.50
1994 Score	120	.05	.04	.02
1994 Score Dream Team	7	5.00	3.75	2.00
1994 Score Hockey Gold Line	120	.40	.30	.15
1994 Topps Premier	110	.05	.04	.02
1994 Topps Premier	127	.05	.04	.02
1994 Topps Stadium Club	56	.05	.04	.02
1994 Upper Deck	150	.10	.08	.04
1994 Upper Deck	232	.10	.08	.04
1994 Upper Deck Electric Ice	150	6.00	4.50	2.50
1994 Upper Deck Electric Ice	232	3.50	2.75	1.50

Lanny McDonald

Set	Card #	NM	EX	VG
1974 O-Pee-Chee	168 (R)	27.00	13.50	8.10
1974 Topps	168 (R)	18.00	9.00	5.40
1975 O-Pee-Chee	23	10.00	5.00	3.00
1975 Topps	23	7.00	3.50	2.00
1976 O-Pee-Chee	348	5.00	2.50	1.50
1977 O-Pee-Chee	5	1.00	.50	.30
1977 O-Pee-Chee	110	3.00	1.50	.90
1977 Topps	5	.40	.20	.12
1977 Topps	110	2.00	1.00	.60
1978 O-Pee-Chee	78	1.75	.90	.50
1978 Topps	78	1.50	.70	.45
1979 O-Pee-Chee	5	3.00	1.50	.90

Set		MT	NM	EX
1979 O-Pee-Chee	153	1.00	.50	.30
1979 Topps	5	1.50	.70	.45
1979 Topps	153	1.25	.60	.40
1980 O-Pee-Chee	62	1.25	.60	.40
1980 Topps	62	.75	.40	.25

Set	Card #	MT	NM	EX
1981 O-Pee-Chee	77	1.00	.70	.40
1981 O-Pee-Chee	85	.30	.25	.12
1981 Topps	82	.50	.40	.20
1981 Topps	50	.20	.15	.08
1982 O-Pee-Chee	38	.20	.15	.08
1982 O-Pee-Chee	51	.50	.40	.20
1983 O-Pee-Chee	74	.15	.11	.06
1983 O-Pee-Chee	75	.15	.11	.06
1983 O-Pee-Chee	87	.30	.25	.12
1983 O-Pee-Chee	208	.15	.11	.06
1984 O-Pee-Chee	231	.75	.60	.30
1984 Topps	26	.25	.20	.10
1985 O-Pee-Chee	1	.60	.45	.25
1985 Topps	1	.50	.40	.20
1986 O-Pee-Chee	8	.75	.60	.30
1986 Topps	8	.50	.40	.20
1987 O-Pee-Chee	20	.12	.09	.05
1987 Topps	20	.50	.40	.20
1988 O-Pee-Chee	234	.35	.25	.14
1989 O-Pee-Chee	7	.35	.25	.14
1989 Topps	7	.35	.25	.14
1990 Upper Deck	508	.20	.15	.08
1992 Pinnacle	242	.06	.05	.02

Marty McSorley

Set	Card #	MT	NM	EX
1987 O-Pee-Chee	205 (R)	8.00	6.00	3.25
1990 O-Pee-Chee	392	.05	.04	.02
1990 Pro Set	124	.05	.04	.02
1990 Score	271	.15	.11	.06
1990 Topps	392	.10	.08	.04
1990 Upper Deck	212	.25	.20	.10
1991 Bowman	184	.15	.11	.06
1991 O-Pee-Chee/Topps	225	.05	.04	.02
1991 O-Pee-Chee/Topps	322	.05	.04	.02
1991 Parkhurst	69	.05	.04	.02
1991 Pinnacle	35	.25	.20	.10
1991 Pro Set	100	.05	.04	.02
1991 Pro Set Platinum	184	.05	.04	.02
1991 Score American	217	.05	.04	.02
1991 Score American	407	.10	.08	.04
1991 Score Canadian	217	.10	.08	.04
1991 Score Canadian	297	.10	.08	.04
1991 Topps Stadium Club	267	.20	.15	.08
1991 Upper Deck	199	.25	.20	.10
1992 Bowman	35	.30	.25	.12
1992 Fleer Ultra	310	.15	.11	.06
1992 O-Pee-Chee	261	.05	.04	.02
1992 Parkhurst	304	.05	.04	.02
1992 Pinnacle	156	.06	.05	.02
1992 Pro Set	69	.05	.04	.02

1992 Score	26	.05	.04	.02
1992 Topps	171	.06	.05	.02
1992 Topps Stadium Club	481	.05	.04	.02
1992 Upper Deck	322	.05	.04	.02
1993 Donruss	256	.10	.08	.04
1993 Donruss	447	.10	.08	.04
1993 Fleer PowerPlay	191	.20	.15	.08
1993 Fleer Ultra	227	.07	.05	.03
1993 Fleer Ultra	394	.07	.05	.03
1993 Leaf	352	.10	.08	.04
1993 Parkhurst	161	.10	.08	.04
1993 Pinnacle	374	.12	.09	.05
1993 Score	212	.05	.04	.02
1993 Score	542	.08	.06	.03
1993 Topps Premier	395	.06	.05	.02
1993 Topps Stadium Club	155	.05	.04	.02
1993 Topps Stadium Club Finest	8	3.50	2.75	1.50
1993 Upper Deck	487	.05	.04	.02
1993 Upper Deck Gretzky's Great Ones	9	2.50	2.00	1.00
1994 Donruss	168	.08	.06	.03
1994 Fleer Flair	82	.25	.20	.10
1994 Fleer Ultra	102	.10	.08	.04
1994 Leaf	174	.15	.11	.06
1994 O-Pee-Chee Premier	146	.08	.06	.03
1994 Parkhurst	106	.06	.05	.02
1994 Pinnacle	61	.10	.08	.04
1994 Pinnacle Artist's Proofs	61	5.00	3.75	2.00
1994 Pinnacle Rink Collection	61	3.00	2.25	1.25
1994 Score	20	.05	.04	.02
1994 Score Hockey Gold Line	20	.25	.20	.10
1994 Topps Premier	146	.08	.06	.03
1994 Upper Deck	33	.10	.08	.04
1994 Upper Deck Electric Ice	33	3.50	2.75	1.50

Mark Messier

Set	Card #	NM	EX	VG
1980 O-Pee-Chee	289 (R)	175.00	87.00	52.00

Set	Card #	MT	NM	EX
1981 O-Pee-Chee	118	50.00	37.00	20.00
1982 O-Pee-Chee	117	20.00	15.00	8.00
1983 O-Pee-Chee	23	20.00	15.00	8.00
1983 O-Pee-Chee	39	14.00	10.50	5.50
1984 O-Pee-Chee	213	2.50	2.00	1.00
1984 O-Pee-Chee	254	8.00	6.00	3.25
1984 Topps	159	1.25	.90	.50
1985 O-Pee-Chee	177	8.00	6.00	3.25
1986 O-Pee-Chee	186	5.00	3.75	2.00
1986 Topps	186	3.00	2.25	1.25
1987 O-Pee-Chee	112	3.00	2.25	1.25
1987 Topps	112	2.00	1.50	.80
1988 O-Pee-Chee	93	1.50	1.25	.60

1988 Topps	93	.75	.60	.30
1989 O-Pee-Chee	65	1.25	.90	.50
1989 Topps	65	.60	.45	.25
1990 Bowman	199	.20	.15	.08
1990 O-Pee-Chee	130	.25	.20	.10
1990 O-Pee-Chee	193	.15	.11	.06
1990 O-Pee-Chee Premier	71	1.00	.70	.40
1990 Pro Set	91	.25	.20	.10
1990 Pro Set	349	.15	.11	.06
1990 Pro Set	381	.15	.11	.06
1990 Pro Set	386	.15	.11	.06
1990 Score	100	.20	.15	.08
1990 Score	315	.15	.11	.06
1990 Score	360	.15	.11	.06
1990 Score Hockey's 100 Hottest Rising Stars	33	.10	.08	.04
1990 Topps	130	.25	.20	.10
1990 Topps	193	.15	.11	.06
1990 Upper Deck	44	.50	.40	.20
1990 Upper Deck	206	.15	.11	.06
1990 Upper Deck	321	.15	.11	.06
1990 Upper Deck	494	.25	.20	.10
1990 Upper Deck Hockey Superstars	(5)	1.25	.90	.50
1990 Upper Deck Hockey Superstars	(7)	1.25	.90	.50
1991 Bowman	114	.25	.20	.10
1991 O-Pee-Chee Premier	51	.20	.15	.08
1991 O-Pee-Chee/Topps	346	.15	.11	.06
1991 Parkhurst	121	.25	.20	.10
1991 Parkhurst	213	.05	.04	.02
1991 Parkhurst	468	3.00	2.25	1.25
1991 Parkhurst	475	3.00	2.25	1.25
1991 Pinnacle	50	.50	.40	.20
1991 Pro Set	74	.20	.15	.08
1991 Pro Set	282	.10	.08	.04
1991 Pro Set	439	.15	.11	.06
1991 Pro Set	579	.10	.08	.04
1991 Pro Set Platinum	81	.15	.11	.06
1991 Pro Set Platinum PC	20	3.00	2.25	1.25
1991 Score American	285	.15	.11	.06
1991 Score American	373	.10	.08	.04
1991 Score American	420	.10	.08	.04
1991 Score Canadian	263	.10	.08	.04
1991 Score Canadian	310	.10	.08	.04
1991 Score Canadian	505	.20	.15	.08
1991 Score Canadian	635	.20	.15	.08
1991 Score Traded	85	.20	.12	.05
1991 Topps Stadium Club	111	.75	.60	.30
1991 Upper Deck	14	.20	.15	.08
1991 Upper Deck	246	.25	.20	.10
1991 Upper Deck	545	.25	.20	.10
1991 Upper Deck	620	.15	.11	.06
1992 Bowman	113	1.25	.90	.50
1992 Bowman	234	4.00	3.00	1.50
1992 Fleer Ultra	139	.30	.25	.12
1992 Fleer Ultra Award Winners	1	3.50	2.75	1.50
1992 Fleer Ultra Award Winners	10	3.50	2.75	1.50
1992 O-Pee-Chee	208	.25	.20	.10
1992 O-Pee-Chee	258	.60	.45	.25
1992 O-Pee-Chee Premier Star Performers	15	.25	.20	.10
1992 O-Pee-Chee 25th Anniversary Series	13	.25	.20	.10
1992 Parkhurst	111	.05	.04	.02
1992 Parkhurst Cherry Picks	4	15.00	11.00	6.00
1992 Pinnacle	1	.30	.25	.12
1992 Pro Set	111	.20	.15	.08
1992 Pro Set Award Winners	1	5.00	3.75	2.00
1992 Score	300	.20	.15	.08
1992 Score	431	.05	.04	.02
1992 Score	493	.05	.04	.02
1992 Score	521	.05	.04	.02
1992 Topps	258	.06	.05	.02
1992 Topps	274	.20	.15	.08
1992 Topps Stadium Club	241	.25	.20	.10
1992 Topps Stadium Club	443	.25	.20	.10

Stan Mikita

1992 Upper Deck	242	.20	.15	.08
1992 Upper Deck	432	.20	.15	.08
1992 Upper Deck	437	.20	.15	.08
1993 Donruss	222	.25	.20	.10
1993 Donruss Special Print	O	4.00	3.00	1.50
1993 Fleer PowerPlay	162	.20	.15	.08
1993 Fleer PowerPlay Point Leaders	9	.60	.45	.25
1993 Fleer Ultra	183	.20	.15	.08
1993 Fleer Ultra Premier Pivots	6	1.00	.70	.40
1993 Leaf	158	.25	.20	.10
1993 Parkhurst	127	.15	.11	.06
1993 Parkhurst Cherry's Playoff Heroes	4D	20.00	15.00	8.00
1993 Pinnacle	125	.25	.20	.10
1993 Pinnacle	238	.10	.08	.04
1993 Pinnacle Hockey Captains	15	11.00	8.25	4.50
1993 Score	200	.10	.08	.04
1993 Score U.S. Dynamic Duos	5	15.00	11.00	6.00
1993 Topps Premier	430	.10	.08	.04
1993 Topps Stadium Club	35	.20	.15	.08
1993 Upper Deck	51	.15	.11	.06
1993 Upper Deck	298	.10	.08	.04
1993 Upper Deck Gretzky's Great Ones	5	1.75	1.25	.70
1993 Upper Deck SP Inserts	103	.75	.60	.30
1994 Donruss	9	.30	.25	.12
1994 Donruss Ice Masters	7	3.00	2.25	1.25
1994 Fleer Flair	115	.60	.45	.25
1994 Fleer Flair Center Spotlight	8	4.00	3.00	1.50
1994 Fleer Ultra	140	.30	.25	.12
1994 Fleer Ultra All-Stars	4	.65	.50	.25
1994 Leaf	11	.20	.15	.08
1994 Leaf Gold Stars	5	35.00	26.00	14.00
1994 Leaf Limited	15	6.50	5.00	2.50
1994 O-Pee-Chee Premier	1	.15	.11	.06
1994 Parkhurst Crash the Game	27	8.00	6.00	3.25
1994 Parkhurst Vintage Parkhurst	33	.60	.45	.25
1994 Pinnacle Team Pinnacle	9	100.00	75.00	40.00
1994 Score Dream Team	16	8.50	6.50	3.50
1994 Score Franchise	15	13.00	9.75	5.25
1994 Topps Premier	1	.15	.11	.06
1994 Topps Stadium Club	1	.20	.15	.08
1994 Topps Stadium Club Dynasty and Destiny	2	20.00	15.00	8.00
1994 Topps Stadium Club Finest	3	6.00	4.50	2.50
1994 Upper Deck	62	.30	.25	.12
1994 Upper Deck	234	.30	.25	.12
1994 Upper Deck Award Predictor	4	6.00	4.50	2.50
1994 Upper Deck Electric Ice	62	12.00	9.00	4.75
1994 Upper Deck Electric Ice	234	6.00	4.50	2.50
1994 Upper Deck SP	51	1.00	.70	.40

1ST TEAM ALL-STAR
STAN MIKITA

Set	Card #	NM	EX	VG
1960 Topps	14	425.00	212.00	127.00
1961 Topps	36	180.00	90.00	54.00
1962 Topps	34	125.00	62.00	37.00
1963 Topps	36	95.00	47.50	28.50
1964 Topps	31	120.00	60.00	36.00
1964 Topps	106	275.00	137.00	82.00
1965 Topps	60	60.00	30.00	18.00
1966 Topps	62	50.00	25.00	15.00
1966 Topps	124	35.00	17.50	10.50
1967 Topps	64	30.00	15.00	9.00
1967 Topps	114	50.00	25.00	15.00
1967 Topps	126	30.00	15.00	9.00
1968 O-Pee-Chee	155	30.00	15.00	9.00
1968 O-Pee-Chee	202	16.00	8.00	4.75
1968 O-Pee-Chee	211	15.00	7.50	4.50
1968 Topps	20	20.00	10.00	6.00
1969 O-Pee-Chee	76	25.00	12.50	7.50
1969 Topps	76	16.00	8.00	4.75
1970 O-Pee-Chee	20	20.00	10.00	6.00
1970 O-Pee-Chee	240	9.00	4.50	2.75
1970 Topps	20	12.50	6.25	3.75
1971 O-Pee-Chee	125	16.00	8.00	4.75
1971 Topps	125	10.00	5.00	3.00
1972 O-Pee-Chee	156	5.00	2.50	1.50
1972 O-Pee-Chee	177	8.00	4.00	2.50
1972 O-Pee-Chee Team Canada	19	12.00	6.00	3.50
1972 Topps	56	6.00	3.00	1.75
1973 O-Pee-Chee	6	8.00	4.00	2.50
1973 Topps	145	6.00	3.00	1.75
1974 O-Pee-Chee	20	7.00	3.50	2.00
1974 O-Pee-Chee	69	1.00	.50	.30
1974 Topps	20	5.00	2.50	1.50
1974 Topps	69	2.00	1.00	.60
1975 O-Pee-Chee	30	5.00	2.50	1.50
1975 O-Pee-Chee	317	.50	.25	.15
1975 Topps	30	4.00	2.00	1.25
1975 Topps	317	2.00	1.00	.60
1976 O-Pee-Chee	225	3.00	1.50	.90
1976 Topps	225	2.75	1.50	.80
1977 O-Pee-Chee	195	4.00	2.00	1.25
1977 Topps	195	3.00	1.50	.90
1978 O-Pee-Chee	75	3.00	1.50	.90
1978 Topps	75	2.50	1.25	.70
1979 O-Pee-Chee	155	3.00	1.50	.90
1979 Topps	155	1.25	.60	.40

Set	Card #	MT	NM	EX
1990 Pro Set	405	.25	.20	.10
1990 Pro Set	655	.25	.20	.10

Non-sports card: A card picturing a subject other than sports. Non-sports cards have depicted movie stars, television shows, U.S. presidents, moments in history, entertainers and other subjects.

Notching: A card-grading term used to describe indentations along the edge of a card, sometimes caused by a rubber band. Notching decreases a card's value.

Off-center: A term used in card grading to describe a card that has uneven borders.

Mike Modano

Set	Card #	MT	NM	EX
1990 Bowman	188 (R)	1.00	.70	.40
1990 O-Pee-Chee	348 (R)	1.25	.90	.50
1990 O-Pee-Chee Premier	74 (R)	8.00	6.00	3.25
1990 Pro Set	142 (R)	.75	.60	.30
1990 Score	120 (R)	.80	.60	.30
1990 Score	327	.30	.25	.12
1990 Score Hockey's 100 Hottest Rising Stars	97	.10	.08	.04
1990 Topps	348 (R)	.60	.45	.25
1990 Upper Deck	46 (R)	2.50	2.00	1.00
1990 Upper Deck	346	.50	.40	.20
1991 Bowman	125	.30	.25	.12
1991 O-Pee-Chee/Topps	367	.15	.11	.06
1991 Parkhurst	81	.60	.45	.25
1991 Pinnacle	5	.80	.60	.30
1991 Pro Set	105	.15	.11	.06
1991 Pro Set Platinum	55	.25	.20	.10
1991 Score American	247	.15	.11	.06
1991 Score American	423	.10	.08	.04
1991 Score Canadian	313	.10	.08	.04
1991 Score Canadian	467	.15	.11	.06
1991 Topps Stadium Club	187	.75	.60	.30
1991 Upper Deck	32	.20	.15	.08
1991 Upper Deck	160	.60	.45	.25
1992 Bowman	151	1.50	1.25	.60
1992 Fleer Ultra	96	.30	.25	.12
1992 O-Pee-Chee	313	.10	.08	.04
1992 Parkhurst	75	.40	.30	.15
1992 Pinnacle	155	.40	.30	.15
1992 Pinnacle	260	.06	.05	.02
1992 Pinnacle Team 2000	2	2.00	1.50	.80
1992 Pro Set	76	.15	.11	.06
1992 Pro Set Gold Team Leaders	7	3.00	2.25	1.25
1992 Score	139	.20	.15	.08
1992 Score	427	.10	.08	.04
1992 Score USA Greats	5	6.00	4.50	2.50
1992 Topps	441	.06	.05	.02
1992 Topps Stadium Club	4	.40	.30	.15
1992 Upper Deck	305	.25	.20	.10
1993 Donruss	76	.35	.25	.14
1993 Donruss Special Print	F	4.50	3.50	1.75
1993 Fleer PowerPlay	63	.40	.30	.15
1993 Fleer PowerPlay Slapshot Artists	8	2.00	1.50	.80
1993 Fleer Ultra	194	.25	.20	.10
1993 Leaf	202	.30	.25	.12
1993 Parkhurst	49	.25	.20	.10
1993 Parkhurst First Overall	6	10.00	7.50	4.00
1993 Pinnacle	40	.35	.25	.14
1993 Pinnacle All-Stars	28	.30	.25	.12
1993 Pinnacle Team 2001	17	1.00	.70	.40
1993 Score	142	.20	.15	.08
1993 Score Franchise	5	8.00	6.00	3.25
1993 Topps Finest Hockey Card Series Roster	6	7.00	5.25	2.75
1993 Topps Premier	46	.15	.11	.06
1993 Topps Stadium Club	130	.30	.25	.12
1993 Topps Stadium Club All-Stars	21	12.00	9.00	4.75
1993 Upper Deck	294	.15	.11	.06
1993 Upper Deck	397	.15	.11	.06
1993 Upper Deck SP Inserts	38	1.00	.70	.40
1994 Donruss	193	.30	.25	.12
1994 Donruss Ice Masters	8	3.50	2.75	1.50
1994 Fleer Flair	43	.60	.45	.25
1994 Fleer Flair Center Spotlight	9	5.00	3.75	2.00
1994 Fleer Flair Scoring Power	7	5.00	3.75	2.00
1994 Fleer Ultra	55	.20	.15	.08
1994 Leaf	9	.25	.20	.10
1994 Leaf Gold Stars	10	32.00	24.00	13.00
1994 Leaf Limited	6	6.00	4.50	2.50
1994 O-Pee-Chee Premier	230	.15	.11	.06
1994 Parkhurst	308	.10	.08	.04
1994 Parkhurst Crash the Game	6	6.00	4.50	2.50
1994 Parkhurst Vintage Parkhurst	2	.80	.60	.30
1994 Pinnacle	3	.30	.25	.12
1994 Pinnacle Artist's Proofs	3	25.00	18.50	10.00
1994 Pinnacle Boomers	5	10.00	7.50	4.00
1994 Pinnacle Rink Collection	3	12.00	9.00	4.75
1994 Score	188	.15	.11	.06
1994 Score Dream Team	17	7.00	5.25	2.75
1994 Score Franchise	6	12.00	9.00	4.75
1994 Score Hockey Gold Line	188	1.50	1.25	.60
1994 Score 90-Plus Club	16	6.00	4.50	2.50
1994 Topps Premier	230	.15	.11	.06
1994 Topps Premier Finest Inserts	9	8.00	6.00	3.25
1994 Upper Deck	58	.35	.25	.14
1994 Upper Deck Electric Ice	58	15.00	11.00	6.00
1994 Upper Deck Ice Gallery	8	9.00	6.75	3.50
1994 Upper Deck SP	21	1.00	.70	.40

Alexander Mogilny

Set	Card #	MT	NM	EX
1990 Bowman	240 (R)	1.25	.90	.50
1990 O-Pee-Chee	42 (R)	1.25	.90	.50
1990 O-Pee-Chee Premier	75 (R)	8.00	6.00	3.25
1990 Pro Set	26 (R)	.70	.50	.30
1990 Score	43 (R)	1.00	.70	.40
1990 Topps	42 (R)	.75	.60	.30
1990 Upper Deck	24 (R)	3.00	2.25	1.25
1991 Bowman	30	.35	.25	.14
1991 O-Pee-Chee/Topps	171	.40	.30	.15
1991 Parkhurst	12	.75	.60	.30

Set	Card #	MT	NM	EX
1991 Pinnacle	163	1.50	1.25	.60
1991 Pro Set	16	.50	.40	.20
1991 Pro Set Platinum	14	.50	.40	.20
1991 Pro Set Platinum	283	.25	.20	.10
1991 Score American	236	.50	.40	.20
1991 Score Canadian	456	.50	.40	.20
1991 Topps Stadium Club	195	1.25	.90	.50
1991 Upper Deck	267	.75	.60	.30
1991 Upper Deck	618	.25	.20	.10
1991 Upper Deck Euro-Stars	2	3.00	1.50	.75
1992 Bowman	34	3.00	2.25	1.25
1992 Bowman	235	7.00	5.25	2.75
1992 Fleer Ultra	18	1.00	.70	.40
1992 Fleer Ultra Imports	16	7.00	5.25	2.75
1992 O-Pee-Chee	279	.50	.40	.20
1992 Parkhurst	13	.50	.40	.20
1992 Parkhurst	218	.05	.04	.02
1992 Pinnacle	77	.75	.60	.30
1992 Pinnacle Team 2000	28	4.50	3.50	1.75
1992 Pro Set	19	.50	.40	.20
1992 Score	248	.60	.45	.25
1992 Topps	382	.50	.40	.20
1992 Topps Stadium Club	320	.75	.60	.30
1992 Upper Deck	167	.50	.40	.20
1992 Upper Deck World Junior Grads	18	8.00	6.00	3.25
1993 Donruss	39	.50	.40	.20
1993 Donruss Elite	8	35.00	26.00	14.00
1993 Fleer PowerPlay	32	.60	.45	.25
1993 Fleer PowerPlay Global Greats	5	1.50	1.25	.60
1993 Fleer PowerPlay Point Leaders	10	1.00	.70	.40
1993 Fleer Ultra	238	.60	.45	.25
1993 Fleer Ultra All-Stars	5	4.50	3.50	1.75
1993 Fleer Ultra Red Light Specials	7	2.00	1.50	.80
1993 Fleer Ultra Speed Merchants	7	10.00	7.50	4.00
1993 Leaf	91	.60	.45	.25
1993 Leaf Gold All-Stars	8	13.00	9.75	5.25
1993 Leaf Hat Trick Artists	2	4.00	3.00	1.50
1993 OPC Premier Black Gold	10	15.00	11.00	6.00
1993 Parkhurst	21	.60	.45	.25
1993 Pinnacle	10	.50	.40	.20
1993 Pinnacle All-Stars	22	.50	.40	.20
1993 Pinnacle Nifty 50	2	16.00	12.00	6.50
1993 Pinnacle Team Pinnacle	12	35.00	26.00	14.00
1993 Pinnacle Team 2001	2	1.50	1.25	.60
1993 Score	222	.25	.20	.10
1993 Score	477	.25	.20	.10
1993 Score Dream Team	20	10.00	7.50	4.00
1993 Score International Stars	8	2.00	1.50	.80
1993 Score U.S. Dynamic Duos	2	12.00	9.00	4.75
1993 Topps Premier	148	.25	.20	.10
1993 Topps Premier	172	.20	.15	.08
1993 Topps Premier	245	.25	.20	.10
1993 Topps Stadium Club	91	.40	.30	.15
1993 Topps Stadium Club All-Stars	12	9.00	6.75	3.50
1993 Upper Deck	234	.30	.25	.12
1993 Upper Deck	488	.40	.30	.15
1993 Upper Deck Future Heroes	34	10.00	7.50	4.00
1993 Upper Deck Hat Tricks	15	1.50	1.25	.60
1993 Upper Deck NHL's Best	1	9.00	6.75	3.50
1993 Upper Deck Silver Skates Dye-Cut Hobby	10H	10.00	7.50	4.00
1993 Upper Deck SP Inserts	18	1.50	1.25	.60
1994 Donruss	92	.35	.25	.14
1994 Fleer Flair	20	.60	.45	.25
1994 Fleer Flair Scoring Power	8	6.00	4.50	2.50
1994 Fleer Ultra	26	.30	.25	.12
1994 Fleer Ultra All-Stars	5	1.00	.70	.40
1994 Leaf	256	.35	.25	.14
1994 Leaf Fire On Ice	10	6.00	4.50	2.50
1994 O-Pee-Chee Premier	50	.25	.20	.10
1994 Parkhurst	21	.35	.25	.14
1994 Pinnacle	125	.50	.40	.20
1994 Pinnacle Artist's Proofs	125	25.00	18.50	10.00
1994 Pinnacle Boomers	17	10.00	7.50	4.00
1994 Pinnacle Rink Collection	125	12.00	9.00	4.75
1994 Score	200	.35	.25	.14
1994 Score Hockey Gold Line	200	1.50	1.25	.60
1994 Topps Premier	50	.25	.20	.10
1994 Upper Deck Award Predictor	9	5.00	3.75	2.00
1994 Upper Deck SP	10	1.50	1.25	.60

Joe Mullen

JOE MULLEN • RW

Set	Card #	MT	NM	EX
1982 O-Pee-Chee	307 (R)	15.00	11.00	6.00
1983 O-Pee-Chee	317	5.00	3.75	2.00
1984 O-Pee-Chee	188	2.50	2.00	1.00
1984 O-Pee-Chee	367	.30	.25	.12
1984 Topps	133	1.50	1.25	.60
1985 O-Pee-Chee	7	2.00	1.50	.80
1985 Topps	7	.75	.60	.30
1986 O-Pee-Chee	44	1.00	.70	.40
1986 Topps	44	.60	.45	.25
1987 O-Pee-Chee	126	.60	.45	.25
1987 Topps	126	.12	.09	.05
1988 O-Pee-Chee	76	.15	.11	.06
1988 Topps	76	.25	.20	.10
1989 O-Pee-Chee	196	.07	.05	.03
1989 O-Pee-Chee Future Stars	23	.15	.11	.06
1989 Topps	196	.15	.11	.06
1990 Bowman	97	.04	.03	.02
1990 O-Pee-Chee	218	.05	.04	.02
1990 O-Pee-Chee Premier	77	.15	.11	.06
1990 Pro Set	343	.05	.04	.02
1990 Pro Set	508	.10	.08	.04
1990 Score	208	.05	.04	.02
1990 Score Hockey's 100 Hottest Rising Stars	88	.10	.08	.04
1990 Score Traded	7	.20	.15	.08
1990 Topps	218	.03	.02	.01
1990 Upper Deck	252	.10	.08	.04
1990 Upper Deck	423	.08	.06	.03
1991 Bowman	79	.05	.04	.02
1991 O-Pee-Chee Premier	153	.05	.04	.02
1991 O-Pee-Chee/Topps	69	.15	.11	.06
1991 Parkhurst	141	.05	.04	.02
1991 Pinnacle	176	.08	.06	.03

Set	Card #	MT	NM	EX
1991 Pro Set	191	.05	.04	.02
1991 Score American	268	.05	.04	.02
1991 Score American	379	.05	.04	.02
1991 Score Canadian	269	.05	.04	.02
1991 Score Canadian	488	.05	.04	.02
1991 Topps Stadium Club	7	.08	.06	.03
1991 Upper Deck	201	.05	.04	.02
1992 Bowman	58	.25	.20	.10
1992 Fleer Ultra	166	.06	.05	.02
1992 O-Pee-Chee	23	.05	.04	.02
1992 Parkhurst	368	.05	.04	.02
1992 Pinnacle	360	.06	.05	.02
1992 Pro Set	142	.05	.04	.02
1992 Pro Set	262	.05	.04	.02
1992 Score	3	.05	.04	.02
1992 Score USA Greats	9	4.00	3.00	1.50
1992 Topps	113	.06	.05	.02
1992 Topps Stadium Club	20	.05	.04	.02
1992 Upper Deck	144	.05	.04	.02
1993 Donruss	257	.10	.08	.04
1993 Fleer PowerPlay	192	.10	.08	.04
1993 Fleer Ultra	171	.07	.05	.03
1993 Leaf	300	.10	.08	.04
1993 Parkhurst	159	.10	.08	.04
1993 Pinnacle	122	.10	.08	.04
1993 Pinnacle	240	.08	.06	.03
1993 Score	7	.05	.04	.02
1993 Topps Premier	498	.05	.04	.02
1993 Topps Stadium Club	19	.05	.04	.02
1993 Upper Deck	186	.05	.04	.02
1994 Fleer Ultra	167	.05	.04	.02
1994 Parkhurst	180	.06	.05	.02
1994 Pinnacle	149	.10	.08	.04
1994 Pinnacle Artist's Proofs	149	5.00	3.75	2.00
1994 Pinnacle Rink Collection	149	3.00	2.25	1.25
1994 Score	57	.05	.04	.02
1994 Score Hockey Gold Line	57	.25	.20	.10
1994 Topps Stadium Club	50	.05	.04	.02
1990 Pro Set	371	.05	.04	.02
1990 Score	160	.05	.04	.02
1990 Score Hockey's 100 Hottest Rising Stars	71	.10	.08	.04
1990 Topps	245	.03	.02	.01
1990 Upper Deck	267	.08	.06	.03
1990 Upper Deck	311	.07	.05	.03
1991 Bowman	274	.05	.04	.02
1991 O-Pee-Chee Premier	86	.05	.04	.02
1991 O-Pee-Chee/Topps	22	.05	.04	.02
1991 Parkhurst	89	.05	.04	.02
1991 Pinnacle	3	.08	.06	.03
1991 Pro Set	134	.05	.04	.02
1991 Pro Set	412	.05	.04	.02
1991 Pro Set Platinum	66	.05	.04	.02
1991 Score American	110	.05	.04	.02
1991 Score American	331	.05	.04	.02
1991 Score Canadian	110	.05	.04	.02
1991 Score Canadian	361	.05	.04	.02
1991 Score Canadian	614	.05	.04	.02
1991 Score Traded	64	.05	.04	.02
1991 Topps Stadium Club	193	.08	.06	.03
1991 Upper Deck	149	.05	.04	.02
1991 Upper Deck	519	.05	.04	.02
1992 Bowman	138	.40	.30	.15
1992 Bowman	236	2.00	1.50	.80
1992 Fleer Ultra	107	.06	.05	.02
1992 O-Pee-Chee	327	.05	.04	.02
1992 Parkhurst	83	.05	.04	.02
1992 Parkhurst	504	.25	.20	.10
1992 Parkhurst Cherry Picks	5	10.00	7.50	4.00
1992 Pinnacle	111	.06	.05	.02
1992 Pro Set	87	.05	.04	.02
1992 Score	225	.05	.04	.02
1992 Score Sharpshooters	29	1.00	.50	.25
1992 Topps	490	.06	.05	.02
1992 Topps Stadium Club	387	.05	.04	.02
1992 Upper Deck	180	.05	.04	.02
1993 Donruss	177	.10	.08	.04
1993 Fleer PowerPlay	131	.10	.08	.04
1993 Fleer Ultra	21	.07	.05	.03
1993 Fleer Ultra All-Stars	9	2.50	2.00	1.00
1993 Leaf	182	.10	.08	.04
1993 OPC Premier Black Gold	24	8.00	6.00	3.25
1993 Parkhurst	378	.10	.08	.04
1993 Pinnacle	180	.10	.08	.04
1993 Pinnacle All-Stars	7	.20	.15	.08
1993 Score	234	.05	.04	.02
1993 Score Canadian Dynamic Duos	6	8.50	6.50	3.50
1993 Topps Premier	509	.05	.04	.02
1993 Topps Stadium Club	67	.05	.04	.02
1993 Upper Deck	148	.05	.04	.02
1993 Upper Deck SP Inserts	80	.30	.25	.12
1994 Donruss	255	.08	.06	.03
1994 Fleer Flair	89	.25	.20	.10
1994 Leaf	163	.10	.08	.04
1994 Parkhurst Vintage Parkhurst	4	.25	.20	.10
1994 Pinnacle	82	.10	.08	.04
1994 Pinnacle Artist's Proofs	82	5.00	3.75	2.00
1994 Pinnacle Northern Lights	2	5.50	4.25	2.25
1994 Pinnacle Rink Collection	82	3.00	2.25	1.25
1994 Score	146	.05	.04	.02
1994 Score Check-It	10	7.50	5.75	3.00
1994 Score Hockey Gold Line	146	.25	.20	.10
1994 Topps Stadium Club	130	.05	.04	.02
1994 Upper Deck	66	.10	.08	.04
1994 Upper Deck Electric Ice	66	3.50	2.75	1.50
1994 Upper Deck Ice Gallery	9	4.00	3.00	1.50
1994 Upper Deck SP	40	.30	.25	.12

Kirk Muller

Set	Card #	MT	NM	EX
1985 O-Pee-Chee	84 (R)	15.00	11.00	6.00
1985 Topps	84 (R)	9.00	6.75	3.50
1986 O-Pee-Chee	94	4.00	3.00	1.50
1986 Topps	94	2.50	2.00	1.00
1987 O-Pee-Chee	157	2.00	1.50	.80
1987 Topps	157	.75	.60	.30
1988 O-Pee-Chee	84	1.00	.70	.40
1988 Topps	84	.50	.40	.20
1989 O-Pee-Chee	117	.07	.05	.03
1989 Topps	117	.20	.15	.08
1990 Bowman	82	.04	.03	.02
1990 O-Pee-Chee	245	.05	.04	.02
1990 O-Pee-Chee Premier	78	.15	.11	.06
1990 Pro Set	172	.07	.05	.03

Larry Murphy

Set	Card #	MT	NM	EX
1981 O-Pee-Chee	148 (R)	15.00	11.00	6.00
1981 O-Pee-Chee	393	3.00	2.25	1.25
1981 Topps	100 (R)	8.00	6.00	3.25
1982 O-Pee-Chee	158	4.00	3.00	1.50
1983 O-Pee-Chee	159	2.00	1.50	.80
1984 O-Pee-Chee	204	.75	.60	.30
1985 O-Pee-Chee	236	1.00	.70	.40
1986 O-Pee-Chee	185	.60	.45	.25
1986 Topps	185	.25	.20	.10
1987 O-Pee-Chee	133	.12	.09	.05
1987 O-Pee-Chee Hockey Leaders	31	.30	.25	.12
1987 Topps	133	.04	.03	.02
1988 O-Pee-Chee	141	.15	.11	.06
1988 Topps	141	.07	.05	.03
1989 O-Pee-Chee	128	.07	.05	.03
1989 Topps	128	.05	.04	.02
1990 Bowman	177	.04	.03	.02
1990 O-Pee-Chee	47	.05	.04	.02
1990 Pro Set	143	.05	.04	.02
1990 Score	206	.05	.04	.02
1990 Topps	47	.03	.02	.01
1990 Upper Deck	229	.08	.06	.03
1991 Bowman	78	.05	.04	.02
1991 O-Pee-Chee/Topps	277	.05	.04	.02
1991 Parkhurst	358	.05	.04	.02
1991 Pinnacle	143	.20	.15	.08
1991 Pro Set	193	.05	.04	.02
1991 Pro Set Platinum	213	.05	.04	.02
1991 Score American	31	.05	.04	.02
1991 Score Canadian	31	.05	.04	.02
1991 Topps Stadium Club	112	.10	.08	.04
1991 Upper Deck	302	.15	.11	.06
1992 Bowman	153	.25	.20	.10
1992 Fleer Ultra	167	.06	.05	.02
1992 O-Pee-Chee	209	.05	.04	.02
1992 Parkhurst	137	.05	.04	.02
1992 Pinnacle	292	.06	.05	.02
1992 Pro Set	146	.05	.04	.02
1992 Score	45	.05	.04	.02
1992 Topps	447	.06	.05	.02
1992 Topps Stadium Club	375	.05	.04	.02
1992 Upper Deck	241	.05	.04	.02
1993 Donruss	263	.10	.08	.04
1993 Fleer PowerPlay	193	.10	.08	.04
1993 Fleer Ultra	184	.07	.05	.03
1993 Leaf	16	.10	.08	.04
1993 Leaf Gold All-Stars	2	6.00	4.50	2.50
1993 Parkhurst	162	.10	.08	.04
1993 Pinnacle	52	.10	.08	.04
1993 Score	23	.05	.04	.02
1993 Topps Premier	173	.05	.04	.02
1993 Topps Premier	189	.05	.04	.02
1993 Topps Premier Black Gold	23	2.00	1.50	.80
1993 Topps Stadium Club	283	.05	.04	.02
1993 Upper Deck	374	.06	.05	.02
1994 Donruss	27	.08	.06	.03
1994 Fleer Flair	137	.25	.20	.10
1994 Fleer Ultra	168	.08	.06	.03
1994 Leaf	249	.15	.11	.06
1994 O-Pee-Chee Premier	10	.10	.08	.04
1994 O-Pee-Chee Premier	492	.04	.04	.04
1994 Parkhurst	179	.06	.05	.02
1994 Pinnacle	215	.10	.08	.04
1994 Pinnacle Artist's Proofs	215	7.00	5.25	2.75
1994 Pinnacle Rink Collection	215	4.00	3.00	1.50
1994 Score	5	.05	.04	.02
1994 Score Hockey Gold Line	5	.35	.25	.14
1994 Topps Premier	10	.10	.08	.04
1994 Topps Premier	492	.04	.04	.04
1994 Upper Deck	99	.10	.08	.04
1994 Upper Deck Electric Ice	99	3.50	2.75	1.50

Petr Nedved

Set	Card #	MT	NM	EX
1990 O-Pee-Chee Premier	81 (R)	4.00	3.00	1.50
1990 Pro Set	402 (R)	.60	.45	.25
1990 Pro Set	643	.75	.60	.30
1990 Score Traded	50 (R)	.75	.60	.30
1990 Upper Deck	351	1.00	.70	.40
1990 Upper Deck	353 (R)	1.50	1.25	.60
1991 Bowman	324	.25	.20	.10
1991 O-Pee-Chee/Topps	141	.25	.20	.10
1991 Parkhurst	178	.05	.04	.02
1991 Pinnacle	192	.20	.15	.08
1991 Pro Set	235	.15	.11	.06
1991 Score American	124	.15	.11	.06
1991 Score Canadian	124	.15	.11	.06
1991 Topps Stadium Club	280	.40	.30	.15
1991 Upper Deck	227	.20	.15	.08
1991 Upper Deck Euro-Stars	5	.60	.40	.20
1992 Bowman	396	1.00	.70	.40
1992 Fleer Ultra	226	.25	.20	.10
1992 Fleer Ultra Imports	17	5.00	3.75	2.00
1992 O-Pee-Chee	89	.15	.11	.06
1992 Parkhurst	418	.10	.08	.04
1992 Parkhurst	449	.08	.06	.03
1992 Pinnacle	127	.20	.15	.08
1992 Pinnacle	249	.65	.50	.25
1992 Score	101	.25	.20	.10
1992 Topps	422	.06	.05	.02
1992 Topps Stadium Club	457	.30	.25	.12
1992 Upper Deck	263	.25	.20	.10
1993 Donruss	356	.10	.08	.04
1993 Donruss	486	.10	.08	.04
1993 Fleer PowerPlay	254	.20	.15	.08
1993 Fleer PowerPlay	490	.15	.11	.06
1993 Fleer Ultra	68	.15	.11	.06
1993 Leaf	78	.20	.15	.08
1993 O-Pee-Chee Team Canada	15	4.00	3.00	1.50

1993 Pinnacle	106	.15	.11	.06
1993 Score	231	.15	.11	.06
1993 Score International Stars	22	.75	.60	.30
1993 Topps Stadium Club	18	.15	.11	.06
1994 Fleer Ultra	141	.07	.05	.03
1994 Parkhurst Vintage Parkhurst	44	.50	.40	.20
1994 Pinnacle	58	.10	.08	.04
1994 Pinnacle Artist's Proofs	58	12.00	9.00	4.75
1994 Pinnacle Rink Collection	58	6.00	4.50	2.50
1994 Score Canadian Team	2	8.50	6.50	3.50
1994 Topps Premier	286	3.50	3.50	3.50
1994 Topps Stadium Club	205	.10	.08	.04
1994 Upper Deck	164	.20	.15	.08
1994 Upper Deck Electric Ice	164	3.50	2.75	1.50

Cam Neely

Set	Card #	MT	NM	EX
1984 O-Pee-Chee	327	40.00	30.00	16.00
1985 O-Pee-Chee	228	15.00	11.00	6.00
1986 O-Pee-Chee	250	8.00	6.00	3.25
1987 O-Pee-Chee	69	5.00	3.75	2.00
1987 Topps	69	4.00	3.00	1.50
1988 O-Pee-Chee	58	3.00	2.25	1.25
1988 Topps	58	1.00	.70	.40
1989 O-Pee-Chee	15	.75	.60	.30
1989 Topps	15	.40	.30	.15
1990 Bowman	29	.15	.11	.06
1990 O-Pee-Chee	69	.15	.11	.06
1990 O-Pee-Chee	201	.15	.11	.06
1990 O-Pee-Chee Premier	82	.75	.60	.30
1990 Pro Set	11	.20	.15	.08
1990 Pro Set	358	.07	.05	.03
1990 Score	4	.20	.15	.08
1990 Score	323	.15	.11	.06
1990 Score	340	.10	.08	.04
1990 Score Hockey's 100 Hottest Rising Stars	67	.10	.08	.04
1990 Topps	69	.20	.15	.08
1990 Topps	201	.15	.11	.06
1990 Upper Deck	156	.25	.20	.10
1990 Upper Deck	493	.25	.20	.10
1991 Bowman	348	.05	.04	.02
1991 Bowman	366	.05	.04	.02
1991 O-Pee-Chee Premier	107	.10	.08	.04
1991 O-Pee-Chee/Topps	192	.12	.09	.05
1991 O-Pee-Chee/Topps	266	.05	.04	.02
1991 Pinnacle	78	.08	.06	.03
1991 Pinnacle B	6	45.00	34.00	18.00
1991 Pro Set	5	.05	.04	.02
1991 Pro Set	300	.05	.04	.02
1991 Pro Set Platinum	1	.05	.04	.02
1991 Score American	6	.05	.04	.02
1991 Score American	301	.05	.04	.02

1991 Score Canadian	6	.05	.04	.02
1991 Score Canadian	305	.05	.04	.02
1991 Topps Stadium Club	64	.10	.08	.04
1991 Upper Deck	234	.05	.04	.02
1992 Bowman	62	.60	.45	.25
1992 Fleer Ultra	7	.15	.11	.06
1992 O-Pee-Chee	174	.05	.04	.02
1992 Parkhurst	248	.05	.04	.02
1992 Parkhurst Cherry Picks	14	15.00	11.00	6.00
1992 Pinnacle	25	.06	.05	.02
1992 Pinnacle	232	.06	.05	.02
1992 Pro Set	8	.05	.04	.02
1992 Score	10	.05	.04	.02
1992 Topps	32	.15	.11	.06
1992 Upper Deck	86	.05	.04	.02
1993 Donruss	29	.15	.11	.06
1993 Donruss Elite	4	35.00	26.00	14.00
1993 Fleer PowerPlay	22	.15	.11	.06
1993 Fleer Ultra	138	.07	.05	.03
1993 Leaf	99	.10	.08	.04
1993 Parkhurst	10	.10	.08	.04
1993 Pinnacle	30	.20	.15	.08
1993 Score	342	.05	.04	.02
1993 Score U.S. Dynamic Duos	3	10.00	7.50	4.00
1993 Topps Premier	254	.05	.04	.02
1993 Topps Stadium Club	216	.05	.04	.02
1993 Upper Deck	356	.08	.06	.03
1993 Upper Deck SP Inserts	10	.40	.30	.15
1994 Donruss	269	.20	.15	.08
1994 Fleer Flair	11	.40	.30	.15
1994 Fleer Ultra	13	.15	.11	.06
1994 Fleer Ultra NHL Award Winners	8	1.00	.70	.40
1994 Fleer Ultra Ultra Power	6	9.00	6.75	3.50
1994 Leaf	267	.20	.15	.08
1994 Leaf Gold Stars	9	28.00	21.00	11.00
1994 O-Pee-Chee Premier	129	.10	.08	.04
1994 Parkhurst	11	.15	.11	.06
1994 Parkhurst Vintage Parkhurst	64	.50	.40	.20
1994 Pinnacle	65	.30	.25	.12
1994 Pinnacle Artist's Proofs	65	15.00	11.00	6.00
1994 Pinnacle Boomers	12	8.00	6.00	3.25
1994 Pinnacle Rink Collection	65	8.00	6.00	3.25
1994 Pinnacle Team Pinnacle	12	70.00	52.00	28.00
1994 Score	4	.15	.11	.06
1994 Score Check-It	8	8.00	6.00	3.25
1994 Score Dream Team	23	6.00	4.50	2.50
1994 Score Franchise	2	10.00	7.50	4.00
1994 Score Hockey Gold Line	4	1.50	1.25	.60
1994 Topps Premier	129	.10	.08	.04
1994 Topps Premier Finest Inserts	8	6.00	4.50	2.50
1994 Topps Stadium Club	8	.15	.11	.06
1994 Topps Stadium Club	266	.10	.08	.04
1994 Upper Deck SP	6	.50	.40	.20

O-Pee-Chee: Topps' Canadian licensee. O-Pee-Chee makes and sells a baseball card set that resembles Topps' set but has fewer cards, and a hockey card set that resembles Topps but has more cards. O-Pee-Chee cards can sometimes be distinguished from Topps cards by the bilingual (French-English) backs.

Out of register: A term used to describe a printing error in which the various colors are not correctly superimposed upon one another, thereby decreasing the value of the card.

Bernie Nicholls

Set	Card #	MT	NM	EX
1983 O-Pee-Chee	160 (R)	9.00	6.75	3.50
1984 Topps	67	1.25	.90	.50
1985 O-Pee-Chee	148	1.50	1.25	.60
1985 Topps	148	1.50	1.25	.60
1986 O-Pee-Chee	159	1.00	.70	.40
1986 Topps	159	.25	.20	.10
1987 O-Pee-Chee	183	.50	.40	.20
1987 Topps	183	.40	.30	.15
1988 O-Pee-Chee	169	.75	.60	.30
1988 Topps	169	.40	.30	.15
1989 O-Pee-Chee	47	.50	.40	.20
1989 Topps	47	.20	.15	.08
1990 Bowman	221	.10	.08	.04
1990 O-Pee-Chee	13	.10	.08	.04
1990 O-Pee-Chee Premier	83	.15	.11	.06
1990 Pro Set	204	.25	.20	.10
1990 Pro Set	352	.10	.08	.04
1990 Score	9	.10	.08	.04
1990 Score Hockey's 100 Hottest Rising Stars	5	.10	.08	.04
1990 Topps	13	.10	.08	.04
1990 Upper Deck	34	.30	.25	.12
1991 Bowman	76	.05	.04	.02
1991 O-Pee-Chee/Topps	174	.05	.04	.02
1991 Parkhurst	278	.05	.04	.02
1991 Pinnacle	300	.20	.15	.08
1991 Pro Set	166	.05	.04	.02
1991 Pro Set	386	.05	.04	.02
1991 Pro Set Platinum	174	.05	.04	.02
1991 Score American	240	.05	.04	.02
1991 Score Canadian	460	.05	.04	.02
1991 Topps Stadium Club	245	.08	.06	.03
1991 Upper Deck	356	.10	.08	.04
1991 Upper Deck	566	.10	.08	.04
1992 Bowman	161	.25	.20	.10
1992 Fleer Ultra	64	.06	.05	.02
1992 O-Pee-Chee	52	.05	.04	.02
1992 Parkhurst	49	.05	.04	.02
1992 Parkhurst	328	.05	.04	.02
1992 Pinnacle	120	.06	.05	.02
1992 Pro Set	52	.05	.04	.02
1992 Score	340	.05	.04	.02
1992 Topps	438	.06	.05	.02
1992 Topps Stadium Club	448	.05	.04	.02
1992 Upper Deck	290	.05	.04	.02
1992 Upper Deck	624	.10	.08	.04
1993 Donruss	188	.10	.08	.04
1993 Fleer PowerPlay	139	.10	.08	.04
1993 Fleer Ultra	86	.07	.05	.03
1993 Leaf	169	.10	.08	.04
1993 Parkhurst	117	.10	.08	.04
1993 Pinnacle	165	.10	.08	.04
1993 Score	19	.05	.04	.02
1993 Topps Premier	274	.05	.04	.02
1993 Topps Stadium Club	111	.05	.04	.02
1993 Upper Deck	58	.05	.04	.02
1993 Upper Deck SP Inserts	85	.30	.25	.12

Set	Card #	MT	NM	EX
1994 Fleer Flair	35	.25	.20	.10
1994 Fleer Ultra	42	.08	.06	.03
1994 Score	74	.05	.04	.02
1994 Score	245	.05	.04	.02
1994 Score Hockey Gold Line	74	.25	.20	.10
1994 Score Hockey Gold Line	245	.25	.20	.10
1994 Upper Deck	83	.10	.08	.04
1994 Upper Deck Electric Ice	83	4.00	3.00	1.50

Rob Niedermayer

Set	Card #	MT	NM	EX
1992 Upper Deck	593 (R)	2.00	1.50	.80
1993 Donruss	134	1.00	.70	.40
1993 Donruss Rated Rookies	4	4.00	3.00	1.50
1993 Donruss Special Print	I	7.00	5.25	2.75
1993 Fleer PowerPlay	349	1.00	.70	.40
1993 Fleer PowerPlay Rookie Standouts	8	2.50	2.00	1.00
1993 Fleer Ultra	330	.50	.40	.20
1993 Fleer Ultra Speed Merchants	8	10.00	7.50	4.00
1993 Fleer Ultra Wave of the Future	11	3.00	2.25	1.25
1993 Leaf	293	.75	.60	.30
1993 Leaf Freshman Phenoms	6	5.00	3.75	2.00
1993 Parkhurst	246	.75	.60	.30
1993 Parkhurst Calder Candidates	4CC	10.00	7.50	4.00
1993 Parkhurst East-West Stars	5E	12.00	9.00	4.75
1993 Parkhurst US Canada Gold-Foiled	5	10.00	7.50	4.00
1993 Pinnacle	439	.75	.60	.30
1993 Pinnacle Super Rookies	4	6.00	4.50	2.50
1993 Score	592	.40	.30	.15
1993 Topps Premier	270	.40	.30	.15
1993 Topps Stadium Club	449	.50	.40	.20
1993 Upper Deck	98	.75	.60	.30
1993 Upper Deck Program of Excellence	11E	11.00	8.25	4.50
1993 Upper Deck Silver Skates Dye-Cut Hobby	4H	10.00	7.50	4.00
1993 Upper Deck SP Inserts	58	1.00	.70	.40
1994 Donruss	113	.40	.30	.15
1994 Fleer Flair	67	.40	.30	.15
1994 Fleer Ultra	84	.50	.40	.20
1994 Leaf	225	.30	.25	.12
1994 O-Pee-Chee Premier Finest Inserts	9	7.00	5.25	2.75
1994 Parkhurst	294	.30	.25	.12

1994 Parkhurst Vintage Parkhurst	22	.50	.40	.20
1994 Pinnacle	168	.50	.40	.20
1994 Pinnacle Artist's Proofs	168	15.00	11.00	6.00
1994 Pinnacle Rink Collection	168	8.00	6.00	3.25
1994 Topps Stadium Club	22	.25	.20	.10
1994 Topps Stadium Club	117	.15	.11	.06
1994 Upper Deck SP	30	.30	.25	.12

Joe Nieuwendyk

Set	Card #	MT	NM	EX
1988 O-Pee-Chee	16 (R)	10.00	7.50	4.00
1988 Topps	16 (R)	7.50	5.75	3.00
1989 O-Pee-Chee	138	1.25	.90	.50
1989 Topps	138	.60	.45	.25
1990 Bowman	91	.15	.11	.06
1990 O-Pee-Chee	87	.30	.25	.12
1990 O-Pee-Chee Premier	84	.50	.40	.20
1990 Pro Set	42	3.00	2.25	1.25
1990 Pro Set	344	.15	.11	.06
1990 Score	30	.40	.30	.15
1990 Score Hockey's 100 Hottest Rising Stars	45	.10	.08	.04
1990 Topps	87	.30	.25	.12
1990 Upper Deck	26	.40	.30	.15
1991 Bowman	252	.05	.04	.02
1991 O-Pee-Chee Premier	48	.05	.04	.02
1991 O-Pee-Chee/Topps	223	.15	.11	.06
1991 Parkhurst	23	.05	.04	.02
1991 Pinnacle	54	.08	.06	.03
1991 Pro Set	29	.05	.04	.02
1991 Pro Set	569	.05	.04	.02
1991 Pro Set Platinum	18	.05	.04	.02
1991 Score American	170	.05	.04	.02
1991 Score Canadian	170	.05	.04	.02
1991 Topps Stadium Club	60	.08	.06	.03
1991 Upper Deck	263	.05	.04	.02
1992 Bowman	59	.60	.45	.25
1992 Fleer Ultra	25	.06	.05	.02
1992 O-Pee-Chee	354	.05	.04	.02
1992 Parkhurst	21	.05	.04	.02
1992 Pinnacle	31	.06	.05	.02
1992 Pro Set	26	.05	.04	.02
1992 Score	193	.05	.04	.02
1992 Topps	105	.06	.05	.02
1992 Topps Stadium Club	37	.05	.04	.02
1992 Upper Deck	128	.05	.04	.02
1993 Donruss	48	.10	.08	.04
1993 Fleer PowerPlay	39	.10	.08	.04
1993 Fleer Ultra	130	.07	.05	.03
1993 Leaf	126	.10	.08	.04
1993 Parkhurst	31	.10	.08	.04
1993 Pinnacle	198	.10	.08	.04
1993 Pinnacle Hockey Captains	4	5.00	3.75	2.00
1993 Score	199	.05	.04	.02

1993 Score Canadian Dynamic Duos	4	8.50	6.50	3.50
1993 Topps Premier	205	.05	.04	.02
1993 Topps Stadium Club	96	.05	.04	.02
1993 Upper Deck	396	.05	.04	.02
1993 Upper Deck SP Inserts	23	.30	.25	.12
1994 Donruss	56	.08	.06	.03
1994 Leaf	228	.10	.08	.04
1994 Parkhurst	33	.06	.05	.02
1994 Parkhurst Crash the Game	4	5.00	3.75	2.00
1994 Pinnacle	90	.10	.08	.04
1994 Pinnacle Artist's Proofs	90	5.00	3.75	2.00
1994 Pinnacle Rink Collection	90	3.00	2.25	1.25
1994 Score	159	.05	.04	.02
1994 Score Hockey Gold Line	159	.25	.20	.10
1994 Topps Stadium Club	166	.05	.04	.02
1994 Upper Deck SP	13	.30	.25	.12

Owen Nolan

Set	Card #	MT	NM	EX
1990 O-Pee-Chee Premier	86 (R)	2.50	2.00	1.00
1990 Pro Set	401 (R)	.50	.40	.20
1990 Pro Set	635	.75	.60	.30
1990 Score	435 (R)	.50	.40	.20
1990 Score Traded	80	.75	.60	.30
1990 Upper Deck	352 (R)	1.00	.70	.40
1991 Bowman	134	.20	.15	.08
1991 O-Pee-Chee Premier	193	.25	.20	.10
1991 O-Pee-Chee/Topps	64	.15	.11	.06
1991 Parkhurst	143	.10	.08	.04
1991 Pinnacle	156	.40	.30	.15
1991 Pro Set	196	.05	.04	.02
1991 Pro Set Platinum	101	.25	.20	.10
1991 Score American	143	.20	.15	.08
1991 Score Canadian	143	.25	.20	.10
1991 Topps Stadium Club	259	.50	.40	.20
1991 Upper Deck	367	.40	.30	.15
1991 Upper Deck	619	.15	.11	.06
1992 Bowman	237	2.00	1.50	.80
1992 Bowman	328	.75	.60	.30
1992 Fleer Ultra	177	.25	.20	.10
1992 O-Pee-Chee	382	.15	.11	.06
1992 Parkhurst	145	.05	.04	.02
1992 Parkhurst	455	.10	.08	.04
1992 Parkhurst Cherry Picks	13	9.00	6.75	3.50
1992 Pinnacle	6	.20	.15	.08
1992 Pinnacle Team 2000	10	.75	.60	.30
1992 Pro Set	153	.15	.11	.06
1992 Score	286	.05	.04	.02
1992 Score Sharpshooters	12	1.00	.50	.25
1992 Topps	349	.15	.11	.06
1992 Topps Stadium Club	78	.20	.15	.08

Set	Card #	MT	NM	EX
1992 Upper Deck	321	.25	.20	.10
1993 Donruss	279	.10	.08	.04
1993 Fleer PowerPlay	201	.20	.15	.08
1993 Fleer Ultra	154	.15	.11	.06
1993 Leaf	42	.20	.15	.08
1993 Parkhurst	163	.15	.11	.06
1993 Parkhurst First Overall	4	6.00	4.50	2.50
1993 Pinnacle	151	.10	.08	.04
1993 Pinnacle Team 2001	28	.50	.40	.20
1993 Score	32	.10	.08	.04
1993 Topps Finest Hockey Card Series Roster	4	4.00	3.00	1.50
1993 Topps Premier	267	.08	.06	.03
1993 Topps Stadium Club	397	.10	.08	.04
1993 Upper Deck	175	.15	.11	.06
1993 Upper Deck Hat Tricks	16	.60	.45	.25
1993 Upper Deck SP Inserts	128	.30	.25	.12
1994 Donruss	45	.08	.06	.03
1994 Fleer Ultra	177	.08	.06	.03
1994 Leaf	144	.10	.08	.04
1994 Parkhurst Vintage Parkhurst	43	.20	.15	.08
1994 Pinnacle	76	.10	.08	.04
1994 Pinnacle Artist's Proofs	76	5.00	3.75	2.00
1994 Pinnacle Rink Collection	76	3.00	2.25	1.25
1994 Topps Stadium Club	102	.05	.04	.02
1994 Upper Deck	103	.10	.08	.04
1994 Upper Deck Electric Ice	103	3.50	2.75	1.50
1994 Upper Deck SP	63	.30	.25	.12

Adam Oates

ADAM OATES
BOSTON BRUINS • CENTER

Set	Card #	MT	NM	EX
1987 O-Pee-Chee	123 (R)	40.00	30.00	16.00
1987 Topps	123 (R)	25.00	18.50	10.00
1988 O-Pee-Chee	161	7.00	5.25	2.75
1988 Topps	161	3.50	2.75	1.50
1989 O-Pee-Chee	185	.50	.40	.20
1989 Topps	185	.75	.60	.30
1990 Bowman	16	.15	.11	.06
1990 O-Pee-Chee	149	.05	.04	.02
1990 O-Pee-Chee Premier	88	1.00	.70	.40
1990 Pro Set	269	.20	.15	.08
1990 Score	85	.12	.09	.05
1990 Score Hockey's 100 Hottest Rising Stars	41	.10	.08	.04
1990 Topps	149	.20	.15	.08
1990 Upper Deck	173	.40	.30	.15
1990 Upper Deck	483	.10	.08	.04
1991 Bowman	384	.15	.11	.06
1991 O-Pee-Chee Premier	7	.15	.11	.06
1991 O-Pee-Chee/Topps	265	.05	.04	.02
1991 O-Pee-Chee/Topps	448	.12	.09	.05
1991 Parkhurst	155	.05	.04	.02
1991 Parkhurst	233	.25	.20	.10
1991 Pinnacle	6	.25	.20	.10
1991 Pinnacle	378	.15	.11	.06
1991 Pro Set	219	.10	.08	.04
1991 Pro Set	291	.05	.04	.02
1991 Pro Set Platinum	113	.05	.04	.02
1991 Score American	238	.10	.08	.04
1991 Score Canadian	458	.10	.08	.04
1991 Score Hot Card	6	2.00	1.50	.80
1991 Topps Stadium Club	108	.25	.20	.10
1991 Upper Deck	252	.15	.11	.06
1991 Upper Deck	627	.10	.08	.04
1992 Bowman	213	2.50	2.00	1.00
1992 Bowman	258	.75	.60	.30
1992 Fleer Ultra	8	.20	.15	.08
1992 O-Pee-Chee	172	.25	.20	.10
1992 O-Pee-Chee	272	.10	.08	.04
1992 O-Pee-Chee Premier Star Performers	13	.25	.20	.10
1992 O-Pee-Chee 25th Anniversary Series	20	.25	.20	.10
1992 Parkhurst	4	.05	.04	.02
1992 Pinnacle	40	.20	.15	.08
1992 Pro Set	3	.15	.11	.06
1992 Score	250	.05	.04	.02
1992 Topps	475	.15	.11	.06
1992 Topps Stadium Club	188	.35	.25	.14
1992 Topps Stadium Club	245	.10	.08	.04
1992 Upper Deck	133	.20	.15	.08
1992 Upper Deck	637	.10	.08	.04
1993 Donruss	18	.25	.20	.10
1993 Donruss Special Print	B	5.00	4.50	2.50
1993 Fleer PowerPlay	23	.25	.20	.10
1993 Fleer PowerPlay Point Leaders	11	.60	.45	.25
1993 Fleer Ultra	156	.15	.11	.06
1993 Fleer Ultra Adam Oates	1	3.00	2.25	1.25
1993 Fleer Ultra Adam Oates	2	3.00	2.25	1.25
1993 Fleer Ultra Adam Oates	3	3.00	2.25	1.25
1993 Fleer Ultra Adam Oates	4	3.00	2.25	1.25
1993 Fleer Ultra Adam Oates	5	3.00	2.25	1.25
1993 Fleer Ultra Adam Oates	6	3.00	2.25	1.25
1993 Fleer Ultra Adam Oates	7	3.00	2.25	1.25
1993 Fleer Ultra Adam Oates	8	3.00	2.25	1.25
1993 Fleer Ultra Adam Oates	9	3.00	2.25	1.25
1993 Fleer Ultra Adam Oates	10	3.00	2.25	1.25
1993 Fleer Ultra All-Stars	7	4.00	3.00	1.50
1993 Fleer Ultra Premier Pivots	7	1.00	.70	.40
1993 Leaf	235	.25	.20	.10
1993 Leaf Hat Trick Artists	8	3.00	2.25	1.25
1993 OPC Premier Black Gold	3	10.00	7.50	4.00
1993 Parkhurst	11	.20	.15	.08
1993 Pinnacle	185	.20	.15	.08
1993 Pinnacle All-Stars	9	.35	.25	.14
1993 Score	125	.15	.11	.06
1993 Score	478	.10	.08	.04
1993 Score Dream Team	17	6.00	4.50	2.50
1993 Score U.S. Dynamic Duos	3	10.00	7.50	4.00
1993 Topps Premier	50	.15	.11	.06
1993 Topps Premier	74	.05	.04	.02
1993 Topps Premier Black Gold	5	2.50	2.00	1.00
1993 Topps Stadium Club	93	.10	.08	.04
1993 Topps Stadium Club All-Stars	11	5.00	3.75	2.00

Set	Card #			
1993 Upper Deck	226	.10	.08	.04
1993 Upper Deck	286	.10	.08	.04
1993 Upper Deck	327	.10	.08	.04
1993 Upper Deck Hat Tricks	5	1.00	.70	.40
1993 Upper Deck Silver Skates Dye-Cut Hobby	6H	7.50	5.75	3.00
1993 Upper Deck SP Inserts	11	.65	.50	.25
1994 Fleer Flair	12	.40	.30	.15
1994 Fleer Flair Hot Numbers	6	12.00	9.00	4.75
1994 Fleer Ultra	14	.12	.09	.05
1994 Leaf	305	.20	.15	.08
1994 Leaf Limited	2	6.00	4.50	2.50
1994 Parkhurst	311	.10	.08	.04
1994 Parkhurst Vintage Parkhurst	46	.40	.30	.15
1994 Pinnacle	120	.30	.25	.12
1994 Pinnacle Artist's Proofs	120	18.00	13.50	7.25
1994 Pinnacle Rink Collection	120	9.00	6.75	3.50
1994 Score	141	.15	.11	.06
1994 Score Hockey Gold Line	141	1.50	1.25	.60
1994 Score 90-Plus Club	3	6.00	4.50	2.50
1994 Upper Deck	11	.20	.15	.08
1994 Upper Deck Electric Ice	11	10.00	7.50	4.00
1994 Upper Deck Scoring Predictor	12	8.00	6.00	3.25
1994 Upper Deck Scoring Predictor	26	6.00	4.50	2.50
1994 Upper Deck SP	7	.70	.50	.30

Bobby Orr

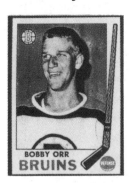

Set	Card #	NM	EX	VG
1966 Topps	35 (R)	2600.	1300.	780.00
1967 Topps	92 (R)	800.00	400.00	240.00
1967 Topps	118	250.00	125.00	75.00
1967 Topps	128	250.00	125.00	75.00
1968 O-Pee-Chee	2	375.00	187.00	112.00
1968 O-Pee-Chee	200	160.00	80.00	48.00
1968 O-Pee-Chee	214	160.00	80.00	48.00
1968 Topps	2	200.00	100.00	60.00
1969 O-Pee-Chee	24	175.00	87.00	52.00
1969 O-Pee-Chee	209	80.00	40.00	24.00
1969 O-Pee-Chee	212	75.00	37.00	22.00
1969 Topps	24	125.00	62.00	37.00
1970 O-Pee-Chee	3	130.00	65.00	39.00
1970 O-Pee-Chee	236	55.00	27.00	16.50
1970 O-Pee-Chee	246	60.00	30.00	18.00
1970 O-Pee-Chee	248	55.00	27.00	16.50
1970 O-Pee-Chee	249	55.00	27.00	16.50
1970 O-Pee-Chee	252	50.00	25.00	15.00
1970 Topps	3	75.00	37.00	22.00
1971 O-Pee-Chee	100	80.00	40.00	24.00
1971 O-Pee-Chee	245	50.00	25.00	15.00
1971 O-Pee-Chee	251	50.00	25.00	15.00
1971 Topps	2	15.00	7.50	4.50
1971 Topps	3	15.00	7.50	4.50
1971 Topps	100	50.00	25.00	15.00
1972 O-Pee-Chee	58	25.00	12.50	7.50
1972 O-Pee-Chee	129	55.00	27.00	16.50
1972 O-Pee-Chee	227	35.00	17.50	10.50
1972 O-Pee-Chee	280	25.00	12.50	7.50
1972 O-Pee-Chee	283	25.00	12.50	7.50
1972 Topps	100	30.00	15.00	9.00
1972 Topps	122	20.00	10.00	6.00
1973 O-Pee-Chee	30	42.00	21.00	12.50
1973 Topps	150	30.00	15.00	9.00
1974 O-Pee-Chee	2	8.00	4.00	2.50
1974 O-Pee-Chee	28	9.00	4.50	2.75
1974 O-Pee-Chee	100	35.00	17.50	10.50
1974 O-Pee-Chee	130	17.00	8.50	5.00
1974 O-Pee-Chee	248	20.00	10.00	6.00
1974 Topps	2	4.50	2.25	1.25
1974 Topps	28	8.00	4.00	2.50
1974 Topps	100	25.00	12.50	7.50
1974 Topps	130	12.00	6.00	3.50
1974 Topps	248	13.00	6.50	4.00
1975 O-Pee-Chee	100	32.00	16.00	9.50
1975 O-Pee-Chee	209	6.00	3.00	1.75
1975 O-Pee-Chee	210	7.50	3.75	2.25
1975 O-Pee-Chee	288	15.00	7.50	4.50
1975 O-Pee-Chee	314	8.00	4.00	2.50
1975 Topps	100	20.00	10.00	6.00
1975 Topps	209	5.50	2.75	1.75
1975 Topps	210	6.50	3.25	2.00
1975 Topps	288	10.00	5.00	3.00
1975 Topps	314	6.00	3.00	1.75
1976 O-Pee-Chee	213	25.00	12.50	7.50
1976 Topps	213	18.00	9.00	5.50
1977 O-Pee-Chee	251	20.00	10.00	6.00
1977 Topps	251	15.00	7.50	4.50
1978 O-Pee-Chee	300	35.00	17.50	10.50

Set	Card #	MT	NM	EX
1991 Score Bobby Orr	(1)	10.00	7.50	4.00
1991 Score Bobby Orr	(2)	200.00	150.00	80.00
1991 Score Bobby Orr	(3)	10.00	7.50	4.00
1991 Score Bobby Orr	(4)	200.00	150.00	80.00
1991 Score Bobby Orr	(5)	10.00	7.50	4.00
1991 Score Bobby Orr	(6)	200.00	150.00	80.00
1991 Score Bobby Orr	(7)	10.00	7.50	4.00
1991 Score Bobby Orr	(8)	200.00	150.00	80.00

Bernie Parent

Set	Card #	NM	EX	VG
1968 O-Pee-Chee	89 (R)	100.00	50.00	30.00
1968 Topps	89 (R)	70.00	35.00	21.00
1969 O-Pee-Chee	89	45.00	22.00	13.50

1969 Topps	89	25.00	12.50	7.50
1970 O-Pee-Chee	78	20.00	10.00	6.00
1970 Topps	78	15.00	7.50	4.50
1971 O-Pee-Chee	131	17.00	8.50	5.00
1971 Topps	131	9.00	4.50	2.75
1973 O-Pee-Chee	66	6.00	3.00	1.75
1973 Topps	66	5.00	2.50	1.50
1974 O-Pee-Chee	4	1.00	.50	.30
1974 O-Pee-Chee	60	5.00	2.50	1.50
1974 O-Pee-Chee	138	2.00	1.00	.60
1974 O-Pee-Chee	249	1.50	.70	.45
1974 O-Pee-Chee	251	1.50	.70	.45
1974 Topps	4	2.00	1.00	.60
1974 Topps	60	3.00	1.50	.90
1974 Topps	138	3.00	1.50	.90
1974 Topps	249	2.00	1.00	.60
1974 Topps	251	2.00	1.00	.60
1975 O-Pee-Chee	213	5.00	2.50	1.50
1975 O-Pee-Chee	291	2.50	1.25	.70
1975 O-Pee-Chee	300	4.00	2.00	1.25
1975 Topps	213	5.00	2.50	1.50
1975 Topps	291	1.50	.70	.45
1975 Topps	300	3.00	1.50	.90
1976 O-Pee-Chee	10	3.00	1.50	.90
1976 Topps	10	2.50	1.25	.70
1977 O-Pee-Chee	8	3.00	1.50	.90
1977 O-Pee-Chee	65	1.75	.90	.50
1977 Topps	8	1.75	.90	.50
1977 Topps	65	1.50	.70	.45
1978 O-Pee-Chee	15	1.75	.90	.50
1978 O-Pee-Chee	68	2.00	1.00	.60
1978 O-Pee-Chee	70	3.00	1.50	.90
1978 Topps	15	1.25	.60	.40
1978 Topps	68	1.50	.70	.45
1978 Topps	70	2.50	1.25	.70
1979 O-Pee-Chee	6	2.50	1.25	.70
1979 O-Pee-Chee	8	3.00	1.50	.90
1979 Topps	6	1.50	.70	.45
1979 Topps	8	1.50	.70	.45

Set	Card #	MT	NM	EX
1992 O-Pee-Chee	217	.20	.15	.08
1992 O-Pee-Chee 25th Anniversary Series	1	.40	.30	.15
1992 Parkhurst	470	.10	.08	.04
1992 Pinnacle	246	.25	.20	.10

Rob Pearson

Set	Card #	MT	NM	EX
1991 O-Pee-Chee Premier	65 (R)	.20	.15	.08
1991 Parkhurst	169 (R)	.05	.04	.02
1991 Pinnacle	304 (R)	.25	.20	.10
1991 Pro Set	562 (R)	.25	.20	.10
1991 Score American	311 (R)	.20	.15	.08
1991 Score Canadian	341 (R)	.20	.15	.08
1991 Score Canadian	385	1.25	.90	.50
1991 Upper Deck	598 (R)	.20	.15	.08
1992 Bowman	381	1.00	.70	.40
1992 Fleer Ultra	423	.25	.20	.10
1992 O-Pee-Chee	136	.05	.04	.02
1992 Parkhurst	414	.25	.20	.10

1992 Pinnacle	245	.25	.20	.10
1992 Pinnacle	287	.25	.20	.10
1992 Pinnacle Team 2000	23	1.50	1.25	.60
1992 Pro Set	191	.10	.08	.04
1992 Pro Set Rookie Goal Leaders	9	3.00	2.25	1.25
1992 Score	333	.05	.04	.02
1992 Topps	168	.20	.15	.08
1992 Topps Stadium Club	377	.25	.20	.10
1992 Upper Deck	318	.25	.20	.10
1993 Donruss	339	.10	.08	.04
1993 Fleer PowerPlay	453	.25	.20	.10
1993 Fleer Ultra	434	.10	.08	.04
1993 Leaf	174	.10	.08	.04
1993 Parkhurst	474	.20	.15	.08
1993 Pinnacle	89	.10	.08	.04
1993 Score	96	.05	.04	.02
1993 Topps Premier	137	.05	.04	.02
1993 Topps Stadium Club	498	.20	.15	.08
1993 Upper Deck	48	.05	.04	.02
1994 Score	137	.05	.04	.02
1994 Score Hockey Gold Line	137	.25	.20	.10
1994 Upper Deck	180	.10	.08	.04
1994 Upper Deck Electric Ice	180	3.50	2.75	1.50

Gilbert Perreault

GIL PERREAULT   CENTER
BUFFALO SABRES

Set	Card #	NM	EX	VG
1970 O-Pee-Chee	131 (R)	90.00	45.00	27.00
1970 Topps	131 (R)	50.00	25.00	15.00
1971 O-Pee-Chee	60	30.00	15.00	9.00
1971 O-Pee-Chee	246	14.00	7.00	4.25
1971 Topps	60	18.00	9.00	5.50
1972 O-Pee-Chee	136	14.00	7.00	4.25
1972 O-Pee-Chee Team Canada	22	10.00	5.00	3.00
1972 Topps	120	6.00	3.00	1.75
1973 O-Pee-Chee	70	10.00	5.00	3.00
1973 Topps	70	6.00	3.00	1.75
1974 O-Pee-Chee	25	6.00	3.00	1.75
1974 Topps	25	4.00	2.00	1.25
1975 O-Pee-Chee	10	5.00	2.50	1.50
1975 Topps	10	3.00	1.50	.90
1976 O-Pee-Chee	2	3.00	1.50	.90
1976 O-Pee-Chee	3	3.00	1.50	.90
1976 O-Pee-Chee	180	3.00	1.50	.90
1976 O-Pee-Chee	214	2.00	1.00	.60
1976 O-Pee-Chee	380	.45	.25	.14
1976 Topps	2	2.00	1.00	.60
1976 Topps	3	2.00	1.00	.60
1976 Topps	180	3.00	1.50	.90
1976 Topps	214	1.50	.70	.45
1977 O-Pee-Chee	7	1.50	.70	.45
1977 O-Pee-Chee	210	2.50	1.25	.70
1977 Topps	7	1.50	.70	.45
1977 Topps	210	1.75	.90	.50
1978 O-Pee-Chee	130	1.00	.50	.30
1978 Topps	130	1.00	.50	.30
1979 O-Pee-Chee	180	1.00	.50	.30

Set	Card #			
1979 Topps	180	1.00	.50	.30
1980 O-Pee-Chee	80	1.00	.50	.30
1980 Topps	80	.75	.40	.25

Set	Card #	MT	NM	EX
1981 O-Pee-Chee	30	.80	.60	.30
1982 O-Pee-Chee	25	.20	.15	.08
1983 O-Pee-Chee	67	.50	.40	.20
1984 O-Pee-Chee	24	.15	.11	.06
1984 Topps	19	.25	.20	.10
1985 O-Pee-Chee	160	.40	.30	.15
1985 Topps	160	1.00	.70	.40
1986 O-Pee-Chee	79	.90	.70	.35
1986 Topps	79	.15	.11	.06
1990 Score	355	.07	.05	.03
1991 Pro Set	596	.05	.04	.02

Pierre Pilote

Set	Card #	NM	EX	VG
1957 Topps	22 (R)	125.00	62.00	37.00
1958 Topps	36	60.00	30.00	18.00
1959 Topps	2	35.00	17.50	10.50
1959 Topps	60	18.00	9.00	5.50
1960 Topps	65	25.00	12.50	7.50
1961 Topps	24	20.00	10.00	6.00
1962 Topps	28	20.00	10.00	6.00
1963 Topps	25	14.00	10.50	5.50
1964 Topps	59	240.00	120.00	72.00
1964 Topps	109	65.00	32.00	19.50
1965 Topps	56	10.00	5.00	3.00
1966 Topps	59	18.00	9.00	5.50
1966 Topps	123	18.00	9.00	5.50
1967 Topps	62	16.00	8.00	4.75
1967 Topps	122	16.00	8.00	4.75
1968 O-Pee-Chee	124	4.00	2.00	1.25
1968 Topps	124	4.50	2.25	1.25

Jacques Plante

Set	Card #	NM	EX	VG
1955 Parkhurst	50 (R)	700.00	350.00	210.00

1955 Parkhurst	71	60.00	30.00	18.00
1957 Parkhurst	15	350.00	175.00	105.00
1958 Parkhurst	21	40.00	20.00	12.00
1958 Parkhurst	22	250.00	125.00	75.00
1958 Parkhurst	26	30.00	15.00	9.00
1958 Parkhurst	39	30.00	15.00	9.00
1959 Parkhurst	41	160.00	80.00	48.00
1960 Parkhurst	53	125.00	62.00	37.00
1961 Parkhurst	49	100.00	50.00	30.00
1962 Parkhurst	49	90.00	45.00	27.00
1963 Topps	45	100.00	50.00	30.00
1964 Parkhurst	100	30.00	30.00	30.00
1964 Topps	68	150.00	75.00	45.00
1968 O-Pee-Chee	181	40.00	20.00	12.00
1969 O-Pee-Chee	180	30.00	15.00	9.00
1969 O-Pee-Chee	207	30.00	15.00	9.00
1970 O-Pee-Chee	222	20.00	10.00	6.00
1971 O-Pee-Chee	195	18.00	9.00	5.50
1971 O-Pee-Chee	256	12.00	6.00	3.50
1971 Topps	6	10.00	5.00	3.00
1971 Topps	10	14.00	7.00	4.25
1972 O-Pee-Chee	92	15.00	7.50	4.50
1972 Topps	24	9.00	4.50	2.75
1974 O-Pee-Chee WHA	64	35.00	17.50	10.50
1975 O-Pee-Chee WHA	34	35.00	17.50	10.50

Set	Card #	MT	NM	EX
1991 Pro Set	341	.05	.04	.02
1993 Parkhurst Parkie Reprints	43	20.00	15.00	8.00
1993 Parkhurst Parkie Reprints	67	20.00	15.00	8.00

Denis Potvin

Set	Card #	NM	EX	VG
1974 O-Pee-Chee	195 (R)	45.00	22.00	13.50
1974 O-Pee-Chee	233	3.00	1.50	.90
1974 O-Pee-Chee	252	10.00	5.00	3.00
1974 Topps	195 (R)	27.00	13.50	8.10
1974 Topps	233	2.00	1.00	.60
1974 Topps	252	8.00	4.00	2.50
1975 O-Pee-Chee	275	15.00	7.50	4.50
1975 O-Pee-Chee	287	5.00	2.50	1.50
1975 O-Pee-Chee	323	2.50	1.25	.70
1975 Topps	275	9.00	4.50	2.75
1975 Topps	287	3.00	1.50	.90
1975 Topps	323	.75	.40	.25
1976 O-Pee-Chee	5	3.00	1.50	.90
1976 O-Pee-Chee	170	8.00	4.00	2.50
1976 O-Pee-Chee	389	.45	.25	.14
1976 Topps	5	2.50	1.25	.70
1976 Topps	170	5.00	2.50	1.50
1977 O-Pee-Chee	10	5.00	2.50	1.50
1977 Topps	10	3.00	1.50	.90
1978 O-Pee-Chee	334	1.75	.90	.50
1978 Topps	245	2.00	1.00	.60
1979 O-Pee-Chee	70	2.00	1.00	.60
1979 Topps	70	1.50	.70	.45
1980 O-Pee-Chee	120	1.50	.70	.45

Set	Card #	MT	NM	EX
1980 Topps	120	1.50	.70	.45
1981 O-Pee-Chee	199	1.00	.70	.40
1981 O-Pee-Chee	209	.60	.45	.25
1981 Topps	27	.50	.40	.20
1981 Topps	130	.40	.30	.15
1982 O-Pee-Chee	210	.75	.60	.30
1983 O-Pee-Chee	2	.25	.20	.10
1983 O-Pee-Chee	16	.50	.40	.20
1984 O-Pee-Chee	134	.60	.45	.25
1984 O-Pee-Chee	216	.40	.30	.15
1984 O-Pee-Chee	389	.50	.40	.20
1984 Topps	100	.25	.20	.10
1984 Topps	162	.20	.15	.08
1985 O-Pee-Chee	25	.25	.20	.10
1985 Topps	25	.90	.70	.35
1986 O-Pee-Chee	129	1.00	.70	.40
1986 Topps	129	.75	.60	.30
1987 O-Pee-Chee	1	.50	.40	.20
1987 Topps	1	.25	.20	.10
1990 Pro Set	656	.20	.15	.08
1990 Upper Deck	515	.20	.15	.08
1992 O-Pee-Chee	57	.20	.15	.08
1992 O-Pee-Chee 25th Anniversary Series	7	.30	.25	.12

Felix Potvin

Set	Card #	MT	NM	EX
1990 Upper Deck	458 (R)	12.00	9.00	4.75
1991 Parkhurst	398	2.75	2.00	1.00
1991 Pinnacle	345	3.50	2.75	1.50
1991 Upper Deck	460	2.00	1.50	.80
1992 Bowman	77	9.50	7.25	3.75
1992 Fleer Ultra	213	2.00	1.50	.80
1992 O-Pee-Chee	73	1.00	.70	.40
1992 O-Pee-Chee Premier	114	1.50	1.25	.60
1992 O-Pee-Chee Premier Top Rookies	4	5.00	3.00	1.50
1992 Parkhurst	187	2.00	1.50	.80
1992 Parkhurst	507	3.00	2.25	1.25
1992 Pinnacle	364	2.50	2.00	1.00
1992 Pinnacle Team 2000	5	6.50	5.00	2.50
1992 Pro Set	242	1.25	.90	.50
1992 Score	472	1.00	.70	.40
1992 Score	501	.75	.60	.30
1992 Topps	3	1.00	.70	.40
1992 Upper Deck	79	1.25	.90	.50
1992 Upper Deck Calder Candidates	3	12.00	9.00	4.75
1993 Donruss	343	1.25	.90	.50
1993 Donruss Elite	3	50.00	37.00	20.00
1993 Donruss Ice Kings	6	6.00	4.50	2.50
1993 Donruss Special Print	W	11.00	10.50	5.50
1993 Fleer PowerPlay	246	1.00	.70	.40
1993 Fleer PowerPlay Gamebreakers	7	4.00	3.00	1.50
1993 Fleer PowerPlay Netminders	5	13.00	9.75	5.25

Set	Card #	MT	NM	EX
1993 Fleer PowerPlay Rising Stars	3	6.00	4.50	2.50
1993 Fleer PowerPlay Second-Year Stars	8	3.00	2.25	1.25
1993 Fleer Ultra	30	1.00	.70	.40
1993 Leaf	409	1.00	.70	.40
1993 Leaf Gold All-Stars	10	9.00	6.75	3.50
1993 Leaf Gold Rookies	4	8.00	6.00	3.25
1993 Leaf Painted Warriors	1	10.00	7.50	4.00
1993 OPC Premier Black Gold	17	20.00	15.00	8.00
1993 Parkhurst	202	1.00	.70	.40
1993 Parkhurst	237	.50	.40	.20
1993 Parkhurst Cherry's Playoff Heroes	14D	40.00	30.00	16.00
1993 Parkhurst East-West Stars	9W	25.00	18.50	10.00
1993 Pinnacle	190	1.00	.70	.40
1993 Pinnacle Team 2001	5	4.00	3.00	1.50
1993 Score	5	.50	.40	.20
1993 Score	484	.40	.30	.15
1993 Topps Premier	30	.60	.45	.25
1993 Topps Premier	111	.30	.25	.12
1993 Topps Premier	126	.40	.30	.15
1993 Topps Premier	385	.40	.30	.15
1993 Topps Premier Black Gold	3	6.00	4.50	2.50
1993 Topps Stadium Club	280	1.00	.70	.40
1993 Topps Stadium Club Finest	5	10.00	7.50	4.00
1993 Upper Deck	159	1.00	.70	.40
1993 Upper Deck	285	.50	.40	.20
1993 Upper Deck Future Heroes	28	20.00	15.00	8.00
1993 Upper Deck Next in Line	6	10.00	7.50	4.00
1993 Upper Deck SP Inserts	160	5.00	3.75	2.00
1994 Donruss	12	.75	.60	.30
1994 Donruss Elite Series	8	25.00	18.50	10.00
1994 Donruss Masked Marvels	7	8.00	6.00	3.25
1994 Fleer Flair	184	1.25	.90	.50
1994 Fleer Ultra	219	.75	.60	.30
1994 Fleer Ultra All-Stars	12	1.25	.90	.50
1994 Fleer Ultra Premier Pad Men	4	24.00	18.00	9.50
1994 Leaf	186	.75	.60	.30
1994 O-Pee-Chee Premier	238	.35	.25	.14
1994 Parkhurst	229	.65	.50	.25
1994 Pinnacle	83	.75	.60	.30
1994 Pinnacle Artist's Proofs	83	45.00	34.00	18.00
1994 Pinnacle Goaltending Greats	8	12.00	9.00	4.75
1994 Pinnacle Northern Lights	9	20.00	15.00	8.00
1994 Pinnacle Rink Collection	83	28.00	21.00	11.00
1994 Pinnacle Team Pinnacle	1	75.00	56.00	30.00
1994 Score	160	.45	.35	.20
1994 Score Dream Team	2	15.00	11.00	6.00
1994 Score Hockey Gold Line	160	3.00	2.25	1.25
1994 Topps Premier	238	.35	.25	.14
1994 Topps Stadium Club	15	.50	.40	.20
1994 Topps Stadium Club	185	.25	.20	.10
1994 Upper Deck SP	80	6.00	4.50	2.50

Plastic sheet: A polyethelyne or polyvinyl sheet designed to store baseball cards, the most common being the nine-pocket sheet (which fits today's standard-sized cards). The sheets have prepunched holes on the left side which allows them to be placed in a three-ring binder.

Bob Probert

Chris Pronger

Set	Card #	MT	NM	EX
1988 O-Pee-Chee	181 (R)	4.00	3.00	1.50
1988 Topps	181 (R)	2.00	1.50	.80
1990 Pro Set	76	.12	.09	.05
1990 Score	143	.12	.09	.05
1990 Upper Deck	448	.80	.60	.30
1991 Bowman	55	.10	.08	.04
1991 O-Pee-Chee/Topps	198	.05	.04	.02
1991 Parkhurst	272	.05	.04	.02
1991 Pinnacle	183	.20	.15	.08
1991 Pro Set	61	.05	.04	.02
1991 Pro Set Platinum	34	.10	.08	.04
1991 Score American	73	.10	.08	.04
1991 Score Canadian	73	.10	.08	.04
1991 Topps Stadium Club	59	.20	.15	.08
1991 Upper Deck	239	.10	.08	.04
1992 Bowman	85	.30	.25	.12
1992 Fleer Ultra	53	.06	.05	.02
1992 O-Pee-Chee	252	.05	.04	.02
1992 Parkhurst	41	.05	.04	.02
1992 Parkhurst Cherry Picks	9	10.00	7.50	4.00
1992 Pinnacle	56	.06	.05	.02
1992 Pro Set	46	.05	.04	.02
1992 Score	52	.05	.04	.02
1992 Score Sharpshooters	17	1.00	.50	.25
1992 Topps	63	.06	.05	.02
1992 Topps Stadium Club	355	.05	.04	.02
1992 Upper Deck	248	.05	.04	.02
1993 Donruss	104	.10	.08	.04
1993 Fleer PowerPlay	335	.08	.06	.03
1993 Fleer Ultra	309	.07	.05	.03
1993 Leaf	186	.10	.08	.04
1993 Parkhurst	333	.10	.08	.04
1993 Pinnacle	7	.10	.08	.04
1993 Score	59	.05	.04	.02
1993 Topps Premier	177	.05	.04	.02
1993 Topps Stadium Club	137	.05	.04	.02
1993 Upper Deck	200	.10	.08	.04
1993 Upper Deck SP Inserts	46	.30	.25	.12
1994 Parkhurst	71	.06	.05	.02

Parkhurst: A Canadian card manufacturer that produced NHL hockey sets in the 1950s and 1960s. Collectors often refer to Parkhurst cards as "Parkies."

Play Ball: The name of baseball cards produced by Gum Inc. (1939-1941).

Polyethylene: A type of plastic used to make card sheets and other collectors' supplies. Very flexible, but not as clear as other types of plastic. Safer than PVC for very long-term card storage.

Set	Card #	MT	NM	EX
1992 Upper Deck	591 (R)	2.00	1.50	.80
1993 Donruss	150	1.00	.70	.40
1993 Donruss Rated Rookies	3	4.00	3.00	1.50
1993 Donruss Special Print	J	6.00	4.50	2.50
1993 Fleer PowerPlay	354	1.00	.70	.40
1993 Fleer PowerPlay Rookie Standouts	12	2.00	1.50	.80
1993 Fleer Ultra	339	.50	.40	.20
1993 Fleer Ultra Wave of the Future	14	4.00	3.00	1.50
1993 Leaf	257	.75	.60	.30
1993 Leaf Freshman Phenoms	2	5.00	3.75	2.00
1993 Parkhurst	249	.75	.60	.30
1993 Parkhurst Calder Candidates	2CC	10.00	7.50	4.00
1993 Parkhurst Cherry's Playoff Heroes	13D	20.00	15.00	8.00
1993 Pinnacle	456	1.00	.70	.40
1993 Pinnacle Super Rookies	2	6.00	4.50	2.50
1993 Score	586	.40	.30	.15
1993 Topps Premier	485	.35	.25	.14
1993 Topps Stadium Club	290	.75	.60	.30
1993 Upper Deck	190	.50	.40	.20
1993 Upper Deck Silver Skates Dye-Cut Hobby	5H	10.00	7.50	4.00
1993 Upper Deck SP Inserts	64	1.00	.70	.40
1994 Donruss	215	.35	.25	.14
1994 Fleer Flair	73	.75	.60	.30
1994 Fleer Ultra	91	.40	.30	.15
1994 Fleer Ultra Ultra All-Rookies	7	10.00	7.50	4.00
1994 Leaf	268	.35	.25	.14
1994 Leaf Gold Rookies	9	3.50	2.75	1.50
1994 Leaf Limited	10	5.00	3.75	2.00
1994 O-Pee-Chee Premier	198	.20	.15	.08
1994 O-Pee-Chee Premier Finest Inserts	11	6.50	5.00	2.50
1994 Parkhurst	274	.30	.25	.12
1994 Pinnacle	11	.50	.40	.20
1994 Pinnacle Artist's Proofs	11	15.00	11.00	6.00
1994 Pinnacle Rink Collection	11	8.00	6.00	3.25
1994 Score	252	.20	.15	.08
1994 Score Hockey Gold Line	252	.50	.40	.20
1994 Topps Premier	198	.20	.15	.08
1994 Topps Stadium Club	111	.15	.11	.06
1994 Topps Stadium Club	235	.30	.25	.12
1994 Topps Stadium Club Dynasty and Destiny	5	5.00	3.75	2.00
1994 Upper Deck	52	.40	.30	.15

1994 Upper Deck Electric Ice	52	10.00	7.50	4.00
1994 Upper Deck SP	33	.60	.45	.25

Mark Recchi

Set	Card #	MT	NM	EX
1990 Bowman	206 (R)	1.00	.70	.40
1990 O-Pee-Chee	280 (R)	1.25	.90	.50
1990 Pro Set	239 (R)	.75	.60	.30
1990 Score	186 (R)	.70	.50	.30
1990 Score Hockey's 100 Hottest Rising Stars	81	.10	.08	.04
1990 Topps	280 (R)	1.00	.70	.40
1990 Upper Deck	178 (R)	3.00	2.25	1.25
1990 Upper Deck	487	.30	.25	.12
1991 Bowman	83	.30	.25	.12
1991 O-Pee-Chee/Topps	196	.25	.20	.10
1991 Parkhurst	134	.60	.45	.25
1991 Parkhurst	347	.75	.60	.30
1991 Pinnacle	151	.75	.60	.30
1991 Pinnacle	360	.25	.20	.10
1991 Pro Set	184	.30	.25	.12
1991 Pro Set	313	.10	.08	.04
1991 Pro Set Platinum	97	.25	.20	.10
1991 Score American	145	.25	.20	.10
1991 Score Canadian	145	.25	.20	.10
1991 Topps Stadium Club	256	1.00	.70	.40
1991 Upper Deck	346	.75	.60	.30
1992 Bowman	314	2.00	1.50	.80
1992 Fleer Ultra	158	.35	.25	.14
1992 O-Pee-Chee	373	.25	.20	.10
1992 Parkhurst	130	.30	.25	.12
1992 Pinnacle	80	.40	.30	.15
1992 Pro Set	131	.20	.15	.08
1992 Score	180	.25	.20	.10
1992 Score Sharpshooters	18	1.00	.50	.25
1992 Topps	267	.06	.05	.02
1992 Topps	410	.15	.11	.06
1992 Topps Stadium Club	183	.40	.30	.15
1992 Upper Deck	327	.25	.20	.10
1993 Donruss	252	.25	.20	.10
1993 Fleer PowerPlay	184	.35	.25	.14
1993 Fleer PowerPlay Point Leaders	12	.60	.45	.25
1993 Fleer Ultra	236	.25	.20	.10
1993 Fleer Ultra Red Light Specials	8	1.00	.70	.40
1993 Leaf	205	.25	.20	.10
1993 Parkhurst	149	.25	.20	.10
1993 Pinnacle	50	.25	.20	.10
1993 Pinnacle All-Stars	6	.40	.30	.15
1993 Pinnacle Nifty 50	13	14.00	10.50	5.50
1993 Pinnacle Team 2001	30	1.00	.70	.40
1993 Score	150	.15	.11	.06
1993 Score	442	.15	.11	.06
1993 Score U.S. Dynamic Duos	1	45.00	34.00	18.00

1993 Topps Premier	230	.15	.11	.06
1993 Topps Stadium Club	136	.25	.20	.10
1993 Topps Stadium Club All-Stars	18	8.00	6.00	3.25
1993 Upper Deck	222	.20	.15	.08
1993 Upper Deck	300	.10	.08	.04
1993 Upper Deck	350	.15	.11	.06
1993 Upper Deck SP Inserts	117	.60	.45	.25
1994 Donruss	121	.20	.15	.08
1994 Fleer Flair	130	.40	.30	.15
1994 Fleer Ultra	158	.10	.08	.04
1994 Leaf	89	.25	.20	.10
1994 O-Pee-Chee Premier	90	.10	.08	.04
1994 Parkhurst	165	.20	.15	.08
1994 Parkhurst	315	.15	.11	.06
1994 Pinnacle	53	.30	.25	.12
1994 Pinnacle Artist's Proofs	53	15.00	11.00	6.00
1994 Pinnacle Rink Collection	53	8.00	6.00	3.25
1994 Score	50	.20	.15	.08
1994 Score Hockey Gold Line	50	1.00	.70	.40
1994 Score 90-Plus Club	7	5.00	3.75	2.00
1994 Topps Premier	90	.10	.08	.04
1994 Topps Premier Finest Inserts	21	6.00	4.50	2.50
1994 Upper Deck	94	.20	.15	.08
1994 Upper Deck Electric Ice	94	10.00	7.50	4.00
1994 Upper Deck SP	58	1.00	.70	.40

Glenn Resch

Set	Card #	NM	EX	VG
1974 O-Pee-Chee	353 (R)	15.00	7.50	4.50
1975 O-Pee-Chee	145	5.00	2.50	1.50
1975 Topps	145	3.50	1.75	1.00
1976 O-Pee-Chee	6	1.50	.70	.45
1976 O-Pee-Chee	250	2.00	1.00	.60
1976 Topps	6	2.00	1.00	.60
1976 Topps	250	1.00	.50	.30
1977 O-Pee-Chee	6	1.50	.70	.45
1977 O-Pee-Chee	50	1.00	.50	.30
1977 Topps	6	.40	.20	.12
1977 Topps	50	1.00	.50	.30
1978 O-Pee-Chee	105	1.00	.50	.30
1978 Topps	105	1.00	.50	.30
1979 O-Pee-Chee	6	2.50	1.25	.70
1979 O-Pee-Chee	20	.50	.25	.15
1979 Topps	6	1.50	.70	.45
1979 Topps	20	.50	.25	.15
1980 O-Pee-Chee	235	.35	.20	.11
1980 Topps	235	1.50	.70	.45

Set	Card #	MT	NM	EX
1981 O-Pee-Chee	80	.30	.25	.12
1981 O-Pee-Chee	389	.30	.25	.12
1981 Topps	85	.20	.15	.08

1982 O-Pee-Chee	145	.20	.15	.08
1982 O-Pee-Chee	146	.20	.15	.08
1983 O-Pee-Chee	236	.15	.11	.06
1984 O-Pee-Chee	119	.15	.11	.06
1984 Topps	89	.50	.40	.20
1985 O-Pee-Chee	36	.25	.20	.10
1985 Topps	36	.35	.25	.14
1986 O-Pee-Chee	158	.15	.11	.06
1986 Topps	158	.25	.20	.10
1990 Upper Deck	507	.20	.15	.08

Henri Richard

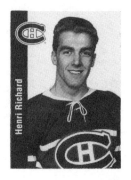

Set	Card #	NM	EX	VG
1957 Parkhurst	4 (R)	350.00	175.00	105.00
1958 Parkhurst	2	140.00	70.00	42.00
1959 Parkhurst	39	80.00	40.00	24.00
1960 Parkhurst	47	70.00	35.00	21.00
1961 Parkhurst	38	10.00	5.00	3.00
1961 Parkhurst	43	50.00	25.00	15.00
1962 Parkhurst	38	40.00	20.00	12.00
1963 Parkhurst	23	40.00	20.00	12.00
1963 Parkhurst	82	40.00	20.00	12.00
1964 Topps	48	65.00	32.00	19.50
1965 Topps	71	22.00	11.00	6.50
1966 Topps	8	20.00	10.00	6.00
1967 Topps	72	20.00	10.00	6.00
1968 O-Pee-Chee	165	12.00	6.00	3.50
1968 Topps	64	8.00	4.00	2.50
1969 O-Pee-Chee	163	10.00	5.00	3.00
1969 Topps	11	7.00	3.50	2.10
1970 O-Pee-Chee	176	8.00	4.00	2.50
1971 O-Pee-Chee	120	5.00	2.50	1.50
1971 Topps	120	3.50	1.75	1.00
1972 O-Pee-Chee	251	6.00	3.00	1.75
1973 O-Pee-Chee	87	3.00	1.50	.90
1973 Topps	87	2.50	1.25	.70
1974 O-Pee-Chee	243	1.00	.50	.30
1974 O-Pee-Chee	321	2.50	1.25	.70
1974 Topps	243	2.00	1.00	.60

Set	Card #	MT	NM	EX
1992 Parkhurst Parkie Reprints	28	30.00	15.00	8.00
1993 Parkhurst Cherry's Playoff Heroes	18D	10.00	7.50	4.00

Restored card: A card which has had "cosmetic surgery" — that is, a card which has had its imperfections fixed long after the card was issued. A card restorer can fix corners and restore gloss to card stock. Restored cards should be clearly labeled as such by whoever is selling them, and should be priced much less than unrestored cards in the same condition.

Reverse: The back of a card.

Maurice Richard

Set	Card #	NM	EX	VG
1951 Parkhurst	4 (R)	1500.	750.00	450.00
1952 Parkhurst	1	1000.	500.00	300.00
1953 Parkhurst	24	450.00	225.00	135.00
1954 Parkhurst	7	400.00	200.00	120.00
1955 Parkhurst	37	375.00	187.00	112.00
1955 Parkhurst	72	80.00	40.00	24.00
1955 Parkhurst	73	80.00	40.00	24.00
1957 Parkhurst	5	350.00	175.00	105.00
1958 Parkhurst	38	300.00	150.00	90.00
1959 Parkhurst	2	250.00	125.00	75.00
1960 Parkhurst	45	200.00	100.00	60.00

Set	Card #	MT	NM	EX
1993 Parkhurst Cherry's Playoff Heroes	16D	30.00	22.00	12.00
1993 Parkhurst Parkie Reprints	40	18.00	13.50	7.25
1993 Parkhurst Parkie Reprints	59	20.00	15.00	8.00

Mike Richter

Set	Card #	MT	NM	EX
1990 Bowman	218 (R)	1.00	.70	.40
1990 O-Pee-Chee	330 (R)	1.25	.90	.50
1990 Pro Set	398	.05	.04	.02
1990 Pro Set	627	.75	.60	.30
1990 Score	74 (R)	.75	.60	.30
1990 Topps	330 (R)	.75	.60	.30
1990 Upper Deck	32 (R)	2.00	1.50	.80
1991 Bowman	70	.15	.11	.06
1991 O-Pee-Chee Premier	78	.15	.11	.06
1991 O-Pee-Chee/Topps	11	.15	.11	.06
1991 O-Pee-Chee/Topps	91	.15	.11	.06
1991 Parkhurst	117	.50	.40	.20
1991 Pinnacle	164	.20	.15	.08

Larry Robinson

Set	Card #		
1991 Pinnacle	384	.08	.06	.03
1991 Pro Set	161	.10	.08	.04
1991 Pro Set Platinum	83	.20	.15	.08
1991 Pro Set Platinum	279	.05	.04	.02
1991 Score American	120	.10	.08	.04
1991 Score Canadian	120	.10	.08	.04
1991 Topps Stadium Club	92	.75	.60	.30
1991 Upper Deck	34	.05	.04	.02
1991 Upper Deck	175	.10	.08	.04
1991 Upper Deck	634	.10	.08	.04
1992 Bowman	238	6.00	4.50	2.50
1992 Bowman	354	2.00	1.50	.80
1992 Fleer Ultra	142	.06	.05	.02
1992 O-Pee-Chee	259	.05	.04	.02
1992 Parkhurst	112	.05	.04	.02
1992 Pinnacle	75	.06	.05	.02
1992 Pinnacle	270	2.50	2.00	1.00
1992 Pinnacle Team Pinnacle	1	20.00	15.00	8.00
1992 Pro Set	116	.05	.04	.02
1992 Score	5	.05	.04	.02
1992 Score USA Greats	6	6.00	4.50	2.50
1992 Topps	367	.06	.05	.02
1992 Topps Stadium Club	242	.10	.08	.04
1992 Topps Stadium Club	266	.05	.04	.02
1992 Upper Deck	145	.05	.04	.02
1993 Donruss	223	.35	.25	.14
1993 Fleer PowerPlay	165	.10	.08	.04
1993 Fleer Ultra	228	.07	.05	.03
1993 Leaf	185	.10	.08	.04
1993 Parkhurst	129	.10	.08	.04
1993 Pinnacle	242	.10	.08	.04
1993 Score	99	.05	.04	.02
1993 Topps Premier	135	.05	.04	.02
1993 Topps Stadium Club	64	.05	.04	.02
1993 Upper Deck	42	.05	.04	.02
1994 Donruss	165	.25	.20	.10
1994 Donruss Masked Marvels	8	6.00	4.50	2.50
1994 Fleer Flair	117	.35	.25	.14
1994 Fleer Ultra	143	.15	.11	.06
1994 Fleer Ultra Premier Pad Men	5	13.00	9.75	5.25
1994 Leaf	18	.20	.15	.08
1994 Leaf Gold Stars	3	70.00	52.00	28.00
1994 O-Pee-Chee Premier	70	.10	.08	.04
1994 O-Pee-Chee Premier	155	.08	.06	.03
1994 Parkhurst Vintage Parkhurst	5	.40	.30	.15
1994 Pinnacle	10	.35	.25	.14
1994 Pinnacle Artist's Proofs	10	18.00	13.50	7.25
1994 Pinnacle Goaltending Greats	2	6.00	4.50	2.50
1994 Pinnacle Rink Collection	10	9.00	6.75	3.50
1994 Pinnacle Team Pinnacle	2	25.00	18.50	10.00
1994 Score	130	.15	.11	.06
1994 Score Hockey Gold Line	130	1.50	1.25	.60
1994 Topps Premier	70	.10	.08	.04
1994 Topps Premier	155	.08	.06	.03
1994 Topps Stadium Club	181	.10	.08	.04
1994 Upper Deck	78	.25	.20	.10
1994 Upper Deck Electric Ice	78	10.00	7.50	4.00
1994 Upper Deck SP	52	.30	.25	.12

Set	Card #	NM	EX	VG
1973 O-Pee-Chee	237 (R)	50.00	25.00	15.00
1974 O-Pee-Chee	280	20.00	10.00	6.00
1975 O-Pee-Chee	241	12.00	6.00	3.50
1975 Topps	241	7.00	3.50	2.00
1976 O-Pee-Chee	151	6.00	3.00	1.75
1976 Topps	151	3.50	1.75	1.00
1977 O-Pee-Chee	2	2.00	1.00	.60
1977 O-Pee-Chee	30	5.00	2.50	1.50
1977 Topps	2	1.50	.70	.45
1977 Topps	30	3.00	1.50	.90
1978 O-Pee-Chee	210	2.50	1.25	.70
1978 O-Pee-Chee	329	1.00	.50	.30
1978 Topps	210	1.50	.70	.45
1979 O-Pee-Chee	50	2.00	1.00	.60
1979 Topps	50	1.25	.60	.40
1980 O-Pee-Chee	84	.75	.40	.25
1980 O-Pee-Chee	230	1.00	.50	.30
1980 O-Pee-Chee Photos	11	2.00	1.00	.60
1980 Topps	84	.50	.25	.15
1980 Topps	230	1.00	.50	.30

Set	Card #	MT	NM	EX
1981 O-Pee-Chee	179	.75	.60	.30
1981 O-Pee-Chee	196	.50	.40	.20
1981 Topps	31	.30	.25	.12
1982 O-Pee-Chee	191	.50	.40	.20
1983 O-Pee-Chee	195	.50	.40	.20
1984 O-Pee-Chee	270	.50	.40	.20
1984 Topps	82	.30	.25	.12
1985 O-Pee-Chee	147	.40	.30	.15
1985 Topps	147	.20	.15	.08
1986 O-Pee-Chee	62	.35	.25	.14
1986 Topps	62	.35	.25	.14
1987 O-Pee-Chee	192	.15	.11	.06
1987 Topps	192	.12	.09	.05
1988 O-Pee-Chee	246	.15	.11	.06
1989 O-Pee-Chee	235	.07	.05	.03
1990 Bowman	150	.07	.05	.03
1990 O-Pee-Chee	261	.05	.04	.02
1990 Pro Set	125	.10	.08	.04
1990 Score	260	.07	.05	.03
1990 Topps	261	.07	.05	.03
1990 Upper Deck	52	.10	.08	.04
1991 Bowman	177	.05	.04	.02
1991 O-Pee-Chee/Topps	458	.05	.04	.02
1991 Parkhurst	74	.05	.04	.02
1991 Pinnacle	208	.08	.06	.03
1991 Pinnacle	403	.08	.06	.03
1991 Pro Set	104	.05	.04	.02
1991 Score American	291	.05	.04	.02
1991 Score Canadian	511	.05	.04	.02
1991 Topps Stadium Club	252	.10	.08	.04
1991 Upper Deck	499	.05	.04	.02
1992 Bowman	215	2.00	1.50	.80
1992 O-Pee-Chee	167	.25	.20	.10
1992 O-Pee-Chee 25th Anniversary Series	6	.25	.20	.10

Premium: An extra. In terms of cards, this can either refer to a card inserted in a package of some other product or something inserted extra inserted in a package of cards. "Premium" can also refer to the extra money a high-series or star card commands.

Price on request (P.O.R.): A dealer will advertise a card P.O.R. if he believes the card will fluctuate in price from the time he places his ad until the time the ad is seen by the public.

Luc Robitaille

Set	Card #	MT	NM	EX
1987 O-Pee-Chee	42 (R)	40.00	30.00	16.00
1987 Topps	42 (R)	28.00	21.00	11.00
1988 O-Pee-Chee	124	7.00	5.25	2.75
1988 Topps	124	4.50	3.50	1.75
1989 O-Pee-Chee	88	.85	.60	.35
1989 Topps	88	1.00	.70	.40
1990 Bowman	152	.30	.25	.12
1990 O-Pee-Chee	194	.10	.08	.04
1990 O-Pee-Chee	209	.20	.15	.08
1990 O-Pee-Chee Premier	99	1.50	1.25	.60
1990 Pro Set	126	.15	.11	.06
1990 Pro Set	341	.15	.11	.06
1990 Score	150	.20	.15	.08
1990 Score	316	.15	.11	.06
1990 Score Hockey's 100 Hottest Rising Stars	66	.10	.08	.04
1990 Topps	194	.12	.09	.05
1990 Topps	209	.25	.20	.10
1990 Upper Deck	73	.50	.40	.20
1991 Bowman	188	.15	.11	.06
1991 O-Pee-Chee Premier	34	.15	.11	.06
1991 O-Pee-Chee/Topps	260	.15	.11	.06
1991 O-Pee-Chee/Topps	405	.12	.09	.05
1991 Parkhurst	68	.25	.20	.10
1991 Parkhurst	224	.10	.08	.04
1991 Pinnacle	17	.50	.40	.20
1991 Pinnacle	385	.30	.25	.12
1991 Pro Set	95	.15	.11	.06
1991 Pro Set	286	.15	.11	.06
1991 Pro Set Platinum	50	.15	.11	.06
1991 Score American	3	.15	.11	.06
1991 Score American	345	.15	.11	.06
1991 Score Canadian	3	.15	.11	.06
1991 Score Canadian	375	.15	.11	.06
1991 Topps Stadium Club	159	.50	.40	.20
1991 Upper Deck	145	.20	.15	.08
1991 Upper Deck	507	.15	.11	.06
1991 Upper Deck	623	.15	.11	.06
1992 Bowman	70	.75	.60	.30
1992 Bowman	216	5.00	3.75	2.00
1992 Fleer Ultra	87	.30	.25	.12
1992 Fleer Ultra All-Stars	11	4.00	3.00	1.50
1992 O-Pee-Chee	6	.20	.15	.08
1992 Parkhurst	68	.25	.20	.10
1992 Parkhurst	501	.60	.45	.25
1992 Pinnacle	175	.30	.25	.12
1992 Pinnacle	251	.15	.11	.06
1992 Pro Set	72	.15	.11	.06
1992 Score	290	.20	.15	.08
1992 Score	498	.08	.06	.03
1992 Topps	101	.15	.11	.06
1992 Topps	266	.20	.15	.08
1992 Topps Stadium Club	44	.25	.20	.10
1992 Topps Stadium Club	247	.25	.20	.10
1992 Upper Deck	216	.30	.25	.12
1992 Upper Deck Gordie Howe Selects	2	6.00	4.50	2.50
1992 Upper Deck World Junior Grads	20	6.00	4.50	2.50
1993 Donruss	162	.25	.20	.10
1993 Fleer PowerPlay	120	.25	.20	.10
1993 Fleer PowerPlay Point Leaders	13	.60	.45	.25
1993 Fleer Ultra	208	.25	.20	.10
1993 Fleer Ultra All-Stars	13	4.00	3.00	1.50
1993 Fleer Ultra Red Light Specials	9	1.00	.70	.40
1993 Leaf	20	.30	.25	.12
1993 Leaf Gold All-Stars	9	6.00	4.50	2.50
1993 Parkhurst	91	.20	.15	.08
1993 Pinnacle	145	.25	.20	.10
1993 Pinnacle All-Stars	37	.40	.30	.15
1993 Pinnacle Nifty 50	5	14.00	10.50	5.50
1993 Pinnacle Team Pinnacle	4	30.00	22.00	12.00
1993 Score	245	.15	.11	.06
1993 Score	451	.10	.08	.04
1993 Score Dream Team	24	6.00	4.50	2.50
1993 Topps Premier	90	.10	.08	.04
1993 Topps Premier	180	.15	.11	.06
1993 Topps Stadium Club	87	.20	.15	.08
1993 Topps Stadium Club All-Stars	18	8.00	6.00	3.25
1993 Topps Stadium Club Finest	7	5.00	3.75	2.00
1993 Upper Deck	231	.20	.15	.08
1993 Upper Deck	293	.15	.11	.06
1993 Upper Deck	414	.15	.11	.06
1993 Upper Deck Gretzky's Great Ones	8	2.50	2.00	1.00
1993 Upper Deck Hat Tricks	17	1.00	.70	.40
1993 Upper Deck SP Inserts	73	.80	.60	.30
1994 Donruss Ice Masters	9	2.00	1.50	.80
1994 Fleer Flair	138	.40	.30	.15
1994 Fleer Flair Hot Numbers	7	10.00	7.50	4.00
1994 Fleer Ultra	103	.10	.08	.04
1994 Leaf	20	.15	.11	.06
1994 Parkhurst Vintage Parkhurst	67	.50	.40	.20
1994 Pinnacle Team Pinnacle	7	20.00	15.00	8.00
1994 Score Dream Team	10	5.00	3.75	2.00
1994 Topps Premier Finest Inserts	13	5.00	3.75	2.00
1994 Topps Stadium Club	57	.08	.06	.03
1994 Topps Stadium Club Dynasty and Destiny	4	7.00	5.25	2.75
1994 Upper Deck	194	.25	.20	.10
1994 Upper Deck Electric Ice	194	8.00	6.00	3.25

Jeremy Roenick

Set	Card #	MT	NM	EX
1990 Bowman	1 (R)	1.75	1.25	.70

1990 O-Pee-Chee	7 (R)	1.75	1.25	.70
1990 O-Pee-Chee Premier	100 (R)	15.00	11.00	6.00
1990 Pro Set	58 (R)	1.00	.70	.40
1990 Score	179 (R)	1.50	1.25	.60
1990 Score Hockey's 100 Hottest Rising Stars	31	.10	.08	.04
1990 Topps	7 (R)	1.50	1.25	.60
1990 Upper Deck	63 (R)	4.50	3.50	1.75
1990 Upper Deck	481	.60	.45	.25
1991 Bowman	386	.15	.11	.06
1991 Bowman	403	.50	.40	.20
1991 O-Pee-Chee Premier	52	1.00	.70	.40
1991 O-Pee-Chee Premier	174	.50	.40	.20
1991 O-Pee-Chee/Topps	106	.60	.45	.25
1991 Parkhurst	29	1.25	.90	.50
1991 Parkhurst	439	.30	.25	.12
1991 Pinnacle	120	2.00	1.50	.80
1991 Pinnacle	359	.40	.30	.15
1991 Pro Set	40	.50	.40	.20
1991 Pro Set	280	.35	.25	.14
1991 Pro Set	605	.20	.15	.08
1991 Pro Set Platinum	24	.50	.40	.20
1991 Score American	220	.50	.40	.20
1991 Score American	305	.20	.15	.08
1991 Score American	418	.25	.20	.10
1991 Score Canadian	220	.50	.40	.20
1991 Score Canadian	309	.20	.15	.08
1991 Score Canadian	334	.15	.11	.06
1991 Score Hot Card	10	4.00	3.00	1.50
1991 Topps Stadium Club	46	2.00	1.50	.80
1991 Upper Deck	36	.50	.40	.20
1991 Upper Deck	166	1.00	.70	.40
1991 Upper Deck	629	.25	.20	.10
1992 Bowman	78	4.00	3.00	1.50
1992 Bowman	217	40.00	30.00	16.00
1992 Fleer Ultra	41	.75	.60	.30
1992 O-Pee-Chee	345	.50	.40	.20
1992 O-Pee-Chee	383	.30	.25	.12
1992 O-Pee-Chee Premier Star Performers	5	1.00	.70	.40
1992 O-Pee-Chee 25th Anniversary Series	23	.30	.25	.12
1992 Parkhurst	31	.75	.60	.30
1992 Parkhurst Cherry Picks	2	20.00	15.00	8.00
1992 Pinnacle	10	1.00	.70	.40
1992 Pinnacle	256	.25	.20	.10
1992 Pinnacle Team 2000	27	3.00	2.25	1.25
1992 Pro Set	30	.65	.50	.25
1992 Pro Set	252	.20	.15	.08
1992 Pro Set Gold Team Leaders	2	5.00	3.75	2.00
1992 Score	200	.60	.45	.25
1992 Score	422	.25	.20	.10
1992 Score	499	.20	.15	.08
1992 Score Sharpshooters	10	.50	.25	.15
1992 Score USA Greats	3	8.00	6.00	3.25
1992 Topps	400	.50	.40	.20
1992 Topps Stadium Club	167	1.00	.70	.40
1992 Topps Stadium Club	255	.75	.60	.30
1992 Upper Deck	274	.75	.60	.30
1992 Upper Deck Gordie Howe Selects	8	9.00	6.75	3.50
1992 Upper Deck World Junior Grads	19	10.00	7.50	4.00
1993 Donruss	67	.75	.60	.30
1993 Donruss Elite	6	50.00	37.00	20.00
1993 Donruss Special Print	E	8.00	6.00	3.25
1993 Fleer PowerPlay	54	.75	.60	.30
1993 Fleer PowerPlay Gamebreakers	8	2.00	1.50	.80
1993 Fleer PowerPlay Point Leaders	14	2.00	1.50	.80
1993 Fleer Ultra	186	.75	.60	.30
1993 Fleer Ultra Premier Pivots	8	4.00	3.00	1.50
1993 Leaf	27	.75	.60	.30
1993 Leaf Studio Signature	7	6.00	4.50	2.50
1993 Parkhurst	309	.75	.60	.30
1993 Parkhurst East-West Stars	6W	15.00	11.00	6.00
1993 Pinnacle	140	.75	.60	.30
1993 Pinnacle All-Stars	39	.50	.40	.20
1993 Pinnacle Nifty 50	15	22.00	16.50	8.75
1993 Pinnacle Team Pinnacle	11	70.00	52.00	28.00
1993 Pinnacle Team 2001	20	2.00	1.50	.80
1993 Score	240	.40	.30	.15
1993 Score Franchise	4	14.00	10.50	5.50
1993 Score U.S. Dynamic Duos	6	13.00	9.75	5.25
1993 Topps Premier	450	.40	.30	.15
1993 Topps Premier	500	.35	.25	.14
1993 Topps Stadium Club	190	.75	.60	.30
1993 Topps Stadium Club All-Stars	20	8.00	6.00	3.25
1993 Upper Deck	235	.35	.25	.14
1993 Upper Deck	289	.30	.25	.12
1993 Upper Deck	314	.35	.25	.14
1993 Upper Deck Hat Tricks	18	2.00	1.50	.80
1993 Upper Deck Silver Skates Dye-Cut Retail	10R	12.00	9.00	4.75
1993 Upper Deck SP Inserts	31	2.25	1.75	.90
1994 Donruss	222	.50	.40	.20
1994 Donruss Elite Series	9	25.00	18.50	10.00
1994 Fleer Flair	36	1.50	1.25	.60
1994 Fleer Flair Center Spotlight	10	7.00	5.25	2.75
1994 Fleer Flair Scoring Power	9	7.00	5.25	2.75
1994 Fleer Ultra	44	.50	.40	.20
1994 Fleer Ultra Ultra Power	8	16.00	12.00	6.50
1994 Leaf	63	.50	.40	.20
1994 Leaf Fire On Ice	2	9.00	6.75	3.50
1994 Leaf Gold Stars	2	40.00	30.00	16.00
1994 Leaf Limited	5	10.00	7.50	4.00
1994 O-Pee-Chee Premier	200	.25	.20	.10
1994 Parkhurst	302	.45	.35	.20
1994 Parkhurst Crash the Game	5	8.00	6.00	3.25
1994 Parkhurst Vintage Parkhurst	65	2.00	1.50	.80
1994 Pinnacle	165	.75	.60	.30
1994 Pinnacle Artist's Proofs	165	60.00	45.00	24.00
1994 Pinnacle Rink Collection	165	25.00	18.50	10.00
1994 Score Check-It	6	25.00	18.50	10.00
1994 Score Dream Team	18	12.00	9.00	4.75
1994 Score Franchise	5	20.00	15.00	8.00
1994 Score 90-Plus Club	6	11.00	8.25	4.50
1994 Topps Premier	200	.25	.20	.10
1994 Topps Premier Finest Inserts	11	10.00	7.50	4.00
1994 Topps Stadium Club	59	.25	.20	.10
1994 Upper Deck Award Predictor	13	9.00	6.75	3.50
1994 Upper Deck Ice Gallery	3	10.00	7.50	4.00
1994 Upper Deck Scoring Predictor	8	10.00	7.50	4.00
1994 Upper Deck SP	17	2.50	2.00	1.00

Price guide: A periodical or book which contains checklists of cards, sets and other memorabilia and their values in varying conditions.

Promo card: A card made for promotional purposes. Promo cards generally have very limited distribution and can be quite valuable.

Proof card: A card made not to be sold but to test the card presses, the card design, photography, colors, paper, statistical accuracy and so forth.

Dominic Roussel

Patrick Roy

Set	Card #	MT	NM	EX
1991 Parkhurst	450	.60	.45	.25
1991 Pinnacle	343 (R)	.75	.60	.30
1991 Pro Set	552 (R)	.20	.15	.08
1991 Upper Deck	583 (R)	.75	.60	.30
1992 Bowman	92	.75	.60	.30
1992 Fleer Ultra	159	.35	.25	.14
1992 O-Pee-Chee	198	.20	.15	.08
1992 O-Pee-Chee Premier	51	.25	.20	.10
1992 O-Pee-Chee Premier Top Rookies	3	2.00	1.25	.60
1992 Parkhurst	129	.30	.25	.12
1992 Pinnacle	96	.40	.30	.15
1992 Pinnacle Team 2000	11	1.50	1.25	.60
1992 Pro Set	235	.25	.20	.10
1992 Score	464	.25	.20	.10
1992 Topps	10	.20	.15	.08
1992 Topps	213	.20	.15	.08
1992 Topps Stadium Club	315	.25	.20	.10
1992 Upper Deck	31	.25	.20	.10
1992 Upper Deck Holograms	6	3.00	2.25	1.25
1993 Donruss	243	.25	.20	.10
1993 Fleer PowerPlay	409	.10	.08	.04
1993 Fleer Ultra	392	.20	.15	.08
1993 Leaf	244	.20	.15	.08
1993 Parkhurst	417	.10	.08	.04
1993 Pinnacle	97	.10	.08	.04
1993 Pinnacle Masks	4	25.00	18.50	10.00
1993 Score	82	.20	.15	.08
1993 Topps Premier	335	.15	.11	.06
1993 Topps Stadium Club	109	.20	.15	.08
1993 Upper Deck	336	.20	.15	.08
1994 Donruss	263	.08	.06	.03
1994 Leaf	223	.10	.08	.04
1994 O-Pee-Chee Premier	56	.05	.04	.02
1994 Pinnacle	208	.10	.08	.04
1994 Pinnacle Artist's Proofs	208	5.00	3.75	2.00
1994 Pinnacle Rink Collection	208	3.00	2.25	1.25
1994 Score	105	.05	.04	.02
1994 Score Hockey Gold Line	105	.25	.20	.10
1994 Topps Premier	56	.05	.04	.02

Reverse negative: A common error in which the picture negative is flip-flopped so the picture comes out backward, or reversed.

SASE: A term used in hobby advertisements and elsewhere to indicate "self-addressed, stamped envelope."

Sell price: The price at which a dealer will sell cards. Generally much higher than his buy price.

Set	Card #	MT	NM	EX
1986 O-Pee-Chee	53 (R)	145.00	109.00	58.00
1986 Topps	53 (R)	70.00	52.00	28.00
1987 O-Pee-Chee	163	40.00	30.00	16.00
1987 Topps	163	23.00	17.00	9.25
1988 O-Pee-Chee	116	12.00	9.00	4.75
1988 Topps	116	5.00	3.75	2.00
1989 O-Pee-Chee	17	1.00	.70	.40
1989 O-Pee-Chee	322	.25	.20	.10
1989 O-Pee-Chee Future Stars	28	1.00	.70	.40
1989 Topps	17	1.50	1.25	.60
1990 Bowman	50	1.00	.70	.40
1990 O-Pee-Chee	198	.10	.08	.04
1990 O-Pee-Chee	219	1.00	.70	.40
1990 O-Pee-Chee Premier	101	3.50	2.75	1.50
1990 Pro Set	157	.50	.40	.20
1990 Pro Set	359	.15	.11	.06
1990 Pro Set	391	.15	.11	.06
1990 Pro Set	399	.15	.11	.06
1990 Score	10	.75	.60	.30
1990 Score	312	.10	.08	.04
1990 Score	344	.10	.08	.04
1990 Score	354	.05	.04	.02
1990 Score	364	.10	.08	.04
1990 Score Hockey's 100 Hottest Rising Stars	25	.10	.08	.04
1990 Topps	198	.10	.08	.04
1990 Topps	219	.75	.60	.30
1990 Upper Deck	153	1.50	1.25	.60
1990 Upper Deck	207	.50	.40	.20
1990 Upper Deck	317	.20	.15	.08
1990 Upper Deck	496	.50	.40	.20
1991 Bowman	335	.50	.40	.20
1991 O-Pee-Chee Premier	14	.80	.60	.30
1991 O-Pee-Chee Premier	170	.60	.45	.25
1991 O-Pee-Chee/Topps	270	.15	.11	.06
1991 O-Pee-Chee/Topps	413	.50	.40	.20
1991 Parkhurst	90	.90	.70	.35
1991 Parkhurst	220	.50	.40	.20
1991 Parkhurst	442	.20	.15	.08
1991 Parkhurst	463	13.00	9.75	5.25
1991 Parkhurst	470	12.00	9.00	4.75
1991 Pinnacle	175	1.25	.90	.50
1991 Pinnacle	387	.40	.30	.15
1991 Pinnacle B	1	100.00	75.00	40.00
1991 Pro Set	1	150.00	112.00	60.00
1991 Pro Set	125	.50	.40	.20
1991 Pro Set	304	.15	.11	.06
1991 Pro Set	599	.10	.08	.04
1991 Pro Set	613	.10	.08	.04
1991 Pro Set Platinum	61	.50	.40	.20
1991 Score American	75	.50	.40	.20
1991 Score American	342	.10	.08	.04
1991 Score American	424	.10	.08	.04
1991 Score Canadian	75	.50	.40	.20
1991 Score Canadian	314	.10	.08	.04
1991 Score Canadian	372	.15	.11	.06
1991 Topps Stadium Club	107	2.00	1.50	.80

		MT	NM	EX
1991 Upper Deck	137	1.00	.70	.40
1991 Upper Deck	614	.20	.15	.08
1992 Bowman	74	5.00	3.75	2.00
1992 Bowman	239	10.00	7.50	4.00
1992 Fleer Ultra	108	1.00	.70	.40
1992 Fleer Ultra All-Stars	3	6.00	4.50	2.50
1992 Fleer Ultra Award Winners	4	6.00	4.50	2.50
1992 O-Pee-Chee	111	1.50	1.25	.60
1992 O-Pee-Chee	164	.50	.40	.20
1992 O-Pee-Chee 25th Anniversary Series	19	.30	.25	.12
1992 Parkhurst	84	1.00	.75	.40
1992 Parkhurst	463	.20	.15	.08
1992 Parkhurst	510	2.50	2.00	1.00
1992 Pinnacle	130	1.00	.70	.40
1992 Pro Set	2	.15	.11	.06
1992 Pro Set	85	1.00	.75	.40
1992 Score	295	.50	.40	.20
1992 Score	418	.15	.11	.06
1992 Score	428	.15	.11	.06
1992 Score	489	.05	.04	.02
1992 Score	527	.15	.11	.06
1992 Topps	110	.25	.20	.10
1992 Topps	263	.25	.20	.10
1992 Topps	491	.25	.20	.10
1992 Topps	508	.75	.60	.30
1992 Topps Stadium Club	133	.75	.60	.30
1992 Topps Stadium Club	252	.50	.40	.20
1992 Upper Deck	149	.80	.60	.30
1992 Upper Deck	438	.15	.11	.06
1992 Upper Deck	440	.15	.11	.06
1992 Upper Deck All-World Team	6	9.00	6.75	3.50
1993 Donruss	178	1.50	1.25	.60
1993 Donruss Elite	9	75.00	56.00	30.00
1993 Donruss Ice Kings	1	5.00	3.75	2.00
1993 Donruss Special Print	L	15.00	9.00	4.75
1993 Fleer PowerPlay	133	1.00	.70	.40
1993 Fleer PowerPlay Gamebreakers	9	4.00	3.00	1.50
1993 Fleer PowerPlay Netminders	7	15.00	11.00	6.00
1993 Fleer Ultra	39	1.00	.70	.40
1993 Fleer Ultra All-Stars	1	7.50	5.75	3.00
1993 Leaf	33	.75	.60	.30
1993 Leaf	100	.75	.60	.30
1993 Leaf Gold All-Stars	5	13.00	9.75	5.25
1993 Leaf Painted Warriors	4	12.00	9.00	4.75
1993 Leaf Studio Signature	6	7.00	5.25	2.75
1993 OPC Premier Black Gold	8	25.00	18.50	10.00
1993 Parkhurst	100	.75	.60	.30
1993 Parkhurst Cherry's Playoff Heroes	10D	65.00	49.00	26.00
1993 Parkhurst East-West Stars	4E	28.00	21.00	11.00
1993 Parkhurst US Canada Gold-Foiled	9	25.00	18.50	10.00
1993 Pinnacle	150	.70	.50	.30
1993 Pinnacle	228	.25	.20	.10
1993 Pinnacle All-Stars	18	.75	.60	.30
1993 Pinnacle Team Pinnacle	1	70.00	52.00	28.00
1993 Score	315	.70	.50	.30
1993 Score Dream Team	2	30.00	22.00	12.00
1993 Score Franchise	10	30.00	22.00	12.00
1993 Topps Premier	1	.50	.40	.20
1993 Topps Premier Black Gold	22	7.00	5.25	2.75
1993 Topps Stadium Club	231	.65	.50	.25
1993 Topps Stadium Club All-Stars	1	20.00	15.00	8.00
1993 Topps Stadium Club Finest	11	10.00	7.50	4.00
1993 Upper Deck	49	.65	.50	.25
1993 Upper Deck Award Winners	4	7.00	5.25	2.75
1993 Upper Deck Next in Line	6	10.00	7.50	4.00
1993 Upper Deck SP Inserts	81	7.00	5.25	2.75
1994 Donruss	328	1.00	.70	.40
1994 Donruss Elite Series	10	45.00	34.00	18.00
1994 Donruss Masked Marvels	9	10.00	7.50	4.00
1994 Fleer Flair	91	1.50	1.25	.60
1994 Fleer Flair Hot Numbers	8	35.00	26.00	14.00
1994 Fleer Ultra	113	1.25	.90	.50
1994 Fleer Ultra All-Stars	6	1.75	1.25	.70
1994 Fleer Ultra Premier Pad Men	6	30.00	22.00	12.00
1994 Leaf	41	.75	.60	.30
1994 Leaf Gold Stars	3	70.00	52.00	28.00
1994 Leaf Limited	12	15.00	11.00	6.00
1994 O-Pee-Chee Premier	125	.25	.20	.10
1994 Parkhurst	113	.60	.45	.25
1994 Parkhurst	312	.40	.30	.15
1994 Parkhurst Crash the Game	12	13.00	9.75	5.25
1994 Pinnacle	30	1.00	.70	.40
1994 Pinnacle Artist's Proofs	30	100.00	75.00	40.00
1994 Pinnacle Goaltending Greats	5	18.00	13.50	7.25
1994 Pinnacle Hockey Masks	1	85.00	64.00	34.00
1994 Pinnacle Northern Lights	1	25.00	18.50	10.00
1994 Pinnacle Rink Collection	30	40.00	30.00	16.00
1994 Pinnacle Team Pinnacle	1	75.00	56.00	30.00
1994 Score Dream Team	1	20.00	15.00	8.00
1994 Score Franchise	12	45.00	34.00	18.00
1994 Topps Premier	125	.25	.20	.10
1994 Topps Stadium Club	33	.75	.60	.30
1994 Topps Stadium Club	178	.25	.20	.10
1994 Topps Stadium Club Finest	9	13.00	9.75	5.25
1994 Upper Deck	121	1.25	.90	.50
1994 Upper Deck Award Predictor	5	14.00	10.50	5.50
1994 Upper Deck Electric Ice	121	50.00	37.00	20.00
1994 Upper Deck SP	42	6.00	4.50	2.50

Joe Sakic

Set	Card #	MT	NM	EX
1989 O-Pee-Chee	113 (R)	4.00	3.00	1.50
1989 Topps	113 (R)	7.00	5.25	2.75
1990 Bowman	169	.75	.60	.30
1990 O-Pee-Chee	384	.50	.40	.20
1990 O-Pee-Chee Premier	102	1.50	1.25	.60
1990 Pro Set	257	.70	.50	.30
1990 Pro Set	375	.20	.15	.08

1990 Score	8	.50	.40	.20
1990 Score Hockey's 100 Hottest Rising Stars	7	.10	.08	.04
1990 Topps	384	.50	.40	.20
1990 Topps Team Scoring Leaders	14	.15	.08	.08
1990 Upper Deck	164	1.00	.70	.40
1990 Upper Deck	490	.25	.20	.10
1991 Bowman	133	.25	.20	.10
1991 O-Pee-Chee Premier	70	.30	.25	.12
1991 O-Pee-Chee/Topps	16	.15	.11	.06
1991 Parkhurst	148	.50	.40	.20
1991 Pinnacle	150	.50	.40	.20
1991 Pinnacle	381	.40	.30	.15
1991 Pro Set	199	.25	.20	.10
1991 Pro Set	315	.10	.08	.04
1991 Pro Set Platinum	102	.25	.20	.10
1991 Score American	25	.25	.20	.10
1991 Score American	336	.10	.08	.04
1991 Score Canadian	25	.25	.20	.10
1991 Score Canadian	366	.10	.08	.04
1991 Topps Promo Cards	(5)	5.00	2.50	2.50
1991 Topps Stadium Club	389	.75	.60	.30
1991 Topps Team Scoring Leaders	8	.10	.05	.05
1991 Upper Deck	333	.40	.30	.15
1991 Upper Deck	616	.15	.11	.06
1992 Bowman	240	16.00	12.00	6.50
1992 Bowman	244	1.00	.70	.40
1992 Fleer Ultra	179	.40	.30	.15
1992 O-Pee-Chee	54	.20	.15	.08
1992 O-Pee-Chee	55	.20	.15	.08
1992 O-Pee-Chee Premier Star Performers	11	.25	.20	.10
1992 O-Pee-Chee 25th Anniversary Series	22	.25	.20	.10
1992 Parkhurst	147	.05	.04	.02
1992 Pinnacle	150	.30	.25	.12
1992 Pinnacle Team 2000	21	1.75	1.25	.70
1992 Pro Set	150	.15	.11	.06
1992 Score	240	.25	.20	.10
1992 Score	434	.05	.04	.02
1992 Topps	495	.20	.15	.08
1992 Topps Stadium Club	3	.25	.20	.10
1992 Upper Deck	36	.05	.04	.02
1992 Upper Deck	255	.20	.15	.08
1992 Upper Deck World Junior Grads	8	7.00	5.25	2.75
1993 Donruss	282	.30	.25	.12
1993 Fleer PowerPlay	204	.20	.15	.08
1993 Fleer PowerPlay Point Leaders	15	.60	.45	.25
1993 Fleer Ultra	242	.25	.20	.10
1993 Leaf	87	.25	.20	.10
1993 OPC Premier Black Gold	15	8.00	6.00	3.25
1993 Parkhurst	169	.10	.08	.04
1993 Parkhurst East-West Stars	9E	12.00	9.00	4.75
1993 Pinnacle	290	.08	.06	.03
1993 Pinnacle All-Stars	13	.30	.25	.12
1993 Pinnacle Hockey Captains	19	6.00	4.50	2.50
1993 Pinnacle Team 2001	25	.75	.60	.30
1993 Score	135	.20	.15	.08
1993 Score Canadian Dynamic Duos	5	10.00	7.50	4.00
1993 Score Dream Team	14	8.00	6.00	3.25
1993 Score Franchise	17	9.00	6.75	3.50
1993 Topps Premier	10	.15	.11	.06
1993 Topps Stadium Club	32	.20	.15	.08
1993 Topps Stadium Club All-Stars	17	12.00	9.00	4.75
1993 Upper Deck	69	.25	.20	.10
1993 Upper Deck	223	.20	.15	.08
1993 Upper Deck Next in Line	3	6.00	4.50	2.50
1993 Upper Deck Silver Skates Dye-Cut Hobby	9H	7.50	5.75	3.00

1993 Upper Deck SP Inserts	130	.75	.60	.30
1994 Donruss	141	.25	.20	.10
1994 Fleer Flair	151	.50	.40	.20
1994 Fleer Ultra	180	.05	.04	.02
1994 Leaf	165	.15	.11	.06
1994 Parkhurst Crash the Game	19	5.00	3.75	2.00
1994 Parkhurst Vintage Parkhurst	34	.50	.40	.20
1994 Pinnacle	50	.30	.25	.12
1994 Pinnacle Artist's Proofs	50	14.00	10.50	5.50
1994 Pinnacle Northern Lights	4	8.00	6.00	3.25
1994 Pinnacle Rink Collection	50	8.00	6.00	3.25
1994 Score Franchise	19	10.00	7.50	4.00
1994 Score 90-Plus Club	19	5.00	3.75	2.00
1994 Upper Deck SP	65	1.00	.70	.40

Borje Salming

Set	Card #	NM	EX	VG
1974 O-Pee-Chee	180 (R)	14.00	7.00	4.25
1974 Topps	180 (R)	9.00	4.50	2.75
1975 O-Pee-Chee	283	5.00	2.50	1.50
1975 O-Pee-Chee	294	.50	.25	.15
1975 Topps	283	2.50	1.25	.70
1975 Topps	294	1.50	.70	.45
1976 O-Pee-Chee	22	.45	.25	.14
1976 Topps	22	1.25	.60	.40
1977 O-Pee-Chee	2	2.00	1.00	.60
1977 O-Pee-Chee	140	2.00	1.00	.60
1977 Topps	2	1.50	.70	.45
1977 Topps	140	1.00	.50	.30
1978 O-Pee-Chee	328	.35	.20	.11
1978 Topps	240	.50	.25	.15
1979 Topps	40	.75	.40	.25
1980 O-Pee-Chee	85	.35	.20	.11
1980 O-Pee-Chee	210	.35	.20	.11
1980 Topps	85	.20	.10	.08
1980 Topps	210	.75	.40	.25

Set	Card #	MT	NM	EX
1981 O-Pee-Chee	307	.30	.25	.12
1981 Topps	33	.75	.60	.30
1982 O-Pee-Chee	332	.20	.15	.08
1983 O-Pee-Chee	341	.15	.11	.06
1984 O-Pee-Chee	311	.15	.11	.06
1985 O-Pee-Chee	248	.25	.20	.10
1986 O-Pee-Chee	169	.15	.11	.06
1986 Topps	169	.20	.15	.08
1987 O-Pee-Chee	237	.12	.09	.05
1988 O-Pee-Chee	247	.15	.11	.06
1989 O-Pee-Chee	278	.07	.05	.03

> Sepia: A dark reddish-brown coloration used in some card sets instead of traditional black-and-white.

Tomas Sandstrom

Denis Savard

Set	Card #	MT	NM	EX
1985 O-Pee-Chee	123 (R)	7.50	5.75	3.00
1985 Topps	123 (R)	5.00	3.75	2.00
1986 O-Pee-Chee	230	2.00	1.50	.80
1987 O-Pee-Chee	28	1.50	1.25	.60
1987 Topps	28	.75	.60	.30
1988 O-Pee-Chee	121	.75	.60	.30
1988 Topps	121	.50	.40	.20
1989 O-Pee-Chee	54	.20	.15	.08
1989 Topps	54	.20	.15	.08
1990 Bowman	141	.07	.05	.03
1990 O-Pee-Chee	301	.07	.05	.03
1990 Pro Set	127	.07	.05	.03
1990 Score	183	.15	.11	.06
1990 Score Hockey's 100	79	.10	.08	.04
Hottest Rising Stars				
1990 Topps	301	.07	.05	.03
1990 Upper Deck	251	.15	.11	.06
1991 Bowman	174	.08	.06	.03
1991 Bowman	179	.05	.04	.02
1991 O-Pee-Chee Premier	82	.05	.04	.02
1991 O-Pee-Chee/Topps	173	.05	.04	.02
1991 Parkhurst	70	.05	.04	.02
1991 Pinnacle	178	.20	.15	.08
1991 Pro Set	97	.05	.04	.02
1991 Pro Set	287	.05	.04	.02
1991 Pro Set Platinum	53	.10	.08	.04
1991 Score American	270	.05	.04	.02
1991 Score Canadian	490	.10	.08	.04
1991 Topps Stadium Club	209	.15	.11	.06
1991 Upper Deck	30	.20	.15	.08
1991 Upper Deck	141	.15	.11	.06
1991 Upper Deck Euro-	7	.60	.40	.20
Stars				
1992 Bowman	22	.25	.20	.10
1992 Fleer Ultra	88	.06	.05	.02
1992 O-Pee-Chee	91	.05	.04	.02
1992 Pinnacle	345	.06	.05	.02
1992 Score	199	.05	.04	.02
1992 Topps	421	.06	.05	.02
1992 Topps Stadium Club	220	.05	.04	.02
1992 Upper Deck	424	.05	.04	.02
1993 Donruss	163	.10	.08	.04
1993 Donruss	475	.10	.08	.04
1993 Fleer PowerPlay	121	.15	.11	.06
1993 Fleer Ultra	246	.07	.05	.03
1993 Leaf	106	.10	.08	.04
1993 Parkhurst	362	.10	.08	.04
1993 Pinnacle	263	.10	.08	.04
1993 Score	129	.05	.04	.02
1993 Score International	21	.75	.60	.30
Stars				
1993 Topps Premier	434	.06	.05	.02
1993 Topps Stadium Club	25	.05	.04	.02
1993 Upper Deck	188	.05	.04	.02
1994 Donruss	271	.08	.06	.03
1994 Leaf	207	.10	.08	.04
1994 O-Pee-Chee Premier	108	.05	.04	.02
1994 Parkhurst	175	.06	.05	.02
1994 Topps Premier	108	.05	.04	.02

Set	Card #	MT	NM	EX
1981 O-Pee-Chee	63 (R)	20.00	15.00	8.00
1981 Topps	75 (R)	12.00	9.00	4.75
1982 O-Pee-Chee	73	5.00	3.75	2.00
1983 O-Pee-Chee	96	.30	.25	.12
1983 O-Pee-Chee	111	3.00	2.25	1.25
1984 O-Pee-Chee	45	2.00	1.50	.80
1984 O-Pee-Chee	355	.20	.15	.08
1984 Topps	35	.65	.50	.25
1985 O-Pee-Chee	73	1.00	.70	.40
1985 Topps	73	1.00	.70	.40
1986 O-Pee-Chee	7	1.00	.70	.40
1986 Topps	7	.50	.40	.20
1987 O-Pee-Chee	127	.60	.45	.25
1987 Topps	127	.50	.40	.20
1988 O-Pee-Chee	26	.50	.40	.20
1988 Topps	26	.40	.30	.15
1989 O-Pee-Chee	5	.50	.40	.20
1989 Topps	5	.25	.20	.10
1990 Bowman	6	.07	.05	.03
1990 O-Pee-Chee	28	.15	.11	.06
1990 O-Pee-Chee Premier	103	.15	.11	.06
1990 Pro Set	59	.20	.15	.08
1990 Pro Set	473	.20	.15	.08
1990 Score	125	.12	.09	.05
1990 Score Hockey's 100	59	.10	.08	.04
Hottest Rising Stars				
1990 Score Traded	1	.25	.20	.10
1990 Topps	28	.20	.15	.08
1990 Upper Deck	244	.20	.15	.08
1990 Upper Deck	426	.25	.20	.10
1991 Bowman	342	.05	.04	.02
1991 O-Pee-Chee Premier	71	.05	.04	.02
1991 O-Pee-Chee/Topps	330	.05	.04	.02
1991 Parkhurst	93	.05	.04	.02
1991 Parkhurst	211	.05	.04	.02
1991 Pinnacle	28	.20	.15	.08
1991 Pro Set	128	.05	.04	.02
1991 Pro Set	305	.05	.04	.02
1991 Pro Set Platinum	64	.05	.04	.02
1991 Pro Set Platinum PC	18	1.50	1.25	.60
1991 Score American	165	.10	.08	.04
1991 Score Canadian	165	.05	.04	.02
1991 Topps Stadium Club	213	.15	.11	.06
1991 Upper Deck	242	.10	.08	.04
1992 Bowman	64	.25	.20	.10
1992 Fleer Ultra	109	.06	.05	.02
1992 O-Pee-Chee	35	.05	.04	.02
1992 O-Pee-Chee Premier	6	.15	.11	.06
Star Performers				
1992 Parkhurst	85	.05	.04	.02
1992 Pinnacle	61	.06	.05	.02
1992 Pro Set	84	.05	.04	.02
1992 Pro Set	260	.05	.04	.02
1992 Score	202	.05	.04	.02
1992 Topps	414	.06	.05	.02
1992 Topps Stadium Club	467	.05	.04	.02
1992 Upper Deck	162	.05	.04	.02
1992 Upper Deck	638	.10	.08	.04

1993 Donruss	319	.10	.08	.04
1993 Fleer PowerPlay	447	.08	.06	.03
1993 Fleer Ultra	428	.07	.05	.03
1993 Leaf	372	.10	.08	.04
1993 Parkhurst	193	.12	.09	.05
1993 Pinnacle	391	.10	.08	.04
1993 Pinnacle Hockey Captains	22	5.00	3.75	2.00
1993 Score	105	.05	.04	.02
1993 Score	555	.08	.06	.03
1993 Topps Premier	305	.07	.05	.03
1993 Topps Stadium Club	297	.10	.08	.04
1993 Upper Deck	502	.05	.04	.02
1993 Upper Deck Gretzky's Great Ones	1	1.75	1.25	.70
1993 Upper Deck SP Inserts	153	.30	.25	.12
1994 Donruss	284	.08	.06	.03
1994 Leaf	166	.10	.08	.04
1994 O-Pee-Chee Premier	69	.08	.06	.03
1994 Parkhurst	217	.06	.05	.02
1994 Topps Premier	69	.08	.06	.03
1994 Upper Deck SP	76	.30	.25	.12

Serge Savard

Set	Card #	NM	EX	VG
1969 O-Pee-Chee	4 (R)	35.00	17.50	10.50
1969 O-Pee-Chee	210	10.00	5.00	3.00
1969 Topps	4 (R)	20.00	10.00	6.00
1970 O-Pee-Chee	51	10.00	5.00	3.00
1970 Topps	51	5.50	2.75	1.75
1971 O-Pee-Chee	143	5.00	2.50	1.50
1972 O-Pee-Chee	185	1.50	.70	.45
1972 O-Pee-Chee Team Canada	25	7.50	3.75	2.25
1973 O-Pee-Chee	24	1.00	.50	.30
1973 Topps	24	1.50	.70	.45
1974 O-Pee-Chee	53	1.00	.50	.30
1974 Topps	53	1.00	.50	.30
1975 O-Pee-Chee	144	.50	.25	.15
1975 Topps	144	1.25	.60	.40
1976 O-Pee-Chee	205	.45	.25	.14
1976 Topps	205	1.00	.50	.30
1977 O-Pee-Chee	45	.60	.30	.20
1977 Topps	45	1.00	.50	.30
1978 O-Pee-Chee	190	.35	.20	.11
1978 O-Pee-Chee	335	.35	.20	.11
1978 Topps	190	.75	.40	.25
1979 O-Pee-Chee	101	.30	.15	.09
1979 Topps	101	.75	.40	.25
1980 O-Pee-Chee	26	.35	.20	.11
1980 Topps	26	.75	.40	.25

Set	Card #	MT	NM	EX
1982 O-Pee-Chee	390	.20	.15	.08
1990 Upper Deck	506	.08	.06	.03

Terry Sawchuk

Set	Card #	NM	EX	VG
1951 Parkhurst	61 (R)	1000.	500.00	300.00
1952 Parkhurst	86	500.00	250.00	150.00
1953 Parkhurst	46	225.00	112.00	67.00
1954 Parkhurst	33	200.00	100.00	60.00
1954 Parkhurst	96	50.00	25.00	15.00
1954 Parkhurst	100	125.00	62.00	37.00
1954 Topps	58	600.00	300.00	180.00
1957 Topps	35 (R)	200.00	100.00	60.00
1958 Topps	2	150.00	75.00	45.00
1959 Topps	42	125.00	62.00	37.00
1960 Parkhurst	31	120.00	60.00	36.00
1961 Parkhurst	31	100.00	50.00	30.00
1963 Parkhurst	53	100.00	50.00	30.00
1964 Topps	6	100.00	50.00	30.00
1965 Topps	12	60.00	30.00	18.00
1966 Topps	13	50.00	25.00	15.00
1968 O-Pee-Chee	34	45.00	22.00	13.50
1968 Topps	34	30.00	15.00	9.00
1969 O-Pee-Chee	189	35.00	17.50	10.50
1970 O-Pee-Chee	231	50.00	25.00	15.00

Set	Card #	MT	NM	EX
1991 Pro Set	343	.05	.04	.02
1993 Parkhurst Parkie Reprints	37	20.00	15.00	8.00
1993 Parkhurst Parkie Reprints	53	20.00	15.00	8.00

Teemu Selanne

Set	Card #	MT	NM	EX
1991 Upper Deck	21 (R)	6.00	4.50	2.50
1992 Fleer Ultra	444	2.00	1.50	.80
1992 Fleer Ultra Imports	21	8.00	6.00	3.25
1992 O-Pee-Chee Premier	68	1.50	1.25	.60
1992 Parkhurst	209	2.25	1.75	.90
1992 Parkhurst	217	1.00	.70	.40
1992 Parkhurst	500	2.50	2.00	1.00
1992 Pinnacle	406	2.00	1.50	.80
1992 Upper Deck	574	1.75	1.25	.70

1992 Upper Deck Calder Candidates	10	10.00	7.50	4.00
1992 Upper Deck Euro-Rookies	6	8.00	6.00	3.25
1992 Upper Deck Gordie Howe Selects	15	10.00	7.50	4.00
1993 Donruss	387	2.00	1.50	.80
1993 Donruss Elite	3	35.00	26.00	14.00
1993 Donruss Ice Kings	10	5.00	3.75	2.00
1993 Donruss Special Print	Z	10.00	7.50	4.00
1993 Fleer PowerPlay	274	1.50	1.25	.60
1993 Fleer PowerPlay Global Greats	7	3.00	2.25	1.25
1993 Fleer PowerPlay Point Leaders	16	2.50	2.00	1.00
1993 Fleer PowerPlay Second-Year Stars	10	3.00	2.25	1.25
1993 Fleer PowerPlay Slapshot Artists	9	4.00	3.00	1.50
1993 Fleer Ultra	48	1.00	.70	.40
1993 Fleer Ultra	250	.25	.20	.10
1993 Fleer Ultra All-Stars	11	7.00	5.25	2.75
1993 Fleer Ultra Award Winners	6	7.00	5.25	2.75
1993 Fleer Ultra Red Light Specials	10	4.00	3.00	1.50
1993 Fleer Ultra Speed Merchants	10	20.00	15.00	8.00
1993 Leaf	13	1.00	.70	.40
1993 Leaf	110	.40	.30	.15
1993 Leaf Gold All-Stars	3	9.00	6.75	3.50
1993 Leaf Gold Rookies	1	6.00	4.50	2.50
1993 Leaf Hat Trick Artists	3	5.00	3.75	2.00
1993 OPC Premier Black Gold	20	15.00	11.00	6.00
1993 Parkhurst	233	1.00	.70	.40
1993 Parkhurst	235	.60	.45	.25
1993 Parkhurst East-West Stars	3W	15.00	11.00	6.00
1993 Parkhurst US Canada Gold-Foiled	8	14.00	10.50	5.50
1993 Pinnacle	4	1.00	.70	.40
1993 Pinnacle	222	.60	.45	.25
1993 Pinnacle All-Stars	32	1.00	.70	.40
1993 Pinnacle Nifty 50	3	20.00	15.00	8.00
1993 Pinnacle Team Pinnacle	12	35.00	26.00	14.00
1993 Pinnacle Team 2001	10	2.50	2.00	1.00
1993 Score	331	.75	.60	.30
1993 Score	477	.25	.20	.10
1993 Score Dream Team	21	15.00	11.00	6.00
1993 Score Franchise	24	18.00	13.50	7.25
1993 Score International Stars	2	4.00	3.00	1.50
1993 Topps Premier	92	.35	.25	.14
1993 Topps Premier	130	.60	.45	.25
1993 Topps Premier	148	.25	.20	.10
1993 Topps Premier	483	.60	.45	.25
1993 Topps Premier Black Gold	1	5.00	3.75	2.00
1993 Topps Stadium Club	141	.40	.30	.15
1993 Topps Stadium Club	210	.75	.60	.30
1993 Topps Stadium Club All-Stars	22	12.00	9.00	4.75
1993 Upper Deck	1	10.00	7.50	4.00
1993 Upper Deck	281	.50	.40	.20
1993 Upper Deck	309	.50	.40	.20
1993 Upper Deck	448	.75	.60	.30
1993 Upper Deck Award Winners	2	5.00	3.75	2.00
1993 Upper Deck Future Heroes	32	15.00	11.00	6.00
1993 Upper Deck Silver Skates Dye-Cut Retail	2R	12.00	9.00	4.75
1993 Upper Deck SP Inserts	177	3.00	2.25	1.25
1994 Donruss	210	.50	.40	.20
1994 Fleer Flair	209	1.00	.70	.40
1994 Fleer Ultra	246	.35	.25	.14
1994 Leaf Fire On Ice	12	8.00	6.00	3.25
1994 O-Pee-Chee Premier	95	.30	.25	.12
1994 O-Pee-Chee Premier	243	.25	.20	.10
1994 Parkhurst	300	.35	.25	.14
1994 Parkhurst Crash the Game	26	9.00	6.75	3.50
1994 Parkhurst Vintage Parkhurst	81	1.75	1.25	.70
1994 Pinnacle	25	.50	.40	.20
1994 Pinnacle Artist's Proofs	25	35.00	26.00	14.00
1994 Pinnacle Boomers	15	15.00	11.00	6.00
1994 Pinnacle Northern Lights	11	15.00	11.00	6.00
1994 Pinnacle Rink Collection	25	20.00	15.00	8.00
1994 Score	178	.45	.35	.20
1994 Score Franchise	26	25.00	18.50	10.00
1994 Score Hockey Gold Line	178	3.50	2.75	1.50
1994 Topps Premier	95	.30	.25	.12
1994 Topps Premier	243	.25	.20	.10
1994 Upper Deck	90	.75	.60	.30
1994 Upper Deck Electric Ice	90	25.00	18.50	10.00
1994 Upper Deck Ice Gallery	13	12.00	9.00	4.75
1994 Upper Deck Scoring Predictor	3	10.00	7.50	4.00
1994 Upper Deck SP	88	3.00	2.25	1.25

Brendan Shanahan

Set	Card #	MT	NM	EX
1988 O-Pee-Chee	122 (R)	20.00	15.00	8.00
1988 Topps	122 (R)	12.00	9.00	4.75
1989 O-Pee-Chee	147	.75	.60	.30
1989 Topps	147	1.50	1.25	.60
1990 Bowman	85	.15	.11	.06
1990 O-Pee-Chee	259	.05	.04	.02
1990 O-Pee-Chee Premier	105	.80	.60	.30
1990 Pro Set	174	.05	.04	.02
1990 Score	146	.25	.20	.10
1990 Topps	259	.20	.15	.08
1990 Upper Deck	269	.50	.40	.20
1991 Bowman	288	.05	.04	.02
1991 O-Pee-Chee Premier	130	.15	.11	.06
1991 O-Pee-Chee/Topps	140	.15	.11	.06
1991 Parkhurst	153	.05	.04	.02
1991 Pinnacle	41	.50	.40	.20
1991 Pro Set	131	.15	.11	.06
1991 Pro Set	475	.05	.04	.02
1991 Pro Set Platinum	111	.15	.11	.06
1991 Score American	286	.15	.11	.06
1991 Score Canadian	588	.10	.08	.04
1991 Score Traded	38	.05	.04	.02
1991 Topps Stadium Club	199	.30	.25	.12
1991 Upper Deck	561	.10	.08	.04
1992 Bowman	183	1.00	.70	.40
1992 Fleer Ultra	189	.06	.05	.02
1992 O-Pee-Chee	244	.05	.04	.02
1992 Parkhurst	156	.05	.04	.02

Set	Card #			
1992 Parkhurst Cherry Picks	10	12.00	9.00	4.75
1992 Pinnacle	114	.06	.05	.02
1992 Pinnacle	248	.06	.05	.02
1992 Pro Set	163	.05	.04	.02
1992 Score	392	.05	.04	.02
1992 Topps	295	.06	.05	.02
1992 Topps Stadium Club	371	.15	.11	.06
1992 Upper Deck	122	.05	.04	.02
1993 Donruss	299	.10	.08	.04
1993 Fleer PowerPlay	216	.20	.15	.08
1993 Fleer PowerPlay Slapshot Artists	10	.75	.60	.30
1993 Fleer Ultra	245	.15	.11	.06
1993 Leaf	30	.20	.15	.08
1993 Leaf Gold All-Stars	9	6.00	4.50	2.50
1993 Parkhurst	172	.10	.08	.04
1993 Pinnacle	205	.20	.15	.08
1993 Pinnacle Nifty 50	14	20.00	15.00	8.00
1993 Pinnacle Team 2001	29	1.00	.70	.40
1993 Score	238	.10	.08	.04
1993 Topps Premier	247	.05	.04	.02
1993 Topps Stadium Club	389	.25	.20	.10
1993 Upper Deck SP Inserts	140	.40	.30	.15
1994 Donruss	174	.30	.25	.12
1994 Fleer Flair	158	.50	.40	.20
1994 Fleer Flair Hot Numbers	9	14.00	10.50	5.50
1994 Fleer Ultra	189	.25	.20	.10
1994 Fleer Ultra Ultra Power	9	10.00	7.50	4.00
1994 Leaf	113	.20	.15	.08
1994 O-Pee-Chee Premier	215	.15	.11	.06
1994 Parkhurst	196	.35	.25	.14
1994 Parkhurst	298	.10	.08	.04
1994 Pinnacle	32	.40	.30	.15
1994 Pinnacle Artist's Proofs	32	20.00	15.00	8.00
1994 Pinnacle Boomers	6	10.00	7.50	4.00
1994 Pinnacle Rink Collection	32	10.00	7.50	4.00
1994 Pinnacle Team Pinnacle	6	25.00	18.50	10.00
1994 Score	155	.15	.11	.06
1994 Score Check-It	5	18.00	13.50	7.25
1994 Score Hockey Gold Line	155	1.50	1.25	.60
1994 Score 90-Plus Club	8	7.00	5.25	2.75
1994 Topps Premier	215	.15	.11	.06
1994 Topps Premier Finest Inserts	5	8.00	6.00	3.25
1994 Upper Deck Ice Gallery	4	7.00	5.25	2.75
1994 Upper Deck Scoring Predictor	7	7.00	5.25	2.75
1994 Upper Deck SP	69	.75	.60	.30

Set	Card #			
1971 O-Pee-Chee	193	40.00	20.00	12.00
1972 O-Pee-Chee	188	24.00	12.00	7.25
1973 O-Pee-Chee	132	20.00	10.00	6.00
1973 Topps	132	7.00	3.50	2.00
1974 O-Pee-Chee	40	9.50	4.75	2.75
1974 O-Pee-Chee	41	1.00	.50	.30
1974 O-Pee-Chee	219	1.00	.50	.30
1974 Topps	40	5.00	2.50	1.50
1974 Topps	219	.30	.15	.09
1975 O-Pee-Chee	150	7.00	3.50	2.00
1975 O-Pee-Chee	328	2.00	1.00	.60
1975 Topps	150	4.00	.40	.25
1975 Topps	328	.75	.40	.25
1976 O-Pee-Chee	66	1.00	.50	.30
1976 O-Pee-Chee	207	5.00	2.50	1.50
1976 O-Pee-Chee	394	.45	.25	.14
1976 Topps	66	.75	.40	.25
1976 Topps	207	2.50	1.25	.70
1977 O-Pee-Chee	38	3.00	1.50	.90
1977 Topps	38	2.00	1.00	.60
1978 O-Pee-Chee	4	.35	.20	.11
1978 O-Pee-Chee	30	2.00	1.00	.60
1978 O-Pee-Chee	64	2.00	1.00	.60
1978 O-Pee-Chee	65	3.00	1.50	.90
1978 O-Pee-Chee	69	1.50	.70	.45
1978 O-Pee-Chee	331	1.00	.50	.30
1978 Topps	4	.40	.20	.12
1978 Topps	30	1.00	.50	.30
1978 Topps	64	1.50	.70	.45
1978 Topps	65	1.50	.70	.45
1978 Topps	69	1.50	.70	.45
1979 O-Pee-Chee	120	1.50	.70	.45
1979 Topps	120	1.00	.50	.30
1980 O-Pee-Chee	50	1.50	.70	.45
1980 O-Pee-Chee	193	.40	.20	.12
1980 Topps	50	1.00	.50	.30
1980 Topps	165	1.00	.50	.30
1980 Topps	193	.30	.15	.09

Set	Card #	MT	NM	EX
1981 O-Pee-Chee	308	1.00	.70	.40
1981 O-Pee-Chee	312	.30	.25	.12
1981 Topps	36	.50	.40	.20
1982 O-Pee-Chee	257	.20	.15	.08
1983 O-Pee-Chee	257	.15	.11	.06
1983 O-Pee-Chee	258	.15	.11	.06
1983 O-Pee-Chee	272	.50	.40	.20
1984 O-Pee-Chee	168	.50	.40	.20
1984 Topps	121	.40	.30	.15
1990 Pro Set	404	.20	.15	.08
1990 Upper Deck	504	.20	.15	.08
1992 O-Pee-Chee	191	.25	.20	.10
1992 O-Pee-Chee 25th Anniversary Series	8	.30	.25	.12
1992 Pinnacle	248	.06	.05	.02

Darryl Sittler

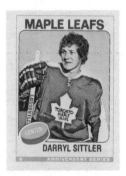

Set	Card #	NM	EX	VG
1970 O-Pee-Chee	218 (R)	120.00	60.00	36.00

Billy Smith

Set	Card #	NM	EX	VG
1973 O-Pee-Chee	142 (R)	35.00	17.50	10.50

1973 Topps	162 (R)	25.00	12.50	7.50
1974 O-Pee-Chee	82	10.00	5.00	3.00
1974 Topps	82	7.00	3.50	2.00
1975 O-Pee-Chee	372	6.00	3.00	1.75
1976 O-Pee-Chee	46	4.00	2.00	1.25
1976 Topps	46	2.00	1.00	.60
1977 O-Pee-Chee	229	2.00	1.00	.60
1977 Topps	229	1.50	.70	.45
1978 O-Pee-Chee	62	1.00	.50	.30
1978 Topps	62	1.00	.50	.30
1979 O-Pee-Chee	242	1.00	.50	.30
1979 Topps	242	1.00	.50	.30
1980 O-Pee-Chee	5	.35	.20	.11
1980 O-Pee-Chee	60	.75	.40	.25
1980 Topps	5	.20	.10	.06
1980 Topps	60	.40	.20	.12

Set	Card #	MT	NM	EX
1981 O-Pee-Chee	207	.60	.45	.25
1981 Topps	93	.40	.30	.15
1982 O-Pee-Chee	211	.20	.15	.08
1983 O-Pee-Chee	17	.15	.11	.06
1984 O-Pee-Chee	135	.35	.25	.14
1984 Topps	101	.75	.60	.30
1986 O-Pee-Chee	228	.25	.20	.10
1988 O-Pee-Chee	17	.25	.20	.10
1988 Topps	17	.25	.20	.10

Tommy Soderstrom

Set	Card #	MT	NM	EX
1992 Fleer Ultra	160 (R)	.75	.60	.30
1992 Fleer Ultra Imports	23	3.00	2.25	1.25
1992 Parkhurst	367 (R)	.50	.40	.20
1992 Parkhurst	448	.30	.25	.12
1992 Upper Deck	377 (R)	.35	.25	.14
1992 Upper Deck	475	.25	.20	.10
1993 Donruss	253	.25	.20	.10
1993 Fleer PowerPlay	185	.30	.25	.12
1993 Fleer PowerPlay Netminders	8	5.00	3.75	2.00
1993 Fleer PowerPlay Second-Year Stars	11	.60	.45	.25
1993 Fleer Ultra	217	.20	.15	.08
1993 Leaf	37	.15	.11	.06
1993 Leaf Gold Rookies	12	5.00	3.75	2.00
1993 Parkhurst	150	.25	.20	.10
1993 Pinnacle	19	.20	.15	.08
1993 Score	336	.20	.15	.08
1993 Score International Stars	5	1.00	.70	.40
1993 Topps Premier	55	.35	.25	.14
1993 Topps Premier	122	.25	.20	.10
1993 Topps Stadium Club	340	.15	.11	.06
1993 Topps Stadium Club	430	.10	.08	.04
1993 Upper Deck	182	.30	.25	.12
1994 Fleer Ultra	160	.05	.04	.02
1994 Leaf	184	.10	.08	.04
1994 Topps Stadium Club	24	.10	.08	.04

Peter Stastny

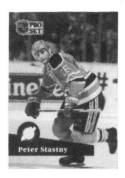

Peter Stastny

Set	Card #	MT	NM	EX
1981 O-Pee-Chee	269 (R)	22.00	11.00	6.50
1981 O-Pee-Chee	286	5.00	3.75	2.00
1981 O-Pee-Chee	287	3.00	2.25	1.25
1981 O-Pee-Chee	395	4.00	3.00	1.50
1981 Topps	39 (R)	4.00	3.00	1.50
1981 Topps	61	.40	.30	.15
1982 O-Pee-Chee	276	.20	.15	.08
1982 O-Pee-Chee	292	5.50	4.25	2.25
1982 O-Pee-Chee	293	1.50	1.25	.60
1983 O-Pee-Chee	304	3.00	2.25	1.25
1984 O-Pee-Chee	293	2.00	1.50	.80
1984 Topps	130	1.50	1.25	.60
1985 O-Pee-Chee	31	1.25	.90	.50
1985 Topps	31	1.00	.70	.40
1986 O-Pee-Chee	20	1.00	.70	.40
1986 Topps	20	.75	.60	.30
1987 O-Pee-Chee	21	.60	.45	.25
1987 Topps	21	.50	.40	.20
1988 O-Pee-Chee	22	.50	.40	.20
1988 Topps	22	.25	.20	.10
1989 O-Pee-Chee	143	.35	.25	.14
1989 Topps	143	.15	.11	.06
1990 Bowman	86	.07	.05	.03
1990 O-Pee-Chee	334	.10	.08	.04
1990 Pro Set	175	.20	.15	.08
1990 Score	96	.12	.09	.05
1990 Score Hockey's 100 Hottest Rising Stars	48	.10	.08	.04
1990 Topps	334	.12	.09	.05
1990 Upper Deck	163	.10	.08	.04
1991 Bowman	287	.05	.04	.02
1991 O-Pee-Chee/Topps	275	.05	.04	.02
1991 Parkhurst	103	.05	.04	.02
1991 Parkhurst	209	.05	.04	.02
1991 Pinnacle	266	.08	.06	.03
1991 Pro Set	143	.05	.04	.02
1991 Pro Set Platinum	194	.05	.04	.02
1991 Score American	66	.05	.04	.02
1991 Score Canadian	66	.05	.04	.02
1991 Topps Stadium Club	263	.08	.06	.03
1991 Upper Deck	113	.05	.04	.02
1992 Bowman	249	.25	.20	.10
1992 Fleer Ultra	118	.06	.05	.02
1992 Fleer Ultra Imports	24	3.00	2.25	1.25
1992 O-Pee-Chee	216	.05	.04	.02
1992 Pinnacle	359	.06	.05	.02
1992 Pro Set	100	.05	.04	.02
1992 Score	291	.05	.04	.02
1992 Topps	469	.06	.05	.02
1992 Topps Stadium Club	140	.05	.04	.02
1993 Donruss	487	.15	.11	.06
1993 Score	22	.05	.04	.02
1994 Donruss	191	.08	.06	.03
1994 Fleer Flair	159	.25	.20	.10
1994 Fleer Ultra	190	.07	.05	.03
1994 O-Pee-Chee Premier	182	.05	.04	.02
1994 Parkhurst	203	.06	.05	.02
1994 Pinnacle	134	.10	.08	.04

1994 Pinnacle Artist's Proofs	134	5.00	3.75	2.00
1994 Pinnacle Rink Collection	134	3.00	2.25	1.25
1994 Topps Premier	182	.05	.04	.02
1994 Upper Deck	60	.10	.08	.04
1994 Upper Deck Electric Ice	60	3.50	2.75	1.50

Kevin Stevens

Set	Card #	MT	NM	EX
1990 Bowman	208	1.00	.70	.40
1990 O-Pee-Chee	360 (R)	1.25	.90	.50
1990 O-Pee-Chee Premier	111 (R)	3.50	2.75	1.50
1990 Pro Set	240 (R)	.70	.50	.30
1990 Score	53 (R)	.70	.50	.30
1990 Topps	360 (R)	.75	.60	.30
1990 Upper Deck	14 (R)	2.00	1.50	.80
1991 Bowman	92	.40	.30	.15
1991 O-Pee-Chee Premier	26	.40	.30	.15
1991 O-Pee-Chee/Topps	267	.05	.04	.02
1991 O-Pee-Chee/Topps	421	.40	.30	.15
1991 Parkhurst	135	.60	.45	.25
1991 Parkhurst	473	2.50	2.00	1.00
1991 Pinnacle	191	.75	.60	.30
1991 Pinnacle B	4	50.00	37.00	20.00
1991 Pro Set	185	.30	.25	.12
1991 Pro Set	314	.10	.08	.04
1991 Pro Set Platinum	93	.25	.20	.10
1991 Score American	248	.25	.20	.10
1991 Score Canadian	468	.25	.20	.10
1991 Topps Stadium Club	234	1.00	.70	.40
1991 Upper Deck	154	.50	.40	.20
1991 Upper Deck	613	.15	.11	.06
1992 Bowman	241	3.50	2.75	1.50
1992 Bowman	366	1.50	1.25	.60
1992 Fleer Ultra	171	.40	.30	.15
1992 Fleer Ultra All-Stars	5	3.00	2.25	1.25
1992 O-Pee-Chee	29	.25	.20	.10
1992 Parkhurst	138	.40	.30	.15
1992 Parkhurst	466	.15	.11	.06
1992 Pinnacle	288	.50	.40	.20
1992 Pro Set	140	.25	.20	.10
1992 Score	25	.25	.20	.10
1992 Score	492	.15	.11	.06
1992 Score USA Greats	10	6.00	4.50	2.50
1992 Topps	259	.06	.05	.02
1992 Topps	343	.06	.05	.02
1992 Topps	429	.06	.05	.02
1992 Topps Stadium Club	110	.40	.30	.15
1992 Topps Stadium Club	257	.40	.30	.15
1992 Upper Deck	275	.30	.25	.12
1992 Upper Deck	630	.25	.20	.10
1992 Upper Deck Gordie Howe Selects	4	6.00	4.50	2.50
1993 Donruss	265	.25	.20	.10
1993 Fleer PowerPlay	195	.35	.25	.14
1993 Fleer PowerPlay Point Leaders	17	.60	.45	.25
1993 Fleer Ultra	229	.25	.20	.10
1993 Fleer Ultra All-Stars	6	4.00	3.00	1.50
1993 Leaf	69	.20	.15	.08
1993 Leaf Hat Trick Artists	9	3.00	2.25	1.25
1993 Parkhurst	158	.25	.20	.10
1993 Pinnacle	149	.25	.20	.10
1993 Pinnacle All-Stars	15	.30	.25	.12
1993 Pinnacle Nifty 50	9	14.00	10.50	5.50
1993 Score	325	.20	.15	.08
1993 Score Dream Team	23	6.00	4.50	2.50
1993 Topps Premier	170	.10	.08	.04
1993 Topps Premier	370	.20	.15	.08
1993 Topps Stadium Club	158	.25	.20	.10
1993 Topps Stadium Club	457	.15	.11	.06
1993 Upper Deck	126	.25	.20	.10
1993 Upper Deck	230	.10	.08	.04
1993 Upper Deck Hat Tricks	19	1.00	.70	.40
1993 Upper Deck SP Inserts	124	.80	.60	.30
1994 Donruss	229	.30	.25	.12
1994 Fleer Flair	140	.40	.30	.15
1994 Fleer Ultra	170	.10	.08	.04
1994 Parkhurst	177	.20	.15	.08
1994 Score	182	.15	.11	.06
1994 Score Check-It	4	9.00	6.75	3.50
1994 Score Hockey Gold Line	182	1.00	.70	.40
1994 Topps Premier Finest Inserts	17	7.00	5.25	2.75
1994 Upper Deck SP	62	.60	.45	.25

Scott Stevens

Set	Card #	MT	NM	EX
1983 O-Pee-Chee	376 (R)	15.00	11.00	6.00
1984 O-Pee-Chee	206	4.00	3.00	1.50
1984 Topps	149	2.50	2.00	1.00
1985 O-Pee-Chee	62	4.00	3.00	1.50
1985 Topps	62	2.00	1.50	.80
1986 O-Pee-Chee	126	1.50	1.25	.60
1986 Topps	126	.25	.20	.10
1987 O-Pee-Chee	25	1.00	.70	.40
1987 Topps	25	.25	.20	.10
1988 O-Pee-Chee	60	.60	.45	.25
1988 Topps	60	.25	.20	.10
1989 O-Pee-Chee	93	.35	.25	.14
1989 Topps	93	.15	.11	.06
1990 O-Pee-Chee	211	.05	.04	.02
1990 O-Pee-Chee Premier	112	.15	.11	.06
1990 Pro Set	321	.10	.08	.04
1990 Pro Set	528	.07	.05	.03
1990 Score	188	.05	.04	.02
1990 Score	341	.05	.04	.02
1990 Score Hockey's 100 Hottest Rising Stars	82	.10	.08	.04
1990 Score Traded	40	.10	.08	.04
1990 Topps	211	.03	.02	.01
1990 Upper Deck	236	.15	.11	.06

1990 Upper Deck	436	.08	.06	.03
1990 Upper Deck	482	.10	.08	.04
1991 Bowman	369	.05	.04	.02
1991 O-Pee-Chee Premier	84	.05	.04	.02
1991 O-Pee-Chee/Topps	481	.05	.04	.02
1991 Parkhurst	102	.05	.04	.02
1991 Pinnacle	81	.08	.06	.03
1991 Pro Set	216	.05	.04	.02
1991 Pro Set	292	.05	.04	.02
1991 Pro Set	423	.05	.04	.02
1991 Pro Set Platinum	72	.05	.04	.02
1991 Score American	40	.05	.04	.02
1991 Score American	303	.05	.04	.02
1991 Score Canadian	40	.05	.04	.02
1991 Score Canadian	307	.05	.04	.02
1991 Score Canadian	595	.05	.04	.02
1991 Score Traded	45	.05	.04	.02
1991 Topps Stadium Club	265	.08	.06	.03
1991 Upper Deck	132	.05	.04	.02
1991 Upper Deck	539	.05	.04	.02
1992 Bowman	160	.25	.20	.10
1992 Bowman	242	2.00	1.50	.80
1992 Fleer Ultra	119	.06	.05	.02
1992 O-Pee-Chee	251	.10	.08	.04
1992 O-Pee-Chee	336	.05	.04	.02
1992 O-Pee-Chee 25th Anniversary Series	16	.25	.20	.10
1992 Parkhurst	92	.05	.04	.02
1992 Parkhurst Cherry Picks	18	9.00	6.75	3.50
1992 Pinnacle	280	.06	.05	.02
1992 Pinnacle Team Pinnacle	4	20.00	15.00	8.00
1992 Pro Set	95	.05	.04	.02
1992 Score	75	.05	.04	.02
1992 Score	429	.05	.04	.02
1992 Topps	156	.06	.05	.02
1992 Topps	269	.06	.05	.02
1992 Topps Stadium Club	151	.05	.04	.02
1992 Upper Deck	297	.05	.04	.02
1993 Donruss	192	.10	.08	.04
1993 Fleer PowerPlay	143	.10	.08	.04
1993 Fleer Ultra	189	.07	.05	.03
1993 Leaf	60	.10	.08	.04
1993 Leaf Gold All-Stars	4	6.00	4.50	2.50
1993 Parkhurst	114	.10	.08	.04
1993 Pinnacle	25	.10	.08	.04
1993 Pinnacle All-Stars	4	.20	.15	.08
1993 Pinnacle Hockey Captains	13	5.00	3.75	2.00
1993 Pinnacle Team Pinnacle	3	25.00	18.50	10.00
1993 Pinnacle Team Pinnacle	4	30.00	22.00	12.00
1993 Score	111	.05	.04	.02
1993 Score Canadian Dynamic Duos	8	30.00	22.00	12.00
1993 Score Dream Team	5	4.00	3.00	1.50
1993 Score Franchise	11	4.00	3.00	1.50
1993 Topps Premier	80	.05	.04	.02
1993 Topps Stadium Club	383	.15	.11	.06
1993 Topps Stadium Club All-Stars	6	15.00	11.00	6.00
1993 Upper Deck	119	.05	.04	.02
1993 Upper Deck SP Inserts	89	.30	.25	.12
1994 Donruss	262	.08	.06	.03
1994 Fleer Flair	100	.25	.20	.10
1994 Fleer Ultra	123	.08	.06	.03
1994 O-Pee-Chee Premier	126	.05	.04	.02
1994 O-Pee-Chee Premier	153	.05	.04	.02
1994 Parkhurst Crash the Game	13	5.00	3.75	2.00
1994 Parkhurst Vintage Parkhurst	41	.20	.15	.08
1994 Pinnacle Team Pinnacle	5	20.00	15.00	8.00
1994 Pinnacle Team Pinnacle	7	20.00	15.00	8.00
1994 Score	193	.05	.04	.02
1994 Score Check-It	2	7.50	5.75	3.00
1994 Score Dream Team	5	5.00	3.75	2.00
1994 Score Franchise	13	8.00	6.00	3.25
1994 Score Hockey Gold Line	193	.25	.20	.10
1994 Topps Premier	126	.05	.04	.02
1994 Topps Premier	153	.05	.04	.02
1994 Topps Stadium Club	4	.05	.04	.02
1994 Upper Deck	73	.10	.08	.04
1994 Upper Deck Electric Ice	73	3.50	2.75	1.50
1994 Upper Deck Ice Gallery	5	4.00	3.00	1.50
1994 Upper Deck SP	45	.30	.25	.12

Mats Sundin

Set	Card #	MT	NM	EX
1990 O-Pee-Chee Premier	114 (R)	7.00	5.25	2.75
1990 Pro Set	636 (R)	.60	.45	.25
1990 Score	398 (R)	.80	.60	.30
1990 Score Traded	100	1.50	1.25	.60
1990 Upper Deck	365 (R)	2.00	1.50	.80
1991 Bowman	137	.20	.15	.08
1991 O-Pee-Chee/Topps	12	.20	.15	.08
1991 O-Pee-Chee/Topps	219	.20	.15	.08
1991 Parkhurst	144	.50	.40	.20
1991 Pinnacle	10	.60	.45	.25
1991 Pinnacle	389	.08	.06	.03
1991 Pro Set	197	.20	.15	.08
1991 Pro Set Platinum	99	.25	.20	.10
1991 Score American	130	.25	.20	.10
1991 Score Canadian	130	.25	.20	.10
1991 Topps Stadium Club	300	.75	.60	.30
1991 Upper Deck	31	.20	.15	.08
1991 Upper Deck	134	.50	.40	.20
1991 Upper Deck Euro-Stars	13	1.50	1.00	.50
1992 Bowman	344	1.00	.70	.40
1992 Fleer Ultra	180	.35	.25	.14
1992 Fleer Ultra Imports	25	5.00	3.75	2.00
1992 O-Pee-Chee	110	.10	.08	.04
1992 Parkhurst	148	.05	.04	.02
1992 Parkhurst	221	.05	.04	.02
1992 Pinnacle	90	.25	.20	.10
1992 Pinnacle Team 2000	7	1.25	.90	.50
1992 Pro Set	149	.25	.20	.10
1992 Score	153	.25	.20	.10
1992 Topps	415	.15	.11	.06
1992 Topps Stadium Club	478	.35	.25	.14
1992 Upper Deck	121	.30	.25	.12
1992 Upper Deck	374	.20	.15	.08
1992 Upper Deck Euro Stars	18	3.00	2.00	1.00
1992 Upper Deck World Junior Grads	17	5.00	3.75	2.00
1993 Donruss	283	.25	.20	.10
1993 Donruss Special Print	S	4.50	3.50	1.75
1993 Fleer PowerPlay	205	.10	.08	.04

1993 Fleer PowerPlay Global Greats	8	.50	.40	.20
1993 Fleer PowerPlay Point Leaders	18	.60	.45	.25
1993 Fleer Ultra	137	.25	.20	.10
1993 Leaf	136	.25	.20	.10
1993 OPC Premier Black Gold	6	10.00	7.50	4.00
1993 Parkhurst	435	.20	.15	.08
1993 Parkhurst First Overall	5	10.00	7.50	4.00
1993 Pinnacle	2	.25	.20	.10
1993 Pinnacle Team 2001	15	.50	.40	.20
1993 Score	9	.15	.11	.06
1993 Score Canadian Dynamic Duos	5	10.00	7.50	4.00
1993 Score International Stars	10	1.00	.70	.40
1993 Topps Finest Hockey Card Series Roster	5	5.00	3.75	2.00
1993 Topps Premier	460	.10	.08	.04
1993 Topps Stadium Club	370	.10	.08	.04
1993 Topps Stadium Club	425	.15	.11	.06
1993 Upper Deck	220	.15	.11	.06
1993 Upper Deck	228	.10	.08	.04
1993 Upper Deck	302	.10	.08	.04
1993 Upper Deck	419	.20	.15	.08
1993 Upper Deck Hat Tricks	20	1.00	.70	.40
1993 Upper Deck SP Inserts	132	1.00	.70	.40
1994 Fleer Flair	186	.40	.30	.15
1994 Fleer Ultra	220	.08	.06	.03
1994 O-Pee-Chee Premier	160	.05	.04	.02
1994 Parkhurst	185	.20	.15	.08
1994 Parkhurst Vintage Parkhurst	52	.20	.15	.08
1994 Pinnacle Northern Lights	10	12.00	9.00	4.75
1994 Score	89	.15	.11	.06
1994 Score Hockey Gold Line	89	1.00	.70	.40
1994 Topps Premier	160	.05	.04	.02
1994 Topps Stadium Club	90	.05	.04	.02
1994 Upper Deck	51	.30	.25	.12
1994 Upper Deck Electric Ice	51	8.00	6.00	3.25

1981 O-Pee-Chee	152	.60	.45	.25
1981 O-Pee-Chee	391	3.00	2.25	1.25
1981 Topps	40	.40	.30	.15
1981 Topps	132	.75	.60	.30
1982 O-Pee-Chee	161	.20	.15	.08
1983 O-Pee-Chee	163	.30	.25	.12
1984 O-Pee-Chee	92	.15	.11	.06
1985 O-Pee-Chee	214	.25	.20	.10
1986 O-Pee-Chee	63	.15	.11	.06
1986 Topps	63	.07	.05	.03
1987 O-Pee-Chee	118	.12	.09	.05
1987 Topps	118	.08	.06	.03
1988 O-Pee-Chee	46	.15	.11	.06
1988 Topps	46	.07	.05	.03
1989 O-Pee-Chee	58	.07	.05	.03
1989 Topps	58	.05	.04	.02
1990 Bowman	149	.04	.03	.02
1990 O-Pee-Chee	314	.05	.04	.02
1990 Pro Set	128	.10	.08	.04
1990 Score	166	.05	.04	.02
1990 Topps	314	.03	.02	.01
1990 Upper Deck	214	.08	.06	.03
1991 Bowman	186	.05	.04	.02
1991 O-Pee-Chee/Topps	138	.05	.04	.02
1991 Parkhurst	67	.05	.04	.02
1991 Parkhurst	214	.05	.04	.02
1991 Pinnacle	249	.08	.06	.03
1991 Pinnacle	373	.08	.06	.03
1991 Pro Set	103	.05	.04	.02
1991 Pro Set	325	.05	.04	.02
1991 Score American	214	.05	.04	.02
1991 Score American	374	.05	.04	.02
1991 Score American	435	.05	.04	.02
1991 Score Canadian	214	.05	.04	.02
1991 Score Canadian	264	.05	.04	.02
1991 Score Canadian	325	.05	.04	.02
1991 Topps Stadium Club	232	.08	.06	.03
1991 Upper Deck	270	.05	.04	.02
1992 Bowman	37	.25	.20	.10
1992 Fleer Ultra	313	.06	.05	.02
1992 Parkhurst	307	.05	.04	.02
1992 Pinnacle	367	.06	.05	.02
1992 Pro Set	258	.05	.04	.02
1992 Score	49	.05	.04	.02
1992 Topps	446	.06	.05	.02
1992 Topps Stadium Club	234	.05	.04	.02
1993 Fleer PowerPlay	364	.10	.08	.04
1993 Fleer Ultra	348	.07	.05	.03
1993 Leaf	374	.10	.08	.04
1993 Parkhurst	367	.10	.08	.04
1993 Pinnacle	412	.08	.06	.03
1993 Score	389	.05	.04	.02

Dave Taylor

Set	Card #	NM	EX	VG
1978 O-Pee-Chee	353 (R)	20.00	10.00	6.00
1979 O-Pee-Chee	232	7.00	3.50	2.00
1979 Topps	232	5.00	2.50	1.50
1980 O-Pee-Chee	137	3.50	1.75	1.00
1980 Topps	137	2.00	1.00	.60

Set	Card #	MT	NM	EX
1981 O-Pee-Chee	143	2.00	1.50	.80

Rick Tocchet

Set	Card #	MT	NM	EX
1987 O-Pee-Chee	2 (R)	14.00	10.50	5.50
1987 Topps	2 (R)	8.00	6.00	3.25
1988 O-Pee-Chee	177	3.00	2.25	1.25

Bryan Trottier

Set	Card #			
1988 Topps	177	2.50	2.00	1.00
1989 O-Pee-Chee	80	.30	.25	.12
1989 Topps	80	.20	.15	.08
1990 Bowman	108	.15	.11	.06
1990 O-Pee-Chee	26	.15	.11	.06
1990 O-Pee-Chee Premier	120	.25	.20	.10
1990 Pro Set	225	.15	.11	.06
1990 Pro Set	374	.15	.11	.06
1990 Score	80	.07	.05	.03
1990 Score Hockey's 100 Hottest Rising Stars	40	.10	.08	.04
1990 Topps	26	.15	.11	.06
1990 Upper Deck	263	.25	.20	.10
1990 Upper Deck	488	.20	.15	.08
1991 Bowman	230	.05	.04	.02
1991 O-Pee-Chee Premier	63	.05	.04	.02
1991 O-Pee-Chee/Topps	160	.05	.04	.02
1991 Parkhurst	129	.05	.04	.02
1991 Parkhurst	354	.05	.04	.02
1991 Pinnacle	20	.08	.06	.03
1991 Pro Set	177	.05	.04	.02
1991 Pro Set	311	.05	.04	.02
1991 Pro Set	580	.05	.04	.02
1991 Pro Set Platinum	88	.05	.04	.02
1991 Score American	9	.05	.04	.02
1991 Score American	302	.05	.04	.02
1991 Score American	334	.05	.04	.02
1991 Score Canadian	9	.05	.04	.02
1991 Score Canadian	306	.05	.04	.02
1991 Score Canadian	364	.10	.08	.04
1991 Topps Stadium Club	35	.10	.08	.04
1991 Upper Deck	122	.10	.08	.04
1991 Upper Deck	503	.05	.04	.02
1992 Bowman	159	.25	.20	.10
1992 Fleer Ultra	172	.06	.05	.02
1992 O-Pee-Chee	148	.05	.04	.02
1992 Parkhurst	139	.05	.04	.02
1992 Parkhurst Cherry Picks	12	9.00	6.75	3.50
1992 Pinnacle	282	.06	.05	.02
1992 Pro Set	138	.05	.04	.02
1992 Score	245	.05	.04	.02
1992 Topps	70	.06	.05	.02
1992 Topps Stadium Club	76	.05	.04	.02
1992 Upper Deck	238	.05	.04	.02
1993 Donruss	267	.10	.08	.04
1993 Fleer PowerPlay	196	.10	.08	.04
1993 Fleer Ultra	225	.07	.05	.03
1993 Leaf	109	.10	.08	.04
1993 Parkhurst	428	.12	.09	.05
1993 Pinnacle	174	.10	.08	.04
1993 Pinnacle All-Stars	14	.20	.15	.08
1993 Score	340	.05	.04	.02
1993 Topps Premier	72	.05	.04	.02
1993 Topps Stadium Club	329	.05	.04	.02
1993 Topps Stadium Club All-Stars	20	8.00	6.00	3.25
1993 Upper Deck	179	.05	.04	.02
1993 Upper Deck	233	.10	.08	.04
1993 Upper Deck Hat Tricks	12	.60	.45	.25
1993 Upper Deck SP Inserts	126	.30	.25	.12
1994 Fleer Flair	83	.25	.20	.10
1994 Leaf	100	.10	.08	.04
1994 Parkhurst Vintage Parkhurst	25	.20	.15	.08
1994 Score Check-It	11	7.50	5.75	3.00
1994 Topps Stadium Club	160	.05	.04	.02
1994 Upper Deck	224	.10	.08	.04
1994 Upper Deck Electric Ice	224	3.50	2.75	1.50

Tab: A portion of a card, usually perforated, which can be removed from the card without damaging the central part of the card.

Team card: A card picturing an entire team.

BRYAN TROTTIER • CENTER

Set	Card #	NM	EX	VG
1976 O-Pee-Chee	67	7.00	3.50	2.00
1976 O-Pee-Chee	115 (R)	50.00	25.00	15.00
1976 O-Pee-Chee	216	4.00	2.00	1.25
1976 Topps	67	5.00	2.50	1.50
1976 Topps	115 (R)	30.00	15.00	9.00
1976 Topps	216	2.50	1.25	.70
1977 O-Pee-Chee	105	22.00	11.00	6.50
1977 Topps	105	12.00	6.00	3.50
1978 O-Pee-Chee	10	10.00	5.00	3.00
1978 O-Pee-Chee	64	2.00	1.00	.60
1978 O-Pee-Chee	65	3.00	1.50	.90
1978 O-Pee-Chee	325	4.00	2.00	1.25
1978 Topps	10	5.00	2.50	1.50
1978 Topps	64	1.50	.70	.45
1978 Topps	65	1.50	.70	.45
1979 O-Pee-Chee	2	3.00	1.50	.90
1979 O-Pee-Chee	3	3.00	1.50	.90
1979 O-Pee-Chee	7	3.00	1.50	.90
1979 O-Pee-Chee	100	4.00	2.00	1.25
1979 O-Pee-Chee	165	1.00	.50	.30
1979 Topps	2	2.00	1.00	.60
1979 Topps	3	2.00	1.00	.60
1979 Topps	7	2.00	1.00	.60
1979 Topps	100	2.50	1.25	.70
1979 Topps	165	1.00	.50	.30
1980 O-Pee-Chee	40	2.00	1.00	.60
1980 Topps	40	1.50	.70	.45

Set	Card #	MT	NM	EX
1981 O-Pee-Chee	200	2.00	1.50	.80
1981 O-Pee-Chee	210	.75	.60	.30
1981 Topps	41	.75	.60	.30
1981 Topps	132	.75	.60	.30
1982 O-Pee-Chee	5	.60	.45	.25
1982 O-Pee-Chee	214	1.00	.70	.40
1982 O-Pee-Chee	215	.60	.45	.25
1983 O-Pee-Chee	21	.50	.40	.20
1984 O-Pee-Chee	139	.75	.60	.30
1984 O-Pee-Chee	214	.75	.60	.30
1984 Topps	104	.35	.25	.14
1984 Topps	160	.25	.20	.10
1985 O-Pee-Chee	60	.50	.40	.20
1985 Topps	60	.90	.70	.35
1986 O-Pee-Chee	155	.60	.45	.25
1986 Topps	155	.25	.20	.10
1987 O-Pee-Chee	60	.30	.25	.12
1987 Topps	60	.50	.40	.20
1988 O-Pee-Chee	97	.30	.25	.12
1988 Topps	97	.20	.15	.08
1989 O-Pee-Chee	149	.50	.40	.20
1989 Topps	149	.75	.60	.30
1990 O-Pee-Chee	6	.07	.05	.03
1990 O-Pee-Chee	291	.10	.08	.04
1990 O-Pee-Chee Premier	121	.15	.11	.06
1990 Pro Set	192	.20	.15	.08
1990 Pro Set	511	.15	.11	.06
1990 Score	270	.12	.09	.05
1990 Score Traded	106	.20	.15	.08
1990 Topps	6	.07	.05	.03

		MT	NM	EX
1990 Topps	291	.10	.08	.04
1990 Upper Deck	137	.30	.25	.12
1990 Upper Deck	425	.25	.20	.10
1991 Bowman	93	.05	.04	.02
1991 O-Pee-Chee/Topps	472	.05	.04	.02
1991 Parkhurst	208	.05	.04	.02
1991 Parkhurst	360	.05	.04	.02
1991 Parkhurst	431	.05	.04	.02
1991 Pinnacle	241	.08	.06	.03
1991 Pro Set	192	.05	.04	.02
1991 Pro Set Platinum	216	.05	.04	.02
1991 Pro Set Platinum PC	19	1.25	.90	.50
1991 Score American	229	.05	.04	.02
1991 Score Canadian	229	.05	.04	.02
1991 Topps Stadium Club	91	.08	.06	.03
1991 Upper Deck	329	.10	.08	.04
1992 Bowman	152	.25	.20	.10
1992 Bowman	243	14.00	10.50	5.50
1992 O-Pee-Chee	107	.20	.15	.08
1992 O-Pee-Chee	130	.05	.04	.02
1992 O-Pee-Chee 25th Anniversary Series	9	.25	.20	.10
1992 Score	157	.05	.04	.02
1992 Topps	416	.06	.05	.02
1992 Topps Stadium Club	26	.05	.04	.02
1993 Donruss	268	.10	.08	.04
1993 Fleer PowerPlay	416	.08	.06	.03
1993 Fleer Ultra	398	.07	.05	.03
1993 Leaf	318	.10	.08	.04
1993 Parkhurst	431	.10	.08	.04
1993 Pinnacle	411	.12	.09	.05
1993 Score	567	.10	.08	.04
1993 Topps Premier	296	.05	.04	.02

Pierre Turgeon

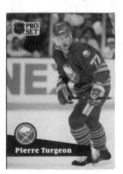

Set	Card #	MT	NM	EX
1988 O-Pee-Chee	194 (R)	27.00	20.00	11.00
1988 O-Pee-Chee Future Stars	20	2.00	1.50	.80
1988 Topps	194 (R)	15.00	11.00	6.00
1989 O-Pee-Chee	25	.80	.60	.30
1989 Topps	25	1.50	1.25	.60
1990 Bowman	241	.25	.20	.10
1990 O-Pee-Chee	66	.10	.08	.04
1990 O-Pee-Chee Premier	124	1.50	1.25	.60
1990 Pro Set	31	.30	.25	.12
1990 Pro Set	366	.05	.04	.02
1990 Score	110	.30	.25	.12
1990 Score Hockey's 100 Hottest Rising Stars	53	.10	.08	.04
1990 Topps	66	.30	.25	.12
1990 Upper Deck	43	.50	.40	.20
1990 Upper Deck	318	.07	.05	.03
1991 Bowman	27	.25	.20	.10
1991 O-Pee-Chee Premier	59	.25	.20	.10
1991 O-Pee-Chee/Topps	416	.15	.11	.06
1991 Parkhurst	106	.05	.04	.02
1991 Pinnacle	30	.50	.40	.20
1991 Pro Set	15	.25	.20	.10

		MT	NM	EX
1991 Pro Set	433	.25	.20	.10
1991 Pro Set Platinum	10	.20	.15	.08
1991 Score American	4	.20	.15	.08
1991 Score American	377	.05	.04	.02
1991 Score American	416	.10	.08	.04
1991 Score Canadian	4	.25	.20	.10
1991 Score Canadian	267	.05	.04	.02
1991 Score Canadian	332	.10	.08	.04
1991 Score Traded	101	.25	.15	.08
1991 Topps Stadium Club	77	1.00	.70	.40
1991 Upper Deck	176	.40	.30	.15
1991 Upper Deck	554	.25	.20	.10
1992 Bowman	23	1.50	1.25	.60
1992 Fleer Ultra	132	.35	.25	.14
1992 O-Pee-Chee	47	.15	.11	.06
1992 Parkhurst	103	.35	.25	.14
1992 Pinnacle	165	.40	.30	.15
1992 Pinnacle Team 2000	17	2.00	1.50	.80
1992 Pro Set	104	.20	.15	.08
1992 Score	325	.20	.15	.08
1992 Score	430	.05	.04	.02
1992 Score Sharpshooters	25	1.50	.75	.35
1992 Topps	289	.06	.05	.02
1992 Topps Stadium Club	276	.25	.20	.10
1992 Upper Deck	175	.25	.20	.10
1993 Donruss	209	.35	.25	.14
1993 Donruss Special Print	N	6.00	4.50	2.50
1993 Fleer PowerPlay	155	.40	.30	.15
1993 Fleer PowerPlay Point Leaders	19	.75	.60	.30
1993 Fleer Ultra	197	.25	.20	.10
1993 Fleer Ultra All-Stars	3	6.00	4.50	2.50
1993 Fleer Ultra Premier Pivots	9	2.50	2.00	1.00
1993 Fleer Ultra Scoring Kings	5	6.00	4.50	2.50
1993 Leaf	25	.40	.30	.15
1993 Leaf Hat Trick Artists	5	3.00	2.25	1.25
1993 Parkhurst	389	.10	.08	.04
1993 Parkhurst East-West Stars	10E	15.00	11.00	6.00
1993 Parkhurst First Overall	7	9.00	6.75	3.50
1993 Pinnacle	160	.25	.20	.10
1993 Pinnacle	225	.20	.15	.08
1993 Pinnacle All-Stars	5	.40	.30	.15
1993 Pinnacle Nifty 50	7	14.00	10.50	5.50
1993 Pinnacle Team 2001	13	1.00	.70	.40
1993 Score	6	.15	.11	.06
1993 Score Canadian Dynamic Duos	9	11.00	8.25	4.50
1993 Score Dream Team	15	9.00	6.75	3.50
1993 Score Franchise	12	10.00	7.50	4.00
1993 Topps Finest Hockey Card Series Roster	7	6.00	4.50	2.50
1993 Topps Premier	190	.10	.08	.04
1993 Topps Premier Black Gold	20	4.00	3.00	1.50
1993 Topps Stadium Club	145	.15	.11	.06
1993 Topps Stadium Club	380	.15	.11	.06
1993 Topps Stadium Club All-Stars	21	12.00	9.00	4.75
1993 Upper Deck	224	.20	.15	.08
1993 Upper Deck	297	.10	.08	.04
1993 Upper Deck	347 (R)	.20	.15	.08
1993 Upper Deck Award Winners	7	4.00	3.00	1.50
1993 Upper Deck Hat Tricks	11	1.00	.70	.40
1993 Upper Deck Silver Skates Dye-Cut Hobby	7H	8.00	6.00	3.25
1993 Upper Deck SP Inserts	96	.75	.60	.30
1994 Donruss	23	.08	.06	.03
1994 Fleer Flair	109	.50	.40	.20
1994 Fleer Ultra	133	.08	.06	.03

1994 Leaf Limited	14	6.50	5.00	2.50
1994 O-Pee-Chee Premier	115	.15	.11	.06
1994 Parkhurst	135	.20	.15	.08
1994 Parkhurst Crash the Game	14	5.00	3.75	2.00
1994 Pinnacle	78	.10	.08	.04
1994 Pinnacle Artist's Proofs	78	18.00	13.50	7.25
1994 Pinnacle Rink Collection	78	9.00	6.75	3.50
1994 Score	166	.15	.11	.06
1994 Score Franchise	14	10.00	7.50	4.00
1994 Score Hockey Gold Line	166	1.00	.70	.40
1994 Score 90-Plus Club	14	6.00	4.50	2.50
1994 Topps Premier	115	.15	.11	.06
1994 Upper Deck	77	.30	.25	.12
1994 Upper Deck Electric Ice	77	10.00	7.50	4.00
1994 Upper Deck SP	48	1.00	.70	.40

Rogatien Vachon

Set	Card #	NM	EX	VG
1967 Topps	75 (R)	75.00	37.00	22.00
1968 O-Pee-Chee	164	25.00	12.50	7.50
1968 O-Pee-Chee	212	18.00	9.00	5.50
1969 O-Pee-Chee	165	15.00	7.50	4.50
1970 O-Pee-Chee	49	10.00	5.00	3.00
1970 Topps	49	4.00	2.00	1.25
1971 O-Pee-Chee	156	2.00	1.00	.60
1972 O-Pee-Chee	100	4.50	2.25	1.25
1972 Topps	51	3.00	1.50	.90
1973 O-Pee-Chee	64	1.00	.50	.30
1973 Topps	64	2.50	1.25	.70
1974 O-Pee-Chee	235	1.00	.50	.30
1974 Topps	235	1.50	.70	.45
1975 O-Pee-Chee	160	.50	.25	.15
1975 O-Pee-Chee	297	.50	.25	.15
1975 Topps	160	1.50	.70	.45
1975 Topps	213	5.00	2.50	1.50
1975 Topps	297	1.25	.60	.40
1976 O-Pee-Chee	40	1.75	.90	.50
1976 Topps	40	1.00	.50	.30
1977 O-Pee-Chee	160	1.00	.50	.30
1977 Topps	8	1.75	.90	.50
1977 Topps	160	.75	.40	.25
1978 O-Pee-Chee	20	.60	.30	.20
1978 Topps	20	.75	.40	.25
1979 O-Pee-Chee	235	.30	.15	.09
1979 Topps	235	.75	.40	.25
1980 O-Pee-Chee	110	.35	.20	.11
1980 O-Pee-Chee	168	1.00	.50	.30
1980 Topps	110	.75	.40	.25
1980 Topps	168	1.00	.50	.30

Set	Card #	MT	NM	EX
1981 O-Pee-Chee	10	.50	.40	.20
1981 Topps	74	.30	.25	.12
1982 O-Pee-Chee	23	.20	.15	.08

John Vanbiesbrouck

Set	Card #	MT	NM	EX
1986 O-Pee-Chee	9 (R)	15.00	11.00	6.00
1986 Topps	9 (R)	6.00	4.50	2.50
1987 O-Pee-Chee	36	4.00	3.00	1.50
1987 Topps	36	2.00	1.50	.80
1988 O-Pee-Chee	102	1.00	.70	.40
1988 Topps	102	.75	.60	.30
1989 O-Pee-Chee	114	.07	.05	.03
1989 Topps	114	.20	.15	.08
1990 Bowman	222	.04	.03	.02
1990 O-Pee-Chee	75	.15	.11	.06
1990 Pro Set	209	.07	.05	.03
1990 Score	175	.07	.05	.03
1990 Score Hockey's 100 Hottest Rising Stars	76	.10	.08	.04
1990 Topps	75	.15	.11	.06
1990 Upper Deck	279	.08	.06	.03
1991 Bowman	68	.05	.04	.02
1991 O-Pee-Chee/Topps	353	.05	.04	.02
1991 Parkhurst	338	.05	.04	.02
1991 Pinnacle	121	.08	.06	.03
1991 Pinnacle	367	.08	.06	.03
1991 Pro Set	447	.05	.04	.02
1991 Pro Set Platinum PC	1	1.25	.90	.50
1991 Score American	10	.05	.04	.02
1991 Score Canadian	10	.05	.04	.02
1991 Topps Stadium Club	323	.08	.06	.03
1991 Upper Deck	324	.05	.04	.02
1992 Bowman	132	.75	.60	.30
1992 Fleer Ultra	144	.06	.05	.02
1992 O-Pee-Chee	275	.05	.04	.02
1992 Parkhurst	349	.05	.04	.02
1992 Pinnacle	186	.06	.05	.02
1992 Score	160	.05	.04	.02
1992 Score USA Greats	7	6.00	4.50	2.50
1992 Topps	169	.06	.05	.02
1992 Topps Stadium Club	58	.05	.04	.02
1992 Upper Deck	44	.05	.04	.02
1993 Donruss	132	.10	.08	.04
1993 Fleer PowerPlay	102	.10	.08	.04
1993 Fleer Ultra	333	.08	.06	.03
1993 Leaf	371	.10	.08	.04
1993 Leaf Painted Warriors	8	5.00	3.75	2.00
1993 Parkhurst	73	.12	.09	.05
1993 Pinnacle	148	.10	.08	.04
1993 Pinnacle Masks	9	30.00	22.00	12.00
1993 Score	162	.05	.04	.02
1993 Score	445	.05	.04	.02
1993 Score	492	.05	.04	.02
1993 Score	501	.15	.11	.06
1993 Topps Premier	160	.05	.04	.02
1993 Topps Premier	314	.08	.06	.03
1993 Topps Stadium Club	85	.05	.04	.02
1993 Topps Stadium Club	330	.10	.08	.04
1993 Upper Deck	8	.05	.04	.02
1993 Upper Deck SP Inserts	60	.30	.25	.12
1994 Donruss	176	.08	.06	.03
1994 Donruss Ice Masters	10	2.00	1.50	.80

1994 Donruss Masked Marvels	10	5.00	3.75	2.00
1994 Fleer Flair	69	.35	.25	.14
1994 Fleer Ultra	86	.12	.09	.05
1994 Leaf	70	.15	.11	.06
1994 Leaf Limited	9	5.00	3.75	2.00
1994 O-Pee-Chee Premier	82	.05	.04	.02
1994 Parkhurst Crash the Game	9	5.00	3.75	2.00
1994 Parkhurst Vintage Parkhurst	13	.20	.15	.08
1994 Pinnacle	100	.10	.08	.04
1994 Pinnacle Artist's Proofs	100	10.00	7.50	4.00
1994 Pinnacle Goaltending Greats	3	6.00	4.50	2.50
1994 Pinnacle Hockey Masks	2	60.00	45.00	24.00
1994 Pinnacle Rink Collection	100	5.00	3.75	2.00
1994 Score Franchise	9	8.00	6.00	3.25
1994 Topps Premier	82	.05	.04	.02
1994 Topps Stadium Club	95	.10	.08	.04
1994 Upper Deck	46	.10	.08	.04
1994 Upper Deck Electric Ice	46	6.00	4.50	2.50
1994 Upper Deck SP	31	.30	.25	.12

Doug Wilson

Set	Card #	NM	EX	VG
1978 O-Pee-Chee	168 (R)	14.00	7.00	4.20
1978 Topps	168 (R)	8.00	4.00	2.50
1980 O-Pee-Chee	12	3.50	1.75	1.00
1980 Topps	12	2.50	1.25	.70

Set	Card #	MT	NM	EX
1981 O-Pee-Chee	66	2.00	1.50	.80
1981 Topps	78 (R)	1.00	.70	.40
1982 O-Pee-Chee	77	1.00	.70	.40
1982 Topps	78	.30	.25	.12
1983 O-Pee-Chee	114	.50	.40	.20
1984 O-Pee-Chee	48	.25	.20	.10
1984 Topps	37	.20	.15	.08
1985 O-Pee-Chee	45	.25	.20	.10
1985 Topps	45	.20	.15	.08
1986 O-Pee-Chee	106	.25	.20	.10
1986 Topps	106	.50	.40	.20
1987 O-Pee-Chee	14	.12	.09	.05
1987 Topps	14	.08	.06	.03
1988 O-Pee-Chee	89	.15	.11	.06
1988 Topps	89	.03	.02	.01
1989 O-Pee-Chee	112	.07	.05	.03
1989 Topps	112	.05	.04	.02
1990 Bowman	2	.04	.03	.02
1990 O-Pee-Chee	111	.05	.04	.02
1990 O-Pee-Chee	203	.07	.05	.03
1990 O-Pee-Chee Premier	129	.15	.11	.06
1990 Pro Set	63	.10	.08	.04
1990 Pro Set	346	.04	.03	.02
1990 Score	280	.07	.05	.03

1990 Score	320	.05	.04	.02
1990 Score Hockey's 100 Hottest Rising Stars	68	.10	.08	.04
1990 Topps	111	.07	.05	.03
1990 Topps	203	.07	.05	.03
1990 Upper Deck	223	.10	.08	.04
1991 Bowman	400	.05	.04	.02
1991 O-Pee-Chee Premier	6	.05	.04	.02
1991 O-Pee-Chee/Topps	49	.05	.04	.02
1991 Parkhurst	168	.05	.04	.02
1991 Pinnacle	13	.08	.06	.03
1991 Pinnacle	369	.08	.06	.03
1991 Pro Set	52	.05	.04	.02
1991 Pro Set	478	.05	.04	.02
1991 Pro Set	584	.05	.04	.02
1991 Pro Set Platinum	107	.05	.04	.02
1991 Score American	35	.05	.04	.02
1991 Score Canadian	35	.05	.04	.02
1991 Score Canadian	551	.05	.04	.02
1991 Score Traded	1	.05	.04	.02
1992 Bowman	75	.25	.20	.10
1992 Bowman	219	2.00	1.50	.80
1992 O-Pee-Chee	281	.05	.04	.02
1992 Parkhurst	167	.05	.04	.02
1992 Pinnacle	52	.06	.05	.02
1992 Pro Set	165	.05	.04	.02
1992 Score	15	.05	.04	.02
1992 Topps	482	.06	.05	.02
1992 Topps Stadium Club	470	.05	.04	.02
1992 Upper Deck	150	.05	.04	.02
1993 Fleer Ultra	230	.07	.05	.03
1993 Score	115	.05	.04	.02
1993 Topps Premier	77	.05	.04	.02

Gump Worsley

Set	Card #	NM	EX	VG
1953 Parkhurst	53 (R)	300.00	150.00	90.00
1954 Topps	10	200.00	100.00	60.00
1957 Topps	53	100.00	50.00	30.00
1958 Topps	39	50.00	25.00	15.00
1959 Topps	15	45.00	22.00	13.50
1959 Topps	54	30.00	15.00	9.00
1960 Topps	36	40.00	20.00	12.00
1961 Topps	50	35.00	17.50	10.50
1961 Topps	65	25.00	12.50	7.50
1962 Topps	45	32.00	16.00	9.50
1963 Parkhurst	35	65.00	32.00	19.50
1963 Parkhurst	39	30.00	15.00	9.00
1963 Parkhurst	98	35.00	17.50	10.50
1965 Topps	2	23.00	11.50	7.00
1966 Topps	2	20.00	10.00	6.00
1966 Topps	130	20.00	10.00	6.00
1967 Topps	1	35.00	17.50	10.50
1968 O-Pee-Chee	56	10.00	5.00	3.00

Set	Card #	MT	NM	EX
1968 O-Pee-Chee	199	7.00	3.50	2.00
1968 O-Pee-Chee	212	18.00	9.00	5.50
1968 Topps	56	8.00	4.00	2.50
1969 O-Pee-Chee	1	20.00	10.00	6.00
1969 Topps	1	15.00	7.50	4.50
1970 O-Pee-Chee	40	7.00	3.50	2.00
1970 Topps	40	4.50	2.25	1.25
1971 O-Pee-Chee	241	5.00	2.50	1.50
1972 O-Pee-Chee	28	5.00	2.50	1.50
1972 O-Pee-Chee	189	5.00	2.50	1.50
1972 O-Pee-Chee	286	10.00	5.00	3.00
1972 Topps	55	4.00	2.00	1.25
1973 O-Pee-Chee	230	4.00	2.00	1.25

Set	Card #	MT	NM	EX
1993 Parkhurst Parkie Reprints	45	18.00	13.50	7.25

Steve Yzerman

Set	Card #	MT	NM	EX
1984 O-Pee-Chee	67 (R)	60.00	45.00	24.00
1984 O-Pee-Chee	385	7.00	5.25	2.75
1984 Topps	49 (R)	12.00	9.00	4.75
1985 O-Pee-Chee	29	25.00	18.50	10.00
1985 Topps	29	15.00	11.00	6.00
1986 O-Pee-Chee	11	12.00	9.00	4.75
1986 Topps	11	7.50	5.75	3.00
1987 O-Pee-Chee	56	7.00	5.25	2.75
1987 Topps	56	3.00	2.25	1.25
1988 O-Pee-Chee	196	4.00	3.00	1.50
1988 Topps	196	2.00	1.50	.80
1989 O-Pee-Chee	83	.50	.40	.20
1989 Topps	83	.50	.40	.20
1990 Bowman	233	.40	.30	.15
1990 O-Pee-Chee	222	.15	.11	.06
1990 O-Pee-Chee Premier	130	1.50	1.25	.60
1990 Pro Set	79	.25	.20	.10
1990 Pro Set	347	.10	.08	.04
1990 Score	3	.50	.40	.20
1990 Score	339	.10	.08	.04
1990 Score Hockey's 100 Hottest Rising Stars	4	.10	.08	.04
1990 Topps	222	.25	.20	.10
1990 Upper Deck	56	.75	.60	.30
1990 Upper Deck	303	.15	.11	.06
1990 Upper Deck	477	.30	.25	.12
1990 Upper Deck Hockey Superstars	(6)	1.25	.90	.50
1990 Upper Deck Hockey Superstars	(7)	1.25	.90	.50
1990 Upper Deck Hockey Superstars	(8)	1.25	.90	.50
1990 Upper Deck Hockey Superstars	(9)	1.25	.90	.50
1991 Bowman	41	.15	.11	.06
1991 Bowman	42	.30	.25	.12
1991 O-Pee-Chee Premier	73	.30	.25	.12
1991 O-Pee-Chee/Topps	424	.20	.15	.08
1991 Parkhurst	44	.50	.40	.20
1991 Parkhurst	434	.10	.08	.04

Set	Card #	MT	NM	EX
1991 Pinnacle	75	.50	.40	.20
1991 Pro Set	62	.20	.15	.08
1991 Pro Set	281	.10	.08	.04
1991 Pro Set	571	.10	.08	.04
1991 Pro Set Platinum	32	.20	.15	.08
1991 Score American	190	.25	.20	.10
1991 Score American	419	.10	.08	.04
1991 Score Canadian	190	.20	.15	.08
1991 Score Canadian	335	.10	.08	.04
1991 Topps Stadium Club	81	1.00	.70	.40
1991 Upper Deck	146	.40	.30	.15
1991 Upper Deck	626	.15	.11	.06
1992 Bowman	103	2.50	2.00	1.00
1992 Bowman	220	5.00	3.75	2.00
1992 Fleer Ultra	55	.30	.25	.12
1992 O-Pee-Chee	61	.15	.11	.06
1992 O-Pee-Chee	321	.60	.45	.25
1992 O-Pee-Chee 25th Anniversary Series	17	.30	.25	.12
1992 Parkhurst	44	.05	.04	.02
1992 Parkhurst	456	.20	.15	.08
1992 Pinnacle	241	.25	.20	.10
1992 Pinnacle	258	.15	.11	.06
1992 Pinnacle	350	.45	.35	.20
1992 Pro Set	39	.15	.11	.06
1992 Pro Set	247	.10	.08	.04
1992 Pro Set Gold Team Leaders	3	5.00	3.75	2.00
1992 Score	400	.25	.20	.10
1992 Score	423	.05	.04	.02
1992 Topps	207	.20	.15	.08
1992 Topps Stadium Club	19	.40	.30	.15
1992 Topps Stadium Club	254	.30	.25	.12
1992 Upper Deck	155	.30	.25	.12
1992 Upper Deck Gordie Howe Selects	10	7.00	5.25	2.75
1992 Upper Deck World Junior Grads	7	8.00	6.00	3.25
1993 Donruss	95	.40	.30	.15
1993 Donruss Special Print	G	6.00	4.50	2.50
1993 Fleer PowerPlay	77	.40	.30	.15
1993 Fleer PowerPlay Gamebreakers	10	2.00	1.50	.80
1993 Fleer PowerPlay Point Leaders	20	2.00	1.50	.80
1993 Fleer Ultra	201	.40	.30	.15
1993 Fleer Ultra All-Stars	12	5.00	3.75	2.00
1993 Fleer Ultra Premier Pivots	10	3.00	2.25	1.25
1993 Fleer Ultra Scoring Kings	6	6.00	4.50	2.50
1993 Leaf	162	.40	.30	.15
1993 Leaf Hat Trick Artists	10	3.00	2.25	1.25
1993 Leaf Studio Signature	5	6.00	4.50	2.50
1993 OPC Premier Black Gold	23	15.00	11.00	6.00
1993 Parkhurst	326	.35	.25	.14
1993 Parkhurst East-West Stars	5W	12.00	9.00	4.75
1993 Pinnacle	175	.40	.30	.15
1993 Pinnacle All-Stars	36	.50	.40	.20
1993 Pinnacle Hockey Captains	7	12.00	9.00	4.75
1993 Pinnacle Nifty 50	8	20.00	15.00	8.00
1993 Score	310	.20	.15	.08
1993 Score	448	.10	.08	.04
1993 Score Dream Team	16	12.00	9.00	4.75
1993 Score Franchise	6	12.00	9.00	4.75
1993 Score U.S. Dynamic Duos	9	20.00	15.00	8.00
1993 Topps Premier	280	.15	.11	.06
1993 Topps Premier Black Gold	16	5.00	3.75	2.00
1993 Topps Stadium Club	70	.25	.20	.10
1993 Topps Stadium Club All-Stars	5	11.00	8.25	4.50
1993 Upper Deck	227	.10	.08	.04
1993 Upper Deck	290	.10	.08	.04

1993 Upper Deck	388	.10	.08	.04
1993 Upper Deck Hat Tricks	6	1.50	1.25	.60
1993 Upper Deck Next in Line	3	6.00	4.50	2.50
1993 Upper Deck Program of Excellence	14E	15.00	11.00	6.00
1993 Upper Deck Silver Skates Dye-Cut Retail	6R	10.00	7.50	4.00
1993 Upper Deck SP Inserts	47	1.00	.70	.40
1994 Donruss	1	.40	.30	.15
1994 Fleer Flair	55	.75	.60	.30
1994 Fleer Flair Hot Numbers	10	16.00	12.00	6.50
1994 Fleer Ultra	67	.40	.30	.15
1994 Fleer Ultra Scoring Kings	7	2.50	2.00	1.00
1994 Leaf	148	.15	.11	.06
1994 O-Pee-Chee Premier	235	.15	.11	.06
1994 Parkhurst	299	.15	.11	.06
1994 Parkhurst Vintage Parkhurst	57	1.25	.90	.50
1994 Score	150	.25	.20	.10
1994 Score Dream Team	20	8.00	6.00	3.25
1994 Score Hockey Gold Line	150	1.50	1.25	.60
1994 Topps Premier	235	.15	.11	.06
1994 Upper Deck Ice Gallery	1	8.00	6.00	3.25
1994 Upper Deck Scoring Predictor	24	8.00	6.00	3.25
1994 Upper Deck SP	25	1.75	1.25	.70

BASEBALL

Hank Aaron

Set	Card #	NM	EX	VG
1954 Topps	128 (R)	1500.	750.00	450.00
1955 Bowman	179	200.00	100.00	60.00
1955 Topps	47	300.00	150.00	90.00
1956 Topps	31	250.00	125.00	75.00
1957 Topps	20	200.00	100.00	55.00
1958 Topps	30a	300.00	150.00	90.00
1958 Topps	30b	170.00	85.00	50.00
1958 Topps	351	30.00	15.00	9.00
1958 Topps	418	180.00	90.00	55.00
1958 Topps	488	50.00	25.00	15.00
1959 Home Run Derby	(1)	450.00	225.00	135.00
1959 Topps	212	60.00	30.00	18.00
1959 Topps	380	100.00	50.00	30.00
1959 Topps	467	22.00	11.00	6.50
1959 Topps	561	115.00	57.50	33.00
1960 Topps	300	100.00	50.00	30.00
1960 Topps	566	120.00	60.00	35.00
1961 Post Cereal	107a	35.00	17.50	10.50
1961 Post Cereal	107b	35.00	17.50	10.50
1961 Topps	43	9.00	4.50	2.75
1961 Topps	415	110.00	55.00	33.00
1961 Topps	484	40.00	20.00	12.00
1961 Topps	577	140.00	70.00	42.00
1962 Post Cereal	149	45.00	22.00	13.50
1962 Topps	320	130.00	65.00	40.00
1962 Topps	394	40.00	20.00	12.00
1963 Post Cereal	152	70.00	35.00	21.00
1963 Topps	1	35.00	17.50	10.50
1963 Topps	3	26.00	13.00	7.75
1963 Topps	242	40.00	20.00	12.00
1963 Topps	390	130.00	65.00	39.00
1964 Topps	7	12.00	6.00	3.50
1964 Topps	9	25.00	12.50	7.50
1964 Topps	11	8.00	4.00	2.50
1964 Topps	300	100.00	50.00	30.00
1964 Topps	423	130.00	65.00	39.00
1965 O-Pee-Chee	2	17.00	8.50	5.00
1965 O-Pee-Chee	170	105.00	52.00	31.00
1965 Topps	2	15.00	7.50	4.50
1965 Topps	170	85.00	42.00	25.00
1966 Topps	215	22.00	11.00	6.50
1966 Topps	500	100.00	50.00	30.00
1967 Topps	242	12.00	6.00	3.50
1967 Topps	244	12.00	6.00	3.50
1967 Topps	250	80.00	40.00	24.00
1968 O-Pee-Chee	3	13.50	6.75	4.00
1968 O-Pee-Chee	5	10.25	5.25	3.00
1968 O-Pee-Chee	110	85.00	42.00	25.00
1968 Topps	3	9.00	4.50	2.75

Set	Card #	NM	EX	VG
1968 Topps	5	8.00	4.00	2.50
1968 Topps	110	62.50	31.00	19.00
1968 Topps	370	15.00	7.50	4.50
1969 O-Pee-Chee	100	65.00	32.00	19.50
1969 O-Pee-Chee	100	55.00	27.00	16.50
1970 O-Pee-Chee	65	2.25	1.25	.70
1970 O-Pee-Chee	462	20.00	10.00	6.00
1970 O-Pee-Chee	500	75.00	37.00	22.00
1970 Topps	65	5.00	2.50	1.50
1970 Topps	462	15.00	7.50	4.50
1970 Topps	500	60.00	30.00	18.00
1971 O-Pee-Chee	400	65.00	32.00	19.50
1971 Topps	400	45.00	22.00	13.50
1972 O-Pee-Chee	87	1.25	.60	.40
1972 O-Pee-Chee	89	1.25	.60	.40
1972 O-Pee-Chee	299	38.00	19.00	11.50
1972 O-Pee-Chee	300	18.00	9.00	5.50
1972 Topps	87	4.50	2.25	1.25
1972 Topps	89	4.50	2.25	1.25
1972 Topps	299	30.00	15.00	9.00
1972 Topps	300	15.00	7.50	4.50
1973 O-Pee-Chee	1	38.00	19.00	11.50
1973 O-Pee-Chee	100	30.00	15.00	9.00
1973 O-Pee-Chee	473	6.75	3.50	2.00
1973 Topps	1	35.00	17.50	10.50
1973 Topps	100	25.00	12.50	7.50
1973 Topps	473	7.50	3.75	2.25
1974 O-Pee-Chee	1	38.00	19.00	11.50
1974 O-Pee-Chee	332	1.50	.70	.45
1974 Topps	1	30.00	15.00	9.00
1974 Topps	2	4.00	2.00	1.25
1974 Topps	3	4.00	2.00	1.25
1974 Topps	4	4.00	2.00	1.25
1974 Topps	5	4.00	2.00	1.25
1974 Topps	6	4.00	2.00	1.25
1974 Topps	332	5.00	2.50	1.50
1975 O-Pee-Chee	1	34.00	17.00	10.00
1975 O-Pee-Chee	195	12.75	6.50	3.75
1975 O-Pee-Chee	660	34.00	17.00	10.00
1975 Topps	1	25.00	12.50	7.50
1975 Topps	195	10.00	5.00	3.00
1975 Topps	660	30.00	15.00	9.00
1975 Topps Mini	1	25.00	12.50	7.50
1975 Topps Mini	195	10.00	5.00	3.00
1975 Topps Mini	660	35.00	17.50	10.50
1976 O-Pee-Chee	1	21.00	10.50	6.25
1976 O-Pee-Chee	550	30.00	15.00	9.00
1976 Topps	1	18.00	9.00	5.50
1976 Topps	550	25.00	12.50	7.50
1979 Topps	412	.70	.35	.20
1979 Topps	413	1.00	.50	.30

Set	Card #	MT	NM	EX
1988 Pacific Trading Cards Baseball Legends	1	.50	.40	.20
1989 Topps	663	.15	.11	.06
1990 Pacific Legends	1	.50	.40	.20
1991 "1953" Topps Archives Promos	(1)	24.00	18.00	9.50
1991 "1953" Topps Archives	317	7.50	5.75	3.00
1991 Upper Deck	----	3.00	2.25	1.25
1993 Upper Deck All-Time Heroes	1	2.00	1.50	.80
1993 Upper Deck All-Time Heroes	149	.10	.08	.04
1993 Upper Deck All-Time Heroes	150	.10	.08	.04
1994 "1954" Topps Archives	128	3.00	2.25	1.25
1994 Topps	715	.50	.40	.20

1994 Topps Gold	715	2.00	1.50	.80
1994 Upper Deck All-Time Heroes	5	.50	.40	.20
1994 Upper Deck All-Time Heroes	144	.75	.60	.30
1994 Upper Deck All-Time Heroes	164	.50	.40	.20
1994 Upper Deck Heroes Gold	5	2.00	1.50	.80
1994 Upper Deck Heroes Gold	144	3.00	2.25	1.25
1994 Upper Deck Heroes Gold	164	2.50	2.00	1.00
1994 Upper Deck/GM "Baseball" Previews	1	.50	.40	.20

Dick Allen

Set	Card #	NM	EX	VG
1964 Topps	243 (R)	32.50	16.00	9.75
1965 Topps	460	15.00	7.50	4.50
1966 O-Pee-Chee	80	6.25	3.25	2.00
1966 Topps	80	3.00	1.50	.90
1967 Topps	242	12.00	6.00	3.50
1967 Topps	244	12.00	6.00	3.50
1967 Topps	309	4.00	2.00	1.25
1967 Topps	450	5.00	2.50	1.50
1968 Topps	225	2.50	1.25	.70
1969 O-Pee-Chee	6	8.50	4.25	2.50
1969 Topps	6	4.00	2.00	1.25
1969 Topps	350	2.00	1.00	.60
1970 O-Pee-Chee	40	1.50	.70	.45
1970 Topps	40	2.00	1.00	.60
1971 O-Pee-Chee	650	30.00	15.00	9.00
1971 Topps	650	15.00	7.50	4.50
1972 O-Pee-Chee	240	1.25	.60	.40
1972 Topps	240	2.00	1.00	.60
1973 O-Pee-Chee	62	1.00	.50	.30
1973 O-Pee-Chee	63	1.00	.50	.30
1973 O-Pee-Chee	310	.75	.40	.25
1973 Topps	62	2.25	1.25	.70
1973 Topps	63	2.25	1.25	.70
1973 Topps	310	.75	.40	.25
1974 O-Pee-Chee	70	.75	.40	.25
1974 O-Pee-Chee	332	1.50	.70	.45
1974 Topps	70	.50	.25	.15
1974 Topps	332	5.00	2.50	1.50
1975 O-Pee-Chee	210	3.00	1.50	.90
1975 O-Pee-Chee	307	4.00	2.00	1.25
1975 O-Pee-Chee	400	.75	.40	.25
1975 Topps	210	1.25	.60	.40
1975 Topps	307	.90	.45	.25
1975 Topps	400	.80	.40	.25
1975 Topps Mini	210	1.75	.90	.50
1975 Topps Mini	307	1.25	.60	.40
1975 Topps Mini	400	1.25	.60	.40
1976 O-Pee-Chee	455	.50	.25	.15
1976 Topps	455	.40	.20	.12

Roberto Alomar

Set	Card #	MT	NM	EX
1988 Donruss	34 (R)	3.00	2.25	1.25
1988 Fleer Update	122	9.00	6.75	3.50
1988 Leaf	34	3.25	2.50	1.25
1988 Score Traded	105T	50.00	38.00	20.00
1988 Score Traded/ Rookie Glossy	105T	150.00	112.00	60.00
1988 Topps Traded	4T	7.00	5.50	3.00
1989 Bowman	458	.75	.60	.30
1989 Donruss	246	.75	.60	.30
1989 Fleer	299	.75	.60	.30
1989 Fleer	630	.50	.40	.20
1989 O-Pee-Chee	206	.45	.35	.20
1989 Score	232	.75	.60	.30
1989 Sportflics	20	.50	.40	.20
1989 Topps	206	.75	.60	.30
1989 Topps	231	.12	.09	.05
1989 Topps All-Star Glossy Set of 60	19	.35	.25	.14
1989 Topps Big Baseball	102	.15	.11	.06
1989 Topps Glossy Rookies Set of 22	1	.25	.20	.10
1989 Upper Deck	471	5.00	3.75	2.00
1990 Bowman	221	.40	.30	.15
1990 Donruss	111	.50	.40	.20
1990 Fleer	149	.30	.25	.12
1990 Leaf	75	6.00	4.00	2.50
1990 O-Pee-Chee	517	.15	.11	.06
1990 Score	12	.30	.25	.12
1990 Sportflics	93	.15	.11	.06
1990 Topps	517	.25	.20	.10
1990 Topps All-Star Glossy Set of 60	27	.30	.25	.12
1990 Topps Big Baseball	9	.15	.11	.06
1990 Upper Deck	346	1.00	.70	.40
1991 Bowman	9	.25	.20	.10
1991 Donruss	12	.10	.08	.04
1991 Donruss	682	.20	.15	.08
1991 Fleer	523	.25	.20	.10
1991 Fleer Ultra	358	1.00	.75	.40
1991 Fleer Update	63	.25	.20	.10
1991 Leaf	267	1.00	.70	.40
1991 O-Pee-Chee Premier	1	.50	.40	.20
1991 Score	25	.30	.25	.12
1991 Score	887	.25	.20	.10
1991 Score Traded	44	.30	.25	.12
1991 Studio	131	.75	.60	.30
1991 Topps	315	.25	.20	.10
1991 Topps Stadium Club	304	5.00	3.75	2.00
1991 Upper Deck	335	.50	.40	.20
1991 Upper Deck	763	.50	.40	.20
1991 Upper Deck Final Edition	83	.30	.25	.12
1992 Bowman	20	2.50	2.00	1.00
1992 Donruss	28	.20	.15	.08
1992 Donruss	58	.25	.20	.10
1992 Donruss Triple Play	84	.25	.15	.06
1992 Fleer	323	.15	.11	.06
1992 Fleer	698	.08	.06	.03
1992 Fleer Ultra	143	.75	.60	.30

Card	#			
1992 Fleer Ultra All-Stars	2	2.00	1.50	.75
1992 Fleer Ultra Award Winners	20	4.00	3.00	1.50
1992 Leaf	233	.40	.30	.15
1992 O-Pee-Chee	225	.15	.11	.06
1992 O-Pee-Chee Premier	130	.50	.40	.20
1992 Pinnacle	45	.75	.60	.30
1992 Pinnacle	306	.30	.25	.12
1992 Pinnacle	586	.25	.20	.10
1992 Pinnacle Team Pinnacle	5	30.00	22.00	12.00
1992 Pinnacle Team 2000	48	1.00	.75	.40
1992 Score	15	.25	.20	.10
1992 Score Impact Players	10	.60	.45	.25
1992 Studio	251	.50	.40	.20
1992 Topps	225	.25	.20	.10
1992 Topps Gold	225	2.00	1.50	.80
1992 Topps Kids	90	.15	.11	.06
1992 Topps Stadium Club	159	.75	.60	.30
1992 Topps Stadium Club Special Edition	5	.60	.45	.25
1992 Upper Deck	81	.10	.08	.04
1992 Upper Deck	355	.25	.20	.10
1992 Upper Deck MVP Holograms	4	.50	.40	.20
1993 Bowman	338	.75	.60	.30
1993 DiamondMarks	(115)	.60	.45	.25
1993 DiamondMarks Inserts	(1)	15.00	11.00	6.00
1993 Donruss	425	.35	.25	.14
1993 Donruss Diamond Kings	20	3.00	2.25	1.25
1993 Donruss Elite	26	60.00	45.00	24.00
1993 Donruss Elite Dominators	20	100.00	75.00	40.00
1993 Donruss Elite Supers	8	15.00	11.00	6.00
1993 Donruss Long Ball Leaders	8	6.00	4.50	2.50
1993 Donruss Masters of the Game	10	3.00	2.25	1.25
1993 Donruss MVP's	6	2.00	1.50	.80
1993 Donruss Spirit of the Game	3	3.00	2.25	1.25
1993 Donruss Triple Play	2	.25	.20	.10
1993 Donruss Triple Play Action Baseball	13	.15	.11	.06
1993 Donruss Triple Play	200	.10	.08	.04
1993 Donruss 1992 Blue Jays Commemorative Set	2	.75	.60	.30
1993 Fleer	330	.25	.20	.10
1993 Fleer	357	.15	.11	.06
1993 Fleer All-Stars	2	3.00	2.25	1.25
1993 Fleer Atlantic	1	.50	.40	.20
1993 Fleer AL Team Leaders	9	9.00	6.75	3.50
1993 Fleer Flair	287	1.50	1.25	.60
1993 Fleer ProVisions I	1	4.00	3.00	1.50
1993 Fleer Ultra	639	.90	.70	.35
1993 Fleer Ultra Award Winners	13	4.00	3.00	1.50
1993 Leaf	245	.80	.60	.30
1993 Leaf Gold All-Stars	13	2.50	2.00	1.00
1993 Leaf Update Gold All-Stars	4	4.00	3.00	1.50
1993 O-Pee-Chee	4	1.00	.75	.40
1993 O-Pee-Chee Premier Star Performers	3	.40	.30	.15
1993 O-Pee-Chee World Champs	1	1.00	.75	.40
1993 Pacific Prism Insert	7	35.00	26.00	14.00
1993 Pinnacle	30	.50	.40	.20
1993 Pinnacle Cooperstown	29	.30	.25	.12
1993 Pinnacle Cooperstown Dufex	29	80.00	60.00	32.00
1993 Post Cereal	22	.35	.25	.14
1993 Score	14	.25	.20	.10
1993 Score	511	.10	.08	.04
1993 Score	542	.10	.08	.04
1993 Score Gold Dream Team	11	1.00	.75	.40
1993 Score Select	8	.40	.30	.15
1993 Score Select Chase Stars	14	12.00	9.00	4.75
1993 Score Select Stat Leaders	39	.35	.25	.14
1993 Score Select Stat Leaders	51	.30	.25	.12
1993 Score The Franchise	14	6.00	4.50	2.50
1993 Studio	4	.60	.45	.25
1993 Topps	50	.15	.11	.06
1993 Topps Black Gold	23	.75	.60	.30
1993 Topps Finest	88	8.00	6.00	3.25
1993 Topps Finest Jumbo All-Stars	88	20.00	15.00	8.00
1993 Topps Finest Refractors	88	80.00	60.00	32.00
1993 Topps Gold	50	.30	.25	.12
1993 Topps Stadium Club	142	.50	.40	.20
1993 Topps Stadium Club	596	.35	.25	.14
1993 Topps Stadium Club First Day Production	142	30.00	22.00	12.00
1993 Topps Stadium Club First Day Production	596	15.00	11.00	6.00
1993 Topps Stadium Club Special	19	.35	.25	.14
1993 Topps Stadium Club Special	191	.40	.30	.15
1993 Upper Deck	42	.12	.09	.05
1993 Upper Deck	125	.25	.20	.10
1993 Upper Deck	815	.15	.11	.06
1993 Upper Deck	840	.06	.05	.02
1993 Upper Deck "Highlights"	1	8.00	6.00	3.25
1993 Upper Deck Clutch Performers	1	1.50	1.25	.60
1993 Upper Deck Diamond Gallery	4	2.00	1.50	.80
1993 Upper Deck Fun Packs All-Star Scratch-Off	4	3.00	2.25	1.25
1993 Upper Deck Fun Packs	10	.50	.40	.20
1993 Upper Deck Fun Packs	22	.15	.11	.06
1993 Upper Deck Fun Packs	54	.25	.20	.10
1993 Upper Deck Fun Packs	55	.25	.20	.10
1993 Upper Deck Future Heroes	55	1.50	1.25	.60
1993 Upper Deck Iooss Collection	4	1.50	1.25	.60
1993 Upper Deck Iooss Collection Super	4	5.00	3.75	2.00
1993 Upper Deck On Deck	2	1.50	1.25	.60
1993 Upper Deck SP	1	2.00	1.50	.80
1993 Upper Deck 5th Anniversary	3	1.50	1.25	.60
1993 Upper Deck 5th Anniversary Super	3	4.00	3.00	1.50
1994 Bowman	609	.40	.30	.15
1994 Bowman's Best	7	3.00	2.25	1.25
1994 Bowman's Best Refractors	7	15.00	11.00	6.00
1994 Donruss	6	.50	.40	.20
1994 Donruss Special Edition - Gold	6	.60	.45	.25
1994 Donruss Triple Play Medalists	5	2.50	2.00	1.00
1994 Donruss Triple Play	31	.30	.25	.12
1994 Fleer	324	.35	.25	.14
1994 Fleer All-Stars	1	1.00	.75	.40
1994 Fleer Extra Bases	186	.50	.40	.20
1994 Fleer Flair	115	1.25	.90	.50
1994 Fleer Flair Hot Numbers	1	14.00	10.50	5.50
1994 Fleer Ultra	434	.40	.30	.15
1994 Fleer Ultra All-Stars	3	1.50	1.25	.60

1994 Fleer Ultra Award Winners	3	1.25	.90	.50
1994 Fleer Ultra Hitting Machines	1	1.25	.90	.50
1994 Fleer Ultra On-Base Leaders	1	14.00	10.50	5.50
1994 Leaf	225	.40	.30	.15
1994 Leaf Gold Stars	1	20.00	15.00	8.00
1994 Leaf Limited	75	4.00	3.00	1.50
1994 Leaf Limited Gold	3	30.00	22.00	12.00
1994 Leaf Slide Show	5	5.00	3.75	2.00
1994 O-Pee-Chee	96	.60	.45	.25
1994 O-Pee-Chee All-Star Redemption Cards	21	1.00	.75	.40
1994 O-Pee-Chee Jumbo All-Stars	21	10.00	7.50	4.00
1994 O-Pee-Chee Toronto Blue Jays	6	8.00	6.00	3.25
1994 Pacific Crown	632	.35	.25	.14
1994 Pacific Crown All Latino All-Star Team	4	7.00	5.50	3.00
1994 Pacific Crown All Latino All-Star Team	17	4.00	3.00	1.50
1994 Pacific Crown Jewels of the Crown	5	6.00	4.50	2.50
1994 Pinnacle	287	.40	.30	.15
1994 Pinnacle Artist's Proof	287	20.00	15.00	8.00
1994 Pinnacle Museum Collection	287	10.00	7.50	4.00
1994 Pinnacle Run Creators	6	4.00	3.00	1.50
1994 Pinnacle The Naturals Box Set	8	.60	.45	.25
1994 Pinnacle Tribute	16	5.00	3.75	2.00
1994 Post Cereal	18	.35	.25	.14
1994 Score	43	.35	.25	.14
1994 Score Gold Stars	42	9.00	6.75	3.50
1994 Score Select	229	.75	.60	.30
1994 Sportflics 2000	31	.60	.45	.25
1994 Sportflics 2000	177	.35	.25	.14
1994 Studio	24	.40	.30	.15
1994 Topps	385	.20	.15	.08
1994 Topps	675	.25	.20	.10
1994 Topps Black Gold	1	1.25	.90	.50
1994 Topps Finest	205	3.00	2.25	1.25
1994 Topps Finest Refractors	205	20.00	15.00	8.00
1994 Topps Finest Superstars	205	12.00	9.00	4.75
1994 Topps Gold	385	.60	.45	.25
1994 Topps Gold	675	.75	.60	.30
1994 Topps Stadium Club	10	.50	.40	.20
1994 Topps Stadium Club First Day Production	10	25.00	18.50	10.00
1994 Topps Stadium Club Members Only Baseball	33	.45	.35	.20
1994 Upper Deck	35	.40	.30	.15
1994 Upper Deck	455	.50	.40	.20
1994 Upper Deck All-Stars Green Foil	16	.50	.40	.20
1994 Upper Deck All-Stars Gold Foil	16	2.50	2.00	1.00
1994 Upper Deck Collector's Choice	33	.25	.20	.10
1994 Upper Deck Collector's Choice	321	.05	.04	.02
1994 Upper Deck Collector's Choice	331	.10	.08	.04
1994 Upper Deck Collector's Choice	631	.10	.08	.04
1994 Upper Deck Diamond Collection	1E	10.00	7.50	4.00
1994 Upper Deck Electric Diamond	35	.60	.45	.25
1994 Upper Deck Electric Diamond	455	1.00	.75	.40
1994 Upper Deck Fun Packs	12	.25	.20	.10

1994 Upper Deck Fun Packs	178	.20	.15	.08
1994 Upper Deck Fun Packs	201	1.00	.70	.40
1994 Upper Deck Fun Packs	211	.15	.11	.06
1994 Upper Deck Fun Packs	217	.35	.25	.14
1994 Upper Deck Next Generation	1	4.00	3.00	1.50
1994 Upper Deck SP	39	.60	.45	.25
1994 Upper Deck SP Baseball Die-Cut	39	1.00	.75	.40
1994 Upper Deck SP Holoview Blue	1	7.50	5.25	2.75
1994 Upper Deck SP Insert	1	8.00	6.00	3.25

Moises Alou

Set	Card #	MT	NM	EX
1990 Bowman	178 (R)	.50	.40	.20
1990 Fleer	650 (R)	.50	.40	.20
1990 Score	592 (R)	.40	.30	.15
1991 Donruss	38	.35	.25	.14
1991 O-Pee-Chee Premier	3	.40	.30	.15
1991 Score	813	.30	.25	.12
1991 Studio	191	.75	.60	.30
1991 Topps	526a	.40	.30	.15
1991 Topps	526b	.50	.40	.20
1991 Topps Stadium Club	31	2.00	1.50	.80
1991 Upper Deck	665	.75	.60	.30
1992 Fleer Ultra	511	.25	.20	.10
1992 Fleer Update	95	4.00	3.00	1.50
1992 Leaf	426	.15	.11	.06
1992 O-Pee-Chee	401	.15	.11	.06
1992 Pinnacle	572	.50	.40	.20
1992 Pinnacle Rookies	16	.60	.45	.25
1992 Score Rising Stars	9	.10	.08	.04
1992 Topps Stadium Club	519	.40	.30	.15
1992 Topps Traded	4	.50	.40	.20
1993 Bowman	452	.20	.15	.08
1993 DiamondMarks	(36)	.25	.20	.10
1993 Donruss	510	.05	.04	.02
1993 Donruss Triple Play	244	.10	.08	.04
1993 Fleer	70	.08	.06	.03
1993 Fleer Flair	78	.50	.40	.20
1993 Fleer Rookie Sensations II	1	4.00	3.00	1.50
1993 Fleer Ultra	61	.15	.11	.06
1993 Leaf	147	.15	.11	.06
1993 O-Pee-Chee	10	.20	.15	.08
1993 Pinnacle	92	.06	.05	.02
1993 Score	187	.08	.06	.03
1993 Score Select	272	.20	.15	.08
1993 Score Select Chase Rookies	2	15.00	11.00	6.00
1993 Studio	11	.15	.11	.06
1993 Topps	123	.08	.06	.03
1993 Topps Finest	189	3.00	2.25	1.25

Set	Card #	NM	EX	VG
1993 Topps Finest Refractors	189	30.00	22.00	12.00
1993 Topps Gold	123	.15	.11	.06
1993 Topps Stadium Club	239	.20	.15	.08
1993 Topps Stadium Club First Day Production	239	12.00	9.00	4.75
1993 Upper Deck	297	.10	.08	.04
1993 Upper Deck SP	100	.40	.30	.15
1994 Bowman	116	.15	.11	.06
1994 Bowman's Best	52	.50	.40	.20
1994 Bowman's Best Refractors	52	2.00	1.50	.80
1994 Donruss	3	.10	.08	.04
1994 Donruss Diamond Kings	23	1.25	.90	.50
1994 Donruss Diamond Kings Super	23	3.50	2.75	1.50
1994 Donruss MVP's	8	.50	.40	.20
1994 Donruss Special Edition - Gold	3	.30	.25	.12
1994 Donruss Triple Play	91	.05	.04	.02
1994 Fleer	531	.10	.08	.04
1994 Fleer Extra Bases	299	.10	.08	.04
1994 Fleer Flair	400	.25	.20	.10
1994 Fleer Ultra	222	.12	.09	.05
1994 Leaf	252	.12	.09	.05
1994 Leaf Limited	123	1.25	.90	.50
1994 O-Pee-Chee	266	.10	.08	.04
1994 Pacific Crown	372	.15	.11	.06
1994 Pinnacle	7	.20	.15	.08
1994 Pinnacle Artist's Proof	7	5.00	3.75	2.00
1994 Pinnacle Museum Collection	7	2.50	2.00	1.00
1994 Score	90	.04	.03	.02
1994 Score Select	159	.20	.15	.08
1994 Sportflics 2000	87	.10	.08	.04
1994 Studio	74	.15	.11	.06
1994 Topps	50	.08	.06	.03
1994 Topps Finest	121	.75	.60	.30
1994 Topps Finest Refractors	121	7.50	5.50	3.00
1994 Topps Gold	50	.20	.15	.08
1994 Topps Stadium Club	141	.15	.11	.06
1994 Topps Stadium Club First Day Production	141	8.00	6.00	3.25
1994 Upper Deck	351	.15	.11	.06
1994 Upper Deck Collector's Choice	35	.08	.06	.03
1994 Upper Deck Electric Diamond	351	.35	.25	.14
1994 Upper Deck SP	82	.15	.11	.06
1994 Upper Deck SP Baseball Die-Cut	82	.25	.20	.10

Walter Alston

Set	Card #	NM	EX	VG
1956 Topps	8 (R)	30.00	15.00	9.00

Set	Card #	NM	EX	VG
1958 Topps	314	17.50	8.75	5.25
1960 Topps	212	9.00	4.50	2.75
1961 Topps	136	5.00	2.50	1.50
1962 Topps	217	5.00	2.50	1.50
1963 Topps	154	5.00	2.50	1.50
1964 Topps	101	4.00	2.00	1.25
1965 O-Pee-Chee	217	6.25	3.25	2.00
1965 Topps	217	5.00	2.50	1.50
1966 O-Pee-Chee	116	2.50	1.25	.70
1966 Topps	116	5.00	2.50	1.50
1967 Topps	294	5.00	2.50	1.50
1968 Topps	472	4.00	2.00	1.25
1969 O-Pee-Chee	24	2.25	1.25	.70
1969 Topps	24	2.50	1.25	.70
1970 O-Pee-Chee	242	1.25	.60	.40
1970 Topps	242	3.50	1.75	1.00
1971 O-Pee-Chee	567	5.00	2.50	1.50
1971 Topps	567	4.00	2.00	1.25
1972 Topps	749	12.00	6.00	3.50
1973 O-Pee-Chee	569	3.50	1.75	1.00
1973 Topps	569	4.00	2.00	1.25
1974 O-Pee-Chee	144	1.25	.60	.40
1974 Topps	144	1.50	.70	.45
1975 O-Pee-Chee	361	.75	.40	.25
1975 Topps	361	3.00	1.50	.90
1975 Topps Mini	361	1.50	.70	.45
1976 O-Pee-Chee	46	1.00	.50	.30
1976 Topps	46	1.00	.50	.30

Sparky Anderson

Set	Card #	NM	EX	VG
1959 Topps	338 (R)	70.00	35.00	21.00
1960 Leaf	125	80.00	40.00	24.00
1960 Topps	34	20.00	10.00	6.00
1970 O-Pee-Chee	181	1.25	.60	.40
1970 Topps	181	3.00	1.50	.90
1971 O-Pee-Chee	688	34.00	17.00	10.00
1971 Topps	688	25.00	12.50	7.50
1972 O-Pee-Chee	358	1.25	.60	.40
1972 Topps	358	1.50	.70	.45
1973 O-Pee-Chee	296	.75	.40	.25
1973 Topps	296	2.00	1.00	.60
1974 O-Pee-Chee	326	.60	.30	.20
1974 Topps	326	1.50	.70	.45
1975 O-Pee-Chee	531	.75	.40	.25
1975 Topps	531	3.00	1.50	.90
1975 Topps Mini	531	1.50	.70	.45
1976 O-Pee-Chee	104	.75	.40	.25
1976 Topps	104	1.00	.50	.30
1977 Topps	287	2.00	1.00	.60
1978 Topps	401	.50	.25	.15
1979 Topps	259	.60	.30	.20
1980 Topps	626	.60	.30	.20

Set	Card #	MT	NM	EX
1981 Donruss	370	.10	.08	.04
1981 Fleer	460	.10	.08	.04
1981 Topps	666	.30	.25	.12
1982 Donruss	29	.10	.08	.04

1983 Donruss	533a	.70	.50	.30
1983 Donruss	533b	.10	.08	.04
1983 Topps	666	.12	.09	.05
1984 Topps	259	.12	.09	.05
1985 Fleer	628	.08	.06	.03
1985 Topps	307	.08	.06	.03
1986 Topps	411	.07	.05	.03
1986 Topps All-Star Glossy Set of 22	1	.20	.15	.08
1987 Topps	218	.07	.05	.03
1987 Topps	631	.07	.05	.03
1988 Topps	14	.06	.05	.02
1989 Topps	193	.06	.05	.02
1990 O-Pee-Chee	609	.03	.02	.01
1990 Topps	609	.03	.02	.01
1991 Topps	519	.04	.03	.02
1992 O-Pee-Chee	381	.03	.02	.01
1992 Topps	381	.03	.02	.01
1992 Topps Gold	381	.25	.20	.10

Luis Aparicio

Set	Card #	NM	EX	VG
1956 Topps	292 (R)	110.00	55.00	32.50
1957 Topps	7	35.00	17.50	10.50
1958 Topps	85a	60.00	30.00	18.00
1958 Topps	85b	27.50	13.50	8.25
1958 Topps	483	12.00	6.00	3.50
1959 Topps	310	15.00	7.50	4.50
1959 Topps	408	12.00	6.00	3.50
1959 Topps	560	27.50	13.50	8.25
1960 Leaf	1	25.00	12.50	7.50
1960 Topps	240	14.00	7.00	4.25
1960 Topps	559	20.00	10.00	6.00
1961 Post Cereal	19a	7.50	3.75	2.25
1961 Post Cereal	19b	7.50	3.75	2.25
1961 Topps	440	14.00	7.00	4.25
1961 Topps	574	45.00	22.00	13.50
1962 Post Cereal	49	9.00	4.50	2.75
1962 Topps	325	15.00	7.50	4.50
1962 Topps	469	9.00	4.50	2.75
1963 Post Cereal	37	9.00	4.50	2.75
1963 Topps	205	12.00	6.00	3.50
1964 Topps	540	15.00	7.50	4.50
1965 Topps	410	9.00	4.50	2.75
1966 O-Pee-Chee	90	10.25	5.25	3.00
1966 Topps	90	7.50	3.75	2.25
1967 O-Pee-Chee	60	8.50	4.25	2.50
1967 Topps	60	6.00	3.00	1.75
1968 Topps	310	5.00	2.50	1.50
1969 O-Pee-Chee	75	2.25	1.25	.70
1969 Topps	75	5.00	2.50	1.50
1970 O-Pee-Chee	315	3.50	1.75	1.00
1970 Topps	315	4.50	2.25	1.25
1971 O-Pee-Chee	740	30.00	15.00	9.00
1971 Topps	740	15.00	7.50	4.50
1972 O-Pee-Chee	313	2.00	1.00	.60
1972 O-Pee-Chee	314	1.25	.60	.40
1972 Topps	313	4.00	2.00	1.25
1972 Topps	314	2.00	1.00	.60

1973 O-Pee-Chee	165	1.75	.90	.50
1973 Topps	165	2.75	1.50	.80
1974 O-Pee-Chee	61	1.75	.90	.50
1974 Topps	61	2.50	1.25	.70

Luke Appling

Set	Card #	NM	EX	VG
1934-36 Diamond Stars	95	395.00	197.00	118.00
1934 Goudey	27	225.00	90.00	43.00
1935 Goudey	(4)	100.00	50.00	30.00
1937 O-Pee-Chee	115	250.00	125.00	75.00
1939 Goudey Premiums (R303-A)	(1)	45.00	22.00	13.50
1939 Goudey Premiums (R303-B)	(1)	40.00	20.00	12.00
1941 Double Play	70	65.00	32.00	19.50
1948 Leaf	59	80.00	40.00	24.00
1949 Bowman	175	125.00	62.00	37.00
1950 Bowman	37	80.00	40.00	24.00
1960 Fleer	27	3.50	1.75	1.00
1960 Topps	461	7.50	3.75	2.25

Set	Card #	MT	NM	EX
1988 Pacific Trading Cards Baseball Legends	4	.15	.11	.06
1990 Pacific Legends	3	.15	.11	.06
1994 Upper Deck All-Time Heroes	41	.05	.04	.02
1994 Upper Deck Heroes Gold	41	.15	.11	.06

Richie Ashburn

Set	Card #	NM	EX	VG
1949 Bowman	214 (R)	495.00	245.00	140.00
1950 Bowman	84	80.00	40.00	24.00
1951 Bowman	186	55.00	27.00	16.50
1951 Topps Blue Backs	3	55.00	27.00	16.50

		MT	NM	EX
1952 Bowman	53	50.00	25.00	15.00
1952 Red Man Tobacco	2N	40.00	20.00	12.00
1952 Topps	216	120.00	60.00	28.00
1953 Bowman Color	10	75.00	37.00	22.00
1953 Red Man Tobacco	3N	40.00	20.00	12.00
1954 Bowman	15	35.00	17.50	10.50
1954 Red Heart Dog Food	(1)	50.00	25.00	15.00
1954 Red Man Tobacco	1N	45.00	22.00	13.50
1954 Topps	45	40.00	20.00	12.00
1955 Bowman	130	25.00	12.50	7.50
1955 Red Man Tobacco	1N	40.00	20.00	12.00
1956 Topps	120	35.00	17.50	10.50
1957 Topps	70	25.00	12.50	7.50
1958 Topps	230	16.00	8.00	4.75
1959 Topps	300	18.00	9.00	5.50
1959 Topps	317	40.00	20.00	12.00
1960 Topps	305	10.00	5.00	3.00
1961 Post Cereal	192a	4.50	2.25	1.25
1961 Post Cereal	192b	4.50	2.25	1.25
1961 Topps	88	8.00	4.00	2.50
1962 Post Cereal	186	5.00	2.50	1.50
1962 Topps	213	8.00	4.00	2.50
1963 Post Cereal	197	20.00	10.00	6.00
1963 Topps	135	10.00	5.00	3.00

Set	Card #	MT	NM	EX
1983 Topps 1952 Reprint Set	216	1.75	1.25	.70
1988 Pacific Trading Cards Baseball Legends	8	.10	.08	.04
1989 Bowman Inserts	(1)	.10	.08	.04
1990 Pacific Legends	70	.10	.08	.04
1991 "1953" Topps Archives	311	.35	.25	.14
1994 "1954" Topps Archives	45	.35	.25	.14

Steve Avery

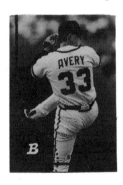

Set	Card #	MT	NM	EX
1989 Bowman	268 (R)	1.00	.70	.40
1989 Topps	784 (R)	1.00	.75	.40
1990 Bowman	9	.50	.40	.20
1990 Donruss	39	.40	.30	.15
1990 Fleer Update	1	.50	.40	.20
1990 Leaf	481	8.00	6.00	3.25
1990 Score Traded	109T	.60	.45	.25
1990 Topps Traded	4T	.50	.40	.20
1990 Upper Deck	65	1.50	1.25	.60
1991 Bowman	566	.20	.15	.08
1991 Donruss	187	.20	.15	.08
1991 Fleer	681	.20	.15	.08
1991 Fleer Ultra	1	.50	.40	.20
1991 Leaf	510	.75	.60	.30
1991 Score	80	.20	.15	.08
1991 Studio	141	.30	.25	.12
1991 Topps	227	.15	.11	.06
1991 Topps Glossy Rookies	3	.35	.25	.14
1991 Topps Stadium Club	48	2.50	2.00	1.00

		MT	NM	EX
1991 Upper Deck	365	.25	.20	.10
1992 Bowman	180	1.50	1.25	.60
1992 Donruss	81	.25	.20	.10
1992 Donruss Triple Play	85	.20	.15	.08
1992 Fleer	349	.20	.15	.08
1992 Fleer Smoke 'N Heat	10	1.00	.75	.40
1992 Fleer Ultra	157	.40	.30	.15
1992 Leaf	59	.30	.25	.12
1992 O-Pee-Chee	574	.20	.15	.08
1992 O-Pee-Chee Premier	170	.15	.11	.06
1992 Pinnacle	231	.25	.20	.10
1992 Pinnacle	585	.20	.15	.08
1992 Pinnacle	612	.25	.20	.10
1992 Pinnacle Team Pinnacle	2	8.00	6.00	3.25
1992 Pinnacle Team 2000	66	.35	.25	.14
1992 Score	241	.20	.15	.08
1992 Score	797	.10	.08	.04
1992 Score Impact Players	12	.30	.25	.12
1992 Studio	1	.25	.20	.10
1992 Topps	574	.20	.15	.08
1992 Topps Gold	574	.75	.60	.30
1992 Topps Kids	36	.10	.08	.04
1992 Topps Stadium Club	60	.30	.25	.12
1992 Topps Stadium Club	594	.25	.20	.10
1992 Topps Stadium Club Special Edition	9	.40	.30	.15
1992 Upper Deck	41	.10	.08	.04
1992 Upper Deck	475	.15	.11	.06
1992 Upper Deck MVP Holograms	6	.40	.30	.15
1993 Bowman	198	.20	.15	.08
1993 DiamondMarks	(1)	.50	.40	.20
1993 Donruss	26	.15	.11	.06
1993 Donruss Triple Play	30	.10	.08	.04
1993 Fleer	1	.10	.08	.04
1993 Fleer Flair	1	.50	.40	.20
1993 Fleer Ultra	1	.20	.15	.08
1993 Leaf	121	.25	.20	.10
1993 Leaf Fasttrack	13	2.50	2.00	1.00
1993 O-Pee-Chee	5	.20	.15	.08
1993 Pinnacle	315	.25	.20	.10
1993 Score	169	.10	.08	.04
1993 Score Select	109	.15	.11	.06
1993 Studio	5	.20	.15	.08
1993 Topps	615	.03	.02	.01
1993 Topps Finest	160	2.50	2.00	1.00
1993 Topps Finest Refractors	160	45.00	34.00	18.00
1993 Topps Gold	615	.10	.08	.04
1993 Topps Stadium Club	626	.25	.20	.10
1993 Topps Stadium Club First Day Production	626	25.00	18.50	10.00
1993 Topps Stadium Club Team Sets	10	.50	.40	.20
1993 Upper Deck	246	.15	.11	.06
1993 Upper Deck	472	.15	.11	.06
1993 Upper Deck	816	.10	.07	.04
1993 Upper Deck "Highlights"	2	4.00	3.00	1.50
1993 Upper Deck Fun Packs	62	.15	.11	.06
1993 Upper Deck Iooss Collection	5	.75	.60	.30
1993 Upper Deck Iooss Collection Super	5	4.00	3.00	1.50
1993 Upper Deck SP	55	.75	.60	.30
1994 Bowman	189	.20	.15	.08
1994 Bowman's Best	109	.50	.40	.20
1994 Bowman's Best	20	1.00	.70	.40
1994 Bowman's Best Refractors	109	5.00	3.75	2.00
1994 Bowman's Best Refractors	20	5.00	3.75	2.00
1994 Donruss	41	.20	.15	.08
1994 Donruss Diamond Kings	3	1.00	.75	.40
1994 Donruss Diamond Kings Super	3	3.00	2.25	1.25

Set	Card #	MT	NM	EX
1994 Donruss Special Edition - Gold	41	.30	.25	.12
1994 Donruss Triple Play	41	.15	.11	.06
1994 Fleer	350	.12	.09	.05
1994 Fleer All-Stars	26	.40	.30	.15
1994 Fleer Extra Bases	199	.20	.15	.08
1994 Fleer Extra Bases Pitcher's Duel	6M	.50	.40	.20
1994 Fleer Flair	352	.40	.30	.15
1994 Fleer Ultra	147	.20	.15	.08
1994 Leaf	138	.20	.15	.08
1994 Leaf Limited	81	1.50	1.25	.60
1994 O-Pee-Chee	196	.15	.11	.06
1994 Pinnacle	8	.20	.15	.08
1994 Pinnacle Artist's Proof	8	7.50	5.25	2.75
1994 Pinnacle Museum Collection	8	3.00	2.25	1.25
1994 Score	166	.10	.08	.04
1994 Score Select	87	.20	.15	.08
1994 Sportflics 2000	60	.25	.20	.10
1994 Studio	33	.25	.20	.10
1994 Topps	137	.10	.08	.04
1994 Topps Finest	359	1.00	.75	.40
1994 Topps Finest Refractors	359	7.00	5.25	2.75
1994 Topps Gold	137	.25	.20	.10
1994 Topps Stadium Club	254	.20	.15	.08
1994 Topps Stadium Club First Day Production	254	10.00	7.50	4.00
1994 Upper Deck	41	.20	.15	.08
1994 Upper Deck	420	.25	.20	.10
1994 Upper Deck All-Stars Green Foil	18	.25	.20	.10
1994 Upper Deck Collector's Choice	44	.15	.11	.06
1994 Upper Deck Electric Diamond	41	.50	.40	.20
1994 Upper Deck Electric Diamond	420	.40	.30	.15
1994 Upper Deck Fun Packs	33	.25	.20	.10
1994 Upper Deck SP	47	.35	.25	.14
1994 Upper Deck SP Baseball Die-Cut	47	.60	.45	.25

Carlos Baerga

Set	Card #	MT	NM	EX
1990 Bowman	339 (R)	.75	.60	.30
1990 Donruss Rookies	19	1.00	.75	.40
1990 Fleer Update	90	1.00	.75	.40
1990 Leaf	443 (R)	16.00	12.00	6.50
1990 Score Traded	74T	2.00	1.50	.80
1990 Topps Big Baseball	229	.50	.40	.20
1990 Topps Traded	6T	1.50	1.25	.60
1990 Upper Deck	737 (R)	3.00	2.25	1.25
1991 Bowman	69	.25	.20	.10
1991 Donruss	274	.25	.20	.10
1991 Fleer	360	.25	.20	.10
1991 Fleer Ultra	106	.75	.60	.30
1991 Leaf	225	1.00	.75	.40
1991 Score	74	.25	.20	.10
1991 Topps	147	.25	.20	.10
1991 Topps Glossy Rookies	4	.75	.60	.30
1991 Topps Stadium Club	115	5.00	3.75	2.00
1991 Upper Deck	125	.60	.45	.25
1992 Bowman	531	3.00	2.25	1.25
1992 Donruss	120	.25	.20	.10
1992 Donruss Triple Play	235	.25	.15	.08
1992 Fleer	104	.20	.15	.08
1992 Fleer Ultra	46	.75	.60	.30
1992 Leaf	202	.40	.30	.15
1992 O-Pee-Chee	33	.20	.15	.08
1992 Pinnacle	3	.75	.60	.30
1992 Pinnacle Team 2000	56	.25	.20	.10
1992 Pinnacle Team 2000	58	.75	.60	.30
1992 Score	128	.25	.20	.10
1992 Studio	163	.50	.40	.20
1992 Topps	33	.20	.15	.08
1992 Topps Gold	33	1.50	1.25	.60
1992 Topps Stadium Club	143	.75	.60	.30
1992 Upper Deck	231	.25	.20	.10
1993 Bowman	585	.60	.45	.25
1993 DiamondMarks	(77)	.50	.40	.20
1993 Donruss	405	.25	.20	.10
1993 Donruss Diamond Kings	13	2.00	1.50	.80
1993 Donruss MVP's	16	1.50	1.25	.60
1993 Donruss Spirit of the Game	15	1.50	1.25	.60
1993 Donruss Triple Play Action Baseball	18	.15	.11	.06
1993 Donruss Triple Play	80	.10	.08	.04
1993 Fleer	213	.25	.20	.10
1993 Fleer	357	.15	.11	.06
1993 Fleer AL Team Leaders	6	6.00	4.50	2.50
1993 Fleer Flair	191	1.50	1.25	.60
1993 Fleer Ultra	183	.40	.30	.15
1993 Fleer Ultra All-Stars	13	2.50	2.00	1.00
1993 Leaf	233	.40	.30	.15
1993 Leaf Fasttrack	11	5.00	3.75	2.00
1993 Leaf Gold All-Stars	4	4.00	3.00	1.50
1993 O-Pee-Chee	39	1.00	.75	.40
1993 O-Pee-Chee Premier	51	.25	.20	.10
1993 Pacific Prism Insert	9	35.00	26.00	14.00
1993 Pinnacle	6	.50	.40	.20
1993 Pinnacle Home Run Club	39	.50	.40	.20
1993 Pinnacle Slugfest	29	2.00	1.50	.80
1993 Pinnacle Team Pinnacle	5	8.00	6.00	3.25
1993 Pinnacle Team 2001	7	2.50	2.00	1.00
1993 Score	9	.25	.20	.10
1993 Score Select	122	.40	.30	.15
1993 Score Select Stat Leaders	8	.35	.25	.14
1993 Score The Franchise	5	5.00	3.75	2.00
1993 Studio	50	.60	.45	.25
1993 Studio Heritage	9	1.50	1.25	.60
1993 Topps	221	.20	.15	.08
1993 Topps	402	.15	.11	.06
1993 Topps Black Gold	25	.60	.45	.25
1993 Topps Finest	57	6.00	4.50	2.50
1993 Topps Finest Refractors	57	60.00	45.00	24.00
1993 Topps Gold	221	.40	.30	.15
1993 Topps Gold	402	.30	.25	.12
1993 Topps Stadium Club	61	.50	.40	.20
1993 Topps Stadium Club	593	.25	.20	.10
1993 Topps Stadium Club First Day Production	61	35.00	26.00	14.00
1993 Topps Stadium Club First Day Production	593	20.00	15.00	8.00
1993 Topps Stadium Club Special	189	.40	.30	.15

1993 Upper Deck	174	.20	.15	.08
1993 Upper Deck Diamond Gallery	12	1.00	.70	.40
1993 Upper Deck Fun Packs	105	.20	.15	.08
1993 Upper Deck Fun Packs	107	.25	.20	.10
1993 Upper Deck On Deck	3	1.50	1.25	.60
1993 Upper Deck SP	119	1.50	1.25	.60
1993 Upper Deck 5th Anniversary	8	1.00	.75	.40
1993 Upper Deck 5th Anniversary Super	8	3.50	2.75	1.50
1994 Bowman	307	.40	.30	.15
1994 Bowman's Best	103	2.00	1.50	.80
1994 Bowman's Best	35	2.00	1.50	.80
1994 Bowman's Best Refractors	103	6.00	4.50	2.50
1994 Bowman's Best Refractors	35	10.00	7.50	4.00
1994 Donruss	14	.40	.30	.15
1994 Donruss Special Edition - Gold	14	.75	.60	.30
1994 Donruss Triple Play Medalists	5	2.50	2.00	1.00
1994 Donruss Triple Play	112	.25	.20	.10
1994 Fleer	99	.25	.20	.10
1994 Fleer All-Stars	2	.60	.45	.25
1994 Fleer Extra Bases	56	.40	.30	.15
1994 Fleer Flair	37	1.00	.75	.40
1994 Fleer Flair Hot Numbers	2	10.00	7.50	4.00
1994 Fleer Golden Moments	2	2.00	1.50	.80
1994 Fleer Golden Moments Super	2	7.50	5.50	3.00
1994 Fleer ProVisions	4	.75	.60	.30
1994 Fleer Team Leaders	5	1.00	.75	.40
1994 Fleer Ultra	342	.40	.30	.15
1994 Fleer Ultra Hitting Machines	2	1.00	.75	.40
1994 Fleer Ultra Rising Stars	1	10.00	7.50	4.00
1994 Fleer Ultra RBI Kings	6	10.00	7.50	4.00
1994 Leaf	247	.40	.30	.15
1994 Leaf Gold Stars	9	20.00	15.00	8.00
1994 Leaf Limited	26	3.50	2.75	1.50
1994 Leaf MVP Contenders	14a	2.50	2.00	1.00
1994 Leaf MVP Contenders	14b	5.00	3.75	2.00
1994 O-Pee-Chee	106	.30	.25	.12
1994 O-Pee-Chee All-Star Redemption Cards	6	1.00	.75	.40
1994 O-Pee-Chee Jumbo All-Stars	6	10.00	7.50	4.00
1994 Pacific Crown	165	.25	.20	.10
1994 Pacific Crown Jewels of the Crown	16	4.00	3.00	1.50
1994 Pacific Crown Promos	1	3.00	2.25	1.25
1994 Pinnacle	2	.40	.30	.15
1994 Pinnacle Artist's Proof	2	20.00	15.00	8.00
1994 Pinnacle Museum Collection	2	10.00	.40	.20
1994 Pinnacle Power Surge	12	.40	.30	.15
1994 Pinnacle Power Surge	12a	3.00	2.25	1.25
1994 Pinnacle Run Creators	15	4.00	3.00	1.50
1994 Pinnacle Team Pinnacle	2	12.00	9.00	4.75
1994 Pinnacle The Naturals Box Set	22	.50	.40	.20
1994 Score	53	.30	.25	.12
1994 Score Dream Team	4	12.00	9.00	4.75
1994 Score Gold Stars	38	8.00	6.00	3.25
1994 Score Select	279	.50	.40	.20
1994 Score The Cycle	4	14.00	10.50	5.50

1994 Sportflics 2000	71	.60	.45	.25
1994 Sportflics 2000 Movers	11	7.00	5.25	2.75
1994 Studio	91	.50	.40	.20
1994 Topps	450	.20	.15	.08
1994 Topps Black Gold	2	1.00	.75	.40
1994 Topps Finest	231	2.00	1.50	.80
1994 Topps Finest Refractors	231	18.00	13.50	7.25
1994 Topps Finest Superstars	231	8.00	6.00	3.25
1994 Topps Gold	450	.60	.45	.25
1994 Topps Stadium Club	169	.40	.30	.15
1994 Topps Stadium Club First Day Production	169	18.00	13.50	7.25
1994 Topps Stadium Club Members Only Baseball	45	.40	.30	.15
1994 Upper Deck	49	.25	.20	.10
1994 Upper Deck	115	.35	.25	.14
1994 Upper Deck Collector's Choice	444	.20	.15	.08
1994 Upper Deck Electric Diamond	49	1.50	1.25	.60
1994 Upper Deck Electric Diamond	115	2.00	1.50	.80
1994 Upper Deck Fun Packs	109	.40	.30	.15
1994 Upper Deck Fun Packs	201	1.00	.70	.40
1994 Upper Deck SP	96	.50	.40	.20
1994 Upper Deck SP Baseball Die-Cut	96	1.00	.75	.40

Jeff Bagwell

Set	Card #	MT	NM	EX
1991 Bowman	183 (R)	2.50	2.00	1.00
1991 Donruss Rookies	30	2.50	2.00	1.00
1991 Fleer Ultra Update	79	18.00	13.50	7.25
1991 Fleer Update	87	2.00	1.50	.80
1991 Leaf Gold Rookies	14	12.00	9.00	4.75
1991 Score Traded	96	2.00	1.50	.80
1991 Studio	172 (R)	3.00	2.25	1.25
1991 Topps Stadium Club	388	14.00	10.50	5.50
1991 Topps Traded	4	2.50	2.00	1.00
1991 Upper Deck	755	2.50	2.00	1.00
1992 Bowman	200	5.00	3.75	2.00
1992 Donruss	358	.60	.45	.25
1992 Donruss Diamond Kings	11	4.00	3.00	1.50
1992 Donruss Triple Play Gallery of Stars	7	2.50	2.00	1.00
1992 Donruss Triple Play	200	.50	.40	.20
1992 Fleer	425	.60	.45	.25
1992 Fleer Rookie Sensations	4	15.00	11.00	6.00
1992 Fleer Ultra	198	1.50	1.25	.60
1992 Fleer Ultra Award Winners	3	6.00	4.50	2.50

1992 Leaf	28	1.00	.75	.40
1992 Leaf Gold Previews	4	2.50	2.00	1.00
1992 O-Pee-Chee	520	.30	.25	.12
1992 O-Pee-Chee Premier	107	.50	.40	.20
1992 Pinnacle	70	1.00	.75	.40
1992 Pinnacle Slugfest	15	4.00	3.00	1.50
1992 Pinnacle Team 2000	10	2.00	1.50	.80
1992 Post Cereal	1	.35	.25	.14
1992 Score	576	.60	.45	.25
1992 Score	793	.25	.20	.10
1992 Score Impact Players	2	1.50	1.25	.60
1992 Score Rising Stars	35	.20	.15	.08
1992 Studio	31	1.00	.75	.40
1992 Studio Heritage	12	3.50	2.75	1.50
1992 Topps	520	.60	.45	.25
1992 Topps Gold	520	7.50	5.75	3.00
1992 Topps Kids	44	.10	.08	.04
1992 Topps Stadium Club	330	2.00	1.50	.80
1992 Topps Stadium Club	606	.75	.60	.30
1992 Topps Stadium Club East Coast National	606	20.00	15.00	8.00
1992 Upper Deck	276	.50	.40	.20
1992 Upper Deck Home Run Heroes	25	2.00	1.50	.80
1992 Upper Deck MVP Holograms	7	1.00	.75	.40
1993 Bowman	420	2.00	1.50	.80
1993 DiamondMarks	(25)	.50	.40	.20
1993 Donruss	428	.75	.60	.30
1993 Donruss Long Ball Leaders	17	10.00	7.50	4.00
1993 Donruss MVP's	24	4.00	3.00	1.50
1993 Donruss Triple Play Action Baseball	12	.10	.08	.04
1993 Donruss Triple Play	43	.25	.20	.10
1993 Fleer	46	.75	.60	.30
1993 Fleer Flair	57	4.00	3.00	1.50
1993 Fleer NL Team Leaders	9	18.00	13.50	7.25
1993 Fleer Ultra	390	1.00	.75	.40
1993 Leaf	125	1.50	1.25	.60
1993 Leaf Fasttrack	17	12.00	9.00	4.75
1993 Leaf Gold All-Stars	3	3.00	2.25	1.25
1993 O-Pee-Chee	29	1.50	1.25	.60
1993 Pinnacle	10	1.50	1.25	.60
1993 Pinnacle	297	.50	.40	.20
1993 Pinnacle Home Run Club	28	.75	.60	.30
1993 Pinnacle Slugfest	14	6.00	4.50	2.50
1993 Pinnacle Team 2001	9	5.00	3.75	2.00
1993 Score	89	.75	.60	.30
1993 Score Select	113	1.00	.75	.40
1993 Score The Franchise	18	15.00	11.00	6.00
1993 Studio	34	1.00	.75	.40
1993 Studio Silhouettes	3	5.00	3.75	2.00
1993 Topps	227	.50	.40	.20
1993 Topps Finest	11	16.00	12.00	6.50
1993 Topps Finest Refractors	11	300.00	220.00	120.00
1993 Topps Full Shot Super	8	4.00	3.00	1.50
1993 Topps Gold	227	.90	.70	.35
1993 Topps Stadium Club	384	1.00	.75	.40
1993 Topps Stadium Club First Day Production	384	35.00	26.00	14.00
1993 Topps Stadium Club Team Sets	8	.50	.40	.20
1993 Upper Deck	256	.60	.45	.25
1993 Upper Deck	452	.40	.30	.15
1993 Upper Deck	475	.12	.09	.05
1993 Upper Deck	813	.25	.20	.10
1993 Upper Deck Diamond Gallery	2	1.00	.75	.40
1993 Upper Deck Fun Packs	42	.40	.30	.15
1993 Upper Deck Fun Packs	43	.75	.60	.30
1993 Upper Deck Iooss Collection	2	2.50	2.00	1.00
1993 Upper Deck Iooss Collection Super	2	4.00	3.00	1.50
1993 Upper Deck SP	28	6.00	4.50	2.50
1994 Bowman	118	1.00	.75	.40
1994 Bowman's Best	53	4.50	3.50	1.75
1994 Bowman's Best Refractors	53	40.00	30.00	15.00
1994 Donruss	365	1.00	.75	.40
1994 Donruss Diamond Kings	27	4.00	3.00	1.50
1994 Donruss MVP's	6	4.00	3.00	1.50
1994 Donruss Special Edition - Gold	365	1.50	1.25	.60
1994 Donruss Triple Play Medalists	4	2.50	2.00	1.00
1994 Donruss Triple Play	21	.60	.45	.25
1994 Fleer	483	1.00	.75	.40
1994 Fleer Extra Bases	268	1.25	.90	.50
1994 Fleer Extra Bases Game Breakers	1	2.00	1.50	.80
1994 Fleer Flair	385	2.00	1.50	.80
1994 Fleer Flair Infield Power	1	8.00	6.00	3.25
1994 Fleer Team Leaders	20	2.50	2.00	1.00
1994 Fleer Ultra	203	1.25	.90	.50
1994 Fleer Ultra Rising Stars	2	25.00	18.00	10.00
1994 Leaf	221	1.25	.90	.50
1994 Leaf Limited	110	10.00	7.50	4.00
1994 Leaf MVP Contenders	2a	60.00	45.00	24.00
1994 Leaf MVP Contenders	2b	125.00	95.00	50.00
1994 O-Pee-Chee	212	.75	.60	.30
1994 O-Pee-Chee All-Star Redemption Cards	5	1.50	1.25	.60
1994 O-Pee-Chee Jumbo All-Stars	5	8.00	6.00	3.25
1994 Pacific Crown	257	.75	.60	.30
1994 Pacific Crown Jewels of the Crown	24	8.00	6.00	3.25
1994 Pinnacle	290	1.00	.70	.40
1994 Pinnacle Artist's Proof	290	75.00	56.00	30.00
1994 Pinnacle Museum Collection	290	25.00	18.00	10.00
1994 Pinnacle Power Surge	16	.30	.25	.12
1994 Pinnacle Run Creators	36	8.00	6.00	3.25
1994 Pinnacle Team Pinnacle	1	70.00	52.00	28.00
1994 Post Cereal	29	.35	.25	.14
1994 Score	4	.75	.60	.30
1994 Score Gold Stars	8	22.00	16.50	8.75
1994 Score Select	234	1.50	1.25	.60
1994 Sportflics 2000	7	1.00	.75	.40
1994 Sportflics 2000 Shakers	3	15.00	11.00	6.00
1994 Studio	16	1.00	.75	.40
1994 Topps	40	.60	.45	.25
1994 Topps Black Gold	23	1.50	1.25	.60
1994 Topps Finest	212	7.00	5.25	2.75
1994 Topps Finest Refractors	212	50.00	38.00	20.00
1994 Topps Finest Superstars	212	18.00	13.50	7.25
1994 Topps Gold	40	2.00	1.50	.80
1994 Topps Stadium Club	108	1.00	.75	.40
1994 Topps Stadium Club Finest	1	4.00	3.00	1.50
1994 Topps Stadium Club First Day Production	108	40.00	30.00	16.00
1994 Upper Deck	272	.75	.60	.30
1994 Upper Deck	480	1.00	.75	.40
1994 Upper Deck All-Stars Green Foil	36	.90	.70	.35
1994 Upper Deck Collector's Choice	329	.10	.08	.04

1994 Upper Deck Collector's Choice	590	.60	.45	.25
1994 Upper Deck Diamond Collection	2C	22.00	16.50	8.75
1994 Upper Deck Electric Diamond	272	1.00	.75	.40
1994 Upper Deck Electric Diamond	480	2.00	1.50	.80
1994 Upper Deck Fun Packs	152	1.00	.75	.40
1994 Upper Deck Mickey Mantle's Long Shots	1MM	8.00	6.00	3.25
1994 Upper Deck SP	27	2.00	1.50	.80
1994 Upper Deck SP Baseball Die-Cut	27	5.00	3.75	2.00
1994 Upper Deck SP Holoview Blue	3	14.00	10.50	5.50
1994 Upper Deck SP Insert	1	12.00	9.00	4.75

1984 Topps Traded	5T	.50	.40	.20
1985 Donruss	445	.10	.08	.04
1985 Fleer	602	.08	.06	.03
1985 Fleer Update	3	.15	.11	.06
1985 O-Pee-Chee	165	.08	.06	.03
1985 Topps	165	.08	.06	.03
1985 Topps Traded	4T	.15	.11	.06
1986 Donruss	467	.08	.06	.03
1986 Fleer	411	.08	.06	.03
1986 Leaf	231	.08	.06	.03
1986 O-Pee-Chee	31	.08	.06	.03
1986 Topps	645	.07	.05	.03
1987 Fleer	387	.08	.06	.03
1987 Topps	565	.07	.05	.03
1990 Pacific Legends	71	.05	.04	.02
1993 Topps	514	.03	.02	.01
1993 Topps Gold	514	.10	.08	.04

Dusty Baker

Sal Bando

Set	Card #	NM	EX	VG
1971 O-Pee-Chee	709	115.00	57.00	34.00
1971 Topps	709 (R)	90.00	45.00	27.00
1972 Topps	764	12.00	6.00	3.50
1973 O-Pee-Chee	215	.75	.40	.25
1973 Topps	215	.75	.40	.25
1974 O-Pee-Chee	320	.60	.30	.20
1974 Topps	320	.40	.20	.12
1975 O-Pee-Chee	33	.55	.30	.15
1975 Topps	33	.40	.20	.12
1975 Topps Mini	33	.90	.45	.25
1976 O-Pee-Chee	28	.35	.20	.11
1976 Topps	28	1.50	.75	.45
1976 Topps Traded	28T	1.25	.60	.40
1977 Topps	146	.25	.13	.08
1978 Topps	668	.25	.13	.08
1979 O-Pee-Chee	290	.25	.13	.08
1979 Topps	562	.25	.13	.08
1980 O-Pee-Chee	135	.20	.10	.06
1980 Topps	255	.12	.06	.04

Set	Card #	MT	NM	EX
1981 Donruss	179	.10	.08	.04
1981 Fleer	115	.10	.08	.04
1981 Topps	495	.12	.09	.05
1982 Donruss	336	.10	.08	.04
1982 Fleer	1	.10	.08	.04
1982 O-Pee-Chee	375	.12	.09	.05
1982 Topps	311	.12	.09	.05
1982 Topps	375	.12	.09	.05
1983 Donruss	462	.10	.08	.04
1983 Fleer	201	.10	.08	.04
1983 O-Pee-Chee	220	.12	.09	.05
1983 Topps	220	.12	.09	.05
1984 Donruss	226	.20	.15	.08
1984 Fleer	96	.12	.09	.05
1984 Fleer Update	5	.25	.20	.10
1984 O-Pee-Chee	40	.20	.15	.08
1984 Topps	40	.12	.09	.05

Set	Card #	NM	EX	VG
1967 O-Pee-Chee	33	2.25	1.25	.70
1967 Topps	33 (R)	1.75	1.00	.50
1968 O-Pee-Chee	146	2.25	1.25	.70
1968 Topps	146	1.50	.70	.45
1969 Topps	371	1.25	.60	.40
1969 Topps	556	2.50	1.25	.70
1970 O-Pee-Chee	120	1.00	.50	.30
1970 Topps	120	.90	.45	.25
1971 O-Pee-Chee	285	1.50	.70	.45
1971 Topps	285	1.00	.50	.30
1972 O-Pee-Chee	348	1.25	.60	.40
1972 Topps	348	.75	.40	.25
1972 Topps	650	2.00	1.00	.60
1973 O-Pee-Chee	155	.75	.40	.25
1973 Topps	155	.40	.20	.12
1974 O-Pee-Chee	103	.60	.30	.20
1974 Topps	103	.30	.15	.09
1975 O-Pee-Chee	380	.55	.30	.15
1975 Topps	380	.30	.15	.09
1975 Topps Mini	380	.60	.30	.20
1976 O-Pee-Chee	90	.35	.20	.11
1976 Topps	90	.25	.13	.08
1977 O-Pee-Chee	145	.30	.15	.09
1977 Topps	498	.20	.10	.06
1978 O-Pee-Chee	174	.25	.13	.08
1978 Topps	265	.20	.10	.06
1979 O-Pee-Chee	283	.25	.13	.08
1979 Topps	550	.20	.10	.06
1980 O-Pee-Chee	363	.15	.08	.05
1980 Topps	715	.20	.10	.06

Set	Card #	MT	NM	EX
1981 Donruss	84	.10	.08	.04
1981 Fleer	510	.10	.08	.04
1981 O-Pee-Chee	276	.12	.09	.05
1981 Topps	623	.12	.09	.05
1982 Donruss	592	.08	.06	.03
1982 Fleer	134	.08	.06	.03

Set		NM	EX	VG
1988 Pacific Trading Cards Baseball Legends	99	.06	.05	.02
1990 Pacific Legends	4	.05	.04	.02
1993 Upper Deck All-Time Heroes	5	.10	.08	.04
1994 Upper Deck All-Time Heroes	88	.05	.04	.02
1994 Upper Deck Heroes Gold	88	.15	.11	.06

Ernie Banks

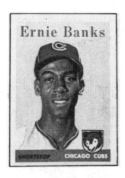

Set	Card #	NM	EX	VG
1954 Topps	94 (R)	675.00	325.00	200.00
1955 Bowman	242	300.00	150.00	90.00
1955 Topps	28	200.00	100.00	60.00
1956 Topps	15	80.00	40.00	24.00
1957 Topps	55	110.00	55.00	33.00
1958 Topps	310	80.00	40.00	24.00
1958 Topps	482	24.00	12.00	7.25
1959 Home Run Derby	(3)	300.00	150.00	90.00
1959 Topps	147	16.00	8.00	4.75
1959 Topps	350	65.00	32.50	19.50
1959 Topps	469	12.00	6.00	3.50
1959 Topps	559	55.00	27.00	16.50
1960 Topps	10	40.00	20.00	12.50
1960 Topps	560	50.00	25.00	15.00
1961 Post Cereal	191a	9.00	4.50	2.75
1961 Post Cereal	191b	9.00	4.50	2.75
1961 Topps	43	9.00	4.50	2.75
1961 Topps	350	37.50	18.50	11.00
1961 Topps	485	30.00	15.00	9.00
1961 Topps	575	85.00	42.00	25.00
1962 Post Cereal	188	15.00	7.50	4.50
1962 Topps	25	40.00	20.00	12.00
1963 Post Cereal	169	10.00	5.00	3.00
1963 Topps	3	26.00	13.00	7.75
1963 Topps	242	40.00	20.00	12.00
1963 Topps	380	60.00	30.00	18.00
1964 Topps	55.	30.00	15.00	9.00
1965 Topps	510	70.00	35.00	21.00
1966 O-Pee-Chee	110	30.00	15.00	9.00
1966 Topps	110	25.00	12.50	7.50
1967 Topps	215	20.00	10.00	6.00
1968 Topps	355	24.00	12.00	7.25
1969 O-Pee-Chee	6	8.50	4.25	2.50
1969 O-Pee-Chee	20	23.00	11.50	7.00
1969 Topps	6	4.00	2.00	1.25
1969 Topps	20	15.00	7.50	4.50
1970 Topps	630	36.00	18.00	11.00
1971 O-Pee-Chee	525	50.00	25.00	15.00
1971 Topps	525	30.00	15.00	9.00
1973 O-Pee-Chee	81	.75	.40	.25
1973 Topps	81a	.90	.45	.25
1973 Topps	81b	.70	.35	.20
1975 O-Pee-Chee	196	3.00	1.50	.90
1975 O-Pee-Chee	197	3.00	1.50	.90
1975 Topps	196	.90	.45	.25
1975 Topps	197	.90	.45	.25
1975 Topps Mini	196	1.25	.60	.40
1975 Topps Mini	197	1.25	.60	.40

Set	Card #	MT	NM	EX
1988 Pacific Trading Cards Baseball Legends	36	.30	.25	.12
1990 Pacific Legends	5	.40	.30	.15

Don Baylor

Set	Card #	NM	EX	VG
1971 O-Pee-Chee	709	115.00	57.00	34.00
1971 Topps	709 (R)	90.00	45.00	27.00
1972 O-Pee-Chee	474	15.00	7.50	4.50
1972 Topps	474	12.00	6.00	3.50
1973 O-Pee-Chee	384	1.00	.50	.30
1973 Topps	384	2.00	1.00	.60
1974 O-Pee-Chee	187	.75	.40	.25
1974 Topps	187	.50	.25	.15
1975 O-Pee-Chee	382	.75	.40	.25
1975 Topps	382	.45	.25	.14
1975 Topps Mini	382	.90	.45	.25
1976 O-Pee-Chee	125	.50	.25	.15
1976 Topps	125	.40	.20	.12
1977 O-Pee-Chee	133	.50	.25	.15
1977 Topps	462	.35	.20	.11
1978 O-Pee-Chee	173	.40	.20	.12
1978 Topps	48	.35	.20	.11
1979 O-Pee-Chee	335	.40	.20	.12
1979 Topps	635	.40	.20	.12
1980 O-Pee-Chee	150	.30	.15	.09
1980 Topps	203	.50	.25	.15
1980 Topps	285	.35	.20	.11

Set	Card #	MT	NM	EX
1981 Donruss	413	.12	.09	.05
1981 Fleer	271	.12	.09	.05
1981 O-Pee-Chee	309	.15	.11	.06
1981 Topps	580	.15	.11	.06
1982 Donruss	493	.12	.09	.05
1982 Fleer	451	.12	.09	.05
1982 O-Pee-Chee	234	.15	.11	.06
1982 Topps	415	.15	.11	.06
1983 Donruss	493	.12	.09	.05
1983 Fleer	77	.12	.09	.05
1983 O-Pee-Chee	105	.15	.11	.06
1983 Topps	105	.15	.11	.06
1983 Topps Traded	8T	.30	.25	.12
1984 Donruss	152	.20	.15	.08
1984 Fleer	119	.15	.11	.06
1984 O-Pee-Chee	335	.30	.25	.12
1984 Topps	335	.15	.11	.06
1984 Topps	486	.15	.11	.06
1985 Donruss	173	.15	.11	.06
1985 Donruss Highlights	35	.15	.11	.06
1985 Fleer	121	.12	.09	.05
1985 Leaf-Donruss	146	.20	.15	.08
1985 O-Pee-Chee	70	.12	.09	.05
1985 Topps	70	.12	.09	.05
1986 Donruss	347	.12	.09	.05

		MT	NM	EX
1986 Fleer	99	.12	.09	.05
1986 Fleer	631	.08	.06	.03
1986 Fleer Update	10	.15	.11	.06
1986 O-Pee-Chee	184	.10	.08	.04
1986 Sportflics	57	.35	.25	.14
1986 Topps	765	.12	.09	.05
1986 Topps Traded	6T	.15	.11	.06
1987 Donruss	339	.12	.09	.05
1987 Fleer	28	.12	.09	.05
1987 Leaf	232	.08	.06	.03
1987 O-Pee-Chee	230	.08	.06	.03
1987 Sportflics	163	.15	.11	.06
1987 Topps	230	.10	.08	.04
1987 Topps All-Star Glossy Set of 60	27	.25	.20	.10
1988 Fleer	2	.10	.08	.04
1988 Score	250	.08	.06	.03
1988 Score Glossy	250	.40	.30	.15
1988 Score Traded	55T	.25	.20	.10
1988 Topps	545	.08	.06	.03
1988 Topps Big Baseball	162	.10	.08	.04
1988 Topps Traded	11T	.10	.08	.04
1989 Fleer	1	.10	.08	.04
1989 Score	205	.08	.06	.03
1989 Topps	673	.08	.06	.03
1989 Upper Deck	601	.10	.08	.04
1990 Pacific Legends	6	.05	.04	.02
1993 Topps	504	.03	.02	.01
1993 Topps Gold	504	.10	.08	.04
1993 Upper Deck All-Time Heroes	7	.10	.08	.04
1994 Upper Deck All-Time Heroes	179	.05	.04	.02
1994 Upper Deck Heroes Gold	179	.15	.11	.06

Albert Belle

ALBERT BELLE

Set	Card #	MT	NM	EX
1989 Fleer Update	25	3.50	2.75	1.50
1989 Score Traded	106T	4.50	3.50	1.75
1990 Bowman	333 (R)	1.25	.90	.50
1990 Donruss	390 (R)	1.25	.90	.50
1990 Fleer	485 (R)	1.50	1.25	.60
1990 Leaf	180	18.00	13.50	7.25
1990 O-Pee-Chee	283	1.00	.75	.40
1990 Score	508 (R)	1.25	.90	.50
1990 Sportflics	159	.80	.60	.30
1990 Topps	283 (R)	1.50	1.25	.60
1990 Topps Glossy Rookies	2	.75	.60	.30
1990 Upper Deck	446 (R)	3.00	2.25	1.25
1991 Bowman	81	.30	.25	.12
1991 Fleer Ultra	107	1.25	.90	.50
1991 Fleer Update	16	.30	.25	.12
1991 Leaf	239	1.00	.70	.40
1991 O-Pee-Chee Premier	8	.50	.40	.20
1991 Topps Stadium Club	465	6.00	4.50	2.50
1991 Upper Deck	764	.50	.40	.20
1992 Bowman	329	4.00	3.00	1.50

		MT	NM	EX
1992 Donruss	500	.40	.30	.15
1992 Donruss Triple Play	103	.25	.20	.10
1992 Fleer	105	.40	.30	.15
1992 Fleer Ultra	47	1.00	.70	.40
1992 Leaf	350	.50	.40	.20
1992 O-Pee-Chee	785	.15	.11	.06
1992 O-Pee-Chee Premier	100	.30	.25	.12
1992 Pinnacle	31	.75	.60	.30
1992 Pinnacle Team 2000	18	1.50	1.25	.60
1992 Score	31	.30	.25	.12
1992 Studio	164	.60	.45	.25
1992 Topps	785	.40	.30	.15
1992 Topps Gold	785	2.00	1.50	.80
1992 Topps Kids	73	.10	.08	.04
1992 Topps Stadium Club	220	1.00	.75	.40
1992 Upper Deck	137	.30	.25	.12
1992 Upper Deck Home Run Heroes	13	1.50	1.25	.60
1992 Upper Deck MVP Holograms	8	1.00	.75	.40
1993 Bowman	445	.75	.60	.30
1993 DiamondMarks	(78)	.50	.40	.20
1993 Donruss	435	.40	.30	.15
1993 Donruss Elite Dominators	17	65.00	49.00	26.00
1993 Donruss Long Ball Leaders	3	6.00	4.50	2.50
1993 Donruss Triple Play	94	.15	.11	.06
1993 Fleer	590	.40	.30	.15
1993 Fleer	712	.15	.11	.06
1993 Fleer Flair	192	2.00	1.50	.80
1993 Fleer Ultra	538	.75	.60	.30
1993 Fleer Ultra Home Run Kings	5	3.50	2.75	1.50
1993 Leaf	18	1.00	.75	.40
1993 O-Pee-Chee	66	1.50	1.25	.60
1993 Pinnacle	93	.75	.60	.30
1993 Pinnacle Home Run Club	5	1.00	.70	.40
1993 Pinnacle Slugfest	11	4.00	3.00	1.50
1993 Score	84	.40	.30	.15
1993 Score Select	50	.75	.60	.30
1993 Studio	95	.80	.60	.30
1993 Topps	635	.30	.25	.12
1993 Topps Finest	16	9.00	6.75	3.50
1993 Topps Finest Refractors	16	100.00	75.00	40.00
1993 Topps Gold	635	.60	.45	.25
1993 Topps Stadium Club	102	.60	.45	.25
1993 Topps Stadium Club First Day Production	102	45.00	34.00	18.00
1993 Upper Deck	586	.30	.25	.12
1993 Upper Deck	823	.15	.11	.06
1993 Upper Deck Fun Packs	108	.40	.30	.15
1993 Upper Deck Home Run Heroes	5	1.50	1.25	.60
1993 Upper Deck Iooss Collection	12	2.00	1.50	.80
1993 Upper Deck Iooss Collection Super	12	3.00	2.25	1.25
1993 Upper Deck On Deck	4	1.75	1.25	.70
1993 Upper Deck SP	120	2.50	2.00	1.00
1993 Upper Deck SP Platinum Power	1	18.00	13.50	7.25
1994 Bowman	411	.50	.40	.20
1994 Bowman's Best	98	2.00	1.50	.80
1994 Bowman's Best	41	3.50	2.75	1.50
1994 Bowman's Best Refractors	98	5.00	3.75	2.00
1994 Bowman's Best Refractors	41	12.00	9.00	4.75
1994 Donruss	351	.60	.45	.25
1994 Donruss Diamond Kings	8	3.00	2.25	1.25
1994 Donruss Diamond Kings Super	8	3.75	2.75	1.50
1994 Donruss Elite	40	30.00	22.00	12.00
1994 Donruss MVP's	19	2.00	1.50	.80

1994 Donruss Special Edition - Gold	351	.75	.60	.30
1994 Donruss Triple Play Bomb Squad	9	3.00	2.25	1.25
1994 Donruss Triple Play Medalists	11	5.00	3.75	2.00
1994 Donruss Triple Play	113	.30	.25	.12
1994 Fleer All-Stars	3	1.00	.75	.40
1994 Fleer Extra Bases	57	.60	.45	.25
1994 Fleer Extra Bases Game Breakers	3	1.00	.75	.40
1994 Fleer Flair	38	1.50	1.25	.60
1994 Fleer Flair Outfield Power	1	5.00	3.75	2.00
1994 Fleer League Leaders	2	1.50	1.25	.60
1994 Fleer Lumber Co.	1	1.50	1.25	.60
1994 Fleer Ultra	41	.75	.60	.30
1994 Fleer Ultra All-Stars	6	1.50	1.25	.60
1994 Fleer Ultra Home Run Kings	4	7.50	5.50	3.00
1994 Fleer Ultra Rising Stars	3	15.00	11.00	6.00
1994 Fleer Ultra RBI Kings	1	16.00	12.00	6.50
1994 Leaf	251	.75	.60	.30
1994 Leaf Clean-Up Crew	11	10.00	7.50	4.00
1994 Leaf Limited	27	5.00	3.75	2.00
1994 Leaf MVP Contenders	1b	15.00	11.00	6.00
1994 Leaf Power Brokers	10	2.50	2.00	1.00
1994 O-Pee-Chee	43	.60	.45	.25
1994 O-Pee-Chee All-Star Redemption Cards	12	1.25	.90	.50
1994 O-Pee-Chee Jumbo All-Stars	12	10.00	7.50	4.00
1994 Pacific Crown	166	.40	.30	.15
1994 Pacific Crown Homerun Leaders	4	8.00	6.00	3.25
1994 Pinnacle	15	.60	.45	.25
1994 Pinnacle Artist's Proof	15	35.00	26.00	14.00
1994 Pinnacle Museum Collection	15	15.00	11.00	6.00
1994 Pinnacle Power Surge	11	.40	.30	.15
1994 Pinnacle Run Creators	8	7.00	5.25	2.75
1994 Pinnacle The Naturals Box Set	6	.60	.45	.25
1994 Post Cereal	27	.35	.25	.14
1994 Score	7	.50	.40	.20
1994 Score Gold Stars	46	15.00	11.00	6.00
1994 Score Select	235	1.00	.70	.40
1994 Score The Cycle	20	18.00	13.50	7.25
1994 Sportflics 2000	10	.60	.45	.25
1994 Studio	92	.60	.45	.25
1994 Topps	390	.35	.25	.14
1994 Topps	480	.30	.25	.12
1994 Topps Black Gold	3	1.25	.90	.50
1994 Topps Finest	208	3.50	2.75	1.50
1994 Topps Finest Refractors	208	25.00	18.00	10.00
1994 Topps Finest Superstars	208	12.00	9.00	4.75
1994 Topps Gold	390	1.25	.90	.50
1994 Topps Gold	480	1.00	.70	.40
1994 Topps Stadium Club	219	.60	.45	.25
1994 Topps Stadium Club	258	.25	.20	.10
1994 Topps Stadium Club Finest	2	3.00	2.25	1.25
1994 Topps Stadium Club First Day Production	219	30.00	22.00	12.00
1994 Topps Stadium Club First Day Production	258	18.00	13.50	7.25
1994 Topps Stadium Club Members Only Baseball	18	.45	.35	.20
1994 Upper Deck	40	.40	.30	.15
1994 Upper Deck	131	.50	.40	.20
1994 Upper Deck	285	.50	.40	.20
1994 Upper Deck Collectors Choice Home Run A	6HA	1.25	.90	.50
1994 Upper Deck Collector's Choice	314	.25	.20	.10
1994 Upper Deck Collector's Choice	339	.15	.11	.06
1994 Upper Deck Collector's Choice	620	.30	.25	.12
1994 Upper Deck Electric Diamond	40	.75	.60	.30
1994 Upper Deck Electric Diamond	131	2.50	2.00	1.00
1994 Upper Deck Electric Diamond	285	1.50	1.25	.60
1994 Upper Deck Fun Packs	130	.50	.40	.20
1994 Upper Deck Fun Packs	183	.30	.25	.12
1994 Upper Deck Fun Packs	204	2.50	2.00	1.00
1994 Upper Deck Mickey Mantle's Long Shots	2MM	5.00	3.75	2.00
1994 Upper Deck SP	97	1.00	.75	.40
1994 Upper Deck SP Baseball Die-Cut	97	2.00	1.50	.80

Johnny Bench

Set	Card #	NM	EX	VG
1968 Topps	247 (R)	200.00	100.00	60.00
1969 O-Pee-Chee	95	135.00	67.00	40.00
1969 Topps	95	100.00	50.00	30.00
1969 Topps	430	11.00	5.50	3.75
1970 O-Pee-Chee	464	15.00	7.50	4.50
1970 Topps	464	10.00	5.00	3.00
1970 Topps	660	125.00	62.50	37.50
1971 O-Pee-Chee	64	1.50	.70	.45
1971 O-Pee-Chee	66	1.50	.70	.45
1971 O-Pee-Chee	250	46.00	23.00	14.00
1971 Topps	64	3.50	1.75	1.00
1971 Topps	66	3.50	1.75	1.00
1971 Topps	250	35.00	17.50	10.50
1972 O-Pee-Chee	433	42.50	21.00	12.50
1972 O-Pee-Chee	434	21.00	10.50	6.25
1972 Topps	433	25.00	12.50	7.50
1972 Topps	434	15.00	7.50	4.50
1973 O-Pee-Chee	62	1.00	.50	.30
1973 O-Pee-Chee	63	1.00	.50	.30
1973 O-Pee-Chee	380	22.00	11.00	6.50
1973 Topps	62	2.25	1.25	.70
1973 Topps	63	2.25	1.25	.70
1973 Topps	380	16.00	8.00	4.75
1974 O-Pee-Chee	10	18.00	9.00	5.50
1974 O-Pee-Chee	331	6.75	3.50	2.00
1974 Topps	10	15.00	7.50	4.50
1974 Topps	331	5.00	2.50	1.50
1975 O-Pee-Chee	208	3.00	1.50	.90
1975 O-Pee-Chee	210	3.00	1.50	.90

1975 O-Pee-Chee	260	15.00	7.50	4.50
1975 O-Pee-Chee	308	2.00	1.00	.60
1975 Topps	208	1.25	.60	.40
1975 Topps	210	1.25	.60	.40
1975 Topps	260	12.00	6.00	3.50
1975 Topps	308	.80	.40	.25
1975 Topps Mini	208	1.75	.90	.50
1975 Topps Mini	210	1.75	.90	.50
1975 Topps Mini	260	15.00	7.50	4.50
1975 Topps Mini	308	1.25	.60	.40
1976 O-Pee-Chee	195	2.00	1.00	.60
1976 O-Pee-Chee	300	12.75	6.50	3.75
1976 Topps	195	2.00	1.00	.60
1976 Topps	300	10.00	5.00	3.00
1977 O-Pee-Chee	100	10.25	5.25	3.00
1977 Topps	70	8.00	4.00	2.50
1977 Topps	411	1.50	.70	.45
1977 Topps	412	1.50	.70	.45
1978 O-Pee-Chee	50	5.00	2.50	1.50
1978 Topps	700	5.00	2.50	1.50
1979 O-Pee-Chee	101	3.00	1.50	.90
1979 Topps	200	2.00	1.00	.60
1980 O-Pee-Chee	55	4.25	2.25	1.25
1980 Topps	100	4.00	2.00	1.25

Set	Card #	MT	NM	EX
1981 Donruss	62	1.25	.90	.50
1981 Donruss	182	1.00	.70	.40
1981 Fleer	196	1.50	1.25	.60
1981 O-Pee-Chee	286	2.50	2.00	1.00
1981 Topps	201	1.00	.75	.40
1981 Topps	600	2.00	1.50	.80
1982 Donruss	400	1.00	.75	.40
1982 Donruss	628	.80	.60	.30
1982 Fleer	57	.80	.60	.30
1982 Fleer	634	.30	.25	.12
1982 O-Pee-Chee	18	1.50	1.25	.60
1982 O-Pee-Chee	304	.40	.30	.15
1982 Topps	400	1.50	1.25	.60
1982 Topps	401	.40	.30	.15
1983 Donruss	22	.60	.45	.25
1983 Donruss	500	1.00	.70	.40
1983 Fleer	584	1.00	.70	.40
1983 O-Pee-Chee	60	1.50	1.25	.60
1983 O-Pee-Chee	61	.75	.60	.30
1983 Topps	60	1.50	1.25	.60
1983 Topps	61	.60	.45	.25
1984 Donruss	B	7.00	5.25	2.75
1984 Fleer	462	.80	.60	.30
1984 Fleer	640	2.00	1.50	.80
1984 Topps	6	.40	.30	.15
1984 Topps All-Star Glossy Set of 22	22	.60	.45	.25
1988 Pacific Trading Cards Baseball Legends	110	.40	.30	.15
1990 O-Pee-Chee	664	.07	.05	.03
1990 Topps	664	.07	.05	.03
1992 Upper Deck Bench/ Morgan Heroes	37	1.00	.70	.40
1992 Upper Deck Bench/ Morgan Heroes	38	1.00	.70	.40
1992 Upper Deck Bench/ Morgan Heroes	39	1.00	.70	.40
1992 Upper Deck Bench/ Morgan Heroes	43	.75	.60	.30
1992 Upper Deck Bench/ Morgan Heroes	44	.75	.60	.30
1992 Upper Deck Bench/ Morgan Heroes	45	.75	.60	.30

* * *

A Yankee official claims that he telephoned Yogi Berra early one morning: "Yogi, did I get you out of bed?" he asked. "No, I had to get up to answer the phone anyway," Yogi said.

* * *

Yogi Berra

Set	Card #	NM	EX	VG
1948 Bowman	6 (R)	500.00	250.00	150.00
1949 Bowman	60	350.00	175.00	105.00
1950 Bowman	46	350.00	175.00	105.00
1951 Bowman	2	300.00	150.00	90.00
1951 Topps Red Backs	1	75.00	38.00	23.50
1952 Bowman	1	600.00	250.00	150.00
1952 Red Man Tobacco	3A	90.00	45.00	27.00
1952 Topps	191	300.00	150.00	69.00
1953 Bowman Color	44	450.00	225.00	125.00
1953 Bowman Color	121	450.00	225.00	135.00
1953 Red Man Tobacco	3A	80.00	40.00	24.00
1953 Topps	104	250.00	125.00	57.00
1954 Bowman	161	145.00	72.50	42.50
1954 Red Man Tobacco	20A	80.00	40.00	24.00
1954 Topps	50	200.00	100.00	60.00
1955 Bowman	168	75.00	35.00	20.00
1955 Red Man Tobacco	16A	80.00	40.00	24.00
1955 Topps	198	160.00	80.00	45.00
1956 Topps	110	110.00	55.00	32.50
1957 Topps	2	110.00	55.00	32.50
1957 Topps	407	325.00	160.00	95.00
1958 Topps	370	90.00	45.00	27.00
1959 Topps	180	70.00	35.00	21.00
1960 Topps	480	70.00	35.00	21.00
1961 Post Cereal	1a	35.00	17.50	10.50
1961 Post Cereal	1b	21.50	10.50	6.50
1961 Topps	425	70.00	35.00	21.00
1961 Topps	472	45.00	22.00	13.50
1962 Post Cereal	7	15.00	7.50	4.50
1962 Topps	360	72.00	36.00	21.50
1963 Post Cereal	17	15.00	7.50	4.50
1963 Topps	340	55.00	27.00	16.50
1964 Topps	21	35.00	17.50	10.50
1965 Topps	470	50.00	25.00	15.00
1973 O-Pee-Chee	257	1.00	.50	.30
1973 Topps	257a	3.00	1.50	.90
1973 Topps	257b	2.50	1.25	.70
1974 O-Pee-Chee	179	1.00	.50	.30
1974 Topps	179	2.00	1.00	.60
1975 O-Pee-Chee	189	3.00	1.50	.90
1975 O-Pee-Chee	192	5.00	2.50	1.50
1975 O-Pee-Chee	193	3.00	1.50	.90
1975 O-Pee-Chee	421	.75	.40	.25
1975 Topps	189	2.00	1.00	.60
1975 Topps	192	2.00	1.00	.60
1975 Topps	193	2.00	1.00	.60
1975 Topps	421	2.50	1.25	.70
1975 Topps Mini	189	2.25	1.25	.70
1975 Topps Mini	192	2.25	1.25	.70
1975 Topps Mini	193	2.25	1.25	.70
1975 Topps Mini	421	1.50	.70	.45

Set	Card #	MT	NM	EX
1981 Donruss	351	.15	.11	.06
1982 Donruss	387	.15	.11	.06
1983 Topps 1952 Reprint Set	101	3.00	2.25	1.25
1984 Topps Traded	13T	.60	.45	.25
1985 Topps	132	.20	.15	.08

1985 Topps	155	.12	.09	.05
1987 Topps	531	.07	.05	.03
1988 Pacific Trading Cards Baseball Legends	53	.30	.25	.12
1990 Pacific Legends	7	.40	.30	.15
1991 "1953" Topps Archives	104	2.50	2.00	1.00
1994 "1954" Topps Archives	50	.60	.45	.25

Craig Biggio

Set	Card #	MT	NM	EX
1988 Fleer Update	89	1.50	1.25	.60
1988 Score Traded	103T	7.50	5.50	3.00
1989 Donruss	561 (R)	.35	.25	.14
1989 Fleer	353 (R)	.50	.40	.20
1989 Score	237 (R)	.50	.40	.20
1989 Topps	49 (R)	.40	.30	.15
1989 Upper Deck	273 (R)	1.50	1.25	.60
1990 Bowman	78	.08	.06	.03
1990 Donruss	306	.15	.11	.06
1990 Fleer	224	.10	.08	.04
1990 Leaf	37	.90	.70	.35
1990 O-Pee-Chee	157	.15	.11	.06
1990 O-Pee-Chee	404	.10	.07	.04
1990 Score	275	.15	.11	.06
1990 Sportflics	22	.70	.50	.30
1990 Topps	157	.10	.07	.04
1990 Topps	404	.10	.07	.04
1990 Topps All-Star Glossy Set of 60	54	.15	.11	.06
1990 Topps Big Baseball	111	.08	.06	.03
1990 Upper Deck	104	.15	.11	.06
1991 Bowman	556	.08	.06	.03
1991 Donruss	2	.05	.04	.02
1991 Donruss	595	.08	.06	.03
1991 Fleer	499	.08	.06	.03
1991 Fleer Ultra	132	.15	.11	.06
1991 Leaf	12	.12	.09	.05
1991 Score	161	.06	.05	.02
1991 Score	872	.08	.06	.03
1991 Studio	173	.20	.15	.08
1991 Topps	565	.08	.06	.03
1991 Topps Stadium Club	176	.50	.40	.20
1991 Upper Deck	158	.08	.06	.03
1992 Bowman	484	.50	.40	.20
1992 Donruss	75	.08	.06	.03
1992 Donruss Triple Play	150	.08	.06	.03
1992 Fleer	426	.08	.06	.03
1992 Fleer Ultra	199	.15	.11	.06
1992 Leaf	315	.15	.11	.06
1992 O-Pee-Chee	715	.08	.06	.03
1992 O-Pee-Chee Premier	135	.15	.11	.06
1992 Pinnacle	140	.12	.09	.05
1992 Score	460	.08	.06	.03
1992 Score Impact Players	22	.20	.15	.08
1992 Studio	32	.15	.11	.06

1992 Topps	393	.05	.04	.02
1992 Topps	715	.08	.06	.03
1992 Topps Gold	393	.25	.20	.10
1992 Topps Gold	715	.35	.25	.14
1992 Topps Kids	43	.05	.04	.02
1992 Topps Stadium Club	200	.15	.11	.06
1992 Topps Stadium Club Special Edition	17	.15	.11	.06
1992 Upper Deck	31	.05	.04	.02
1992 Upper Deck	162	.10	.08	.04
1993 Bowman	560	.10	.08	.04
1993 DiamondMarks	(26)	.50	.40	.20
1993 Donruss	84	.08	.06	.03
1993 Donruss Diamond Kings	24	.75	.60	.30
1993 Donruss Triple Play	100	.07	.05	.03
1993 Fleer	47	.08	.06	.03
1993 Fleer Flair	58	.25	.15	.08
1993 Fleer Ultra	37	.10	.08	.04
1993 Leaf	223	.10	.08	.04
1993 Leaf Gold All-Stars	13	2.50	2.00	1.00
1993 O-Pee-Chee	56	.15	.11	.06
1993 Pinnacle	50	.08	.06	.03
1993 Score	18	.06	.05	.02
1993 Score Select	25	.10	.08	.04
1993 Studio	86	.08	.06	.03
1993 Topps Finest	119	1.00	.70	.40
1993 Topps Finest Refractors	119	20.00	15.00	8.00
1993 Topps Gold	680	.10	.08	.04
1993 Topps Stadium Club	183	.10	.08	.04
1993 Topps Stadium Club First Day Production	183	5.00	3.75	2.00
1993 Topps Stadium Club Special	115	.10	.08	.04
1993 Topps Stadium Club Team Sets	14	.50	.40	.20
1993 Upper Deck	114	.08	.06	.03
1993 Upper Deck Fun Packs	44	.05	.04	.02
1993 Upper Deck SP	29	.25	.20	.10
1994 Bowman	390	.10	.08	.04
1994 Donruss	12	.05	.04	.02
1994 Donruss Special Edition - Gold	12	.25	.20	.10
1994 Donruss Triple Play Medalists	6	2.00	1.50	.80
1994 Donruss Triple Play	22	.05	.04	.02
1994 Fleer	485	.05	.04	.02
1994 Fleer Extra Bases	269	.10	.08	.04
1994 Fleer Flair	386	.20	.15	.08
1994 Fleer Ultra	499	.10	.08	.04
1994 Leaf	236	.12	.09	.05
1994 Leaf Limited	111	1.00	.70	.40
1994 O-Pee-Chee	230	.05	.04	.02
1994 Pacific Crown	259	.05	.04	.02
1994 Pinnacle	20	.10	.08	.04
1994 Pinnacle Artist's Proof	20	3.00	2.25	1.25
1994 Pinnacle Museum Collection	20	1.50	1.25	.60
1994 Pinnacle Run Creators	33	1.50	1.25	.60
1994 Score	48	.04	.03	.02
1994 Score Select	296	.10	.08	.04
1994 Studio	17	.10	.08	.04
1994 Topps	305	.04	.03	.02
1994 Topps Finest	382	.50	.40	.20
1994 Topps Finest Refractors	382	3.50	2.75	1.50
1994 Topps Gold	305	.15	.11	.06
1994 Topps Stadium Club	374	.10	.08	.04
1994 Topps Stadium Club First Day Production	374	2.50	2.00	1.00
1994 Upper Deck	312	.10	.08	.04
1994 Upper Deck Collector's Choice	456	.06	.05	.02
1994 Upper Deck Electric Diamond	312	.25	.20	.10

Set	Card #			
1994 Upper Deck Fun Packs	158	.05	.04	.02
1994 Upper Deck Fun Packs	218	.10	.08	.04
1994 Upper Deck SP	28	.15	.11	.06

Paul Blair

Set	Card #	NM	EX	VG
1965 Topps	473 (R)	15.00	7.50	4.50
1966 O-Pee-Chee	48	2.25	1.25	.70
1966 Topps	48	1.50	.70	.45
1967 Topps	319	2.50	1.25	.70
1968 O-Pee-Chee	135	2.25	1.25	.70
1968 Topps	135	1.50	.70	.45
1969 Topps	506	1.00	.50	.30
1970 O-Pee-Chee	285	1.75	.90	.50
1970 Topps	285	.90	.45	.25
1971 O-Pee-Chee	53	1.50	.70	.45
1971 Topps	53	1.00	.50	.30
1972 Topps	660	6.00	3.00	1.75
1973 O-Pee-Chee	528	1.25	.60	.40
1973 Topps	528	.70	.35	.20
1974 O-Pee-Chee	92	.60	.30	.20
1974 Topps	92	.30	.15	.09
1975 O-Pee-Chee	275	.55	.30	.15
1975 Topps	275	.30	.15	.09
1975 Topps Mini	275	.60	.30	.20
1976 O-Pee-Chee	473	.35	.20	.11
1976 Topps	473	.25	.13	.08
1977 Topps	313	.20	.10	.06
1978 Topps	114	.20	.10	.06
1979 O-Pee-Chee	304	.25	.13	.08
1979 Topps	582	.20	.10	.06
1980 O-Pee-Chee	149	.15	.08	.05
1980 Topps	281	.20	.10	.06

Vida Blue

Set	Card #	NM	EX	VG
1970 O-Pee-Chee	21	1.00	.50	.30

Set	Card #			
1970 Topps	21 (R)	7.00	3.50	2.00
1971 O-Pee-Chee	544	5.00	2.50	1.50
1971 Topps	544	3.50	1.75	1.00
1972 O-Pee-Chee	92	1.00	.50	.30
1972 O-Pee-Chee	94	.75	.40	.25
1972 O-Pee-Chee	96	.75	.40	.25
1972 O-Pee-Chee	169	1.00	.50	.30
1972 O-Pee-Chee	170	.75	.40	.25
1972 Topps	92	3.00	1.50	.90
1972 Topps	94	2.00	1.00	.60
1972 Topps	96	2.00	1.00	.60
1972 Topps	169	1.00	.50	.30
1972 Topps	170	.75	.40	.25
1973 O-Pee-Chee	430	1.25	.60	.40
1973 Topps	430	1.00	.50	.30
1974 O-Pee-Chee	290	.60	.30	.20
1974 Topps	290	.40	.20	.12
1975 O-Pee-Chee	209	.55	.30	.15
1975 O-Pee-Chee	510	.55	.30	.15
1975 Topps	209	.50	.25	.15
1975 Topps	510	.50	.25	.15
1975 Topps Mini	209	.80	.40	.25
1975 Topps Mini	510	.80	.40	.25
1976 O-Pee-Chee	140	.40	.20	.12
1976 O-Pee-Chee	200	2.00	1.00	.60
1976 Topps	140	.40	.20	.12
1976 Topps	200	2.00	1.00	.60
1977 O-Pee-Chee	75	.30	.15	.09
1977 Topps	230	.40	.20	.12
1978 O-Pee-Chee	177	.25	.13	.08
1978 Topps	680	.30	.15	.09
1979 O-Pee-Chee	49	.25	.13	.08
1979 Topps	110	.30	.15	.09
1980 O-Pee-Chee	14	.20	.10	.06
1980 Topps	30	.15	.08	.05

Set	Card #	MT	NM	EX
1981 Donruss	433	.12	.09	.05
1981 Fleer	432	.12	.09	.05
1981 O-Pee-Chee	310	.12	.09	.05
1981 Topps	310	.08	.06	.03
1982 Donruss	4	.12	.09	.05
1982 Donruss	222	.12	.09	.05
1982 Fleer	384	.12	.09	.05
1982 O-Pee-Chee	82	.12	.09	.05
1982 O-Pee-Chee	267	.12	.09	.05
1982 Topps	430	.15	.11	.06
1982 Topps	431	.10	.08	.04
1982 Topps	576	.15	.11	.06
1983 Donruss	34	.12	.09	.05
1983 Donruss	648	.15	.11	.06
1983 Fleer	106	.12	.09	.05
1983 Fleer	643	.10	.08	.04
1983 O-Pee-Chee	178	.12	.09	.05
1983 Topps	471	.15	.11	.06
1983 Topps	570	.15	.11	.06
1985 Fleer Update	7	.20	.15	.08
1986 Donruss	509	.10	.08	.04
1986 Fleer	533	.10	.08	.04
1986 Leaf	247	.08	.06	.03
1986 Sportflics	132	.15	.11	.06
1986 Sportflics	142	.15	.11	.06
1986 Sportflics Decade Greats	63	.30	.25	.12
1986 Topps	770	.10	.08	.04
1987 Donruss	362	.10	.08	.04
1987 Fleer	266	.10	.08	.04
1987 O-Pee-Chee	260	.08	.06	.03
1987 Topps	260	.07	.05	.03
1989 Pacific Trading Cards Legends II	198	.10	.08	.04
1990 Pacific Legends	8	.05	.04	.02
1990 Pacific Senior League	215	.15	.11	.06
1990 Topps Senior League	48	.15	.11	.06
1991 Pacific Senior League	81	.15	.11	.06

Bert Blyleven

Set	Card #	NM	EX	VG
1971 O-Pee-Chee	26	46.00	23.00	14.00
1971 Topps	26 (R)	25.00	12.50	7.50
1972 O-Pee-Chee	515	11.00	5.50	3.25
1972 Topps	515	7.00	3.50	2.00
1973 O-Pee-Chee	199	6.00	3.00	1.75
1973 Topps	199	3.00	1.50	.90
1974 O-Pee-Chee	98	1.00	.50	.30
1974 Topps	98	1.00	.50	.30
1974 Topps Stamps	(24)	10.00	5.00	3.00
1975 O-Pee-Chee	30	.75	.40	.25
1975 Topps	30	1.00	.50	.30
1975 Topps Mini	30	2.00	1.00	.60
1976 O-Pee-Chee	204	.50	.25	.15
1976 O-Pee-Chee	235	1.00	.50	.30
1976 Topps	204	1.00	.50	.30
1976 Topps	235	.50	.25	.15
1977 O-Pee-Chee	101	.50	.25	.15
1977 Topps	630	.90	.45	.25
1978 O-Pee-Chee	113	.75	.40	.25
1978 Topps	131	.60	.30	.20
1979 O-Pee-Chee	155	.30	.15	.09
1979 Topps	308	.30	.15	.09
1980 O-Pee-Chee	238	.30	.15	.09
1980 Topps	457	.50	.25	.15

Set	Card #	MT	NM	EX
1981 Donruss	135	.12	.09	.05
1981 Fleer	383	.12	.09	.05
1981 O-Pee-Chee	294	.20	.15	.08
1981 Topps	554	.15	.11	.06
1981 Topps Traded	738	.30	.25	.12
1982 Donruss	111	.12	.09	.05
1982 Fleer	361	.12	.09	.05
1982 O-Pee-Chee	164	.20	.15	.08
1982 Topps	559	.15	.11	.06
1982 Topps	685	.20	.15	.08
1983 Donruss	589	.12	.09	.05
1983 O-Pee-Chee	280	.15	.11	.06
1983 Topps	280	.20	.15	.08
1984 Donruss	129	.30	.25	.12
1984 Fleer	536	.20	.15	.08
1984 O-Pee-Chee	126	.30	.25	.12
1984 Topps	716	.15	.11	.06
1984 Topps	789	.20	.15	.08
1985 Donruss	4	.15	.11	.06
1985 Donruss	224	.15	.11	.06
1985 Donruss Diamond Kings Supers	4	.25	.20	.10
1985 Fleer	440	.15	.11	.06
1985 Leaf-Donruss	4	.12	.09	.05
1985 O-Pee-Chee	355	.15	.11	.06
1985 Topps	355	.12	.09	.05
1985 Topps All-Star Glossy Set of 40	17	.20	.15	.08
1986 Donruss	649	.15	.11	.06
1986 Fleer	386	.15	.11	.06
1986 Leaf	88	.12	.09	.05
1986 O-Pee-Chee	272	.10	.08	.04
1986 Sportflics	64	.10	.08	.04
1986 Sportflics	103	.15	.11	.06
1986 Sportflics	142	.15	.11	.06
1986 Topps	445	.12	.09	.05
1987 Donruss	71	.12	.09	.05
1987 Fleer	536	.12	.09	.05
1987 Leaf	100	.10	.08	.04
1987 O-Pee-Chee	25	.10	.08	.04
1987 Sportflics	81	.15	.11	.06
1987 Topps	25	.12	.09	.05
1988 Donruss	71	.12	.09	.05
1988 Fleer	4	.12	.09	.05
1988 Leaf	52	.10	.08	.04
1988 O-Pee-Chee	295	.09	.07	.04
1988 Score	90	.10	.08	.04
1988 Sportflics	92	.15	.11	.06
1988 Topps	295	.10	.08	.04
1988 Topps Big Baseball	180	.10	.08	.04
1989 Bowman	41	.08	.06	.03
1989 Donruss	119	.10	.08	.04
1989 Fleer	105	.12	.09	.05
1989 Fleer Update	12	.06	.05	.02
1989 O-Pee-Chee	204	.08	.06	.03
1989 Score	215	.25	.20	.10
1989 Score Traded	17T	.08	.06	.03
1989 Topps	555	.10	.08	.04
1989 Topps Traded	11T	.05	.04	.02
1989 Upper Deck	225	.10	.08	.04
1989 Upper Deck	712	.10	.08	.04
1990 Bowman	285	.06	.05	.02
1990 Donruss	331	.08	.06	.03
1990 Fleer	128	.09	.07	.04
1990 Leaf	63	.35	.25	.14
1990 O-Pee-Chee	130	.05	.04	.02
1990 Score	180	.09	.07	.04
1990 Sportflics	193	.10	.08	.04
1990 Topps	130	.05	.04	.02
1990 Topps Big Baseball	114	.10	.08	.04
1990 Upper Deck	527	.09	.07	.04
1991 Donruss	453	.06	.05	.02
1991 Fleer	308	.08	.06	.03
1991 Score	235	.08	.06	.03
1991 Studio	23	.15	.11	.06
1991 Topps	615	.08	.06	.03
1991 Topps Stadium Club	175	.20	.15	.08
1991 Upper Deck	571	.10	.08	.04
1992 O-Pee-Chee	375	.05	.04	.02
1992 Topps	375	.05	.04	.02
1992 Topps Gold	375	.35	.25	.14
1992 Upper Deck	632	.06	.05	.02
1993 Fleer	568	.05	.04	.02
1993 Pinnacle	83	.06	.05	.02
1993 Pinnacle	296	.06	.05	.02
1993 Score	577	.08	.06	.03
1993 Score Select	252	.08	.06	.03
1993 Topps	48	.06	.05	.02
1993 Topps Gold	48	.10	.08	.04

Wade Boggs

Set	Card #	MT	NM	EX
1983 Donruss	586 (R)	25.00	18.50	10.00

1983 Fleer	179 (R)	22.00	16.50	8.75
1983 Topps	498 (R)	30.00	22.00	12.00
1984 Donruss	26a	3.00	2.25	1.25
1984 Donruss	26b	4.00	3.00	1.50
1984 Donruss	151	15.00	11.00	6.00
1984 Fleer	392	10.00	7.50	4.00
1984 Fleer	630	1.00	.70	.40
1984 O-Pee-Chee	30	3.75	2.75	1.50
1984 Topps	30	4.00	3.00	1.50
1984 Topps	131	.50	.40	.20
1984 Topps	786	.40	.30	.15
1984 Topps All-Star Glossy Set of 40	8	3.00	2.25	1.25
1985 Donruss	172	5.00	3.75	2.00
1985 Fleer	151	4.00	3.00	1.50
1985 Leaf-Donruss	179	4.50	3.50	1.75
1985 O-Pee-Chee	350	1.50	1.25	.60
1985 Topps	350	1.75	1.25	.70
1986 Donruss	371	2.50	2.00	1.00
1986 Fleer	341	2.25	1.75	.90
1986 Fleer	634	1.00	.70	.40
1986 Fleer	639	1.00	.70	.40
1986 Leaf	168	2.50	2.00	1.00
1986 O-Pee-Chee	262	1.00	.70	.40
1986 Sportflics	3	1.50	1.25	.60
1986 Sportflics	75	1.50	1.25	.60
1986 Sportflics	180	1.25	.90	.50
1986 Sportflics	183	1.25	.90	.50
1986 Sportflics	184	1.50	1.25	.60
1986 Sportflics Decade Greats	68	1.50	1.25	.60
1986 Topps	510	.90	.70	.35
1986 Topps All-Star Glossy Set of 60	26	1.25	.90	.50
1987 Donruss	252	.75	.60	.30
1987 Fleer	29	1.50	1.25	.60
1987 Fleer	637	.35	.25	.14
1987 Fleer All Stars	3	.60	.45	.25
1987 Fleer Headliners	1	1.50	1.25	.60
1987 Leaf	193	.80	.60	.30
1987 O-Pee-Chee	150	.40	.30	.15
1987 Sportflics	2	1.50	1.25	.60
1987 Sportflics	114	.60	.45	.25
1987 Sportflics	197	.80	.60	.30
1987 Topps	150	.40	.30	.15
1987 Topps	608	.20	.15	.08
1987 Topps All-Star Glossy Set of 22	15	.50	.40	.20
1987 Topps All-Star Glossy Set of 60	18	1.25	.90	.50
1988 Donruss	153	.25	.20	.10
1988 Donruss MVP	7	.40	.30	.15
1988 Fleer	345	.35	.25	.14
1988 Fleer All Stars	8	1.00	.70	.40
1988 Leaf	65	.70	.50	.30
1988 O-Pee-Chee	200	.70	.50	.30
1988 Score	2	.25	.15	.08
1988 Score Glossy	2	1.25	.90	.50
1988 Sportflics	50	.90	.70	.35
1988 Sportflics Gamewinners	3	.80	.60	.30
1988 Topps	21	.15	.11	.06
1988 Topps	200	.30	.25	.12
1988 Topps	388	.12	.09	.05
1988 Topps All-Star Glossy Set of 22	4	.80	.60	.30
1988 Topps All-Star Glossy Set of 60	51	.80	.60	.30
1988 Topps Big Baseball	32	.90	.70	.35
1989 Bowman	32	.25	.20	.10
1989 Donruss	68	.25	.20	.10
1989 Fleer	81	.25	.20	.10
1989 Fleer	633	.10	.08	.04
1989 Fleer For The Record	1	1.00	.70	.40
1989 O-Pee-Chee	184	.35	.25	.14
1989 Score	175	.25	.20	.10
1989 Score	654a	3.00	2.25	1.25
1989 Score	654b	.10	.06	.03
1989 Sportflics	100	.60	.45	.25
1989 Sportflics	221	1.50	1.25	.60
1989 Topps	2	.12	.09	.05
1989 Topps	399	.15	.11	.06
1989 Topps	600	.25	.20	.10
1989 Topps All-Star Glossy Set of 22	4	.15	.11	.06
1989 Topps All-Star Glossy Set of 60	5	.70	.50	.30
1989 Topps Big Baseball	241	.80	.60	.30
1989 Upper Deck	389	.60	.45	.25
1989 Upper Deck	687	.20	.15	.08
1990 Bowman	281	.20	.15	.08
1990 Donruss	68	.20	.15	.08
1990 Donruss	712	.09	.07	.04
1990 Fleer	268	.25	.20	.10
1990 Fleer League Standouts	6	.60	.45	.25
1990 Leaf	51	2.00	1.50	.80
1990 O-Pee-Chee	387	.20	.15	.08
1990 O-Pee-Chee	760	.30	.25	.12
1990 Post Cereal	17	.80	.60	.30
1990 Score	245	.25	.20	.10
1990 Score	683	.10	.07	.04
1990 Score	704	.10	.07	.04
1990 Sportflics	2	.50	.40	.20
1990 Topps	387	.15	.11	.06
1990 Topps	760	.25	.20	.10
1990 Topps All-Star Glossy Set of 22	15	.25	.20	.10
1990 Topps All-Star Glossy Set of 60	22	.60	.45	.25
1990 Topps Big Baseball	77	.50	.40	.20
1990 Upper Deck	555	.25	.20	.10
1991 Bowman	129	.12	.09	.05
1991 Donruss	55	.10	.08	.04
1991 Donruss	178	.10	.08	.04
1991 Fleer	86	.12	.09	.05
1991 Fleer Ultra	27	.25	.20	.10
1991 Leaf	273	.20	.15	.08
1991 O-Pee-Chee Premier	11	.25	.20	.10
1991 Score	12	.20	.15	.08
1991 Score	393	.12	.09	.05
1991 Score	889	.20	.15	.08
1991 Score Cooperstown	1	1.00	.70	.40
1991 Studio	11	.30	.25	.12
1991 Topps	450	.12	.09	.05
1991 Topps All-Star Glossy Set of 22	4	.40	.30	.15
1991 Topps Stadium Club	170	.90	.70	.35
1991 Upper Deck	546	.20	.15	.08
1991 Upper Deck Final Edition	84	.10	.08	.04
1992 Bowman	70	1.00	.75	.40
1992 Donruss	23	.10	.08	.04
1992 Donruss	210	.20	.15	.08
1992 Donruss Diamond Kings	9	1.00	.75	.40
1992 Donruss Elite	9	40.00	30.00	15.00
1992 Donruss Triple Play	211	.15	.11	.06
1992 Fleer	32	.15	.11	.06
1992 Fleer	707	.08	.06	.03
1992 Fleer Team Leaders	13	3.00	2.25	1.25
1992 Fleer Ultra	311	.30	.25	.12
1992 Fleer Ultra All-Stars	4	1.25	.75	.40
1992 Leaf	286	.15	.11	.06
1992 O-Pee-Chee	10	.15	.11	.06
1992 O-Pee-Chee Premier	1	.40	.30	.15
1992 Pinnacle	175	.20	.15	.08
1992 Pinnacle	282	.15	.11	.06
1992 Post Cereal	19	.40	.30	.15
1992 Score	434	.10	.08	.04
1992 Score	660	.12	.09	.05
1992 Score	885	.20	.15	.08
1992 Studio	131	.30	.25	.12
1992 Studio Heritage	3	1.25	.90	.50
1992 Topps	10	.15	.11	.06
1992 Topps	399	.10	.08	.04
1992 Topps Gold	10	1.50	1.25	60
1992 Topps Gold	399	.50	.40	.20
1992 Topps Kids	68	.20	.15	.08
1992 Topps Stadium Club	520	.25	.20	.10

1992 Topps Stadium Club Master Photos	(1)	4.50	3.50	1.75
1992 Topps Stadium Club Members Only	(1)	1.00	.70	.40
1992 Topps Stadium Club Special Edition	18	.30	.25	.12
1992 Upper Deck	443	.15	.11	.06
1992 Upper Deck	646	.10	.08	.04
1992 Upper Deck MVP Holograms	10	.40	.30	.15
1993 Bowman	399	.30	.25	.12
1993 DiamondMarks	(99)	.50	.40	.20
1993 Donruss	619	.05	.04	.02
1993 Donruss Spirit of the Game	7	1.50	1.25	.60
1993 Donruss Triple Play Gallery	3	1.75	1.25	.70
1993 Donruss Triple Play	143	.25	.20	.10
1993 Donruss Triple Play	258	.25	.20	.10
1993 Fleer	554	.10	.08	.04
1993 Fleer Final Edition	1DT	.50	.40	.20
1993 Fleer Final Edition	243	.15	.11	.06
1993 Fleer Flair	245	.75	.60	.30
1993 Fleer Ultra	591	.25	.20	.10
1993 Leaf	285	.25	.20	.10
1993 Leaf Update Gold All-Stars	5	1.00	.75	.40
1993 O-Pee-Chee	196	.40	.30	.15
1993 O-Pee-Chee Premier	49	.20	.15	.08
1993 Pinnacle	424	.20	.15	.08
1993 Pinnacle	476	.15	.11	.06
1993 Pinnacle Cooperstown	13	.35	.25	.14
1993 Pinnacle Cooperstown Dufex	13	100.00	75.00	40.00
1993 Score	592	.20	.15	.08
1993 Score Select	48	.20	.15	.08
1993 Score Select Rookie/Traded	17	.75	.60	.30
1993 Studio	31	.20	.15	.08
1993 Topps Finest	90	3.00	2.25	1.25
1993 Topps Finest Jumbo All-Stars	90	10.00	7.50	4.00
1993 Topps Finest Refractors	90	45.00	34.00	18.00
1993 Topps Stadium Club	134	.30	.25	.12
1993 Topps Stadium Club	601	.20	.15	.08
1993 Topps Stadium Club First Day Production	134	25.00	18.50	10.00
1993 Topps Stadium Club First Day Production	601	20.00	15.00	8.00
1993 Topps Stadium Club Special	15	.25	.20	.10
1993 Topps Stadium Club Team Sets	5	.75	.60	.30
1993 Topps Traded	47	.10	.08	.04
1993 Upper Deck	556	.15	.11	.06
1993 Upper Deck Clutch Performers	2	1.00	.75	.40
1993 Upper Deck Fun Packs	206	.25	.20	.10
1993 Upper Deck Iooss Collection	20	1.00	.75	.40
1993 Upper Deck Iooss Collection Super	20	4.00	3.00	1.50
1993 Upper Deck On Deck	5	.75	.60	.30
1993 Upper Deck SP	2	1.00	.75	.40
1993 Upper Deck Then And Now	1	1.50	1.25	.60
1994 Bowman	305	.25	.20	.10
1994 Bowman's Best	42	1.00	.70	.40
1994 Bowman's Best Refractors	42	8.00	6.00	3.25
1994 Donruss	36	.25	.20	.10
1994 Donruss Anniversary-1984	7	2.50	2.00	1.00
1994 Donruss Special Edition - Gold	36	.45	.35	.20
1994 Donruss Triple Play Medalists	9	1.50	1.25	.60

1994 Donruss Triple Play	272	.10	.07	.04
1994 Fleer	226	.15	.11	.06
1994 Fleer All-Stars	4	.35	.25	.14
1994 Fleer Extra Bases	128	.25	.20	.10
1994 Fleer Flair	319	.40	.30	.15
1994 Fleer Ultra	93	.15	.11	.06
1994 Leaf	257	.30	.25	.12
1994 Leaf Limited	54	2.50	2.00	1.00
1994 Leaf Limited Gold	5	15.00	11.00	6.00
1994 O-Pee-Chee	193	.25	.20	.10
1994 Pacific Crown	421	.20	.15	.08
1994 Pacific Crown Jewels of the Crown	9	3.00	2.25	1.25
1994 Pinnacle	31	.15	.11	.06
1994 Pinnacle Artist's Proof	31	8.00	6.00	3.25
1994 Pinnacle Museum Collection	31	2.00	1.50	.80
1994 Score	101	.20	.15	.08
1994 Score Gold Stars	50	6.00	4.50	2.50
1994 Score Select	156	.30	.25	.12
1994 Sportflics 2000	102	.35	.25	.14
1994 Studio	212	.30	.25	.12
1994 Topps	386	.10	.08	.04
1994 Topps	520	.20	.15	.08
1994 Topps	603	.08	.06	.03
1994 Topps Finest	173	1.50	1.25	.60
1994 Topps Finest Refractors	173	18.00	13.50	7.25
1994 Topps Gold	386	.25	.20	.10
1994 Topps Gold	520	.60	.45	.25
1994 Topps Gold	603	.20	.15	.08
1994 Topps Stadium Club	349	.20	.15	.08
1994 Topps Stadium Club First Day Production	349	15.00	11.00	6.00
1994 Upper Deck	112	.20	.15	.08
1994 Upper Deck All-Stars Green Foil	8	.75	.60	.30
1994 Upper Deck All-Stars Gold Foil	8	4.00	3.00	1.50
1994 Upper Deck Collector's Choice	380	.10	.08	.04
1994 Upper Deck Electric Diamond	112	1.00	.75	.40
1994 Upper Deck Fun Packs	126	.15	.11	.06
1994 Upper Deck SP	196	.40	.30	.15
1994 Upper Deck SP Baseball Die-Cut	196	1.00	.75	.40

Barry Bonds

Set	Card #	MT	NM	EX
1986 Fleer Update	14	15.00	11.00	6.00
1986 Sportflics Rookies	13	3.00	2.25	1.25
1986 Topps Traded	11T	8.00	6.00	3.25
1987 Donruss	361 (R)	10.00	7.50	4.00
1987 Fleer	604 (R)	35.00	26.00	14.00
1987 Leaf	219	10.25	7.75	4.00

1987 O-Pee-Chee	320	3.00	2.25	1.25
1987 Topps	320 (R)	2.75	2.00	1.00
1987 Topps All-Star Glossy Set of 60	30	.80	.60	.30
1988 Donruss	326	.50	.40	.20
1988 Fleer	322	2.00	1.50	.80
1988 Leaf	113	.60	.45	.25
1988 O-Pee-Chee	267	.60	.45	.25
1988 Score	265	.60	.45	.25
1988 Sportflics	119	1.00	.70	.40
1988 Topps	231	.15	.11	.06
1988 Topps	450	.60	.45	.25
1988 Topps Big Baseball	89	.75	.60	.30
1989 Bowman	426	.50	.40	.20
1989 Donruss	92	.60	.45	.25
1989 Fleer	202	.60	.45	.25
1989 O-Pee-Chee	263	.45	.35	.20
1989 Score	127	.60	.45	.25
1989 Sportflics	146	.20	.15	.08
1989 Topps	620	.40	.30	.15
1989 Topps Big Baseball	5	.08	.06	.03
1989 Upper Deck	440	2.00	1.50	.80
1990 Bowman	181	.40	.30	.15
1990 Donruss	126	.30	.25	.12
1990 Fleer	461	.40	.30	.15
1990 Leaf	91	6.00	4.50	2.50
1990 O-Pee-Chee	220	.10	.08	.04
1990 Score	4	.50	.40	.20
1990 Sportflics	143	.15	.11	.06
1990 Topps	220	.50	.40	.20
1990 Topps Big Baseball	128	.40	.30	.15
1990 Upper Deck	227	1.00	.75	.40
1991 Bowman	380	.35	.25	.14
1991 Bowman	513	.35	.25	.14
1991 Donruss	4	.20	.15	.08
1991 Donruss	495	.40	.30	.15
1991 Donruss	762	.25	.20	.10
1991 Donruss Elite	1	115.00	85.00	46.00
1991 Donruss Grand Slammers	5	.30	.25	.12
1991 Fleer	33	.25	.20	.10
1991 Fleer	710	.50	.40	.20
1991 Fleer All Stars	5	2.50	2.00	1.00
1991 Fleer ProVisions	1F	1.00	.75	.40
1991 Fleer Ultra	275	1.00	.75	.40
1991 Fleer Ultra	391	.30	.25	.12
1991 Fleer Ultra Gold	1	1.50	.90	.50
1991 Leaf	261	.75	.60	.30
1991 Leaf	364	.08	.06	.03
1991 O-Pee-Chee Premier	12	.60	.45	.25
1991 Post Cereal	21	.80	.60	.30
1991 Score	330	.40	.30	.15
1991 Score	668	.20	.15	.05
1991 Score	868	.25	.15	.10
1991 Score	876	.25	.08	.04
1991 Studio	222	1.00	.75	.40
1991 Topps	401	.15	.11	.06
1991 Topps	570	.40	.30	.15
1991 Topps Stadium Club	220	6.00	4.50	2.50
1991 Topps Stadium Club Charter Members	(3)	1.50	1.25	.60
1991 Upper Deck	154	.60	.45	.25
1991 Upper Deck Silver Sluggers	5	4.50	3.50	1.75
1992 Bowman	60	4.00	3.00	1.50
1992 Bowman	590	4.00	3.00	1.50
1992 Donruss	243	.35	.25	.14
1992 Donruss Triple Play	116	.30	.20	.10
1992 Fleer	550	.40	.30	.15
1992 Fleer All-Stars	3	3.50	2.75	1.50
1992 Fleer Lumber Co.	8	4.50	3.50	1.75
1992 Fleer Ultra	251	1.50	1.25	.60
1992 Fleer Ultra All-Stars	16	4.00	3.00	1.50
1992 Fleer Ultra Award Winners	11	6.00	4.50	2.50
1992 Leaf	275	.60	.45	.25
1992 O-Pee-Chee	380	.40	.30	.15
1992 O-Pee-Chee Premier	157	.50	.40	.20
1992 Pinnacle	500	1.00	.70	.40
1992 Pinnacle Slugfest	4	4.00	3.00	1.50
1992 Pinnacle Team Pinnacle	8	25.00	18.50	10.00
1992 Post Cereal	15	.40	.30	.15
1992 Score	555	.40	.30	.15
1992 Score	777	.25	.20	.10
1992 Score Impact Players	55	1.00	.75	.40
1992 Studio	82	.60	.45	.25
1992 Topps	380	.40	.30	.15
1992 Topps	390	.10	.08	.04
1992 Topps Gold	380	4.00	3.00	1.50
1992 Topps Gold	390	1.50	1.25	.60
1992 Topps Kids	21	.20	.15	.08
1992 Topps Stadium Club	604	.75	.60	.30
1992 Topps Stadium Club	620	1.50	1.25	.60
1992 Topps Stadium Club East Coast National	604	20.00	15.00	8.00
1992 Topps Stadium Club East Coast National	620	25.00	18.50	10.00
1992 Topps Stadium Club Master Photos	(2)	6.00	4.50	2.50
1992 Upper Deck	134	.30	.25	.12
1992 Upper Deck	711	.06	.05	.02
1992 Upper Deck	721	.20	.15	.08
1992 Upper Deck Home Run Heroes	21	1.50	1.25	.60
1992 Upper Deck MVP Holograms	11	1.25	.90	.50
1993 Bowman	140	1.00	.75	.40
1993 DiamondMarks	(61)	1.50	1.25	.60
1993 DiamondMarks Inserts	(2)	20.00	15.00	8.00
1993 Donruss	678	.50	.40	.20
1993 Donruss Elite	31	90.00	67.00	36.00
1993 Donruss Elite Dominators	16	125.00	94.00	50.00
1993 Donruss Elite Supers	13	35.00	26.00	14.00
1993 Donruss Masters of the Game	14	4.00	3.00	1.50
1993 Donruss MVP's	25	3.00	2.25	1.25
1993 Donruss Triple Play Gallery	1	7.00	5.25	2.75
1993 Donruss Triple Play League Leaders	1	7.50	5.75	3.00
1993 Fleer	112	.50	.40	.20
1993 Fleer	350	.15	.11	.06
1993 Fleer Final Edition	150	.50	.40	.20
1993 Fleer Flair	138	3.50	2.75	1.50
1993 Fleer Ultra	483	1.00	.70	.40
1993 Fleer Ultra All-Stars	6	6.00	4.50	2.50
1993 Fleer Ultra Award Winners	7	6.00	4.50	2.50
1993 Fleer Ultra Award Winners	24	6.00	4.50	2.50
1993 Fleer Ultra Home Run Kings	6	5.00	3.75	2.00
1993 Fleer Ultra Performers	1	3.00	2.25	1.25
1993 Leaf	269	1.00	.70	.40
1993 Leaf Gold All-Stars	16	5.00	3.75	2.00
1993 Leaf Update Gold All-Stars	7	7.50	5.75	3.00
1993 O-Pee-Chee	46	2.00	1.50	.80
1993 O-Pee-Chee Premier	1	1.00	.70	.40
1993 O-Pee-Chee Premier Star Performers	14	1.00	.70	.40
1993 Pinnacle	484	.50	.40	.20
1993 Pinnacle	504	.75	.60	.30
1993 Pinnacle Cooperstown	15	.35	.25	.14
1993 Pinnacle Cooperstown Dufex	15	125.00	94.00	50.00
1993 Pinnacle Home Run Club	4	2.00	1.50	.80
1993 Pinnacle Slugfest	6	5.00	3.75	2.00
1993 Pinnacle Team Pinnacle	8	25.00	18.00	10.00
1993 Post Cereal	15	.75	.60	.30
1993 Score	482	.20	.15	.08

1993 Score	523	.15	.11	.06
1993 Score	560	.40	.30	.15
1993 Score Select	1	.75	.60	.30
1993 Score Select Chase Stars	7	15.00	11.00	6.00
1993 Score Select Rookie/ Traded	23	3.00	2.25	1.25
1993 Score Select Stat Leaders	29	.40	.30	.15
1993 Score Select Stat Leaders	40	.40	.30	.15
1993 Score Select Stat Leaders	46	.40	.30	.15
1993 Score Select Stat Leaders	52	.40	.30	.15
1993 Studio	12	1.00	.75	.40
1993 Studio Silhouettes	2	4.00	3.00	1.50
1993 Studio Superstars on Canvas	10	4.00	3.00	1.50
1993 Topps	2	.40	.30	.15
1993 Topps	407	.15	.11	.06
1993 Topps Black Gold	1	1.00	.75	.40
1993 Topps Finest	103	13.00	9.75	5.25
1993 Topps Finest Jumbo All-Stars	103	30.00	22.00	12.00
1993 Topps Finest Refractors	103	175.00	130.00	70.00
1993 Topps Gold	2	.90	.70	.35
1993 Topps Gold	407	.30	.25	.12
1993 Topps Stadium Club	51	1.00	.70	.40
1993 Topps Stadium Club	684	1.00	.70	.40
1993 Topps Stadium Club	747	.50	.40	.20
1993 Topps Stadium Club First Day Production	51	100.00	75.00	40.00
1993 Topps Stadium Club First Day Production	684	70.00	52.00	28.00
1993 Topps Stadium Club First Day Production	747	45.00	34.00	18.00
1993 Topps Stadium Club Master Photos	(25)	6.00	4.50	2.50
1993 Topps Stadium Club Members Only	(2)	2.00	1.50	.80
1993 Topps Stadium Club Special	161	.75	.60	.30
1993 Topps Stadium Club Team Sets	1	.75	.60	.30
1993 Topps Traded	1	.50	.40	.20
1993 Upper Deck	210	.10	.07	.04
1993 Upper Deck	471	.20	.15	.08
1993 Upper Deck	476	.20	.15	.08
1993 Upper Deck	486	.25	.20	.10
1993 Upper Deck	567	.50	.40	.20
1993 Upper Deck "Highlights"	5	14.00	10.50	5.50
1993 Upper Deck Clutch Performers	3	2.50	2.00	1.00
1993 Upper Deck Diamond Gallery	11	3.00	2.25	1.25
1993 Upper Deck Fun Packs All-Star Scratch-Off	7	4.00	3.00	1.50
1993 Upper Deck Fun Packs	11	.60	.45	.25
1993 Upper Deck Fun Packs	99	.25	.20	.10
1993 Upper Deck Fun Packs	100	.35	.25	.14
1993 Upper Deck Fun Packs	222	.25	.20	.10
1993 Upper Deck Future Heroes	56	2.50	2.00	1.00
1993 Upper Deck Home Run Heroes	6	2.50	2.00	1.00
1993 Upper Deck SP	10	3.00	2.25	1.25
1993 Upper Deck SP Jumbos	10	25.00	18.50	10.00
1993 Upper Deck SP Platinum Power	2	25.00	18.00	10.00
1993 Upper Deck Triple Crown	1	3.50	2.75	1.50
1994 Bowman	135	.75	.60	.30
1994 Bowman's Best	97	2.00	1.50	.80
1994 Bowman's Best	59	4.00	3.00	1.50
1994 Bowman's Best Refractors	97	6.00	4.50	2.50
1994 Bowman's Best Refractors	59	35.00	26.00	14.00
1994 Donruss	349	.75	.60	.30
1994 Donruss Award Winners Supers	1	6.00	4.50	2.50
1994 Donruss Award Winners Supers	4	6.00	4.50	2.50
1994 Donruss Decade Dominators	2	4.00	3.00	1.50
1994 Donruss Decade Dominators Supers	2	7.50	5.75	3.00
1994 Donruss Decade Dominators	7	4.00	3.00	1.50
1994 Donruss Decade Dominators Supers	7	6.00	4.50	2.50
1994 Donruss Diamond Kings	1	4.50	3.50	1.75
1994 Donruss Diamond Kings Super	1	6.00	4.50	2.50
1994 Donruss Elite	44	40.00	30.00	15.00
1994 Donruss Long Ball Leaders	9	7.50	5.50	3.00
1994 Donruss MVP's	14	3.00	2.25	1.25
1994 Donruss Special Edition - Gold	349	1.50	1.25	.60
1994 Donruss Spirit of the Game	2	7.00	5.25	2.75
1994 Donruss Spirit of the Game Super	2	15.00	11.00	6.00
1994 Donruss Triple Play Promos	3	5.00	3.75	2.00
1994 Donruss Triple Play Bomb Squad	4	3.50	2.75	1.50
1994 Donruss Triple Play Medalists	12	3.00	2.25	1.25
1994 Donruss Triple Play	102	.50	.40	.20
1994 Fleer	684	.50	.40	.20
1994 Fleer All-Stars	31	1.50	1.25	.60
1994 Fleer Award Winners	2	2.00	1.50	.80
1994 Fleer Extra Bases	383	.50	.40	.20
1994 Fleer Extra Bases Game Breakers	4	1.50	1.25	.60
1994 Fleer Flair	239	2.00	1.50	.80
1994 Fleer Flair Hot Glove	1	25.00	18.00	10.00
1994 Fleer Flair Outfield Power	2	6.00	4.50	2.50
1994 Fleer League Leaders	8	2.50	2.00	1.00
1994 Fleer Lumber Co.	2	2.50	2.00	1.00
1994 Fleer Ultra	286	1.00	.75	.40
1994 Fleer Ultra All-Stars	16	2.50	2.00	1.00
1994 Fleer Ultra Award Winners	15	2.50	2.00	1.00
1994 Fleer Ultra Award Winners	20	2.50	2.00	1.00
1994 Fleer Ultra Hitting Machines	3	2.00	1.50	.80
1994 Fleer Ultra Home Run Kings	7	10.00	7.50	4.00
1994 Fleer Ultra On-Base Leaders	2	20.00	15.00	8.00
1994 Fleer Ultra RBI Kings	7	20.00	15.00	8.00
1994 Fleer Update Diamond Tribute	1	1.50	1.25	.60
1994 Leaf	264	1.00	.70	.40
1994 Leaf Gamers	8	8.00	6.00	3.25
1994 Leaf Gold Stars	2	35.00	25.00	14.00
1994 Leaf Limited	156	8.00	6.00	3.25
1994 Leaf Limited Gold	10	40.00	30.00	15.00
1994 Leaf MVP Contenders	4a	10.00	7.50	4.00
1994 Leaf MVP Contenders	4b	20.00	15.00	8.00
1994 Leaf Power Brokers	3	2.50	2.00	1.00

1994 Leaf Slide Show	6	7.00	5.25	2.75
1994 Leaf Statistical Standouts	2	2.50	2.00	1.00
1994 O-Pee-Chee	200	1.00	.70	.40
1994 O-Pee-Chee All-Star Redemption Cards	3	1.25	.90	.50
1994 Pacific Crown	540	.50	.40	.20
1994 Pacific Crown	655	.40	.30	.15
1994 Pacific Crown Homerun Leaders	11	8.00	6.00	3.25
1994 Pacific Crown Jewels of the Crown	28	8.00	6.00	3.25
1994 Pinnacle	26	.75	.60	.30
1994 Pinnacle Artist's Proof	26	75.00	56.00	30.00
1994 Pinnacle Museum Collection	26	25.00	18.00	10.00
1994 Pinnacle Run Creators	23	10.00	7.50	4.00
1994 Pinnacle Team Pinnacle	7	35.00	26.00	14.00
1994 Pinnacle The Naturals Box Set	2	.75	.60	.30
1994 Pinnacle Tribute	8	8.00	6.00	3.25
1994 Post Cereal	11	.75	.60	.30
1994 Score	1	.50	.40	.20
1994 Score	632	.25	.20	.10
1994 Score Gold Stars	1	20.00	15.00	8.00
1994 Score Select	211	1.00	.70	.40
1994 Score Select Crown Contenders	6	15.00	11.00	6.00
1994 Score Select Skills	6	18.00	13.50	7.25
1994 Score The Cycle	16	35.00	26.00	14.00
1994 Sportflics 2000	91	1.25	.90	.50
1994 Sportflics 2000	190	.75	.60	.30
1994 Studio	83	.75	.60	.30
1994 Studio Editor's Choice	1	6.00	4.50	2.50
1994 Studio Gold Stars	2	35.00	26.00	14.00
1994 Studio Heritage	1	3.00	2.25	1.25
1994 Studio Silver Stars	2	20.00	15.00	8.00
1994 Topps	390	.35	.25	.14
1994 Topps	605	.30	.25	.12
1994 Topps	700	.40	.30	.15
1994 Topps Black Gold	27	1.50	1.25	.60
1994 Topps Finest	230	4.00	3.00	1.50
1994 Topps Finest Bronze	1	10.00	7.50	4.00
1994 Topps Finest Refractors	230	45.00	34.00	18.00
1994 Topps Finest Superstars	230	15.00	11.00	6.00
1994 Topps Gold	390	1.25	.90	.50
1994 Topps Gold	605	1.00	.70	.40
1994 Topps Gold	700	1.50	1.25	.60
1994 Topps Stadium Club	238	.75	.60	.30
1994 Topps Stadium Club	259	.40	.30	.15
1994 Topps Stadium Club	532	.40	.30	.15
1994 Topps Stadium Club Dugout Dirt	6	1.25	.90	.50
1994 Topps Stadium Club Finest	3	4.00	3.00	1.50
1994 Topps Stadium Club First Day Production	238	40.00	30.00	16.00
1994 Topps Stadium Club First Day Production	259	20.00	15.00	8.00
1994 Topps Stadium Club First Day Production	532	18.00	13.50	7.25
1994 Topps Stadium Club Members Only Baseball	24	1.50	1.25	.60
1994 Upper Deck	38	.60	.45	.25
1994 Upper Deck	280	.50	.40	.20
1994 Upper Deck	400	.75	.60	.30
1994 Upper Deck All-Stars Green Foil	35	1.00	.70	.40
1994 Upper Deck All-Stars Gold Foil	35	5.00	3.75	2.00
1994 Upper Deck Collector's Choice	311	.40	.30	.15
1994 Upper Deck Collector's Choice	313	.50	.40	.20
1994 Upper Deck Collector's Choice	316	.10	.07	.04
1994 Upper Deck Collector's Choice	338	.15	.11	.06
1994 Upper Deck Collector's Choice	610	.50	.40	.20
1994 Upper Deck Collector's Choice	632	.25	.20	.10
1994 Upper Deck Diamond Collection	1W	17.50	13.00	7.00
1994 Upper Deck Electric Diamond	38	1.25	.90	.50
1994 Upper Deck Electric Diamond	280	2.00	1.50	.80
1994 Upper Deck Electric Diamond	400	1.50	1.25	.60
1994 Upper Deck Fun Packs	25	.75	.60	.30
1994 Upper Deck Fun Packs	190	.35	.25	.14
1994 Upper Deck Fun Packs	194	.40	.30	.15
1994 Upper Deck Fun Packs	199	1.50	1.25	.60
1994 Upper Deck Fun Packs	212	.35	.25	.14
1994 Upper Deck Fun Packs	225	.75	.60	.30
1994 Upper Deck Fun Packs	226	.40	.30	.15
1994 Upper Deck Fun Packs	237	.20	.15	.08
1994 Upper Deck Mickey Mantle's Long Shots	3MM	6.00	4.50	2.50
1994 Upper Deck SP	90	1.25	.90	.50

Bobby Bonds

Set	Card #	NM	EX	VG
1969 Topps	630 (R)	45.00	22.00	13.50
1970 O-Pee-Chee	425	12.00	6.00	3.50
1970 Topps	425	2.00	1.00	.60
1971 O-Pee-Chee	295	1.50	.70	.45
1971 Topps	295	1.25	.60	.40
1972 Topps	711	12.00	6.00	3.50
1972 Topps	712	6.00	3.00	1.75
1973 O-Pee-Chee	145	.75	.40	.25
1973 Topps	145	.90	.45	.25
1974 O-Pee-Chee	30	.60	.30	.20
1974 Topps	30	.50	.25	.15
1975 O-Pee-Chee	55	.55	.30	.15
1975 Topps	55	.35	.20	.11
1975 Topps Mini	55	.80	.40	.25
1976 O-Pee-Chee	2	.40	.20	.12
1976 O-Pee-Chee	380	.35	.20	.11
1976 Topps	2	.40	.20	.12
1976 Topps	380	.25	.13	.08
1976 Topps Traded	380T	.90	.45	.25
1977 O-Pee-Chee	173	.30	.15	.09

1977 Topps	570	.35	.20	.11
1978 O-Pee-Chee	206	.30	.15	.09
1978 Topps	150	.20	.10	.06
1979 O-Pee-Chee	142	.25	.13	.08
1979 Topps	285	.30	.15	.09
1980 O-Pee-Chee	215	.25	.13	.08
1980 Topps	410	.25	.13	.08

Set	Card #	MT	NM	EX
1981 Donruss	71a	.30	.25	.12
1981 Donruss	71b	.15	.11	.06
1981 Fleer	548	.10	.08	.04
1981 O-Pee-Chee	223	.12	.09	.05
1981 Topps	635	.15	.11	.06
1981 Topps Traded	740	.20	.15	.08
1982 Fleer	588	.10	.08	.04
1982 O-Pee-Chee	27	.12	.09	.05
1982 Topps	580	.15	.11	.06
1990 Pacific Senior League	128	.10	.08	.04
1990 Topps Senior League	40	.15	.11	.06

Bobby Bonilla

Set	Card #	MT	NM	EX
1986 Fleer Update	15	2.50	2.00	1.00
1986 Sportflics Rookies	26	.60	.45	.25
1986 Topps Traded	12T	1.50	1.25	.60
1987 Donruss	558 (R)	1.50	1.25	.60
1987 Fleer	605 (R)	3.00	2.25	1.25
1987 Topps	184 (R)	.60	.45	.25
1988 Donruss	238	.20	.15	.08
1988 Fleer	323	.35	.25	.14
1988 Leaf	188	.35	.25	.14
1988 O-Pee-Chee	189	.09	.07	.04
1988 Score	116	.20	.15	.08
1988 Sportflics	131	.40	.30	.15
1988 Topps	231	.15	.11	.06
1988 Topps	681	.15	.11	.06
1988 Topps Big Baseball	25	.15	.11	.06
1989 Bowman	422	.10	.08	.04
1989 Donruss	2	.08	.06	.03
1989 Donruss	151	.10	.08	.04
1989 Fleer	203	.10	.08	.04
1989 Fleer	637	.10	.08	.04
1989 Fleer All-Stars	1	.25	.20	.10
1989 O-Pee-Chee	142	.10	.08	.04
1989 Score	195	.12	.09	.05
1989 Sportflics	182	.15	.11	.06
1989 Topps	388	.08	.06	.03
1989 Topps	440	.15	.11	.06
1989 Topps All-Star Glossy Set of 22	15	.10	.08	.04
1989 Topps All-Star Glossy Set of 60	24	.25	.20	.10
1989 Topps Big Baseball	159	.08	.06	.03
1989 Upper Deck	578	.25	.20	.10
1990 Bowman	169	.10	.08	.04
1990 Donruss	290	.10	.08	.04
1990 Fleer	462	.10	.08	.04

1990 Fleer MVP	4	.15	.11	.06
1990 Leaf	196	.60	.45	.25
1990 O-Pee-Chee	273	.15	.11	.06
1990 Score	170	.15	.11	.06
1990 Sportflics	195	.12	.09	.05
1990 Topps	273	.15	.11	.06
1990 Topps Big Baseball	208	.15	.11	.06
1990 Upper Deck	366	.12	.09	.05
1991 Bowman	381	.10	.08	.04
1991 Bowman	525	.10	.08	.04
1991 Donruss	325	.10	.08	.04
1991 Fleer	34	.12	.09	.05
1991 Fleer	711	.15	.11	.06
1991 Fleer Ultra	276	.10	.08	.04
1991 Leaf	357	.15	.11	.06
1991 Post Cereal	14	.40	.30	.15
1991 Score	315	.10	.08	.04
1991 Score	402	.10	.08	.04
1991 Score	670	.08	.06	.03
1991 Studio	223	.15	.11	.06
1991 Topps	403	.10	.08	.04
1991 Topps	750	.10	.08	.04
1991 Topps Stadium Club	139	.75	.60	.30
1991 Upper Deck	152	.15	.11	.06
1991 Upper Deck Final Edition	99	.12	.09	.05
1991 Upper Deck Silver Sluggers	15	.60	.45	.25
1992 Bowman	235	.50	.40	.20
1992 Donruss	427	.10	.08	.04
1992 Donruss	610	.12	.09	.05
1992 Donruss Triple Play Gallery of Stars	1	1.50	1.25	.60
1992 Fleer	551	.12	.09	.05
1992 Fleer	699	.10	.08	.04
1992 Fleer All-Stars	4	.75	.60	.30
1992 Fleer Team Leaders	9	1.00	.75	.40
1992 Fleer Ultra	527	.15	.11	.06
1992 Fleer Update	101	.40	.30	.15
1992 Leaf	308	.15	.10	.05
1992 O-Pee-Chee	160	.12	.09	.05
1992 O-Pee-Chee Premier	143	.40	.30	.15
1992 Pinnacle	310	.10	.08	.04
1992 Pinnacle	395	.15	.11	.06
1992 Pinnacle Slugfest	6	1.00	.70	.40
1992 Post Cereal	21	.30	.25	.12
1992 Score	225	.10	.08	.04
1992 Score Rookie & Traded	5	.15	.11	.06
1992 Studio	61	.12	.09	.05
1992 Topps	160	.12	.09	.05
1992 Topps	392	.08	.06	.03
1992 Topps Gold	160	.35	.25	.14
1992 Topps Gold	392	.25	.20	.10
1992 Topps Kids	22	.10	.08	.04
1992 Topps Stadium Club	608	.15	.11	.06
1992 Topps Stadium Club	780	.20	.15	.08
1992 Topps Stadium Club East Coast National	608	4.00	3.00	1.50
1992 Topps Stadium Club Special Edition	19	.25	.20	.10
1992 Topps Traded	14	.10	.08	.04
1992 Topps Traded Gold	14	.20	.15	.08
1992 Upper Deck	225	.12	.09	.05
1992 Upper Deck	755	.10	.07	.04
1993 Bowman	158	.10	.08	.04
1993 DiamondMarks	(41)	.50	.40	.20
1993 Donruss	594	.05	.04	.02
1993 Donruss Triple Play Action Baseball	2	.10	.08	.04
1993 Donruss Triple Play	173	.12	.09	.05
1993 Fleer	84	.08	.06	.03
1993 Fleer Flair	89	.30	.25	.12
1993 Fleer Ultra	422	.15	.11	.06
1993 Leaf	236	.10	.08	.04
1993 O-Pee-Chee	15	.20	.15	.08
1993 Pinnacle	43	.06	.05	.02
1993 Pinnacle Home Run Club	41	.35	.25	.14
1993 Post Cereal	24	.30	.25	.12

1993 Score	8	.08	.06	.03
1993 Score Select	11	.12	.09	.05
1993 Score The Franchise	21	1.00	.70	.40
1993 Studio	16	.12	.09	.05
1993 Topps	52	.08	.06	.03
1993 Topps Finest	66	1.50	1.25	.60
1993 Topps Finest Refractors	66	20.00	15.00	8.00
1993 Topps Gold	52	.15	.11	.06
1993 Topps Stadium Club	163	.12	.09	.05
1993 Topps Stadium Club First Day Production	163	7.00	5.25	2.75
1993 Upper Deck	275	.10	.08	.04
1993 Upper Deck	484	.08	.06	.03
1993 Upper Deck	826	.06	.05	.02
1993 Upper Deck Fun Packs	124	.15	.11	.06
1993 Upper Deck Home Run Heroes	23	.50	.40	.20
1993 Upper Deck SP	146	.15	.11	.06
1994 Bowman	128	.10	.08	.04
1994 Bowman's Best	50	.50	.40	.20
1994 Bowman's Best Refractors	50	2.00	1.50	.80
1994 Donruss	347	.08	.06	.03
1994 Donruss Diamond Kings	13	1.00	.75	.40
1994 Donruss Diamond Kings Super	13	3.50	2.75	1.50
1994 Donruss MVP's	9	.50	.40	.20
1994 Donruss Triple Play	141	.05	.04	.02
1994 Fleer	558	.06	.05	.02
1994 Fleer All-Stars	32	.30	.25	.12
1994 Fleer Extra Bases	315	.15	.11	.06
1994 Fleer Flair	407	.30	.25	.12
1994 Fleer Team Leaders	23	.50	.40	.20
1994 Fleer Ultra	529	.12	.09	.05
1994 Leaf	31	.12	.09	.05
1994 Leaf Clean-Up Crew	4	2.00	1.50	.80
1994 Leaf Limited	129	1.00	.70	.40
1994 O-Pee-Chee	202	.05	.04	.02
1994 Pacific Crown	396	.10	.08	.04
1994 Pacific Crown All Latino All-Star Team	18	1.50	1.25	.60
1994 Pacific Crown Homerun Leaders	17	2.00	1.50	.80
1994 Pinnacle	33	.15	.11	.06
1994 Pinnacle Artist's Proof	33	3.50	2.75	1.50
1994 Pinnacle Museum Collection	33	2.00	1.50	.80
1994 Post Cereal	10	.25	.20	.10
1994 Score	378	.06	.05	.02
1994 Score Gold Stars	26	2.50	2.00	1.00
1994 Score Select	238	.10	.08	.04
1994 Sportflics 2000	49	.15	.11	.06
1994 Studio	113	.10	.08	.04
1994 Topps	730	.06	.05	.02
1994 Topps Finest	234	.50	.40	.20
1994 Topps Finest Refractors	234	3.75	3.00	1.50
1994 Topps Finest Superstars	234	2.50	2.00	1.00
1994 Topps Gold	730	.15	.11	.06
1994 Topps Stadium Club	59	.15	.11	.06
1994 Topps Stadium Club First Day Production	59	3.50	2.75	1.50
1994 Upper Deck	275	.12	.09	.05
1994 Upper Deck	344	.10	.08	.04
1994 Upper Deck Collector's Choice	58	.07	.05	.03
1994 Upper Deck Electric Diamond	275	.25	.20	.10
1994 Upper Deck Electric Diamond	344	.25	.20	.10
1994 Upper Deck Fun Packs	127	.07	.05	.03
1994 Upper Deck Fun Packs	223	.10	.08	.04
1994 Upper Deck SP	115	.20	.15	.08

Bob Boone

Set	Card #	NM	EX	VG
1973 O-Pee-Chee	613	42.50	21.00	12.50
1973 Topps	613 (R)	30.00	15.00	9.00
1974 O-Pee-Chee	131	.60	.30	.20
1974 Topps	131	2.50	1.25	.70
1975 O-Pee-Chee	351	.55	.30	.15
1975 Topps	351	.40	.20	.12
1975 Topps Mini	351	2.00	1.00	.60
1976 O-Pee-Chee	67	.35	.20	.11
1976 O-Pee-Chee	318	.35	.20	.11
1976 Topps	67	.40	.20	.12
1976 Topps	318	.25	.13	.08
1977 O-Pee-Chee	68	.30	.15	.09
1977 Topps	545	.35	.20	.11
1978 O-Pee-Chee	141	.25	.13	.08
1978 Topps	161	.25	.13	.08
1979 O-Pee-Chee	38	.25	.13	.08
1979 Topps	90	.25	.13	.08
1980 O-Pee-Chee	246	.15	.08	.05
1980 Topps	470	.20	.10	.06

Set	Card #	MT	NM	EX
1981 Donruss	262	.10	.08	.04
1981 Fleer	4	.10	.08	.04
1981 O-Pee-Chee	290	.12	.09	.05
1981 Topps	290	.08	.06	.03
1982 Donruss	471	.10	.08	.04
1982 Fleer	240	.10	.08	.04
1982 O-Pee-Chee	23	.12	.09	.05
1982 O-Pee-Chee	392	.12	.09	.05
1982 Topps	615	.12	.09	.05
1982 Topps	616	.10	.08	.04
1982 Topps Traded	9T	.30	.25	.12
1983 Donruss	192	.10	.08	.04
1983 Fleer	79	.10	.08	.04
1983 O-Pee-Chee	366	.12	.09	.05
1983 Topps	765	.12	.09	.05
1984 Donruss	158	.15	.11	.06
1984 Fleer	509	.10	.08	.04
1984 Fleer	637	.15	.11	.06
1984 O-Pee-Chee	174	.20	.15	.08
1984 Topps	520	.10	.08	.04
1985 Donruss	230	.10	.08	.04
1985 Fleer	295	.08	.06	.03
1985 O-Pee-Chee	348	.08	.06	.03
1985 Topps	133	.12	.09	.05
1985 Topps	348	.08	.06	.03
1986 Donruss	17	.10	.08	.04
1986 Donruss	230	.08	.06	.03
1986 Fleer	149	.08	.06	.03
1986 Leaf	17	.08	.06	.03
1986 O-Pee-Chee	62	.08	.06	.03
1986 Topps	62	.07	.05	.03
1987 Donruss	233	.07	.05	.03
1987 Fleer	73	.08	.06	.03
1987 Leaf	202	.08	.06	.03
1987 O-Pee-Chee	166	.08	.06	.03
1987 Topps	166	.07	.05	.03
1987 Topps	556	.07	.05	.03
1988 Donruss	305	.07	.05	.03

1988 Fleer	485	.08	.06	.03
1988 Leaf	151	.08	.06	.03
1988 O-Pee-Chee	158	.08	.06	.03
1988 Score	63	.06	.05	.02
1988 Sportflics	212	.10	.08	.04
1988 Topps	498	.06	.05	.02
1988 Topps Big Baseball	30	.05	.04	.02
1989 Bowman	119	.05	.04	.02
1989 Donruss	170	.06	.05	.02
1989 Donruss Traded	5	.10	.08	.04
1989 Fleer	469	.07	.05	.03
1989 Fleer Update	36	.06	.05	.02
1989 O-Pee-Chee	243	.05	.04	.02
1989 Score	233	.06	.05	.02
1989 Score Traded	74T	.08	.06	.03
1989 Sportflics	40	.10	.08	.04
1989 Topps	243	.06	.05	.02
1989 Topps	404	.06	.05	.02
1989 Topps Big Baseball	269	.05	.04	.02
1989 Topps Traded	12T	.05	.04	.02
1989 Upper Deck	119	.08	.06	.03
1989 Upper Deck	767	.15	.11	.06
1990 Bowman	373	.06	.05	.02
1990 Donruss	326	.09	.07	.04
1990 Fleer	102	.07	.05	.03
1990 Leaf	46	.35	.25	.14
1990 O-Pee-Chee	671	.09	.07	.04
1990 Score	60	.08	.06	.03
1990 Sportflics	40	.10	.08	.04
1990 Topps	671	.09	.07	.04
1990 Topps Big Baseball	268	.08	.06	.03
1990 Upper Deck	271	.09	.07	.04
1991 Donruss	356	.06	.05	.02
1991 Fleer	551	.08	.06	.03
1991 Upper Deck	502	.08	.06	.03

Lou Boudreau

Set	Card #	NM	EX	VG
1941 Double Play	132	80.00	40.00	24.00
1948 Leaf	106	100.00	50.00	30.00
1949 Bowman	11	60.00	30.00	18.00
1950 Bowman	94	45.00	22.00	13.50
1951 Bowman	62	55.00	27.00	16.50
1953 Bowman Color	57	50.00	25.00	15.00
1955 Bowman	89	30.00	15.00	9.00
1960 Fleer	16	3.50	1.75	1.00
1961-62 Fleer	94	10.00	5.00	3.00

Set	Card #	MT	NM	EX
1988 Pacific Trading Cards Baseball Legends	106	.15	.11	.06
1989 Pacific Trading Cards Legends II	166	.15	.11	.08
1990 Pacific Legends	9	.10	.08	.04
1991 "1953" Topps Archives	304	.50	.40	.20

Larry Bowa

Set	Card #	NM	EX	VG
1970 O-Pee-Chee	539	7.50	3.75	2.25
1970 Topps	539 (R)	3.00	1.50	.90
1971 O-Pee-Chee	233	1.50	.70	.45
1971 Topps	233	2.00	1.00	.60
1972 O-Pee-Chee	520	1.75	.90	.50
1972 Topps	520	1.25	.60	.40
1973 O-Pee-Chee	119	.75	.40	.25
1973 Topps	119	.75	.40	.25
1974 O-Pee-Chee	255	.60	.30	.20
1974 Topps	255	.40	.20	.12
1975 O-Pee-Chee	420	.55	.30	.15
1975 Topps	420	.40	.20	.12
1976 O-Pee-Chee	145	.35	.20	.11
1976 Topps	145	.35	.20	.11
1977 O-Pee-Chee	17	.30	.15	.09
1977 Topps	310	.30	.15	.09
1978 O-Pee-Chee	68	.25	.13	.08
1978 Topps	90	.30	.15	.09
1979 O-Pee-Chee	104	.25	.13	.08
1979 Topps	210	.30	.15	.09
1980 O-Pee-Chee	330	.20	.10	.06
1980 Topps	630	.25	.13	.08

Set	Card #	MT	NM	EX
1981 Donruss	142	.15	.11	.06
1981 Fleer	2	.15	.11	.06
1981 Fleer	645a	2.00	1.50	.80
1981 O-Pee-Chee	120	.12	.09	.05
1981 Topps	120	.20	.15	.08
1982 Donruss	63	.15	.11	.06
1982 Fleer	241	.15	.11	.06
1982 O-Pee-Chee	194	.12	.09	.05
1982 O-Pee-Chee	374	.12	.09	.05
1982 Topps	515	.20	.15	.08
1982 Topps	516	.12	.09	.05
1982 Topps Traded	10T	.25	.20	.10
1983 Donruss	435	.12	.09	.05
1983 Fleer	491	.12	.09	.05
1983 O-Pee-Chee	305	.12	.09	.05
1983 Topps	305	.15	.11	.06
1984 Donruss	239	.25	.20	.10
1984 Fleer	486	.15	.11	.06
1984 O-Pee-Chee	346	.25	.20	.10
1984 Topps	705	.12	.09	.05
1984 Topps	757	.15	.11	.06
1985 Donruss	361	.12	.09	.05
1985 Fleer	50	.12	.09	.05
1985 O-Pee-Chee	56	.10	.08	.04
1985 Topps	484	.10	.08	.04
1987 Topps Traded	8T	.10	.08	.04
1988 Topps	284	.06	.05	.02

* * *

SCD's 1990 Baseball Card Shop Directory contained more than 2,000 listings of shops across the country.

* * *

Ralph Branca

Set	Card #	NM	EX	VG
1949 Bowman	194	80.00	40.00	24.00
1950 Bowman	59	50.00	25.00	15.00
1951 Bowman	56	30.00	15.00	9.00
1951 Topps Blue Backs	20	45.00	22.50	13.50
1952 Bowman	96	24.00	12.00	7.20
1952 Topps	274	75.00	37.00	17.00
1953 Bowman Black & White	52	45.00	22.50	13.50

Set	Card #	MT	NM	EX
1983 Topps 1952 Reprint Set	274	.40	.30	.15
1990 Pacific Legends	13	.05	.04	.02
1991 "1953" Topps Archives	293	.25	.20	.10

George Brett

Set	Card #	NM	EX	VG
1975 O-Pee-Chee	228	245.00	122.00	73.00
1975 Topps	228 (R)	220.00	110.00	65.00
1975 Topps Mini	228	250.00	125.00	75.00
1976 O-Pee-Chee	19	65.00	32.00	19.50
1976 Topps	19	60.00	30.00	18.00
1977 O-Pee-Chee	1	6.00	3.00	1.75
1977 O-Pee-Chee	170	38.00	19.00	11.50
1977 O-Pee-Chee	261	11.00	5.50	3.25
1977 Topps	1	5.00	2.50	1.50
1977 Topps	231	10.00	5.00	3.00
1977 Topps	580	35.00	17.50	10.50
1977 Topps	631	5.00	2.50	1.50
1978 O-Pee-Chee	215	25.00	12.50	7.50
1978 Topps	100	25.00	12.50	7.50
1979 O-Pee-Chee	167	21.00	10.50	6.25
1979 Topps	330	20.00	10.00	6.00
1980 O-Pee-Chee	235	15.00	7.50	4.50
1980 Topps	450	15.00	7.50	4.50

Set	Card #	MT	NM	EX
1981 Donruss	100	4.00	3.00	1.50
1981 Donruss	491	2.50	2.00	1.00
1981 Donruss	537	2.00	1.50	.80
1981 Fleer	28a	4.00	3.00	1.50
1981 Fleer	28b	1.00	.70	.40
1981 Fleer	655	4.00	3.00	1.50
1981 O-Pee-Chee	113	5.50	4.25	2.25
1981 Topps	1	2.00	1.50	.80
1981 Topps	700	6.00	4.50	2.50
1982 Donruss	15	1.50	1.25	.60
1982 Donruss	34	3.00	2.25	1.25
1982 Fleer	405	4.00	3.00	1.50
1982 O-Pee-Chee	200	3.75	2.75	1.50
1982 O-Pee-Chee	201	2.00	1.50	.80
1982 O-Pee-Chee	261	.60	.45	.25
1982 Topps	96	.35	.25	.14
1982 Topps	200	5.00	3.75	2.00
1982 Topps	201	2.50	2.00	1.00
1982 Topps	549	2.00	1.50	.80
1983 Donruss	338	3.50	2.75	1.50
1983 Fleer	108	3.50	2.75	1.50
1983 O-Pee-Chee	3	3.00	2.25	1.25
1983 O-Pee-Chee	388	.40	.30	.15
1983 Topps	388	1.50	1.25	.60
1983 Topps	600	4.00	3.00	1.50
1983 Topps All-Star Glossy Set of 40	31	.80	.60	.30
1984 Donruss	53	12.00	9.00	4.75
1984 Fleer	344	7.50	5.50	3.00
1984 Fleer	638	.30	.25	.12
1984 O-Pee-Chee	212	.40	.30	.15
1984 O-Pee-Chee	223	1.75	1.25	.70
1984 Topps	399	1.00	.75	.40
1984 Topps	500	3.00	2.25	1.25
1984 Topps	710	.30	.25	.12
1984 Topps All-Star Glossy Set of 22	4	.80	.60	.30
1984 Topps All-Star Glossy Set of 40	12	1.00	.70	.40
1985 Donruss	53	4.50	3.50	1.75
1985 Fleer	199	4.00	3.00	1.50
1985 Leaf-Donruss	176	3.50	2.75	1.50
1985 O-Pee-Chee	100	1.00	.70	.40
1985 Topps	100	2.00	1.50	.80
1985 Topps	703	.50	.40	.20
1985 Topps All-Star Glossy Set of 22	15	.80	.60	.30
1986 Donruss	53	2.50	2.00	1.00
1986 Fleer	5	2.25	1.75	.90
1986 Fleer	634	1.00	.70	.40
1986 Fleer All Stars	3	5.00	3.75	2.00
1986 Leaf	42	1.75	1.25	.70
1986 O-Pee-Chee	300	.75	.60	.30
1986 Sportflics	1	2.00	1.50	.80
1986 Sportflics	52	.35	.25	.14
1986 Sportflics	63	.30	.25	.12
1986 Sportflics	179	1.25	.90	.50
1986 Sportflics	180	1.25	.90	.50
1986 Sportflics	186	.40	.30	.15
1986 Sportflics Decade Greats	64	.80	.60	.30
1986 Topps	300	1.00	.75	.40
1986 Topps	714	.40	.30	.15
1986 Topps All-Star Glossy Set of 22	4	.80	.60	.30
1986 Topps All-Star Glossy Set of 60	18	.90	.70	.35
1987 Donruss	15	.60	.45	.25
1987 Donruss	54	1.00	.70	.40
1987 Donruss Diamond Kings Supers	15	.70	.50	.30
1987 Fleer	366	2.00	1.50	.80
1987 Leaf	15	.30	.25	.12
1987 Leaf	96	.60	.45	.25
1987 O-Pee-Chee	126	.30	.25	.12
1987 Sportflics	5	2.00	1.50	.80
1987 Sportflics	114	.60	.45	.25
1987 Sportflics	197	.80	.60	.30
1987 Topps	256	.15	.11	.06
1987 Topps	400	.50	.40	.20

Card	#			
1987 Topps All-Star Glossy Set of 60	31	.90	.70	.35
1988 Donruss	102	.40	.30	.15
1988 Fleer	254	.75	.60	.30
1988 Leaf	93	.50	.40	.20
1988 O-Pee-Chee	312	.25	.20	.10
1988 Score	11	.35	.25	.14
1988 Sportflics	150	1.00	.70	.40
1988 Topps	141	.12	.09	.05
1988 Topps	700	.30	.25	.12
1988 Topps All-Star Glossy Set of 60	53	.70	.50	.30
1988 Topps Big Baseball	157	.45	.35	.20
1989 Bowman	121	.35	.25	.14
1989 Donruss	204	.30	.25	.12
1989 Donruss MVP	7	.50	.40	.20
1989 Fleer	277	.30	.25	.12
1989 Fleer MVP	4	.70	.50	.30
1989 O-Pee-Chee	200	.50	.40	.20
1989 Score	75a	1.00	.70	.40
1989 Score	75b	.30	.25	.12
1989 Sportflics	64	.60	.45	.25
1989 Topps	200	.30	.25	.12
1989 Topps All-Star Glossy Set of 60	14	.40	.30	.15
1989 Topps Big Baseball	46	.15	.11	.06
1989 Topps Coins	34	.45	.35	.20
1989 Upper Deck	215	1.50	1.25	.60
1989 Upper Deck	689	.25	.20	.10
1990 Bowman	382	.25	.20	.10
1990 Donruss	144	.25	.20	.10
1990 Fleer	103	.30	.25	.12
1990 Fleer	621a	2.00	1.50	.80
1990 Fleer	621b	.20	.15	.08
1990 Fleer MVP	5	.60	.45	.25
1990 Leaf	178	2.50	2.00	1.00
1990 O-Pee-Chee	60	.20	.15	.08
1990 Post Cereal	4	.90	.70	.35
1990 Score	140	.30	.25	.12
1990 Sportflics	214	.60	.20	.10
1990 Topps	60	.25	.20	.10
1990 Upper Deck	124	.50	.40	.20
1991 Bowman	300	.25	.20	.10
1991 Donruss	201	.25	.20	.10
1991 Donruss	396	.15	.11	.06
1991 Donruss Elite	2	125.00	94.00	50.00
1991 Fleer	552	.25	.20	.10
1991 Fleer Ultra	144	.50	.40	.20
1991 Leaf	335	.40	.30	.15
1991 O-Pee-Chee Premier	14	.40	.30	.15
1991 Post Cereal	26	.80	.60	.30
1991 Score	120	.20	.15	.08
1991 Score	769	.20	.15	.08
1991 Score	853	.15	.11	.06
1991 Score Cooperstown	5	1.50	1.25	.60
1991 Studio	62	.50	.40	.20
1991 Topps	2	.15	.11	.06
1991 Topps	540	.20	.15	.08
1991 Topps Stadium Club	159	2.00	1.50	.80
1991 Topps Stadium Club Charter Members	(2)	2.00	1.50	.80
1991 Upper Deck	525	.35	.25	.14
1992 Bowman	500	2.50	2.00	1.00
1992 Donruss	143	.15	.11	.06
1992 Donruss Triple Play	115	.20	.15	.08
1992 Fleer	154	.15	.11	.06
1992 Fleer Ultra	68	.40	.30	.15
1992 Leaf	255	.40	.30	.15
1992 O-Pee-Chee	620	.12	.09	.05
1992 O-Pee-Chee Premier	114	.25	.20	.10
1992 Pinnacle	60	.75	.60	.30
1992 Pinnacle	282	.15	.11	.06
1992 Pinnacle Rookie Idols	3	10.00	7.50	4.00
1992 Post Cereal	11	.50	.40	.20
1992 Score	650	.20	.15	.08
1992 Studio	181	.50	.40	.20
1992 Topps	620	.25	.20	.10
1992 Topps Gold	620	2.00	1.50	.80
1992 Topps Kids	105	.20	.15	.08
1992 Topps Stadium Club	150	.75	.60	.30
1992 Topps Stadium Club	609	.50	.40	.20
1992 Topps Stadium Club East Coast National	609	30.00	22.00	12.00
1992 Topps Stadium Club Members Only	(2)	2.00	1.50	.80
1992 Upper Deck	444	.25	.20	.10
1992 Upper Deck MVP Holograms	12	.75	.60	.30
1993 Bowman	265	1.00	.75	.40
1993 Donruss Elite Dominators	15	125.00	94.00	50.00
1993 Donruss MVP's	3	2.50	2.00	1.00
1993 Donruss Triple Play	64	.10	.08	.04
1993 Donruss Triple Play	214	.50	.40	.20
1993 Fleer	236	.40	.30	.15
1993 Fleer Final Edition	2DT	1.50	1.25	.60
1993 Fleer Flair	213	2.50	2.00	1.00
1993 Fleer Golden Moments I	(1)	3.00	2.25	1.25
1993 Fleer Ultra	206	.75	.60	.30
1993 Leaf	146	.75	.60	.30
1993 Leaf Heading for the Hall	7	5.00	3.75	2.00
1993 O-Pee-Chee	50	1.00	.70	.40
1993 Pinnacle	131	.75	.60	.30
1993 Pinnacle	294	.40	.30	.15
1993 Pinnacle Cooperstown	2	.50	.40	.20
1993 Pinnacle Cooperstown Dufex	2	150.00	112.00	60.00
1993 Pinnacle Tribute	1	6.00	4.50	2.50
1993 Pinnacle Tribute	2	6.00	4.50	2.50
1993 Pinnacle Tribute	4	6.00	4.50	2.50
1993 Pinnacle Tribute	5	6.00	4.50	2.50
1993 Post Cereal	25	.75	.60	.30
1993 Score	57	.40	.30	.15
1993 Score	517	.30	.25	.12
1993 Studio	25	.75	.60	.30
1993 Studio Heritage	1	4.00	3.00	1.50
1993 Topps	397	.30	.25	.12
1993 Topps Finest	63	13.00	9.75	5.25
1993 Topps Finest Refractors	63	350.00	260.00	140.00
1993 Topps Gold	397	.60	.45	.25
1993 Topps Stadium Club	424	.60	.45	.25
1993 Topps Stadium Club First Day Production	424	75.00	56.00	30.00
1993 Topps Stadium Club I Inserts	2	6.00	4.50	2.50
1993 Topps Stadium Club Master Photos	(13)	4.00	3.00	1.50
1993 Topps Stadium Club Members Only	(4)	2.00	1.50	.80
1993 Topps Stadium Club Team Sets	1	1.00	.70	.40
1993 Upper Deck	54	.20	.15	.08
1993 Upper Deck	56	.30	.25	.12
1993 Upper Deck "Highlights"	7	12.00	9.00	4.75
1993 Upper Deck Diamond Gallery	24	4.00	3.00	1.50
1993 Upper Deck Fun Packs	181	.40	.30	.15
1993 Upper Deck Iooss Collection	22	1.50	1.25	.60
1993 Upper Deck Iooss Collection Super	22	5.00	3.75	2.00
1993 Upper Deck On Deck	6	1.75	1.25	.70
1993 Upper Deck SP	227	3.50	2.75	1.50
1993 Upper Deck Then And Now	2	4.00	3.00	1.50
1994 Donruss	107	.75	.60	.30
1994 Donruss Anniversary-1984	3	6.00	4.50	2.50
1994 Fleer	149	.50	.40	.20
1994 Fleer Golden Moments	6	2.50	2.00	1.00
1994 Fleer Golden Moments Super	6	10.00	7.50	4.00

1994 Topps	180	.40	.30	.15
1994 Topps Gold	180	1.50	1.25	.60
1994 Topps Stadium Club	5	.75	.60	.30
1994 Topps Stadium Club First Day Production	5	40.00	30.00	16.00
1994 Upper Deck All-Time Heroes	20	.35	.25	.14
1994 Upper Deck Collector's Choice	65	.35	.25	.14
1994 Upper Deck Heroes Autographed Inserts	(3)	80.00	60.00	32.00
1994 Upper Deck Heroes Gold	20	.50	.40	.20

Lou Brock

Set	Card #	NM	EX	VG
1962 Topps	387 (R)	175.00	85.00	50.00
1963 Topps	472	110.00	55.00	32.50
1964 Topps	29	35.00	17.50	10.50
1965 Topps	540	40.00	20.00	12.00
1966 O-Pee-Chee	125	30.00	15.00	9.00
1966 Topps	125	18.00	9.00	5.50
1967 O-Pee-Chee	63	10.25	5.25	3.00
1967 Topps	63	13.00	6.50	4.00
1967 Topps	285	20.00	10.00	6.00
1968 Topps	372	6.00	3.00	1.75
1968 Topps	520	20.00	10.00	6.00
1969 O-Pee-Chee	85	30.00	15.00	9.00
1969 Topps	85	21.00	10.50	6.25
1969 Topps	428	4.00	2.00	1.25
1970 O-Pee-Chee	330	12.75	6.50	3.75
1970 Topps	330	8.00	4.00	2.50
1971 O-Pee-Chee	625	34.00	17.00	10.00
1971 Topps	625	20.00	10.00	6.00
1972 O-Pee-Chee	200	7.50	3.75	2.25
1972 Topps	200	6.00	3.00	1.75
1973 O-Pee-Chee	64	.75	.40	.25
1973 O-Pee-Chee	320	7.50	3.75	2.25
1973 Topps	64	2.00	1.00	.60
1973 Topps	320	6.00	3.00	1.75
1974 O-Pee-Chee	60	6.75	3.50	2.00
1974 O-Pee-Chee	204	1.00	.50	.30
1974 Topps	60	5.00	2.50	1.50
1974 Topps	204	1.50	.70	.45
1975 O-Pee-Chee	2	1.25	.60	.40
1975 O-Pee-Chee	309	.75	.40	.25
1975 O-Pee-Chee	540	5.50	2.75	1.75
1975 Topps	2	2.00	1.00	.60
1975 Topps	309	.75	.40	.25
1975 Topps	540	4.00	2.00	1.25
1975 Topps Mini	2	3.50	1.75	1.00
1975 Topps Mini	309	1.25	.60	.40
1975 Topps Mini	540	7.00	3.50	2.00
1976 O-Pee-Chee	10	5.00	2.50	1.50
1976 O-Pee-Chee	197	2.00	1.00	.60
1976 Topps	10	4.00	2.00	1.25
1976 Topps	197	1.00	.50	.30
1977 O-Pee-Chee	51	4.25	2.25	1.25

1977 Topps	355	4.00	2.00	1.25
1978 O-Pee-Chee	204	3.50	1.75	1.00
1978 O-Pee-Chee	236	3.00	1.50	.90
1978 Topps	1	2.00	1.00	.60
1978 Topps	170	3.00	1.50	.90
1979 O-Pee-Chee	350	3.00	1.50	.90
1979 Topps	415	.50	.25	.15
1979 Topps	665	2.00	1.00	.60
1980 Topps	1	2.00	1.00	.60

Set	Card #	MT	NM	EX
1986 Sportflics Decade Greats	59	.30	.25	.12
1989 Topps	662	.08	.06	.03
1990 Pacific Legends	12	.30	.25	.12

Bill Buckner

Bill Buckner
FIRST BASE

Set	Card #	NM	EX	VG
1970 O-Pee-Chee	286	10.25	5.25	3.00
1970 Topps	286 (R)	6.00	3.00	1.75
1971 O-Pee-Chee	529	5.00	2.50	1.50
1971 Topps	529	4.00	2.00	1.25
1972 O-Pee-Chee	114	.75	.40	.25
1972 Topps	114	1.25	.60	.40
1973 O-Pee-Chee	368	.75	.40	.25
1973 Topps	368	.60	.30	.20
1974 O-Pee-Chee	505	.60	.30	.20
1974 Topps	505	.30	.15	.09
1975 O-Pee-Chee	244	.55	.30	.15
1975 Topps	244	.30	.15	.09
1975 Topps Mini	244	.80	.40	.25
1976 O-Pee-Chee	253	.40	.20	.12
1976 Topps	253	.25	.13	.08
1977 Topps	27	.30	.15	.09
1978 O-Pee-Chee	127	.25	.13	.08
1978 Topps	473	.30	.15	.09
1979 O-Pee-Chee	177	.25	.13	.08
1979 Topps	346	.30	.15	.09
1980 O-Pee-Chee	75	.25	.13	.08
1980 Topps	135	.15	.08	.05

Set	Card #	MT	NM	EX
1981 Donruss	482	.12	.09	.05
1981 Fleer	292	.12	.09	.05
1981 O-Pee-Chee	202	.60	.45	.25
1981 Topps	1	2.00	1.50	.80
1981 Topps	625	.15	.11	.06
1982 Donruss	403	.12	.09	.05
1982 Fleer	589	.12	.09	.05
1982 O-Pee-Chee	124	.15	.11	.06
1982 Topps	456	.08	.06	.03
1982 Topps	760	.15	.11	.06
1983 Donruss	14	.12	.09	.05
1983 Donruss	99	.12	.09	.05
1983 Fleer	492	.12	.09	.05
1983 O-Pee-Chee	250	.15	.11	.06
1983 Topps	250	.15	.11	.06
1983 Topps All-Star Glossy Set of 40	24	.15	.11	.06
1984 Donruss	117	.20	.15	.08

1984 Fleer	488	.15	.11	.06
1984 Fleer Update	18	.50	.40	.20
1984 O-Pee-Chee	96	.30	.25	.12
1984 Topps	545	.15	.11	.06
1984 Topps Traded	17T	.25	.20	.10
1985 Donruss	416	.15	.11	.06
1985 Fleer	153	.12	.09	.05
1985 Leaf-Donruss	254	.20	.15	.08
1985 O-Pee-Chee	65	.10	.08	.04
1985 Topps	65	.12	.09	.05
1986 Donruss	151	.12	.09	.05
1986 Fleer	343	.12	.09	.05
1986 Leaf	77	.08	.06	.03
1986 O-Pee-Chee	239	.08	.06	.03
1986 Sportflics	81	.10	.08	.04
1986 Sportflics	140	.20	.15	.08
1986 Topps	443	.10	.08	.04
1987 Donruss	462	.10	.08	.04
1987 Fleer	31	.10	.08	.04
1987 Leaf	241	.08	.06	.03
1987 O-Pee-Chee	306	.08	.06	.03
1987 Sportflics	70	.10	.08	.04
1987 Topps	764	.07	.05	.03
1988 Donruss	456	.10	.08	.04
1988 Fleer	486	.10	.08	.04
1988 O-Pee-Chee	147	.08	.06	.03
1988 Score	591	.08	.06	.03
1988 Score Traded	36T	.20	.15	.08
1988 Topps	147	.08	.06	.03
1989 Fleer	278	.10	.08	.04
1989 Score	214	.08	.06	.03
1989 Upper Deck	639	.10	.08	.04
1990 Donruss	474	.05	.04	.02
1990 Score	396	.06	.05	.02
1990 Upper Deck	252	.07	.05	.03

Roy Campanella

Set	Card #	NM	EX	VG
1949 Bowman	84 (R)	800.00	400.00	240.00
1950 Bowman	75	240.00	120.00	72.50
1951 Bowman	31	240.00	120.00	72.50
1952 Bowman	44	200.00	100.00	60.00
1952 Topps	314	1750.	875.00	402.00
1953 Bowman Color	46	235.00	115.00	70.00
1953 Red Man Tobacco	5N	85.00	42.00	25.00
1953 Topps	27	200.00	100.00	46.00
1954 Bowman	90	160.00	80.00	47.50
1954 Red Man Tobacco	13N	80.00	40.00	24.00
1955 Bowman	22	100.00	50.00	30.00
1956 Topps	101	130.00	65.00	39.00
1957 Topps	210	100.00	50.00	30.00
1957 Topps	400	175.00	85.00	50.00
1959 Topps	550	150.00	75.00	45.00
1961 Topps	480	30.00	15.00	9.00
1975 O-Pee-Chee	189	3.00	1.50	.90
1975 O-Pee-Chee	191	.75	.40	.25
1975 O-Pee-Chee	193	3.00	1.50	.90
1975 Topps	189	2.00	1.00	.60
1975 Topps	191	.90	.45	.25
1975 Topps	193	2.00	1.00	.60
1975 Topps Mini	189	2.25	1.25	.70
1975 Topps Mini	191	1.25	.60	.40
1975 Topps Mini	193	2.25	1.25	.70

Set	Card #	MT	NM	EX
1983 Topps 1952 Reprint Set	314	12.50	9.50	5.00
1986 Sportflics Decade Greats	33	.70	.50	.30
1988 Pacific Trading Cards Baseball Legends	47	.30	.25	.12
1991 "1953" Topps Archives Promos	(2)	20.00	15.00	8.00
1991 "1953" Topps Archives	27	2.50	2.00	1.00

Bert Campaneris

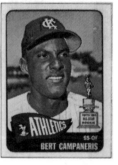

Set	Card #	NM	EX	VG
1965 O-Pee-Chee	266	11.00	5.50	3.25
1965 Topps	266 (R)	7.00	3.50	2.00
1966 O-Pee-Chee	175	2.50	1.25	.70
1966 Topps	175	3.00	1.50	.90
1967 Topps	515	9.00	4.50	2.75
1968 O-Pee-Chee	109	2.25	1.25	.70
1968 Topps	109	2.00	1.00	.60
1969 Topps	423	1.00	.50	.30
1969 Topps	495	1.00	.50	.30
1969 Topps	556	2.50	1.25	.70
1970 O-Pee-Chee	205	1.00	.50	.30
1970 Topps	205	.90	.45	.25
1971 O-Pee-Chee	440	2.50	1.25	.70
1971 Topps	440	2.00	1.00	.60
1972 O-Pee-Chee	75	.75	.40	.25
1972 Topps	75	.90	.45	.25
1973 O-Pee-Chee	64	.75	.40	.25
1973 O-Pee-Chee	295	.75	.40	.25
1973 Topps	64	2.00	1.00	.60
1973 Topps	295	.75	.40	.25
1974 O-Pee-Chee	155	.60	.30	.20
1974 O-Pee-Chee	335	.60	.30	.20
1974 Topps	155	.30	.15	.09
1974 Topps	335	.40	.20	.12
1975 O-Pee-Chee	170	.55	.30	.15
1975 Topps	170	.40	.20	.12
1975 Topps Mini	170	.60	.30	.20
1976 O-Pee-Chee	580	.35	.20	.11
1976 Topps	580	.25	.13	.08
1977 O-Pee-Chee	74	.30	.15	.09
1977 Topps	373	.30	.15	.09
1978 Topps	260	.25	.13	.08
1979 O-Pee-Chee	326	.25	.13	.08
1979 Topps	620	.25	.13	.08
1980 O-Pee-Chee	264	.15	.08	.05
1980 Topps	505	.20	.10	.06

Set	Card #	MT	NM	EX
1981 Donruss	50	.10	.08	.04
1981 Fleer	280	.10	.08	.04

1981 Topps	410	.12	.09	.05
1982 Donruss	593	.10	.08	.04
1982 Fleer	454	.10	.08	.04
1982 Topps	772	.12	.09	.05
1983 Topps Traded	18T	.20	.15	.08
1984 Fleer	120	.12	.09	.05
1984 Topps	139	.12	.09	.05
1984 Topps	711	.30	.25	.12
1984 Topps	714	.10	.08	.04
1989 Pacific Trading Cards Legends II	157	.06	.05	.02
1990 Pacific Legends	15	.05	.04	.02
1990 Pacific Senior League	63	.10	.08	.04
1990 Topps Senior League	32	.15	.11	.06

Jose Canseco

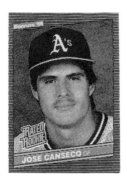

Set	Card #	MT	NM	EX
1986 Donruss	39 (R)	35.00	26.00	14.00
1986 Fleer	649 (R)	22.00	16.50	8.75
1986 Fleer Update	20	5.00	3.75	2.00
1986 Sportflics	178a	8.00	6.00	3.25
1986 Sportflics	178b	60.00	45.00	24.00
1986 Sportflics Rookies	11	3.00	2.25	1.25
1986 Topps Traded	20T	4.00	3.00	1.50
1987 Donruss	6	.40	.30	.15
1987 Donruss	97	3.00	2.25	1.25
1987 Donruss Diamond Kings Supers	6	2.00	1.50	.80
1987 Fleer	389	5.00	3.75	2.00
1987 Fleer	625	.75	.60	.30
1987 Fleer	628	.75	.60	.30
1987 Fleer	633	.75	.60	.30
1987 Fleer All Stars	6	1.00	.70	.40
1987 Fleer Headliners	2	1.50	1.25	.60
1987 Leaf	6	.50	.40	.20
1987 Leaf	151	2.25	1.75	.90
1987 O-Pee-Chee	247	.85	.60	.35
1987 Sportflics	80	.50	.40	.20
1987 Sportflics	90	2.00	1.50	.80
1987 Topps	620	1.00	.75	.40
1987 Topps All-Star Glossy Set of 60	59	2.00	1.50	.80
1987 Topps Glossy Rookies	3	3.00	2.25	1.25
1988 Donruss	302	.30	.25	.12
1988 Fleer	276	1.00	.70	.40
1988 Fleer	624	.50	.40	.20
1988 Fleer MVP	3	.80	.60	.30
1988 Leaf	138	.30	.25	.12
1988 O-Pee-Chee	370	.35	.25	.14
1988 Score	45	.40	.30	.15
1988 Sportflics	201	1.50	1.25	.60
1988 Topps	370	.40	.30	.15
1988 Topps	759	.30	.25	.12
1988 Topps All-Star Glossy Set of 60	55	2.00	1.50	.80
1988 Topps Big Baseball	13	1.25	.90	.50

1989 Bowman	201	.40	.30	.15
1989 Donruss	91	.35	.25	.14
1989 Donruss	643	.20	.15	.08
1989 Donruss Grand Slammers	1	.30	.25	.12
1989 Donruss MVP	5	.75	.60	.30
1989 Fleer	5	.30	.25	.12
1989 Fleer	628	.25	.20	.10
1989 Fleer	634	.30	.25	.12
1989 Fleer All-Stars	2	1.50	1.25	.60
1989 Fleer MVP	6	.90	.70	.35
1989 O-Pee-Chee	389	.45	.35	.20
1989 Score	1	.35	.25	.14
1989 Score	582	.10	.06	.03
1989 Score	655	.25	.20	.10
1989 Sportflics	1	.60	.45	.25
1989 Sportflics	221	1.50	1.25	.60
1989 Topps	401	.20	.15	.08
1989 Topps	500	.25	.20	.10
1989 Topps All-Star Glossy Set of 22	6	.20	.15	.08
1989 Topps All-Star Glossy Set of 60	12	1.25	.90	.50
1989 Topps Big Baseball	190	1.00	.70	.40
1989 Upper Deck	371	.75	.60	.30
1989 Upper Deck	659	.40	.30	.15
1989 Upper Deck	670	.25	.20	.10
1990 Bowman	460	.35	.25	.14
1990 Donruss	125	.20	.15	.08
1990 Fleer	3	.25	.20	.10
1990 Fleer	629	.20	.15	.08
1990 Fleer League Standouts	5	1.25	.90	.50
1990 Fleer MVP	6	.70	.50	.30
1990 Leaf	108	2.50	2.00	1.00
1990 O-Pee-Chee	250	.70	.50	.30
1990 Post Cereal	16	.90	.70	.35
1990 Score	375	.25	.20	.10
1990 Sportflics	23	.50	.40	.20
1990 Topps	250	.30	.25	.12
1990 Topps All-Star Glossy Set of 60	31	.80	.60	.30
1990 Topps Big Baseball	270	.50	.40	.20
1990 Upper Deck	66	.40	.30	.15
1991 Bowman	227	.20	.15	.08
1991 Bowman	372	.10	.08	.04
1991 Donruss	50	.12	.09	.05
1991 Donruss	536	.20	.15	.08
1991 Donruss Elite	3	70.00	52.00	28.00
1991 Donruss Grand Slammers	4	.30	.25	.12
1991 Fleer	5	.15	.11	.06
1991 Fleer All Stars	8	1.00	.75	.40
1991 Fleer ProVisions	6	.50	.40	.20
1991 Fleer Ultra	244	.40	.30	.15
1991 Leaf	182	.40	.30	.15
1991 O-Pee-Chee Premier	18	.35	.25	.14
1991 Post Cereal	4	.80	.60	.30
1991 Score	1	.20	.15	.08
1991 Score	398	.10	.08	.04
1991 Score	441	.60	.45	.25
1991 Score	690	.12	.09	.05
1991 Studio	101	.50	.40	.20
1991 Topps	390	.10	.08	.04
1991 Topps	700	.20	.15	.08
1991 Topps All-Star Glossy Set of 22	8	.30	.25	.12
1991 Topps Stadium Club	155	1.75	1.25	.70
1991 Upper Deck	155	.30	.25	.12
1991 Upper Deck Silver Sluggers	4	2.00	1.50	.80
1992 Bowman	600	1.25	.90	.50
1992 Donruss	548	.20	.15	.08
1992 Donruss Triple Play	214	.15	.11	.06
1992 Fleer	252	.15	.11	.06
1992 Fleer	688	.15	.11	.06
1992 Fleer All-Stars	24	2.00	1.50	.80
1992 Fleer Lumber Co.	5	2.00	1.50	.75
1992 Fleer Team Leaders	19	4.00	3.00	1.50
1992 Fleer Ultra	110	.40	.30	.15
1992 Fleer Update	59	2.50	2.00	1.00

1992 Leaf	267	.25	.15	.08
1992 O-Pee-Chee	100	.10	.08	.04
1992 O-Pee-Chee Premier	24	.50	.40	.20
1992 Pinnacle	130	.40	.30	.15
1992 Pinnacle Slugfest	3	2.50	2.00	1.00
1992 Post Cereal	25	.35	.25	.14
1992 Score	500	.15	.11	.06
1992 Score Impact Players	52	.60	.45	.25
1992 Score Rookie & Traded	9	1.25	.90	.50
1992 Studio	222	.35	.25	.14
1992 Studio Heritage	4	1.50	1.25	.60
1992 Topps	100	.10	.08	.04
1992 Topps	401	.10	.08	.04
1992 Topps Gold	100	2.00	1.50	.80
1992 Topps Gold	401	.60	.45	.25
1992 Topps Kids	115	.20	.15	.08
1992 Topps Stadium Club	370	.50	.40	.20
1992 Topps Stadium Club Master Photos	(3)	4.00	3.00	1.50
1992 Upper Deck	333	.25	.20	.10
1992 Upper Deck	640	.05	.04	.02
1992 Upper Deck	649	.10	.08	.04
1992 Upper Deck Home Run Heroes	1	1.00	.75	.40
1992 Upper Deck MVP Holograms	14	.75	.60	.30
1993 Bowman	545	.35	.25	.14
1993 Donruss	159	.20	.15	.08
1993 Donruss Long Ball Leaders	6	3.00	2.25	1.25
1993 Donruss Masters of the Game	7	3.00	2.25	1.25
1993 Donruss Spirit of the Game	5	4.00	3.00	1.50
1993 Donruss Triple Play	243	.25	.20	.10
1993 Fleer	319	.25	.20	.10
1993 Fleer Flair	278	.75	.60	.30
1993 Fleer Ultra	627	.35	.25	.14
1993 Leaf	241	.35	.25	.14
1993 Leaf Gold All-Stars	9	2.00	1.50	.80
1993 O-Pee-Chee	47	.50	.40	.20
1993 O-Pee-Chee Premier	81	.20	.15	.08
1993 Pacific Prism Insert	11	20.00	15.00	8.00
1993 Pinnacle	49	.35	.25	.14
1993 Pinnacle Home Run Club	10	1.00	.70	.40
1993 Pinnacle Slugfest	24	2.00	1.50	.80
1993 Score	13	.25	.20	.10
1993 Score Select	364	.25	.20	.10
1993 Studio	47	.35	.25	.14
1993 Studio Superstars on Canvas	2	2.00	1.50	.80
1993 Topps	500	.20	.15	.08
1993 Topps Finest	99	5.00	3.75	2.00
1993 Topps Finest Jumbo All-Stars	99	15.00	11.00	6.00
1993 Topps Finest Refractors	99	50.00	37.00	20.00
1993 Topps Gold	500	.40	.30	.15
1993 Topps Stadium Club	499	.35	.25	.14
1993 Topps Stadium Club First Day Production	499	35.00	26.00	14.00
1993 Topps Stadium Club Master Photos	(14)	4.00	3.00	1.50
1993 Topps Stadium Club Team Sets	28	.40	.30	.15
1993 Upper Deck	52	.25	.20	.10
1993 Upper Deck	365	.25	.20	.10
1993 Upper Deck Clutch Performers	4	1.00	.75	.40
1993 Upper Deck Fun Packs	12	.20	.15	.08
1993 Upper Deck Fun Packs	155	.20	.15	.08
1993 Upper Deck On Deck	7	1.00	.75	.40
1993 Upper Deck SP	191	1.00	.75	.40
1993 Upper Deck Triple Crown	2	2.00	1.50	.80
1994 Bowman	600	.35	.25	.14
1994 Bowman's Best	24	1.50	1.25	.60
1994 Bowman's Best Refractors	24	12.00	9.00	4.75
1994 Donruss	372	.40	.30	.15
1994 Donruss Decade Dominators	7	2.00	1.50	.80
1994 Donruss Decade Dominators Supers	7	5.00	3.75	2.00
1994 Donruss Special Edition - Gold	372	.40	.30	.15
1994 Donruss Triple Play	192	.25	.20	.10
1994 Fleer	304	.25	.20	.10
1994 Fleer Extra Bases	176	.40	.30	.15
1994 Fleer Extra Bases Game Breakers	5	.50	.40	.20
1994 Fleer Flair	344	.75	.60	.30
1994 Fleer Ultra	426	.40	.30	.15
1994 Leaf	249	.40	.30	.15
1994 Leaf Limited	70	3.00	2.25	1.25
1994 Leaf MVP Contenders	2a	4.00	3.00	1.50
1994 Leaf MVP Contenders	2b	8.00	6.00	3.25
1994 O-Pee-Chee	169	.25	.20	.10
1994 Pacific Crown	611	.30	.25	.12
1994 Pacific Crown All Latino All-Star Team	8	4.00	3.00	1.50
1994 Pinnacle	306	.30	.25	.12
1994 Pinnacle Artist's Proof	306	10.00	7.50	4.00
1994 Pinnacle Museum Collection	306	4.00	3.00	1.50
1994 Score	61	.30	.25	.12
1994 Score Select	76	.10	.08	.04
1994 Score Select	276	.30	.25	.12
1994 Sportflics 2000	141	.40	.30	.15
1994 Studio	152	.40	.30	.15
1994 Topps	80	.25	.20	.10
1994 Topps Finest	222	1.75	1.25	.70
1994 Topps Finest Refractors	222	8.00	6.00	3.25
1994 Topps Finest Superstars	222	6.00	4.50	2.50
1994 Topps Gold	80	.75	.60	.30
1994 Topps Stadium Club	171	.30	.25	.12
1994 Topps Stadium Club First Day Production	171	15.00	11.00	6.00
1994 Topps Team Stadium Club	250	6.00	6.00	6.00
1994 Topps Team Stadium Club 1st Day Issue	250	6.00	6.00	6.00
1994 Upper Deck	140	.35	.25	.14
1994 Upper Deck Collector's Choice	560	.15	.11	.06
1994 Upper Deck Electric Diamond	140	1.25	.90	.50
1994 Upper Deck Fun Packs	133	.35	.25	.14
1994 Upper Deck Fun Packs	209	.15	.11	.06
1994 Upper Deck Mickey Mantle's Long Shots	4MM	2.50	2.00	1.00
1994 Upper Deck SP	146	.50	.40	.20
1994 Upper Deck SP Holoview Blue	4	4.50	3.50	1.75
1994 Upper Deck SP Holoview Red	4	30.00	22.00	12.00

* * *

Wade Boggs, about his first appearance on a base-ball card: "Well, it's a big thrill because when you're growing up you put them in your bicycle tires and that kind of thing. And now you're on one and you know that you're in somebody's bicycle spokes, so that makes you feel good."

* * *

Rod Carew

Set	Card #	NM	EX	VG
1967 Topps	569 (R)	325.00	160.00	97.50
1968 O-Pee-Chee	80	135.00	67.00	40.00
1968 Topps	80	70.00	35.00	21.00
1968 Topps	363	7.00	3.50	2.00
1969 Topps	419	7.50	3.75	2.25
1969 Topps	510	55.00	27.00	16.50
1970 O-Pee-Chee	62	1.75	.90	.50
1970 O-Pee-Chee	290	46.00	23.00	14.00
1970 O-Pee-Chee	453	10.25	5.25	3.00
1970 Topps	62	3.50	1.75	1.00
1970 Topps	290	30.00	15.00	9.00
1970 Topps	453	6.00	3.00	1.75
1971 O-Pee-Chee	210	46.00	23.00	14.00
1971 Topps	210	30.00	15.00	9.00
1972 Topps	695	75.00	37.00	22.00
1972 Topps	696	35.00	17.50	10.50
1973 O-Pee-Chee	61	1.25	.60	.40
1973 O-Pee-Chee	330	12.75	6.50	3.75
1973 Topps	61	2.25	1.25	.70
1973 Topps	330	10.00	5.00	3.00
1974 O-Pee-Chee	50	12.00	6.00	3.50
1974 O-Pee-Chee	201	6.75	3.50	2.00
1974 O-Pee-Chee	333	1.50	.70	.45
1974 Topps	50	8.00	4.00	2.50
1974 Topps	201	4.00	2.00	1.25
1974 Topps	333	3.00	1.50	.90
1975 O-Pee-Chee	306	.75	.40	.25
1975 O-Pee-Chee	600	10.25	5.25	3.00
1975 Topps	306	.80	.40	.25
1975 Topps	600	9.00	4.50	2.75
1975 Topps Mini	306	1.25	.60	.40
1975 Topps Mini	600	12.00	6.00	3.50
1976 O-Pee-Chee	192	2.00	1.00	.60
1976 O-Pee-Chee	400	8.50	4.25	2.50
1976 Topps	192	2.00	1.00	.60
1976 Topps	400	8.00	4.00	2.50
1977 O-Pee-Chee	143	7.50	3.75	2.25
1977 Topps	120	8.00	4.00	2.50
1978 O-Pee-Chee	1	.75	.40	.25
1978 O-Pee-Chee	230	6.00	3.00	1.75
1978 Topps	201	1.00	.50	.30
1978 Topps	580	6.00	3.00	1.75
1979 O-Pee-Chee	151	4.25	2.25	1.25
1979 Topps	1	3.00	1.50	.90
1979 Topps	300	4.00	2.00	1.25
1980 O-Pee-Chee	353	2.00	1.00	.60
1980 Topps	700	1.50	.70	.45

Set	Card #	MT	NM	EX
1981 Donruss	49	1.50	1.25	.60
1981 Donruss	169	1.50	1.25	.60
1981 Donruss	537	2.00	1.50	.80
1981 Fleer	268	1.50	1.25	.60
1981 O-Pee-Chee	100	2.50	2.00	1.00
1981 Topps	100	2.00	1.50	.80
1982 Donruss	8	.60	45	.25
1982 Donruss	216	1.00	.70	.40
1982 Fleer	455	1.00	.70	.40
1982 O-Pee-Chee	36	.30	.25	.12
1982 O-Pee-Chee	187	2.00	1.50	.80
1982 O-Pee-Chee	363	.30	.25	.12
1982 Topps	276	.25	.20	.10
1982 Topps	500	1.00	.70	.40
1982 Topps	501	.40	.30	.15
1982 Topps	547	.35	.25	.14
1983 Donruss	90	1.00	.70	.40
1983 Fleer	81	1.00	.70	.40
1983 O-Pee-Chee	200	1.50	1.25	.60
1983 O-Pee-Chee	201	.30	.25	.12
1983 O-Pee-Chee	386	.30	.25	.12
1983 Topps	200	.90	.70	.35
1983 Topps	201	.35	.25	.14
1983 Topps	386	.50	.40	.20
1983 Topps	651	.30	.25	.12
1983 Topps All-Star Glossy Set of 40	29	.60	.45	.25
1984 Donruss	352	4.00	3.00	1.50
1984 Fleer	511	1.25	.90	.50
1984 Fleer	629	.25	.20	.10
1984 O-Pee-Chee	26	1.00	.70	.40
1984 Topps	276	.20	.15	.08
1984 Topps	600	.50	.40	.20
1984 Topps	710	.30	.25	.12
1984 Topps	711	.30	.25	.12
1984 Topps All-Star Glossy Set of 22	2	.50	.40	.20
1984 Topps All-Star Glossy Set of 40	26	.60	.45	.25
1985 Donruss	85	1.00	.70	.40
1985 Fleer	297	1.50	1.25	.60
1985 Leaf-Donruss	132	.35	.25	.14
1985 O-Pee-Chee	300	.30	.25	.12
1985 Topps	300	.50	.40	.20
1985 Topps All-Star Glossy Set of 22	13	.50	.40	.20
1986 Donruss	280	.70	.50	.30
1986 Fleer	151	.70	.50	.30
1986 Fleer	629	.50	.40	.20
1986 Fleer Future Hall Of Famers	4	1.75	1.25	.70
1986 O-Pee-Chee	371	.25	.20	.10
1986 Sportflics	69	1.00	.70	.40
1986 Sportflics	74	.20	.15	.08
1986 Sportflics	106	1.25	.90	.50
1986 Sportflics	146	.25	.20	.10
1986 Sportflics	180	1.25	.90	.50
1986 Sportflics	182	1.50	1.25	.60
1986 Topps	400	.30	.25	.12
1986 Topps All-Star Glossy Set of 60	16	.60	.45	.25
1991 Bowman	1	.08	.06	.03
1991 Bowman	2	.08	.06	.03
1991 Bowman	3	.08	.06	.03
1991 Bowman	4	.08	.06	.03
1991 Bowman	5	.08	.06	.03
1992 Pinnacle	584	.20	.15	.08

* * *

Rod Carew, about his favorite baseball card: "I'd have to say that my favorite Rod Carew card is my Topps rookie card. And, I don't think that just on sentiment. Even though it was my first card, I really think that photo captured me."

* * *

Jim Palmer, on teammate Moe Drabowsky's pranks: "When we won our first World Series (1966), we won it in Kansas City and immediately got on the plane to L.A. The next thing you know, Moe had wrapped this snake around Luis Aparicio's neck and put little garter snakes in Paul Blair's uniform. Blair ended up dressing in the dugout. He wouldn't go back in. He just hated snakes."

* * *

Steve Carlton

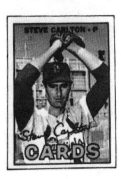

Set	Card #	NM	EX	VG
1965 Topps	477 (R)	400.00	200.00	120.00
1967 O-Pee-Chee	146	150.00	75.00	45.00
1967 Topps	146	90.00	45.00	27.00
1968 Topps	408	40.00	20.00	12.00
1969 Topps	255	45.00	22.00	13.50
1970 O-Pee-Chee	67	7.50	3.75	2.25
1970 O-Pee-Chee	220	42.50	21.00	12.50
1970 Topps	67	4.00	2.00	1.25
1970 Topps	220	35.00	17.00	10.50
1971 O-Pee-Chee	55	32.00	16.00	9.50
1971 Topps	55	25.00	12.50	7.50
1972 O-Pee-Chee	93	5.00	2.50	1.50
1972 O-Pee-Chee	420	30.00	15.00	9.00
1972 Topps	93	3.50	1.75	1.00
1972 Topps	420	15.00	7.50	4.50
1972 Topps	751	50.00	25.00	15.00
1973 O-Pee-Chee	65	.75	.40	.25
1973 O-Pee-Chee	66	1.00	.50	.30
1973 O-Pee-Chee	67	23.00	11.50	7.00
1973 O-Pee-Chee	300	17.00	8.50	5.00
1973 Topps	65	2.00	1.00	.60
1973 Topps	66	2.00	1.00	.60
1973 Topps	67	18.00	9.00	5.50
1973 Topps	300	15.00	7.50	4.50
1974 O-Pee-Chee	95	12.75	6.50	3.75
1974 Topps	95	9.00	4.50	2.75
1975 O-Pee-Chee	185	10.25	5.25	3.00
1975 O-Pee-Chee	312	18.00	9.00	5.50
1975 Topps	185	10.00	5.00	3.00
1975 Topps	312	9.00	4.50	2.75
1975 Topps Mini	185	15.00	7.50	4.50
1975 Topps Mini	312	2.50	1.25	.70
1976 O-Pee-Chee	355	8.50	4.25	2.50
1976 Topps	355	7.00	3.50	2.00
1977 O-Pee-Chee	93	7.50	3.75	2.25
1977 Topps	110	8.00	4.00	2.50
1978 O-Pee-Chee	5	.50	.25	.15
1978 O-Pee-Chee	170	6.00	3.00	1.75
1978 Topps	205	1.50	.70	.45
1978 Topps	540	5.00	2.50	1.50
1979 O-Pee-Chee	9	4.25	2.25	1.25
1979 Topps	25	4.50	3.50	1.75
1980 O-Pee-Chee	113	4.25	2.25	1.25
1980 Topps	210	4.00	2.00	1.25

Set	Card #	MT	NM	EX
1981 Donruss	33	2.00	1.50	.80
1981 Donruss	481	.40	.30	.15
1981 Fleer	6a	1.00	.70	.40
1981 Fleer	6b	2.00	1.50	.80
1981 Fleer	6c	3.00	2.25	1.25
1981 Fleer	660a	1.00	.70	.40
1981 Fleer	660b	2.00	1.50	.80
1981 O-Pee-Chee	203	2.50	2.00	1.00
1981 Topps	5	.20	.15	.08
1981 Topps	6	.20	.15	.08
1981 Topps	202	1.00	.75	.40
1981 Topps	630	3.25	2.50	1.50
1982 Donruss	42	1.00	.70	.40

1982 Fleer	243	1.00	.70	.40
1982 Fleer	632	.25	.20	.10
1982 Fleer	641	.50	.40	.20
1982 O-Pee-Chee	68	.75	.60	.30
1982 O-Pee-Chee	122	.30	.25	.12
1982 Topps	1	.50	.40	.20
1982 Topps	480	1.00	.70	.40
1982 Topps	481	.40	.30	.15
1982 Topps	636	.50	.40	.20
1983 Donruss	16	.40	.30	.15
1983 Donruss	219	1.00	.70	.40
1983 Fleer	155	1.00	.70	.40
1983 O-Pee-Chee	70	.50	.40	.20
1983 O-Pee-Chee	71	.25	.20	.10
1983 O-Pee-Chee	384	.30	.25	.12
1983 Topps	70	1.25	.90	.50
1983 Topps	71	.30	.25	.12
1983 Topps	229	.20	.15	.08
1983 Topps	406	.50	.40	.20
1983 Topps	705	.20	.15	.08
1983 Topps	706	.20	.15	.08
1983 Topps All-Star Glossy Set of 40	36	.50	.40	.20
1984 Donruss	111	5.00	3.75	2.00
1984 Fleer	25	3.50	2.75	1.50
1984 Fleer	642	.20	.15	.08
1984 O-Pee-Chee	214	.70	.50	.30
1984 O-Pee-Chee	395	.40	.30	.15
1984 Topps	1	.30	.25	.12
1984 Topps	4	1.00	.75	.40
1984 Topps	136	.25	.20	.10
1984 Topps	395	.25	.20	.10
1984 Topps	706	.30	.25	.12
1984 Topps	707	.35	.25	.14
1984 Topps	708	.25	.20	.10
1984 Topps	780	1.00	.70	.40
1984 Topps All-Star Glossy Set of 40	27	.50	.40	.20
1985 Donruss	305	1.25	.90	.50
1985 Fleer	246	1.50	1.25	.60
1985 Leaf-Donruss	113	1.00	.70	.40
1985 O-Pee-Chee	360	.30	.25	.12
1985 Topps	360	.60	.45	.25
1986 Donruss	183	.60	.45	.25
1986 Fleer	435	.60	.45	.25
1986 Fleer Future Hall Of Famers	2	1.75	1.25	.70
1986 Leaf	117	.30	.25	.12
1986 O-Pee-Chee	120	.25	.20	.10
1986 Sportflics	27	.75	.60	.30
1986 Sportflics	70	.25	.20	.10
1986 Sportflics Decade Greats	54	.40	.30	.15
1986 Topps	120	.40	.30	.15
1986 Topps	246	.15	.11	.06
1987 Donruss	617	.25	.20	.10
1987 Fleer	490	.40	.30	.15
1987 Fleer	635	.12	.09	.05
1987 Fleer Update	17	.40	.30	.15
1987 O-Pee-Chee	271	.20	.15	.08
1987 Sportflics	200	.75	.60	.30
1987 Topps	718	.20	.15	.08
1987 Topps Traded	19T	.30	.25	.12
1988 Fleer	7	.35	.25	.14
1990 Pacific Legends	16	.30	.25	.12

* * *

Philadelphia Phillies Hall of Fame pitcher Steve Carlton, also known by his nickname "Lefty," signs autographs with his right hand.

* * *

Andre Dawson, on why he likes signing autographs for kids: "I like to see the expressions on their faces. I've always felt the kids are the backbone of the business. The kids are the ones that get the biggest thrill out of it. They make it enjoyable for me."

* * *

Gary Carter

Set	Card #	NM	EX	VG
1975 O-Pee-Chee	620	46.00	23.00	14.00
1975 Topps	620 (R)	30.00	15.00	9.00
1975 Topps Mini	620	50.00	25.00	15.00
1976 O-Pee-Chee	441	10.25	5.25	3.00
1976 Topps	441	5.00	2.50	1.50
1977 O-Pee-Chee	45	6.75	3.50	2.00
1977 Topps	295	4.00	2.00	1.25
1978 O-Pee-Chee	135	5.00	2.50	1.50
1978 Topps	120	3.00	1.50	.90
1979 O-Pee-Chee	270	3.75	2.00	1.25
1979 Topps	520	2.00	1.00	.60
1980 O-Pee-Chee	37	2.75	1.50	.80
1980 Topps	70	1.25	.60	.40

Set	Card #	MT	NM	EX
1981 Donruss	90	.50	.40	.20
1981 Fleer	142	.40	.30	.15
1981 O-Pee-Chee	6	1.00	.70	.40
1981 Topps	660	.80	.60	.30
1982 Donruss	2	.50	.40	.20
1982 Donruss	114	.50	.40	.20
1982 Fleer	185	.35	.25	.14
1982 Fleer	635	.30	.25	.12
1982 Fleer	638	.25	.20	.10
1982 O-Pee-Chee	244	.75	.60	.30
1982 O-Pee-Chee	344	.30	.25	.12
1982 Topps	344	.20	.15	.08
1982 Topps	730	.80	.60	.30
1983 Donruss	340	.40	.30	.15
1983 Fleer	278	.35	.25	.14
1983 Fleer	637	.15	.11	.06
1983 Fleer	638	.20	.15	.08
1983 O-Pee-Chee	314	.30	.25	.12
1983 O-Pee-Chee	370	.50	.40	.20
1983 Topps	370	.25	.20	.10
1983 Topps	404	.20	.15	.08
1983 Topps All-Star Glossy Set of 40	20	.30	.25	.12
1984 Donruss	55	1.00	.70	.40
1984 Fleer	271	.40	.30	.15
1984 O-Pee-Chee	366	.70	.50	.30
1984 O-Pee-Chee	393	.40	.30	.15
1984 Topps	393	.20	.15	.08
1984 Topps	450	.40	.30	.15
1984 Topps All-Star Glossy Set of 40	9	.50	.40	.20
1984 Topps All-Star Glossy Set of 22	20	.35	.25	.14
1985 Donruss	55	.40	.30	.15
1985 Fleer	393	.35	.25	.14
1985 Fleer	631	.25	.20	.10
1985 Fleer	632	.12	.09	.05
1985 Fleer Update	21	.40	.30	.15
1985 Leaf-Donruss	241	.30	.25	.12
1985 O-Pee-Chee	230	.30	.25	.12
1985 Topps	230	.35	.25	.14
1985 Topps	719	.15	.11	.06
1985 Topps All-Star Glossy Set of 22	9	.30	.25	.12
1985 Topps All-Star Glossy Set of 40	36	.35	.25	.14
1985 Topps Traded	17T	.60	.45	.25
1986 Donruss	68	.35	.25	.14
1986 Fleer	76	.25	.20	.10
1986 Fleer All Stars	4	.75	.60	.30
1986 Leaf	63	1.00	.70	.40
1986 O-Pee-Chee	170	.25	.20	.10
1986 Sportflics	28	.35	.25	.14
1986 Sportflics	126	.15	.11	.06
1986 Sportflics	137	.20	.15	.08
1986 Sportflics Decade Greats	72	.30	.25	.12
1986 Topps	170	.20	.15	.08
1986 Topps	708	.10	.07	.04
1986 Topps All-Star Glossy Set of 60	23	.50	.40	.20
1987 Donruss	69	.12	.09	.05
1987 Fleer	4	.15	.11	.06
1987 Fleer	629	.15	.11	.06
1987 Fleer	634	.40	.30	.15
1987 Fleer All Stars	2	.50	.40	.20
1987 Fleer All Stars	7	.25	.20	.10
1987 Leaf	109	.60	.45	.25
1987 O-Pee-Chee	20	.20	.15	.08
1987 Sportflics	50	.30	.25	.12
1987 Sportflics	151	.15	.11	.06
1987 Topps	20	.10	.08	.04
1987 Topps	331	.10	.08	.04
1987 Topps	602	.15	.11	.06
1987 Topps All-Star Glossy Set of 22	9	.30	.25	.12
1987 Topps All-Star Glossy Set of 60	11	.30	.25	.12
1988 Donruss	199	.10	.08	.04
1988 Fleer	130	.10	.08	.04
1988 Fleer	636	.25	.20	.10
1988 Leaf	156	.40	.30	.15
1988 O-Pee-Chee	157	.15	.11	.06
1988 Score	325	.10	.08	.04
1988 Sportflics	28	.25	.20	.10
1988 Sportflics Gamewinners	14	.30	.25	.12
1988 Topps	530	.15	.11	.06
1988 Topps	579	.08	.06	.03
1988 Topps All-Star Glossy Set of 60	7	.30	.25	.12
1988 Topps All-Star Glossy Set of 22	20	.25	.20	.10
1989 Bowman	379	.03	.02	.01
1989 Donruss	53	.10	.08	.04
1989 Fleer	30	.08	.06	.03
1989 O-Pee-Chee	324	.25	.20	.10
1989 Score	240	.15	.11	.06
1989 Sportflics	155	.25	.20	.10
1989 Topps	3	.10	.08	.04
1989 Topps	393	.10	.08	.04
1989 Topps	680	.15	.11	.06
1989 Topps All-Star Glossy Set of 60	17	.15	.11	.06
1989 Topps All-Star Glossy Set of 22	20	.05	.04	.02
1989 Upper Deck	390	.10	.08	.04
1990 Bowman	236	.05	.04	.02
1990 Donruss	147	.06	.05	.02
1990 Fleer	199	.06	.05	.02
1990 Fleer Update	62	.10	.08	.04
1990 Leaf	134	.35	.25	.14
1990 O-Pee-Chee	790	.06	.05	.02
1990 Score	416	.07	.05	.03
1990 Score Traded	35T	.10	.08	.04
1990 Topps	790	.06	.05	.02
1990 Topps Traded	19T	.10	.08	.04
1990 Upper Deck	168	.10	.08	.04
1990 Upper Deck	774	.10	.07	.04
1991 Bowman	598	.06	.05	.02
1991 Donruss	151	.08	.06	.03
1991 Fleer	258	.08	.06	.03
1991 Fleer Ultra Update	86	.20	.15	.08
1991 Fleer Update	93	.08	.06	.03
1991 Leaf	457	.15	.11	.06

Set	Card #	MT	NM	EX
1991 O-Pee-Chee Premier	19	.05	.04	.02
1991 Score	215	.08	.06	.03
1991 Score Traded	26	.10	.08	.04
1991 Topps	310	.08	.06	.03
1991 Topps Traded	19	.08	.06	.03
1991 Upper Deck	176	.10	.08	.04
1991 Upper Deck	758	.12	.09	.05
1992 Bowman	385	.35	.25	.14
1992 Donruss	36	.08	.06	.03
1992 Donruss Triple Play	26	.05	.04	.02
1992 Fleer	450	.08	.06	.03
1992 Fleer Ultra	514	.15	.11	.06
1992 Leaf	442	.10	.07	.04
1992 O-Pee-Chee	45	.08	.06	.03
1992 O-Pee-Chee	387	.10	.08	.04
1992 O-Pee-Chee	389	.10	.08	.04
1992 O-Pee-Chee	399	.10	.08	.04
1992 O-Pee-Chee	402	.10	.08	.04
1992 O-Pee-Chee Premier	29	.15	.11	.06
1992 Pinnacle	321	.15	.11	.06
1992 Score	489	.08	.06	.03
1992 Score Rookie & Traded	59	.10	.08	.04
1992 Topps	45	.08	.06	.03
1992 Topps Gold	45	.50	.40	.20
1992 Topps Stadium Club	845	.15	.11	.06
1992 Topps Stadium Club Members Only	(3)	.40	.30	.15
1992 Topps Stadium Club National Convention	845	20.00	15.00	8.00
1992 Topps Traded	22	.10	.08	.04
1992 Topps Traded Gold	22	.20	.15	.08
1992 Upper Deck	267	.08	.06	.03
1992 Upper Deck	767	.08	.06	.03
1993 Score Select	55	.12	.09	.05
1993 Topps	205	.08	.06	.03
1993 Topps Gold	205	.15	.11	.06
1993 Upper Deck	219	.10	.08	.04

Joe Carter

Set	Card #	MT	NM	EX
1984 Donruss	41 (R)	65.00	49.00	26.00
1985 Donruss	616	15.00	11.00	6.00
1985 Fleer	443	15.00	11.00	6.00
1985 Topps	694	5.00	3.75	2.00
1986 Donruss	224	5.00	3.75	2.00
1986 Fleer	583	3.50	2.75	1.50
1986 O-Pee-Chee	377	1.25	.90	.50
1986 Topps	377	1.50	1.25	.60
1987 Donruss	156a	.15	.11	.06
1987 Donruss	156b	1.00	.70	.40
1987 Fleer	249	2.00	1.50	.80
1987 Fleer All Stars	8	.25	.20	.10
1987 Leaf	133	1.00	.70	.40
1987 O-Pee-Chee	220	.60	.45	.25
1987 Sportflics	176	.35	.25	.14
1987 Topps	220	.40	.30	.15
1987 Topps All-Star Glossy Set of 60	16	.40	.30	.15
1988 Donruss	254	.30	.25	.12
1988 Donruss MVP	9	.25	.20	.10
1988 Fleer	605	.50	.40	.20
1988 Leaf	184	.10	.08	.04
1988 O-Pee-Chee	75	.09	.07	.04
1988 Score	80	.30	.25	.12
1988 Sportflics	5	.15	.11	.06
1988 Topps	75	.30	.25	.12
1988 Topps	789	.10	.07	.04
1988 Topps All-Star Glossy Set of 60	44	.35	.25	.14
1988 Topps Big Baseball	71	.20	.15	.08
1989 Bowman	91	.25	.20	.10
1989 Donruss	83	.25	.20	.10
1989 Donruss MVP	3	.30	.25	.12
1989 Fleer	400	.25	.20	.10
1989 O-Pee-Chee	164	.35	.25	.14
1989 Score	213	.25	.15	.08
1989 Sportflics	104	.15	.11	.06
1989 Topps	420	.10	.08	.04
1989 Topps All-Star Glossy Set of 60	3	.30	.25	.12
1989 Topps Big Baseball	155	.08	.06	.03
1989 Upper Deck	190	1.00	.75	.40
1990 Bowman	220	.15	.11	.06
1990 Donruss	114	.10	.07	.04
1990 Fleer	489	.12	.09	.05
1990 Fleer Update	55	.35	.25	.14
1990 Leaf	379	2.50	2.00	1.00
1990 O-Pee-Chee	580	.15	.11	.06
1990 Post Cereal	30	.40	.30	.15
1990 Score	319	.25	.20	.10
1990 Score Traded	19T	.20	.15	.08
1990 Sportflics	120	.15	.11	.06
1990 Topps	580	.15	.11	.06
1990 Topps All-Star Glossy Set of 60	33	.25	.20	.10
1990 Topps Big Baseball	245	.12	.09	.05
1990 Topps Traded	20T	.25	.20	.10
1990 Upper Deck	375	.50	.40	.20
1990 Upper Deck	754	.40	.30	.15
1991 Bowman	11	.15	.11	.06
1991 Donruss	298	.20	.15	.08
1991 Donruss	409	.08	.06	.03
1991 Donruss Grand Slammers	1	.20	.15	.08
1991 Fleer	525	.15	.11	.06
1991 Fleer Ultra	360	.50	.40	.20
1991 Fleer Update	65	.20	.15	.08
1991 Leaf	353	.25	.20	.10
1991 O-Pee-Chee Premier	20	.25	.20	.10
1991 Score	9	.20	.15	.08
1991 Score Traded	11	.20	.15	.08
1991 Studio	133	.35	.25	.14
1991 Topps	120	.15	.11	.06
1991 Topps Traded	20	.20	.15	.08
1991 Upper Deck	226	.25	.20	.10
1991 Upper Deck	765	.20	.15	.08
1992 Bowman	573	1.50	1.25	.60
1992 Bowman	667	3.50	2.75	1.50
1992 Donruss	677	.08	.06	.03
1992 Donruss	693	.20	.15	.08
1992 Donruss Diamond Kings	3	2.00	1.50	.80
1992 Donruss Elite	10	60.00	45.00	24.00
1992 Donruss Triple Play	108	.12	.09	.05
1992 Fleer	327	.10	.07	.04
1992 Fleer	685	.06	.05	.02
1992 Fleer	703	.15	.11	.06
1992 Fleer All-Stars	21	2.00	1.50	.80
1992 Fleer Team Leaders	14	5.00	3.75	2.00
1992 Fleer Ultra	145	.50	.40	.20
1992 Leaf	375	.25	.20	.10
1992 O-Pee-Chee	790	.10	.08	.04
1992 O-Pee-Chee Premier	194	.20	.15	.08
1992 Pinnacle	148	.40	.30	.15
1992 Post Cereal	12	.30	.25	.12
1992 Score	90	.15	.11	.06

Card	#			
1992 Score	435	.10	.08	.04
1992 Studio	254	.25	.20	.10
1992 Topps	402	.08	.06	.03
1992 Topps	790	.10	.08	.04
1992 Topps Gold	402	.25	.20	.10
1992 Topps Gold	790	.60	.45	.25
1992 Topps Kids	89	.10	.08	.04
1992 Topps Stadium Club	10	.40	.30	.15
1992 Topps Stadium Club Special Edition	25	.40	.30	.15
1992 Upper Deck	224	.20	.15	.08
1992 Upper Deck Home Run Heroes	6	1.00	.75	.40
1993 Bowman	575	.30	.25	.12
1993 DiamondMarks	(117)	.35	.25	.14
1993 Donruss	615	.25	.20	.10
1993 Donruss Triple Play Action Baseball	30	.15	.11	.06
1993 Donruss Triple Play	123	.15	.11	.06
1993 Fleer	333	.20	.15	.08
1993 Fleer	713	.10	.08	.04
1993 Fleer All-Stars	8	2.00	1.50	.80
1993 Fleer Flair	289	1.00	.75	.40
1993 Fleer Ultra	288	.30	.25	.12
1993 Fleer Ultra Home Run Kings	7	2.50	2.00	1.00
1993 Leaf	228	.35	.25	.14
1993 Leaf Gold All-Stars	8	3.00	2.25	1.25
1993 Leaf Update Gold All-Stars	9	2.00	1.50	.80
1993 O-Pee-Chee	83	.75	.60	.30
1993 O-Pee-Chee Premier Star Performers	13	.40	.30	.15
1993 Pinnacle	427	.40	.30	.15
1993 Pinnacle Cooperstown	21	.25	.20	.10
1993 Pinnacle Cooperstown Dufex	21	50.00	37.00	20.00
1993 Pinnacle Home Run Club	7	.50	.40	.20
1993 Pinnacle Slugfest	4	2.00	1.50	.80
1993 Pinnacle Team Pinnacle	10	8.00	6.00	3.25
1993 Score	506	.10	.08	.04
1993 Score	575	.25	.20	.10
1993 Score Select	96	.25	.20	.10
1993 Score Select Chase Stars	20	8.00	6.00	3.25
1993 Score Select Stat Leaders	32	.20	.15	.08
1993 Studio	87	.30	.25	.12
1993 Studio Superstars on Canvas	5	2.00	1.50	.80
1993 Topps	350	.20	.15	.08
1993 Topps	407	.15	.11	.06
1993 Topps Black Gold	26	.50	.40	.20
1993 Topps Finest	94	5.00	3.75	2.00
1993 Topps Finest Jumbo All-Stars	94	15.00	11.00	6.00
1993 Topps Finest Refractors	94	50.00	37.00	20.00
1993 Topps Gold	350	.40	.30	.15
1993 Topps Gold	407	.30	.25	.12
1993 Topps Stadium Club	279	.40	.30	.15
1993 Topps Stadium Club	749	.20	.15	.08
1993 Topps Stadium Club First Day Production	279	25.00	18.50	10.00
1993 Topps Stadium Club First Day Production	749	15.00	11.00	6.00
1993 Topps Stadium Club Members Only	(6)	.75	.60	.30
1993 Topps Stadium Club Members Only	(7)	.75	.60	.30
1993 Topps Stadium Club Special	74	.35	.25	.14
1993 Upper Deck	42	.12	.09	.05
1993 Upper Deck	223	.20	.15	.08
1993 Upper Deck Clutch Performers	5	1.00	.75	.40
1993 Upper Deck Fun Packs	56	.15	.11	.06
1993 Upper Deck Home Run Heroes	7	1.00	.75	.40
1993 Upper Deck SP	3	1.50	1.25	.60
1993 Upper Deck SP Platinum Power	3	10.00	7.50	4.00
1994 Bowman	1	.30	.25	.12
1994 Bowman's Best	16	2.00	1.50	.80
1994 Bowman's Best Refractors	16	10.00	7.50	4.00
1994 Donruss	366	.25	.20	.10
1994 Donruss Anniversary-1984	1	3.50	2.75	1.50
1994 Donruss Decade Dominators	5	2.50	2.00	1.00
1994 Donruss Decade Dominators Supers	5	4.00	3.00	1.50
1994 Donruss Special Edition - Gold	366	.35	.25	.14
1994 Donruss Triple Play Nicknames	4	3.00	2.25	1.25
1994 Donruss Triple Play	32	.20	.15	.08
1994 Fleer	326	.25	.20	.10
1994 Fleer All-Stars	5	.60	.45	.25
1994 Fleer Extra Bases	188	.40	.30	.15
1994 Fleer Extra Bases Game Breakers	6	.50	.40	.20
1994 Fleer Flair	116	.75	.60	.30
1994 Fleer Flair Outfield Power	3	2.50	2.00	1.00
1994 Fleer Ultra	136	.35	.25	.14
1994 Fleer Ultra Career Achievement Awards	1	2.00	1.50	.80
1994 Fleer Ultra Home Run Kings	6	4.00	3.00	1.50
1994 Fleer Ultra RBI Kings	3	10.00	7.50	4.00
1994 Fleer Update Diamond Tribute	2	.50	.40	.20
1994 Leaf	193	.40	.30	.15
1994 Leaf Clean-Up Crew	8	5.00	3.75	2.00
1994 Leaf Limited	76	3.00	2.25	1.25
1994 Leaf Limited Gold	13	16.00	12.00	6.50
1994 Leaf MVP Contenders	3a	4.00	3.00	1.50
1994 Leaf MVP Contenders	3b	8.00	6.00	3.25
1994 Leaf Power Brokers	9	1.50	1.25	.60
1994 Leaf Statistical Standouts	7	1.50	1.25	.60
1994 O-Pee-Chee	145	.35	.25	.14
1994 O-Pee-Chee All-Star Redemption Cards	23	.85	.60	.35
1994 O-Pee-Chee Toronto Blue Jays	4	6.00	4.50	2.50
1994 Pacific Crown	636	.25	.20	.10
1994 Pacific Crown Homerun Leaders	6	3.50	2.75	1.50
1994 Pacific Crown Promos	2	3.00	2.25	1.25
1994 Pinnacle	345	.35	.25	.14
1994 Pinnacle Artist's Proof	345	20.00	15.00	8.00
1994 Pinnacle Museum Collection	345	10.00	7.50	4.00
1994 Score	73	.25	.20	.10
1994 Score	625	.10	.08	.04
1994 Score Gold Stars	31	8.00	6.00	3.25
1994 Score Select	12	.50	.40	.20
1994 Sportflics 2000	12	.40	.30	.15
1994 Sportflics 2000	183	.35	.25	.14
1994 Sportflics 2000 Movers	10	7.00	5.25	2.75
1994 Studio	26	.40	.30	.15
1994 Studio Gold Stars	5	25.00	18.00	10.00
1994 Studio Heritage	3	1.50	1.25	.60
1994 Studio Silver Stars	5	12.00	9.00	4.75
1994 Topps	645	.25	.20	.10
1994 Topps Black Gold	4	.75	.60	.30
1994 Topps Finest	207	2.00	1.50	.80

1994 Topps Finest Refractors	207	15.00	11.00	6.00
1994 Topps Finest Superstars	207	9.00	6.50	3.50
1994 Topps Gold	645	.75	.60	.30
1994 Topps Stadium Club	300	.40	.30	.15
1994 Topps Stadium Club	527	.20	.15	.08
1994 Topps Stadium Club First Day Production	300	20.00	15.00	8.00
1994 Topps Stadium Club First Day Production	527	10.00	7.50	4.00
1994 Topps Stadium Club Members Only Baseball	11	.40	.30	.15
1994 Upper Deck	91	.30	.25	.12
1994 Upper Deck Collector's Choice	455	.20	.15	.08
1994 Upper Deck Electric Diamond	91	2.00	1.50	.80
1994 Upper Deck Fun Packs	29	.25	.20	.10
1994 Upper Deck Fun Packs	227	.20	.15	.08
1994 Upper Deck Mickey Mantle's Long Shots	5MM	2.50	2.00	1.00
1994 Upper Deck SP	40	.50	.40	.20

Rico Carty

Set	Card #	NM	EX	VG
1964 Topps	476 (R)	9.50	4.75	2.75
1965 O-Pee-Chee	2	17.00	8.50	5.00
1965 Topps	2	15.00	7.50	4.50
1965 Topps	305	3.50	1.75	1.00
1966 O-Pee-Chee	153	2.50	1.25	.70
1966 Topps	153	2.50	1.25	.70
1967 O-Pee-Chee	35	2.25	1.25	.70
1967 Topps	35	1.50	.70	.45
1967 Topps	240	3.00	1.50	.90
1968 Topps	455	1.50	.70	.45
1969 Topps	590	2.50	1.25	.70
1970 O-Pee-Chee	145	1.00	.50	.30
1970 Topps	145	.90	.45	.25
1971 O-Pee-Chee	62	1.50	.70	.45
1971 O-Pee-Chee	270	1.50	.70	.45
1971 Topps	62	1.50	.70	.45
1971 Topps	270	1.00	.50	.30
1972 Topps	740	6.00	3.00	1.75
1973 O-Pee-Chee	435	1.25	.60	.40
1973 Topps	435	.70	.35	.20
1975 O-Pee-Chee	655	.55	.30	.15
1975 Topps	655	.30	.15	.09
1976 O-Pee-Chee	156	.35	.20	.11
1976 Topps	156	.25	.13	.08
1977 O-Pee-Chee	114	.30	.15	.09
1977 Topps	465	.20	.10	.06
1978 Topps	305	.20	.10	.06
1979 O-Pee-Chee	291	.25	.13	.08

1979 Topps	565	.25	.13	.08
1980 O-Pee-Chee	25	.15	.08	.05
1980 Topps	46	.12	.06	.04

Orlando Cepeda

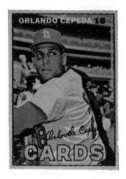

Set	Card #	NM	EX	VG
1958 Topps	343 (R)	100.00	50.00	30.00
1959 Topps	390	22.00	11.00	6.50
1959 Topps	553	25.00	12.50	7.50
1960 Leaf	128	60.00	30.00	18.00
1960 Topps	450	18.00	9.00	5.50
1961 Post Cereal	144a	7.50	3.75	2.25
1961 Post Cereal	144b	7.50	3.75	2.25
1961 Topps	435	12.00	6.00	3.50
1962 Post Cereal	136	4.50	2.25	1.25
1962 Topps	40	9.00	4.50	2.75
1962 Topps	54	12.00	6.00	3.50
1962 Topps	390	7.50	3.75	2.25
1962 Topps	401	40.00	20.00	12.00
1963 Fleer	64	25.00	12.50	7.50
1963 Post Cereal	101	4.00	2.00	1.25
1963 Topps	3	26.00	13.00	7.75
1963 Topps	520	24.00	12.00	7.25
1964 Topps	9	25.00	12.50	7.50
1964 Topps	306	22.00	11.00	6.50
1964 Topps	390	9.00	4.50	2.75
1965 O-Pee-Chee	66	3.50	1.75	1.00
1965 Topps	4	15.00	7.50	4.50
1965 Topps	360	7.50	3.75	2.25
1966 O-Pee-Chee	132	6.25	3.25	2.00
1966 Topps	132	8.00	4.00	2.50
1967 O-Pee-Chee	20	8.50	4.25	2.50
1967 Topps	20	10.00	5.00	3.00
1968 O-Pee-Chee	3	13.50	6.75	4.00
1968 Topps	3	9.00	4.50	2.75
1968 Topps	200	4.00	2.00	1.25
1968 Topps	278a	3.00	1.50	.90
1968 Topps	278b	5.00	2.50	1.50
1968 Topps	362	2.75	1.50	.80
1969 Topps	385	4.00	2.00	1.25
1970 Topps	555	4.50	2.25	1.25
1971 O-Pee-Chee	605	5.00	2.50	1.50
1971 Topps	605	7.50	3.75	2.25
1972 O-Pee-Chee	195	1.25	.60	.40
1972 Topps	195	2.00	1.00	.60
1973 O-Pee-Chee	545	3.50	1.75	1.00
1973 Topps	545	4.00	2.00	1.25
1974 O-Pee-Chee	83	1.00	.50	.30
1974 Topps	83	2.00	1.00	.60
1975 O-Pee-Chee	205	3.00	1.50	.90
1975 Topps	205	1.25	.60	.40

Set	Card #	MT	NM	EX
1986 Sportflics Decade Greats	48	.30	.25	.12
1988 Pacific Trading Cards Baseball Legends	94	.10	.08	.04
1990 Pacific Legends	65	.10	.08	.04

Ron Cey

Chris Chambliss

Set	Card #	NM	EX	VG
1972 Topps	761 (R)	20.00	10.00	6.00
1973 O-Pee-Chee	615	535.00	267.00	160.00
1973 Topps	615	450.00	225.00	135.00
1974 O-Pee-Chee	315	.60	.30	.20
1974 Topps	315	.60	.30	.20
1975 O-Pee-Chee	390	.55	.30	.15
1975 Topps	390	.30	.15	.09
1975 Topps Mini	390	.60	.30	.20
1976 O-Pee-Chee	370	.35	.20	.11
1976 Topps	370	.25	.13	.08
1977 O-Pee-Chee	199	.30	.15	.09
1977 Topps	50	.35	.20	.11
1978 O-Pee-Chee	130	.25	.13	.08
1978 Topps	630	.25	.13	.08
1979 O-Pee-Chee	94	.25	.13	.08
1979 Topps	190	.25	.13	.08
1980 O-Pee-Chee	267	.20	.10	.06
1980 Topps	510	.25	.13	.08

Set	Card #	MT	NM	EX
1981 Donruss	296	.12	.09	.05
1981 Fleer	126a	.12	.09	.05
1981 Fleer	126b	1.00	.70	.40
1981 O-Pee-Chee	260	.15	.11	.06
1981 Topps	260	.15	.11	.06
1982 Donruss	210	.12	.09	.05
1982 Fleer	3	.12	.09	.05
1982 O-Pee-Chee	216	.12	.09	.05
1982 O-Pee-Chee	367	.12	.09	.05
1982 Topps	410	.15	.11	.06
1982 Topps	411	.10	.08	.04
1983 Donruss	84	.12	.09	.05
1983 Fleer	204	.12	.09	.05
1983 O-Pee-Chee	15	.12	.09	.05
1983 Topps	15	.15	.11	.06
1983 Topps Traded	19T	.25	.20	.10
1984 Donruss	361	.20	.15	.08
1984 Fleer	490	.12	.09	.05
1984 O-Pee-Chee	357	.25	.20	.10
1984 Topps	357	.12	.09	.05
1985 Donruss	320	.12	.09	.05
1985 Fleer	52	.10	.08	.04
1985 Leaf-Donruss	84	.08	.06	.03
1985 O-Pee-Chee	366	.10	.08	.04
1985 Topps	768	.10	.08	.04
1986 Donruss	198	.10	.08	.04
1986 Fleer	363	.10	.08	.04
1986 O-Pee-Chee	194	.08	.06	.03
1986 Sportflics	130	.50	.40	.20
1986 Topps	669	.10	.08	.04
1987 Fleer	556	.10	.08	.04
1987 O-Pee-Chee	322	.08	.06	.03
1987 Topps	581	.07	.05	.03
1987 Topps	767	.07	.05	.03
1987 Topps Traded	22T	.10	.08	.04

* * *

NBC's Bob Costas idolizes Mickey Mantle so much that he has carried his 1958 Mantle card in his wallet.

* * *

Set	Card #	NM	EX	VG
1972 O-Pee-Chee	142	1.00	.50	.30
1972 Topps	142 (R)	3.00	1.50	.90
1973 O-Pee-Chee	11	.75	.40	.25
1973 Topps	11	.40	.20	.12
1974 O-Pee-Chee	384	.60	.30	.20
1974 Topps	384	.30	.15	.09
1975 O-Pee-Chee	585	.55	.30	.15
1975 Topps	585	.30	.15	.09
1975 Topps Mini	585	.60	.30	.20
1976 O-Pee-Chee	65	.35	.20	.11
1976 Topps	65	.25	.13	.08
1977 O-Pee-Chee	49	.30	.15	.09
1977 Topps	220	.20	.10	.06
1978 O-Pee-Chee	145	.25	.13	.08
1978 Topps	485	.20	.10	.06
1979 O-Pee-Chee	171	.25	.13	.08
1979 Topps	335	.25	.13	.08
1980 O-Pee-Chee	328	.15	.08	.05
1980 Topps	625	.12	.06	.04

Set	Card #	MT	NM	EX
1981 Donruss	219	.08	.06	.03
1981 Fleer	252	.08	.06	.03
1981 O-Pee-Chee	155	.12	.09	.05
1981 Topps	155	.12	.09	.05
1982 Donruss	47	.08	.06	.03
1982 Fleer	433	.08	.06	.03
1982 O-Pee-Chee	320	.12	.09	.05
1982 O-Pee-Chee	321	.12	.09	.05
1982 Topps	320	.10	.08	.04
1982 Topps	321	.10	.08	.04
1983 Donruss	123	.08	.06	.03
1983 Fleer	134	.08	.06	.03
1983 O-Pee-Chee	11	.12	.09	.05
1983 Topps	792	.10	.08	.04
1984 Donruss	537	.12	.09	.05
1984 Fleer	175	.08	.06	.03
1984 O-Pee-Chee	50	.20	.15	.08
1984 Topps	50	.10	.08	.04
1985 Donruss	287	.10	.08	.04
1985 Fleer	322	.08	.06	.03
1985 Leaf-Donruss	168	.08	.06	.03
1985 O-Pee-Chee	187	.08	.06	.03
1985 Topps	518	.08	.06	.03
1986 Donruss	618	.08	.06	.03
1986 Fleer	512	.08	.06	.03
1986 Topps	293	.07	.05	.03
1987 Fleer	513	.08	.06	.03
1987 O-Pee-Chee	204	.08	.06	.03
1987 Topps	777	.07	.05	.03

* * *

Bubble gum will begin to dissolve in a couple of years if you leave it in an unopened pack of cards. Eventually, it will weld itself onto the card on which it is resting.

* * *

Will Clark

Will Clark

Set	Card #	MT	NM	EX
1986 Fleer Update	25	8.00	6.00	3.25
1986 Sportflics Rookies	6	3.00	2.25	1.25
1986 Topps Traded	24T	4.50	3.50	1.75
1987 Donruss	66 (R)	6.00	4.50	2.50
1987 Fleer	269 (R)	20.00	15.00	8.00
1987 Leaf	144	6.25	4.75	2.50
1987 O-Pee-Chee	361	1.75	1.25	.70
1987 Sportflics	95	2.00	1.50	.80
1987 Sportflics	195	.50	.40	.20
1987 Topps	420 (R)	1.75	1.25	.70
1987 Topps Glossy Rookies	4	3.00	2.25	1.25
1988 Donruss	21	.25	.20	.10
1988 Donruss	204	.30	.25	.12
1988 Donruss MVP	24	.50	.40	.20
1988 Fleer	78	1.00	.70	.40
1988 Fleer MVP	5	.80	.60	.30
1988 Leaf	21	.40	.30	.15
1988 Leaf	170	.40	.30	.15
1988 O-Pee-Chee	350	.40	.30	.15
1988 Score	78	.40	.25	.15
1988 Sportflics	9	1.00	.70	.40
1988 Sportflics Gamewinners	4	1.00	.70	.40
1988 Topps	261	.10	.08	.04
1988 Topps	350	.40	.30	.15
1988 Topps Big Baseball	9	.80	.60	.30
1989 Bowman	476	.25	.20	.10
1989 Donruss	249	.35	.25	.14
1989 Donruss MVP	22	.30	.25	.12
1989 Fleer	325	.40	.30	.15
1989 Fleer	631	.40	.30	.15
1989 Fleer	632	.25	.20	.10
1989 Fleer All-Stars	3	1.00	.75	.40
1989 Fleer MVP	7	.70	.50	.30
1989 O-Pee-Chee	321	.25	.20	.10
1989 Score	450	.40	.30	.15
1989 Sportflics	170	.80	.60	.30
1989 Topps	660	.50	.40	.20
1989 Topps All-Star Glossy Set of 60	11	1.00	.70	.40
1989 Topps All-Star Glossy Set of 22	13	.20	.15	.08
1989 Topps Big Baseball	146	.90	.70	.35
1989 Upper Deck	155	1.25	.90	.50
1989 Upper Deck	678	.30	.25	.12
1990 Bowman	231	.35	.25	.14
1990 Bowman Inserts	(1)	.10	.08	.04
1990 Donruss	230	.25	.20	.10
1990 Donruss	707	.15	.11	.06
1990 Fleer	54	.25	.20	.10
1990 Fleer	630a	1.50	1.25	.60
1990 Fleer	630b	.20	.15	.08
1990 Fleer	637	.10	.08	.04
1990 Fleer All-Stars	2	.80	.60	.30
1990 Fleer MVP	7	.40	.30	.15
1990 Leaf	172	3.00	2.25	1.25
1990 O-Pee-Chee	100	.50	.40	.20
1990 O-Pee-Chee	397	.25	.20	.10
1990 Post Cereal	7	.80	.60	.30
1990 Score	300	.25	.20	.10
1990 Score	684	.20	.15	.08
1990 Score	699	.15	.11	.06
1990 Sportflics	5	.20	.15	.08
1990 Topps	100	.30	.25	.12
1990 Topps	397	.15	.11	.06
1990 Topps All-Star Glossy Set of 22	2	.35	.25	.14
1990 Topps All-Star Glossy Set of 60	52	.50	.40	.20
1990 Topps Big Baseball	224	.40	.30	.15
1990 Upper Deck	50	.30	.25	.12
1990 Upper Deck	556	.40	.30	.15
1991 Bowman	616	.20	.15	.08
1991 Donruss	86	.25	.20	.10
1991 Donruss	441	.10	.08	.04
1991 Fleer	259	.25	.20	.10
1991 Fleer ProVisions	2	.60	.45	.25
1991 Fleer Ultra	318	.40	.30	.15
1991 Fleer Ultra Gold	2	1.25	.90	.50
1991 Leaf	238	.50	.40	.20
1991 O-Pee-Chee Premier	22	.35	.25	.14
1991 Post Cereal	3	.80	.60	.30
1991 Score	7	.20	.15	.08
1991 Score	664	.15	.11	.06
1991 Score	871	.12	.10	.08
1991 Score	886	.30	.25	.12
1991 Studio	254	.40	.30	.15
1991 Topps	500	.20	.15	.08
1991 Topps All-Star Glossy Set of 22	13	.30	.25	.12
1991 Upper Deck	445	.30	.25	.12
1991 Upper Deck Final Edition	92	.20	.15	.08
1992 Bowman	260	1.50	1.25	.60
1992 Bowman	673	2.00	1.50	.80
1992 Donruss	214	.20	.15	.08
1992 Donruss	428	.15	.11	.06
1992 Donruss Diamond Kings	2	2.00	1.50	.80
1992 Donruss Elite	11	60.00	45.00	24.00
1992 Donruss Triple Play	155	.20	.15	.08
1992 Fleer	631	.25	.20	.10
1992 Fleer	699	.10	.08	.04
1992 Fleer All-Stars	13	2.00	1.50	.80
1992 Fleer Team Leaders	8	5.00	3.75	2.00
1992 Fleer Ultra	287	.75	.60	.30
1992 Fleer Ultra All-Stars	11	2.00	1.50	.80
1992 Fleer Ultra Award Winners	14	2.50	2.00	1.00
1992 Leaf	241	.30	.20	.10
1992 O-Pee-Chee	330	.20	.15	.08
1992 O-Pee-Chee Premier	146	.50	.40	.20
1992 Pinnacle	122	.50	.40	.20
1992 Pinnacle Slugfest	12	3.00	2.25	1.25
1992 Pinnacle Team Pinnacle	4	50.00	37.00	20.00
1992 Post Cereal	14	.35	.25	.14
1992 Score	3	.25	.20	.10
1992 Score	773	.10	.08	.04
1992 Score	883	.20	.15	.08
1992 Score Impact Players	51	.60	.45	.25
1992 Studio	114	.30	.25	.12
1992 Studio Heritage	8	2.00	1.50	.80
1992 Topps	330	.20	.15	.08
1992 Topps	386	.10	.08	.04
1992 Topps Gold	330	2.00	1.50	.80
1992 Topps Gold	386	.50	.40	.20
1992 Topps Kids	58	.20	.15	.08
1992 Topps Stadium Club	460	.50	.40	.20
1992 Topps Stadium Club	598	.35	.25	.14
1992 Topps Stadium Club Master Photos	(4)	4.00	3.00	1.50
1992 Topps Stadium Club Special Edition	28	.40	.30	.15
1992 Upper Deck	175	.25	.20	.10
1992 Upper Deck	718	.15	.11	.06
1992 Upper Deck MVP Holograms	15	.50	.40	.20

1993 Bowman	252	.40	.30	.15
1993 DiamondMarks	(63)	1.50	1.25	.60
1993 DiamondMarks Promos	(2)	20.00	15.00	8.00
1993 Donruss	446	.25	.20	.10
1993 Donruss Elite	----	250.00	180.00	100.00
1993 Donruss Masters of the Game	9	4.00	3.00	1.50
1993 Donruss MVP's	13	1.50	1.25	.60
1993 Donruss Spirit of the Game	8	2.00	1.50	.80
1993 Donruss Triple Play Nicknames	4	2.50	2.00	1.00
1993 Donruss Triple Play Action Baseball	11	.20	.15	.08
1993 Donruss Triple Play	107	.20	.15	.08
1993 Fleer	154	.20	.15	.08
1993 Fleer Flair	140	1.00	.75	.40
1993 Fleer NL Team Leaders	1	5.00	3.75	2.00
1993 Fleer Ultra	130	.40	.30	.20
1993 Fleer Ultra All-Stars	2	3.00	2.25	1.20
1993 Leaf	247	.40	.30	.15
1993 Leaf Gold All-Stars	11	1.50	1.25	.60
1993 O-Pee-Chee	113	.75	.60	.30
1993 O-Pee-Chee Premier Star Performers	12	.35	.25	.14
1993 Pinnacle	16	.30	.25	.12
1993 Pinnacle Cooperstown	16	.35	.25	.14
1993 Pinnacle Cooperstown Dufex	16	125.00	94.00	50.00
1993 Pinnacle Home Run Club	38	.75	.60	.30
1993 Pinnacle Slugfest	20	2.00	1.50	.80
1993 Post Cereal	2	.75	.60	.30
1993 Score	22	.20	.15	.08
1993 Score Select	3	.25	.20	.10
1993 Score The Franchise	26	5.00	3.75	2.00
1993 Studio	48	.40	.30	.15
1993 Topps	10	.15	.11	.06
1993 Topps Black Gold	2	.60	.45	.25
1993 Topps Finest	108	6.00	4.50	2.50
1993 Topps Finest Jumbo All-Stars	108	20.00	15.00	8.00
1993 Topps Finest Refractors	108	60.00	45.00	24.00
1993 Topps Gold	10	.30	.25	.12
1993 Topps Stadium Club	562	.30	.25	.12
1993 Topps Stadium Club First Day Production	562	35.00	26.00	14.00
1993 Topps Stadium Club II Inserts	1	4.50	3.50	1.75
1993 Topps Stadium Club Master Photos	(15)	3.00	2.25	1.25
1993 Topps Stadium Club Special	139	.40	.30	.15
1993 Topps Stadium Club Team Sets	9	.75	.60	.30
1993 Upper Deck	315	.05	.04	.02
1993 Upper Deck	471	.20	.15	.08
1993 Upper Deck	476	.20	.15	.08
1993 Upper Deck	576	.25	.20	.10
1993 Upper Deck Clutch Performers	6	1.50	1.25	.60
1993 Upper Deck Fun Packs All-Star Scratch-Off	3	2.50	2.00	1.00
1993 Upper Deck Fun Packs	13	.50	.40	.20
1993 Upper Deck Fun Packs	101	.35	.25	.14
1993 Upper Deck Iooss Collection	11	1.00	.75	.40
1993 Upper Deck Iooss Collection Super	11	4.00	3.00	1.50
1993 Upper Deck On Deck	8	1.00	.70	.40
1993 Upper Deck SP	111	1.50	1.25	.60
1993 Upper Deck SP Platinum Power	4	10.00	7.50	4.00
1993 Upper Deck Triple Crown	3	2.00	1.50	.80
1994 Bowman	485	.40	.30	.15
1994 Bowman's Best	79	2.00	1.50	.80
1994 Bowman's Best Refractors	79	14.00	10.50	5.50
1994 Donruss	38	.40	.30	.15
1994 Donruss Special Edition - Gold	38	.40	.30	.15
1994 Donruss Triple Play	193	.20	.15	.08
1994 Fleer	689	.25	.20	.10
1994 Fleer Extra Bases	177	.40	.30	.15
1994 Fleer Flair	108	.75	.60	.30
1994 Fleer Flair Hot Glove	2	12.00	9.00	4.75
1994 Fleer Flair Hot Numbers	3	10.00	7.50	4.00
1994 Fleer Flair Infield Power	2	2.50	2.00	1.00
1994 Fleer Team Leaders	28	1.00	.75	.40
1994 Fleer Ultra	427	.40	.30	.15
1994 Fleer Update	90	.50	.40	.20
1994 Fleer Update Diamond Tribute	3	.75	.60	.30
1994 Leaf	404	.40	.30	.15
1994 Leaf Gamers	10	4.00	3.00	1.50
1994 Leaf Limited	71	3.00	2.25	1.25
1994 Leaf MVP Contenders	4a	4.00	3.00	1.50
1994 Leaf MVP Contenders	4b	8.00	6.00	3.25
1994 O-Pee-Chee	187	.50	.40	.20
1994 Pacific Crown	544	.25	.20	.10
1994 Pinnacle	513	.40	.30	.15
1994 Pinnacle Artist's Proof	513	10.00	7.50	4.00
1994 Pinnacle Museum Collection	513	6.00	4.50	2.50
1994 Post Cereal	22	.60	.45	.25
1994 Score	10	.25	.20	.10
1994 Score Rookie and Traded	1	.40	.30	.15
1994 Score Rookie/ Traded Samples	2RT	4.00	3.00	1.50
1994 Score Select	319	.50	.40	.20
1994 Sportflics 2000	146	.50	.40	.20
1994 Studio	153	.40	.30	.15
1994 Topps	240	.15	.11	.06
1994 Topps Finest	238	2.00	1.50	.80
1994 Topps Finest Refractors	238	12.00	9.00	4.75
1994 Topps Finest Superstars	238	6.00	4.50	2.50
1994 Topps Gold	240	.45	.35	.20
1994 Topps Stadium Club	203	.40	.30	.15
1994 Topps Stadium Club	666	.35	.25	.14
1994 Topps Stadium Club First Day Production	203	20.00	15.00	8.00
1994 Topps Stadium Club First Day Production	666	25.00	18.50	10.00
1994 Topps Traded	115	.25	.20	.10
1994 Upper Deck	350	.40	.30	.15
1994 Upper Deck Collector's Choice	540	.20	.15	.08
1994 Upper Deck Electric Diamond	350	1.00	.75	.40
1994 Upper Deck Fun Packs	22	.25	.20	.10

* * *

The top five most valuable baseball cards, according to a 1980 issue of Money Magazine: 1. American Tobacco Honus Wagner, issued 1909, $12,500; 2. Goudey Napoleon Lajoie, issued 1934, $6,500; 3. American Tobacco Eddie Plank, issued 1919, $5,000; 4. Topps Jim Konstanty standup, issued 1951, $2,500; 5. Topps Mickey Mantle, issued 1952, $1,700.

* * *

Roger Clemens

Set	Card #	MT	NM	EX
1984 Fleer Update	27	350.00	260.00	140.00
1985 Donruss	273 (R)	35.00	26.00	14.00
1985 Fleer	155 (R)	35.00	26.00	14.00
1985 Leaf-Donruss	99	32.50	24.00	13.00
1985 Topps	181 (R)	15.00	11.00	6.00
1986 Donruss	172	7.00	5.25	2.75
1986 Fleer	345	7.50	5.50	3.00
1986 O-Pee-Chee	98	3.25	2.50	1.25
1986 Topps	661	3.50	2.75	1.50
1987 Donruss	2	.50	.40	.20
1987 Donruss	276	2.00	1.50	.80
1987 Donruss Diamond Kings Supers	2	.90	.70	.35
1987 Fleer	32	3.00	2.25	1.25
1987 Fleer	634	.40	.30	.15
1987 Fleer	640	.50	.40	.20
1987 Fleer All Stars	10	.50	.40	.20
1987 Fleer All Stars	11	5.00	3.00	1.50
1987 Leaf	2	.50	.40	.20
1987 Leaf	190	1.75	1.25	.70
1987 O-Pee-Chee	340	.85	.60	.35
1987 Sportflics	10	1.00	.70	.40
1987 Sportflics	111	.25	.20	.10
1987 Sportflics	159	1.25	.90	.50
1987 Sportflics	196	.35	.25	.14
1987 Topps	1	.30	.25	.12
1987 Topps	340	.75	.60	.30
1987 Topps	614	.20	.15	.08
1987 Topps All-Star Glossy Set of 60	5	.45	.35	.20
1987 Topps All-Star Glossy Set of 22	21	.30	.25	.12
1988 Donruss	51	.50	.40	.20
1988 Fleer	349	.75	.60	.30
1988 Fleer All Stars	4	3.00	2.25	1.25
1988 Fleer MVP	6	.40	.30	.15
1988 Leaf	56	.30	.25	.12
1988 O-Pee-Chee	70	.30	.25	.12
1988 Score	110	.35	.20	.10
1988 Sportflics	207	.90	.70	.35
1988 Sportflics Gamewinners	20	.80	.60	.30
1988 Topps	70	.50	.40	.20
1988 Topps	394	.15	.11	.06
1988 Topps All-Star Glossy Set of 60	13	.60	.45	.25
1988 Topps Big Baseball	118	.50	.40	.20
1989 Bowman	26	.35	.25	.14
1989 Donruss	280	.30	.25	.12
1989 Fleer	85	.40	.30	.15
1989 Fleer For The Record	2	1.50	1.25	.60
1989 O-Pee-Chee	121	.15	.11	.06
1989 Score	350a	3.00	2.25	1.25
1989 Score	350b	.40	.30	.15
1989 Scoremasters	20	.60	.45	.25
1989 Sportflics	3	.60	.45	.25
1989 Topps	405	.15	.11	.06
1989 Topps	450	.40	.30	.15
1989 Topps All-Star Glossy Set of 60	23	.40	.30	.15
1989 Topps Big Baseball	42	.25	.20	.10
1989 Upper Deck	195	1.00	.75	.40
1990 Bowman	268	.25	.20	.10
1990 Donruss	184	.25	.20	.10
1990 Fleer	271	.25	.20	.10
1990 Fleer	627	.25	.20	.10
1990 Fleer MVP	8	.30	.25	.12
1990 Leaf	12	4.00	3.00	1.50
1990 O-Pee-Chee	245	.25	.20	.10
1990 Post Cereal	2	.50	.40	.20
1990 Score	310	.25	.20	.10
1990 Sportflics	149	.25	.20	.10
1990 Topps	245	.25	.20	.10
1990 Topps Big Baseball	22	.30	.25	.12
1990 Upper Deck	323	.50	.40	.20
1991 Bowman	118	.25	.20	.10
1991 Donruss	9	.10	.08	.04
1991 Donruss	81	.20	.15	.08
1991 Donruss	395	.15	.11	.06
1991 Fleer	90	.25	.20	.10
1991 Fleer All Stars	10	1.50	1.00	.50
1991 Fleer ProVisions	9	.40	.30	.15
1991 Fleer Ultra	31	.50	.40	.20
1991 Leaf	488	.50	.40	.20
1991 O-Pee-Chee Premier	23	.35	.25	.14
1991 Post Cereal	12	.60	.45	.25
1991 Score	399	.15	.11	.06
1991 Score	655	.20	.15	.08
1991 Score	684	.15	.11	.06
1991 Score	850	.12	.09	.05
1991 Studio	14	.75	.60	.30
1991 Topps	530	.20	.15	.08
1991 Topps Stadium Club	309	2.00	1.50	.80
1991 Topps Stadium Club Members Only	(6)	.90	.70	.35
1991 Upper Deck	655	.25	.20	.10
1992 Bowman	691	2.00	1.50	.80
1992 Donruss	244	.20	.15	.08
1992 Donruss Triple Play	216	.20	.15	.08
1992 Fleer	37	.20	.15	.08
1992 Fleer Smoke 'N Heat	4	2.50	2.00	1.00
1992 Fleer Ultra	15	.75	.60	.30
1992 Fleer Ultra Award Winners	6	3.50	2.75	1.50
1992 Leaf	19	.35	.25	.14
1992 O-Pee-Chee	150	.15	.11	.06
1992 Pinnacle	95	.50	.40	.20
1992 Pinnacle Rookie Idols	4	8.00	6.00	3.25
1992 Pinnacle Team Pinnacle	1	15.00	11.00	6.00
1992 Post Cereal	16	.30	.25	.12
1992 Score	21	.15	.11	.06
1992 Score	790	.10	.08	.04
1992 Score Impact Players	57	.30	.25	.12
1992 Studio	132	.40	.30	.15
1992 Topps	150	.20	.15	.08
1992 Topps	405	.12	.09	.05
1992 Topps Gold	150	1.50	1.25	.60
1992 Topps Gold	405	.45	.35	.20
1992 Topps Kids	67	.15	.11	.06
1992 Topps Stadium Club	80	.75	.60	.30
1992 Topps Stadium Club	593	.40	.30	.15
1992 Topps Stadium Club Members Only	(4)	.25	.20	.10
1992 Topps Stadium Club Special Edition	29	.30	.25	.12
1992 Upper Deck	545	.20	.15	.08
1992 Upper Deck	641	.10	.08	.04
1992 Upper Deck MVP Holograms	16	.40	.30	.15
1993 Bowman	635	.60	.45	.25
1993 DiamondMarks	(68)	.50	.40	.20
1993 Donruss	119	.35	.25	.14
1993 Donruss Diamond Kings	3	3.00	2.25	1.25
1993 Donruss MVP's	15	2.50	2.00	1.00

Set	#			
1993 Donruss Triple Play Nicknames	2	3.00	2.25	1.25
1993 Donruss Triple Play Action Baseball	14	.20	.15	.08
1993 Donruss Triple Play	118	.15	.11	.06
1993 Fleer	177	.35	.25	.14
1993 Fleer	348	.12	.09	.05
1993 Fleer	717	.10	.08	.04
1993 Fleer AL Team Leaders	4	8.00	6.00	3.25
1993 Fleer Flair	160	1.50	1.25	.60
1993 Fleer Ultra	508	.75	.60	.30
1993 Fleer Ultra Strikeout Kings	1	4.00	3.00	1.50
1993 Leaf	279	.60	.45	.25
1993 Leaf Gold All-Stars	20	2.00	1.50	.80
1993 Leaf Heading for the Hall	6	5.00	3.75	2.00
1993 O-Pee-Chee	259	1.50	1.25	.60
1993 O-Pee-Chee Premier Star Performers	18	.50	.40	.20
1993 Pinnacle	25	.75	.60	.30
1993 Pinnacle Cooperstown	18	.30	.25	.12
1993 Pinnacle Cooperstown Dufex	18	60.00	45.00	24.00
1993 Post Cereal	4	.35	.25	.14
1993 Score	7	.25	.20	.10
1993 Score Select	14	.40	.30	.15
1993 Score Select Aces	1	13.00	9.75	5.25
1993 Score Select Chase Stars	21	12.00	9.00	4.75
1993 Score Select Stat Leaders	75	.30	.25	.12
1993 Score Select Stat Leaders	79	.30	.25	.12
1993 Score Select Stat Leaders	87	.30	.25	.12
1993 Score The Franchise	2	7.50	5.50	3.00
1993 Studio	22	.40	.30	.15
1993 Studio Heritage	3	3.00	2.25	1.25
1993 Topps	4	.20	.15	.08
1993 Topps	409	.10	.08	.04
1993 Topps Black Gold	27	.60	.45	.25
1993 Topps Finest	104	7.00	5.50	3.00
1993 Topps Finest Jumbo All-Stars	104	20.00	15.00	8.00
1993 Topps Finest Refractors	104	70.00	52.00	28.00
1993 Topps Full Shot Super	15	4.00	3.00	1.50
1993 Topps Gold	4	.30	.25	.12
1993 Topps Gold	409	.20	.15	.08
1993 Topps Stadium Club	220	.50	.40	.20
1993 Topps Stadium Club	748	.25	.20	.10
1993 Topps Stadium Club First Day Production	220	45.00	34.00	18.00
1993 Topps Stadium Club First Day Production	748	25.00	18.50	10.00
1993 Topps Stadium Club Special	97	.60	.45	.25
1993 Upper Deck	48	.12	.09	.05
1993 Upper Deck	135	.25	.20	.10
1993 Upper Deck	630	.06	.05	.02
1993 Upper Deck Clutch Performers	7	1.50	1.25	.60
1993 Upper Deck Diamond Gallery	21	1.50	1.25	.60
1993 Upper Deck Fun Packs	14	.35	.25	.14
1993 Upper Deck Fun Packs	23	.05	.04	.02
1993 Upper Deck Fun Packs	29	.05	.04	.02
1993 Upper Deck Fun Packs	161	.20	.15	.08
1993 Upper Deck Fun Packs	162	.20	.15	.08
1993 Upper Deck Future Heroes	57	1.50	1.25	.60
1993 Upper Deck On Deck	9	1.50	1.25	.60
1993 Upper Deck SP	199	2.00	1.50	.80
1993 Upper Deck SP Jumbos	199	25.00	18.50	10.00
1994 Bowman	475	.50	.40	.20
1994 Bowman's Best	100	2.00	1.50	.80
1994 Bowman's Best	37	2.50	2.00	1.00
1994 Bowman's Best Refractors	100	6.00	4.50	2.50
1994 Bowman's Best Refractors	37	10.00	7.50	4.00
1994 Donruss	356	.40	.30	.15
1994 Donruss Special Edition - Gold	356	.35	.25	.14
1994 Donruss Triple Play	201	.20	.15	.08
1994 Fleer	26	.30	.25	.12
1994 Fleer Extra Bases	16	.25	.20	.10
1994 Fleer Extra Bases Game Breakers	7	.75	.60	.30
1994 Fleer Extra Bases Pitcher's Duel	1M	1.00	.75	.40
1994 Fleer Flair	261	1.00	.75	.40
1994 Fleer Smoke N' Heat	1	15.00	11.00	6.00
1994 Fleer Ultra	11	.40	.30	.15
1994 Fleer Update Diamond Tribute	4	.75	.60	.30
1994 Leaf	255	.60	.45	.25
1994 Leaf Limited	7	5.00	3.75	2.00
1994 O-Pee-Chee	67	.50	.40	.20
1994 O-Pee-Chee All-Star Redemption Cards	18	1.00	.75	.40
1994 Pacific Crown	49	.25	.20	.10
1994 Pinnacle	25	.50	.40	.20
1994 Pinnacle Artist's Proof	25	30.00	22.00	12.00
1994 Pinnacle Museum Collection	25	8.00	6.00	3.25
1994 Pinnacle The Naturals Box Set	25	.60	.45	.25
1994 Score	25	.40	.30	.15
1994 Score Select	61	.75	.60	.30
1994 Score Select Crown Contenders	3	10.00	7.50	4.00
1994 Sportflics 2000	15	.60	.45	.25
1994 Studio	159	.50	.40	.20
1994 Topps	720	.20	.15	.08
1994 Topps Finest	217	3.00	2.25	1.25
1994 Topps Finest Refractors	217	25.00	18.00	10.00
1994 Topps Finest Superstars	217	10.00	7.50	4.00
1994 Topps Gold	720	.60	.45	.25
1994 Topps Stadium Club	534	.20	.15	.08
1994 Topps Stadium Club	650	.50	.40	.20
1994 Topps Stadium Club First Day Production	534	10.00	7.50	4.00
1994 Topps Stadium Club First Day Production	650	15.00	11.00	6.00
1994 Upper Deck	450	.40	.30	.15
1994 Upper Deck Collector's Choice	322	.05	.04	.02
1994 Upper Deck Collector's Choice	348	.10	.08	.04
1994 Upper Deck Collector's Choice	550	.15	.11	.06
1994 Upper Deck Diamond Collection	2E	10.00	7.50	4.00
1994 Upper Deck Electric Diamond	450	1.50	1.25	.60
1994 Upper Deck Fun Packs	21	.25	.20	.10
1994 Upper Deck Fun Packs	207	1.25	.90	.50
1994 Upper Deck SP Holoview Blue	5	5.00	3.75	2.00
1994 Upper Deck SP Holoview Red	5	40.00	30.00	15.00

Roberto Clemente

Set	Card #	NM	EX	VG
1955 Topps	164 (R)	1575.	775.00	475.00
1956 Topps	33	375.00	185.00	100.00
1957 Topps	76	200.00	100.00	60.00
1958 Topps	52a	375.00	185.00	110.00
1958 Topps	52b	200.00	100.00	60.00
1959 Topps	478	120.00	60.00	36.00
1959 Topps	543	90.00	45.00	27.00
1960 Topps	326	130.00	65.00	40.00
1961 Post Cereal	132a	35.00	17.50	10.50
1961 Post Cereal	132b	35.00	17.50	10.50
1961 Topps	41	11.00	5.50	3.25
1961 Topps	388	100.00	50.00	30.00
1962 Post Cereal	173a	40.00	20.00	12.00
1962 Post Cereal	173b	25.00	12.50	7.50
1962 Topps	10	100.00	50.00	30.00
1962 Topps	52	10.00	5.00	3.00
1963 Fleer	56	185.00	90.00	54.00
1963 Post Cereal	143	25.00	12.50	7.50
1963 Topps	18	25.00	12.50	7.50
1963 Topps	540	250.00	125.00	75.00
1964 Topps	7	12.00	6.00	3.50
1964 Topps	440	170.00	85.00	51.00
1965 O-Pee-Chee	2	17.00	8.50	5.00
1965 O-Pee-Chee	160	85.00	42.00	25.00
1965 Topps	2	15.00	7.50	4.50
1965 Topps	160	80.00	40.00	24.00
1966 Topps	215	22.00	11.00	6.50
1966 Topps	300	100.00	50.00	30.00
1967 Topps	242	12.00	6.00	3.50
1967 Topps	400	80.00	40.00	24.00
1968 O-Pee-Chee	1	25.00	12.50	7.50
1968 O-Pee-Chee	3	13.50	6.75	4.00
1968 O-Pee-Chee	150	65.00	32.00	19.50
1968 Topps	1	17.50	8.75	5.25
1968 Topps	3	9.00	4.50	2.75
1968 Topps	150	62.50	31.00	19.00
1968 Topps	374	15.00	7.50	4.50
1968 Topps	480	35.00	17.50	10.50
1969 O-Pee-Chee	50	60.00	30.00	18.00
1969 Topps	50	40.00	20.00	12.00
1970 O-Pee-Chee	61	8.50	4.25	2.50
1970 O-Pee-Chee	350	63.00	31.00	19.00
1970 Topps	61	7.00	3.50	2.00
1970 Topps	350	45.00	22.00	13.50
1971 O-Pee-Chee	630	80.00	40.00	24.00
1971 Topps	630	80.00	40.00	24.00
1972 O-Pee-Chee	309	42.50	21.00	12.50
1972 O-Pee-Chee	310	21.00	10.50	6.25
1972 Topps	309	25.00	12.50	7.50
1972 Topps	310	15.00	7.50	4.50
1973 O-Pee-Chee	50	38.00	19.00	11.50
1973 Topps	50	35.00	17.50	10.50
1975 O-Pee-Chee	204	4.00	2.00	1.25
1975 Topps	204	2.00	1.00	.60
1975 Topps Mini	204	2.25	1.25	.70

Set	Card #	MT	NM	EX
1986 Sportflics Decade Greats	43	1.00	.70	.40
1987 Topps	313	.10	.08	.04
1989 Pacific Trading Cards Legends II	135	.50	.40	.20
1994 "1954" Topps Archives	251	3.00	2.25	1.25

Rocky Colavito

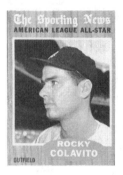

Set	Card #	NM	EX	VG
1957 Topps	212 (R)	130.00	65.00	40.00
1958 Topps	368	35.00	17.50	10.50
1959 Topps	166	12.00	6.00	3.50
1959 Topps	420	20.00	10.00	6.00
1959 Topps	462	9.00	4.50	2.75
1960 Topps	260	6.00	3.00	1.75
1960 Topps	400	20.00	10.00	6.00
1961 Post Cereal	36a	9.00	4.50	2.75
1961 Post Cereal	36b	5.00	2.50	1.50
1961 Topps	44	50.00	25.00	15.00
1961 Topps	330	12.00	6.00	3.50
1962 Post Cereal	19	4.50	2.25	1.25
1962 Topps	20	9.00	4.50	2.75
1962 Topps	314	7.00	3.50	2.00
1962 Topps	472	12.00	6.00	3.50
1963 Post Cereal	50	5.00	2.50	1.50
1963 Topps	4	11.00	5.50	3.25
1963 Topps	240	12.00	6.00	3.50
1964 Topps	320	7.00	3.50	2.00
1965 Topps	380	10.00	5.00	3.00
1966 O-Pee-Chee	150	7.50	3.75	2.25
1966 Topps	150	8.00	4.00	2.50
1966 Topps	220	5.00	2.50	1.50
1967 O-Pee-Chee	109	2.25	1.25	.70
1967 Topps	109	2.50	1.25	.70
1967 Topps	580	75.00	37.00	22.00
1968 O-Pee-Chee	99	2.25	1.25	.70
1968 Topps	99	3.00	1.50	.90
1973 O-Pee-Chee	449	1.25	.60	.40
1973 Topps	449a	1.50	.70	.45
1973 Topps	449b	2.00	1.00	.60

Set	Card #	MT	NM	EX
1990 Pacific Legends	18	.15	.11	.06

* * *

Price increases from 1984 to 1989:1968 Topps
Nolan Ryan rookie, from $25 to $550; 1954 Topps
Henry Aaron rookie, from $130 to $1,000; 1967
Topps Tom Seaver rookie, from $73 to $675; 1984
Donruss Don Mattingly rookie, from $1.50 to $65;
1952 Topps Mickey Mantle rookie,
from $1,000 to $6,500.

* * *

In the June 5, 1987, Sports Collectors Digest issue,
Lee Temanson reported there had been 119 different
baseball card sets issued in 1987 at that point.

* * *

Dave Concepcion

Set	Card #	NM	EX	VG
1971 O-Pee-Chee	14	30.00	15.00	9.00
1971 Topps	14 (R)	20.00	10.00	6.00
1972 O-Pee-Chee	267	1.50	.70	.45
1972 Topps	267	1.75	.90	.50
1973 O-Pee-Chee	554	3.50	1.75	1.00
1973 Topps	554	2.50	1.25	.70
1974 O-Pee-Chee	435	.60	.30	.20
1974 Topps	435	.50	.25	.15
1975 O-Pee-Chee	17	.55	.30	.15
1975 Topps	17	.45	.25	.14
1975 Topps Mini	17	.90	.45	.25
1976 O-Pee-Chee	48	.40	.20	.12
1976 Topps	48	.40	.20	.12
1977 O-Pee-Chee	258	.30	.15	.09
1977 Topps	560	.35	.20	.11
1978 O-Pee-Chee	220	.25	.13	.08
1978 Topps	180	.35	.20	.11
1979 O-Pee-Chee	234	.25	.13	.08
1979 Topps	450	.30	.15	.09
1980 O-Pee-Chee	117	.25	.13	.08
1980 Topps	220	.30	.15	.09

Set	Card #	MT	NM	EX
1981 Donruss	181	.15	.11	.06
1981 Fleer	197	.15	.11	.06
1981 O-Pee-Chee	83	.15	.11	.06
1981 Topps	375	.20	.15	.08
1982 Donruss	421	.12	.09	.05
1982 Fleer	63	.12	.09	.05
1982 Fleer	630	.15	.11	.06
1982 O-Pee-Chee	86	.15	.11	.06
1982 O-Pee-Chee	221	.12	.09	.05
1982 O-Pee-Chee	340	.12	.09	.05
1982 Topps	340	.12	.09	.05
1982 Topps	660	.15	.11	.06
1982 Topps	661	.10	.08	.04
1983 Donruss	148	.12	.09	.05
1983 Fleer	588	.12	.09	.05
1983 Fleer	631	.10	.08	.04
1983 O-Pee-Chee	32	.12	.09	.05
1983 O-Pee-Chee	102	.12	.09	.05
1983 Topps	400	.12	.09	.05
1983 Topps	720	.15	.11	.06
1984 Donruss	2a	.30	.25	.12
1984 Donruss	2b	.60	.45	.25
1984 Donruss	121	.20	.15	.08
1984 Fleer	466	.15	.11	.06
1984 O-Pee-Chee	55	.25	.20	.10
1984 Topps	55	.15	.11	.06
1985 Donruss	203	.15	.11	.06
1985 Fleer	532	.12	.09	.05
1985 Leaf-Donruss	131	.08	.06	.03
1985 O-Pee-Chee	21	.10	.08	.04
1985 Topps	515	.12	.09	.05
1986 Donruss	243	.12	.09	.05
1986 Fleer	174	.12	.09	.05
1986 O-Pee-Chee	195	.08	.06	.03
1986 Sportflics	131	.10	.08	.04
1986 Sportflics	153	.15	.11	.06
1986 Topps	195	.12	.09	.05
1986 Topps	366	.07	.05	.03
1987 Fleer	196	.12	.09	.05
1987 O-Pee-Chee	193	.08	.06	.03
1987 Topps	731	.10	.08	.04
1988 Donruss	329	.07	.05	.03
1988 Fleer	229	.08	.06	.03
1988 O-Pee-Chee	336	.08	.06	.03
1988 Score	210	.06	.05	.02
1988 Sportflics	218	.10	.08	.04
1988 Topps	422	.06	.05	.02
1988 Topps Big Baseball	144	.08	.06	.03
1989 Fleer	156	.10	.08	.04
1989 Score	166	.08	.06	.03
1989 Upper Deck	196	.10	.08	.04

David Cone

Set	Card #	MT	NM	EX
1987 Donruss	502 (R)	2.50	2.00	1.00
1987 Sportflics Rookies	39	.70	.50	.30
1987 Topps Traded	24T	.75	.60	.30
1988 Donruss	653	.60	.45	.25
1988 Fleer	131	.75	.60	.30
1988 Score	49	.35	.25	.14
1988 Topps	181	.30	.25	.12
1989 Bowman	375	.10	.08	.04
1989 Donruss	9	.08	.06	.03
1989 Donruss	388	.12	.09	.05
1989 Fleer	31	.15	.11	.06
1989 Fleer	636	.10	.07	.04
1989 O-Pee-Chee	384	.07	.05	.03
1989 Score	221	.10	.06	.03
1989 Sportflics	51	.25	.20	.10
1989 Topps	710	.15	.11	.06
1989 Topps All-Star Glossy Set of 60	6	.25	.20	.10
1989 Upper Deck	584	.35	.25	.14
1990 Bowman	125	.08	.06	.03
1990 Donruss	265	.10	.08	.04
1990 Fleer	200	.10	.08	.04
1990 Leaf	40	1.00	.75	.40
1990 O-Pee-Chee	30	.10	.08	.04
1990 Score	430	.15	.11	.06
1990 Sportflics	201	.12	.09	.05
1990 Topps	30	.10	.08	.04
1990 Upper Deck	224	.15	.11	.06
1991 Bowman	460	.08	.06	.03
1991 Donruss	154	.08	.06	.03
1991 Fleer	143	.06	.05	.02
1991 Fleer Ultra	213	.10	.08	.04
1991 Leaf	253	.15	.11	.06
1991 Score	409	.10	.08	.04
1991 Score	549	.08	.06	.03
1991 Topps	680	.06	.05	.02
1991 Topps Stadium Club	367	.30	.25	.12
1991 Topps Stadium Club Members Only	(7)	.25	.20	.10
1991 Upper Deck	366	.10	.07	.04
1992 Bowman	238	.40	.30	.15

1992 Donruss	97	.08	.06	.03
1992 Donruss Triple Play	35	.12	.09	.05
1992 Fleer	501	.08	.06	.03
1992 Fleer	687	.06	.05	.02
1992 Fleer Smoke 'N Heat	3	.50	.40	.20
1992 Fleer Ultra	230	.15	.11	.06
1992 Fleer Ultra All-Stars	19	.50	.40	.20
1992 Fleer Update	63	.20	.15	.08
1992 Leaf	92	.15	.11	.06
1992 O-Pee-Chee	195	.08	.06	.03
1992 O-Pee-Chee Premier	175	.15	.11	.06
1992 Pinnacle	450	.10	.08	.04
1992 Pinnacle	611	.10	.08	.04
1992 Score	680	.08	.06	.03
1992 Score	795	.06	.05	.02
1992 Score Impact Players	90	.10	.08	.04
1992 Score Rookie & Traded	27	.08	.06	.03
1992 Topps	195	.08	.06	.03
1992 Topps Gold	195	.35	.25	.14
1992 Topps Kids	16	.05	.04	.02
1992 Topps Stadium Club	17	.20	.15	.08
1992 Upper Deck	364	.10	.07	.04
1992 Upper Deck MVP Holograms	17	.25	.20	.10
1993 Bowman	97	.10	.08	.04
1993 Donruss	712	.05	.04	.02
1993 Donruss 1992 Blue Jays Commemorative Set	15	.15	.11	.06
1993 Fleer	691	.05	.04	.02
1993 Fleer Final Edition	216	.05	.04	.02
1993 Fleer Flair	214	.25	.15	.08
1993 Fleer Ultra	558	.10	.08	.04
1993 Leaf	250	.10	.08	.04
1993 O-Pee-Chee	107	.15	.11	.06
1993 O-Pee-Chee Premier	92	.10	.08	.04
1993 O-Pee-Chee World Champs	4	.35	.25	.14
1993 Pinnacle	489	.10	.08	.04
1993 Pinnacle	544	.06	.05	.02
1993 Score	654	.06	.05	.02
1993 Score Select	361	.15	.11	.06
1993 Score Select Rookie/ Traded	18	.25	.20	.10
1993 Score Select Stat Leaders	77	.10	.08	.04
1993 Topps Finest	115	1.00	.70	.40
1993 Topps Finest Jumbo All-Stars	115	7.00	5.25	2.75
1993 Topps Finest Refractors	115	20.00	15.00	8.00
1993 Topps Gold	720	.10	.08	.04
1993 Topps Stadium Club	703	.10	.08	.04
1993 Topps Stadium Club First Day Production	703	5.00	3.75	2.00
1993 Topps Stadium Club Special	154	.10	.08	.04
1993 Topps Stadium Club Team Sets	17	.20	.15	.08
1993 Topps Traded	125	.05	.04	.02
1993 Upper Deck	335	.08	.06	.03
1993 Upper Deck	534	.08	.06	.03
1993 Upper Deck Fun Packs	179	.15	.11	.06
1993 Upper Deck Fun Packs	182	.05	.04	.02
1993 Upper Deck SP	228	.15	.11	.06
1994 Bowman	593	.10	.08	.04
1994 Bowman's Best	46	.50	.40	.20
1994 Bowman's Best Refractors	46	2.00	1.50	.80
1994 Donruss	194	.05	.04	.02
1994 Donruss Triple Play	232	.05	.04	.02
1994 Fleer	152	.05	.04	.02
1994 Fleer Extra Bases	85	.10	.08	.04
1994 Fleer Extra Bases Pitcher's Duel	3M	.40	.30	.15
1994 Fleer Flair	297	.20	.15	.08

1994 Fleer Smoke N' Heat	2	4.00	3.00	1.50
1994 Fleer Ultra	361	.10	.08	.04
1994 Leaf	274	.12	.09	.05
1994 Leaf Limited	36	1.00	.70	.40
1994 O-Pee-Chee	260	.05	.04	.02
1994 Pacific Crown	281	.05	.04	.02
1994 Pinnacle	325	.12	.09	.05
1994 Pinnacle Artist's Proof	325	3.00	2.25	1.25
1994 Pinnacle Museum Collection	325	1.50	1.25	.60
1994 Score	405	.04	.03	.02
1994 Score Select	76	.10	.08	.04
1994 Sportflics 2000	39	.10	.08	.04
1994 Studio	182	.10	.08	.04
1994 Topps	510	.04	.03	.02
1994 Topps Finest	52	.50	.40	.20
1994 Topps Finest Refractors	52	3.50	2.75	1.50
1994 Topps Gold	510	.15	.11	.06
1994 Topps Stadium Club	292	.10	.08	.04
1994 Topps Stadium Club First Day Production	292	2.50	2.00	1.00
1994 Upper Deck	413	.10	.08	.04
1994 Upper Deck Collector's Choice	81	.05	.04	.02
1994 Upper Deck Electric Diamond	413	.25	.20	.10

Cecil Cooper

Cecil Cooper
FIRST BASE

Set	Card #	NM	EX	VG
1972 O-Pee-Chee	79	120.00	60.00	36.00
1972 Topps	79 (R)	90.00	45.00	27.00
1974 O-Pee-Chee	523	1.25	.60	.40
1974 Topps	523	.50	.25	.15
1975 O-Pee-Chee	489	.75	.40	.25
1975 Topps	489	.45	.25	.14
1975 Topps Mini	489	.75	.40	.25
1976 O-Pee-Chee	78	.75	.40	.25
1976 Topps	78	.50	.25	.15
1977 O-Pee-Chee	102	.50	.25	.15
1977 Topps	235	.20	.10	.06
1978 O-Pee-Chee	71	.25	.13	.08
1978 Topps	154	.20	.10	.06
1979 O-Pee-Chee	163	.30	.15	.09
1979 Topps	325	.20	.10	.06
1980 O-Pee-Chee	52	.30	.15	.09
1980 Topps	95	.35	.20	.11

Set	Card #	MT	NM	EX
1981 Donruss	83	.15	.11	.06
1981 Fleer	639	.15	.11	.06
1981 O-Pee-Chee	356	.15	.11	.06
1981 Topps	3	.30	.25	.12
1981 Topps	555	.10	.08	.04
1982 Donruss	258	.15	.11	.06
1982 Fleer	138	.15	.11	.06
1982 O-Pee-Chee	167	.15	.11	.06
1982 Topps	675	.08	.06	.03

1982 Topps	703	.15	.11	.06
1983 Donruss	106	.15	.11	.06
1983 Fleer	30	.15	.11	.06
1983 O-Pee-Chee	190	.12	.09	.05
1983 Topps	190	.10	.08	.04
1983 Topps All-Star Glossy Set of 40	15	.20	.15	.08
1984 Donruss	351	.25	.20	.10
1984 Fleer	198	.15	.11	.06
1984 O-Pee-Chee	43	.25	.20	.10
1984 Topps	133	.40	.30	.15
1984 Topps	420	.15	.11	.06
1984 Topps	710	.30	.25	.12
1984 Topps All-Star Glossy Set of 40	34	.20	.15	.08
1985 Donruss	170	.15	.11	.06
1985 Fleer	580	.15	.11	.06
1985 Leaf-Donruss	246	.08	.06	.03
1985 O-Pee-Chee	290	.12	.09	.05
1985 Topps	290	.12	.09	.05
1986 Donruss	7	.12	.09	.05
1986 Donruss	170	.12	.09	.05
1986 Donruss Diamond Kings Supers	7	.25	.20	.10
1986 Fleer	484	.12	.09	.05
1986 Fleer Limited Edition	12	.07	.05	.03
1986 Leaf	7	.08	.06	.03
1986 O-Pee-Chee	385	.08	.06	.03
1986 Sportflics	29	.10	.08	.04
1986 Sportflics	145	.15	.11	.06
1986 Sportflics	180	1.25	.90	.50
1986 Topps	385	.10	.08	.04
1987 Donruss	363	.12	.09	.05
1987 Fleer	343	.12	.09	.05
1987 Leaf	230	.08	.06	.03
1987 O-Pee-Chee	10	.10	.08	.04
1987 Sportflics	169	.15	.11	.06
1987 Topps	10	.10	.08	.04
1988 Fleer	161	.10	.08	.04
1988 Score	169	.08	.06	.03
1988 Topps	769	.08	.06	.03
1990 Pacific Senior League	42	.10	.08	.04

1957 Topps	98	10.00	5.00	3.00
1958 Topps	125	6.50	3.25	2.00
1959 Topps	502	4.00	2.00	1.25
1960 Topps	472	5.75	3.00	1.75
1961 Topps	220	3.00	1.50	.90
1962 Topps	322	3.50	1.75	1.00
1963 Topps	258	3.25	1.75	1.00
1964 Topps	529	9.50	4.75	2.75
1966 Topps	433	4.00	2.00	1.25
1967 Topps	389	3.00	1.50	.90
1968 Topps	237	1.50	.70	.45
1969 O-Pee-Chee	91	2.25	1.25	.70
1969 Topps	91	1.00	.50	.30
1970 O-Pee-Chee	524	2.25	1.25	.70
1970 Topps	524	1.50	.70	.45
1971 O-Pee-Chee	397	2.50	1.25	.70
1971 Topps	397	2.00	1.00	.60
1975 O-Pee-Chee	561	.75	.40	.25
1975 Topps	561	2.00	1.00	.60
1975 Topps Mini	561	1.25	.60	.40
1978 Topps	467	.20	.10	.06

Set	Card #	MT	NM	EX
1983 Topps 1952 Reprint Set	351	.40	.30	.15
1988 Pacific Trading Cards Baseball Legends	28	.10	.08	.04
1990 Pacific Legends	69	.05	.04	.02
1991 "1953" Topps Archives	109	.20	.15	.08

Darren Daulton

Set	Card #	MT	NM	EX
1985 Fleer Update	33	18.00	13.50	7.25
1986 Donruss	477 (R)	4.00	3.00	1.50
1986 Fleer	438 (R)	4.00	3.00	1.50
1986 Topps	264 (R)	1.25	.90	.50
1987 Donruss	262	.60	.45	.25
1987 Fleer	172	1.00	.75	.40
1987 O-Pee-Chee	57	.08	.06	.03
1987 Topps	636	.30	.25	.12
1988 Donruss	309	.05	.04	.02
1988 Score	473	.15	.11	.06
1988 Topps	468	.04	.03	.02
1989 Donruss	549	.04	.03	.02
1989 Score	413	.15	.10	.05
1989 Topps	187	.15	.11	.06
1989 Upper Deck	448	.40	.30	.15
1990 Bowman	158	.05	.04	.02
1990 Donruss	194	.04	.03	.02
1990 Fleer	555	.05	.04	.02
1990 Leaf	369	1.50	1.25	.60
1990 O-Pee-Chee	542	.03	.02	.01
1990 Score	389	.04	.03	.02
1990 Topps	542	.03	.02	.01
1990 Upper Deck	418	.20	.15	.08
1991 Bowman	507	.15	.11	.06
1991 Donruss	316	.10	.08	.04

Alvin Dark

Set	Card #	NM	EX	VG
1948 Leaf	51 (R)	350.00	175.00	105.00
1949 Bowman	67	24.00	12.00	7.20
1950 Bowman	64	45.00	22.00	13.50
1951 Bowman	14	24.00	12.00	7.25
1952 Bowman	34	24.00	12.00	7.25
1952 Topps	351	250.00	125.00	57.00
1953 Bowman Color	19	30.00	15.00	9.00
1953 Topps	109	20.00	10.00	4.50
1954 Bowman	41a	10.00	5.00	3.00
1954 Bowman	41b	10.00	5.00	3.00
1954 Red Heart Dog Food	(5)	35.00	17.50	10.50
1955 Bowman	2	10.00	5.00	3.00
1956 Topps	148	12.00	6.00	3.50

1991 Fleer	393	.06	.05	.02
1991 Fleer Ultra	260	.06	.05	.02
1991 Leaf	192	.08	.06	.03
1991 Score	246	.06	.05	.02
1991 Studio	212	.12	.09	.05
1991 Topps	89	.06	.05	.02
1991 Topps Stadium Club	4	.40	.30	.15
1991 Upper Deck	408	.08	.06	.03
1992 Bowman	440	.40	.30	.15
1992 Donruss	198	.06	.05	.02
1992 Donruss Triple Play	143	.08	.06	.03
1992 Fleer	527	.05	.04	.02
1992 Fleer Ultra	240	.15	.11	.06
1992 Leaf	335	.15	.11	.06
1992 O-Pee-Chee	244	.04	.03	.02
1992 Pinnacle	241	.15	.11	.06
1992 Score	506	.06	.05	.02
1992 Studio	73	.15	.11	.06
1992 Studio Heritage	13	1.00	.70	.40
1992 Topps	244	.04	.03	.02
1992 Topps Gold	244	1.00	.70	.40
1992 Topps Stadium Club	529	.25	.20	.10
1992 Upper Deck	429	.06	.05	.02
1993 Bowman	160	.10	.08	.04
1993 DiamondMarks	(45)	.25	.20	.10
1993 Donruss	92	.08	.06	.03
1993 Donruss Diamond Kings	17	1.00	.75	.40
1993 Donruss Elite	29	20.00	15.00	8.00
1993 Donruss Elite Supers	11	6.00	4.50	2.50
1993 Donruss MVP's	11	1.00	.75	.40
1993 Donruss Triple Play League Leaders	5	3.00	2.25	1.25
1993 Donruss Triple Play Action Baseball	5	.10	.08	.04
1993 Donruss Triple Play	7	.10	.08	.04
1993 Donruss Triple Play	229	.10	.08	.04
1993 Fleer	100	.08	.06	.03
1993 Fleer	352	.08	.06	.03
1993 Fleer	705	.08	.06	.03
1993 Fleer	715	.10	.08	.04
1993 Fleer All-Stars	9	1.00	.75	.40
1993 Fleer Flair	97	.40	.30	.15
1993 Fleer Ultra	86	.20	.15	.08
1993 Fleer Ultra All-Stars	1	1.00	.75	.40
1993 Fleer Ultra Home Run Kings	9	2.00	1.50	.80
1993 Leaf	95	.15	.11	.06
1993 Leaf Gold All-Stars	1	1.25	.90	.50
1993 Leaf Update Gold All-Stars	2	1.00	.75	.40
1993 O-Pee-Chee	71	.20	.15	.08
1993 O-Pee-Chee Premier	12	.15	.11	.06
1993 Pinnacle	99	.06	.05	.02
1993 Pinnacle Home Run Club	9	.35	.25	.14
1993 Pinnacle Team Pinnacle	3	6.00	4.50	2.50
1993 Post Cereal	18	.25	.20	.10
1993 Score	10	.08	.06	.03
1993 Score	526	.06	.05	.02
1993 Score Select	13	.12	.09	.05
1993 Score Select Chase Stars	5	2.50	2.00	1.00
1993 Score Select Stat Leaders	34	.10	.08	.04
1993 Score The Franchise	22	2.00	1.50	.80
1993 Studio	51	.15	.11	.06
1993 Studio Superstars on Canvas	7	1.00	.70	.40
1993 Topps	180	.08	.06	.03
1993 Topps	408	.03	.02	.01
1993 Topps Black Gold	3	.30	.25	.12
1993 Topps Finest	171	2.00	1.50	.80
1993 Topps Finest Refractors	171	25.00	18.50	10.00
1993 Topps Full Shot Super	13	3.00	2.25	1.25
1993 Topps Gold	180	.15	.11	.06
1993 Topps Gold	408	.10	.08	.04

1993 Topps Stadium Club	313	.15	.11	.06
1993 Topps Stadium Club First Day Production	313	12.00	9.00	4.75
1993 Topps Stadium Club Special	91	.10	.08	.04
1993 Topps Stadium Club Team Sets	1	.25	.20	.10
1993 Upper Deck	137	.10	.07	.04
1993 Upper Deck	498	.08	.06	.03
1993 Upper Deck	829	.08	.06	.03
1993 Upper Deck Fun Packs All-Star Scratch-Off	2	1.00	.70	.40
1993 Upper Deck Fun Packs	142	.15	.11	.06
1993 Upper Deck Fun Packs	143	.12	.09	.05
1993 Upper Deck Home Run Heroes	8	.60	.45	.25
1993 Upper Deck Iooss Collection	17	.75	.60	.30
1993 Upper Deck Iooss Collection Super	17	3.00	2.25	1.25
1993 Upper Deck SP	11	.20	.15	.08
1993 Upper Deck SP Platinum Power	5	5.00	3.75	2.00
1994 Bowman	140	.10	.08	.04
1994 Bowman	384	.10	.08	.04
1994 Bowman's Best	11	.50	.40	.20
1994 Bowman's Best Refractors	11	2.00	1.50	.80
1994 Donruss	333	.05	.04	.02
1994 Donruss Special Edition - Gold	333	.25	.20	.10
1994 Donruss Triple Play Medalists	2	1.00	.75	.40
1994 Donruss Triple Play	171	.05	.04	.02
1994 Fleer	585	.08	.06	.03
1994 Fleer All-Stars	34	.30	.25	.12
1994 Fleer Extra Bases	330	.15	.11	.06
1994 Fleer Extra Bases Game Breakers	8	.25	.20	.10
1994 Fleer Flair	204	.35	.25	.14
1994 Fleer Flair Infield Power	3	1.00	.75	.40
1994 Fleer ProVisions	1	.30	.25	.12
1994 Fleer Ultra	243	.12	.09	.05
1994 Fleer Ultra Phillies Finest	1	1.00	.70	.40
1994 Fleer Ultra Phillies Finest	1M	1.50	1.25	.60
1994 Fleer Ultra Phillies Finest	2	1.00	.70	.40
1994 Fleer Ultra Phillies Finest	3	1.00	.70	.40
1994 Fleer Ultra Phillies Finest	3M	1.50	1.25	.60
1994 Fleer Ultra Phillies Finest	4	1.00	.70	.40
1994 Fleer Ultra Phillies Finest	5	1.00	.70	.40
1994 Fleer Ultra Phillies Finest	11	1.00	.70	.40
1994 Fleer Ultra Phillies Finest	12	1.00	.70	.40
1994 Fleer Ultra Phillies Finest	13	1.00	.70	.40
1994 Fleer Ultra Phillies Finest	14	1.00	.70	.40
1994 Fleer Ultra Phillies Finest	15	1.00	.70	.40
1994 Fleer Ultra RBI Kings	12	2.50	2.00	1.00
1994 Leaf	170	.12	.09	.05
1994 Leaf Limited	134	1.50	1.25	.60
1994 Leaf MVP Contenders	5a	2.50	2.00	1.00
1994 Leaf MVP Contenders	5b	5.00	3.75	2.00
1994 Leaf Slide Show	3	3.00	2.25	1.25
1994 O-Pee-Chee	123	.05	.04	.02

1994 Pacific Crown	471	.10	.08	.04
1994 Pacific Crown Jewels of the Crown	31	2.50	2.00	1.00
1994 Pinnacle	91	.10	.08	.04
1994 Pinnacle Artist's Proof	91	3.00	2.25	1.25
1994 Pinnacle Museum Collection	91	1.50	1.25	.60
1994 Pinnacle Run Creators	31	2.00	1.50	.80
1994 Post Cereal	9	.25	.20	.10
1994 Score	34	.04	.03	.02
1994 Score Gold Stars	4	3.00	2.25	1.25
1994 Score Select	9	.10	.08	.04
1994 Sportflics 2000	128	.10	.08	.04
1994 Studio	136	.10	.08	.04
1994 Topps	380	.04	.03	.02
1994 Topps	608	.06	.05	.02
1994 Topps Black Gold	28	.50	.40	.20
1994 Topps Finest	220	.50	.40	.20
1994 Topps Finest Refractors	220	3.50	2.75	1.50
1994 Topps Finest Superstars	220	2.50	2.00	1.00
1994 Topps Gold	380	.15	.11	.06
1994 Topps Gold	608	.15	.11	.06
1994 Topps Stadium Club	450	.10	.08	.04
1994 Topps Stadium Club Dugout Dirt	12	.35	.25	.14
1994 Topps Stadium Club First Day Production	450	2.50	2.00	1.00
1994 Upper Deck	65	.10	.08	.04
1994 Upper Deck All-Stars Green Foil	7	.25	.20	.10
1994 Upper Deck All-Stars Gold Foil	7	1.00	.70	.40
1994 Upper Deck Collector's Choice	358	.05	.04	.02
1994 Upper Deck Electric Diamond	65	.25	.20	.10
1994 Upper Deck Fun Packs	140	.05	.04	.02

Willie Davis

Set	Card #	NM	EX	VG
1961 Topps	506 (R)	12.00	6.00	3.50
1962 Post Cereal	106	3.00	1.50	.90
1962 Topps	108	5.00	2.50	1.50
1963 Post Cereal	119	150.00	75.00	45.00
1963 Topps	229	3.50	1.75	1.00
1964 Topps	68	3.50	1.75	1.00
1965 Topps	435	7.00	3.50	2.00
1966 Topps	535	30.00	15.00	9.00
1967 O-Pee-Chee	160	3.00	1.50	.90
1967 Topps	160	2.50	1.25	.70
1968 Topps	208	1.50	.70	.45
1969 O-Pee-Chee	65	2.25	1.25	.70
1969 Topps	65	1.00	.50	.30

1970 O-Pee-Chee	390	1.75	.90	.50
1970 Topps	390	1.75	.90	.50
1971 O-Pee-Chee	585	5.00	2.50	1.50
1971 Topps	585	3.50	1.75	1.00
1972 O-Pee-Chee	390	1.25	.60	.40
1972 Topps	390	.75	.40	.25
1973 O-Pee-Chee	35	.75	.40	.25
1973 Topps	35	.40	.20	.12
1974 O-Pee-Chee	165	.60	.30	.20
1974 Topps	165	.30	.15	.09
1974 Topps Traded	165T	.40	.30	.15
1975 O-Pee-Chee	10	.55	.30	.15
1975 Topps	10	.35	.20	.11
1975 Topps Mini	10	.60	.30	.20
1976 O-Pee-Chee	265	.35	.20	.11
1976 Topps	265	.25	.13	.08
1977 Topps	603	.25	.13	.08

Set	Card #	MT	NM	EX
1992 Pinnacle	591	.15	.11	.06

Andre Dawson

Set	Card #	NM	EX	VG
1977 Topps	473 (R)	70.00	35.00	21.00
1978 O-Pee-Chee	180	23.00	11.50	7.00
1978 Topps	72	20.00	10.00	6.00
1979 O-Pee-Chee	179	13.50	6.75	4.00
1979 Topps	348	10.00	5.00	3.00
1980 O-Pee-Chee	124	9.25	4.75	2.75
1980 Topps	235	8.00	4.00	2.50

Set	Card #	MT	NM	EX
1981 Donruss	212	1.50	1.25	.60
1981 Fleer	145	2.00	1.50	.80
1981 O-Pee-Chee	125	3.00	2.25	1.25
1981 Topps	125	2.50	2.00	1.00
1982 Donruss	88	1.25	.90	.50
1982 Fleer	187	2.00	1.50	.80
1982 O-Pee-Chee	341	.20	.15	.08
1982 O-Pee-Chee	379	2.75	2.00	1.00
1982 Topps	341	.50	.40	.20
1982 Topps	540	.80	.60	.30
1983 Donruss	518	1.25	.90	.50
1983 Fleer	280	1.25	.90	.50
1983 O-Pee-Chee	173	.15	.11	.06
1983 O-Pee-Chee	303	2.25	1.75	.90
1983 Topps	402	.60	.45	.25
1983 Topps	680	2.00	1.50	.80
1984 Donruss	97	5.00	3.75	2.00
1984 Fleer	273	3.00	2.25	1.25
1984 O-Pee-Chee	200	1.00	.70	.40
1984 O-Pee-Chee	392	.30	.25	.12
1984 Topps	200	.75	.60	.30
1984 Topps	392	.40	.30	.15
1984 Topps All-Star Glossy Set of 22	18	.35	.25	.14
1904 Topps All-Star Glossy Set of 40	35	.35	.25	.14
1985 Donruss	421	2.00	1.50	.80
1985 Fleer	394	2.00	1.50	.80

1985 Leaf-Donruss	133	.25	.20	.10
1985 O-Pee-Chee	133	.25	.20	.10
1985 Topps	420	.75	.60	.30
1986 Donruss	25	.40	.30	.15
1986 Donruss	87	1.00	.70	.40
1986 Donruss Diamond Kings Supers	25	.60	.45	.25
1986 Fleer	246	.30	.25	.12
1986 Leaf	25	.25	.20	.10
1986 O-Pee-Chee	256	.15	.11	.06
1986 Sportflics	66	.30	.20	.10
1986 Sportflics	110	.25	.20	.10
1986 Topps	576	.12	.09	.05
1986 Topps	760	.40	.30	.15
1987 Donruss	458	.30	.25	.12
1987 Fleer	316	.75	.60	.30
1987 Fleer Update	24	.40	.30	.15
1987 Leaf	212	.50	.40	.20
1987 O-Pee-Chee	345	.15	.11	.06
1987 Sportflics	139	.35	.25	.14
1987 Topps	345	.25	.20	.10
1987 Topps Traded	27T	.40	.30	.15
1988 Donruss	9	.10	.08	.04
1988 Donruss	269	.20	.15	.08
1988 Donruss Diamond Kings Supers	9	.30	.25	.12
1988 Donruss MVP	10	.25	.20	.10
1988 Fleer	415	.30	.25	.12
1988 Fleer All Stars	6	.60	.45	.25
1988 Fleer MVP	9	.15	.11	.06
1988 Leaf	9	.15	.11	.06
1988 Leaf	126	.15	.11	.06
1988 O-Pee-Chee	247	.12	.09	.05
1988 Score	4	.20	.15	.08
1988 Score Glossy	4	1.00	.70	.40
1988 Sportflics	3	.25	.20	.10
1988 Topps	401	.10	.08	.04
1988 Topps	500	.15	.11	.06
1988 Topps All-Star Glossy Set of 60	1	.30	.25	.12
1988 Topps All-Star Glossy Set of 22	18	.25	.20	.10
1988 Topps Big Baseball	153	.15	.11	.06
1989 Bowman	298	.12	.09	.05
1989 Donruss	167	.20	.15	.08
1989 Donruss MVP	8	.25	.20	.10
1989 Fleer	422	.15	.11	.06
1989 Fleer MVP	11	.12	.09	.05
1989 O-Pee-Chee	10	.10	.08	.04
1989 Score	2	.15	.11	.06
1989 Sportflics	95	.25	.20	.10
1989 Topps	4	.08	.06	.03
1989 Topps	10	.15	.11	.06
1989 Topps	391	.10	.08	.04
1989 Topps All-Star Glossy Set of 22	18	.10	.08	.04
1989 Topps Big Baseball	120	.08	.06	.03
1989 Upper Deck	205	.25	.20	.10
1990 Bowman	39	.10	.08	.04
1990 Donruss	223	.12	.09	.05
1990 Fleer	29	.12	.09	.05
1990 Leaf	177	.75	.60	.30
1990 O-Pee-Chee	140	.12	.09	.05
1990 Score	265	.12	.09	.05
1990 Sportflics	108	.15	.11	.06
1990 Topps	140	.12	.09	.05
1990 Topps All-Star Glossy Set of 60	41	.25	.20	.10
1990 Topps Big Baseball	91	.15	.11	.06
1990 Upper Deck	357	.15	.11	.06
1991 Bowman	429	.10	.08	.04
1991 Donruss	129	.10	.08	.04
1991 Donruss	435	.10	.08	.04
1991 Donruss Elite	4	45.00	34.00	18.00
1991 Fleer	419a	.10	.08	.04
1991 Fleer	419b	.10	.08	.04
1991 Fleer	713	.15	.11	.06
1991 Fleer Ultra	58	.12	.09	.05
1991 Leaf	400	.15	.11	.06
1991 Score	445	.10	.08	.04
1991 Studio	153	.15	.11	.06
1991 Topps	640	.10	.08	.04
1991 Topps Stadium Club	310	.50	.40	.20
1991 Upper Deck	454	.15	.11	.06
1991 Upper Deck Final Edition	98	.10	.08	.04
1992 Bowman	625	.60	.45	.25
1992 Donruss	119	.15	.11	.06
1992 Donruss	422	.10	.08	.04
1992 Donruss Triple Play	113	.05	.04	.02
1992 Donruss Triple Play	174	.12	.09	.05
1992 Fleer	379	.12	.09	.05
1992 Fleer Team Leaders	20	1.00	.75	.40
1992 Fleer Ultra	468	.15	.11	.06
1992 Leaf	183	.15	.10	.05
1992 O-Pee-Chee	460	.12	.09	.05
1992 Pinnacle	115	.15	.11	.06
1992 Score	75	.12	.09	.05
1992 Studio	12	.15	.11	.06
1992 Studio Heritage	9	1.00	.70	.40
1992 Topps	460	.12	.09	.05
1992 Topps Gold	460	.60	.45	.25
1992 Topps Kids	2	.10	.08	.04
1992 Topps Stadium Club	810	.15	.11	.06
1992 Topps Stadium Club Special Edition	33	.25	.20	.10
1992 Upper Deck	124	.15	.11	.06
1992 Upper Deck Home Run Heroes	9	.50	.40	.20
1993 Bowman	495	.20	.15	.08
1993 DiamondMarks	(69)	.40	.30	.15
1993 Donruss	632	.10	.08	.04
1993 Donruss Triple Play Gallery	2	1.25	.90	.50
1993 Fleer	377	.08	.06	.03
1993 Fleer Final Edition	3DT	.20	.15	.08
1993 Fleer Final Edition	173	.05	.04	.02
1993 Fleer Flair	162	.35	.25	.14
1993 Leaf	310	.15	.11	.06
1993 O-Pee-Chee	35	.20	.15	.08
1993 Pinnacle	497	.15	.11	.06
1993 Pinnacle Cooperstown	11	.25	.20	.10
1993 Pinnacle Cooperstown Dufex	11	50.00	37.00	20.00
1993 Pinnacle Home Run Club	16	.35	.25	.14
1993 Pinnacle Slugfest	26	.75	.60	.30
1993 Score	552	.06	.05	.02
1993 Score Select	9	.15	.11	.06
1993 Score Select Rookie/ Traded	11	.25	.20	.10
1993 Studio	104	.12	.09	.05
1993 Topps	265	.10	.08	.04
1993 Topps Black Gold	4	.30	.25	.12
1993 Topps Finest	84	1.50	1.25	.60
1993 Topps Finest Jumbo All-Stars	84	8.00	6.00	3.25
1993 Topps Finest Refractors	84	20.00	15.00	8.00
1993 Topps Gold	265	.20	.15	.08
1993 Topps Stadium Club	203	.15	.11	.06
1993 Topps Stadium Club	655	.15	.11	.06
1993 Topps Stadium Club First Day Production	203	20.00	15.00	8.00
1993 Topps Stadium Club First Day Production	655	20.00	15.00	8.00
1993 Topps Traded	92	.05	.04	.02
1993 Upper Deck	308	.10	.07	.04
1993 Upper Deck	777	.10	.08	.04
1993 Upper Deck	832	.08	.06	.03
1993 Upper Deck Fun Packs	163	.20	.15	.08
1993 Upper Deck SP	201	.15	.11	.06
1994 Bowman	531	.15	.11	.06
1994 Donruss	448	.10	.08	.04
1994 Donruss Triple Play	203	.05	.04	.02
1994 Fleer	29	.05	.04	.02
1994 Fleer Extra Bases	19	.10	.08	.04
1994 Fleer Flair	13	.20	.15	.08

1994 Fleer Ultra	13	.10	.08	.04
1994 Leaf	142	.12	.09	.05
1994 Leaf Limited	9	1.50	1.25	.60
1994 O-Pee-Chee	138	.15	.11	.06
1994 Pacific Crown	52	.10	.08	.04
1994 Pinnacle	320	.15	.11	.06
1994 Pinnacle Artist's Proof	320	5.00	3.75	2.00
1994 Pinnacle Museum Collection	320	2.00	1.50	.80
1994 Score	471	.06	.05	.02
1994 Score Select	93	.20	.15	.08
1994 Sportflics 2000	79	.10	.08	.04
1994 Studio	161	.15	.11	.06
1994 Topps	595	.06	.05	.02
1994 Topps Finest	50	.75	.60	.30
1994 Topps Finest Refractors	50	7.00	5.25	2.75
1994 Topps Gold	595	.15	.11	.06
1994 Topps Stadium Club	371	.12	.09	.05
1994 Topps Stadium Club	525	.10	.08	.04
1994 Topps Stadium Club First Day Production	371	8.00	6.00	3.25
1994 Topps Stadium Club First Day Production	525	2.50	2.00	1.00
1994 Upper Deck	96	.10	.08	.04
1994 Upper Deck Collector's Choice	412	.06	.05	.02
1994 Upper Deck Electric Diamond	96	.25	.20	.10
1994 Upper Deck Fun Packs	100	.05	.04	.02

Dizzy Dean

Set	Card #	NM	EX	VG
1933 Goudey	223	700.00	280.00	133.00
1934 Batter-Up	64	450.00	225.00	135.00
1934 Goudey	6	800.00	320.00	152.00
1935 Goudey	(22)	375.00	187.00	112.00

Set	Card #	MT	NM	EX
1986 Sportflics Decade Greats	14	.30	.25	.12
1991 "1953" Topps Archives	326	1.00	.70	.40

* * *

Steve Blass, on memorabilia he's collected: "When the last game at Forbes Field was played, I joined the herd of people that ran to the big scoreboard in left field. I was able to get a "2" and an "8" since my number was 28. Some people came to the last game with tools to remove seats, signs, etc. One guy even got a toilet!"

* * *

Bucky Dent

Set	Card #	NM	EX	VG
1974 O-Pee-Chee	582	.75	.40	.25
1974 Topps	582 (R)	.50	.25	.15
1975 O-Pee-Chee	299	.55	.30	.15
1975 Topps	299	.40	.20	.12
1975 Topps Mini	299	.60	.30	.20
1976 O-Pee-Chee	154	.35	.20	.11
1976 Topps	154	.25	.13	.08
1977 O-Pee-Chee	122	.30	.15	.09
1977 Topps	29	.25	.13	.08
1978 O-Pee-Chee	164	.25	.13	.08
1978 Topps	335	.30	.15	.09
1979 O-Pee-Chee	254	.25	.13	.08
1979 Topps	485	.25	.13	.08
1980 O-Pee-Chee	33	.20	.10	.06
1980 Topps	60	.15	.08	.05

Set	Card #	MT	NM	EX
1981 Donruss	465	.10	.08	.04
1981 Fleer	80	.10	.08	.04
1981 O-Pee-Chee	164	.12	.09	.05
1981 Topps	650	.12	.09	.05
1982 Donruss	209	.10	.08	.04
1982 Fleer	33	.10	.08	.04
1982 Fleer	629	.10	.08	.04
1982 O-Pee-Chee	240	.12	.09	.05
1982 O-Pee-Chee	241	.12	.09	.05
1982 O-Pee-Chee	298	.12	.09	.05
1982 Topps	240	.12	.09	.05
1982 Topps	241	.10	.08	.04
1982 Topps	550	.12	.09	.05
1983 Fleer	566	.10	.08	.04
1983 O-Pee-Chee	279	.12	.09	.05
1983 Topps	565	.12	.09	.05
1984 Donruss	300	.15	.11	.06
1984 Fleer	417	.12	.09	.05
1984 O-Pee-Chee	331	.20	.15	.08
1984 Topps	331	.12	.09	.05
1990 O-Pee-Chee	519	.03	.02	.01
1990 Topps	519	.03	.02	.01

* * *

Cards which have team logos missing from helmets, caps or uniforms generally have been airbrushed to avoid having to pay a royalty to the teams for the depiction of their insignias.

* * *

In 1987, Sports Collectors Digest readers selected the 1957 set as Topps' best issue, with 15 percent of the votes, followed by the 1953 set, with 8 percent. The 1972 Topps set, with 20 percent of the votes, took the booby prize as the worst set, followed by the 1982 set, with 11 percent.

* * *

Mike Devereaux

Set	Card #	MT	NM	EX
1988 Donruss	546 (R)	.30	.25	.12
1988 Fleer	512 (R)	.75	.60	.30
1988 Score	637 (R)	.40	.30	.15
1988 Score Glossy	637 (R)	2.00	1.50	.80
1989 Donruss	603	.15	.11	.06
1989 Donruss Traded	30	.10	.08	.04
1989 Fleer	56	.15	.11	.06
1989 Fleer Update	2	.15	.11	.06
1989 Topps Traded	23T	.15	.11	.06
1989 Upper Deck	68	.15	.11	.06
1990 Bowman	260	.05	.04	.02
1990 Donruss	282	.07	.05	.03
1990 Fleer	175	.07	.05	.03
1990 Leaf	223	.40	.30	.15
1990 O-Pee-Chee	127	.06	.05	.02
1990 Score	232	.09	.07	.04
1990 Sportflics	114	.10	.08	.04
1990 Topps	127	.06	.05	.02
1990 Topps Big Baseball	178	.06	.05	.02
1990 Topps Glossy Rookies	7	.35	.25	.14
1990 Upper Deck	681	.09	.07	.04
1991 Bowman	93	.06	.05	.02
1991 Donruss	444	.06	.05	.02
1991 Fleer	469a	.06	.05	.02
1991 Fleer	469b	.06	.05	.02
1991 Fleer Ultra	15	.08	.06	.03
1991 Leaf	138	.10	.08	.04
1991 Score	258	.05	.04	.02
1991 Topps	758	.06	.05	.02
1991 Topps Stadium Club	555	.20	.15	.08
1991 Upper Deck	308	.06	.05	.02
1992 Bowman	688	.20	.15	.08
1992 Donruss	354	.06	.05	.02
1992 Fleer	5	.05	.04	.02
1992 Fleer Ultra	2	.15	.11	.06
1992 Leaf	79	.15	.11	.06
1992 O-Pee-Chee	492	.04	.03	.02
1992 Pinnacle	165	.12	.09	.05
1992 Score	36	.05	.04	.02
1992 Studio	123	.10	.08	.04
1992 Topps	492	.04	.03	.02
1992 Topps Gold	492	.25	.20	.10
1992 Topps Stadium Club	199	.20	.15	.08
1992 Upper Deck	209	.06	.05	.02
1993 Bowman	605	.10	.08	.04
1993 Donruss	455	.05	.04	.02
1993 Donruss Triple Play	34	.07	.05	.03
1993 Donruss Triple Play	78	.05	.04	.02
1993 Fleer	165	.08	.06	.03
1993 Fleer Flair	150	.25	.15	.08
1993 Fleer Ultra	493	.10	.08	.04
1993 Leaf	67	.10	.08	.04
1993 O-Pee-Chee	93	.15	.11	.06
1993 Pinnacle	400	.06	.05	.02
1993 Score	170	.04	.03	.02
1993 Score Select	170	.10	.08	.04
1993 Score Select Stat Leaders	20	.10	.08	.04
1993 Studio	55	.08	.06	.03
1993 Topps	741	.03	.02	.01
1993 Topps Black Gold	28	.25	.20	.10
1993 Topps Finest	74	1.00	.70	.40
1993 Topps Finest Refractors	74	20.00	15.00	8.00
1993 Topps Gold	741	.10	.08	.04
1993 Topps Stadium Club	56	.10	.08	.04
1993 Topps Stadium Club First Day Production	56	4.00	3.00	1.50
1993 Upper Deck	167	.08	.06	.03
1993 Upper Deck Fun Packs	132	.05	.04	.02
1993 Upper Deck Home Run Heroes	14	.50	.40	.20
1993 Upper Deck SP	155	.15	.11	.06
1994 Bowman	403	.10	.08	.04
1994 Donruss	69	.05	.04	.02
1994 Donruss Triple Play	153	.05	.04	.02
1994 Fleer	3	.05	.04	.02
1994 Fleer Extra Bases	3	.10	.08	.04
1994 Fleer Flair	252	.20	.15	.08
1994 Fleer Ultra	304	.10	.08	.04
1994 Leaf	154	.10	.08	.04
1994 O-Pee-Chee	203	.05	.04	.02
1994 Pacific Crown	29	.05	.04	.02
1994 Pinnacle	13	.10	.08	.04
1994 Pinnacle Artist's Proof	13	3.00	2.25	1.25
1994 Pinnacle Museum Collection	13	1.50	1.25	.60
1994 Score	386	.04	.03	.02
1994 Score Select	131	.10	.08	.04
1994 Studio	122	.10	.08	.04
1994 Topps	534	.04	.03	.02
1994 Topps Finest	117	.50	.40	.20
1994 Topps Finest Refractors	117	3.50	2.75	1.50
1994 Topps Gold	534	.15	.11	.06
1994 Topps Stadium Club	424	.10	.08	.04
1994 Topps Stadium Club First Day Production	424	2.50	2.00	1.00
1994 Upper Deck	356	.10	.08	.04
1994 Upper Deck Collector's Choice	502	.05	.04	.02
1994 Upper Deck Electric Diamond	356	.25	.20	.10

Delino DeShields

Delino DeShields

Set	Card #	MT	NM	EX
1988 O-Pee-Chee	88	6.25	4.75	2.50
1990 Bowman	119 (R)	.30	.25	.12
1990 Donruss	42 (R)	.30	.25	.12
1990 Fleer	653 (R)	.40	.30	.15
1990 Fleer Update	27	.25	.20	.10
1990 Leaf	193 (R)	3.00	2.25	1.25
1990 O-Pee-Chee	224 (R)	.60	.45	.25

Set	#			
1990 Score	645 (R)	.40	.30	.15
1990 Topps	224 (R)	.40	.30	.15
1990 Topps Big Baseball	231	.50	.40	.20
1990 Upper Deck	702	1.00	.70	.40
1990 Upper Deck	746 (R)	.50	.40	.20
1991 Bowman	445	.12	.09	.05
1991 Donruss	11	.08	.06	.03
1991 Donruss	555	.08	.06	.03
1991 Fleer	228	.15	.11	.06
1991 Fleer Ultra	200	.12	.09	.05
1991 Leaf	139	.15	.11	.06
1991 O-Pee-Chee Premier	34	.08	.06	.03
1991 Score	545	.12	.09	.05
1991 Studio	195	.20	.15	.08
1991 Topps	432	.10	.08	.04
1991 Topps Glossy Rookies	8	.35	.25	.14
1991 Topps Stadium Club	194	.60	.45	.25
1991 Topps Stadium Club Charter Members	(6)	.35	.25	.14
1991 Upper Deck	364	.15	.11	.06
1992 Bowman	47	.40	.30	.15
1992 Donruss	277	.08	.06	.03
1992 Donruss Triple Play	209	.10	.08	.04
1992 Fleer	476	.08	.06	.03
1992 Fleer Ultra	220	.15	.11	.06
1992 Leaf	138	.15	.11	.06
1992 O-Pee-Chee	515	.08	.06	.03
1992 O-Pee-Chee Premier	163	.20	.15	.08
1992 Pinnacle	24	.15	.11	.06
1992 Pinnacle Team 2000	22	.20	.15	.08
1992 Score	16	.08	.06	.03
1992 Studio	54	.10	.08	.04
1992 Topps	515	.08	.06	.03
1992 Topps Gold	515	.40	.30	.15
1992 Topps Kids	9	.05	.04	.02
1992 Topps Stadium Club	505	.15	.11	.06
1992 Upper Deck	36	.05	.04	.02
1992 Upper Deck	167	.08	.06	.03
1993 Bowman	424	.15	.11	.06
1993 DiamondMarks	(37)	.35	.25	.14
1993 Donruss	564	.05	.04	.02
1993 Donruss Triple Play	102	.10	.08	.04
1993 Fleer	74	.08	.06	.03
1993 Fleer All-Stars	2	.75	.60	.30
1993 Fleer Flair	81	.35	.25	.14
1993 Fleer Ultra	66	.20	.15	.08
1993 Leaf	268	.15	.11	.06
1993 Leaf Gold All-Stars	5	1.00	.75	.40
1993 O-Pee-Chee	183	.20	.15	.08
1993 O-Pee-Chee Premier	7	.15	.11	.06
1993 Pinnacle	121	.06	.05	.02
1993 Pinnacle	302	.06	.05	.02
1993 Pinnacle Team Pinnacle	5	8.00	6.00	3.25
1993 Pinnacle Team 2001	12	.50	.40	.20
1993 Score	145	.08	.06	.03
1993 Score Select	43	.12	.09	.05
1993 Score Select Stat Leaders	59	.15	.11	.06
1993 Studio	150	.12	.09	.05
1993 Topps	368	.06	.05	.02
1993 Topps Black Gold	5	.30	.25	.12
1993 Topps Finest	168	2.00	1.50	.80
1993 Topps Finest Refractors	168	25.00	18.50	10.00
1993 Topps Gold	368	.10	.08	.04
1993 Topps Stadium Club	78	.20	.15	.08
1993 Topps Stadium Club First Day Production	78	25.00	18.50	10.00
1993 Topps Stadium Club Master Photos	(2)	1.50	1.25	.60
1993 Upper Deck	142	.12	.09	.05
1993 Upper Deck	454	.08	.06	.03
1993 Upper Deck Fun Packs	94	.20	.15	.08
1993 Upper Deck Iooss Collection	10	.60	.45	.25
1993 Upper Deck Iooss Collection Super	10	3.00	2.25	1.25
1993 Upper Deck SP	102	.15	.11	.06
1994 Bowman	454	.10	.08	.04
1994 Bowman's Best	39	.50	.40	.20
1994 Bowman's Best Refractors	39	2.00	1.50	.80
1994 Donruss	350	.08	.06	.03
1994 Donruss Special Edition - Gold	350	.30	.25	.12
1994 Donruss Triple Play	83	.05	.04	.02
1994 Fleer	535	.08	.06	.03
1994 Fleer Extra Bases	286	.10	.08	.04
1994 Fleer Flair	395	.20	.15	.08
1994 Fleer Ultra	515	.10	.08	.04
1994 Fleer Update	149	.10	.08	.04
1994 Leaf	277	.10	.08	.04
1994 Leaf Limited	117	1.00	.70	.40
1994 O-Pee-Chee	59	.05	.04	.02
1994 Pacific Crown	377	.10	.08	.04
1994 Pinnacle	147	.15	.11	.06
1994 Pinnacle Artist's Proof	147	4.00	3.00	1.50
1994 Pinnacle Museum Collection	147	2.00	1.50	.80
1994 Score	38	.08	.06	.03
1994 Score Rookie & Traded Gold Rush	6	.25	.20	.10
1994 Score Rookie & Traded Changing Places	9	1.50	1.25	.60
1994 Score Rookie and Traded	6	.05	.04	.02
1994 Score Rookie/ Traded Samples	6RT	2.00	1.50	.80
1994 Score Select	227	.10	.08	.04
1994 Studio	67	.10	.08	.04
1994 Topps	109a	.15	.11	.06
1994 Topps	109b	.05	.04	.02
1994 Topps Finest	270	.50	.40	.20
1994 Topps Finest Refractors	270	3.50	2.75	1.50
1994 Topps Gold	109a	.45	.35	.20
1994 Topps Gold	109b	.15	.11	.06
1994 Topps Stadium Club	549	.10	.08	.04
1994 Topps Stadium Club First Day Production	549	3.50	2.75	1.50
1994 Upper Deck	465	.10	.08	.04
1994 Upper Deck Collector's Choice	92	.05	.04	.02
1994 Upper Deck Collector's Choice	524	.05	.04	.02
1994 Upper Deck Electric Diamond	465	.25	.20	.10
1994 Upper Deck Fun Packs	94	.05	.04	.02

* * *

The Oct. 23, 1992, Sports Collectors Digest cited an article in the Chicago Tribune which listed baseball cards, desktop publishing and message therapy as the fastest-growing businesses in 1991, based on the number of businesses listed under those categories in 5,000 telephone books nationwide. The number of listings under the heading "baseball cards" increased from 3,274 in 1990 to 5,755 in 1991, a 76 percent increase, according to the American Business Institute, a market-research firm that compiled the data.

* * *

The first National Sports Collectors Convention was held in Los Angeles, Aug. 28-Sept. 1, 1980. The show sponsors were Gavin Riley, Mike Berkus and Steve Brunner.

* * *

Joe DiMaggio

JOE DI MAGGIO, Yankees

Set	Card #	NM	EX	VG
1937 O-Pee-Chee	118	5000.	2500.	1500.
1938 Goudey	250	4000.	2100.	1100.
1938 Goudey	274	4500.	2200.	1200.
1939 Goudey Premiums (R303-B)	(6)	300.00	150.00	90.00
1939 Goudey Premiums (R303-A)	(13)	275.00	137.00	82.00
1939 Play Ball	26a	2000.	1000.	600.00
1939 Play Ball	26b	2000.	1000.	600.00
1940 Play Ball	1	2500.	900.00	550.00
1941 Double Play	63	550.00	550.00	550.00
1941 Play Ball	71	2500.	1175.	700.00
1948 Leaf	1	2000.	750.00	475.00

Set	Card #	MT	NM	EX
1986 Sportflics Decade Greats	20	1.50	1.25	.60
1992 Score Joe DiMaggio	1	20.00	15.00	8.00
1992 Score Joe DiMaggio	2	20.00	15.00	8.00
1992 Score Joe DiMaggio	3	20.00	15.00	8.00
1992 Score Joe DiMaggio	4	20.00	15.00	8.00
1992 Score Joe DiMaggio	5	20.00	15.00	8.00

Larry Doby

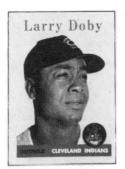

Set	Card #	NM	EX	VG
1948 Leaf	138 (R)	500.00	250.00	150.00
1949 Bowman	233	175.00	87.00	52.00
1950 Bowman	39	65.00	32.50	19.50
1951 Bowman	151	20.00	10.00	6.00
1952 Bowman	115	25.00	12.50	7.50
1952 Red Man Tobacco	6A	35.00	17.50	10.50
1952 Topps	243	45.00	22.00	10.50
1953 Bowman Color	40	35.00	17.50	10.50
1954 Bowman	84	12.00	6.00	3.50
1954 Topps	70	60.00	30.00	18.00
1955 Red Man Tobacco	18A	35.00	17.50	10.50
1956 Topps	250	22.00	11.00	6.50

1957 Topps	85	10.00	5.00	3.00
1958 Topps	424	5.50	2.75	1.75
1959 Topps	166	12.00	6.00	3.50
1959 Topps	455	4.00	2.00	1.25
1973 O-Pee-Chee	377	.75	.40	.25
1973 Topps	377	.60	.30	.20
1974 O-Pee-Chee	531	.60	.30	.20
1974 Topps	531	.40	.20	.12

Set	Card #	MT	NM	EX
1983 Topps 1952 Reprint Set	243	.30	.25	.12
1988 Pacific Trading Cards Baseball Legends	102	.15	.11	.06
1990 Pacific Legends	20	.05	.04	.02
1991 "1953" Topps Archives	333	.25	.20	.10
1994 "1954" Topps Archives	70	.25	.20	.10

Doug Drabek

Set	Card #	MT	NM	EX
1986 Fleer Update	36	1.00	.75	.40
1987 Donruss	251 (R)	.60	.45	.25
1987 Fleer	96 (R)	1.00	.70	.40
1987 Topps	283 (R)	.40	.30	.15
1987 Topps Traded	29T	.30	.25	.12
1988 Donruss	79	.07	.05	.03
1988 Fleer	327	.08	.06	.03
1988 Leaf	88	.08	.06	.03
1988 O-Pee-Chee	143	.08	.06	.03
1988 Score	51	.10	.08	.04
1988 Topps	591	.06	.05	.02
1988 Topps Big Baseball	124	.08	.06	.03
1989 Bowman	416	.03	.02	.01
1989 Donruss	211	.06	.05	.02
1989 Fleer	206	.07	.05	.03
1989 O-Pee-Chee	37	.07	.05	.02
1989 Score	117	.06	.05	.02
1989 Sportflics	27	.10	.08	.04
1989 Topps	478	.06	.05	.02
1989 Upper Deck	597	.08	.06	.03
1990 Bowman	164	.08	.06	.03
1990 Donruss	92	.05	.04	.02
1990 Fleer	465	.06	.05	.02
1990 Leaf	296	.35	.25	.14
1990 O-Pee-Chee	197	.07	.05	.03
1990 Score	505	.06	.05	.02
1990 Topps	197	.07	.05	.03
1990 Topps Big Baseball	185	.10	.08	.04
1990 Upper Deck	422	.10	.08	.04
1991 Bowman	515	.06	.05	.02
1991 Donruss	269	.10	.08	.04
1991 Donruss	411	.06	.05	.02
1991 Donruss	750	.08	.06	.03
1991 Donruss Elite	5	35.00	26.00	14.00
1991 Fleer	36	.10	.08	.04
1991 Fleer Ultra	277	.10	.08	.04

1991 Fleer Ultra Gold	3	.40	.30	.15
1991 Leaf	516	.10	.08	.04
1991 Score	472	.08	.06	.03
1991 Score	661	.08	.06	.03
1991 Score	878	.06	.05	.03
1991 Studio	224	.15	.11	.06
1991 Topps	405	.08	.06	.03
1991 Topps	685	.08	.06	.03
1991 Topps Stadium Club	202	.30	.25	.12
1991 Topps Stadium Club Charter Members	(7)	.25	.20	.10
1991 Upper Deck	278	.10	.08	.04
1992 Bowman	465	.40	.30	.15
1992 Donruss	209	.10	.08	.04
1992 Donruss Triple Play	106	.12	.09	.05
1992 Fleer	553	.08	.06	.03
1992 Fleer Ultra	253	.15	.11	.06
1992 Leaf	11	.05	.04	.02
1992 O-Pee-Chee	440	.08	.06	.03
1992 O-Pee-Chee Premier	32	.20	.15	.08
1992 Pinnacle	96	.15	.11	.06
1992 Score	115	.08	.06	.03
1992 Studio	84	.15	.11	.06
1992 Topps	440	.08	.06	.03
1992 Topps Gold	440	.25	.20	.10
1992 Topps Kids	24	.05	.04	.02
1992 Topps Stadium Club	170	.20	.15	.08
1992 Upper Deck	39	.05	.04	.02
1992 Upper Deck	221	.08	.06	.03
1992 Upper Deck MVP Holograms	18	.25	.20	.10
1993 Bowman	208	.10	.08	.04
1993 Donruss	622	.05	.04	.02
1993 Donruss Triple Play	232	.05	.04	.02
1993 Fleer	500	.05	.04	.02
1993 Fleer Final Edition	77	.05	.04	.02
1993 Fleer Flair	61	.25	.15	.08
1993 Fleer Ultra	392	.10	.08	.04
1993 Leaf	293	.10	.08	.04
1993 Leaf Gold All-Stars	20	2.00	1.50	.80
1993 O-Pee-Chee	72	.15	.11	.06
1993 O-Pee-Chee Premier	73	.10	.08	.04
1993 Pinnacle	423	.06	.05	.02
1993 Pinnacle	485	.08	.06	.03
1993 Score	580	.08	.06	.03
1993 Score Select	153	.12	.09	.05
1993 Score Select Aces	16	3.00	2.25	1.25
1993 Score Select Rookie/Traded	97	.25	.20	.10
1993 Score Select Stat Leaders	66	.10	.08	.04
1993 Studio	194	.08	.06	.03
1993 Topps	190	.08	.06	.03
1993 Topps Finest	127	1.00	.70	.40
1993 Topps Finest Refractors	127	20.00	15.00	8.00
1993 Topps Gold	190	.15	.11	.06
1993 Topps Stadium Club	167	.25	.20	.10
1993 Topps Stadium Club	672	.10	.08	.04
1993 Topps Stadium Club First Day Production	167	5.00	3.75	2.00
1993 Topps Stadium Club First Day Production	672	5.00	3.75	2.00
1993 Topps Traded	94	.05	.04	.02
1993 Upper Deck	475	.12	.09	.05
1993 Upper Deck	664	.07	.05	.03
1993 Upper Deck Fun Packs	46	.05	.04	.02
1993 Upper Deck SP	32	.15	.11	.06
1994 Bowman	174	.10	.08	.04
1994 Donruss	632	.07	.05	.03
1994 Donruss Triple Play	25	.05	.04	.02
1994 Fleer	489	.05	.04	.02
1994 Fleer Extra Bases	272	.10	.08	.04
1994 Fleer Extra Bases Pitcher's Duel	10M	.40	.30	.15
1994 Fleer Flair	388	.20	.15	.08
1994 Fleer Ultra	501	.10	.08	.04

1994 Leaf	271	.10	.08	.04
1994 Leaf Limited	114	1.00	.70	.40
1994 O-Pee-Chee	248	.05	.04	.02
1994 Pacific Crown	263	.05	.04	.02
1994 Pinnacle	104	.10	.08	.04
1994 Pinnacle Artist's Proof	104	3.00	2.25	1.25
1994 Pinnacle Museum Collection	104	1.50	1.25	.60
1994 Score	426	.04	.03	.02
1994 Score Select	349	.10	.08	.04
1994 Sportflics 2000	17	.10	.08	.04
1994 Studio	20	.10	.08	.04
1994 Topps	220	.04	.03	.02
1994 Topps Finest	345	.50	.40	.20
1994 Topps Finest Refractors	345	3.50	2.75	1.50
1994 Topps Gold	220	.15	.11	.06
1994 Topps Stadium Club	408	.10	.08	.04
1994 Topps Stadium Club First Day Production	408	2.50	2.00	1.00
1994 Upper Deck	452	.10	.08	.04
1994 Upper Deck Collector's Choice	95	.05	.04	.02
1994 Upper Deck Electric Diamond	452	.25	.20	.10
1994 Upper Deck Fun Packs	138	.05	.04	.02

Don Drysdale

Set	Card #	NM	EX	VG
1957 Topps	18 (R)	195.00	95.00	57.50
1958 Topps	25	70.00	35.00	21.00
1959 Topps	262	10.00	5.00	3.00
1959 Topps	387	35.00	17.50	10.50
1960 Post Cereal	(2)	400.00	200.00	120.00
1960 Topps	475	35.00	17.50	10.50
1960 Topps	570	25.00	12.50	7.50
1961 Post Cereal	160a	7.00	3.50	2.00
1961 Post Cereal	160b	8.00	4.00	2.50
1961 Topps	45	6.00	3.00	1.75
1961 Topps	49	10.00	5.00	3.00
1961 Topps	260	30.00	15.00	9.00
1962 Post Cereal	110	10.00	5.00	3.00
1962 Topps	60	10.00	5.00	3.00
1962 Topps	340	35.00	17.50	10.50
1962 Topps	398	15.00	7.50	4.50
1963 Fleer	41	50.00	25.00	15.00
1963 Post Cereal	123	12.00	6.00	3.50
1963 Topps	5	15.00	7.50	4.50
1963 Topps	7	7.50	3.75	2.25
1963 Topps	9	12.00	6.00	3.50
1963 Topps	360	40.00	20.00	12.00
1963 Topps	412	35.00	17.50	10.50
1964 Topps	5	12.00	6.00	3.50
1964 Topps	120	20.00	10.00	6.00
1965 O-Pee-Chee	8	17.00	8.50	5.00
1965 O-Pee-Chee	12	2.75	1.50	.80

1965 O-Pee-Chee	260	30.00	15.00	9.00
1965 Topps	8	11.00	5.50	3.25
1965 Topps	12	7.00	3.50	2.00
1965 Topps	260	20.00	10.00	6.00
1966 Topps	223	8.00	4.00	2.50
1966 Topps	430	20.00	10.00	6.00
1967 O-Pee-Chee	55	21.00	10.50	6.25
1967 Topps	55	13.50	6.75	4.00
1968 O-Pee-Chee	145	15.00	7.50	4.50
1968 Topps	145	12.00	6.00	3.50
1969 Topps	314	3.50	1.75	1.00
1969 Topps	400	11.00	5.50	3.25

Set	Card #	MT	NM	EX
1990 Pacific Legends	29	.15	.11	.06
1990 Topps All-Star Glossy Set of 22	11	.20	.15	.08

Len Dykstra

Set	Card #	MT	NM	EX
1986 Donruss	482 (R)	5.00	3.75	2.00
1986 Fleer	78 (R)	6.00	4.50	2.50
1986 O-Pee-Chee	53	2.50	2.00	1.00
1986 Topps	53 (R)	1.75	1.25	.70
1987 Donruss	611	.75	.60	.30
1987 Fleer	6	.75	.60	.30
1987 Leaf	88	.10	.08	.04
1987 O-Pee-Chee	295	.10	.08	.04
1987 Sportflics	58	.30	.25	.12
1987 Topps	295	.30	.25	.12
1988 Donruss	364	.20	.15	.08
1988 Fleer	133	.35	.25	.14
1988 Leaf	135	.08	.06	.03
1988 O-Pee-Chee	299	.08	.06	.03
1988 Score	370	.15	.11	.06
1988 Sportflics	106	.20	.15	.08
1988 Topps	655	.12	.09	.05
1988 Topps Big Baseball	203	.15	.11	.06
1989 Donruss	353	.20	.15	.08
1989 Fleer	33	.15	.11	.06
1989 O-Pee-Chee	349	.10	.08	.04
1989 Score	84	.20	.15	.08
1989 Score Traded	28T	.15	.11	.06
1989 Sportflics	123	.10	.08	.04
1989 Topps	435	.10	.08	.04
1989 Topps Big Baseball	41	.05	.04	.02
1989 Topps Traded	27T	.15	.11	.06
1989 Upper Deck	369	.50	.40	.20
1990 Bowman	152	.08	.06	.03
1990 Donruss	313	.15	.11	.06
1990 Fleer	556	.15	.11	.06
1990 Leaf	262	1.00	.75	.40
1990 O-Pee-Chee	515	.06	.05	.02
1990 Score	427	.15	.11	.06
1990 Sportflics	156	.10	.08	.04
1990 Topps	515	.10	.07	.04
1990 Topps Big Baseball	300	.15	.11	.06
1990 Upper Deck	472	.20	.15	.08
1991 Bowman	501	.12	.09	.05

1991 Donruss	7	.06	.05	.02
1991 Donruss	410	.08	.06	.03
1991 Donruss	434	.06	.05	.02
1991 Donruss	523	.12	.09	.05
1991 Fleer	395	.10	.08	.04
1991 Fleer Ultra	262	.15	.11	.06
1991 Leaf	163	.15	.11	.06
1991 Post Cereal	8	.40	.30	.15
1991 Score	250	.15	.11	.06
1991 Score	867	.10	.07	.04
1991 Studio	213	.20	.15	.08
1991 Topps	345	.15	.11	.06
1991 Topps All-Star Glossy Set of 22	18	.20	.15	.08
1991 Topps Stadium Club	150	.60	.45	.25
1991 Upper Deck	267	.15	.11	.06
1992 Bowman	635	.50	.40	.20
1992 Donruss	57	.15	.11	.06
1992 Fleer	529	.08	.06	.03
1992 Fleer Team Leaders	10	2.50	2.00	1.00
1992 Fleer Ultra	241	.30	.25	.12
1992 Leaf	504	.15	.11	.06
1992 O-Pee-Chee	200	.08	.06	.03
1992 O-Pee-Chee Premier	184	.15	.11	.06
1992 Pinnacle	12	.25	.20	.10
1992 Score	560	.12	.09	.05
1992 Score Impact Players	74	.20	.15	.08
1992 Studio	75	.15	.11	.06
1992 Topps	200	.08	.06	.03
1992 Topps Gold	200	1.25	.90	.50
1992 Topps Kids	17	.10	.08	.04
1992 Topps Stadium Club	470	.25	.20	.10
1992 Upper Deck	246	.10	.08	.04
1993 Bowman	300	.15	.11	.06
1993 DiamondMarks	(46)	.60	.45	.25
1993 Donruss	544	.15	.11	.06
1993 Donruss Triple Play	185	.15	.11	.06
1993 Fleer	488	.10	.08	.04
1993 Fleer Flair	99	.40	.30	.15
1993 Fleer Ultra	439	.15	.11	.06
1993 Leaf	59	.15	.11	.06
1993 O-Pee-Chee	119	.20	.15	.08
1993 Pinnacle	45	.15	.11	.06
1993 Pinnacle	477	.12	.09	.05
1993 Score	30	.10	.08	.04
1993 Score Select	59	.15	.11	.06
1993 Studio	101	.15	.11	.06
1993 Topps	740	.06	.05	.02
1993 Topps Finest	177	3.00	2.25	1.25
1993 Topps Finest Refractors	177	40.00	30.00	16.00
1993 Topps Gold	740	.10	.08	.04
1993 Topps Stadium Club	477	.15	.11	.06
1993 Topps Stadium Club First Day Production	477	15.00	11.00	6.00
1993 Topps Stadium Club Team Sets	15	.50	.40	.20
1993 Upper Deck	69	.10	.07	.04
1993 Upper Deck Fun Packs	144	.15	.11	.06
1993 Upper Deck SP	173	.40	.30	.15
1993 Upper Deck SP Jumbos	173	25.00	18.50	10.00
1994 Bowman	440	.20	.15	.08
1994 Bowman's Best	47	.75	.60	.30
1994 Bowman's Best Refractors	47	3.00	2.25	1.25
1994 Donruss	373	.10	.08	.04
1994 Donruss Decade Dominators	9	1.50	1.25	.60
1994 Donruss Decade Dominators Supers	9	3.50	2.75	1.50
1994 Donruss MVP's	10	.75	.60	.30
1994 Donruss Special Edition - Gold	373	.30	.25	.12
1994 Donruss Spirit of the Game	10	3.00	2.25	1.25
1994 Donruss Spirit of the Game Super	10	10.00	7.50	4.00

1994 Donruss Triple Play Promos	8	3.00	2.25	1.25
1994 Donruss Triple Play Medalists	12	3.00	2.25	1.25
1994 Donruss Triple Play	173	.05	.04	.02
1994 Fleer	587	.10	.07	.04
1994 Fleer Extra Bases	332	.15	.11	.06
1994 Fleer Extra Bases Game Breakers	9	.35	.25	.14
1994 Fleer Flair	205	.50	.40	.20
1994 Fleer Flair Outfield Power	4	3.00	2.25	1.25
1994 Fleer League Leaders	9	.40	.30	.15
1994 Fleer Team Leaders	24	.50	.40	.20
1994 Fleer Ultra	544	.15	.11	.06
1994 Fleer Ultra All-Stars	17	.75	.60	.30
1994 Fleer Ultra League Leaders	7	.50	.40	.20
1994 Fleer Ultra On-Base Leaders	3	5.00	3.75	2.00
1994 Leaf	97	.15	.11	.06
1994 Leaf Gamers	2	2.00	1.50	.80
1994 Leaf Gold Stars	5	10.00	7.50	4.00
1994 Leaf Limited	136	1.75	1.25	.70
1994 O-Pee-Chee	168	.20	.15	.08
1994 Pacific Crown	473	.12	.09	.05
1994 Pacific Crown Jewels of the Crown	33	2.50	2.00	1.00
1994 Pinnacle	34	.15	.11	.06
1994 Pinnacle Artist's Proof	34	5.00	3.75	2.00
1994 Pinnacle Museum Collection	34	3.00	2.25	1.25
1994 Pinnacle Run Creators	24	2.00	1.50	.80
1994 Pinnacle Team Pinnacle	6	60.00	45.00	24.00
1994 Pinnacle The Naturals Box Set	17	.25	.20	.10
1994 Pinnacle Tribute	6	2.00	1.50	.80
1994 Post Cereal	20	.35	.25	.14
1994 Score	60	.10	.08	.04
1994 Score	624	.06	.05	.02
1994 Score Gold Stars	17	3.00	2.25	1.25
1994 Score Select	89	.15	.11	.06
1994 Score Select Crown Contenders	1	5.00	3.75	2.00
1994 Score Select Skills	3	5.00	3.75	2.00
1994 Score The Cycle	8	8.00	6.00	3.25
1994 Sportflics 2000	1	.25	.20	.10
1994 Sportflics 2000	191	.10	.08	.04
1994 Sportflics 2000 Movers	12	4.00	3.00	1.50
1994 Sportflics 2000 Promos	1	2.00	1.50	.80
1994 Studio	138	.20	.15	.08
1994 Topps	388	.40	.30	.15
1994 Topps	635	.06	.05	.02
1994 Topps Black Gold	29	.40	.30	.15
1994 Topps Finest	237	.75	.60	.30
1994 Topps Finest Refractors	237	4.50	3.50	1.75
1994 Topps Finest Superstars	237	2.50	2.00	1.00
1994 Topps Gold	388	1.50	1.25	.60
1994 Topps Gold	635	.15	.11	.06
1994 Topps Stadium Club	165	.15	.11	.06
1994 Topps Stadium Club First Day Production	165	8.00	6.00	3.25
1994 Topps Stadium Club Members Only Baseball	13	.35	.25	.14
1994 Upper Deck	172	.15	.11	.06
1994 Upper Deck Collector's Choice	345	.05	.04	.02
1994 Upper Deck Collector's Choice	369	.05	.04	.02
1994 Upper Deck Diamond Collection	3E	5.00	3.75	2.00

1994 Upper Deck Electric Diamond	172	.50	.40	.20
1994 Upper Deck Fun Packs	69	.10	.08	.04
1994 Upper Deck Fun Packs	191	.10	.08	.04

Dennis Eckersley

Set	Card #	NM	EX	VG
1976 O-Pee-Chee	98	63.00	31.00	19.00
1976 O-Pee-Chee	202	5.00	2.50	1.50
1976 Topps	98 (R)	45.00	22.00	13.50
1976 Topps	202	5.00	2.50	1.50
1977 O-Pee-Chee	15	12.75	6.50	3.75
1977 Topps	525	8.00	4.00	2.50
1978 O-Pee-Chee	138	8.50	4.25	2.50
1978 Topps	122	7.00	3.50	2.00
1979 O-Pee-Chee	16	6.00	3.00	1.75
1979 Topps	40	7.00	3.50	2.00
1980 O-Pee-Chee	169	2.75	1.50	.80
1980 Topps	320	2.00	1.00	.60

Set	Card #	MT	NM	EX
1981 Donruss	96	1.50	1.25	.60
1981 Fleer	226	1.50	1.25	.60
1981 O-Pee-Chee	109	1.75	1.25	.70
1981 Topps	620	1.50	1.25	.60
1982 Donruss	30	1.00	.75	.40
1982 Fleer	292	1.50	1.25	.60
1982 O-Pee-Chee	287	1.50	1.25	.60
1982 Topps	490	.20	.15	.08
1983 Donruss	487	1.00	.70	.40
1983 Fleer	182	.60	.45	.25
1983 Fleer	629	.25	.20	.10
1983 O-Pee-Chee	270	.12	.09	.05
1983 Topps	270	1.00	.75	.40
1984 Donruss	639	3.00	2.25	1.25
1984 Fleer	396	.15	.11	.06
1984 Fleer Update	34	10.00	7.50	4.00
1984 O-Pee-Chee	218	.85	.60	.35
1984 Topps	745	.15	.11	.06
1984 Topps Traded	34T	4.00	3.00	1.50
1985 Donruss	442	1.50	1.25	.60
1985 Fleer	57	1.00	.75	.40
1985 O-Pee-Chee	163	.10	.08	.04
1985 Topps	163	.25	.20	.10
1986 Donruss	239	.12	.09	.05
1986 Fleer	368	.20	.15	.08
1986 Leaf	113	.10	.08	.04
1986 O-Pee-Chee	199	.10	.08	.04
1986 Sportflics	129	.10	.08	.04
1986 Topps	538	.20	.15	.08
1987 Donruss	365	.20	.15	.08
1987 Fleer	563	.25	.20	.10
1987 Fleer Update	30	.30	.25	.12
1987 O-Pee-Chee	381	.10	.08	.04
1987 Topps	459	.10	.08	.04
1987 Topps Traded	31T	.30	.25	.12
1988 Donruss	349	.12	.09	.05

1988 Fleer	279	.12	.09	.05
1988 O-Pee-Chee	72	.08	.06	.03
1988 Score	104	.10	.08	.04
1988 Topps	72	.10	.08	.04
1989 Bowman	190	.08	.06	.03
1989 Donruss	67	.10	.08	.04
1989 Fleer	7	.12	.09	.05
1989 Fleer All-Stars	4	.20	.15	.05
1989 O-Pee-Chee	370	.08	.06	.03
1989 Score	276	.10	.08	.04
1989 Sportflics	101	.15	.11	.06
1989 Sportflics	222	.25	.20	.10
1989 Topps	370	.10	.08	.04
1989 Topps All-Star Glossy Set of 60	16	.20	.15	.08
1989 Upper Deck	289	.25	.20	.10
1989 Upper Deck	664	.08	.06	.03
1990 Bowman	451	.06	.05	.02
1990 Donruss	210	.09	.07	.04
1990 Fleer	6	.12	.09	.05
1990 Leaf	29	.50	.40	.20
1990 O-Pee-Chee	670	.09	.07	.04
1990 Score	315	.08	.06	.03
1990 Sportflics	170	.10	.08	.04
1990 Topps	670	.09	.07	.04
1990 Topps All-Star Glossy Set of 60	53	.20	.15	.08
1990 Topps Big Baseball	50	.15	.11	.06
1990 Upper Deck	513	.10	.08	.04
1991 Bowman	237	.10	.08	.04
1991 Donruss	270	.10	.08	.04
1991 Fleer	6	.10	.08	.04
1991 Fleer Ultra	245	.10	.08	.04
1991 Leaf	285	.20	.15	.08
1991 O-Pee-Chee Premier	38	.08	.06	.03
1991 Score	485	.12	.09	.05
1991 Studio	102	.15	.11	.06
1991 Topps	250	.10	.08	.04
1991 Upper Deck	172	.15	.11	.06
1992 Bowman	431	.40	.30	.15
1992 Donruss	147	.10	.08	.04
1992 Donruss Triple Play	195	.10	.08	.04
1992 Fleer	255	.07	.05	.03
1992 Fleer Ultra	421	.15	.11	.06
1992 Leaf	100	.10	.07	.04
1992 O-Pee-Chee	738	.08	.06	.03
1992 O-Pee-Chee Premier	188	.20	.15	.08
1992 Pinnacle	25	.15	.11	.06
1992 Pinnacle Team Pinnacle	11	6.00	4.50	2.50
1992 Score	190	.08	.06	.03
1992 Studio	223	.20	.15	.08
1992 Topps	738	.08	.06	.03
1992 Topps Gold	738	.40	.30	.15
1992 Topps Kids	119	.10	.08	.04
1992 Topps Stadium Club	190	.25	.20	.10
1992 Topps Stadium Club Special Edition	42	.20	.15	.08
1992 Upper Deck	331	.08	.06	.03
1992 Upper Deck MVP Holograms	19	.35	.25	.14
1993 Bowman	485	.10	.08	.04
1993 Donruss	215	.08	.06	.03
1993 Donruss Elite	25	20.00	15.00	8.00
1993 Donruss Elite Supers	7	8.00	6.00	3.25
1993 Donruss Spirit of the Game	4	1.00	.75	.40
1993 Donruss Triple Play League Leaders	1	7.50	5.75	3.00
1993 Donruss Triple Play League Leaders	2	3.00	2.25	1.25
1993 Donruss Triple Play	9	.07	.05	.03
1993 Fleer	293	.10	.08	.04
1993 Fleer	717	.10	.08	.04
1993 Fleer Flair	257	.25	.15	.08
1993 Fleer Golden Moments II	(1)	.75	.60	.30
1993 Fleer ProVisions I	2	.75	.60	.30
1993 Fleer Ultra	257	.15	.11	.06
1993 Fleer Ultra Award Winners	23	1.00	.75	.40
1993 Leaf	72	.10	.08	.04
1993 Leaf Gold All-Stars	10	1.00	.70	.40
1993 O-Pee-Chee	106	.15	.11	.06
1993 Pinnacle	100	.06	.05	.02
1993 Pinnacle	474	.10	.07	.04
1993 Pinnacle Cooperstown	6	.25	.20	.10
1993 Pinnacle Cooperstown Dufex	6	35.00	26.00	14.00
1993 Score	21	.08	.06	.03
1993 Score	481	.06	.05	.02
1993 Score	483	.06	.05	.02
1993 Score	509	.04	.03	.02
1993 Score	513	.06	.05	.02
1993 Score	540	.06	.05	.02
1993 Score Gold Dream Team	9	.75	.60	.30
1993 Score Select	38	.12	.09	.05
1993 Score Select Chase Stars	24	2.50	2.00	1.00
1993 Score Select Stat Leaders	67	.15	.11	.06
1993 Score The Franchise	11	1.00	.70	.40
1993 Studio	1	.08	.06	.03
1993 Topps	411	.03	.02	.01
1993 Topps Black Gold	29	.25	.20	.10
1993 Topps Finest	100	1.25	.90	.50
1993 Topps Finest Jumbo All-Stars	100	7.00	5.25	2.75
1993 Topps Finest Refractors	100	24.00	18.00	9.50
1993 Topps Gold	155	.15	.11	.06
1993 Topps Gold	411	.10	.08	.04
1993 Topps Stadium Club	291	.50	.40	.20
1993 Topps Stadium Club	461	.10	.08	.04
1993 Topps Stadium Club First Day Production	291	12.00	9.00	4.75
1993 Topps Stadium Club First Day Production	461	15.00	11.00	6.00
1993 Topps Stadium Club Special	179	.10	.08	.04
1993 Topps Stadium Club Team Sets	1	.50	.40	.20
1993 Upper Deck	271	.12	.09	.05
1993 Upper Deck	487	.06	.05	.02
1993 Upper Deck	489	.06	.05	.02
1993 Upper Deck Clutch Performers	8	.75	.60	.30
1993 Upper Deck Fun Packs	49	.12	.09	.05
1993 Upper Deck On Deck	10	.50	.40	.20
1993 Upper Deck SP	38	.15	.11	.06
1993 Upper Deck Then And Now	10	1.50	1.25	.60
1994 Bowman	520	.10	.08	.04
1994 Donruss	16	.05	.04	.02
1994 Donruss Special Edition - Gold	16	.25	.20	.10
1994 Donruss Triple Play	2	.06	.04	.02
1994 Fleer	260	.05	.04	.02
1994 Fleer Extra Bases	148	.10	.08	.04
1994 Fleer Flair	91	.20	.15	.08
1994 Fleer Ultra	405	.12	.09	.05
1994 Fleer Ultra Firemen	5	1.00	.75	.40
1994 Leaf	234	.12	.09	.05
1994 Leaf Limited	59	1.00	.70	.40
1994 O-Pee-Chee	144	.05	.04	.02
1994 Pacific Crown	448	.10	.08	.04
1994 Pinnacle	32	.10	.08	.04
1994 Pinnacle Artist's Proof	32	3.00	2.25	1.25
1994 Pinnacle Museum Collection	32	1.50	1.25	.60
1994 Score	109	.04	.03	.02
1994 Score Select	245	.10	.08	.04
1994 Sportflics 2000	50	.10	.08	.04
1994 Studio	1	.10	.08	.04

1994 Topps	465	.05	.04	.02
1994 Topps Finest	206	.50	.40	.20
1994 Topps Finest Refractors	206	3.50	2.75	1.50
1994 Topps Finest Superstars	206	2.50	2.00	1.00
1994 Topps Gold	465	.15	.11	.06
1994 Topps Stadium Club	125	.12	.09	.05
1994 Topps Stadium Club First Day Production	125	2.50	2.00	1.00
1994 Upper Deck	365	.10	.08	.04
1994 Upper Deck Collector's Choice	495	.05	.04	.02
1994 Upper Deck Electric Diamond	365	.25	.20	.10
1994 Upper Deck Fun Packs	43	.05	.04	.02

Dwight Evans

Set	Card #	NM	EX	VG
1973 O-Pee-Chee	614	42.50	21.00	12.50
1973 Topps	614 (R)	25.00	12.50	7.50
1974 O-Pee-Chee	351	6.75	3.50	2.00
1974 Topps	351	5.00	2.50	1.50
1975 O-Pee-Chee	255	6.00	3.00	1.75
1975 Topps	255	4.00	2.00	1.25
1975 Topps Mini	255	1.50	.70	.45
1976 O-Pee-Chee	575	3.00	1.50	.90
1976 Topps	575	2.00	1.00	.60
1977 O-Pee-Chee	259	.75	.40	.25
1977 Topps	25	1.50	.70	.45
1978 Topps	695	1.00	.50	.30
1979 O-Pee-Chee	73	.40	.20	.12
1979 Topps	155	.75	.40	.25
1980 O-Pee-Chee	210	.50	.25	.15
1980 Topps	405	.90	.45	.25

Set	Card #	MT	NM	EX
1981 Donruss	458	.15	.11	.06
1981 Fleer	232	.15	.11	.06
1981 O-Pee-Chee	275	.25	.20	.10
1981 Topps	275	.15	.11	.06
1982 Donruss	7	.15	.11	.06
1982 Donruss	109	.15	.11	.06
1982 Fleer	293	.15	.11	.06
1982 Fleer	642	.15	.11	.06
1982 O-Pee-Chee	355	.20	.15	.08
1982 Topps	162	.25	.20	.10
1982 Topps	355	.15	.11	.06
1983 Donruss	452	.15	.11	.06
1983 Fleer	183	.15	.11	.06
1983 O-Pee-Chee	135	.15	.11	.06
1983 Topps	135	.15	.11	.06
1984 Donruss	395	.30	.25	.12
1984 Fleer	397	.20	.15	.08
1984 O-Pee-Chee	244	.30	.25	.12
1984 Topps	720	.20	.15	.08
1985 Donruss	294	.15	.11	.06
1985 Fleer	158	.12	.09	.05

1985 Leaf-Donruss	150	.20	.15	.08
1985 O-Pee-Chee	271	.15	.11	.06
1985 Topps	580	.12	.09	.05
1986 Donruss	249	.12	.09	.05
1986 Fleer	348	.12	.09	.05
1986 Leaf	127	.10	.08	.04
1986 O-Pee-Chee	60	.10	.08	.04
1986 Sportflics	32	.15	.11	.06
1986 Topps	60	.12	.09	.05
1986 Topps	396	.07	.05	.03
1987 Donruss	129	.12	.09	.05
1987 Fleer	34	.12	.09	.05
1987 Leaf	57	.08	.06	.03
1987 O-Pee-Chee	368	.10	.08	.04
1987 Sportflics	128	.15	.11	.06
1987 Topps	3	.07	.05	.03
1987 Topps	645	.12	.09	.05
1988 Donruss	16	.08	.06	.03
1988 Donruss	216	.12	.09	.05
1988 Donruss All-Stars	23	.12	.09	.05
1988 Donruss Diamond Kings Supers	16	.25	.20	.10
1988 Fleer	351	.12	.09	.05
1988 Leaf	16	.08	.06	.03
1988 Leaf	171	.10	.08	.04
1988 O-Pee-Chee	221	.08	.06	.03
1988 Score	65	.10	.08	.04
1988 Sportflics	137	.15	.11	.06
1988 Topps	470	.10	.08	.04
1988 Topps All-Star Glossy Set of 60	21	.20	.15	.08
1988 Topps Big Baseball	6	.10	.08	.04
1989 Bowman	35	.15	.11	.06
1989 Donruss	240	.10	.08	.04
1989 Fleer	87	.10	.08	.04
1989 O-Pee-Chee	205	.07	.05	.03
1989 Score	193	.10	.08	.04
1989 Sportflics	204	.15	.11	.06
1989 Topps	205	.10	.08	.04
1989 Topps All-Star Glossy Set of 60	36	.15	.11	.06
1989 Topps Big Baseball	193	.05	.04	.02
1989 Upper Deck	366	.10	.08	.04
1990 Bowman	279	.06	.05	.02
1990 Donruss	122	.08	.06	.03
1990 Donruss Grand Slammers	5	.15	.11	.06
1990 Fleer	274	.09	.07	.05
1990 Leaf	235	.35	.25	.14
1990 O-Pee-Chee	375	.08	.06	.03
1990 Score	3	.08	.06	.03
1990 Sportflics	217	.10	.08	.04
1990 Topps	375	.08	.06	.03
1990 Topps Big Baseball	1	.08	.06	.03
1990 Upper Deck	113	.10	.08	.04
1991 Bowman	103	.06	.05	.02
1991 Donruss	122	.08	.06	.03
1991 Fleer	93	.06	.05	.02
1991 Fleer Ultra Update	1	.15	.11	.06
1991 Fleer Update	2	.08	.06	.03
1991 Leaf	266	.10	.08	.04
1991 O-Pee-Chee Premier	39	.05	.04	.02
1991 Score	225	.08	.06	.03
1991 Score Traded	62	.08	.06	.03
1991 Topps	155a	.08	.06	.03
1991 Topps	155b	.12	.09	.05
1991 Topps Stadium Club	351	.30	.25	.12
1991 Topps Traded	37	.08	.06	.03
1991 Upper Deck	549	.08	.06	.03
1991 Upper Deck	776	.12	.09	.05
1992 Donruss	502	.06	.05	.02
1992 Donruss Triple Play	67	.08	.06	.03
1992 Fleer	6	.08	.06	.03
1992 Fleer Ultra	3	.10	.08	.04
1992 O-Pee-Chee	705	.06	.05	.02
1992 Score	150	.08	.06	.03
1992 Topps	705	.06	.05	.02
1992 Topps Gold	705	.35	.25	.14
1992 Topps Stadium Club	463	.15	.11	.06
1992 Upper Deck	248	.08	.06	.03

Bob Feller

Tony Fernandez

Set	Card #	NM	EX	VG
1937 O-Pee-Chee	120	900.00	450.00	270.00
1938 Goudey	264	800.00	344.00	200.00
1938 Goudey	288	900.00	387.00	225.00
1939 Goudey Premiums (R303-B)	(7)	60.00	30.00	18.00
1939 Goudey Premiums (R303-A)	(14)	80.00	40.00	24.00
1941 Double Play	78	165.00	80.00	48.00
1948 Bowman	5	195.00	95.00	57.50
1948 Leaf	93	1200.	600.00	360.00
1949 Bowman	27	150.00	75.00	45.00
1950 Bowman	6	175.00	85.00	50.00
1951 Bowman	30	125.00	62.00	37.00
1951 Topps Red Backs	22	45.00	22.50	13.50
1952 Bowman	43	135.00	65.00	40.00
1952 Red Man Tobacco	8A	80.00	40.00	24.00
1952 Topps	88	175.00	87.00	40.00
1953 Bowman Color	114	250.00	125.00	75.00
1953 Topps	54	90.00	45.00	21.00
1954 Bowman	132	100.00	50.00	30.00
1955 Bowman	134	55.00	27.00	16.50
1956 Topps	200	105.00	55.00	35.00
1960 Fleer	26	8.00	4.00	2.50
1961-62 Fleer	25	6.00	3.00	1.75

Set	Card #	MT	NM	EX
1983 Topps 1952 Reprint Set	88	3.00	2.25	1.25
1986 Sportflics Decade Greats	16	.60	.45	.25
1988 Pacific Trading Cards Baseball Legends	101	.30	.25	.12
1989 Pacific Trading Cards Legends II	156	.20	.15	.08
1990 Pacific Legends	85	.20	.15	.08
1991 "1953" Topps Archives Promos	(4)	15.00	11.00	6.00
1991 "1953" Topps Archives	54	1.00	.70	.40

* * *

A 1954 Topps cello pack with Hank Aaron's rookie card on top made history when it sold for $25,000, a record for any type of unopened pack in hobby history, the Dec. 6, 1991, Sports Collectors Digest reported. Tony Galovich, who sold the card to a Canadian collector, said the amount more than doubled the previous record.

* * *

Card prices reported in an Aug. 6, 1979, Wall Street Journal story, entitled "If you never made a buck out of baseball, take a look at those bubble gum cards": 1954 Topps Hank Aaron, $100; 1952 Topps Mickey Mantle, $680.

* * *

Set	Card #	MT	NM	EX
1984 Donruss	32 (R)	5.00	3.75	2.00
1984 Fleer	152 (R)	4.00	3.00	1.50
1985 Donruss	390	.70	.50	.30
1985 Fleer	103	.25	.20	.10
1985 Leaf-Donruss	91	.15	.11	.06
1985 O-Pee-Chee	48	.75	.60	.30
1985 Topps	48	.25	.20	.10
1986 Donruss	119	.20	.15	.08
1986 Fleer	57	.20	.15	.08
1986 Leaf	45	.15	.11	.06
1986 O-Pee-Chee	241	.10	.08	.04
1986 Sportflics	112	.15	.11	.06
1986 Topps	241	.20	.15	.08
1987 Donruss	72	.12	.09	.05
1987 Fleer	225	.20	.15	.08
1987 Fleer All Stars	3	.40	.30	.15
1987 Leaf	106	.10	.08	.04
1987 O-Pee-Chee	329	.10	.08	.04
1987 Sportflics	113	.25	.20	.10
1987 Sportflics	187	.15	.11	.06
1987 Topps	485	.10	.08	.04
1988 Donruss	12	.12	.09	.05
1988 Donruss	319	.12	.09	.05
1988 Donruss Diamond Kings Supers	12	.30	.25	.12
1988 Fleer	109	.12	.09	.05
1988 Fleer	635	.30	.25	.12
1988 Leaf	12	.10	.08	.04
1988 Leaf	133	.10	.08	.04
1988 O-Pee-Chee	290	.08	.06	.03
1988 Score	20	.10	.08	.04
1988 Score	651	.25	.20	.10
1988 Sportflics	26	.15	.11	.06
1988 Topps	290	.10	.08	.04
1988 Topps All-Star Glossy Set of 60	15	.20	.15	.08
1988 Topps Big Baseball	187	.10	.08	.04
1989 Bowman	254	.08	.06	.03
1989 Donruss	206	.10	.08	.04
1989 Fleer	231	.12	.09	.05
1989 O-Pee-Chee	170	.08	.06	.03
1989 Score	57	.10	.08	.04
1989 Sportflics	93	.15	.11	.06
1989 Topps	170	.10	.08	.04
1989 Topps All-Star Glossy Set of 60	52	.20	.15	.08
1989 Topps Big Baseball	157	.08	.06	.03
1989 Upper Deck	139	.12	.09	.05
1990 Bowman	524	.06	.05	.02
1990 Donruss	149	.07	.05	.03
1990 Fleer	80	.09	.07	.04
1990 Fleer	634	.10	.08	.04
1990 Leaf	53	.35	.25	.14
1990 O-Pee-Chee	685	.09	.07	.04
1990 Score	89	.09	.07	.04
1990 Sportflics	6	.10	.08	.04
1990 Topps	685	.09	.07	.04
1990 Topps Big Baseball	165	.08	.06	.03
1990 Upper Deck	130	.15	.11	.06

1991 Bowman	642	.06	.05	.02
1991 Donruss	524	.06	.05	.02
1991 Fleer	174	.08	.06	.03
1991 Fleer Ultra Update	111	.15	.11	.06
1991 Fleer Update	123	.08	.06	.03
1991 Leaf	315	.15	.11	.06
1991 O-Pee-Chee Premier	43	.12	.09	.05
1991 Score	432	.08	.06	.03
1991 Score Traded	66	.08	.06	.03
1991 Studio	244	.12	.09	.05
1991 Topps	320	.08	.06	.03
1991 Topps Stadium Club	515	.25	.20	.10
1991 Topps Traded	41	.08	.06	.03
1991 Upper Deck	126	.12	.09	.05
1991 Upper Deck	754	.15	.11	.06
1992 Bowman	293	.08	.06	.03
1992 Donruss	362	.08	.06	.03
1992 Donruss Triple Play	102	.05	.04	.02
1992 Donruss Triple Play	165	.06	.05	.02
1992 Fleer	604	.06	.05	.02
1992 Fleer Ultra	276	.10	.08	.04
1992 Leaf	187	.10	.08	.04
1992 O-Pee-Chee	60	.05	.04	.02
1992 Pinnacle	137	.12	.09	.05
1992 Score	645	.06	.05	.02
1992 Studio	103	.10	.08	.04
1992 Topps	60	.05	.04	.02
1992 Topps Gold	60	.35	.25	.14
1992 Topps Kids	57	.05	.04	.02
1992 Topps Stadium Club	203	.15	.11	.06
1992 Upper Deck	272	.08	.06	.03
1993 Bowman	18	.10	.08	.04
1993 Donruss	674	.05	.04	.02
1993 Fleer	470	.06	.05	.02
1993 Fleer Final Edition	293	.05	.04	.02
1993 Fleer Ultra	426	.10	.08	.04
1993 Leaf	273	.10	.08	.04
1993 O-Pee-Chee	70	.15	.11	.06
1993 O-Pee-Chee Premier	20	.10	.08	.04
1993 Pinnacle	533	.06	.05	.02
1993 Score	572	.04	.03	.02
1993 Score Select	93	.08	.06	.03
1993 Score Select Rookie/ Traded	19	.25	.20	.10
1993 Studio	98	.08	.06	.03
1993 Topps	465	.03	.02	.01
1993 Topps Finest	36	1.00	.70	.40
1993 Topps Finest Refractors	36	20.00	15.00	8.00
1993 Topps Gold	465	.10	.08	.04
1993 Topps Stadium Club	644	.10	.08	.04
1993 Topps Stadium Club First Day Production	644	4.00	3.00	1.50
1993 Topps Stadium Club Special	32	.10	.08	.04
1993 Topps Traded	9	.05	.04	.02
1993 Upper Deck	672	.06	.05	.02
1993 Upper Deck Fun Packs	125	.12	.09	.05
1993 Upper Deck SP	47	.15	.11	.06
1994 Donruss	172	.05	.04	.02
1994 Donruss Triple Play Medalists	7	2.50	2.00	1.00
1994 Fleer	331	.05	.04	.02
1994 Fleer Flair	366	.20	.15	.08
1994 Fleer Update	117	.10	.08	.04
1994 Leaf	266	.10	.08	.04
1994 O-Pee-Chee Toronto Blue Jays	9	2.00	1.50	.80
1994 Pacific Crown	639	.05	.04	.02
1994 Pinnacle	427	.10	.08	.04
1994 Pinnacle Artist's Proof	427	3.00	2.25	1.25
1994 Pinnacle Museum Collection	427	1.50	1.25	.60
1994 Score	62	.04	.03	.02
1994 Score Rookie & Traded Gold Rush	39	.25	.20	.10
1994 Score Rookie and Traded	39	.05	.04	.02

1994 Score Select	310	.10	.08	.04
1994 Score The Cycle	13	6.00	4.50	2.50
1994 Topps	702	.04	.03	.02
1994 Topps Gold	702	.15	.11	.06
1994 Topps Stadium Club	214	.10	.08	.04
1994 Topps Stadium Club First Day Production	214	2.50	2.00	1.00
1994 Topps Traded	127	.05	.04	.02
1994 Upper Deck	437	.10	.08	.04
1994 Upper Deck Collector's Choice	619	.05	.04	.02
1994 Upper Deck Electric Diamond	437	.25	.20	.10

Mark Fidrych

Set	Card #	NM	EX	VG
1977 O-Pee-Chee	7	.30	.15	.09
1977 O-Pee-Chee	115	.40	.20	.12
1977 Topps	7	.20	.10	.06
1977 Topps	265 (R)	.70	.35	.20
1978 O-Pee-Chee	235	.25	.13	.08
1978 Topps	45	.25	.13	.08
1979 O-Pee-Chee	329	.25	.13	.08
1979 Topps	625	.25	.13	.08
1980 O-Pee-Chee	231	.15	.08	.05
1980 Topps	445	.20	.10	.06

Set	Card #	MT	NM	EX
1981 Donruss	8	.08	.06	.03
1981 Fleer	462	.08	.06	.03
1981 O-Pee-Chee	150	.12	.09	.05
1981 Topps	150	.12	.09	.05
1988 Pacific Trading Cards Baseball Legends	62	.06	.05	.02

* * *

Mark Fidrych, on his quirk of talking to the ball while he was on the mound: "A batter tips his hat and hits his spikes and nobody pays attention. My pitching coach says that I can go out there and stand on my head if it'll help me. What I'm really doing, I'm talking out loud to myself, not the ball. I'll tell myself to bring my arm down, things like that. Haven't you ever talked to yourself walking down the street? Yeah, but if I went 9-19 instead of 19-9, they'd be saying, 'Put this kid in the loony bin.'"

* * *

The legendary T206 Honus Wagner card first topped the $100,000 mark when it was sold in early 1988 by a seller and buyer who wished to remain anonymous. The card had been listed at $36,000 in NR MT in the 1988 edition of the Sports Collectors Digest Baseball Card Price Guide.

* * *

Cecil Fielder

Set	Card #	MT	NM	EX
1986 Donruss	512 (R)	18.00	13.50	7.25
1986 Fleer	653 (R)	17.00	12.50	6.75
1986 O-Pee-Chee	386	5.50	4.25	2.25
1986 Topps	386 (R)	3.00	2.25	1.25
1987 Fleer Update	31	1.00	.70	.40
1987 O-Pee-Chee	178	.85	.60	.35
1987 Topps	178	.75	.60	.30
1988 Donruss	565	.25	.20	.10
1988 Fleer	110	.75	.60	.30
1988 O-Pee-Chee	21	.30	.25	.12
1988 Score	399	.30	.25	.12
1988 Topps	618	.30	.25	.12
1989 Donruss	442	.25	.20	.10
1989 Fleer	232	.25	.20	.10
1989 O-Pee-Chee	224	.25	.20	.10
1989 Score	120	.25	.15	.08
1989 Topps	541	.30	.25	.12
1989 Upper Deck	364	1.00	.70	.40
1990 Bowman	357	.25	.20	.10
1990 Fleer Update	95	.25	.20	.10
1990 Leaf	165	2.00	1.50	.80
1990 Score Traded	9T	.30	.25	.12
1990 Topps Big Baseball	313	.50	.40	.20
1990 Topps Traded	31T	.25	.20	.10
1990 Upper Deck	786	.25	.20	.10
1991 Bowman	136	.15	.11	.06
1991 Bowman	367	.10	.08	.04
1991 Donruss	3	.12	.09	.05
1991 Donruss	397	.15	.11	.06
1991 Donruss	451	.20	.15	.08
1991 Donruss Elite	6	50.00	38.00	20.00
1991 Donruss Grand Slammers	7	.30	.25	.12
1991 Fleer	335	.15	.11	.06
1991 Fleer	709	.15	.11	.06
1991 Fleer All Stars	4	1.00	.75	.40
1991 Fleer Ultra	121	.30	.25	.12
1991 Fleer Ultra	392	.20	.15	.08
1991 Leaf	106	.30	.25	.12
1991 O-Pee-Chee Premier	44	.30	.25	.12
1991 Post Cereal	23	.60	.45	.25
1991 Score	168	.25	.20	.10
1991 Score	395	.15	.10	.08
1991 Score	693	.12	.09	.05
1991 Score	770	.08	.06	.03
1991 Studio	53	.35	.25	.14
1991 Topps	386	.08	.06	.03
1991 Topps	720	.15	.11	.06
1991 Topps Stadium Club	186	2.00	1.50	.80
1991 Topps Stadium Club Charter Members	(8)	.60	.45	.25
1991 Topps Stadium Club Members Only	(1)	.40	.30	.15
1991 Upper Deck	244	.20	.15	.08
1991 Upper Deck Final Edition	82	.25	.20	.10
1991 Upper Deck Silver Sluggers	12	1.50	1.25	.60
1992 Bowman	90	1.00	.75	.40
1992 Donruss	27	.10	.07	.04
1992 Donruss	206	.20	.15	.08
1992 Donruss Triple Play	29	.20	.15	.10
1992 Fleer	133	.15	.11	.06
1992 Fleer	692	.10	.08	.04
1992 Fleer	705	.15	.11	.06
1992 Fleer Lumber Co.	1	1.50	1.25	.60
1992 Fleer Team Leaders	6	4.00	3.00	1.50
1992 Fleer Ultra	59	.40	.30	.15
1992 Fleer Update	H4	4.00	3.00	1.50
1992 Leaf	153	.25	.15	.08
1992 O-Pee-Chee	425	.15	.11	.06
1992 O-Pee-Chee Premier	70	.40	.30	.15
1992 Pinnacle	4	.30	.25	.12
1992 Pinnacle Slugfest	1	1.50	1.25	.60
1992 Post Cereal	13	.35	.25	.14
1992 Score	50	.15	.11	.06
1992 Score	431	.10	.08	.04
1992 Score Impact Players	60	.30	.25	.12
1992 Studio	173	.30	.25	.12
1992 Topps	397	.10	.08	.04
1992 Topps	425	.15	.11	.06
1992 Topps Gold	397	.40	.30	.15
1992 Topps Gold	425	1.50	1.25	.60
1992 Topps Kids	76	.20	.15	.08
1992 Topps Stadium Club	250	.50	.40	.20
1992 Topps Stadium Club	599	.15	.11	.06
1992 Topps Stadium Club Master Photos	(5)	4.00	3.00	1.50
1992 Topps Stadium Club Special Edition	48	.25	.20	.10
1992 Upper Deck	96	.10	.08	.04
1992 Upper Deck	255	.20	.15	.08
1992 Upper Deck	647	.10	.08	.04
1992 Upper Deck Home Run Heroes	2	.75	.60	.30
1993 Bowman	475	.25	.20	.10
1993 DiamondMarks	(72)	.60	.45	.25
1993 Donruss	541	.12	.09	.05
1993 Donruss Diamond Kings	15	1.00	.75	.40
1993 Donruss Elite	34	25.00	18.00	10.00
1993 Donruss Elite Supers	16	15.00	11.00	6.00
1993 Donruss Long Ball Leaders	13	2.50	2.00	1.00
1993 Donruss MVP's	17	1.00	.75	.40
1993 Donruss Spirit of the Game	10	1.50	1.25	.60
1993 Donruss Triple Play	5	.20	.15	.08
1993 Donruss Triple Play League Leaders	5	3.00	2.25	1.25
1993 Donruss Triple Play Action Baseball	15	.15	.11	.06
1993 Fleer	227	.12	.09	.05
1993 Fleer	345	.10	.08	.04
1993 Fleer	711	.10	.08	.04
1993 Fleer	714	.40	.30	.15
1993 Fleer All-Stars	5	1.25	.90	.50
1993 Fleer Flair	201	.50	.40	.20
1993 Fleer ProVisions II	3	1.50	1.25	.60
1993 Fleer Ultra	548	.25	.20	.10
1993 Fleer Ultra Home Run Kings	3	2.00	1.50	.80
1993 Leaf	283	.25	.20	.10
1993 Leaf Gold All-Stars	3	3.00	2.25	1.25
1993 O-Pee-Chee	51	.50	.40	.20
1993 O-Pee-Chee Premier	96	.20	.15	.08
1993 Pinnacle	26	.20	.15	.08
1993 Pinnacle Cooperstown	28	.30	.25	.12
1993 Pinnacle Cooperstown Dufex	28	60.00	45.00	24.00
1993 Pinnacle Home Run Club	3	.75	.60	.30
1993 Pinnacle Slugfest	3	1.25	.90	.50
1993 Post Cereal	10	.40	.30	.15
1993 Score	31	.15	.11	.06
1993 Score Select	20	.25	.20	.10

Card	#			
1993 Score Select Chase Stars	13	6.00	4.50	2.50
1993 Score Select Stat Leaders	27	.20	.15	.08
1993 Score Select Stat Leaders	31	.20	.15	.08
1993 Score The Franchise	6	3.50	2.75	1.50
1993 Studio	37	.25	.20	.10
1993 Topps	80	.10	.08	.04
1993 Topps Black Gold	30	.40	.30	.15
1993 Topps Finest	111	3.00	2.25	1.25
1993 Topps Finest Jumbo All-Stars	111	12.00	9.00	4.75
1993 Topps Finest Refractors	111	35.00	26.00	14.00
1993 Topps Gold	80	.20	.15	.08
1993 Topps Stadium Club	503	.25	.20	.10
1993 Topps Stadium Club First Day Production	503	25.00	18.50	10.00
1993 Upper Deck	46	.12	.09	.05
1993 Upper Deck	499	.10	.08	.04
1993 Upper Deck	564	.15	.11	.06
1993 Upper Deck Clutch Performers	9	1.00	.75	.40
1993 Upper Deck Fun Packs	185	.20	.15	.08
1993 Upper Deck Fun Packs	186	.20	.15	.08
1993 Upper Deck Home Run Heroes	3	.75	.60	.30
1993 Upper Deck Iooss Collection	23	.75	.60	.30
1993 Upper Deck Iooss Collection Super	23	4.00	3.00	1.50
1993 Upper Deck On Deck	11	1.00	.70	.40
1993 Upper Deck SP	236	1.00	.75	.40
1993 Upper Deck SP Platinum Power	6	8.00	6.00	3.25
1994 Bowman	69	.25	.20	.10
1994 Bowman's Best	32	1.00	.70	.40
1994 Bowman's Best Refractors	32	7.50	5.75	3.00
1994 Donruss	27	.20	.15	.08
1994 Donruss Decade Dominators	1	1.50	1.25	.60
1994 Donruss Decade Dominators Supers	1	4.50	3.50	1.75
1994 Donruss Diamond Kings	22	1.25	.90	.50
1994 Donruss Diamond Kings Super	22	4.50	3.50	1.75
1994 Donruss Long Ball Leaders	1	2.50	2.00	1.00
1994 Donruss MVP's	20	1.00	.75	.40
1994 Donruss Special Edition - Gold	27	.30	.25	.12
1994 Donruss Triple Play Nicknames	1	2.50	2.00	1.00
1994 Donruss Triple Play Bomb Squad	2	1.50	1.25	.60
1994 Donruss Triple Play	243	.15	.11	.06
1994 Fleer	128	.15	.11	.06
1994 Fleer All-Stars	7	.30	.25	.12
1994 Fleer Extra Bases	73	.25	.20	.10
1994 Fleer Extra Bases Game Breakers	10	.30	.25	.12
1994 Fleer Flair	49	.30	.25	.12
1994 Fleer Team Leaders	6	.60	.45	.25
1994 Fleer Ultra	52	.20	.15	.08
1994 Fleer Ultra RBI Kings	5	8.00	6.00	3.25
1994 Leaf	50	.20	.15	.08
1994 Leaf Clean-Up Crew	5	3.00	2.25	1.25
1994 Leaf Limited	31	2.00	1.50	.80
1994 Leaf MVP Contenders	5a	2.50	2.00	1.00
1994 Leaf MVP Contenders	5b	5.00	3.75	2.00
1994 Leaf Power Brokers	7	1.50	1.25	.60
1994 O-Pee-Chee	126	.15	.11	.06
1994 O-Pee-Chee All-Star Redemption Cards	20	.75	.60	.30
1994 O-Pee-Chee Jumbo All-Stars	20	6.00	4.50	2.50
1994 O-Pee-Chee Jumbo All-Stars Factory Set	20	1.75	1.25	.70
1994 Pacific Crown	216	.20	.15	.08
1994 Pacific Crown Jewels of the Crown	18	2.50	2.00	1.00
1994 Pinnacle	10	.25	.20	.10
1994 Pinnacle Artist's Proof	10	7.50	5.25	2.75
1994 Pinnacle Museum Collection	10	4.00	3.00	1.50
1994 Post Cereal	17	.35	.25	.14
1994 Score	393	.15	.11	.06
1994 Score Gold Stars	40	4.00	3.00	1.50
1994 Score Select	233	.30	.25	.12
1994 Sportflics 2000	78	.25	.20	.10
1994 Sportflics 2000 Movers	3	4.00	3.00	1.50
1994 Studio	190	.25	.20	.10
1994 Topps	190	.15	.11	.06
1994 Topps Black Gold	5	.50	.40	.20
1994 Topps Finest	219	1.25	.90	.50
1994 Topps Finest Refractors	219	7.50	5.50	3.00
1994 Topps Finest Superstars	219	5.00	3.75	2.00
1994 Topps Gold	190	.45	.35	.20
1994 Topps Stadium Club	25	.25	.20	.10
1994 Topps Stadium Club	535	.20	.15	.08
1994 Topps Stadium Club First Day Production	25	12.00	9.00	4.75
1994 Topps Stadium Club First Day Production	535	10.00	7.50	4.00
1994 Topps Stadium Club Members Only Baseball	34	.50	.40	.20
1994 Upper Deck	220	.25	.20	.10
1994 Upper Deck	286	.20	.15	.08
1994 Upper Deck All-Stars Green Foil	23	.50	.40	.20
1994 Upper Deck All-Stars Gold Foil	23	2.50	2.00	1.00
1994 Upper Deck Collectors Choice Home Run A	4HAb	1.00	.70	.40
1994 Upper Deck Collector's Choice	100	.15	.11	.06
1994 Upper Deck Collector's Choice	352	.05	.04	.02
1994 Upper Deck Diamond Collection	4E	6.00	4.50	2.50
1994 Upper Deck Electric Diamond	220	1.00	.75	.40
1994 Upper Deck Electric Diamond	286	1.00	.75	.40
1994 Upper Deck Fun Packs	45	.20	.15	.08
1994 Upper Deck Mickey Mantle's Long Shots	7MM	1.50	1.25	.60
1994 Upper Deck SP	176	.40	.30	.15
1994 Upper Deck SP Baseball Die-Cut	176	.75	.60	.30
1994 Upper Deck SP Holoview Blue	7	4.00	3.00	1.50
1994 Upper Deck SP Holoview Red	7	25.00	18.00	10.00

* * *

The latest collector mania among kids at Philadelphia's Veterans Stadium is getting players' "tire tracks" on paper. The kids stick a clean piece of white paper under the wheels of players' cars as they drive by, then note their names next to the tread marks, the Nov. 11, 1983, Sports Collectors Digest reported.

* * *

Rollie Fingers

Set	Card #	NM	EX	VG
1969 Topps	597 (R)	65.00	32.00	20.00
1970 O-Pee-Chee	502	34.00	17.00	10.00
1970 Topps	502	22.00	11.00	6.50
1971 O-Pee-Chee	384	13.50	6.75	4.00
1971 Topps	384	7.50	3.75	2.25
1972 O-Pee-Chee	241	8.50	4.25	2.50
1972 Topps	241	6.00	3.00	1.75
1973 O-Pee-Chee	84	7.25	3.75	2.25
1973 Topps	84	5.00	2.50	1.50
1974 O-Pee-Chee	212	6.00	3.00	1.75
1974 Topps	212	5.00	2.50	1.50
1975 O-Pee-Chee	21	5.00	2.50	1.50
1975 Topps	21	5.00	2.50	1.50
1975 Topps Mini	21	6.00	3.00	1.75
1976 O-Pee-Chee	405	4.25	2.25	1.25
1976 Topps	405	3.50	1.75	1.00
1977 O-Pee-Chee	52	3.75	2.00	1.25
1977 Topps	523	3.00	1.50	.90
1978 O-Pee-Chee	8	1.00	.50	.30
1978 O-Pee-Chee	201	3.00	1.50	.90
1978 Topps	140	2.50	1.25	.70
1978 Topps	208	.50	.25	.15
1979 O-Pee-Chee	203	2.00	1.00	.60
1979 Topps	8	.40	.20	.12
1979 Topps	390	2.50	1.25	.70
1980 O-Pee-Chee	343	.40	.20	.12
1980 Topps	651	1.00	.50	.30

Set	Card #	MT	NM	EX
1981 Donruss	2	.75	.60	.30
1981 Fleer	485	1.00	.70	.40
1981 O-Pee-Chee	229	.50	.40	.20
1981 Topps	8	.10	.08	.04
1981 Topps	229	.90	.70	.35
1981 Topps Traded	761	2.50	2.00	1.00
1982 Donruss	28	.35	.25	.14
1982 Fleer	141	.50	.40	.20
1982 Fleer	644	.15	.11	.06
1982 O-Pee-Chee	44	.12	.09	.05
1982 O-Pee-Chee	176	.20	.15	.08
1982 Topps	168	.20	.15	.08
1982 Topps	585	.30	.25	.12
1982 Topps	586	.15	.11	.06
1983 Donruss	2	.20	.15	.08
1983 Donruss	78	.60	.45	.25
1983 Fleer	33	.60	.45	.25
1983 O-Pee-Chee	35	.25	.20	.10
1983 O-Pee-Chee	36	.15	.11	.06
1983 Topps	35	.60	.45	.25
1983 Topps	36	.15	.11	.06
1984 Donruss	A	5.00	3.75	2.00
1984 Fleer	199	.25	.20	.10
1984 O-Pee-Chee	283	.40	.30	.15
1984 Topps	495	.20	.15	.08
1984 Topps	717	.15	.11	.06
1984 Topps	718	.15	.11	.06
1985 Donruss	292	.40	.30	.15
1985 Fleer	581	.20	.15	.08
1985 Leaf-Donruss	190	.12	.09	.05

1985 O-Pee-Chee	182	.15	.11	.06
1985 Topps	750	.20	.15	.08
1986 Donruss	229	.15	.11	.06
1986 Fleer	486	.20	.15	.08
1986 O-Pee-Chee	185	.15	.11	.06
1986 Sportflics	65	.15	.11	.06
1986 Sportflics	130	.50	.40	.20
1986 Sportflics	146	.25	.20	.10
1986 Topps	185	.20	.15	.08
1988 Pacific Trading Cards Baseball Legends	103	.15	.11	.06
1990 Pacific Senior League	161	.50	.40	.20
1990 Topps Senior League	65	.50	.40	.20
1991 Pacific Senior League	126	.50	.40	.20
1992 Upper Deck Hall of Fame Heroes	7	9.00	6.75	3.50
1992 Upper Deck Hall of Fame Heroes	8	10.00	7.50	4.00
1992 Upper Deck Heroes Highlights	3	2.00	1.50	.80

Carlton Fisk

Set	Card #	NM	EX	VG
1972 O-Pee-Chee	79	120.00	60.00	36.00
1972 Topps	79 (R)	90.00	45.00	27.00
1973 O-Pee-Chee	193	46.00	23.00	14.00
1973 Topps	193	30.00	15.00	9.00
1974 O-Pee-Chee	105	23.00	11.50	7.00
1974 O-Pee-Chee	331	6.75	3.50	2.00
1974 Topps	105	15.00	7.50	4.50
1974 Topps	331	5.00	2.50	1.50
1975 O-Pee-Chee	80	20.00	10.00	6.00
1975 Topps	80	15.00	7.50	4.50
1975 Topps Mini	80	12.00	6.00	3.50
1976 O-Pee-Chee	365	10.25	5.25	3.00
1976 Topps	365	7.00	3.50	2.00
1977 O-Pee-Chee	137	9.25	4.75	2.75
1977 Topps	640	4.00	2.00	1.25
1978 O-Pee-Chee	210	6.75	3.50	2.00
1978 Topps	270	5.00	2.50	1.50
1979 O-Pee-Chee	360	5.00	2.50	1.50
1979 Topps	680	3.00	1.50	.90
1980 O-Pee-Chee	20	4.50	2.25	1.25
1980 Topps	40	3.00	1.50	.90

Set	Card #	MT	NM	EX
1981 Donruss	335	1.50	1.25	.60
1981 Fleer	224	1.00	.75	.40
1981 O-Pee-Chee	116	2.50	2.00	1.00
1981 Topps	480	1.50	1.25	.60
1981 Topps Traded	762	5.00	3.75	2.00
1982 Donruss	20	.80	.60	.30
1982 Donruss	495	1.50	1.25	.60
1982 Fleer	343	1.50	1.25	.60
1982 Fleer	632	.25	.20	.10
1982 O-Pee-Chee	58	.12	.09	.05

1982 O-Pee-Chee	110	2.00	1.50	.80
1982 O-Pee-Chee	111	1.00	.70	.40
1982 Topps	110	1.00	.70	.40
1982 Topps	111	.60	.45	.25
1982 Topps	554	.20	.15	.08
1983 Donruss	104	.75	.60	.30
1983 Fleer	235	1.00	.70	.40
1983 Fleer	638	.20	.15	.08
1983 O-Pee-Chee	20	2.00	1.50	.80
1983 O-Pee-Chee	393	.12	.09	.05
1983 Topps	20	1.00	.70	.40
1983 Topps	393	.15	.11	.06
1983 Topps All-Star Glossy Set of 40	17	.30	.25	.12
1984 Donruss	302	4.00	3.00	1.50
1984 Fleer	58	2.75	2.00	1.00
1984 O-Pee-Chee	127	.40	.30	.15
1984 Topps	216	.15	.11	.06
1984 Topps	560	.70	.50	.30
1984 Topps All-Star Glossy Set of 40	40	.30	.25	.12
1985 Donruss	208	.75	.60	.30
1985 Fleer	513	1.00	.70	.40
1985 Leaf-Donruss	155	.15	.11	.06
1985 O-Pee-Chee	49	.15	.11	.06
1985 Topps	1	.25	.20	.10
1985 Topps	770	.30	.25	.12
1986 Donruss	366	.60	.45	.25
1986 Fleer	204	.50	.40	.20
1986 Fleer	643	.10	.08	.04
1986 Leaf	163	1.00	.70	.40
1986 O-Pee-Chee	290	.15	.11	.06
1986 Sportflics	67	.15	.11	.06
1986 Sportflics	125	.25	.20	.10
1986 Sportflics Decade Greats	62	.25	.20	.10
1986 Topps	290	.30	.25	.12
1986 Topps	719	.12	.09	.05
1986 Topps All-Star Glossy Set of 22	9	.30	.25	.12
1986 Topps All-Star Glossy Set of 60	28	.25	.20	.10
1987 Donruss	247	.25	.20	.12
1987 Fleer	496	.60	.45	.25
1987 Leaf	199	.60	.45	.25
1987 O-Pee-Chee	164	.12	.09	.05
1987 Sportflics	140	.35	.25	.14
1987 Topps	756	.20	.15	.08
1988 Donruss	260	.15	.11	.06
1988 Fleer	397	.15	.11	.06
1988 Leaf	208	.12	.09	.05
1988 O-Pee-Chee	385	.09	.07	.04
1988 Score	592	.20	.15	.08
1988 Sportflics	43	.25	.20	.10
1988 Topps	321	.08	.06	.03
1988 Topps	385	.15	.11	.06
1988 Topps Big Baseball	197	.12	.09	.05
1989 Bowman	62	.10	.08	.04
1989 Donruss	7	.10	.08	.04
1989 Donruss	101	.12	.09	.05
1989 Fleer	495	.15	.11	.06
1989 O-Pee-Chee	46	.10	.08	.04
1989 Score	449	.12	.09	.05
1989 Sportflics	219	.30	.25	.12
1989 Topps	695	.20	.15	.08
1989 Topps Big Baseball	24	.08	.06	.03
1989 Upper Deck	609	.40	.30	.15
1990 Bowman	314	.08	.06	.03
1990 Donruss	58	.12	.09	.05
1990 Donruss MVP	19	.12	.09	.05
1990 Fleer	530	.10	.08	.04
1990 Leaf	10	.75	.60	.30
1990 O-Pee-Chee	392	.08	.06	.03
1990 O-Pee-Chee	420	.08	.06	.03
1990 Score	290	.09	.07	.04
1990 Sportflics	204	.10	.08	.04
1990 Topps	392	.08	.06	.03
1990 Topps	420	.08	.06	.03
1990 Topps All-Star Glossy Set of 60	46	.20	.15	.08
1990 Topps Big Baseball	176	.15	.11	.06
1990 Upper Deck	367	.10	.08	.04
1991 Bowman	345	.10	.08	.04
1991 Donruss	108	.10	.08	.04
1991 Fleer	118	.10	.08	.04
1991 Fleer Ultra	72	.12	.09	.05
1991 Leaf	384	.15	.11	.06
1991 O-Pee-Chee Premier	45	.10	.08	.04
1991 Score	265	.10	.08	.04
1991 Score	421	.10	.08	.04
1991 Studio	32	.15	.11	.06
1991 Topps	3	.08	.06	.03
1991 Topps	170	.10	.08	.04
1991 Topps	393	.08	.06	.03
1991 Topps Stadium Club	180	.80	.60	.30
1991 Topps Stadium Club Charter Members	(9)	.50	.40	.20
1991 Topps Stadium Club Members Only	(8)	.40	.30	.15
1991 Upper Deck	643	.12	.09	.05
1992 Bowman	585	.40	.30	.15
1992 Donruss	543	.10	.08	.04
1992 Donruss Triple Play	149	.15	.11	.06
1992 Fleer	79	.10	.08	.04
1992 Fleer Team Leaders	4	1.00	.75	.40
1992 Fleer Ultra	33	.15	.11	.06
1992 Leaf	303	.10	.07	.04
1992 O-Pee-Chee	630	.12	.09	.05
1992 O-Pee-Chee Premier	86	.25	.20	.10
1992 Pinnacle	361	.15	.11	.06
1992 Score	72	.10	.08	.04
1992 Studio Heritage	2	1.00	.70	.40
1992 Topps	630	.12	.09	.05
1992 Topps Gold	630	.60	.45	.25
1992 Topps Stadium Club	480	.15	.11	.06
1992 Topps Stadium Club Special Edition	49	.20	.15	.08
1992 Upper Deck	571	.08	.06	.03
1993 Bowman	175	.10	.08	.04
1993 Donruss	519	.08	.06	.03
1993 Fleer	582	.05	.04	.02
1993 Fleer Final Edition	4DT	.20	.15	.08
1993 Fleer Ultra	530	.10	.08	.04
1993 Leaf	284	.10	.08	.04
1993 O-Pee-Chee	78	.15	.11	.06
1993 Pinnacle	421	.12	.09	.05
1993 Pinnacle	475	.12	.09	.05
1993 Pinnacle Cooperstown	4	.30	.25	.12
1993 Pinnacle Cooperstown Dufex	4	35.00	26.00	14.00
1993 Score	579	.12	.09	.05
1993 Score Select	76	.15	.11	.06
1993 Topps	230	.08	.06	.03
1993 Topps Finest	125	1.50	1.25	.60
1993 Topps Finest Refractors	125	20.00	15.00	8.00
1993 Topps Gold	230	.15	.11	.06
1993 Topps Stadium Club	221	.15	.11	.06
1993 Topps Stadium Club First Day Production	221	12.00	9.00	4.75
1993 Topps Stadium Club Members Only	(8)	.75	.60	.30
1993 Topps Stadium Club Team Sets	16	.50	.40	.20
1993 Upper Deck	272	.12	.09	.05

* * *

What's missing on these Topps cards: 1969, #597; 1970 , #502; 1971, #384; and 1972, #241? Don't they look a little bare? Although Rollie Fingers was pictured on these four cards, his trademark mustache didn't appear on a card until 1973, when Oakland A's owner Charles Finley offered $300 to each player who sported a promotional mustache for Opening Day.

* * *

Whitey Ford

Set	Card #	NM	EX	VG
1951 Bowman	1 (R)	1000.	400.00	240.00
1953 Bowman Color	153	400.00	200.00	100.00
1953 Topps	207	130.00	65.00	30.00
1954 Bowman	177	85.00	42.00	25.00
1954 Red Man Tobacco	16A	80.00	40.00	24.00
1954 Topps	37	75.00	37.00	22.00
1955 Bowman	59	75.00	38.00	23.00
1955 Red Man Tobacco	3A	65.00	32.00	19.50
1956 Topps	240	110.00	55.00	32.50
1957 Topps	25	55.00	27.00	16.50
1958 Topps	320	40.00	20.00	12.00
1959 Topps	430	30.00	15.00	9.00
1960 Topps	35	39.00	19.00	11.50
1961 Post Cereal	6a	12.50	6.25	3.75
1961 Post Cereal	6b	12.50	6.25	3.75
1961 Topps	160	35.00	17.50	10.50
1961 Topps	586	85.00	42.00	25.00
1962 Post Cereal	9	10.00	5.00	3.00
1962 Topps	57	8.00	4.00	2.50
1962 Topps	59	8.00	4.00	2.50
1962 Topps	310	30.00	15.00	9.00
1962 Topps	315	9.00	4.50	2.75
1962 Topps	475	10.00	5.00	3.00
1963 Post Cereal	19	10.00	5.00	3.00
1963 Topps	6	6.50	3.25	2.00
1963 Topps	446	35.00	17.50	10.50
1964 Topps	4a	9.50	4.75	2.75
1964 Topps	4b	5.00	2.50	1.50
1964 Topps	380	24.00	12.00	7.25
1965 Topps	330	24.00	12.00	7.25
1966 O-Pee-Chee	160	30.00	15.00	9.00
1966 Topps	160	20.00	10.00	6.00
1967 O-Pee-Chee	5	25.00	12.50	7.50
1967 Topps	5	15.00	7.50	4.50

Set	Card #	MT	NM	EX
1986 Sportflics Decade Greats	44	.40	.30	.15
1989 Pacific Trading Cards Legends II	210	.20	.15	.08
1991 "1953" Topps Archives Promos	(5)	15.00	11.00	6.00
1991 "1953" Topps Archives	207	2.00	1.50	.80
1994 "1954" Topps Archives	37	.45	.35	.20

* * *

Teammate Johnny Antonelli, on Willie Mays: "When Willie Mays would tap his glove you knew he was going to catch the ball and if you see the highlights (of Mays' catch of Vic Wertz's 460-foot drive at the Polo Grounds in the '54 Series), you can see that when Willie is running back, he is tapping his glove with the ball squarely in sight."

* * *

George Foster

Set	Card #	NM	EX	VG
1971 O-Pee-Chee	276	10.25	5.25	3.00
1971 Topps	276 (R)	6.00	3.00	1.75
1972 O-Pee-Chee	256	1.25	.60	.40
1972 Topps	256	1.00	.50	.30
1973 O-Pee-Chee	399	1.25	.60	.40
1973 Topps	399	1.50	.70	.45
1974 O-Pee-Chee	646	1.25	.60	.40
1974 Topps	646	.75	.40	.25
1975 O-Pee-Chee	87	1.00	.50	.30
1975 Topps	87	.75	.40	.25
1975 Topps Mini	87	1.75	.90	.50
1976 O-Pee-Chee	179	.75	.40	.25
1976 Topps	179	1.00	.50	.30
1977 O-Pee-Chee	3	.40	.20	.12
1977 O-Pee-Chee	120	.75	.40	.25
1977 Topps	3	.20	.10	.06
1977 Topps	347	.60	.30	.20
1978 O-Pee-Chee	2	.25	.13	.08
1978 O-Pee-Chee	3	.25	.13	.08
1978 O-Pee-Chee	70	.60	.30	.20
1978 Topps	202	.25	.13	.08
1978 Topps	203	.25	.13	.08
1978 Topps	500	.50	.25	.15
1979 O-Pee-Chee	316	.50	.25	.15
1979 Topps	2	.30	.15	.09
1979 Topps	3	.30	.15	.09
1979 Topps	600	.30	.15	.09
1980 O-Pee-Chee	209	.40	.20	.12
1980 Topps	400	.25	.13	.08

Set	Card #	MT	NM	EX
1981 Donruss	65	.20	.15	.08
1981 Fleer	202	.12	.09	.05
1981 Fleer	216a	.25	.20	.10
1981 Fleer	216b	.20	.15	.08
1981 O-Pee-Chee	200	.12	.09	.05
1981 Topps	200	.25	.20	.10
1982 Donruss	274	.20	.15	.08
1982 Fleer	66	.20	.15	.08
1982 Fleer	630	.15	.11	.06
1982 O-Pee-Chee	177	.12	.09	.05
1982 O-Pee-Chee	336	.15	.11	.06
1982 O-Pee-Chee	342	.12	.09	.05
1982 Topps	342a	2.25	1.75	.90
1982 Topps	342b	.20	.15	.08
1982 Topps	700	.25	.20	.10
1982 Topps	701	.12	.09	.05
1982 Topps Traded	36T	.40	.30	.15
1983 Donruss	6	.20	.15	.08
1983 Donruss	427	.15	.11	.06
1983 Donruss	542	.15	.11	.06
1983 O-Pee-Chee	80	.15	.11	.06
1983 Topps	80	.12	.09	.05
1984 Donruss	312	.30	.25	.12
1984 Fleer	584	.20	.15	.08
1984 O-Pee-Chee	350	.30	.25	.12
1984 Topps	350	.10	.08	.04
1985 Donruss	603	.15	.11	.06
1985 Fleer	79	.15	.11	.06

1985 Leaf-Donruss	42	.12	.09	.05
1985 O-Pee-Chee	170	.12	.09	.05
1985 Topps	170	.15	.11	.06
1986 Donruss	116	.15	.11	.06
1986 Fleer	80	.15	.11	.06
1986 O-Pee-Chee	69	.10	.08	.04
1986 Sportflics	68	.30	.25	.12
1986 Sportflics	126	.15	.11	.06
1986 Sportflics	131	.10	.08	.04
1986 Sportflics	139	.30	.25	.12
1986 Topps	680	.15	.11	.06
1989 Pacific Trading Cards Legends II	173	.06	.05	.02
1990 Pacific Legends	72	.05	.04	.02
1990 Pacific Senior League	114	.10	.08	.04
1990 Topps Senior League	1	.15	.11	.06

Set	Card #	MT	NM	EX
1986 Sportflics Decade Greats	37	.25	.20	.10
1988 Pacific Trading Cards Baseball Legends	57	.15	.11	.06
1991 "1953" Topps Archives	331	.35	.25	.14

Jimmie Foxx

Set	Card #	NM	EX	VG
1933 DeLong	21	600.00	300.00	175.00
1933 Goudey	29	650.00	260.00	123.00
1933 Goudey	154	500.00	200.00	95.00
1934-36 Diamond Stars	64	350.00	175.00	105.00
1934 Goudey	1	1450.	700.00	170.00
1935 Goudey	(31)	275.00	137.00	82.00
1937 O-Pee-Chee	106	800.00	400.00	240.00
1938 Goudey	249	550.00	236.00	137.00
1938 Goudey	273	600.00	258.00	150.00
1939 Goudey Premiums (R303-B)	(8)	60.00	30.00	18.00
1939 Goudey Premiums (R303-A)	(15)	80.00	40.00	24.00
1940 Play Ball	133	275.00	107.00	52.00
1941 Double Play	60	200.00	100.00	60.00
1941 Play Ball	13	375.00	176.00	94.00
1960 Fleer	53	4.00	2.00	1.25
1961-62 Fleer	28	6.00	3.00	1.75

Set	Card #	MT	NM	EX
1986 Sportflics Decade Greats	2	.40	.30	.15

Nellie Fox

Set	Card #	NM	EX	VG
1951 Bowman	232 (R)	120.00	60.00	36.00
1952 Bowman	21	35.00	17.50	10.50
1952 Red Man Tobacco	9A	40.00	20.00	12.00
1953 Bowman Color	18	65.00	32.50	19.50
1953 Red Man Tobacco	5A	40.00	20.00	12.00
1954 Bowman	6	27.50	13.50	8.25
1954 Red Heart Dog Food	(9)	40.00	20.00	12.00
1954 Red Man Tobacco	3A	45.00	22.00	13.50
1955 Bowman	33	20.00	10.00	6.00
1955 Red Man Tobacco	4A	40.00	20.00	12.00
1956 Topps	118	35.00	17.50	10.50
1957 Topps	38	20.00	10.00	6.00
1958 Topps	400	15.00	7.50	4.50
1958 Topps	479	10.00	5.00	3.00
1959 Topps	30	17.50	9.00	5.25
1959 Topps	408	12.00	6.00	3.50
1959 Topps	556	22.00	11.00	6.50
1960 Topps	100	7.00	3.50	2.00
1960 Topps	429	6.00	3.00	1.75
1960 Topps	555	22.00	11.00	6.50
1961 Post Cereal	20a	6.00	3.00	1.75
1961 Post Cereal	20b	6.00	3.00	1.75
1961 Topps	30	6.00	3.00	1.75
1961 Topps	477	9.00	4.50	2.75
1961 Topps	570	40.00	20.00	12.00
1962 Post Cereal	47	6.00	3.00	1.75
1962 Topps	73	8.00	4.00	2.50
1963 Post Cereal	36a	4.50	2.25	1.25
1963 Post Cereal	36b	10.00	5.00	3.00
1963 Topps	525	25.00	12.50	7.25
1964 Topps	81	9.50	4.75	2.75
1964 Topps	205	7.00	3.50	2.00
1965 Topps	485	14.00	7.00	4.25
1975 O-Pee-Chee	19?	3.00	1.50	.90
1975 Topps	197	.90	.45	.25
1975 Topps Mini	197	1.25	.60	.40

Julio Franco

Set	Card #	MT	NM	EX
1983 Donruss	525 (R)	5.00	3.75	2.00
1983 Topps Traded	34T	5.00	3.75	2.00

Card	Number	Price 1	Price 2	Price 3
1984 Donruss	216	4.50	3.50	1.75
1984 Fleer	542	2.00	1.50	.80
1984 O-Pee-Chee	48	.85	.60	.35
1984 Topps	48	.75	.60	.30
1985 Donruss	94	.75	.60	.30
1985 Fleer	448	.60	.45	.25
1985 Leaf-Donruss	213	.20	.15	.08
1985 O-Pee-Chee	237	1.00	.70	.40
1985 Topps	237	.50	.40	.20
1986 Donruss	216	.50	.40	.20
1986 Fleer	586	.10	.08	.04
1986 Leaf	93	.10	.08	.04
1986 O-Pee-Chee	391	.10	.08	.04
1986 Sportflics	33	.15	.11	.06
1986 Topps	391	.10	.08	.04
1987 Donruss	131	.10	.08	.04
1987 Fleer	251	.25	.20	.10
1987 Leaf	131	.25	.20	.10
1987 O-Pee-Chee	160	.10	.08	.04
1987 Sportflics	84	.15	.11	.06
1987 Topps	160	.10	.08	.04
1988 Donruss	10	.10	.08	.04
1988 Donruss	156	.10	.08	.04
1988 Donruss Diamond Kings Supers	10	.25	.20	.10
1988 Fleer	609	.10	.08	.04
1988 Leaf	10	.08	.06	.03
1988 Leaf	71	.20	.15	.08
1988 O-Pee-Chee	49	.08	.06	.03
1988 Score	60	.08	.06	.03
1988 Sportflics	58	.15	.11	.06
1988 Topps	683	.08	.06	.03
1988 Topps Big Baseball	135	.10	.08	.04
1989 Bowman	228	.15	.11	.06
1989 Donruss	310	.10	.08	.04
1989 Donruss Traded	31	.15	.11	.06
1989 Fleer	404	.10	.08	.04
1989 Fleer All-Stars	5	.15	.11	.06
1989 Fleer Update	64	.08	.06	.03
1989 O-Pee-Chee	55	.07	.05	.03
1989 Score	11	.08	.06	.03
1989 Score Traded	35T	.10	.08	.04
1989 Sportflics	149	.15	.11	.06
1989 Topps	55	.08	.06	.03
1989 Topps	398	.06	.05	.02
1989 Topps Big Baseball	288	.08	.06	.03
1989 Upper Deck	186	.10	.08	.04
1989 Upper Deck	793	.30	.25	.12
1990 Bowman	497	.08	.06	.03
1990 Donruss	142	.09	.07	.04
1990 Donruss	701	.09	.07	.04
1990 Donruss MVP	14	.15	.11	.06
1990 Fleer	296	.07	.05	.03
1990 Leaf	205	.35	.25	.14
1990 O-Pee-Chee	386	.10	.08	.04
1990 O-Pee-Chee	550	.09	.07	.04
1990 Score	160	.10	.08	.04
1990 Sportflics	158	.12	.09	.05
1990 Topps	386	.10	.08	.04
1990 Topps	550	.09	.07	.04
1990 Topps All-Star Glossy Set of 22	14	.15	.11	.06
1990 Topps All-Star Glossy Set of 60	35	.15	.11	.06
1990 Topps Big Baseball	205	.12	.09	.05
1990 Upper Deck	103	.10	.08	.04
1991 Bowman	265	.08	.06	.03
1991 Bowman	368	.10	.08	.04
1991 Donruss	192	.08	.06	.03
1991 Fleer	285	.10	.08	.04
1991 Fleer Ultra	348	.10	.08	.04
1991 Leaf	228	.10	.08	.04
1991 Score	392	.10	.08	.04
1991 Score	493	.10	.08	.04
1991 Studio	123	.20	.15	.08
1991 Topps	387	.08	.06	.03
1991 Topps	775	.08	.06	.03
1991 Topps Stadium Club	173	.40	.30	.15
1991 Topps Stadium Club Members Only	(9)	.25	.20	.10
1991 Upper Deck	227	.10	.08	.04
1991 Upper Deck Silver Sluggers	1	.50	.40	.20
1992 Bowman	206	.20	.15	.08
1992 Donruss	741	.08	.06	.03
1992 Donruss Diamond Kings	4	.50	.40	.20
1992 Donruss Triple Play	83	.12	.09	.05
1992 Fleer	303	.08	.06	.03
1992 Fleer	690	.08	.06	.03
1992 Fleer All-Stars	18	.40	.30	.15
1992 Fleer Ultra	131	.15	.11	.06
1992 Leaf	119	.20	.15	.08
1992 O-Pee-Chee	490	.10	.08	.04
1992 O-Pee-Chee Premier	15	.10	.08	.04
1992 Pinnacle	150	.12	.09	.05
1992 Pinnacle Rookie Idols	5	5.00	3.75	2.00
1992 Score	108	.10	.08	.04
1992 Score	432	.08	.06	.03
1992 Studio	241	.15	.11	.06
1992 Topps	398	.08	.06	.03
1992 Topps	490	.10	.08	.04
1992 Topps Gold	398	.25	.20	.10
1992 Topps Gold	490	.35	.25	.14
1992 Topps Kids	129	.05	.04	.02
1992 Topps Stadium Club	440	.15	.11	.06
1992 Topps Stadium Club Special Edition	52	.15	.11	.06
1992 Upper Deck	241	.08	.06	.03
1993 Bowman	657	.10	.08	.04
1993 Donruss	451	.05	.04	.02
1993 Donruss Triple Play	148	.05	.04	.02
1993 Fleer	320	.08	.06	.03
1993 Fleer Flair	279	.25	.15	.08
1993 Fleer Ultra	277	.10	.08	.04
1993 Leaf	27	.10	.08	.04
1993 O-Pee-Chee	73	.15	.11	.06
1993 Pacific Prism Insert	13	15.00	11.00	6.00
1993 Pinnacle	104	.06	.05	.02
1993 Score	394	.04	.03	.02
1993 Score Select	58	.10	.08	.04
1993 Studio	103	.08	.06	.03
1993 Topps	670	.03	.02	.01
1993 Topps Finest	161	1.00	.70	.40
1993 Topps Finest Refractors	161	20.00	15.00	8.00
1993 Topps Gold	670	.10	.08	.04
1993 Topps Stadium Club	651	.10	.08	.04
1993 Topps Stadium Club First Day Production	651	5.00	3.75	2.00
1993 Topps Stadium Club Team Sets	25	.10	.08	.04
1993 Upper Deck	656	.07	.05	.03
1993 Upper Deck SP	192	.15	.11	.06
1994 Bowman	399	.10	.08	.04
1994 Bowman's Best	74	.50	.40	.20
1994 Bowman's Best Refractors	74	2.00	1.50	.80
1994 Donruss	481	.07	.05	.03
1994 Fleer	306	.05	.04	.02
1994 Fleer Extra Bases	46	.10	.08	.04
1994 Fleer Flair	276	.20	.15	.08
1994 Fleer Ultra	332	.10	.08	.04
1994 Fleer Update	25	.10	.08	.04
1994 Leaf	364	.10	.08	.04
1994 Leaf Limited	21	1.00	.70	.40
1994 O-Pee-Chee	142	.05	.04	.02
1994 Pacific Crown	615	.05	.04	.02
1994 Pinnacle	520	.10	.08	.04
1994 Pinnacle Artist's Proof	520	3.00	2.25	1.25
1994 Pinnacle Museum Collection	520	1.50	1.25	.60
1994 Score	413	.04	.03	.02
1994 Score Rookie & Traded Gold Rush	29	.25	.20	.10
1994 Score Rookie and Traded	29	.05	.04	.02
1994 Score Select	288	.10	.08	.04
1994 Studio	205	.10	.08	.04

		MT	NM	EX
1994 Topps	260	.04	.03	.02
1994 Topps Finest	278	.75	.60	.30
1994 Topps Finest Refractors	278	3.50	2.75	1.50
1994 Topps Gold	260	.15	.11	.06
1994 Topps Stadium Club	680	.10	.08	.04
1994 Topps Stadium Club First Day Production	680	3.00	2.25	1.25
1994 Topps Traded	25	.05	.04	.02
1994 Upper Deck	57	.10	.08	.04
1994 Upper Deck Collector's Choice	415	.05	.04	.02
1994 Upper Deck Electric Diamond	57	.25	.20	.10
1994 Upper Deck SP	191	.15	.11	.06
1994 Upper Deck SP Baseball Die-Cut	191	.25	.20	.10

Travis Fryman

Set	Card #	MT	NM	EX
1990 Bowman	360 (R)	1.00	.75	.40
1990 Fleer Update	96	1.00	.75	.40
1990 Topps Traded	33T	1.25	.90	.50
1991 Bowman	145	.50	.40	.20
1991 Donruss	768	.50	.40	.20
1991 Fleer	336	.50	.40	.20
1991 Fleer Ultra	122	1.25	.90	.50
1991 Leaf	149	1.50	1.25	.60
1991 Score	570	.50	.40	.20
1991 Studio	54	1.50	1.25	.60
1991 Topps	128	.60	.45	.25
1991 Topps Glossy Rookies	9	.35	.25	.14
1991 Topps Stadium Club	355	6.00	4.50	2.50
1991 Upper Deck	225	1.50	1.25	.60
1992 Bowman	37	2.00	1.50	.80
1992 Donruss	349	.25	.20	.10
1992 Donruss Triple Play	86	.25	.20	.10
1992 Fleer	134	.25	.20	.10
1992 Fleer Ultra	60	1.00	.75	.40
1992 Leaf	304	.50	.40	.20
1992 O-Pee-Chee	750	.15	.11	.06
1992 Pinnacle	110	.60	.45	.25
1992 Pinnacle Team 2000	4	1.00	.75	.40
1992 Score	65	.20	.15	.08
1992 Score Impact Players	47	.50	.40	.20
1992 Studio	174	.30	.25	.12
1992 Topps	750	.15	.11	.06
1992 Topps Gold	750	.50	.40	.20
1992 Topps Kids	78	.10	.08	.04
1992 Topps Stadium Club	59	.75	.60	.30
1992 Upper Deck	466	.20	.15	.08
1992 Upper Deck	643	.20	.15	.08
1993 Bowman	67	.30	.25	.12
1993 Donruss	127	.20	.15	.08
1993 Donruss Triple Play	59	.10	.08	.04
1993 Fleer	228	.20	.12	.06
1993 Fleer Flair	202	.75	.60	.30
1993 Fleer Ultra	197	.25	.20	.10
1993 Leaf	16	.30	.25	.12
1993 Leaf Fasttrack	19	3.50	2.75	1.50
1993 O-Pee-Chee	76	.75	.60	.30
1993 O-Pee-Chee Premier	102	.25	.20	.10
1993 Pinnacle	79	.25	.20	.10
1993 Pinnacle Home Run Club	48	.35	.25	.14
1993 Pinnacle Slugfest	30	1.50	1.25	.60
1993 Pinnacle Team 2001	10	1.50	1.25	.60
1993 Score	11	.20	.15	.08
1993 Score Select	44	.25	.20	.10
1993 Studio	108	.35	.25	.14
1993 Studio Silhouettes	5	1.00	.70	.40
1993 Topps	392	.15	.11	.06
1993 Topps	404	.10	.08	.04
1993 Topps Black Gold	31	.50	.40	.20
1993 Topps Finest	135	4.00	3.00	1.50
1993 Topps Finest Refractors	135	50.00	37.00	20.00
1993 Topps Gold	392	.30	.25	.12
1993 Topps Gold	404	.20	.15	.08
1993 Topps Stadium Club	298	.25	.20	.10
1993 Topps Stadium Club	448	.30	.25	.12
1993 Topps Stadium Club First Day Production	298	15.00	11.00	6.00
1993 Topps Stadium Club First Day Production	448	8.00	6.00	3.25
1993 Topps Stadium Club Master Photos	(16)	1.50	1.25	.60
1993 Topps Stadium Club Members Only	(9)	.50	.40	.20
1993 Topps Stadium Club Special	168	.25	.20	.10
1993 Upper Deck	364	.20	.15	.08
1993 Upper Deck	455	.15	.11	.06
1993 Upper Deck	836	.12	.09	.05
1993 Upper Deck Diamond Gallery	25	.75	.60	.30
1993 Upper Deck Fun Packs	187	.15	.11	.06
1993 Upper Deck SP	237	1.00	.75	.40
1994 Bowman	621	.25	.20	.10
1994 Bowman's Best	108	1.50	1.25	.60
1994 Bowman's Best	61	1.00	.70	.40
1994 Bowman's Best Refractors	108	6.00	4.50	2.50
1994 Bowman's Best Refractors	61	5.00	3.75	2.00
1994 Donruss	378	.25	.20	.10
1994 Donruss Special Edition - Gold	378	.25	.20	.10
1994 Donruss Triple Play Medalists	9	1.50	1.25	.60
1994 Donruss Triple Play	244	.20	.15	.08
1994 Fleer	129	.25	.20	.10
1994 Fleer All-Stars	8	.50	.40	.20
1994 Fleer Extra Bases	74	.25	.20	.10
1994 Fleer Flair	292	.40	.30	.15
1994 Fleer Ultra	53	.25	.20	.10
1994 Fleer Ultra Rising Stars	5	6.00	4.50	2.50
1994 Leaf	405	.25	.20	.10
1994 Leaf Limited	32	2.50	2.00	1.00
1994 O-Pee-Chee	209	.25	.20	.10
1994 Pacific Crown	217	.25	.20	.10
1994 Pinnacle	183	.25	.20	.10
1994 Pinnacle Artist's Proof	183	9.00	6.75	3.50
1994 Pinnacle Museum Collection	183	4.00	3.00	1.50
1994 Pinnacle Power Surge	14	.30	.25	.12
1994 Pinnacle Run Creators	9	2.00	1.50	.80
1994 Pinnacle The Naturals Box Set	21	.40	.30	15
1994 Score	11	.25	.20	.10
1994 Score Gold Stars	48	5.00	3.75	2.00

Set	Card #	MT	NM	EX
1994 Score Select	295	.30	.25	.12
1994 Score Select Skills	10	6.00	4.50	2.50
1994 Sportflics 2000	16	.40	.30	.15
1994 Sportflics 2000	178	.35	.25	.14
1994 Studio	191	.25	.20	.10
1994 Topps	285	.15	.11	.06
1994 Topps Black Gold	6	.60	.45	.25
1994 Topps Finest	228	1.25	.90	.50
1994 Topps Finest Refractors	228	8.00	6.00	3.25
1994 Topps Finest Superstars	228	4.00	3.00	1.50
1994 Topps Gold	285	.45	.35	.20
1994 Topps Stadium Club	309	.25	.20	.10
1994 Topps Stadium Club First Day Production	309	15.00	11.00	6.00
1994 Upper Deck	37	.20	.15	.08
1994 Upper Deck	51	.20	.15	.08
1994 Upper Deck	345	.25	.20	.10
1994 Upper Deck All-Stars Green Foil	23	.50	.40	.20
1994 Upper Deck All-Stars Gold Foil	23	2.50	2.00	1.00
1994 Upper Deck Collector's Choice	375	.15	.11	.06
1994 Upper Deck Electric Diamond	37	.50	.40	.20
1994 Upper Deck Electric Diamond	51	1.00	.75	.40
1994 Upper Deck Electric Diamond	345	.50	.40	.20
1994 Upper Deck Fun Packs	80	.25	.20	.10
1994 Upper Deck Fun Packs	179	.15	.11	.06
1994 Upper Deck SP	177	.40	.30	.15
1994 Upper Deck SP Baseball Die-Cut	177	.75	.60	.30
1994 Upper Deck SP Holoview Blue	9	4.00	3.00	1.50
1994 Upper Deck SP Holoview Red	9	25.00	18.00	10.00

Andres Galarraga

Set	Card #	MT	NM	EX
1986 Donruss	33a (R)	6.00	4.50	2.50
1986 Donruss	33b (R)	6.00	4.50	2.50
1986 Fleer	647 (R)	6.00	4.50	2.50
1986 Fleer Update	44	2.50	2.00	1.00
1986 Leaf	27	5.00	3.75	2.00
1986 Sportflics Rookies	27	.60	.45	.25
1986 Topps Traded	40T	2.00	1.50	.80
1987 Donruss	303	.75	.60	.30
1987 Fleer	319	1.00	.70	.40
1987 Fleer All Stars	18	.15	.11	.06
1987 Leaf	221	.12	.09	.05
1987 O-Pee-Chee	272	.20	.15	.08
1987 Topps	272	.50	.40	.20

Set	Card #	MT	NM	EX
1988 Donruss	282	.30	.25	.12
1988 Fleer	184	.35	.25	.14
1988 Leaf	121	.15	.11	.06
1988 O-Pee-Chee	25	.10	.08	.04
1988 Score	19	.25	.20	.10
1988 Sportflics	182	.50	.40	.20
1988 Topps	25	.30	.25	.12
1988 Topps All-Star Glossy Set of 60	58	.30	.25	.12
1988 Topps Big Baseball	55	.25	.20	.10
1989 Bowman	365	.20	.15	.08
1989 Donruss	14	.15	.11	.06
1989 Donruss	130	.20	.15	.08
1989 Donruss MVP	16	.15	.11	.06
1989 Fleer	376	.25	.20	.10
1989 Fleer	638	.10	.08	.04
1989 Fleer For The Record	3	.80	.60	.30
1989 O-Pee-Chee	93	.15	.11	.06
1989 Score	144	.25	.20	.10
1989 Sportflics	139	.20	.15	.08
1989 Topps	386	.08	.06	.03
1989 Topps	590	.12	.09	.05
1989 Topps All-Star Glossy Set of 60	44	.30	.25	.12
1989 Topps Big Baseball	173	.08	.06	.03
1989 Upper Deck	115	.50	.40	.20
1989 Upper Deck	677	.08	.06	.03
1990 Bowman	113	.08	.06	.03
1990 Donruss	97	.15	.11	.06
1990 Fleer	345	.15	.11	.06
1990 Leaf	450	1.50	1.25	.60
1990 O-Pee-Chee	720	.25	.20	.10
1990 Score	25	.15	.11	.06
1990 Sportflics	148	.12	.09	.05
1990 Topps	720	.25	.20	.10
1990 Topps Big Baseball	108	.08	.06	.03
1990 Upper Deck	356	.20	.15	.08
1991 Bowman	446	.06	.05	.02
1991 Donruss	68	.08	.06	.03
1991 Donruss Grand Slammers	9	.10	.08	.04
1991 Fleer	232	.08	.06	.03
1991 Fleer Ultra	203	.08	.06	.03
1991 Leaf	110	.15	.11	.06
1991 O-Pee-Chee Premier	48	.15	.11	.06
1991 Score	443	.08	.06	.03
1991 Studio	197	.20	.15	.08
1991 Topps	610	.08	.06	.03
1991 Topps Stadium Club	69	.75	.60	.30
1991 Upper Deck	456	.15	.11	.06
1992 Bowman	320	.08	.06	.03
1992 Donruss	355	.06	.05	.02
1992 Fleer	480	.06	.05	.02
1992 Leaf	449	.10	.08	.04
1992 O-Pee-Chee	240	.06	.05	.02
1992 O-Pee-Chee Premier	191	.10	.08	.04
1992 Pinnacle	381	.12	.09	.05
1992 Score	35	.06	.05	.02
1992 Score Rookie & Traded	60	.60	.45	.25
1992 Topps	240	.06	.05	.02
1992 Topps Gold	240	.75	.60	.30
1992 Topps Stadium Club	652	.15	.11	.06
1992 Topps Stadium Club National Convention	652	15.00	11.00	6.00
1992 Topps Traded	36	.06	.05	.02
1992 Topps Traded Gold	36	.25	.20	.10
1992 Upper Deck	474	.08	.06	.03
1992 Upper Deck	758	.08	.06	.03
1993 Bowman	204	.20	.15	.08
1993 DiamondMarks	(19)	.60	.45	.25
1993 Donruss	764	.05	.04	.02
1993 Fleer	409	.15	.11	.06
1993 Fleer Final Edition	30	.15	.11	.06
1993 Fleer Flair	39	.50	.30	.15
1993 Fleer Ultra	347	.10	.08	.04
1993 Leaf	322	.15	.11	.06
1993 O-Pee-Chee Premier	58	.15	.11	.06
1993 Pinnacle	434	.12	.09	.05

Set	Card #			
1993 Pinnacle Expansion Opening Day	3	3.00	2.25	1.20
1993 Score	649	.08	.06	.03
1993 Score Select Rookie/ Traded	102	.25	.20	.10
1993 Studio	163	.20	.15	.08
1993 Studio Superstars on Canvas	9	1.50	1.25	.60
1993 Topps	173	.08	.06	.03
1993 Topps Finest	130	2.50	2.00	1.00
1993 Topps Finest Refractors	130	30.00	22.00	12.00
1993 Topps Full Shot Super	20	4.00	3.00	1.50
1993 Topps Gold	173	.15	.11	.06
1993 Topps Stadium Club	454	.15	.11	.06
1993 Topps Stadium Club First Day Production	454	15.00	11.00	6.00
1993 Topps Stadium Club Team Sets	11	.50	.40	.20
1993 Topps Traded	31	.10	.08	.04
1993 Upper Deck	478	.12	.09	.05
1993 Upper Deck	593	.08	.06	.03
1993 Upper Deck Fun Packs	173	.20	.15	.08
1993 Upper Deck Fun Packs	176	.20	.15	.08
1993 Upper Deck SP	220	.12	.09	.05
1994 Bowman	526	.15	.11	.06
1994 Bowman's Best	43	.75	.60	.30
1994 Bowman's Best Refractors	43	3.00	2.25	1.25
1994 Donruss	346	.20	.15	.08
1994 Donruss Diamond Kings	7	1.50	1.25	.60
1994 Donruss Diamond Kings Super	7	4.50	3.50	1.75
1994 Donruss Elite	48	15.00	11.00	6.00
1994 Donruss Long Ball Leaders	3	2.00	1.50	.80
1994 Donruss MVP's	4	.75	.60	.30
1994 Donruss Special Edition - Gold	346	.35	.25	.14
1994 Donruss Triple Play	223	.05	.04	.02
1994 Fleer	440	.05	.04	.02
1994 Fleer All-Stars	35	.30	.25	.12
1994 Fleer Extra Bases	244	.20	.15	.08
1994 Fleer Flair	373	.40	.30	.15
1994 Fleer League Leaders	7	.35	.25	.14
1994 Fleer Team Leaders	18	.75	.60	.30
1994 Fleer Ultra	480	.10	.08	.04
1994 Fleer Ultra Hitting Machines	4	.75	.60	.30
1994 Fleer Ultra League Leaders	6	.50	.40	.20
1994 Fleer Ultra On-Base Leaders	4	5.00	3.75	2.00
1994 Leaf	156	.10	.08	.04
1994 Leaf Clean-Up Crew	2	3.00	2.25	1.25
1994 Leaf Gold Stars	7	10.00	7.50	4.00
1994 Leaf Limited	102	1.50	1.25	.60
1994 Leaf MVP Contenders	6a	2.50	2.00	1.00
1994 Leaf MVP Contenders	6b	5.00	3.75	2.00
1994 O-Pee-Chee	69	.15	.11	.06
1994 Pacific Crown	195	.10	.08	.04
1994 Pacific Crown All Latino All-Star Team	13	1.50	1.25	.60
1994 Pacific Crown Jewels of the Crown	20	2.50	2.00	1.00
1994 Pinnacle	446	.15	.11	.06
1994 Pinnacle Artist's Proof	446	5.00	3.75	2.00
1994 Pinnacle Museum Collection	446	2.00	1.50	.80
1994 Pinnacle Run Creators	30	2.50	2.00	1.00
1994 Post Cereal	23	.40	.30	.15
1994 Score	8	.10	.08	.04
1994 Score Gold Stars	11	3.00	2.25	1.25
1994 Score Select	63	.10	.08	.04
1994 Sportflics 2000	55	.10	.08	.04
1994 Sportflics 2000 Movers	6	3.00	2.25	1.25
1994 Studio	177	.10	.08	.04
1994 Studio Editor's Choice	4	3.00	2.25	1.25
1994 Topps	525	.05	.04	.02
1994 Topps Black Gold	30	.40	.30	.15
1994 Topps Finest	35	.90	.70	.35
1994 Topps Finest Promos	35	3.00	2.25	1.25
1994 Topps Finest Refractors	35	4.00	3.00	1.50
1994 Topps Gold	525	.15	.11	.06
1994 Topps Stadium Club	454	.10	.08	.04
1994 Topps Stadium Club First Day Production	454	4.00	3.00	1.50
1994 Topps Stadium Club Members Only Baseball	15	.35	.25	.14
1994 Upper Deck	270	.12	.09	.05
1994 Upper Deck	315	.15	.11	.06
1994 Upper Deck All-Stars Green Foil	39	.25	.20	.10
1994 Upper Deck All-Stars Gold Foil	39	1.00	.70	.40
1994 Upper Deck Collector's Choice	312	.10	.08	.04
1994 Upper Deck Collector's Choice	350	.05	.04	.02
1994 Upper Deck Collector's Choice	360	.07	.05	.03
1994 Upper Deck Diamond Collection	2W	5.00	3.75	2.00
1994 Upper Deck Electric Diamond	270	.25	.20	.10
1994 Upper Deck Electric Diamond	315	.50	.40	.20
1994 Upper Deck Fun Packs	14	.05	.04	.02
1994 Upper Deck SP	166	.25	.20	.10
1994 Upper Deck SP Baseball Die-Cut	166	.35	.25	.14
1994 Upper Deck SP Holoview Blue	10	4.00	3.00	1.50
1994 Upper Deck SP Holoview Red	10	20.00	15.00	8.00

Joe Garagiola

Set	Card #	NM	EX	VG
1951 Bowman	122 (R)	100.00	60.00	30.00
1952 Bowman	27	60.00	30.00	18.00
1952 Topps	227	75.00	37.00	17.00
1953 Bowman Color	21	60.00	30.00	18.00
1954 Bowman	141	35.00	17.50	10.50

Set	Card #	MT	NM	EX
1983 Topps 1952 Reprint Set	227	.60	.45	.25
1990 Pacific Legends	24	.25	.20	.10
1991 "1953" Topps Archives	314	.75	.60	.30

Steve Garvey

Set	Card #	NM	EX	VG
1971 O-Pee-Chee	341	75.00	37.00	22.00
1971 Topps	341 (R)	50.00	25.00	15.00
1972 Topps	686	37.50	18.50	11.00
1973 O-Pee-Chee	213	12.75	6.50	3.75
1973 Topps	213	7.50	3.75	2.25
1974 O-Pee-Chee	575	9.25	4.75	2.75
1974 Topps	575	7.00	3.50	2.00
1975 O-Pee-Chee	140	6.75	3.50	2.00
1975 O-Pee-Chee	212	.75	.40	.25
1975 Topps	140	5.00	2.50	1.50
1975 Topps	212	.75	.40	.25
1975 Topps Mini	140	9.00	4.50	2.75
1975 Topps Mini	212	1.25	.60	.40
1976 O-Pee-Chee	150	4.50	2.25	1.25
1976 Topps	150	4.00	2.00	1.25
1977 O-Pee-Chee	255	4.00	2.00	1.25
1977 Topps	400	3.50	1.75	1.00
1978 O-Pee-Chee	190	3.50	1.75	1.00
1978 Topps	350	3.00	1.50	.90
1979 O-Pee-Chee	21	1.75	.90	.50
1979 Topps	50	.90	.45	.25
1980 O-Pee-Chee	152	1.75	.90	.50
1980 Topps	290	1.25	.60	.40

Set	Card #	MT	NM	EX
1981 Donruss	56a	1.75	1.25	.70
1981 Donruss	56b	.60	.45	.25
1981 Donruss	176	.50	.40	.20
1981 Fleer	110	.40	.30	.15
1981 Fleer	606	.50	.40	.20
1981 O-Pee-Chee	251	1.00	.70	.40
1981 Topps	530	.75	.60	.30
1982 Donruss	3	.25	.20	.10
1982 Donruss	84	.30	.25	.12
1982 Fleer	5	.30	.25	.12
1982 O-Pee-Chee	179	.75	.60	.30
1982 O-Pee-Chee	180	.30	.25	.12
1982 Topps	179	.60	.45	.25
1982 Topps	180	.40	.30	.15
1983 Donruss	488	.40	.30	.15
1983 Fleer	206	.25	.20	.10
1983 O-Pee-Chee	198	.60	.45	.25
1983 Topps	610	.50	.40	.20
1983 Topps Traded	37T	1.50	1.25	.60
1984 Donruss	63	.75	.60	.30
1984 Fleer	300	.50	.40	.20
1984 Fleer	628	.20	.15	.08
1984 O-Pee-Chee	380	.70	.50	.30
1984 Topps	380	.35	.25	.14
1985 Donruss	307	.40	.30	.15
1985 Fleer	32	.05	.25	.14

Set	Card #	MT	NM	EX
1985 Fleer	631	.25	.20	.10
1985 Fleer	633	.20	.15	.08
1985 Leaf-Donruss	94	.30	.25	.12
1985 O-Pee-Chee	177	.30	.25	.12
1985 Topps	2	.20	.15	.08
1985 Topps	450	.25	.20	.10
1985 Topps All-Star Glossy Set of 22	2	.30	.25	.12
1986 Donruss	63	.30	.25	.12
1986 Fleer	321	.30	.25	.12
1986 Fleer	640	.30	.25	.12
1986 Leaf	56	.30	.25	.12
1986 O-Pee-Chee	4	.25	.20	.10
1986 Sportflics	35	.40	.30	.15
1986 Sportflics	51	.70	.50	.30
1986 Sportflics	137	.20	.15	.08
1986 Sportflics Decade Greats	61	.40	.30	.15
1986 Topps	660	.15	.11	.06
1986 Topps All-Star Glossy Set of 22	13	.30	.25	.12
1986 Topps All-Star Glossy Set of 60	38	.50	.40	.20
1987 Donruss	81	.20	.15	.08
1987 Fleer	414	.25	.20	.10
1987 Leaf	114	.20	.15	.08
1987 O-Pee-Chee	100	.20	.15	.08
1987 Sportflics	40	.40	.30	.15
1987 Topps	100	.12	.09	.05
1988 Score	225	.12	.08	.04
1990 Pacific Legends	27	.20	.15	.08

Lou Gehrig

Set	Card #	NM	EX	VG
1933 DeLong	7	3500.	1750.	1050.
1933 Goudey	92	4000.	1500.	850.00
1933 Goudey	160	4000.	2100.	1000.
1934 Goudey	37	3500.	1750.	800.00
1934 Goudey	61	3250.	1650.	900.00
1960 Fleer	28	50.00	25.00	15.00
1961-62 Fleer	31	50.00	25.00	15.00
1973 O-Pee-Chee	472	6.75	3.50	2.00
1973 Topps	472	7.50	3.75	2.25
1976 O-Pee-Chee	341	7.25	3.75	2.25
1976 Topps	341	5.00	2.50	1.50

Set	Card #	MT	NM	EX
1986 Sportflics Decade Greats	10	1.50	1.25	.60
1992 Pinnacle	286	.25	.20	.10
1992 Score	881	.30	.25	.12

* * *

NBC sportscaster Joe Garagiola has his own Topps baseball card, which was produced by Topps in 1976. The card, #1, says he's a catcher for the NBC All-Stars and gives his New York City NBC address.

* * *

Bob Gibson

Set	Card #	NM	EX	VG
1959 Topps	514 (R)	300.00	150.00	90.00
1960 Topps	73	50.00	25.00	15.00
1961 Topps	211	30.00	15.00	9.00
1962 Topps	530	160.00	80.00	47.50
1963 Fleer	61	45.00	22.00	13.50
1963 Post Cereal	166	10.00	5.00	3.00
1963 Topps	5	15.00	7.50	4.50
1963 Topps	9	12.00	6.00	3.50
1963 Topps	415	45.00	22.00	13.50
1964 Topps	460	30.00	15.00	9.00
1965 O-Pee-Chee	12	2.75	1.50	.80
1965 Topps	12	7.00	3.50	2.00
1965 Topps	320	32.00	16.00	9.50
1966 Topps	225	8.00	4.00	2.50
1966 Topps	320	18.00	9.00	5.50
1967 Topps	210	18.00	8.00	4.75
1967 Topps	236	12.00	6.00	3.50
1968 O-Pee-Chee	100	30.00	15.00	9.00
1968 Topps	100	20.00	10.00	6.00
1968 Topps	378	7.00	3.50	2.00
1969 O-Pee-Chee	8	2.25	1.25	.70
1969 O-Pee-Chee	10	8.50	4.25	2.50
1969 O-Pee-Chee	12	2.25	1.25	.70
1969 O-Pee-Chee	107	2.25	1.25	.70
1969 O-Pee-Chee	200	21.00	10.50	6.25
1969 Topps	8	3.00	1.50	.90
1969 Topps	10	3.50	1.75	1.00
1969 Topps	12	3.00	1.50	.90
1969 Topps	107a	3.00	1.50	.90
1969 Topps	107b	6.00	3.00	1.75
1969 Topps	200	10.00	5.00	3.00
1969 Topps	432	4.00	2.00	1.25
1970 O-Pee-Chee	67	7.50	3.75	2.25
1970 O-Pee-Chee	71	1.75	.90	.50
1970 O-Pee-Chee	530	17.00	8.50	5.00
1970 Topps	67	4.00	2.00	1.25
1970 Topps	71	4.00	2.00	1.25
1970 Topps	530	10.00	5.00	3.00
1971 O-Pee-Chee	70	1.50	.70	.45
1971 O-Pee-Chee	72	7.50	3.75	2.25
1971 O-Pee-Chee	450	18.00	9.00	5.50
1971 Topps	70	3.50	1.75	1.00
1971 Topps	72	3.50	1.75	1.00
1971 Topps	450	12.00	6.00	3.50
1972 O-Pee-Chee	130	7.50	3.75	2.25
1972 Topps	130	6.00	3.00	1.75
1973 O-Pee-Chee	190	6.75	3.50	2.00
1973 Topps	190	5.00	2.50	1.50
1974 O-Pee-Chee	350	6.75	3.50	2.00
1974 Topps	350	6.00	3.00	1.75
1975 O-Pee-Chee	3	1.25	.60	.40
1975 O-Pee-Chee	150	6.25	3.25	2.00
1975 O-Pee-Chee	206	2.00	1.00	.60
1975 Topps	3	2.00	1.00	.60
1975 Topps	150	5.00	2.50	1.50
1975 Topps	206	1.25	.60	.40
1975 Topps Mini	3	3.25	1.75	1.00
1975 Topps Mini	150	7.00	3.50	2.00

Set	Card #		NM	EX
1975 Topps Mini	206		1.75	.90	.50

Set	Card #	MT	NM	EX
1986 Sportflics Decade Greats	42	.30	.25	.12
1988 Topps	664	.08	.06	.03
1990 Pacific Legends	28	.25	.20	.10

Kirk Gibson

Set	Card #	MT	NM	EX
1981 Fleer	481 (R)	3.00	2.25	1.25
1981 O-Pee-Chee	315	4.50	3.50	1.75
1981 Topps	315 (R)	4.00	3.00	1.50
1982 Donruss	407	.90	.70	.35
1982 Fleer	267	.40	.30	.15
1982 O-Pee-Chee	105	.60	.45	.25
1982 Topps	105	.50	.40	.20
1983 Donruss	459	.40	.30	.15
1983 Fleer	329	.60	.45	.25
1983 O-Pee-Chee	321	.30	.25	.12
1983 Topps	430	.60	.45	.25
1984 Donruss	593	1.00	.70	.40
1984 Fleer	80	1.00	.70	.40
1984 O-Pee-Chee	65	.60	.45	.25
1984 Topps	65	.40	.30	.15
1985 Donruss	471	.40	.30	.15
1985 Fleer	8	.20	.15	.08
1985 Leaf-Donruss	103	.20	.15	.08
1985 O-Pee-Chee	372	.25	.20	.10
1985 Topps	565	.20	.15	.08
1986 Donruss	1	.15	.11	.06
1986 Donruss	125	.35	.25	.14
1986 Donruss Diamond Kings Supers	1	.50	.40	.20
1986 Fleer	226	.15	.11	.06
1986 Leaf	1	.20	.15	.08
1986 O-Pee-Chee	295	.20	.15	.08
1986 Sportflics	21	.20	.15	.08
1986 Topps	295	.10	.08	.04
1986 Topps All-Star Glossy Set of 60	29	.35	.25	.14
1987 Donruss	50	.15	.11	.06
1987 Fleer	151	.15	.11	.06
1987 Leaf	104	.20	.15	.08
1987 O-Pee-Chee	386	.20	.15	.08
1987 Sportflics	48	.20	.15	.08
1987 Topps	765	.10	.08	.04
1988 Donruss	275	.08	.06	.03
1988 Fleer	55	.08	.06	.03
1988 Fleer Update	93	.20	.15	.08
1988 Leaf	136	.20	.15	.08
1988 O-Pee-Chee	201	.12	.09	.05
1988 Score	525	.15	.11	.06
1988 Score Traded	10T	.40	.30	.15
1988 Score Traded/ Rookie Glossy	10T	1.50	1.25	.60
1988 Sportflics	111	.25	.20	.10
1988 Topps	429	.08	.06	.03
1988 Topps	605	.15	.11	.06
1988 Topps Big Baseball	191	.10	.08	.04

1988 Topps Traded	40T	.10	.08	.04
1989 Bowman	351	.05	.04	.02
1989 Donruss	15	.08	.06	.03
1989 Donruss	132	.08	.06	.03
1989 Fleer	57	.08	.06	.03
1989 Fleer For The Record	4	.25	.20	.10
1989 O-Pee-Chee	340	.07	.05	.03
1989 O-Pee-Chee	382	.07	.05	.03
1989 Score	210	.08	.05	.02
1989 Score	582	.10	.06	.03
1989 Sportflics	65	.25	.20	.10
1989 Topps	340	.15	.11	.06
1989 Topps	396	.08	.06	.03
1989 Topps All-Star Glossy Set of 60	55	.20	.15	.08
1989 Topps Big Baseball	299	.05	.04	.02
1989 Upper Deck	633	.10	.08	.04
1989 Upper Deck	662	.08	.06	.03
1989 Upper Deck	666	.08	.06	.03
1989 Upper Deck	676	.08	.06	.03
1990 Bowman	97	.06	.05	.02
1990 Donruss	368	.09	.07	.04
1990 Fleer	393	.09	.07	.04
1990 Leaf	173	.35	.25	.14
1990 O-Pee-Chee	150	.09	.07	.04
1990 Score	487	.09	.07	.04
1990 Topps	150	.09	.07	.04
1990 Topps Big Baseball	326	.10	.08	.04
1990 Upper Deck	264	.09	.07	.04
1991 Bowman	302	.06	.05	.02
1991 Donruss	445	.06	.05	.02
1991 Fleer	199	.08	.06	.03
1991 Fleer Ultra Update	27	.15	.11	.06
1991 Fleer Update	26	.08	.06	.03
1991 Leaf	249	.12	.09	.05
1991 O-Pee-Chee Premier	50	.15	.11	.06
1991 Score	800	.08	.06	.03
1991 Score Traded	18	.08	.06	.03
1991 Topps	490	.08	.06	.03
1991 Topps Stadium Club	344	.30	.25	.12
1991 Topps Traded	46	.08	.06	.03
1991 Upper Deck	634	.12	.09	.05
1991 Upper Deck	737	.12	.09	.05
1992 Donruss	39	.08	.06	.03
1992 Fleer	157	.08	.06	.03
1992 O-Pee-Chee	720	.06	.05	.02
1992 Pinnacle	481	.10	.08	.04
1992 Score	520	.06	.05	.02
1992 Topps	720	.06	.05	.02
1992 Topps Gold	720	.35	.25	.14
1992 Topps Stadium Club	495	.10	.08	.04
1992 Topps Stadium Club	784	.10	.08	.04
1992 Topps Stadium Club East Coast National	784	4.00	3.00	1.50
1992 Upper Deck	180	.08	.06	.03
1993 Fleer Final Edition	209	.05	.04	.02
1993 Fleer Flair	203	.25	.15	.08
1993 Fleer Ultra	549	.10	.08	.04
1993 Leaf	314	.10	.08	.04
1993 Topps Stadium Club	673	.10	.08	.04
1993 Topps Stadium Club First Day Production	673	6.00	4.50	2.50
1993 Topps Traded	8	.05	.04	.02
1993 Upper Deck	766	.06	.05	.02
1994 Donruss	108	.05	.04	.02
1994 Fleer	130	.05	.04	.02
1994 Fleer Extra Bases	75	.10	.08	.04
1994 Fleer Flair	50	.20	.15	.08
1994 Leaf	342	.10	.08	.04
1994 Pacific Crown	218	.05	.04	.02
1994 Pinnacle	453	.10	.08	.04
1994 Pinnacle Artist's Proof	453	3.00	2.25	1.25
1994 Pinnacle Museum Collection	453	1.50	1.25	.60
1994 Score	421	.05	.04	.02
1994 Score Select	266	.10	.08	.04
1994 Topps	228	.04	.03	.02
1994 Topps Gold	228	.15	.11	.06
1994 Upper Deck Collector's Choice	403	.06	.05	.02

Tom Glavine

Set	Card #	MT	NM	EX
1988 Donruss	644 (R)	1.50	1.25	.60
1988 Fleer	539 (R)	4.00	3.00	1.50
1988 Score	638 (R)	1.50	1.25	.60
1988 Topps	779 (R)	1.50	1.25	.60
1989 Bowman	267	.30	.25	.12
1989 Donruss	381	.25	.20	.10
1989 Fleer	591	.40	.30	.15
1989 Score	442	.40	.30	.15
1989 Topps	157	.40	.30	.15
1989 Upper Deck	360	2.00	1.50	.80
1990 Bowman	2	.25	.20	.10
1990 Donruss	145	.20	.15	.08
1990 Fleer	583	.09	.07	.04
1990 Leaf	13	2.50	2.00	1.00
1990 O-Pee-Chee	506	.20	.15	.08
1990 Score	481	.15	.07	.03
1990 Sportflics	34	.15	.11	.06
1990 Topps	506	.20	.15	.08
1990 Topps Big Baseball	99	.06	.05	.02
1990 Upper Deck	571	.40	.30	.15
1991 Bowman	576	.15	.11	.06
1991 Donruss	132	.15	.11	.06
1991 Fleer	689	.15	.11	.06
1991 Fleer Ultra	5	.40	.30	.15
1991 Leaf	172	.40	.30	.15
1991 Score	206	.06	.05	.02
1991 Studio	145	.30	.25	.12
1991 Topps	82	.12	.09	.05
1991 Topps Stadium Club	558	1.50	1.25	.60
1991 Topps Stadium Club Members Only	(10)	.25	.20	.10
1991 Upper Deck	480	.25	.20	.10
1991 Upper Deck Final Edition	90	.15	.11	.06
1992 Bowman	699	1.00	.70	.40
1992 Donruss	426	.10	.08	.04
1992 Donruss	629	.10	.08	.04
1992 Donruss Triple Play	7	.15	.11	.06
1992 Fleer	358	.15	.11	.06
1992 Fleer	694	.08	.06	.03
1992 Fleer All-Stars	6	.60	.45	.25
1992 Fleer Smoke 'N Heat	7	.90	.70	.35
1992 Fleer Team Leaders	11	2.50	2.00	1.00
1992 Fleer Ultra	162	.35	.25	.14
1992 Fleer Ultra All-Stars	20	.75	.60	.30
1992 Fleer Ultra Award Winners	7	1.50	1.25	.60
1992 Leaf	279	.20	.15	.08
1992 O-Pee-Chee	305	.08	.06	.03
1992 O-Pee-Chee Premier	49	.20	.15	.08
1992 Pinnacle	75	.25	.20	.10
1992 Pinnacle	594	.15	.11	.06
1992 Score	450	.08	.06	.03
1992 Score	791	.08	.06	.03

Card	#			
1992 Score	890	.15	.11	.06
1992 Score Impact Players	49	.25	.20	.10
1992 Studio	4	.20	.15	.08
1992 Topps	305	.08	.06	.03
1992 Topps	395	.05	.04	.02
1992 Topps Gold	305	.45	.35	.20
1992 Topps Gold	395	.25	.20	.10
1992 Topps Kids	34	.05	.04	.02
1992 Topps Stadium Club	395	.40	.30	.15
1992 Topps Stadium Club Special Edition	62	.25	.20	.10
1992 Upper Deck	342	.10	.08	.04
1992 Upper Deck	713	.10	.08	.04
1993 Bowman	410	.20	.15	.08
1993 DiamondMarks	(3)	.50	.40	.20
1993 Donruss	554	.12	.09	.05
1993 Donruss Diamond Kings	19	1.00	.75	.40
1993 Donruss Elite Dominators	14	65.00	49.00	26.00
1993 Donruss Triple Play	117	.07	.05	.03
1993 Donruss Triple Play	209	.10	.08	.04
1993 Fleer	4	.10	.08	.04
1993 Fleer All-Stars	11	1.00	.75	.40
1993 Fleer Flair	4	.50	.40	.20
1993 Fleer ProVisions II	2	1.25	.90	.50
1993 Fleer Tom Glavine Career Highlights	1	.50	.40	.20
1993 Fleer Tom Glavine Career Highlights	2	.50	.40	.20
1993 Fleer Tom Glavine Career Highlights	3	.50	.40	.20
1993 Fleer Tom Glavine Career Highlights	4	.50	.40	.20
1993 Fleer Tom Glavine Career Highlights	5	.50	.40	.20
1993 Fleer Tom Glavine Career Highlights	6	.50	.40	.20
1993 Fleer Tom Glavine Career Highlights	7	.50	.40	.20
1993 Fleer Tom Glavine Career Highlights	8	.50	.40	.20
1993 Fleer Tom Glavine Career Highlights	9	.50	.40	.20
1993 Fleer Tom Glavine Career Highlights	10	.50	.40	.20
1993 Fleer Tom Glavine Career Highlights	11	.50	.40	.20
1993 Fleer Tom Glavine Career Highlights	12	.50	.40	.20
1993 Fleer Tom Glavine Career Highlights	13	.50	.40	.20
1993 Fleer Tom Glavine Career Highlights	14	.50	.40	.20
1993 Fleer Tom Glavine Career Highlights	15	.50	.40	.20
1993 Fleer Ultra	6	.20	.15	.08
1993 Leaf	295	.15	.11	.06
1993 Leaf Gold All-Stars	18	1.25	.90	.50
1993 O-Pee-Chee	132	.20	.15	.08
1993 O-Pee-Chee Premier Star Performers	21	.20	.15	.08
1993 Pinnacle	90	.15	.11	.06
1993 Pinnacle Team Pinnacle	2	6.00	4.50	2.50
1993 Post Cereal	21	.25	.20	.10
1993 Score	15	.10	.08	.04
1993 Score	539	.10	.08	.04
1993 Score Gold Dream Team	8	.75	.60	.30
1993 Score Select	7	.15	.11	.06
1993 Score Select Aces	2	4.00	3.00	1.50
1993 Score Select Chase Stars	10	3.00	2.25	1.25
1993 Score Select Stat Leaders	88	.10	.08	.04
1993 Studio	145	.15	.11	.06
1993 Topps	280	.10	.08	.04
1993 Topps	410	.08	.06	.03
1993 Topps Black Gold	6	.40	.30	.15
1993 Topps Finest	87	2.00	1.50	.80
1993 Topps Finest Jumbo All-Stars	87	10.00	7.50	4.00
1993 Topps Finest Refractors	87	40.00	30.00	15.00
1993 Topps Full Shot Super	19	3.00	2.25	1.25
1993 Topps Gold	280	.20	.15	.08
1993 Topps Gold	410	.15	.11	.06
1993 Topps Stadium Club	296	.15	.11	.06
1993 Topps Stadium Club	650	.20	.15	.08
1993 Topps Stadium Club First Day Production	296	15.00	11.00	6.00
1993 Topps Stadium Club First Day Production	650	15.00	11.00	6.00
1993 Topps Stadium Club Special Master Photo	(2)	.50	.40	.20
1993 Topps Stadium Club Special	106	.10	.08	.04
1993 Topps Stadium Club Team Sets	1	.50	.40	.20
1993 Upper Deck	75	.15	.11	.06
1993 Upper Deck	472	.15	.11	.06
1993 Upper Deck Fun Packs	61	.15	.11	.06
1993 Upper Deck Fun Packs	63	.12	.09	.05
1993 Upper Deck SP	58	.40	.30	.15
1993 Upper Deck SP Jumbos	58	25.00	18.50	10.00
1994 Bowman	21	.15	.11	.06
1994 Bowman's Best	12	1.00	.70	.40
1994 Bowman's Best Refractors	12	5.00	3.75	2.00
1994 Donruss	364	.15	.11	.06
1994 Donruss Special Edition - Gold	364	.25	.20	.10
1994 Donruss Triple Play	44	.15	.11	.06
1994 Fleer	359	.15	.11	.06
1994 Fleer All-Stars	36	.35	.25	.14
1994 Fleer Extra Bases	201	.20	.15	.08
1994 Fleer Extra Bases Game Breakers	11	.30	.25	.12
1994 Fleer Extra Bases Pitcher's Duel	9M	.50	.40	.20
1994 Fleer Flair	125	.35	.25	.14
1994 Fleer League Leaders	11	.35	.25	.14
1994 Fleer Ultra	151	.15	.11	.06
1994 Fleer Ultra All-Stars	19	.60	.45	.25
1994 Fleer Ultra League Leaders	9	.50	.40	.20
1994 Leaf	235	.20	.15	.08
1994 Leaf Limited	82	1.50	1.25	.60
1994 O-Pee-Chee	250	.15	.11	.06
1994 Pacific Crown	9	.15	.11	.06
1994 Pinnacle	284	.15	.11	.06
1994 Pinnacle Artist's Proof	284	6.00	4.50	2.50
1994 Pinnacle Museum Collection	284	3.00	2.25	1.25
1994 Post Cereal	16	.25	.20	.10
1994 Score	30	.15	.11	.06
1994 Score Dream Team	2	6.00	4.50	2.50
1994 Score Gold Stars	16	3.00	2.25	1.25
1994 Score Select	250	.15	.11	.06
1994 Sportflics 2000	80	.25	.20	.10
1994 Studio	34	.25	.20	.10
1994 Topps	393	.10	.08	.04
1994 Topps	475	.15	.11	.06
1994 Topps Black Gold	32	.40	.30	.15
1994 Topps Finest	267	.75	.60	.30
1994 Topps Finest Refractors	267	7.00	5.25	2.75
1994 Topps Gold	393	.25	.20	.10
1994 Topps Gold	475	.45	.35	.20
1994 Topps Stadium Club	538	.15	.11	.06
1994 Topps Stadium Club	574	.15	.11	.06

1994 Topps Stadium Club First Day Production	538	6.00	4.50	2.50
1994 Topps Stadium Club First Day Production	574	12.00	9.00	4.75
1994 Topps Stadium Club Members Only Baseball	23	.25	.20	.10
1994 Upper Deck	144	.25	.20	.10
1994 Upper Deck All-Stars Green Foil	11	.25	.20	.10
1994 Upper Deck All-Stars Gold Foil	11	1.00	.70	.40
1994 Upper Deck Collector's Choice	306	.10	.08	.04
1994 Upper Deck Collector's Choice	430	.10	.08	.04
1994 Upper Deck Electric Diamond	144	1.00	.75	.40
1994 Upper Deck Fun Packs	47	.20	.15	.08
1994 Upper Deck SP	49	.25	.20	.10
1994 Upper Deck SP Baseball Die-Cut	49	.50	.40	.20

Lefty Gomez

Set	Card #	NM	EX	VG
1933 DeLong	14	335.00	167.00	100.00
1933 Goudey	216	350.00	140.00	66.00
1936 Goudey	(14)	225.00	110.00	65.00
1939 Goudey Premiums (R303-B)	(9)	40.00	20.00	12.00
1939 Goudey Premiums (R303-A)	(17)	45.00	22.00	13.50
1939 Play Ball	48a	175.00	85.00	50.00
1939 Play Ball	48b	200.00	100.00	60.00
1940 Play Ball	6	200.00	78.00	38.00
1941 Double Play	61	38.00	38.00	38.00
1941 Play Ball	72	600.00	300.00	160.00
1960 Fleer	54	3.50	1.75	1.00
1961-62 Fleer	34	4.00	2.00	1.25

Set	Card #	MT	NM	EX
1986 Sportflics Decade Greats	9	.30	.25	.12

* * *

The National Chicle Co. and the Goudey Gum Co., the major card producers during the 1930s, were the first companies to team bubble gum with baseball cards. Each sold slabs of gum with one card in a colorful wrapper for one cent.

* * *

Post Cereal put baseball cards on the backs of its cereal boxes from 1960-63 and again during the 1990s.

* * *

Juan Gonzalez

Set	Card #	MT	NM	EX
1990 Bowman	492 (R)	2.00	1.50	.80
1990 Donruss	33a (R)	4.00	3.00	1.50
1990 Donruss	33b (R)	2.00	1.50	.80
1990 Fleer	297 (R)	2.00	1.50	.80
1990 O-Pee-Chee	331 (R)	1.50	1.25	.60
1990 Score	637 (R)	2.00	1.50	.80
1990 Topps	331 (R)	1.75	1.25	.70
1990 Upper Deck	72 (R)	7.00	5.25	2.75
1991 Bowman	180	.75	.60	.30
1991 Donruss	371	.60	.45	.25
1991 Fleer	286	.60	.45	.25
1991 Fleer Ultra Update	55	18.00	13.50	7.25
1991 Leaf	119	3.00	2.25	1.25
1991 O-Pee-Chee Premier	54	1.50	1.25	.60
1991 Score	805	.60	.45	.25
1991 Studio	124	2.00	1.50	.80
1991 Topps	224	.60	.45	.25
1991 Topps Stadium Club	237	15.00	11.00	6.00
1991 Upper Deck	646	1.25	.90	.50
1992 Bowman	84	6.00	4.50	2.50
1992 Donruss	393	.60	.45	.25
1992 Donruss Triple Play	112	.60	.45	.25
1992 Fleer	304	.60	.45	.25
1992 Fleer Ultra	132	2.00	1.50	.80
1992 Leaf	62	1.50	1.25	.60
1992 O-Pee-Chee	27	.60	.45	.25
1992 Pinnacle	127	1.50	1.25	.60
1992 Pinnacle Team 2000	26	2.50	2.00	1.00
1992 Score	11	.60	.45	.25
1992 Score Impact Players	27	1.50	1.25	.60
1992 Studio	242	1.00	.75	.40
1992 Topps	27	.60	.45	.25
1992 Topps Gold	27	6.00	4.50	2.50
1992 Topps Kids	131	.20	.15	.08
1992 Topps Stadium Club	240	1.50	1.25	.60
1992 Upper Deck	243	.60	.45	.25
1992 Upper Deck Home Run Heroes	19	1.50	1.25	.60
1993 Bowman	305	1.00	.75	.40
1993 DiamondMarks	(112)	1.50	1.25	.60
1993 DiamondMarks Promos	(5)	20.00	15.00	8.00
1993 Donruss	555	.60	.45	.25
1993 Donruss Diamond Kings	7	3.50	2.75	1.50
1993 Donruss Elite	36	80.00	60.00	32.00
1993 Donruss Elite Dominators	11	300.00	225.00	120.00
1993 Donruss Elite Dominators	11	175.00	131.00	70.00
1993 Donruss Elite Supers	18	45.00	34.00	18.00
1993 Donruss Long Ball Leaders	14	8.00	6.00	3.25
1993 Donruss Masters of the Game	11	4.00	3.00	1.50
1993 Donruss MVP's	21	3.00	2.25	1.25

Card	#	High	Mid	Low
1993 Donruss Spirit of the Game	5	4.00	3.00	1.50
1993 Donruss Triple Play League Leaders	4	9.00	6.75	3.50
1993 Donruss Triple Play Action Baseball	22	.20	.15	.08
1993 Donruss Triple Play	221	1.00	.75	.40
1993 Fleer	322	.60	.45	.25
1993 Fleer	709	.25	.20	.10
1993 Fleer All-Stars	6	4.00	3.00	1.50
1993 Fleer AL Team Leaders	8	14.00	10.50	5.50
1993 Fleer Flair	280	3.00	2.25	1.25
1993 Fleer Golden Moments II	(3)	7.00	5.25	2.75
1993 Fleer Ultra	279	1.00	.75	.40
1993 Fleer Ultra All-Stars	16	5.00	3.75	2.00
1993 Fleer Ultra Home Run Kings	1	5.00	3.75	2.00
1993 Fleer Ultra Performers	2	3.00	2.25	1.25
1993 Leaf	170	1.00	.75	.40
1993 Leaf Fasttrack	5	10.00	7.50	4.00
1993 Leaf Gold All-Stars	16	5.00	3.75	2.00
1993 O-Pee-Chee	97	2.00	1.50	.80
1993 O-Pee-Chee Premier Star Performers	7	1.00	.75	.40
1993 Pacific Prism Insert	14	45.00	34.00	18.00
1993 Pinnacle	191	1.00	.75	.40
1993 Pinnacle Cooperstown	25	.50	.40	.20
1993 Pinnacle Cooperstown Dufex	25	100.00	75.00	40.00
1993 Pinnacle Home Run Club	1	2.00	1.50	.80
1993 Pinnacle Slugfest	1	5.00	3.75	2.00
1993 Pinnacle Team Pinnacle	8	25.00	18.00	10.00
1993 Pinnacle Team 2001	13	5.00	3.75	2.00
1993 Post Cereal	23	.75	.60	.30
1993 Score	51	.60	.45	.25
1993 Score Select	40	1.00	.75	.40
1993 Score Select Stat Leaders	25	.75	.60	.30
1993 Score The Franchise	13	12.00	9.00	4.75
1993 Studio	160	1.00	.75	.40
1993 Studio Heritage	2	5.00	3.75	2.00
1993 Studio Silhouettes	4	5.00	3.75	2.00
1993 Topps	34	.60	.45	.25
1993 Topps Black Gold	32	1.50	1.25	.60
1993 Topps Finest	116	12.00	9.00	4.75
1993 Topps Finest Jumbo All-Stars	116	25.00	18.00	10.00
1993 Topps Finest Refractors	116	150.00	110.00	60.00
1993 Topps Full Shot Super	4	9.00	6.75	3.50
1993 Topps Gold	34	1.75	1.25	.70
1993 Topps Stadium Club	297	.50	.40	.20
1993 Topps Stadium Club	540	1.00	.75	.40
1993 Topps Stadium Club First Day Production	297	75.00	56.00	30.00
1993 Topps Stadium Club First Day Production	540	100.00	75.00	40.00
1993 Upper Deck	52	.25	.20	.10
1993 Upper Deck	497	.35	.25	.14
1993 Upper Deck	755	.75	.60	.30
1993 Upper Deck	831	.40	.30	.15
1993 Upper Deck Clutch Performers	10	2.50	2.00	1.00
1993 Upper Deck Diamond Gallery	20	3.50	2.75	1.50
1993 Upper Deck Fun Packs All-Star Scratch-Off	7	4.00	3.00	1.50
1993 Upper Deck Fun Packs	15	.50	.40	.20
1993 Upper Deck Fun Packs	153	.25	.20	.10
1993 Upper Deck Fun Packs	156	.35	.25	.14
1993 Upper Deck Fun Packs	223	.20	.15	.08
1993 Upper Deck Future Heroes	58	2.50	2.00	1.00
1993 Upper Deck Home Run Heroes	1	2.50	2.00	1.00
1993 Upper Deck On Deck	12	2.50	2.00	1.00
1993 Upper Deck SP	194	4.00	3.00	1.50
1993 Upper Deck SP Platinum Power	8	18.00	13.50	7.25
1993 Upper Deck 5th Anniversary	6	2.50	2.00	1.00
1993 Upper Deck 5th Anniversary Super	6	5.00	3.75	2.00
1994 Bowman	45	1.00	.75	.40
1994 Bowman's Best	19	3.50	2.75	1.50
1994 Bowman's Best Refractors	19	20.00	15.00	8.00
1994 Donruss	49	1.00	.75	.40
1994 Donruss Award Winners Supers	9	9.00	6.75	3.50
1994 Donruss Decade Dominators	6	3.50	2.75	1.50
1994 Donruss Decade Dominators Supers	6	7.50	5.75	3.00
1994 Donruss Elite	42	35.00	26.00	14.00
1994 Donruss Long Ball Leaders	10	7.00	5.25	2.75
1994 Donruss MVP's	27	3.00	2.25	1.25
1994 Donruss Special Edition - Gold	49	1.50	1.25	.60
1994 Donruss Spirit of the Game	5	7.00	5.25	2.75
1994 Donruss Spirit of the Game Super	5	15.00	11.00	6.00
1994 Donruss Triple Play Promos	1	6.00	4.50	2.50
1994 Donruss Triple Play Bomb Squad	3	3.50	2.75	1.50
1994 Donruss Triple Play	194	.75	.60	.30
1994 Fleer	307	.75	.60	.30
1994 Fleer	710	.25	.20	.10
1994 Fleer All-Stars	9	1.50	1.25	.60
1994 Fleer Extra Bases	178	1.00	.75	.40
1994 Fleer Extra Bases Game Breakers	12	1.50	1.25	.60
1994 Fleer Flair	109	2.00	1.50	.80
1994 Fleer Flair Outfield Power	5	5.00	3.75	2.00
1994 Fleer Lumber Co.	4	2.50	2.00	1.00
1994 Fleer ProVisions	6	1.25	.90	.50
1994 Fleer Team Leaders	13	2.00	1.50	.80
1994 Fleer Ultra	127	1.00	.75	.40
1994 Fleer Ultra All-Stars	7	2.00	1.50	.80
1994 Fleer Ultra Hitting Machines	5	2.00	1.50	.80
1994 Fleer Ultra Home Run Kings	1	8.00	6.00	3.25
1994 Fleer Ultra RBI Kings	4	15.00	11.00	6.00
1994 Leaf	418	1.00	.75	.40
1994 Leaf Clean-Up Crew	7	10.00	7.50	4.00
1994 Leaf Gamers	3	6.00	4.50	2.50
1994 Leaf Gold Stars	13	30.00	22.00	12.00
1994 Leaf Limited	72	7.00	5.25	2.75
1994 Leaf MVP Contenders	6a	9.00	6.75	3.50
1994 Leaf MVP Contenders	6b	18.00	12.00	6.50
1994 Leaf Power Brokers	4	2.50	2.00	1.00
1994 Leaf Slide Show	7	7.00	5.25	2.75
1994 Leaf Statistical Standouts	3	2.50	2.00	1.00
1994 O-Pee-Chee	28	.75	.60	.30
1994 O-Pee-Chee All-Star Redemption Cards	4	1.50	1.25	.60
1994 O-Pee-Chee Jumbo All-Stars	4	30.00	22.00	12.00
1994 O-Pee-Chee Jumbo All-Stars Factory Set	4	3.50	2.75	1.50

1994 Pacific Crown	617	1.00	.75	.40
1994 Pacific Crown All Latino All-Star Team	7	8.00	6.00	3.25
1994 Pacific Crown Homerun Leaders	1	7.00	5.25	2.75
1994 Pacific Crown Jewels of the Crown	2	8.00	6.00	3.25
1994 Pacific Crown Promos	3	6.00	4.50	2.50
1994 Pinnacle	350	1.00	.70	.40
1994 Pinnacle Artist's Proof	350	50.00	38.00	20.00
1994 Pinnacle Museum Collection	350	20.00	15.00	8.00
1994 Pinnacle Power Surge	24	.60	.45	.25
1994 Pinnacle Run Creators	7	8.00	6.00	3.25
1994 Pinnacle Team Pinnacle	7	35.00	26.00	14.00
1994 Pinnacle The Naturals Box Set	4	1.00	.75	.40
1994 Pinnacle Tribute	15	7.50	5.25	2.75
1994 Post Cereal	3	.75	.60	.30
1994 Score	27	.60	.45	.25
1994 Score Dream Team	7	24.00	18.00	9.50
1994 Score Gold Stars	33	17.50	13.00	7.00
1994 Score Select	212	1.00	.70	.40
1994 Score Select Crown Contenders	7	12.00	9.00	4.75
1994 Score Select Skills	5	18.00	13.50	7.25
1994 Score The Cycle	16	35.00	26.00	14.00
1994 Sportflics 2000	35	1.25	.90	.50
1994 Sportflics 2000	182	.75	.60	.30
1994 Studio	154	1.00	.75	.40
1994 Studio Editor's Choice	5	6.00	4.50	2.50
1994 Studio Gold Stars	9	35.00	26.00	14.00
1994 Studio Silver Stars	9	20.00	15.00	8.00
1994 Topps	389	.30	.25	.12
1994 Topps	685	.60	.45	.25
1994 Topps Black Gold	7	1.50	1.25	.60
1994 Topps Finest	211	4.00	3.00	1.50
1994 Topps Finest Refractors	211	40.00	30.00	15.00
1994 Topps Finest Superstars	211	15.00	11.00	6.00
1994 Topps Gold	389	1.00	.70	.40
1994 Topps Gold	685	2.50	2.00	1.00
1994 Topps Stadium Club	261	.60	.45	.25
1994 Topps Stadium Club	568	1.00	.75	.40
1994 Topps Stadium Club Finest	4	4.00	3.00	1.50
1994 Topps Stadium Club First Day Production	261	15.00	11.00	6.00
1994 Topps Stadium Club First Day Production	568	50.00	37.00	20.00
1994 Topps Stadium Club Members Only Baseball	1	1.50	1.25	.60
1994 Upper Deck	52	.60	.45	.25
1994 Upper Deck	155	1.00	.75	.40
1994 Upper Deck	293	.60	.45	.25
1994 Upper Deck All-Stars Green Foil	25	1.00	.70	.40
1994 Upper Deck All-Stars Gold Foil	25	5.00	3.75	2.00
1994 Upper Deck Collector's Choice	313	.50	.40	.20
1994 Upper Deck Collector's Choice	323	.15	.11	.06
1994 Upper Deck Collector's Choice	347	.25	.20	.10
1994 Upper Deck Collector's Choice	630	.60	.45	.25
1994 Upper Deck Collector's Choice	633	.40	.30	.15
1994 Upper Deck Diamond Collection	3W	17.50	13.00	7.00
1994 Upper Deck Electric Diamond	52	7.00	5.25	2.75
1994 Upper Deck Electric Diamond	155	7.00	5.25	2.75
1994 Upper Deck Electric Diamond	293	2.50	2.00	1.00
1994 Upper Deck Fun Packs	19	1.00	.70	.40
1994 Upper Deck Fun Packs	181	.60	.45	.25
1994 Upper Deck Fun Packs	196	.50	.40	.20
1994 Upper Deck Fun Packs	199	1.50	1.25	.60
1994 Upper Deck Fun Packs	215	.60	.45	.25
1994 Upper Deck Fun Packs	240	.25	.20	.10
1994 Upper Deck Mickey Mantle's Long Shots	9MM	6.00	4.50	2.50
1994 Upper Deck Next Generation	5	6.00	4.50	2.50
1994 Upper Deck SP	148	1.50	1.25	.60
1994 Upper Deck SP Baseball Die-Cut	148	3.00	2.25	1.25
1994 Upper Deck SP Holoview Blue	11	10.00	7.50	4.00
1994 Upper Deck SP Holoview Red	11	75.00	60.00	32.00
1994 Upper Deck SP Insert	2	10.00	7.50	4.00

Dwight Gooden

Set	Card #	MT	NM	EX
1984 Fleer Update	43	30.00	22.00	12.00
1984 Topps Traded	42T	14.00	10.50	5.50
1985 Donruss	190 (R)	3.50	2.75	1.50
1985 Fleer	82 (R)	4.00	3.00	1.50
1985 Fleer	634	.25	.20	.10
1985 Leaf-Donruss	234	6.25	4.75	2.50
1985 O-Pee-Chee	41	3.00	2.25	1.25
1985 Topps	3	.25	.20	.10
1985 Topps	620 (R)	2.00	1.50	.80
1985 Topps All-Star Glossy Set of 40	38	.80	.60	.30
1986 Donruss	26	.35	.25	.14
1986 Donruss	75	.50	.40	.20
1986 Donruss Diamond Kings Supers	26	.90	.70	.35
1986 Fleer	81	.60	.45	.25
1986 Fleer	626	.40	.30	.15
1986 Fleer	638	.50	.40	.20
1986 Fleer	641	.40	.30	.15
1986 Fleer All Stars	10	.40	.30	.15
1986 Leaf	26	.80	.60	.30
1986 O-Pee-Chee	250	.40	.30	.15
1986 Sportflics	100	2.00	1.50	.80
1986 Sportflics	136	.80	.60	.30
1986 Sportflics	143	1.25	.90	.50
1986 Sportflics	176	1.00	.70	.40

1986 Sportflics	184	1.50	1.25	.60
1986 Sportflics	185	.60	.45	.25
1986 Sportflics Decade Greats	75	1.00	.70	.40
1986 Sportflics Rookies	47	.40	.30	.15
1986 Topps	202	.20	.15	.08
1986 Topps	250	.40	.30	.15
1986 Topps	709	.10	.07	.04
1986 Topps All-Star Glossy Set of 60	41	.75	.60	.30
1987 Donruss	199	.25	.20	.10
1987 Fleer	9	.35	.25	.14
1987 Fleer	629	.15	.11	.06
1987 Fleer	640	.50	.40	.20
1987 Fleer All Stars	19	.25	.20	.10
1987 Leaf	84	.70	.50	.30
1987 O-Pee-Chee	130	.50	.40	.20
1987 Sportflics	100	.50	.40	.20
1987 Sportflics	120	.25	.20	.10
1987 Sportflics	159	1.25	.90	.50
1987 Topps	130	.10	.08	.04
1987 Topps	603a	.80	.60	.30
1987 Topps	603b	.10	.08	.04
1987 Topps All-Star Glossy Set of 22	10	.30	.25	.12
1987 Topps All-Star Glossy Set of 60	51	.40	.30	.15
1988 Donruss	69	.10	.08	.04
1988 Fleer	135	.10	.08	.04
1988 Leaf	48	.40	.30	.15
1988 O-Pee-Chee	287	.30	.25	.12
1988 Score	350	.08	.06	.03
1988 Sportflics	200	.30	.25	.12
1988 Sportflics Gamewinners	9	.60	.45	.25
1988 Topps	405	.10	.08	.04
1988 Topps	480	.10	.08	.04
1988 Topps All-Star Glossy Set of 60	54	.35	.25	.14
1988 Topps Big Baseball	11	.25	.20	.10
1989 Bowman	376	.10	.07	.04
1989 Donruss	270	.10	.08	.04
1989 Fleer	36	.12	.09	.05
1989 Fleer	635	.12	.09	.05
1989 O-Pee-Chee	30	.10	.08	.04
1989 Score	200	.08	.05	.02
1989 Sportflics	140	.40	.30	.15
1989 Topps	30	.08	.06	.03
1989 Topps	661	.10	.08	.04
1989 Topps All-Star Glossy Set of 22	21	.10	.08	.04
1989 Topps All-Star Glossy Set of 60	37	.25	.20	.10
1989 Topps Big Baseball	304	.10	.08	.04
1989 Upper Deck	565	.15	.11	.06
1990 Bowman	126	.10	.07	.04
1990 Donruss	171	.08	.06	.03
1990 Fleer	204	.10	.07	.04
1990 Leaf	139	.40	.30	.15
1990 O-Pee-Chee	510	.25	.20	.10
1990 Post Cereal	29	.60	.45	.25
1990 Score	313	.08	.06	.03
1990 Sportflics	145	.30	.25	.12
1990 Topps	510	.10	.07	.04
1990 Topps All-Star Glossy Set of 60	23	.25	.20	.10
1990 Topps Big Baseball	174	.20	.15	.08
1990 Upper Deck	114	.10	.08	.04
1991 Bowman	472	.08	.06	.03
1991 Donruss	266	.08	.06	.03
1991 Fleer	148	.10	.07	.04
1991 Fleer ProVisions	7	.25	.20	.10
1991 Fleer Ultra	218	.10	.07	.04
1991 Leaf	165	.10	.08	.04
1991 O-Pee-Chee Premier	55	.05	.04	.02
1991 Score	540	.08	.06	.03
1991 Score	685	.06	.05	.02
1991 Score	866	.08	.06	.03
1991 Studio	204	.30	.25	.12
1991 Topps	330	.10	.07	.04
1991 Upper Deck	224	.10	.07	.04
1992 Bowman	480	.60	.45	.25
1992 Donruss	446	.10	.08	.04
1992 Donruss Diamond Kings	15	.50	.40	.20
1992 Donruss Elite	12	25.00	18.00	10.00
1992 Donruss Triple Play	167	.15	.11	.06
1992 Fleer	505	.12	.09	.05
1992 Fleer Smoke 'N Heat	8	.75	.60	.30
1992 Fleer Ultra	232	.15	.11	.06
1992 Leaf	112	.12	.09	.05
1992 O-Pee-Chee	725	.12	.09	.05
1992 O-Pee-Chee Premier	47	.35	.25	.14
1992 Pinnacle	111	.10	.07	.04
1992 Pinnacle Rookie Idols	6	5.00	3.75	2.00
1992 Post Cereal	5	.30	.25	.12
1992 Score	10	.12	.09	.05
1992 Score Impact Players	54	.15	.11	.06
1992 Studio	65	.25	.20	.10
1992 Topps	725	.12	.09	.05
1992 Topps Gold	725	.45	.35	.20
1992 Topps Kids	11	.10	.08	.04
1992 Topps Stadium Club	455	.15	.11	.06
1992 Topps Stadium Club	602	.15	.11	.06
1992 Topps Stadium Club East Coast National	602	4.00	3.00	1.50
1992 Topps Stadium Club Master Photos	(6)	4.00	3.00	1.50
1992 Topps Stadium Club Members Only	(6)	.35	.25	.14
1992 Upper Deck	84	.10	.08	.04
1992 Upper Deck	135	.08	.06	.03
1993 Bowman	242	.10	.08	.04
1993 DiamondMarks	(42)	.50	.40	.20
1993 Donruss	462	.05	.04	.02
1993 Donruss Triple Play Nicknames	6	1.00	.70	.40
1993 Donruss Triple Play	146	.15	.11	.06
1993 Fleer	474	.08	.06	.03
1993 Fleer Flair	91	.25	.15	.08
1993 Fleer Ultra	427	.10	.08	.04
1993 Leaf	203	.10	.08	.04
1993 O-Pee-Chee	92	.15	.11	.06
1993 Pinnacle	96	.06	.05	.02
1993 Pinnacle Cooperstown	19	.25	.20	.10
1993 Pinnacle Cooperstown Dufex	19	45.00	34.00	18.00
1993 Score	53	.05	.04	.02
1993 Score Select	57	.15	.11	.06
1993 Score Select Aces	8	3.00	2.25	1.25
1993 Studio	155	.08	.06	.03
1993 Topps	640	.03	.02	.01
1993 Topps Finest	113	1.25	.90	.50
1993 Topps Finest Jumbo All-Stars	113	7.00	5.25	2.75
1993 Topps Finest Refractors	113	24.00	18.00	9.50
1993 Topps Gold	640	.10	.08	.04
1993 Topps Stadium Club	514	.10	.08	.04
1993 Topps Stadium Club First Day Production	514	7.00	5.25	2.75
1993 Topps Stadium Club II Inserts	2	4.00	3.00	1.50
1993 Topps Stadium Club Master Photos	(17)	1.50	1.25	.60
1993 Upper Deck	665	.08	.06	.03
1993 Upper Deck Diamond Gallery	15	.50	.40	.20
1993 Upper Deck Fun Packs	123	.20	.15	.08
1993 Upper Deck Fun Packs	126	.20	.15	.08
1993 Upper Deck SP	149	.15	.11	.06
1994 Bowman	400	.10	.08	.04
1994 Donruss	17	.05	.04	.02
1994 Donruss Special Edition - Gold	17	.25	.20	.10

1994 Donruss Triple Play	143	.05	.04	.02
1994 Fleer	563	.05	.04	.02
1994 Fleer Extra Bases	317	.10	.08	.04
1994 Fleer Flair	197	.20	.15	.08
1994 Fleer Ultra	236	.10	.08	.04
1994 Leaf	10	.12	.09	.05
1994 O-Pee-Chee	24	.15	.11	.06
1994 Pacific Crown	402	.05	.04	.02
1994 Pinnacle	62	.10	.08	.04
1994 Pinnacle Artist's Proof	62	3.00	2.25	1.25
1994 Pinnacle Museum Collection	62	1.50	1.25	.60
1994 Score	22	.04	.03	.02
1994 Score Select	54	.10	.08	.04
1994 Sportflics 2000	94	.10	.08	.04
1994 Studio	114	.10	.08	.04
1994 Topps	150	.04	.03	.02
1994 Topps Finest	82	.60	.45	.25
1994 Topps Finest Refractors	82	3.50	2.75	1.50
1994 Topps Gold	150	.15	.11	.06
1994 Topps Stadium Club	220	.10	.08	.04
1994 Topps Stadium Club First Day Production	220	2.50	2.00	1.00
1994 Upper Deck	205	.10	.08	.04
1994 Upper Deck All-Stars Green Foil	38	.25	.20	.10
1994 Upper Deck All-Stars Gold Foil	38	1.00	.70	.40
1994 Upper Deck Collector's Choice	342	.05	.04	.02
1994 Upper Deck Collector's Choice	519	.07	.05	.03
1994 Upper Deck Diamond Collection	6E	4.00	3.00	1.50
1994 Upper Deck Electric Diamond	205	.25	.20	.10
1994 Upper Deck Fun Packs	16	.05	.04	.02
1994 Upper Deck SP	116	.15	.11	.06
1994 Upper Deck SP Baseball Die-Cut	116	.25	.20	.10

Rich Gossage

RICH GOSSAGE

Set	Card #	NM	EX	VG
1973 O-Pee-Chee	174	21.00	10.50	6.25
1973 Topps	174 (R)	15.00	7.50	4.50
1974 O-Pee-Chee	542	4.50	2.25	1.25
1974 Topps	542	2.00	1.00	.60
1975 O-Pee-Chee	554	1.00	.50	.30
1975 Topps	554	.45	.25	.14
1975 Topps Mini	554	1.75	.90	.50
1976 O-Pee-Chee	180	1.00	.50	.30
1976 O-Pee-Chee	205	.40	.20	.12
1976 Topps	180	1.50	.75	.45
1976 Topps	205	.40	.20	.12
1977 Topps	319	.60	.30	.20

1978 Topps	70	.75	.40	.25
1979 O-Pee-Chee	114	.60	.30	.20
1979 Topps	8	.40	.20	.12
1979 Topps	225	.40	.20	.12
1980 O-Pee-Chee	77	.50	.25	.15
1980 Topps	140	.30	.15	.09

Set	Card #	MT	NM	EX
1981 Donruss	347	.20	.15	.08
1981 Fleer	89	.20	.15	.08
1981 O-Pee-Chee	48	.30	.25	.12
1981 Topps	460	.20	.15	.08
1982 Donruss	283	.20	.15	.08
1982 Fleer	37	.20	.15	.08
1982 O-Pee-Chee	117	.12	.09	.05
1982 O-Pee-Chee	286	.12	.09	.05
1982 O-Pee-Chee	396	.25	.20	.10
1982 Topps	557	.20	.15	.08
1982 Topps	770	.15	.11	.06
1982 Topps	771	.08	.06	.03
1983 Donruss	157	.20	.15	.08
1983 Fleer	381	.20	.15	.08
1983 O-Pee-Chee	240	.25	.20	.10
1983 O-Pee-Chee	241	.12	.09	.05
1983 Topps	240	.20	.15	.08
1983 Topps	241	.15	.11	.06
1983 Topps All-Star Glossy Set of 40	11	.25	.20	.10
1984 Donruss	396	.25	.20	.10
1984 Fleer	125	.25	.20	.10
1984 Fleer Update	44	.50	.40	.20
1984 O-Pee-Chee	121	.40	.30	.15
1984 Topps	670	.10	.08	.04
1984 Topps	718	.15	.11	.06
1984 Topps Traded	43T	.40	.30	.15
1985 Donruss	185	.25	.20	.10
1985 Fleer	33	.20	.15	.08
1985 Fleer	633	.20	.15	.08
1985 Leaf-Donruss	204	.15	.11	.06
1985 O-Pee-Chee	90	.15	.11	.06
1985 Topps	90	.10	.08	.04
1985 Topps All-Star Glossy Set of 40	19	.25	.20	.10
1986 Donruss	2	.20	.15	.08
1986 Donruss	185	.20	.15	.08
1986 Donruss Diamond Kings Supers	2	.30	.25	.12
1986 Fleer	322	.10	.08	.04
1986 Leaf	2	.12	.09	.05
1986 O-Pee-Chee	104	.12	.09	.05
1986 Sportflics	55	.10	.08	.04
1986 Sportflics	190	.15	.11	.06
1986 Topps	530	.10	.08	.04
1986 Topps All-Star Glossy Set of 60	56	.25	.20	.10
1987 Donruss	483	.15	.11	.06
1987 Fleer	415	.15	.11	.06
1987 O-Pee-Chee	380	.10	.08	.04
1987 Topps	380	.15	.11	.06
1988 Donruss	434	.15	.11	.06
1988 Fleer	583	.15	.11	.06
1988 Fleer Update	76	.10	.08	.04
1988 O-Pee-Chee	170	.08	.06	.03
1988 Score	331	.12	.09	.05
1988 Score Traded	14T	.25	.20	.10
1988 Score Traded/ Rookie Glossy	14T	1.00	.70	.40
1988 Topps	170	.06	.05	.02
1988 Topps Traded	41T	.15	.11	.06
1989 Donruss	158	.10	.08	.04
1989 Fleer	425	.12	.09	.05
1989 O-Pee-Chee	162	.05	.04	.02
1989 Score	223	.10	.08	.04
1989 Topps	415	.10	.08	.04
1989 Upper Deck	452	.12	.09	.05
1990 Donruss	678	.04	.03	.02
1991 Bowman	271	.06	.05	.02
1991 Fleer Update	59	.08	.06	.03
1991 Leaf	236	.10	.08	.04
1991 Studio	125	.15	.11	.06
1992 Donruss	555	.20	.15	.08

1992 Fleer	305	.05	.04	.02
1992 Leaf	474	.10	.08	.04
1992 O-Pee-Chee	215	.05	.04	.02
1992 Score	538	.04	.03	.02
1992 Topps	215	.05	.04	.02
1992 Topps Gold	215	.25	.20	.10
1992 Topps Stadium Club	719	.20	.15	.08
1993 Fleer Flair	259	.25	.15	.08
1993 Fleer Ultra	606	.10	.08	.04
1993 Topps Stadium Club	17	.10	.08	.04
1993 Topps Stadium Club First Day Production	17	4.00	3.00	1.50
1994 Fleer	262	.05	.04	.02
1994 Pacific Crown	450	.05	.04	.02
1994 Score	260	.04	.03	.02

Mark Grace

Set	Card #	MT	NM	EX
1988 Donruss	40 (R)	1.25	.90	.50
1988 Fleer	641 (R)	3.50	2.75	1.50
1988 Fleer Update	77	2.00	1.50	.80
1988 Leaf	40	1.25	.90	.50
1988 Score Traded	80T	10.00	7.50	4.00
1988 Score Traded/ Rookie Glossy	80T	40.00	30.00	16.00
1988 Topps Traded	42T	1.50	1.25	.60
1989 Bowman	291	.25	.20	.10
1989 Donruss	17	.12	.09	.05
1989 Donruss	255	.15	.11	.06
1989 Fleer	426	.30	.25	.12
1989 O-Pee-Chee	297	.12	.09	.05
1989 Score	362	.40	.30	.15
1989 Sportflics	15	.20	.15	.08
1989 Topps	465	.20	.15	.08
1989 Topps All-Star Glossy Set of 60	29	.35	.25	.14
1989 Topps Big Baseball	189	.15	.11	.06
1989 Topps Glossy Rookies Set of 22	11	.45	.35	.20
1989 Upper Deck	140	.75	.60	.30
1990 Bowman	29	.20	.15	.08
1990 Donruss	577	.10	.07	.04
1990 Fleer	32	.25	.20	.10
1990 Fleer League Standouts	2	.60	.45	.25
1990 Leaf	137	1.00	.75	.40
1990 O-Pee-Chee	240	.40	.30	.15
1990 Post Cereal	19	.40	.30	.15
1990 Score	150	.20	.15	.08
1990 Sportflics	15	.20	.15	.08
1990 Topps	240	.15	.11	.06
1990 Topps All-Star Glossy Set of 60	12	.40	.30	.15
1990 Topps Big Baseball	19	.20	.15	.08
1990 Upper Deck	128	.30	.25	.12
1991 Bowman	433	.10	.08	.04
1991 Donruss	199	.08	.06	.03
1991 Fleer	422	.10	.08	.04
1991 Fleer Ultra	61	.12	.09	.05

1991 Leaf	170	.15	.11	.06
1991 Post Cereal	22	.40	.30	.15
1991 Score	175	.10	.08	.04
1991 Studio	157	.15	.11	.06
1991 Topps	520	.08	.06	.03
1991 Upper Deck	134	.15	.11	.06
1992 Bowman	580	.40	.30	.15
1992 Donruss	281	.15	.11	.06
1992 Donruss Triple Play	114	.12	.09	.05
1992 Fleer	381	.08	.06	.03
1992 Fleer Ultra	175	.15	.11	.06
1992 Leaf	26	.15	.11	.06
1992 O-Pee-Chee	140	.12	.09	.05
1992 Pinnacle	136	.20	.15	.08
1992 Score	445	.08	.06	.03
1992 Studio	14	.15	.11	.06
1992 Topps	140	.12	.09	.05
1992 Topps Gold	140	.45	.35	.20
1992 Topps Kids	4	.10	.08	.04
1992 Topps Stadium Club	174	.15	.11	.06
1992 Upper Deck	143	.15	.11	.06
1993 Bowman	440	.20	.15	.08
1993 DiamondMarks	(8)	.50	.40	.20
1993 Donruss	532	.08	.06	.03
1993 Donruss Triple Play	11	.35	.25	.14
1993 Donruss Triple Play	211	.12	.09	.05
1993 Fleer	20	.08	.06	.03
1993 Fleer Flair	14	.50	.30	.15
1993 Fleer Ultra	18	.20	.15	.08
1993 Fleer Ultra Award Winners	3	1.25	.90	.50
1993 Leaf	198	.15	.11	.06
1993 Leaf Gold All-Stars	12	8.00	6.00	3.25
1993 Leaf Update Gold All-Stars	10	1.50	1.25	.60
1993 O-Pee-Chee	86	.25	.20	.10
1993 Pinnacle	34	.06	.05	.02
1993 Score	50	.08	.06	.03
1993 Score Select	73	.12	.09	.05
1993 Score Select Stat Leaders	12	.20	.15	.08
1993 Studio	42	.15	.11	.06
1993 Studio Heritage	5	1.00	.70	.40
1993 Studio Superstars on Canvas	8	1.00	.70	.40
1993 Topps	630	.03	.02	.01
1993 Topps Finest	73	1.50	1.25	.60
1993 Topps Finest Refractors	73	20.00	15.00	8.00
1993 Topps Gold	630	.10	.08	.04
1993 Topps Stadium Club	419	.15	.11	.06
1993 Topps Stadium Club First Day Production	419	7.50	5.75	3.00
1993 Topps Stadium Club Master Photos	(18)	1.50	1.25	.60
1993 Topps Stadium Club Members Only	(10)	.75	.60	.30
1993 Topps Stadium Club Team Sets	8	.25	.20	.10
1993 Upper Deck	483	.15	.11	.06
1993 Upper Deck	573	.10	.08	.04
1993 Upper Deck Fun Packs	81	.15	.11	.06
1993 Upper Deck Iooss Collection	8	.50	.40	.20
1993 Upper Deck Iooss Collection Super	8	3.00	2.25	1.25
1993 Upper Deck SP	83	.15	.11	.06
1994 Bowman	410	.10	.08	.04
1994 Bowman's Best	9	.75	.60	.30
1994 Bowman's Best Refractors	9	4.00	3.00	1.50
1994 Donruss	358	.05	.04	.02
1994 Donruss MVP's	2	.50	.40	.20
1994 Donruss Special Edition - Gold	358	.25	.20	.10
1994 Donruss Triple Play Medalists	4	2.50	2.00	1.00
1994 Donruss Triple Play	72	.05	.04	.02
1994 Fleer	383	.10	.08	.04

Set	Card #	MT	NM	EX
1994 Fleer All-Stars	37	.25	.20	.10
1994 Fleer Extra Bases	218	.10	.08	.04
1994 Fleer Extra Bases Game Breakers	13	.25	.20	.10
1994 Fleer Flair	360	.25	.20	.10
1994 Fleer Ultra	455	.12	.09	.05
1994 Fleer Ultra Award Winners	11	.60	.45	.25
1994 Fleer Ultra On-Base Leaders	5	5.00	3.75	2.00
1994 Leaf	43	.12	.09	.05
1994 Leaf Gamers	6	1.50	1.25	.60
1994 Leaf Limited	90	1.25	.90	.50
1994 O-Pee-Chee	146	.05	.04	.02
1994 Pacific Crown	98	.10	.08	.04
1994 Pacific Crown Jewels of the Crown	25	3.00	2.25	1.25
1994 Pinnacle	336	.12	.09	.05
1994 Pinnacle Artist's Proof	336	3.00	2.25	1.25
1994 Pinnacle Museum Collection	336	1.75	1.25	.70
1994 Pinnacle Run Creators	34	1.50	1.25	.60
1994 Post Cereal	14	.35	.25	.14
1994 Score	42	.10	.08	.04
1994 Score Gold Stars	3	3.00	2.25	1.25
1994 Score Select	230	.20	.15	.08
1994 Sportflics 2000	120	.20	.15	.08
1994 Studio	60	.10	.08	.04
1994 Topps	360	.08	.06	.03
1994 Topps Black Gold	33	.60	.45	.25
1994 Topps Finest	390	.75	.60	.30
1994 Topps Finest Refractors	390	4.00	3.00	1.50
1994 Topps Gold	360	.20	.15	.08
1994 Topps Stadium Club	403	.12	.09	.05
1994 Topps Stadium Club First Day Production	403	6.00	4.50	2.50
1994 Topps Stadium Club Members Only Baseball	10	.35	.25	.14
1994 Upper Deck	440	.10	.08	.04
1994 Upper Deck All-Stars Green Foil	30	.25	.20	.10
1994 Upper Deck All-Stars Gold Foil	30	1.00	.70	.40
1994 Upper Deck Collector's Choice	114	.05	.04	.02
1994 Upper Deck Electric Diamond	440	.25	.20	.10
1994 Upper Deck Fun Packs	17	.05	.04	.02
1994 Upper Deck SP	69	.15	.11	.06
1994 Upper Deck SP Baseball Die-Cut	69	.25	.20	.10

Mike Greenwell

Set	Card #	MT	NM	EX
1986 Sportflics	178a	8.00	6.00	3.25
1986 Sportflics	178b	60.00	45.00	24.00
1987 Donruss	585 (R)	1.00	.75	.40
1987 Fleer Update	37	.60	.45	.25
1987 Sportflics Rookies	8	1.00	.70	.40
1987 Topps	259 (R)	.50	.40	.20
1988 Donruss	339	.12	.09	.05
1988 Fleer	354	.30	.25	.12
1988 Fleer	630	.25	.20	.10
1988 Leaf	153	1.00	.70	.40
1988 O-Pee-Chee	274	.80	.60	.30
1988 Score	175	.12	.08	.04
1988 Sportflics	118	.60	.45	.25
1988 Topps	493	.12	.09	.05
1988 Topps All-Star Glossy Set of 60	20	.60	.45	.25
1988 Topps Big Baseball	233	.40	.30	.15
1988 Topps Glossy Rookies	3	1.00	.70	.40
1989 Bowman	34	.15	.11	.06
1989 Donruss	1	.08	.06	.03
1989 Donruss	186	.08	.06	.03
1989 Donruss Grand Slammers	5	.25	.20	.10
1989 Donruss MVP	13	.30	.25	.12
1989 Fleer	90	.08	.06	.03
1989 Fleer All-Stars	6	.25	.20	.10
1989 O-Pee-Chee	374	.12	.09	.05
1989 Score	66	.08	.05	.02
1989 Score	659	.15	.11	.06
1989 Sportflics	143	.20	.15	.08
1989 Sportflics	221	1.50	1.25	.60
1989 Topps	402	.15	.11	.06
1989 Topps	630	.08	.06	.03
1989 Topps All-Star Glossy Set of 60	31	.35	.25	.14
1989 Topps Big Baseball	211	.50	.40	.20
1989 Upper Deck	432	.10	.08	.04
1990 Bowman	274	.08	.06	.03
1990 Donruss	66	.10	.08	.04
1990 Fleer	277	.12	.09	.05
1990 Fleer	632	.10	.08	.04
1990 Leaf	143	.40	.30	.15
1990 O-Pee-Chee	70	.30	.25	.12
1990 Score	345	.10	.08	.04
1990 Sportflics	50	.20	.15	.08
1990 Topps	70	.10	.07	.04
1990 Topps Big Baseball	61	.30	.25	.12
1990 Upper Deck	354	.10	.08	.04
1991 Bowman	116	.10	.08	.04
1991 Donruss	553	.12	.09	.05
1991 Donruss Grand Slammers	14	.20	.15	.08
1991 Fleer	96	.10	.08	.04
1991 Fleer ProVisions	8	.25	.20	.10
1991 Fleer Ultra	32	.15	.11	.06
1991 Leaf	19	.20	.15	.08
1991 Score	130	.15	.11	.06
1991 Studio	15	.20	.15	.08
1991 Topps	792	.15	.11	.06
1991 Topps Stadium Club	253	.30	.25	.12
1991 Upper Deck	165	.10	.08	.04
1992 Bowman	615	.08	.06	.03
1992 Donruss	523	.08	.06	.03
1992 Donruss Triple Play	252	.12	.09	.05
1992 Fleer	39	.08	.06	.03
1992 Fleer Ultra	16	.10	.08	.04
1992 Leaf	89	.15	.11	.06
1992 O-Pee-Chee	113	.10	.08	.04
1992 Pinnacle	131	.15	.11	.06
1992 Score	545	.08	.06	.03
1992 Topps	113	.10	.08	.04
1992 Topps Gold	113	.60	.45	.25
1992 Topps Kids	69	.10	.08	.04
1992 Topps Stadium Club	446	.15	.11	.06
1992 Upper Deck	275	.10	.08	.04
1993 Bowman	607	.10	.08	.04
1993 DiamondMarks	(70)	.25	.20	.10
1993 Donruss	223	.08	.06	.03
1993 Donruss Triple Play	46	.07	.05	.03
1993 Fleer	559	.05	.04	.02
1993 Fleer Flair	164	.25	.15	.08

1993 Fleer Ultra	152	.10	.08	.04
1993 Leaf	197	.10	.08	.04
1993 O-Pee-Chee	285	.20	.15	.08
1993 Pinnacle	102	.06	.05	.02
1993 Score	385	.08	.06	.03
1993 Score Select	228	.08	.06	.03
1993 Studio	161	.08	.06	.03
1993 Topps	323	.06	.05	.02
1993 Topps Finest	197	1.00	.70	.40
1993 Topps Finest Refractors	197	20.00	15.00	8.00
1993 Topps Gold	323	.10	.08	.04
1993 Topps Stadium Club	86	.10	.08	.04
1993 Topps Stadium Club First Day Production	86	8.00	6.00	3.25
1993 Upper Deck	154	.08	.06	.03
1993 Upper Deck Fun Packs	164	.15	.11	.06
1993 Upper Deck SP	202	.15	.11	.06
1994 Bowman	259	.10	.08	.04
1994 Donruss	163	.05	.04	.02
1994 Donruss Triple Play	204	.05	.04	.02
1994 Fleer	33	.05	.04	.02
1994 Fleer Extra Bases	20	.10	.08	.04
1994 Fleer Flair	263	.20	.15	.08
1994 Fleer Ultra	313	.10	.08	.04
1994 Leaf	182	.10	.08	.04
1994 Leaf Limited	10	1.00	.70	.40
1994 O-Pee-Chee	49	.05	.04	.02
1994 Pinnacle	285	.10	.08	.04
1994 Pinnacle Artist's Proof	285	3.00	2.25	1.25
1994 Pinnacle Museum Collection	285	1.50	1.25	.60
1994 Score	83	.04	.03	.02
1994 Score Select	10	.10	.08	.04
1994 Sportflics 2000	110	.10	.08	.04
1994 Studio	162	.10	.08	.04
1994 Topps	502	.04	.03	.02
1994 Topps Finest	322	.50	.40	.20
1994 Topps Finest Refractors	322	3.50	2.75	1.50
1994 Topps Gold	502	.15	.11	.06
1994 Topps Stadium Club	386	.10	.08	.04
1994 Topps Stadium Club First Day Production	386	2.50	2.00	1.00
1994 Upper Deck	187	.10	.08	.04
1994 Upper Deck Collector's Choice	440	.05	.04	.02
1994 Upper Deck Electric Diamond	187	.25	.20	.10
1994 Upper Deck Fun Packs	39	.05	.04	.02
1994 Upper Deck Fun Packs	228	.10	.08	.04
1994 Upper Deck SP	155	.15	.11	.06
1994 Upper Deck SP Baseball Die-Cut	155	.25	.20	.10

* * *

The Famous Chicken often aids the home team between innings - he replaces the first baseman during infield warm-ups. "I really enjoy doing that," (Ted) Giannoulas said. "In fact, this summer I took a lawn chair, a drink, a towel and a magazine out to Cecil Fielder. And to see him squeeze into the lawn chair was the funniest sight - even Lou Whitaker was busting up at second base, watching Cecil ease himself into that lawn chair. It was hysterical. Upper Deck has a picture of (the Famous Chicken/Fielder act) and they're going to use it for a 1992 card. I'm really looking forward to seeing that card."

* * *

Bobby Grich

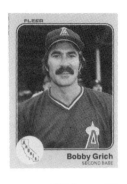

Bobby Grich
SECOND BASE

Set	Card #	NM	EX	VG
1971 O-Pee-Chee	193	1.50	.70	.45
1971 Topps	193 (R)	3.50	1.75	1.00
1972 O-Pee-Chee	338	1.25	.60	.40
1972 Topps	338	.75	.40	.25
1973 O-Pee-Chee	418	1.25	.60	.40
1973 Topps	418	.70	.35	.20
1974 O-Pee-Chee	109	.60	.30	.20
1974 Topps	109	.40	.20	.12
1975 O-Pee-Chee	225	.55	.30	.15
1975 Topps	225	.30	.15	.09
1976 O-Pee-Chee	335	.35	.20	.11
1976 Topps	335	.25	.13	.08
1977 O-Pee-Chee	28	.30	.15	.09
1977 Topps	521	.25	.13	.08
1978 O-Pee-Chee	133	.25	.13	.08
1978 Topps	18	.25	.13	.08
1979 O-Pee-Chee	248	.25	.13	.08
1979 Topps	477	.25	.13	.08
1980 O-Pee-Chee	326	.20	.10	.06
1980 Topps	621	.20	.10	.06

Set	Card #	MT	NM	EX
1981 Donruss	289	.10	.08	.04
1981 Fleer	269	.10	.08	.04
1981 O-Pee-Chee	182	.12	.09	.05
1981 Topps	182	.15	.11	.06
1982 Donruss	90	.10	.08	.04
1982 Fleer	461	.10	.08	.04
1982 O-Pee-Chee	284	.12	.09	.05
1982 Topps	162	.25	.20	.10
1982 Topps	284	.15	.11	.06
1983 Donruss	468	.10	.08	.04
1983 Fleer	91	.10	.08	.04
1983 O-Pee-Chee	381	.12	.09	.05
1983 O-Pee-Chee	387	.12	.09	.05
1983 Topps	387	.10	.08	.04
1983 Topps	790	.12	.09	.05
1984 Donruss	179	.20	.15	.08
1984 Fleer	518	.12	.09	.05
1984 O-Pee-Chee	315	.25	.20	.10
1984 Topps	315	.12	.09	.05
1985 Donruss	280	.12	.09	.05
1985 Fleer	302	.10	.08	.04
1985 Leaf-Donruss	88	.08	.06	.03
1985 O-Pee-Chee	155	.10	.08	.04
1985 Topps	465	.10	.08	.04
1986 Donruss	207	.10	.08	.04
1986 Fleer	157	.10	.08	.04
1986 O-Pee-Chee	155	.08	.06	.03
1986 Topps	155	.10	.08	.04
1986 Topps	486	.07	.05	.03
1987 Donruss	456	.10	.08	.04
1987 Fleer	81	.10	.08	.04
1987 O-Pee-Chee	4	.08	.06	.03
1987 Sportflics	184	.10	.08	.04
1990 Pacific Legends	31	.05	.04	.02

Ken Griffey Jr.

Ken Griffey Jr.

Set	Card #	MT	NM	EX
1989 Bowman	220 (R)	5.00	3.75	2.00
1989 Bowman	259	1.00	.70	.40
1989 Donruss	33 (R)	4.50	3.50	1.75
1989 Fleer	548 (R)	6.00	4.50	2.50
1989 Score Traded	100T	6.00	4.50	2.50
1989 Topps Traded	41T	4.00	3.00	1.50
1989 Upper Deck	1 (R)	70.00	52.00	28.00
1990 Bowman	481	2.00	1.50	.80
1990 Donruss	4	.50	.40	.20
1990 Donruss	365	2.00	1.50	.80
1990 Donruss Diamond Kings Supers	4	2.00	1.50	.80
1990 Fleer	513	2.00	1.50	.80
1990 Fleer Soaring Stars	6	8.00	6.00	3.25
1990 Leaf	245	32.00	24.00	13.00
1990 O-Pee-Chee	336	1.25	.90	.50
1990 Post Cereal	23	1.50	1.25	.60
1990 Score	560	2.00	1.50	.80
1990 Sportflics	7	3.00	2.25	1.25
1990 Topps	336	2.00	1.50	.80
1990 Topps All-Star Glossy Set of 60	20	1.75	1.25	.70
1990 Topps Big Baseball	250	1.25	.90	.50
1990 Topps Glossy Rookies	11	3.00	2.25	1.25
1990 Upper Deck	24	.40	.30	.15
1990 Upper Deck	156	6.00	4.50	2.50
1991 Bowman	246	1.50	1.25	.60
1991 Donruss	49	.50	.40	.20
1991 Donruss	77	1.00	.75	.40
1991 Donruss	392	.40	.30	.15
1991 Fleer	450	1.00	.75	.40
1991 Fleer	710	.50	.40	.20
1991 Fleer All Stars	7	6.00	4.00	2.00
1991 Fleer Ultra	336	5.00	3.75	2.00
1991 Fleer Ultra Gold	4	4.00	3.00	1.50
1991 Leaf	372	4.00	3.00	1.50
1991 O-Pee-Chee Premier	56	3.50	2.75	1.50
1991 Post Cereal	11	1.50	1.25	.60
1991 Score	2	1.25	.90	.50
1991 Score	396	.40	.30	.15
1991 Score	697	.50	.40	.20
1991 Score	841	.50	.30	.15
1991 Score	858	.50	.40	.20
1991 Score	892	1.50	1.25	.60
1991 Studio	112	4.00	3.00	1.50
1991 Topps	392	.40	.30	.15
1991 Topps	790	1.00	.75	.40
1991 Topps All-Star Glossy Set of 22	7	.70	.50	.30
1991 Topps Stadium Club	270	20.00	15.00	8.00
1991 Topps Stadium Club Charter Members	(10)	2.00	1.50	.80
1991 Upper Deck	555	2.50	2.00	1.00
1991 Upper Deck Final Edition	79	.40	.30	.15
1991 Upper Deck Final Edition	87	.75	.60	.30
1992 Bowman	100	15.00	11.00	6.00
1992 Donruss	24	.75	.60	.30
1992 Donruss	165	1.50	1.25	.60
1992 Donruss Elite	13	175.00	130.00	70.00
1992 Donruss Triple Play Gallery of Stars	8	7.00	5.25	2.75
1992 Donruss Triple Play	152	.75	.50	.25
1992 Fleer	279	1.50	1.25	.60
1992 Fleer	709	1.00	.75	.40
1992 Fleer All-Stars	23	9.00	6.75	3.50
1992 Fleer Team Leaders	15	40.00	30.00	15.00
1992 Fleer Ultra	123	5.00	3.75	2.00
1992 Fleer Ultra All-Stars	6	10.00	7.50	4.00
1992 Fleer Ultra Award Winners	22	12.00	9.00	4.75
1992 Fleer Update	H1	25.00	20.00	10.00
1992 Leaf	392	3.00	2.25	1.25
1992 Leaf Gold Previews	24	12.00	9.00	4.75
1992 O-Pee-Chee	50	.60	.45	.25
1992 O-Pee-Chee Premier	167	.80	.60	.30
1992 Pinnacle	283	.75	.60	.30
1992 Pinnacle	549	4.00	3.00	1.50
1992 Pinnacle Slugfest	7	10.00	7.50	4.00
1992 Pinnacle Team Pinnacle	9	45.00	34.00	18.00
1992 Pinnacle Team 2000	47	6.00	4.50	2.50
1992 Post Cereal	20	.80	.60	.30
1992 Score	1	1.50	1.25	.60
1992 Score	436	.60	.45	.25
1992 Score Impact Players	28	4.00	3.00	1.50
1992 Studio	232	3.00	2.25	1.25
1992 Topps	50	1.50	1.25	.60
1992 Topps Gold	50	15.00	11.00	6.00
1992 Topps Kids	122	.35	.25	.14
1992 Topps Stadium Club	400	6.00	4.50	2.50
1992 Topps Stadium Club	603	2.75	2.00	1.00
1992 Topps Stadium Club East Coast National	603	40.00	30.00	16.00
1992 Topps Stadium Club Master Photos	(7)	8.00	6.00	3.25
1992 Topps Stadium Club Special Edition	70	2.50	2.00	1.00
1992 Upper Deck	85	.50	.40	.20
1992 Upper Deck	424	1.50	1.25	.60
1992 Upper Deck	650	.50	.40	.20
1992 Upper Deck MVP Holograms	22	3.50	2.75	1.50
1993 Bowman	375	4.00	3.00	1.50
1993 Bowman	703	1.00	.75	.40
1993 DiamondMarks	(107)	3.00	2.25	1.25
1993 DiamondMarks Inserts	(3)	25.00	18.50	10.00
1993 Donruss	553	1.50	1.25	.60
1993 Donruss Diamond Kings	1	8.00	6.00	3.25
1993 Donruss Elite Dominators	12	175.00	131.00	70.00
1993 Donruss Long Ball Leaders	9	20.00	15.00	8.00
1993 Donruss Masters of the Game	8	6.00	4.50	2.50
1993 Donruss MVP's	20	8.00	6.00	3.25
1993 Donruss Triple Play	1	1.00	.75	.40
1993 Donruss Triple Play Nicknames	5	8.00	6.00	3.25
1993 Donruss Triple Play Action Baseball	24	.35	.25	.14
1993 Fleer	307	1.50	1.25	.60
1993 Fleer All-Stars	7	10.00	7.50	4.00
1993 Fleer AL Team Leaders	10	40.00	30.00	15.00
1993 Fleer Flair	270	10.00	7.50	4.00
1993 Fleer Ultra	619	4.00	3.00	1.50
1993 Fleer Ultra All-Stars	17	14.00	10.50	5.50
1993 Fleer Ultra Award Winners	16	14.00	10.50	5.50
1993 Fleer Ultra Performers	3	7.50	5.50	3.00
1993 Leaf	319	4.00	3.00	1.50

Card	#			
1993 Leaf Gold All-Stars	7	8.00	6.00	3.25
1993 Leaf Update Gold All-Stars	8	8.00	6.00	3.25
1993 O-Pee-Chee	91	6.00	4.50	2.50
1993 O-Pee-Chee Premier Star Performers	9	3.00	2.25	1.25
1993 Pinnacle	110	3.50	2.75	1.50
1993 Pinnacle Cooperstown	22	.75	.60	.30
1993 Pinnacle Cooperstown Dufex	22	400.00	300.00	160.00
1993 Pinnacle Home Run Club	13	3.00	2.25	1.25
1993 Pinnacle Slugfest	28	15.00	11.00	6.00
1993 Post Cereal	7	1.00	.70	.40
1993 Score	1	1.75	1.25	.70
1993 Score	504	.75	.60	.30
1993 Score	536	.75	.60	.30
1993 Score Gold Dream Team	5	5.00	3.75	2.00
1993 Score Select	2	3.50	2.75	1.50
1993 Score Select Chase Stars	19	50.00	38.00	20.00
1993 Score Select Stat Leaders	15	1.00	.70	.40
1993 Score The Franchise	12	30.00	22.00	12.00
1993 Studio	96	3.00	2.25	1.25
1993 Studio Superstars on Canvas	1	12.00	9.00	4.75
1993 Topps	179	1.50	1.25	.60
1993 Topps	405	.40	.30	.15
1993 Topps Black Gold	33	3.50	2.75	1.50
1993 Topps Finest	110	35.00	26.00	14.00
1993 Topps Finest Jumbo All-Stars	110	80.00	60.00	32.00
1993 Topps Finest Refractors	110	700.00	520.00	280.00
1993 Topps Full Shot Super	2	12.00	9.00	4.75
1993 Topps Gold	179	4.00	3.00	1.50
1993 Topps Gold	405	.90	.70	.35
1993 Topps Stadium Club	591	2.00	1.50	.80
1993 Topps Stadium Club	707	3.50	2.75	1.50
1993 Topps Stadium Club First Day Production	591	75.00	56.00	30.00
1993 Topps Stadium Club First Day Production	707	125.00	94.00	50.00
1993 Topps Stadium Club II Inserts	4	7.00	5.25	2.75
1993 Topps Stadium Club Master Photos	(26)	9.00	6.75	3.50
1993 Topps Stadium Club Members Only	(11)	4.00	3.00	1.50
1993 Topps Stadium Club Special Master Photo	(3)	3.00	2.25	1.25
1993 Topps Stadium Club Special	56	3.00	2.25	1.25
1993 Upper Deck	55	.50	.40	.20
1993 Upper Deck	355	2.00	1.50	.80
1993 Upper Deck	355a	25.00	18.50	10.00
1993 Upper Deck	525	.10	.07	.04
1993 Upper Deck "Highlights"	9	40.00	30.00	15.00
1993 Upper Deck Clutch Performers	11	8.00	6.00	3.25
1993 Upper Deck Diamond Gallery	13	7.00	5.25	2.75
1993 Upper Deck Fun Packs All-Star Scratch-Off	8	5.00	3.75	2.00
1993 Upper Deck Fun Packs	16	3.00	2.25	1.25
1993 Upper Deck Fun Packs	24	1.00	.75	.40
1993 Upper Deck Fun Packs	30	1.00	.75	.40
1993 Upper Deck Fun Packs	111	1.00	.75	.40
1993 Upper Deck Fun Packs	114	2.00	1.50	.80
1993 Upper Deck Fun Packs	224	.50	.40	.20
1993 Upper Deck Future Heroes	59	6.00	4.50	2.50
1993 Upper Deck Home Run Heroes	9	6.00	4.50	2.50
1993 Upper Deck Iooss Collection	13	5.00	3.75	2.00
1993 Upper Deck Iooss Collection Super	13	7.50	5.75	3.00
1993 Upper Deck On Deck	13	6.00	4.50	2.50
1993 Upper Deck SP	4	14.00	10.50	5.50
1993 Upper Deck SP Platinum Power	9	60.00	45.00	24.00
1993 Upper Deck Triple Crown	4	10.00	7.50	4.00
1993 Upper Deck 5th Anniversary	1	7.50	5.50	3.00
1993 Upper Deck 5th Anniversary Super	1	9.00	6.75	3.50
1994 Bowman	5	3.00	2.25	1.25
1994 Bowman's Best	96	8.00	6.00	3.25
1994 Bowman's Best	40	10.00	7.50	4.00
1994 Bowman's Best Refractors	96	35.00	26.00	14.00
1994 Bowman's Best Refractors	40	100.00	75.00	40.00
1994 Donruss	4	3.00	2.25	1.25
1994 Donruss Decade Dominators	6	10.00	7.50	4.00
1994 Donruss Decade Dominators Supers	6	7.50	5.75	3.00
1994 Donruss Decade Dominators	9	10.00	7.50	4.00
1994 Donruss Decade Dominators Supers	9	8.00	6.00	3.25
1994 Donruss Diamond Kings	14	10.00	7.50	4.00
1994 Donruss Diamond Kings Super	14	7.50	5.75	3.00
1994 Donruss Elite	45	100.00	75.00	40.00
1994 Donruss Long Ball Leaders	5	20.00	15.00	8.00
1994 Donruss MVP's	26	8.00	6.00	3.25
1994 Donruss Special Edition - Gold	4	5.00	3.75	2.00
1994 Donruss Spirit of the Game	3	15.00	11.00	6.00
1994 Donruss Spirit of the Game Super	3	25.00	18.00	10.00
1994 Donruss Triple Play Promos	4	6.00	4.50	2.50
1994 Donruss Triple Play Bomb Squad	8	10.00	7.50	4.00
1994 Donruss Triple Play Medalists	11	5.00	3.75	2.00
1994 Donruss Triple Play	127	1.50	1.25	.60
1994 Fleer	286	2.50	2.00	1.00
1994 Fleer All-Stars	10	4.00	3.00	1.50
1994 Fleer Extra Bases	166	2.50	2.00	1.00
1994 Fleer Extra Bases Game Breakers	14	4.00	3.00	1.50
1994 Fleer Flair	103	6.00	4.50	2.50
1994 Fleer Flair Hot Glove	3	75.00	56.00	30.00
1994 Fleer Flair Outfield Power	6	15.00	11.00	6.00
1994 Fleer Golden Moments	4	5.00	3.75	2.00
1994 Fleer Golden Moments Super	4	15.00	11.00	6.00
1994 Fleer Lumber Co.	5	6.00	4.50	2.50
1994 Fleer Team Leaders	12	5.00	3.75	2.00
1994 Fleer Ultra	120	3.00	2.25	1.25
1994 Fleer Ultra All-Stars	8	6.00	4.50	2.50
1994 Fleer Ultra Award Winners	6	6.00	4.50	2.50
1994 Fleer Ultra Home Run Kings	2	22.00	16.50	8.75
1994 Fleer Ultra On-Base Leaders	6	60.00	45.00	24.00

1994 Leaf	368	3.00	2.25	1.25
1994 Leaf Gamers	1	25.00	18.00	10.00
1994 Leaf Gold Stars	4	80.00	60.00	32.00
1994 Leaf Limited	66	20.00	15.00	8.00
1994 Leaf Limited Gold	11	95.00	71.00	38.00
1994 Leaf MVP Contenders	7a	25.00	18.00	10.00
1994 Leaf MVP Contenders	7b	50.00	38.00	20.00
1994 Leaf Power Brokers	5	10.00	7.50	4.00
1994 Leaf Slide Show	9	20.00	15.00	8.00
1994 Leaf Statistical Standouts	6	10.00	7.50	4.00
1994 O-Pee-Chee	22	3.00	2.25	1.25
1994 O-Pee-Chee All-Star Redemption Cards	8	3.50	2.75	1.50
1994 O-Pee-Chee Jumbo All-Stars	8	40.00	30.00	15.00
1994 O-Pee-Chee Jumbo All-Stars Factory Set	8	6.00	4.50	2.50
1994 Pacific Crown	570	2.50	2.00	1.00
1994 Pacific Crown Homerun Leaders	2	18.00	13.50	7.25
1994 Pacific Crown Jewels of the Crown	8	18.00	13.50	7.25
1994 Pinnacle	100	3.00	2.25	1.25
1994 Pinnacle Artist's Proof	100	180.00	135.00	75.00
1994 Pinnacle Museum Collection	100	65.00	49.00	26.00
1994 Pinnacle Power Surge	23	1.50	1.25	.60
1994 Pinnacle Run Creators	3	20.00	15.00	8.00
1994 Pinnacle Team Pinnacle	6	60.00	45.00	24.00
1994 Pinnacle The Naturals Box Set	3	2.50	2.00	1.00
1994 Pinnacle Tribute	17	20.00	15.00	8.00
1994 Post Cereal	15	.80	.60	.30
1994 Score	3	1.50	1.25	.60
1994 Score	628	1.00	.75	.40
1994 Score Gold Stars	32	45.00	34.00	18.00
1994 Score Select	1	3.50	2.75	1.50
1994 Score Select Crown Contenders	10	40.00	30.00	15.00
1994 Score The Cycle	17	60.00	45.00	24.00
1994 Sportflics 2000	143	4.00	3.00	1.50
1994 Sportflics 2000	181	2.50	2.00	1.00
1994 Studio	101	3.50	2.75	1.50
1994 Studio Editor's Choice	3	18.00	13.50	7.25
1994 Studio Gold Stars	4	100.00	75.00	40.00
1994 Studio Silver Stars	4	50.00	38.00	20.00
1994 Topps	388	.40	.30	.15
1994 Topps	400	1.50	1.25	.60
1994 Topps	606	.75	.60	.30
1994 Topps Black Gold	8	4.00	3.00	1.50
1994 Topps Finest	232	14.00	10.50	5.50
1994 Topps Finest Bronze	2	12.50	9.50	5.00
1994 Topps Finest Refractors	232	150.00	110.00	60.00
1994 Topps Finest Superstars	232	50.00	38.00	20.00
1994 Topps Gold	388	1.50	1.25	.60
1994 Topps Gold	400	4.00	3.00	1.50
1994 Topps Gold	606	3.00	2.25	1.25
1994 Topps Stadium Club	85	3.00	2.25	1.25
1994 Topps Stadium Club	262	1.50	1.25	.60
1994 Topps Stadium Club	529	1.50	1.25	.60
1994 Topps Stadium Club Dugout Dirt	7	4.00	3.00	1.50
1994 Topps Stadium Club Finest	5	10.00	7.50	4.00
1994 Topps Stadium Club First Day Production	85	90.00	67.00	36.00
1994 Topps Stadium Club First Day Production	262	50.00	37.00	20.00
1994 Topps Stadium Club First Day Production	529	55.00	41.00	22.00
1994 Topps Stadium Club Members Only Baseball	17	4.00	3.00	1.50
1994 Topps Traded Finest Inserts	5	3.50	2.75	1.50
1994 Upper Deck	53	2.00	1.50	.80
1994 Upper Deck	224	3.00	2.25	1.25
1994 Upper Deck	224a	6.00	4.50	2.50
1994 Upper Deck	292	2.00	1.50	.80
1994 Upper Deck All-Stars Green Foil	1	2.00	1.50	.80
1994 Upper Deck All-Stars Gold Foil	1	10.00	7.50	4.00
1994 Upper Deck All-Stars Green Foil	48	2.00	1.50	.80
1994 Upper Deck All-Stars Gold Foil	48	10.00	7.50	4.00
1994 Upper Deck Collector's Choice Promos	50	6.00	4.50	2.50
1994 Upper Deck Collector's Choice	117	1.50	1.25	.60
1994 Upper Deck Collector's Choice	317	.25	.20	.10
1994 Upper Deck Collector's Choice	324	.30	.25	.12
1994 Upper Deck Collector's Choice	340	.50	.40	.20
1994 Upper Deck Collector's Choice	634	.75	.60	.30
1994 Upper Deck Diamond Collection	4W	50.00	37.00	20.00
1994 Upper Deck Electric Diamond	53	12.00	9.00	4.75
1994 Upper Deck Electric Diamond	224	12.00	9.00	4.75
1994 Upper Deck Electric Diamond	292	7.00	5.25	2.75
1994 Upper Deck Fun Packs	24	2.50	2.00	1.00
1994 Upper Deck Fun Packs	182	1.00	.70	.40
1994 Upper Deck Fun Packs	193	1.00	.70	.40
1994 Upper Deck Fun Packs	200	2.50	2.00	1.00
1994 Upper Deck Fun Packs	216	1.00	.70	.40
1994 Upper Deck Fun Packs	224	2.50	2.00	1.00
1994 Upper Deck Fun Packs	229	1.00	.70	.40
1994 Upper Deck Fun Packs	235	.50	.40	.20
1994 Upper Deck Jumbo Checklists	1CL	3.00	2.25	1.25
1994 Upper Deck Jumbo Checklists	2CL	3.00	2.25	1.25
1994 Upper Deck Jumbo Checklists	3CL	3.00	2.25	1.25
1994 Upper Deck Jumbo Checklists	4CL	3.00	2.25	1.25
1994 Upper Deck Mickey Mantle's Long Shots	10MM	20.00	15.00	8.00
1994 Upper Deck Next Generation	6	18.00	13.50	7.25
1994 Upper Deck SP	105	5.00	3.75	2.00
1994 Upper Deck SP Baseball Die-Cut	105	15.00	11.00	6.00
1994 Upper Deck SP Holoview Blue	12	30.00	22.00	12.00
1994 Upper Deck SP Holoview Red	12	200.00	150.00	80.00
1994 Upper Deck SP Insert	3	32.00	24.00	13.00

Ken Griffey Sr.

Set	Card #	NM	EX	VG
1974 O-Pee-Chee	598	21.00	10.50	6.25
1974 Topps	598 (R)	15.00	7.50	4.50
1975 O-Pee-Chee	284	4.25	2.25	1.25
1975 Topps	284	.70	.35	.20
1975 Topps Mini	284	3.00	1.50	.90
1976 O-Pee-Chee	128	.35	.20	.11
1976 Topps	128	.40	.20	.12
1977 O-Pee-Chee	11	.30	.15	.09
1977 Topps	320	.30	.15	.09
1978 O-Pee-Chee	140	.25	.13	.08
1978 Topps	80	.25	.13	.08
1979 O-Pee-Chee	216	.25	.13	.08
1979 Topps	420	.25	.13	.08
1980 O-Pee-Chee	285	.20	.10	.06
1980 Topps	550	.25	.13	.08

Set	Card #	MT	NM	EX
1981 Donruss	184	.12	.09	.05
1981 Fleer	199	.12	.09	.05
1981 O-Pee-Chee	280	.12	.09	.05
1981 Topps	280	.15	.11	.06
1982 Donruss	634	.12	.09	.05
1982 Fleer	67	.12	.09	.05
1982 O-Pee-Chee	171	.12	.09	.05
1982 O-Pee-Chee	330	.15	.11	.06
1982 Topps	620	.15	.11	.06
1982 Topps	621	.10	.08	.04
1982 Topps	756	.30	.25	.12
1982 Topps Traded	40T	.25	.20	.10
1983 Donruss	486	.12	.09	.05
1983 Fleer	382	.12	.09	.05
1983 O-Pee-Chee	110	.12	.09	.05
1983 Topps	110	.15	.11	.06
1984 Donruss	613	.15	.11	.06
1984 Fleer	126	.12	.09	.05
1984 O-Pee-Chee	306	.25	.20	.10
1984 Topps	770	.12	.09	.05
1985 Donruss	347	.12	.09	.05
1985 Fleer	128	.10	.08	.04
1985 Leaf-Donruss	193	.08	.06	.03
1985 O-Pee-Chee	380	.10	.08	.04
1985 Topps	380	.10	.08	.04
1986 Donruss	126	.12	.09	.05
1986 Fleer	105	.10	.08	.04
1986 Leaf	48	.08	.06	.03
1986 O-Pee-Chee	40	.08	.06	.03
1986 Topps	40	.10	.08	.04
1986 Topps Traded	41T	.12	.09	.05
1987 Donruss	513	.10	.08	.04
1987 Fleer	516	.10	.08	.04
1987 O-Pee-Chee	114	.08	.06	.03
1987 Topps	711	.07	.05	.03
1988 Donruss	202	.07	.05	.03
1988 Fleer	540	.08	.06	.03
1988 Leaf	165	.08	.06	.03
1988 O-Pee-Chee	255	.08	.06	.03
1988 Score	390	.06	.05	.02
1988 Sportflics	178	.10	.08	.04
1988 Topps	443	.06	.05	.02

1988 Topps	549	.08	.06	.03
1988 Topps Big Baseball	110	.08	.06	.03
1989 Fleer Update	84	.10	.08	.04
1989 Score	609	.08	.06	.03
1989 Topps Traded	40T	.15	.11	.06
1990 Bowman	60	.06	.05	.02
1990 Donruss	469	.06	.05	.02
1990 Fleer	420	.07	.05	.03
1990 O-Pee-Chee	581	.05	.04	.02
1990 Score	338a	.25	.20	.10
1990 Score	338b	3.00	2.25	1.25
1990 Topps	581	.05	.04	.02
1990 Topps Big Baseball	100	.06	.05	.02
1990 Upper Deck	682	.08	.06	.03
1991 Bowman	255	.08	.06	.03
1991 Donruss	452	.08	.06	.03
1991 Fleer Ultra	335	.08	.06	.03
1991 Leaf	503	.10	.08	.04
1991 Score	835	.08	.06	.03
1991 Score	841	.50	.30	.15
1991 Studio	113	.12	.09	.05
1991 Topps	465	.05	.04	.02
1991 Topps Stadium Club	342	.20	.15	.08
1991 Topps Stadium Club Charter Members	(10)	2.00	1.50	.80
1991 Upper Deck	572	.10	.08	.04
1992 O-Pee-Chee	250	.05	.04	.02
1992 Topps	250	.05	.04	.02
1992 Topps Gold	250	.25	.20	.10
1992 Upper Deck	85	.50	.40	.20
1992 Upper Deck	335	.06	.05	.02
1993 Bowman	703	1.00	.75	.40

Marquis Grissom

Set	Card #	MT	NM	EX
1990 Bowman	115 (R)	.60	.45	.25
1990 Donruss	36 (R)	.60	.45	.25
1990 Fleer	347 (R)	.60	.45	.25
1990 Leaf	107 (R)	6.00	4.50	2.50
1990 O-Pee-Chee	714 (R)	.50	.40	.20
1990 Score	591 (R)	.60	.45	.25
1990 Sportflics	134	.20	.15	.08
1990 Topps	714 (R)	.60	.45	.25
1990 Topps Big Baseball	138	.50	.40	.20
1990 Upper Deck	9 (R)	1.50	1.25	.60
1990 Upper Deck	702	1.00	.70	.40
1991 Bowman	435	.12	.09	.05
1991 Donruss	307	.12	.09	.05
1991 Fleer	234	.20	.15	.08
1991 Fleer Ultra	204	.25	.20	.10
1991 Leaf	22	.20	.15	.08
1991 Score	234	.10	.08	.04
1991 Studio	198	.35	.25	.14
1991 Topps	283	.10	.08	.04
1991 Topps Glossy Rookies	10	.35	.25	.14
1991 Topps Stadium Club	8	2.00	1.50	.80
1991 Upper Deck	477	.20	.15	.08

1992 Bowman	14	.75	.60	.30
1992 Donruss	137	.15	.11	.06
1992 Donruss Triple Play	47	.12	.09	.05
1992 Fleer	482	.12	.09	.05
1992 Fleer Ultra	518	.30	.25	.12
1992 Leaf	273	.20	.15	.08
1992 O-Pee-Chee	647	.12	.09	.05
1992 O-Pee-Chee Premier	176	.20	.15	.08
1992 Pinnacle	129	.20	.15	.08
1992 Pinnacle Team 2000	11	.25	.20	.10
1992 Score	66	.10	.08	.04
1992 Score Impact Players	63	.20	.15	.08
1992 Studio	55	.20	.15	.08
1992 Topps	647	.12	.09	.05
1992 Topps Gold	647	.40	.30	.15
1992 Topps Kids	8	.05	.04	.02
1992 Topps Stadium Club	120	.25	.20	.10
1992 Upper Deck	455	.10	.08	.04
1992 Upper Deck	719	.08	.06	.03
1993 Bowman	268	.15	.11	.06
1993 DiamondMarks	(38)	.25	.20	.10
1993 Donruss	300	.10	.08	.04
1993 Donruss Triple Play	159	.07	.05	.03
1993 Fleer	461	.10	.08	.04
1993 Fleer	706	.08	.06	.03
1993 Fleer Flair	83	.50	.40	.20
1993 Fleer NL Team Leaders	7	3.00	2.25	1.25
1993 Fleer Ultra	415	.20	.15	.08
1993 Leaf	129	.15	.11	.06
1993 Leaf Fasttrack	20	3.00	2.25	1.25
1993 Leaf Gold All-Stars	17	3.00	2.25	1.25
1993 Leaf Update Gold All-Stars	8	8.00	6.00	3.25
1993 O-Pee-Chee	209	.40	.30	.15
1993 Pinnacle	346	.15	.11	.06
1993 Pinnacle Team 2001	17	.90	.70	.35
1993 Score	28	.10	.08	.04
1993 Score Select	99	.15	.11	.06
1993 Score Select Stat Leaders	18	.10	.08	.04
1993 Score Select Stat Leaders	58	.10	.08	.04
1993 Studio	178	.15	.11	.06
1993 Topps	15	.08	.06	.03
1993 Topps Black Gold	7	.35	.25	.14
1993 Topps Finest	40	2.00	1.50	.80
1993 Topps Finest Refractors	40	25.00	18.50	10.00
1993 Topps Gold	15	.15	.11	.06
1993 Topps Stadium Club	529	.15	.11	.06
1993 Topps Stadium Club	598	.15	.11	.06
1993 Topps Stadium Club First Day Production	529	10.00	7.50	4.00
1993 Topps Stadium Club First Day Production	598	10.00	7.50	4.00
1993 Upper Deck	356	.10	.07	.04
1993 Upper Deck Diamond Gallery	10	.50	.40	.20
1993 Upper Deck Fun Packs All-Star Scratch-Off	8	5.00	3.75	2.00
1993 Upper Deck Fun Packs	93	.15	.11	.06
1993 Upper Deck Fun Packs	95	.15	.11	.06
1993 Upper Deck Fun Packs	216	.20	.15	.08
1993 Upper Deck SP	12	.20	.15	.08
1994 Bowman	284	.10	.08	.04
1994 Bowman's Best	69	.75	.60	.30
1994 Bowman's Best Refractors	69	3.00	2.25	1.25
1994 Donruss	37	.10	.08	.04
1994 Donruss Special Edition - Gold	37	.30	.25	.12
1994 Donruss Triple Play	95	.05	.04	.02
1994 Fleer	540	.10	.08	.04
1994 Fleer All-Stars	38	.35	.25	.14
1994 Fleer Extra Bases	306	.10	.08	.04
1994 Fleer Flair	190	.30	.25	.12
1994 Fleer Team Leaders	22	.75	.60	.30
1994 Fleer Ultra	228	.12	.09	.05
1994 Fleer Ultra Award Winners	16	.60	.45	.25
1994 Fleer Ultra Rising Stars	6	4.00	3.00	1.50
1994 Leaf	174	.12	.09	.05
1994 Leaf Limited	125	1.00	.70	.40
1994 O-Pee-Chee	18	.10	.08	.04
1994 O-Pee-Chee All-Star Redemption Cards	11	.35	.25	.14
1994 O-Pee-Chee Jumbo All-Stars	11	5.00	3.75	2.00
1994 O-Pee-Chee Jumbo All-Stars Factory Set	11	1.00	.75	.40
1994 Pacific Crown	382	.15	.11	.06
1994 Pinnacle	358	.12	.09	.05
1994 Pinnacle Artist's Proof	358	3.00	2.25	1.25
1994 Pinnacle Museum Collection	358	2.00	1.50	.80
1994 Pinnacle Run Creators	38	1.50	1.25	.60
1994 Score	352	.07	.05	.03
1994 Score Gold Stars	25	2.00	1.50	.80
1994 Score Select	242	.20	.15	.08
1994 Score Select Skills	7	6.00	4.50	2.50
1994 Sportflics 2000	48	.15	.11	.06
1994 Studio	78	.10	.08	.04
1994 Topps	590	.07	.05	.03
1994 Topps Finest	229	.75	.60	.30
1994 Topps Finest Refractors	229	4.00	3.00	1.50
1994 Topps Finest Superstars	229	2.50	2.00	1.00
1994 Topps Gold	590	.15	.11	.06
1994 Topps Stadium Club	706	.12	.09	.05
1994 Topps Stadium Club Finest	6	2.00	1.50	.80
1994 Topps Stadium Club First Day Production	706	4.00	3.00	1.50
1994 Topps Stadium Club Members Only Baseball	35	.35	.25	.14
1994 Upper Deck	39	.12	.09	.05
1994 Upper Deck	390	.15	.11	.06
1994 Upper Deck All-Stars Green Foil	28	.25	.20	.10
1994 Upper Deck All-Stars Gold Foil	28	1.00	.70	.40
1994 Upper Deck Collector's Choice	465	.07	.05	.03
1994 Upper Deck Electric Diamond	39	.25	.20	.10
1994 Upper Deck Electric Diamond	390	.35	.25	.14
1994 Upper Deck Fun Packs	159	.07	.05	.03
1994 Upper Deck SP	84	.15	.11	.06
1994 Upper Deck SP Baseball Die-Cut	84	.25	.20	.10

* * *

SCD's Top 7 most valuable baseball cards, in June 1989: the 1909 T206 Honus Wagner, at $95,000; the 1932 U.S. Caramel Charles (Lindy) Lindstrom, at $18,000; the 1909 T206 Joe Doyle (rare variation), at $15,000; the 1933 Goudey Napoleon Lajoie, at $15,000; the 1909 T206 Eddie Plank, at $9,000; the 1909 T206 Sherry Magie, at $8,000; and the 1952 Topps Mickey Mantle, at $6,500.

* * *

Dick Groat

Pedro Guerrero

Set	Card #	NM	EX	VG
1952 Topps	369 (R)	350.00	175.00	80.00
1953 Topps	154	32.50	16.00	7.50
1954 Topps	43	16.00	8.00	4.75
1955 Topps	26	12.00	6.00	3.50
1956 Topps	24	10.50	5.25	3.25
1957 Topps	12	10.00	5.00	3.00
1958 Topps	45	9.00	4.50	2.75
1959 Topps	160	4.00	2.00	1.25
1960 Topps	258	5.00	2.50	1.50
1961 Post Cereal	129a	4.50	2.25	1.25
1961 Post Cereal	129b	3.00	1.50	.90
1961 Topps	1	20.00	9.00	4.00
1961 Topps	41	11.00	5.50	3.25
1961 Topps	486	7.50	3.75	2.25
1962 Post Cereal	172	3.00	1.50	.90
1962 Topps	270	3.50	1.75	1.00
1963 Post Cereal	139	3.50	1.75	1.00
1963 Topps	130	3.25	1.75	1.00
1964 Topps	7	12.00	6.00	3.50
1964 Topps	40	3.00	1.50	.90
1965 O-Pee-Chee	275	6.25	3.25	2.00
1965 Topps	275	2.50	1.25	.70
1966 O-Pee-Chee	103	2.25	1.25	.70
1966 Topps	103a	25.00	12.50	7.50
1966 Topps	103b	3.00	1.50	.90
1967 Topps	205	2.50	1.25	.70
1975 O-Pee-Chee	198	3.00	1.50	.90
1975 Topps	198	1.25	.60	.40
1975 Topps Mini	198	1.75	.90	.50

Set	Card #	MT	NM	EX
1983 Topps 1952 Reprint Set	369	.45	.35	.20
1988 Pacific Trading Cards Baseball Legends	108	.06	.05	.02
1990 Pacific Legends	26	.10	.08	.04
1991 "1953" Topps Archives	154	.25	.20	.10
1994 "1954" Topps Archives	43	.20	.15	.08

* * *

A Sotheby's $4.6 million auction brought national attention to the T206 Honus Wagner card in March 1991, when the card, graded as Mint and having a pre-estimate value of between $125,000 and $150,000, sold for a new record - $451,000. Hockey superstar Wayne Gretzky, and the owner of his team, Bruce McNall, a major Beverly Hills coin dealer, were co-partners on the winning bid.

* * *

Set	Card #	NM	EX	VG
1979 Topps	719 (R)	2.50	1.25	.70

Set	Card #	MT	NM	EX
1981 Topps	651	.20	.15	.08
1982 Donruss	136	.30	.25	.12
1982 Fleer	7	.10	.08	.04
1982 O-Pee-Chee	247	.60	.45	.25
1982 Topps	247	.20	.15	.08
1983 Donruss	110	.15	.11	.06
1983 Fleer	207	.12	.09	.05
1983 O-Pee-Chee	116	.30	.25	.12
1983 Topps	425	.15	.11	.06
1983 Topps	681	.25	.20	.10
1984 Donruss	24a	.25	.20	.10
1984 Donruss	24b	.60	.45	.25
1984 Donruss	174	.25	.20	.10
1984 Fleer	100	.15	.11	.06
1984 O-Pee-Chee	90	.60	.45	.25
1984 Topps	90	.10	.08	.04
1984 Topps	306	.15	.11	.06
1984 Topps All-Star Glossy Set of 40	25	.25	.20	.10
1985 Donruss	174	.15	.11	.06
1985 Fleer	370	.10	.08	.04
1985 Leaf-Donruss	211	.15	.11	.06
1985 O-Pee-Chee	34	.20	.15	.08
1985 Topps	575	.10	.08	.04
1986 Donruss	174	.20	.15	.08
1986 Fleer	130	.08	.06	.03
1986 Fleer All Stars	8	.25	.20	.10
1986 Leaf	105	.15	.11	.06
1986 O-Pee-Chee	145	.15	.11	.06
1986 Sportflics	14	.15	.11	.06
1986 Sportflics	148	.20	.15	.08
1986 Sportflics	181	.70	.50	.30
1986 Sportflics Decade Greats	74	.30	.25	.12
1986 Topps	145	.06	.05	.02
1986 Topps	706	.12	.09	.05
1986 Topps All-Star Glossy Set of 60	25	.30	.25	.12
1987 Donruss	53	.15	.11	.06
1987 Fleer	440	.15	.11	.06
1987 Leaf	237	.12	.09	.05
1987 O-Pee-Chee	360	.12	.09	.05
1987 Sportflics	27	.20	.15	.08
1987 Topps	360	.08	.06	.03
1988 Donruss	278	.15	.11	.06
1988 Donruss MVP	16	.20	.15	.08
1988 Fleer	514	.15	.11	.06
1988 Fleer	623	.12	.09	.05
1988 Leaf	101	.12	.09	.05
1988 O-Pee-Chee	111	.09	.07	.04
1988 Score	9	.15	.11	.06
1988 Sportflics	97	.20	.15	.08
1988 Topps	489	.08	.06	.03
1988 Topps	550	.15	.11	.06
1988 Topps All-Star Glossy Set of 60	24	.20	.15	.08

Set	Card #			
1988 Topps Big Baseball	171	.12	.09	.05
1989 Bowman	440	.10	.08	.04
1989 Donruss	418	.08	.06	.03
1989 Fleer	451	.15	.11	.06
1989 O-Pee-Chee	68	.07	.05	.03
1989 Score	564	.12	.09	.05
1989 Topps	780	.06	.05	.02
1989 Topps Big Baseball	285	.10	.08	.04
1989 Upper Deck	306	.15	.11	.06
1990 Bowman	201	.06	.05	.02
1990 Donruss	63	.12	.09	.05
1990 Donruss	674	.09	.07	.04
1990 Donruss MVP	6	.10	.08	.04
1990 Fleer	250	.09	.07	.04
1990 Leaf	44	.35	.25	.14
1990 O-Pee-Chee	610	.12	.09	.05
1990 Post Cereal	22	.30	.25	.12
1990 Score	13	.09	.07	.04
1990 Sportflics	66	.15	.11	.06
1990 Topps	610	.12	.09	.05
1990 Topps All-Star Glossy Set of 60	32	.10	.08	.04
1990 Topps Big Baseball	13	.10	.08	.04
1990 Upper Deck	244	.06	.05	.02
1991 Bowman	403	.08	.06	.03
1991 Donruss	25	.05	.04	.02
1991 Donruss	558	.08	.06	.03
1991 Fleer	634	.08	.06	.03
1991 Fleer Ultra	289	.10	.08	.04
1991 Leaf	204	.15	.11	.06
1991 O-Pee-Chee Premier	58	.05	.04	.02
1991 Score	140	.08	.06	.03
1991 Studio	232	.20	.15	.08
1991 Topps	20	.08	.06	.03
1991 Upper Deck	327	.10	.08	.04
1992 Bowman	377	.40	.30	.15
1992 Donruss	158	.08	.06	.03
1992 Donruss Triple Play	9	.08	.06	.03
1992 Fleer	579	.08	.06	.03
1992 Fleer Ultra	263	.15	.11	.06
1992 Leaf	18	.15	.11	.06
1992 O-Pee-Chee	470	.08	.06	.03
1992 Pinnacle	392	.12	.09	.05
1992 Score	376	.10	.08	.04
1992 Studio	91	.10	.08	.04
1992 Topps	470	.08	.06	.03
1992 Topps Gold	470	.25	.20	.10
1992 Topps Kids	26	.05	.04	.02
1992 Topps Stadium Club	320	.15	.11	.06
1992 Upper Deck	357	.06	.05	.02
1993 Donruss	600	.05	.04	.02
1993 Fleer	509	.05	.04	.02

Ron Guidry

Set	Card #	NM	EX	VG
1976 O-Pee-Chee	599	8.50	4.25	2.50
1976 Topps	599 (R)	6.00	3.00	1.75
1977 Topps	656	.90	.45	.25
1978 Topps	135	.30	.15	.09

Set	Card #			
1979 O-Pee-Chee	264	.75	.40	.25
1979 Topps	5	.30	.15	.09
1979 Topps	7	.25	.13	.08
1979 Topps	202	.35	.20	.11
1979 Topps	500	.30	.15	.09
1980 O-Pee-Chee	157	.75	.40	.25
1980 Topps	207	.25	.13	.08
1980 Topps	300	.30	.15	.09

Set	Card #	MT	NM	EX
1981 Donruss	227	.25	.20	.10
1981 Fleer	88	.25	.20	.10
1981 O-Pee-Chee	250	.40	.30	.15
1981 Topps	250	.20	.15	.08
1982 Donruss	548	.25	.20	.10
1982 Donruss	558	.15	.11	.06
1982 Fleer	38	.25	.20	.10
1982 O-Pee-Chee	9	.30	.25	.12
1982 O-Pee-Chee	10	.15	.11	.06
1982 Topps	9	.15	.11	.06
1982 Topps	10	.15	.11	.06
1983 Donruss	17	.15	.11	.06
1983 Donruss	31	.25	.20	.10
1983 Fleer	383	.25	.20	.10
1983 O-Pee-Chee	104	.25	.20	.10
1983 Topps	440	.30	.25	.12
1984 Donruss	173	.20	.15	.08
1984 Fleer	127	.10	.08	.04
1984 O-Pee-Chee	110	.50	.40	.20
1984 O-Pee-Chee	204	.50	.40	.20
1984 Topps	110	.10	.08	.04
1984 Topps	406	.20	.15	.08
1984 Topps	486	.15	.11	.06
1984 Topps	717	.15	.11	.06
1984 Topps All-Star Glossy Set of 40	14	.30	.25	.12
1985 Donruss	214	.10	.08	.04
1985 Fleer	129	.25	.20	.10
1985 Leaf-Donruss	237	.15	.11	.06
1985 O-Pee-Chee	388	.20	.15	.08
1985 Topps	790	.10	.08	.04
1986 Donruss	103	.12	.09	.05
1986 Fleer	106	.20	.15	.08
1986 Leaf	36	.15	.11	.06
1986 O-Pee-Chee	109	.15	.11	.06
1986 Sportflics	18	.15	.11	.06
1986 Sportflics	59	.10	.08	.04
1986 Sportflics	149	.10	.08	.04
1986 Sportflics	179	1.25	.90	.50
1986 Sportflics	185	.60	.45	.25
1986 Sportflics Decade Greats	71	.25	.20	.10
1986 Topps	610	.08	.06	.03
1986 Topps	721	.10	.08	.04
1986 Topps All-Star Glossy Set of 60	12	.30	.25	.12
1987 Donruss	93	.15	.11	.06
1987 Fleer	100	.15	.11	.06
1987 Leaf	101	.12	.09	.05
1987 O-Pee-Chee	375	.12	.09	.05
1987 Sportflics	83	.20	.15	.08
1987 Topps	375	.12	.09	.05
1988 Donruss	175	.15	.11	.06
1988 Fleer	207	.15	.11	.06
1988 Leaf	180	.10	.08	.04
1988 O-Pee-Chee	127	.09	.07	.04
1988 Score	310	.12	.09	.05
1988 Topps	535	.12	.09	.05
1988 Topps Big Baseball	50	.10	.08	.04
1989 Score	342	.12	.09	.05
1989 Topps	255	.12	.09	.05

* * *

Bob Uecker, about the most memorable moment from his playing days: "Seeing someone fall out of the upper deck in Philadelphia. That was my greatest thrill in baseball." SCD: "What happened to the fan?" "He got up and walked away and they booed him."

* * *

Tony Gwynn

Set	Card #	MT	NM	EX
1983 Donruss	598 (R)	30.00	22.00	12.00
1983 Fleer	360 (R)	25.00	18.50	10.00
1983 O-Pee-Chee	143	30.00	22.00	12.00
1983 Topps	482 (R)	35.00	26.00	14.00
1984 Donruss	324	20.00	15.00	8.00
1984 Fleer	301	12.00	9.00	4.75
1984 Topps	251	4.00	3.00	1.50
1985 Donruss	25	2.50	2.00	1.00
1985 Donruss	63	6.00	4.50	2.50
1985 Donruss Diamond Kings Supers	25	.40	.30	.15
1985 Fleer	34	6.00	4.50	2.50
1985 Leaf-Donruss	25	2.50	2.00	1.00
1985 O-Pee-Chee	383	2.00	1.50	.80
1985 Topps	660	2.00	1.50	.80
1985 Topps	717	.50	.40	.20
1985 Topps All-Star Glossy Set of 22	6	.40	.30	.15
1985 Topps All-Star Glossy Set of 40	29	.60	.45	.25
1986 Donruss	112	3.00	2.25	1.25
1986 Fleer	323	3.00	2.25	1.25
1986 Leaf	41	2.50	2.00	1.00
1986 O-Pee-Chee	10	1.00	.70	.40
1986 Sportflics	13	.45	.35	.20
1986 Sportflics	140	.20	.15	.08
1986 Sportflics	181	.70	.50	.30
1986 Topps	10	1.00	.70	.40
1986 Topps All-Star Glossy Set of 22	17	.60	.45	.25
1986 Topps All-Star Glossy Set of 60	57	.60	.45	.25
1987 Donruss	64	1.00	.70	.40
1987 Fleer	416	2.00	1.50	.80
1987 Fleer All Stars	20	.25	.20	.10
1987 Leaf	235	.75	.60	.30
1987 O-Pee-Chee	198	.40	.30	.15
1987 Sportflics	31	.50	.40	.20
1987 Sportflics	117	.25	.20	.10
1987 Sportflics	197	.80	.60	.30
1987 Topps	530	.30	.25	.12
1987 Topps	599	.20	.15	.08
1987 Topps All-Star Glossy Set of 60	2	.60	.45	.25
1987 Topps All-Star Glossy Set of 22	6	.30	.25	.12
1988 Donruss	164	.35	.25	.14
1988 Donruss MVP	6	.30	.25	.12
1988 Fleer	585	.50	.40	.20
1988 Fleer	631	.20	.15	.08
1988 Fleer	634	.12	.09	.05
1988 Leaf	90	.30	.25	.12
1988 O-Pee-Chee	360	.30	.25	.12
1988 Score	385	.30	.25	.12
1988 Sportflics	16	.40	.30	.15
1988 Topps	360	.30	.25	.12
1988 Topps	402	.15	.11	.06
1988 Topps	699	.12	.09	.05
1988 Topps All-Star Glossy Set of 60	38	.50	.40	.20
1988 Topps Big Baseball	161	.25	.20	.10
1989 Bowman	461	.30	.25	.12
1989 Donruss	6	.12	.09	.05
1989 Donruss	128	.30	.25	.12
1989 Donruss MVP	20	.20	.15	.08
1989 Fleer	305	.25	.20	.10
1989 O-Pee-Chee	51	.40	.30	.15
1989 Score	90	.25	.20	.10
1989 Sportflics	160	.50	.40	.20
1989 Topps	570	.30	.25	.12
1989 Topps All-Star Glossy Set of 60	58	.40	.30	.15
1989 Topps Big Baseball	58	.15	.11	.06
1989 Upper Deck	384	.75	.60	.30
1989 Upper Deck	683	.25	.20	.10
1990 Bowman	217	.20	.15	.08
1990 Donruss	86	.20	.15	.08
1990 Donruss	705	.15	.11	.06
1990 Donruss MVP	4	.15	.11	.06
1990 Fleer	157	.25	.20	.10
1990 Leaf	154	3.00	2.25	1.25
1990 O-Pee-Chee	403	.15	.11	.06
1990 O-Pee-Chee	730	.20	.15	.08
1990 Post Cereal	5	.50	.40	.20
1990 Score	255	.25	.20	.10
1990 Score	685	.20	.15	.08
1990 Sportflics	98	.40	.30	.15
1990 Topps	403	.15	.11	.06
1990 Topps	730	.20	.15	.08
1990 Topps All-Star Glossy Set of 22	8	.20	.15	.08
1990 Topps All-Star Glossy Set of 60	56	.20	.15	.08
1990 Topps Big Baseball	93	.15	.11	.06
1990 Upper Deck	344	.25	.20	.10
1991 Bowman	647	.20	.15	.08
1991 Donruss	243	.20	.15	.08
1991 Fleer	529	.20	.15	.08
1991 Fleer Ultra	303	.25	.20	.10
1991 Leaf	290	.40	.30	.15
1991 O-Pee-Chee Premier	59	.25	.20	.10
1991 Post Cereal	10	.40	.30	.15
1991 Score	500	.15	.11	.06
1991 Studio	245	.35	.25	.14
1991 Topps	180	.12	.09	.05
1991 Upper Deck	255	.30	.25	.12
1991 Upper Deck Final Edition	97	.15	.11	.06
1992 Bowman	50	1.50	1.25	.60
1992 Donruss	425	.10	.08	.04
1992 Donruss	441	.15	.11	.06
1992 Donruss Elite	14	40.00	30.00	15.00
1992 Donruss Triple Play	219	.15	.10	.05
1992 Fleer	605	.20	.15	.08
1992 Fleer All-Stars	2	1.50	1.25	.60
1992 Fleer Team Leaders	7	5.00	3.75	2.00
1992 Fleer Ultra	277	.40	.30	.15
1992 Fleer Ultra Award Winners	12	2.50	2.00	1.00
1992 Fleer Ultra Tony Gwynn	1	1.00	.75	.40
1992 Fleer Ultra Tony Gwynn	1	1.00	.75	.40
1992 Fleer Ultra Tony Gwynn	2	1.00	.75	.40
1992 Fleer Ultra Tony Gwynn	2	1.00	.75	.40
1992 Fleer Ultra Tony Gwynn	3	1.00	.75	.40
1992 Fleer Ultra Tony Gwynn	4	1.00	.75	.40
1992 Fleer Ultra Tony Gwynn	5	1.00	.75	.40
1992 Fleer Ultra Tony Gwynn	6	1.00	.75	.40
1992 Fleer Ultra Tony Gwynn	7	1.00	.75	.40
1992 Fleer Ultra Tony Gwynn	8	1.00	.75	.40

Card	No.			
1992 Fleer Ultra Tony Gwynn	9	1.00	.75	.40
1992 Fleer Ultra Tony Gwynn	10	1.00	.75	.40
1992 Leaf	206	.20	.15	.08
1992 O-Pee-Chee	270	.12	.09	.05
1992 O-Pee-Chee Premier	106	.40	.30	.15
1992 Pinnacle	400	.30	.25	.12
1992 Pinnacle	591	.15	.11	.06
1992 Post Cereal	26	.30	.25	.12
1992 Score	625	.15	.11	.06
1992 Score	779	.10	.08	.04
1992 Score	887	.20	.15	.08
1992 Studio	104	.30	.25	.12
1992 Topps	270	.20	.15	.08
1992 Topps Gold	270	2.00	1.50	.80
1992 Topps Kids	53	.15	.11	.06
1992 Topps Stadium Club	825	.40	.30	.15
1992 Topps Stadium Club National Convention	825	48.00	36.00	19.00
1992 Topps Stadium Club Special Edition	73	.30	.25	.12
1992 Upper Deck	83	.10	.08	.04
1992 Upper Deck	274	.15	.11	.06
1992 Upper Deck	717	.15	.11	.06
1993 Bowman	630	.40	.30	.15
1993 DiamondMarks	(58)	.50	.40	.20
1993 Donruss	126	.35	.25	.14
1993 Donruss Triple Play	51	.10	.08	.04
1993 Fleer	138	.25	.20	.10
1993 Fleer Flair	133	1.25	.90	.50
1993 Fleer Ultra	472	.50	.40	.20
1993 Leaf	28	.40	.30	.15
1993 Leaf Gold All-Stars	9	2.00	1.50	.80
1993 Leaf Heading for the Hall	2	2.50	2.00	1.00
1993 O-Pee-Chee	94	.50	.40	.20
1993 Pinnacle	98	.35	.25	.14
1993 Pinnacle	289	.20	.15	.08
1993 Pinnacle Cooperstown	20	.30	.25	.12
1993 Pinnacle Cooperstown Dufex	20	75.00	56.00	30.00
1993 Post Cereal	8	.40	.30	.15
1993 Score	24	.20	.15	.08
1993 Score	525	.08	.06	.03
1993 Score Select	5	.40	.30	.15
1993 Score Select Chase Stars	8	8.00	6.00	3.25
1993 Studio	100	.20	.15	.08
1993 Topps	5	.20	.15	.08
1993 Topps Black Gold	8	.60	.45	.25
1993 Topps Finest	77	5.00	3.75	2.00
1993 Topps Finest Refractors	77	60.00	45.00	25.00
1993 Topps Full Shot Super	7	4.00	3.00	1.50
1993 Topps Gold	5	.25	.20	.10
1993 Topps Stadium Club	538	.25	.20	.10
1993 Topps Stadium Club First Day Production	538	40.00	30.00	16.00
1993 Topps Stadium Club Special	3	.35	.25	.14
1993 Topps Stadium Club Special Master Photo	(4)	.75	.60	.30
1993 Upper Deck	165	.20	.15	.08
1993 Upper Deck	474	.20	.15	.08
1993 Upper Deck Diamond Gallery	17	1.00	.70	.40
1993 Upper Deck Fun Packs All-Star Scratch-Off	9	2.00	1.50	.80
1993 Upper Deck Fun Packs	138	.20	.15	.08
1993 Upper Deck Fun Packs	211	.10	.08	.04
1993 Upper Deck On Deck	14	1.00	.75	.40
1993 Upper Deck SP	167	2.00	1.50	.80
1993 Upper Deck Then And Now	11	2.00	1.50	.80
1994 Bowman	120	.30	.25	.12
1994 Bowman's Best	78	2.00	1.50	.80
1994 Bowman's Best Refractors	78	14.00	10.50	5.50
1994 Donruss	10	.50	.40	.20
1994 Donruss Anniversary-1984	10	4.00	3.00	1.50
1994 Donruss Decade Dominators	1	2.00	2.00	1.00
1994 Donruss Decade Dominators Supers	1	3.50	2.75	1.50
1994 Donruss Diamond Kings	11	2.50	1.75	.90
1994 Donruss Diamond Kings Super	11	3.50	2.75	1.50
1994 Donruss Elite	38	20.00	15.00	8.00
1994 Donruss MVP's	13	1.50	1.25	.60
1994 Donruss Special Edition - Gold	10	.75	.60	.30
1994 Donruss Triple Play	167	.10	.07	.04
1994 Fleer	665	.25	.20	.10
1994 Fleer	711	.05	.04	.02
1994 Fleer All-Stars	39	.60	.45	.25
1994 Fleer Extra Bases	372	.35	.25	.14
1994 Fleer Flair	436	.75	.60	.30
1994 Fleer ProVisions	9	.50	.40	.20
1994 Fleer Team Leaders	27	1.00	.75	.40
1994 Fleer Ultra	280	.25	.20	.10
1994 Fleer Ultra Hitting Machines	6	1.00	.75	.40
1994 Fleer Update Diamond Tribute	5	.75	.60	.30
1994 Leaf	254	.40	.30	.15
1994 Leaf Limited	152	3.00	2.25	1.25
1994 Leaf Limited Gold	12	25.00	18.00	10.00
1994 Leaf Statistical Standouts	9	2.00	1.50	.80
1994 O-Pee-Chee	109	.40	.30	.15
1994 Pacific Crown	525	.25	.20	.10
1994 Pacific Crown Jewels of the Crown	35	3.00	2.25	1.25
1994 Pinnacle	4	.30	.25	.12
1994 Pinnacle Artist's Proof	4	20.00	15.00	8.00
1994 Pinnacle Museum Collection	4	5.00	3.75	2.00
1994 Pinnacle Run Creators	35	4.00	3.00	1.50
1994 Pinnacle The Naturals Box Set	12	.40	.30	.15
1994 Post Cereal	13	.40	.30	.15
1994 Score	12	.30	.25	.12
1994 Score Gold Stars	23	8.00	6.00	3.25
1994 Score Select	77	.50	.40	.20
1994 Sportflics 2000	25	.40	.30	.15
1994 Sportflics 2000 Movers	5	7.00	5.25	2.75
1994 Studio	132	.35	.25	.14
1994 Studio Gold Stars	1	25.00	18.00	10.00
1994 Studio Silver Stars	1	12.00	9.00	4.75
1994 Topps	620	.15	.11	.06
1994 Topps Finest	201	2.50	2.00	1.00
1994 Topps Finest Refractors	201	24.00	18.00	9.50
1994 Topps Finest Superstars	201	6.00	4.50	2.50
1994 Topps Gold	620	.45	.35	.20
1994 Topps Stadium Club	151	.25	.20	.10
1994 Topps Stadium Club	537	.20	.15	.08
1994 Topps Stadium Club First Day Production	151	10.00	7.50	4.00
1994 Topps Stadium Club First Day Production	537	4.00	3.00	1.50
1994 Topps Stadium Club Members Only Baseball	43	.40	.30	.15
1994 Upper Deck	219	.40	.30	.15
1994 Upper Deck	279	.25	.20	.10

		MT	NM	EX
1994 Upper Deck All-Stars Green Foil	17	.45	.35	.20
1994 Upper Deck All-Stars Gold Foil	17	2.00	1.50	.80
1994 Upper Deck Collector's Choice	122	.15	.11	.06
1994 Upper Deck Collector's Choice	344	.08	.06	.03
1994 Upper Deck Diamond Collection	5W	7.50	5.50	3.00
1994 Upper Deck Electric Diamond	219	1.25	.90	.50
1994 Upper Deck Electric Diamond	279	.50	.40	.20
1994 Upper Deck Fun Packs	119	.30	.25	.12
1994 Upper Deck Fun Packs	206	1.50	1.25	.60
1994 Upper Deck SP	130	.75	.60	.30
1994 Upper Deck SP Baseball Die-Cut	130	1.75	1.25	.70
1994 Upper Deck SP Holoview Blue	13	5.00	3.75	2.00
1994 Upper Deck SP Holoview Red	13	25.00	18.00	10.00

Darryl Hamilton

Set	Card #	MT	NM	EX
1988 Fleer Update	38	.40	.30	.15
1988 Score Traded	72T	1.50	1.25	.60
1988 Score Traded/Rookie Glossy	72T	6.00	4.50	2.50
1989 Fleer	187 (R)	.25	.20	.10
1989 Topps	88 (R)	.25	.20	.10
1989 Upper Deck	301 (R)	.35	.25	.14
1990 Bowman	397	.10	.08	.04
1990 Fleer	325	.08	.06	.03
1990 Topps Traded	35T	.15	.11	.06
1991 Donruss	517	.08	.06	.03
1991 Fleer	585	.06	.05	.02
1991 Fleer Ultra Update	30	.35	.25	.14
1991 Score	107	.06	.05	.02
1991 Topps	781	.05	.04	.02
1991 Topps Stadium Club	234	.20	.15	.08
1991 Upper Deck	43	.06	.05	.02
1992 Bowman	74	.20	.15	.08
1992 Donruss	593	.08	.06	.03
1992 Donruss Triple Play	250	.08	.06	.03
1992 Fleer	177	.05	.04	.02
1992 Fleer Ultra	383	.10	.08	.04
1992 Leaf	12	.15	.11	.06
1992 O-Pee-Chee	278	.04	.03	.02
1992 Pinnacle	151	.12	.09	.05
1992 Score	497	.06	.05	.02
1992 Topps	278	.04	.03	.02
1992 Topps Gold	278	.25	.20	.10
1992 Topps Stadium Club	253	.10	.08	.04
1992 Upper Deck	460	.06	.05	.02
1993 Bowman	239	.10	.08	.04
1993 DiamondMarks	(91)	.25	.20	.10

		MT	NM	EX
1993 Donruss	527	.05	.04	.02
1993 Fleer	250	.08	.06	.03
1993 Fleer Flair	224	.25	.15	.08
1993 Fleer Ultra	219	.10	.08	.04
1993 Leaf	199	.10	.08	.04
1993 O-Pee-Chee	158	.15	.11	.06
1993 Pinnacle	144	.06	.05	.02
1993 Score	118	.04	.03	.02
1993 Score Select	168	.08	.06	.03
1993 Studio	40	.08	.06	.03
1993 Topps	556	.03	.02	.01
1993 Topps Finest	45	1.00	.70	.40
1993 Topps Finest Refractors	45	20.00	15.00	8.00
1993 Topps Gold	556	.10	.08	.04
1993 Topps Stadium Club	303	.10	.08	.04
1993 Topps Stadium Club First Day Production	303	4.00	3.00	1.50
1993 Upper Deck	192	.08	.06	.03
1993 Upper Deck SP	65	.15	.11	.06
1994 Bowman	289	.10	.08	.04
1994 Donruss	398	.05	.04	.02
1994 Donruss Triple Play	53	.05	.04	.02
1994 Fleer	177	.05	.04	.02
1994 Fleer Extra Bases	102	.10	.08	.04
1994 Fleer Flair	67	.20	.15	.08
1994 Fleer Ultra	74	.10	.08	.04
1994 Leaf	281	.10	.08	.04
1994 O-Pee-Chee	58	.05	.04	.02
1994 Pinnacle	94	.10	.08	.04
1994 Pinnacle Artist's Proof	94	3.00	2.25	1.25
1994 Pinnacle Museum Collection	94	1.50	1.25	.60
1994 Score	395	.04	.03	.02
1994 Score Select	307	.10	.08	.04
1994 Sportflics 2000	57	.10	.08	.04
1994 Studio	43	.10	.08	.04
1994 Topps	435	.04	.03	.02
1994 Topps Finest	142	.50	.40	.20
1994 Topps Finest Refractors	142	3.50	2.75	1.50
1994 Topps Gold	435	.15	.11	.06
1994 Topps Stadium Club	188	.10	.08	.04
1994 Topps Stadium Club First Day Production	188	2.50	2.00	1.00
1994 Upper Deck	326	.10	.08	.04
1994 Upper Deck Collector's Choice	386	.05	.04	.02
1994 Upper Deck Electric Diamond	326	.25	.20	.10
1994 Upper Deck Fun Packs	98a	.05	.04	.02

Pete Harnisch

Set	Card #	MT	NM	EX
1989 Bowman	4 (R)	.20	.15	.08

1989 Donruss	44	.15	.11	.06
1989 Score Traded	110T	.35	.25	.14
1989 Upper Deck	744	.50	.40	.20
1990 Bowman	247	.06	.05	.02
1990 Donruss	596	.08	.06	.03
1990 Fleer	177	.10	.08	.04
1990 Leaf	39	.75	.60	.30
1990 O-Pee-Chee	324z	.10	.08	.04
1990 Score	355	.15	.11	.06
1990 Topps	324	.10	.08	.04
1990 Topps Glossy Rookies	12	.30	.25	.12
1990 Upper Deck	623	.10	.08	.04
1991 Bowman	555	.06	.05	.02
1991 Donruss	181	.05	.04	.02
1991 Fleer	474	.06	.05	.02
1991 Fleer Ultra Update	83	.15	.11	.06
1991 Fleer Update	89	.08	.06	.03
1991 Leaf	245	.10	.08	.04
1991 Score	492	.06	.05	.02
1991 Score Traded	36	.08	.06	.03
1991 Studio	177	.15	.11	.06
1991 Topps	179	.06	.05	.02
1991 Topps Stadium Club	343	.20	.15	.08
1991 Topps Stadium Club Members Only	(12)	.25	.20	.10
1991 Topps Traded	53	.08	.06	.03
1991 Upper Deck	302	.08	.06	.03
1991 Upper Deck	772	.12	.09	.05
1992 Bowman	514	.08	.06	.03
1992 Donruss	235	.06	.05	.02
1992 Fleer	435	.06	.05	.02
1992 Fleer Ultra	204	.15	.11	.06
1992 Leaf	77	.10	.08	.04
1992 O-Pee-Chee	765	.06	.05	.02
1992 Pinnacle	196	.12	.09	.05
1992 Pinnacle Team 2000	67	.10	.08	.04
1992 Score	224	.06	.05	.02
1992 Studio	36	.12	.09	.05
1992 Topps	765	.06	.05	.02
1992 Topps Gold	765	.35	.25	.14
1992 Topps Stadium Club	391	.15	.11	.06
1992 Topps Stadium Club Special Edition	77	.15	.11	.06
1992 Upper Deck	635	.08	.06	.03
1992 Upper Deck MVP Holograms	25	.25	.20	.10
1993 Bowman	448	.10	.08	.04
1993 Donruss	272	.06	.05	.02
1993 Fleer	52	.08	.06	.03
1993 Fleer Flair	64	.25	.15	.08
1993 Fleer Ultra	42	.10	.08	.04
1993 Leaf	51	.10	.08	.04
1993 O-Pee-Chee	185	.15	.11	.06
1993 Pinnacle	113	.06	.05	.02
1993 Score	395	.04	.03	.02
1993 Score Select	219	.10	.08	.04
1993 Topps	195	.06	.05	.02
1993 Topps Finest	62	1.00	.70	.40
1993 Topps Finest Refractors	62	20.00	15.00	8.00
1993 Topps Gold	195	.10	.08	.04
1993 Topps Stadium Club	110	.10	.08	.04
1993 Topps Stadium Club First Day Production	110	8.00	6.00	3.25
1993 Upper Deck	97	.06	.05	.02
1993 Upper Deck SP	35	.15	.11	.06
1994 Bowman	286	.10	.08	.04
1994 Donruss	113	.05	.04	.02
1994 Donruss Triple Play	28	.05	.04	.02
1994 Fleer	492	.05	.04	.02
1994 Fleer Extra Bases	275	.10	.08	.04
1994 Fleer Flair	171	.20	.15	.08
1994 Fleer Smoke N' Heat	4	4.00	3.00	1.50
1994 Fleer Ultra	504	.10	.08	.04
1994 Leaf	398	.10	.08	.04
1994 O-Pee-Chee	73	.05	.04	.02
1994 Pacific Crown	267	.05	.04	.02
1994 Pinnacle	45	.10	.08	.04

1994 Pinnacle Artist's Proof	45	3.00	2.25	1.25
1994 Pinnacle Museum Collection	45	1.50	1.25	.60
1994 Score	78	.04	.03	.02
1994 Score Select	284	.10	.08	.04
1994 Sportflics 2000	113	.10	.08	.04
1994 Topps	456	.04	.03	.02
1994 Topps Finest	120	.50	.40	.20
1994 Topps Finest Refractors	120	3.50	2.75	1.50
1994 Topps Gold	456	.15	.11	.06
1994 Topps Stadium Club	190	.10	.08	.04
1994 Topps Stadium Club First Day Production	190	2.50	2.00	1.00
1994 Upper Deck	379	.10	.08	.04
1994 Upper Deck Collector's Choice	534	.05	.04	.02
1994 Upper Deck Electric Diamond	379	.25	.20	.10

Rickey Henderson

Set	Card #	NM	EX	VG
1980 Topps	482 (R)	70.00	35.00	21.00

Set	Card #	MT	NM	EX
1981 Donruss	119	7.00	5.25	2.75
1981 Fleer	351	6.00	4.50	2.50
1981 Fleer	574	7.00	5.25	2.75
1981 O-Pee-Chee	261	11.00	8.25	4.50
1981 Topps	4	1.00	.75	.40
1981 Topps	261	8.00	6.00	3.25
1982 Donruss	113	4.00	3.00	1.50
1982 Fleer	92	4.00	3.00	1.50
1982 Fleer	643	2.00	1.50	.80
1982 O-Pee-Chee	268	6.00	4.50	2.50
1982 Topps	156	.25	.20	.10
1982 Topps	164	.90	.70	.35
1982 Topps	610	4.00	3.00	1.50
1983 Donruss	11	2.00	1.50	.80
1983 Donruss	35	3.00	2.25	1.25
1983 Fleer	519	3.00	2.25	1.25
1983 Fleer	639	1.00	.75	.40
1983 Fleer	646	.30	.25	.12
1983 O-Pee-Chee	180	4.25	3.25	1.75
1983 O-Pee-Chee	391	1.50	1.25	.60
1983 Topps	2	1.00	.75	.40
1983 Topps	180	3.00	2.25	1.25
1983 Topps	391	.50	.40	.20
1983 Topps	531	.30	.25	.12
1983 Topps	704	.35	.25	.14
1983 Topps All-Star Glossy Set of 40	33	.70	.50	.30
1984 Donruss	54	8.00	6.00	3.25
1984 Fleer	447	6.00	4.50	2.50
1984 O-Pee-Chee	230	3.00	2.25	1.25
1984 Topps	2	.50	.40	.20
1984 Topps	134	.30	.25	.12
1984 Topps	156	.25	.20	.10

1984 Topps	230	2.50	2.00	1.00
1984 Topps All-Star Glossy Set of 40	6	.70	.50	.30
1985 Donruss	176	2.50	2.00	1.00
1985 Fleer	425	4.00	3.00	1.50
1985 Fleer	629	1.00	.70	.40
1985 Fleer Update	51	4.00	3.00	1.50
1985 Leaf-Donruss	208	3.00	2.25	1.25
1985 O-Pee-Chee	115	.85	.60	.35
1985 Topps	115	1.25	.90	.50
1985 Topps	706	.25	.20	.10
1985 Topps Traded	49T	3.50	2.75	1.50
1986 Donruss	51	1.75	1.25	.80
1986 Fleer	108	2.00	1.50	.80
1986 Fleer All Stars	7	3.00	2.25	1.25
1986 Leaf	37	1.75	1.25	.70
1986 O-Pee-Chee	243	.75	.60	.30
1986 Sportflics	6	1.00	.70	.40
1986 Sportflics	184	1.50	1.25	.60
1986 Sportflics Decade Greats	69	.60	.45	.25
1986 Topps	500	.60	.45	.25
1986 Topps	716	.25	.20	.10
1986 Topps All-Star Glossy Set of 60	5	.70	.50	.30
1986 Topps All-Star Glossy Set of 22	7	.60	.45	.25
1987 Donruss	228	.40	.30	.15
1987 Fleer	101	1.50	1.25	.60
1987 Leaf	191	.75	.60	.30
1987 O-Pee-Chee	7	.30	.25	.12
1987 Sportflics	4	1.00	.70	.40
1987 Sportflics	157	.25	.20	.10
1987 Sportflics	159	1.25	.90	.50
1987 Sportflics	198	.25	.20	.10
1987 Topps	311	.12	.09	.05
1987 Topps	406	.25	.20	.10
1987 Topps	735	.25	.20	.10
1987 Topps All-Star Glossy Set of 22	18	.50	.40	.20
1987 Topps All-Star Glossy Set of 60	21	.70	.50	.30
1988 Donruss	277	.20	.15	.08
1988 Fleer	209	.60	.45	.25
1988 Leaf	145	.30	.25	.12
1988 O-Pee-Chee	60	.30	.25	.12
1988 Score	13	.25	.15	.08
1988 Sportflics	11	.75	.60	.30
1988 Sportflics Gamewinners	8	.60	.45	.25
1988 Topps	60	.30	.25	.12
1988 Topps All-Star Glossy Set of 22	7	.50	.40	.20
1988 Topps All-Star Glossy Set of 60	25	.60	.45	.25
1988 Topps Big Baseball	165	.25	.20	.10
1989 Bowman	181	.25	.20	.10
1989 Donruss	245	.20	.15	.08
1989 Fleer	254	.25	.20	.10
1989 Fleer Update	54	.20	.15	.08
1989 O-Pee-Chee	282	.25	.20	.10
1989 Score	70	.20	.12	.06
1989 Score	657	.12	.09	.05
1989 Score Traded	50T	.30	.25	.12
1989 Sportflics	145	.50	.40	.20
1989 Topps	380	.30	.25	.12
1989 Topps All-Star Glossy Set of 22	7	.15	.11	.06
1989 Topps All-Star Glossy Set of 60	35	.70	.50	.30
1989 Topps Big Baseball	271	.15	.11	.06
1989 Topps Traded	48T	.20	.15	.08
1989 Upper Deck	210	.50	.40	.20
1990 Bowman	457	.20	.15	.08
1990 Donruss	304	.15	.11	.06
1990 Fleer	10	.20	.15	.08
1990 Leaf	160	1.50	1.25	.60
1990 O-Pee-Chee	7	.20	.15	.08
1990 O-Pee-Chee	450	.25	.20	.10
1990 Post Cereal	25	.80	.60	.30
1990 Score	360	.15	.11	.06
1990 Score	686	.10	.07	.04
1990 Score	698	.12	.09	.05
1990 Sportflics	208	.40	.30	.15
1990 Topps	7	.15	.11	.06
1990 Topps	450	.20	.15	.08
1990 Topps All-Star Glossy Set of 60	37	.40	.30	.15
1990 Topps Big Baseball	292	.35	.25	.14
1990 Upper Deck	334	.25	.20	.10
1991 Bowman	213	.15	.11	.06
1991 Bowman	371	.10	.08	.04
1991 Bowman	692	.10	.08	.04
1991 Donruss	53	.15	.11	.06
1991 Donruss	387	.15	.11	.06
1991 Donruss	648	.12	.09	.05
1991 Donruss	761	.12	.09	.05
1991 Donruss Elite	7	50.00	38.00	20.00
1991 Fleer	10	.15	.11	.06
1991 Fleer All Stars	6	.75	.60	.30
1991 Fleer ProVisions	2F	.50	.40	.20
1991 Fleer Ultra	248	.30	.25	.12
1991 Fleer Ultra	393	.20	.15	.08
1991 Fleer Ultra Gold	5	.75	.60	.30
1991 Fleer World Series	4	.35	.25	.14
1991 Leaf	101	.25	.20	.10
1991 Leaf Gold Rookies	26	1.50	1.25	.60
1991 O-Pee-Chee Premier	62	.25	.20	.10
1991 Post Cereal	27	.80	.60	.30
1991 Score	10	.25	.20	.10
1991 Score	397	.15	.10	.08
1991 Score	857	.12	.10	.06
1991 Score	875	.10	.08	.04
1991 Score	890	.15	.11	.06
1991 Studio	104	.30	.25	.12
1991 Topps	391	.10	.08	.04
1991 Topps	670	.12	.09	.05
1991 Topps All-Star Glossy Set of 22	6	.40	.30	.15
1991 Topps Stadium Club	120	1.00	.75	.40
1991 Topps Stadium Club Charter Members	(13)	.60	.45	.25
1991 Topps Stadium Club Charter Members	(14)	.60	.45	.25
1991 Topps Stadium Club Members Only	(13)	.50	.40	.20
1991 Topps Stadium Club Members Only	(14)	.50	.40	.20
1991 Upper Deck	444	.20	.15	.08
1991 Upper Deck	----	4.00	3.00	1.50
1991 Upper Deck Final Edition	86	.15	.11	.06
1991 Upper Deck Silver Sluggers	3	1.00	.75	.40
1992 Bowman	166	.75	.60	.30
1992 Donruss	30	.15	.11	.06
1992 Donruss	193	.20	.15	.08
1992 Donruss	215	.10	.08	.04
1992 Donruss Elite	----	100.00	75.00	40.00
1992 Donruss Triple Play	63	.15	.10	.05
1992 Fleer	258	.20	.15	.08
1992 Fleer	681	.15	.11	.06
1992 Fleer Ultra	114	.40	.30	.15
1992 Leaf	116	.25	.15	.08
1992 O-Pee-Chee	2	.10	.08	.04
1992 O-Pee-Chee	560	.15	.11	.06
1992 O-Pee-Chee Premier	147	.30	.25	.12
1992 Pinnacle	283	.75	.60	.30
1992 Pinnacle	401	.30	.25	.12
1992 Pinnacle	614	.25	.20	.10
1992 Pinnacle Rookie Idols	7	18.00	13.50	7.25
1992 Score	430	.10	.08	.04
1992 Score	441	.15	.11	.06
1992 Score	480	.15	.11	.06
1992 Topps	2	.10	.08	.04
1992 Topps	560	.15	.11	.06
1992 Topps Gold	2	.35	.25	.14
1992 Topps Gold	560	1.75	1.25	.70
1992 Topps Kids	118	.15	.11	.06

1992 Topps Stadium Club	750	.35	.25	.14
1992 Topps Stadium Club Master Photos	(8)	4.00	3.00	1.50
1992 Topps Stadium Club Special Edition	83	.35	.25	.14
1992 Upper Deck	90	.05	.04	.02
1992 Upper Deck	155	.20	.15	.08
1992 Upper Deck	640	.05	.04	.02
1992 Upper Deck	648	.10	.08	.04
1992 Upper Deck	782	.15	.11	.06
1993 Bowman	625	.20	.15	.08
1993 DiamondMarks	(103)	.60	.45	.25
1993 Donruss	315	.12	.09	.05
1993 Donruss Triple Play	219	.25	.20	.10
1993 Fleer	294	.15	.11	.06
1993 Fleer Flair	260	.40	.30	.15
1993 Fleer Ultra	258	.20	.15	.08
1993 Leaf	291	.15	.11	.06
1993 O-Pee-Chee	130	.20	.15	.08
1993 Pinnacle	29	.15	.11	.06
1993 Pinnacle	308	.06	.05	.02
1993 Pinnacle Cooperstown	7	.30	.25	.12
1993 Pinnacle Cooperstown Dufex	7	75.00	56.00	30.00
1993 Pinnacle Home Run Club	21	.50	.40	.20
1993 Score	71	.15	.11	.06
1993 Score Select	106	.15	.11	.06
1993 Score Select Rookie/ Traded	1	.40	.30	.15
1993 Studio	84	.15	.11	.06
1993 Topps	750	.15	.11	.06
1993 Topps Finest	86	3.00	2.25	1.25
1993 Topps Finest Jumbo All-Stars	86	10.00	7.50	4.00
1993 Topps Finest Refractors	86	30.00	22.00	12.00
1993 Topps Gold	750	.30	.25	.12
1993 Topps Stadium Club	558	.20	.15	.08
1993 Topps Stadium Club First Day Production	558	30.00	22.00	12.00
1993 Topps Stadium Club Master Photos	(19)	2.50	2.00	1.00
1993 Upper Deck	136	.15	.11	.06
1993 Upper Deck "Highlights"	10	3.00	2.25	1.25
1993 Upper Deck Clutch Performers	12	1.25	.90	.50
1993 Upper Deck Diamond Gallery	29	2.00	1.50	.80
1993 Upper Deck Fun Packs	50	.20	.15	.08
1993 Upper Deck Fun Packs	212	.05	.04	.02
1993 Upper Deck SP	40	.75	.60	.30
1993 Upper Deck Then And Now	3	1.50	1.25	.60
1994 Bowman	80	.20	.15	.08
1994 Bowman's Best	4	1.00	.70	.40
1994 Bowman's Best Refractors	4	8.00	6.00	3.25
1994 Donruss	19	.20	.15	.08
1994 Donruss	290	.05	.04	.02
1994 Donruss Anniversary-1984	4	2.50	2.00	1.00
1994 Donruss Special Edition - Gold	19	.30	.25	.12
1994 Donruss Triple Play	4	.05	.04	.02
1994 Fleer	334	.10	.08	.04
1994 Fleer Extra Bases	150	.20	.15	.08
1994 Fleer Flair	331	.40	.30	.15
1994 Fleer Ultra	406	.15	.11	.06
1994 Fleer Update	74	.15	.11	.06
1994 Leaf	259	.15	.11	.06
1994 Leaf Limited	60	1.50	1.25	.60
1994 O-Pee-Chee	37	.15	.11	.06
1994 O-Pee-Chee Toronto Blue Jays	1	4.00	3.00	1.50
1994 Pacific Crown	643	.20	.15	.08
1994 Pinnacle	450	.25	.20	.10
1994 Pinnacle Artist's Proof	450	5.00	3.75	2.00
1994 Pinnacle Museum Collection	450	3.00	2.25	1.25
1994 Pinnacle Run Creators	10	2.00	1.50	.80
1994 Score	35	.10	.08	.04
1994 Score Gold Stars	34	3.00	2.25	1.25
1994 Score Rookie & Traded Changing Places	6	2.50	2.00	1.00
1994 Score Rookie & Traded Gold Rush	13	.60	.45	.25
1994 Score Rookie and Traded	13	.25	.20	.10
1994 Score Select	254	.25	.20	.10
1994 Sportflics 2000 Movers	8	4.00	3.00	1.50
1994 Studio	3	.20	.15	.08
1994 Topps	248	.10	.08	.04
1994 Topps Finest	223	1.00	.75	.40
1994 Topps Finest Refractors	223	6.00	4.50	2.50
1994 Topps Finest Superstars	223	3.00	2.25	1.25
1994 Topps Gold	248	.25	.20	.10
1994 Topps Stadium Club	107	.15	.11	.06
1994 Topps Stadium Club	654	.20	.15	.08
1994 Topps Stadium Club First Day Production	107	10.00	7.50	4.00
1994 Topps Stadium Club First Day Production	654	15.00	11.00	6.00
1994 Topps Stadium Club Members Only Baseball	38	.40	.30	.15
1994 Topps Traded	65	.08	.06	.03
1994 Upper Deck	60	.15	.11	.06
1994 Upper Deck Collector's Choice	131	.15	.11	.06
1994 Upper Deck Collector's Choice	510	.07	.05	.03
1994 Upper Deck Diamond Collection	6W	4.50	3.50	1.75
1994 Upper Deck Electric Diamond	60	.60	.45	.25
1994 Upper Deck Fun Packs	124	.15	.11	.06
1994 Upper Deck Fun Packs	213	.08	.06	.03
1994 Upper Deck SP	34	.30	.25	.12
1994 Upper Deck SP Baseball Die-Cut	34	.40	.30	.15

Keith Hernandez

Set	Card #	NM	EX	VG
1975 O-Pee-Chee	623	17.00	8.50	5.00
1975 Topps	623 (R)	10.00	5.00	3.00
1975 Topps Mini	623	40.00	20.00	12.00

1976 O-Pee-Chee	542	5.00	2.50	1.50
1976 Topps	542	3.00	1.50	.90
1977 O-Pee-Chee	150	2.50	1.25	.70
1977 Topps	95	1.00	.50	.30
1978 O-Pee-Chee	109	3.00	1.50	.90
1978 Topps	143	1.00	.50	.30
1979 O-Pee-Chee	371	1.50	.70	.45
1979 Topps	695	1.00	.50	.30
1980 O-Pee-Chee	170	1.25	.60	.40
1980 Topps	201	.50	.25	.15
1980 Topps	321	.75	.40	.25

Set	Card #	MT	NM	EX
1981 Donruss	67	.20	.15	.08
1981 Fleer	545	.25	.20	.10
1981 O-Pee-Chee	195	.60	.45	.25
1981 Topps	420	.25	.20	.10
1982 Donruss	278	.20	.15	.08
1982 Fleer	114	.20	.15	.08
1982 O-Pee-Chee	210	.50	.40	.20
1982 Topps	186	.15	.11	.06
1982 Topps	210	.15	.11	.06
1983 Donruss	20	.20	.15	.08
1983 Donruss	152	.20	.15	.08
1983 Fleer	8	.15	.11	.06
1983 O-Pee-Chee	262	.40	.30	.15
1983 Topps	700	.25	.20	.10
1983 Topps All-Star Glossy Set of 40	4	.20	.15	.08
1983 Topps Traded	43T	.30	.25	.12
1984 Donruss	238	.25	.20	.10
1984 Fleer	587	.20	.15	.08
1984 O-Pee-Chee	120	.60	.45	.25
1984 Topps	120	.15	.11	.06
1985 Donruss	68	.20	.15	.08
1985 Fleer	85	.15	.11	.06
1985 Leaf-Donruss	62	.30	.25	.12
1985 O-Pee-Chee	80	.25	.20	.10
1985 Topps	80	.12	.09	.05
1985 Topps	712	.10	.08	.04
1985 Topps All-Star Glossy Set of 40	13	.20	.15	.08
1986 Donruss	190	.20	.15	.08
1986 Fleer	84	.15	.11	.06
1986 Leaf	124	.25	.20	.10
1986 O-Pee-Chee	252	.25	.20	.10
1986 Sportflics	15	.15	.11	.06
1986 Sportflics	62	.50	.40	.20
1986 Sportflics	127	.25	.20	.10
1986 Sportflics	179	1.25	.90	.50
1986 Sportflics	181	.70	.50	.30
1986 Topps	203	.08	.06	.03
1986 Topps	520	.12	.09	.05
1986 Topps	701	.10	.08	.04
1986 Topps All-Star Glossy Set of 60	7	.40	.30	.15
1987 Donruss	76	.15	.11	.06
1987 Donruss All-Stars	11	.10	.08	.04
1987 Fleer	12	.10	.08	.04
1987 Fleer	629	.15	.11	.06
1987 Fleer	637	.35	.25	.14
1987 Leaf	233	.20	.15	.08
1987 O-Pee-Chee	350	.20	.15	.08
1987 Sportflics	133	.15	.11	.06
1987 Sportflics	195	.50	.40	.20
1987 Topps	331	.10	.08	.04
1987 Topps	350	.10	.08	.04
1987 Topps	595	.12	.09	.05
1987 Topps All-Star Glossy Set of 22	2	.20	.15	.08
1987 Topps All-Star Glossy Set of 60	26	.20	.15	.08
1988 Donruss	316	.08	.06	.03
1988 Donruss All-Stars	49	.15	.11	.06
1988 Fleer	136	.08	.06	.03
1988 Fleer	639	.15	.11	.06
1988 Leaf	117	.15	.11	.06
1988 O-Pee-Chee	68	.12	.09	.05
1988 Score	400	.15	.11	.06
1988 Sportflics	31	.25	.20	.10
1988 Sportflics Gamewinners	11	.20	.15	.08
1988 Topps	610	.06	.05	.02
1988 Topps All-Star Glossy Set of 60	32	.25	.20	.10
1988 Topps Big Baseball	59	.10	.08	.04
1989 Bowman	385	.05	.04	.02
1989 Donruss	117	.08	.06	.03
1989 Donruss Grand Slammers	8	.15	.11	.06
1989 Fleer	37	.08	.06	.03
1989 O-Pee-Chee	63	.07	.05	.03
1989 Score	41	.20	.15	.08
1989 Sportflics	60	.25	.20	.10
1989 Topps	480	.15	.11	.06
1989 Topps Big Baseball	185	.05	.04	.02
1989 Upper Deck	612	.08	.06	.03
1990 Bowman	342	.06	.05	.02
1990 Donruss	388	.07	.05	.03
1990 Fleer	205	.06	.05	.02
1990 Leaf	470	.25	.20	.10
1990 O-Pee-Chee	230	.07	.05	.03
1990 Score	193	.09	.07	.04
1990 Score Traded	57T	.08	.06	.03
1990 Sportflics	106	.10	.08	.04
1990 Topps	230	.07	.05	.03
1990 Topps Big Baseball	301	.06	.05	.02
1990 Topps Traded	39T	.08	.06	.03
1990 Upper Deck	222	.10	.08	.04
1990 Upper Deck	777	.12	.09	.05
1991 Fleer	368	.08	.06	.03
1991 Score	89	.06	.05	.02

Orel Hershiser

Set	Card #	MT	NM	EX
1985 Donruss	581 (R)	2.50	2.00	1.00
1985 Fleer	371 (R)	2.00	1.50	.80
1985 Leaf-Donruss	38	2.50	2.00	1.00
1985 O-Pee-Chee	273	1.00	.70	.40
1985 Topps	493 (R)	1.00	.75	.40
1986 Donruss	18	.20	.15	.08
1986 Donruss	226	.30	.25	.12
1986 Donruss Diamond Kings Supers	18	.70	.50	.30
1986 Fleer	131	.30	.25	.12
1986 Leaf	18	.60	.45	.25
1986 O-Pee-Chee	159	.70	.50	.30
1986 Sportflics	9	.25	.20	.10
1986 Topps	159	.15	.11	.06
1986 Topps All-Star Glossy Set of 60	24	.40	.30	.15
1987 Donruss	106	.15	.11	.06
1987 Fleer	441	.25	.20	.10
1987 Leaf	246	.20	.15	.08
1987 O-Pee-Chee	385	.20	.15	.08
1987 Sportflics	43	.30	.25	.12
1987 Topps	385	.12	.09	.05
1988 Donruss	94	.08	.06	.03
1988 Fleer	518	.10	.08	.04

Card	No.			
1988 Fleer	632	.12	.09	.05
1988 Leaf	62	.20	.15	.08
1988 O-Pee-Chee	40	.15	.11	.06
1988 Score	470	.08	.06	.03
1988 Sportflics	160	.30	.25	.12
1988 Topps	40	.08	.06	.03
1988 Topps Big Baseball	91	.25	.20	.10
1989 Bowman	341	.08	.06	.03
1989 Donruss	197	.08	.06	.03
1989 Donruss	648	.15	.11	.06
1989 Donruss MVP	4	.25	.20	.10
1989 Fleer	62	.08	.06	.03
1989 Fleer All-Stars	7	.15	.11	.06
1989 O-Pee-Chee	41	.07	.05	.03
1989 O-Pee-Chee	380	.07	.05	.03
1989 Score	370	.08	.05	.02
1989 Score	582	.10	.06	.03
1989 Score	653	.10	.08	.04
1989 Sportflics	36	.40	.30	.15
1989 Sportflics	222	.25	.20	.10
1989 Topps	5	.10	.08	.04
1989 Topps	394	.12	.09	.05
1989 Topps	550	.08	.06	.03
1989 Topps	669	.12	.09	.05
1989 Topps All-Star Glossy Set of 60	48	.20	.15	.08
1989 Topps Big Baseball	1	.15	.11	.06
1989 Upper Deck	130	.10	.08	.04
1989 Upper Deck	661	.08	.06	.03
1989 Upper Deck	665	.08	.06	.03
1989 Upper Deck	667	.08	.06	.03
1990 Bowman	84	.10	.08	.04
1990 Donruss	197	.20	.15	.08
1990 Donruss MVP	5	.10	.08	.04
1990 Fleer	399	.12	.09	.05
1990 Leaf	280	.35	.25	.14
1990 O-Pee-Chee	780	.15	.11	.06
1990 Post Cereal	8	.40	.30	.15
1990 Score	50	.12	.09	.05
1990 Sportflics	197	.20	.15	.08
1990 Topps	780	.08	.06	.03
1990 Topps Big Baseball	82	.12	.09	.05
1990 Upper Deck	256	.10	.08	.04
1991 Bowman	595	.08	.06	.03
1991 Donruss	280	.10	.08	.04
1991 Fleer	208	.10	.08	.04
1991 Fleer Ultra Update	88	.15	.11	.06
1991 Leaf	243	.15	.11	.06
1991 O-Pee-Chee Premier	64	.05	.04	.02
1991 Score	550	.12	.09	.05
1991 Studio	183	.20	.15	.08
1991 Topps	690	.10	.08	.04
1991 Upper Deck	524	.10	.07	.04
1992 Bowman	517	.40	.30	.15
1992 Donruss	247	.10	.08	.04
1992 Donruss Triple Play	212	.08	.06	.03
1992 Fleer	459	.08	.06	.03
1992 Fleer Ultra	507	.10	.08	.04
1992 Leaf	81	.15	.11	.06
1992 O-Pee-Chee	175	.08	.06	.03
1992 O-Pee-Chee Premier	162	.15	.11	.06
1992 Pinnacle	21	.10	.08	.04
1992 Pinnacle	592	.15	.11	.06
1992 Score	653	.06	.05	.02
1992 Studio	44	.15	.11	.06
1992 Topps	175	.08	.06	.03
1992 Topps Gold	175	.35	.25	.14
1992 Topps Kids	52	.10	.08	.04
1992 Topps Stadium Club	431	.10	.08	.04
1992 Upper Deck	261	.08	.06	.03
1993 Bowman	394	.10	.08	.04
1993 DiamondMarks	(31)	.50	.40	.20
1993 Donruss	274	.08	.06	.03
1993 Donruss Diamond Kings	14	.75	.60	.30
1993 Donruss Triple Play	121	.15	.11	.06
1993 Fleer	63	.08	.06	.03
1993 Fleer Flair	70	.25	.15	.08
1993 Fleer Ultra	55	.10	.08	.04
1993 Leaf	53	.10	.08	.04
1993 O-Pee-Chee	136	.15	.11	.06
1993 Pinnacle	319	.06	.05	.02
1993 Score	90	.10	.08	.04
1993 Score Select	49	.12	.09	.05
1993 Topps	255	.08	.06	.03
1993 Topps Finest	184	1.00	.70	.40
1993 Topps Finest Refractors	184	20.00	15.00	8.00
1993 Topps Gold	255	.15	.11	.06
1993 Topps Stadium Club	544	.10	.08	.04
1993 Topps Stadium Club First Day Production	544	6.00	4.50	2.50
1993 Upper Deck	169	.08	.06	.03
1993 Upper Deck Fun Packs	88	.15	.11	.06
1993 Upper Deck SP	93	.15	.11	.06
1994 Bowman	566	.10	.08	.04
1994 Donruss	151	.05	.04	.02
1994 Donruss Triple Play	84	.05	.04	.02
1994 Fleer	513	.05	.04	.02
1994 Fleer Extra Bases	288	.10	.08	.04
1994 Fleer Extra Bases Pitcher's Duel	10M	.40	.30	.15
1994 Fleer Flair	178	.20	.15	.08
1994 Fleer Ultra	518	.10	.08	.04
1994 Leaf	16	.10	.08	.04
1994 O-Pee-Chee	133	.05	.04	.02
1994 Pacific Crown	311	.05	.04	.02
1994 Pinnacle	58	.10	.08	.04
1994 Pinnacle Artist's Proof	58	3.00	2.25	1.25
1994 Pinnacle Museum Collection	58	1.50	1.25	.60
1994 Score	102	.04	.03	.02
1994 Score Select	134	.10	.08	.04
1994 Sportflics 2000	125	.10	.08	.04
1994 Studio	68	.10	.08	.04
1994 Topps	460	.05	.04	.02
1994 Topps Finest	98	.50	.40	.20
1994 Topps Finest Refractors	98	3.50	2.75	1.50
1994 Topps Gold	460	.15	.11	.06
1994 Topps Stadium Club	400	.10	.08	.04
1994 Topps Stadium Club First Day Production	400	2.50	2.00	1.00
1994 Upper Deck	355	.10	.08	.04
1994 Upper Deck All-Stars Green Foil	32	.25	.20	.10
1994 Upper Deck All-Stars Gold Foil	32	1.00	.70	.40
1994 Upper Deck Collector's Choice	135	.05	.04	.02
1994 Upper Deck Electric Diamond	355	.25	.20	.10
1994 Upper Deck Fun Packs	155	.05	.04	.02
1994 Upper Deck SP	77	.15	.11	.06
1994 Upper Deck SP Baseball Die-Cut	77	.25	.20	.10

* * *

As part of a pregame publicity stunt, a snake handler performed at Philadelphia's Veterans Stadium. The handler took the snake into both locker rooms before the game; most players avoided it. But Atlanta Braves pitcher Glenn Hubbard posed with the snake around his shoulders for his 1984 Fleer card.

* * *

Where was Rocky Bridges when Bobby Thomson lined an 0-1 pitch into the stands to give the Giants the National League pennant and send Rocky and the rest of the Dodgers home for the winter? "Oh, I was at my accustomed spot, sitting on my butt in the Dodger dugout."

* * *

Whitey Herzog

Elston Howard

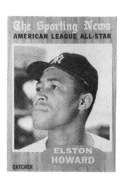

Set	Card #	NM	EX	VG
1957 Topps	29 (R)	30.00	15.00	9.00
1958 Topps	438	7.50	3.75	2.25
1959 Topps	392	6.00	3.00	1.75
1960 Leaf	71	8.00	4.00	2.50
1960 Topps	92	4.50	2.25	1.25
1961 Post Cereal	88a	3.00	1.50	.90
1961 Post Cereal	88b	3.00	1.50	.90
1961 Topps	106	4.00	2.00	1.25
1962 Topps	513	7.50	3.75	2.25
1963 Topps	302	4.50	2.25	1.25
1973 O-Pee-Chee	549	3.50	1.75	1.00
1973 Topps	549	2.50	1.25	.70
1976 O-Pee-Chee	236	.60	.30	.20
1976 Topps	236	.80	.40	.25
1977 Topps	371	2.00	1.00	.60
1978 Topps	299	.30	.15	.09
1979 Topps	451	.50	.25	.15

Set	Card #	MT	NM	EX
1981 Topps	684	.30	.25	.12
1982 Donruss	190	.08	.06	.03
1983 Donruss	530a	.70	.50	.30
1983 Donruss	530b	.10	.08	.04
1983 Topps	186	.10	.08	.04
1984 Topps	561	.10	.08	.04
1984 Topps All-Star Glossy Set of 22	12	.20	.15	.08
1985 Topps	683	.08	.06	.03
1986 Topps	441	.07	.05	.03
1987 Topps	243	.07	.05	.03
1987 Topps All-Star Glossy Set of 22	1	.15	.11	.06
1988 Topps	744	.06	.05	.02
1989 Topps	654	.06	.05	.02
1989 Topps All-Star Glossy Set of 22	12	.05	.04	.02
1990 O-Pee-Chee	261	.03	.02	.01
1990 Topps	261	.03	.02	.01

* * *

Set	Card #	NM	EX	VG
1955 Bowman	68 (R)	65.00	32.50	19.50
1956 Topps	208	40.00	20.00	12.00
1957 Topps	82	18.00	9.00	5.50
1958 Topps	275	10.00	5.00	3.00
1959 Topps	395	7.00	3.50	2.00
1960 Topps	65	6.00	3.00	1.75
1961 Post Cereal	2a	7.50	3.75	2.25
1961 Post Cereal	2b	4.50	2.25	1.25
1961 Topps	495	6.00	3.00	1.75
1962 Post Cereal	8	4.50	2.25	1.25
1962 Topps	51	8.00	4.00	2.50
1962 Topps	400	7.00	3.50	2.00
1962 Topps	473	8.00	4.00	2.50
1963 Post Cereal	18	4.00	2.00	1.25
1963 Topps	60	5.50	2.75	1.75
1963 Topps	306	4.50	2.25	1.25
1964 Topps	100	4.00	2.00	1.25
1965 O-Pee-Chee	1	21.00	10.50	6.25
1965 Topps	1	15.00	7.50	4.50
1965 Topps	450	7.00	3.50	2.00
1966 Topps	405	8.00	4.00	2.50
1967 O-Pee-Chee	25	2.25	1.25	.70
1967 Topps	25	3.00	1.50	.90
1968 O-Pee-Chee	167	2.25	1.25	.70
1968 Topps	167	2.50	1.25	.70
1973 O-Pee-Chee	116	.75	.40	.25
1973 Topps	116a	2.25	1.25	.70
1973 Topps	116b	.90	.45	.25
1975 O-Pee-Chee	201	3.00	1.50	.90
1975 Topps	201	1.50	.70	.45
1975 Topps Mini	201	2.25	1.25	.70

Set	Card #	MT	NM	EX
1986 Sportflics Decade Greats	49	.15	.11	.06
1988 Pacific Trading Cards Baseball Legends	19	.10	.08	.04
1994 "1954" Topps Archives	253	.30	.25	.12

* * *

Catfish Hunter isn't a card collector. Instead, he used to "put them in the spokes of a bicycle, so they'd make a noise." The Hall of Fame pitcher "can tell you when each one (of the pictures for my cards) was taken, as well as most of the (8x10) pictures that I sign."

* * *

Steve Garvey has a least favorite card. It's the one he calls the "Wes Parker Memorial," a 1973 Topps card (#213) which pictures him heading to home plate after a home run. But Parker, waiting to greet him, fills up most of the card space.

* * *

Hank Aaron believes was one of the first autograph guests at a card show. "Let me tell you, I think I can be referred to as a pioneer on the card show circuit. When I was playing for the Milwaukee Brewers in 1976, I was invited to a card show in Detroit to sign autographs. Not many people at the time even knew what a card show was because the Detroit event was the first of its kind. I was paid something like $2,000 for my appearance there, and that was considered big money for a personal appearance at the time."

* * *

Frank Howard

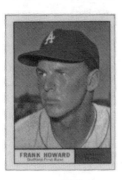

Kent Hrbek

Set	Card #	NM	EX	VG
1960 Topps	132 (R)	22.00	11.00	6.50
1961 Topps	280	6.00	3.00	1.75
1962 Topps	175	5.00	2.50	1.50
1963 Topps	123	3.50	1.75	1.00
1964 Topps	371	6.00	3.00	1.75
1965 O-Pee-Chee	40	2.75	1.50	.80
1965 Topps	40	5.00	2.50	1.50
1966 Topps	515	9.00	4.50	2.75
1967 Topps	255	3.00	1.50	.90
1968 O-Pee-Chee	6	10.25	5.25	3.00
1968 Topps	6	8.00	4.00	2.50
1968 Topps	320	2.50	1.25	.70
1969 O-Pee-Chee	3	2.25	1.25	.70
1969 O-Pee-Chee	5	2.25	1.25	.70
1969 O-Pee-Chee	170	2.25	1.25	.70
1969 Topps	3	2.00	1.00	.60
1969 Topps	5	2.00	1.00	.60
1969 Topps	170	1.50	.70	.45
1970 O-Pee-Chee	66	2.00	1.00	.60
1970 Topps	66	5.00	2.50	1.50
1970 Topps	550	4.50	2.25	1.25
1971 O-Pee-Chee	63	1.50	.70	.45
1971 O-Pee-Chee	65	1.50	.70	.45
1971 O-Pee-Chee	620	5.00	2.50	1.50
1971 Topps	63	1.50	.70	.45
1971 Topps	65	3.50	1.75	1.00
1971 Topps	620	4.00	2.00	1.25
1972 O-Pee-Chee	350	1.25	.60	.40
1972 Topps	350	1.00	.50	.30
1973 O-Pee-Chee	560	3.50	1.75	1.00
1973 Topps	560	2.00	1.00	.60

Set	Card #	MT	NM	EX
1981 Topps	685	.25	.20	.10
1984 Topps	621	.10	.08	.04
1988 Pacific Trading Cards Baseball Legends	17	.10	.08	.04

* * *

Gary Carter, about his card collection: "Right now I have the whole collection stored at my home in Florida, and there's enough stuff there to fill a good-sized museum building...and I feel the public will be interested in examining this collection. Maybe I'll have to wait until I retire as an active player before I realize my museum objective, but this is one project I want to complete."

* * *

Free-lance photographer Brad Newton, on shooting baseball cards for card companies: "When I'm shooting for Score I'll shoot 20 or 30 rolls of film a game."

* * *

Set	Card #	MT	NM	EX
1982 Donruss	557 (R)	2.00	1.50	.80
1982 Topps	766 (R)	2.00	1.50	.80
1982 Topps Traded	44T	4.00	3.00	1.50
1983 Donruss	19	.20	.15	.08
1983 Donruss	179	.80	.60	.30
1983 Fleer	616	.60	.45	.25
1983 Fleer	633	.25	.20	.10
1983 O-Pee-Chee	251	.50	.40	.20
1983 Topps	690	.70	.50	.30
1983 Topps	771	.20	.15	.08
1983 Topps All-Star Glossy Set of 40	35	.30	.25	.12
1984 Donruss	70	.40	.30	.15
1984 Fleer	567	.40	.30	.15
1984 O-Pee-Chee	345	.60	.45	.25
1984 Topps	11	.20	.15	.08
1984 Topps	345	.40	.30	.15
1985 Donruss	70	.30	.25	.12
1985 Fleer	281	.25	.20	.10
1985 Leaf-Donruss	200	.20	.15	.08
1985 O-Pee-Chee	308	.20	.15	.08
1985 Topps	510	.15	.11	.06
1986 Donruss	70	.25	.20	.10
1986 Fleer	397	.20	.15	.08
1986 Leaf	67	.20	.15	.08
1986 O-Pee-Chee	63	.15	.11	.06
1986 Sportflics	36	.25	.20	.10
1986 Topps	430	.10	.08	.04
1987 Donruss	73	.15	.11	.06
1987 Fleer	544	.15	.11	.06
1987 Leaf	99	.15	.11	.06
1987 O-Pee-Chee	161	.15	.11	.06
1987 Sportflics	15	.20	.15	.08
1987 Topps	679	.10	.08	.04
1987 Topps All-Star Glossy Set of 60	25	.30	.25	.12
1988 Donruss	320	.15	.11	.06
1988 Fleer	13	.15	.11	.06
1988 Leaf	139	.15	.11	.06
1988 O-Pee-Chee	45	.12	.09	.05
1988 Score	43	.12	.09	.05
1988 Sportflics	95	.20	.15	.08
1988 Topps	45	.12	.09	.05
1988 Topps	609	.08	.06	.03
1988 Topps All-Star Glossy Set of 60	8	.30	.25	.12
1988 Topps Big Baseball	84	.15	.11	.06
1989 Bowman	157	.08	.06	.03
1989 Donruss	199	.15	.11	.06
1989 Fleer	116	.08	.06	.03
1989 O-Pee-Chee	265	.08	.06	.03
1989 Score	382	.15	.11	.06
1989 Sportflics	188	.20	.15	.08
1989 Topps	265	.15	.11	.06
1989 Topps All-Star Glossy Set of 60	7	.15	.11	.06
1989 Topps Big Baseball	209	.08	.06	.03
1989 Upper Deck	213	.10	.08	.04
1990 Bowman	418	.08	.06	.03

1990 Donruss	81	.10	.08	.04
1990 Fleer	378	.10	.08	.04
1990 Leaf	228	.40	.30	.15
1990 O-Pee-Chee	125	.07	.05	.03
1990 Score	381	.12	.09	.05
1990 Sportflics	203	.10	.08	.04
1990 Topps	125	.07	.05	.03
1990 Topps Big Baseball	27	.12	.09	.05
1990 Upper Deck	452	.15	.11	.06
1991 Bowman	321	.08	.06	.03
1991 Donruss	95	.08	.06	.03
1991 Fleer	614	.08	.06	.03
1991 Fleer Ultra	189	.08	.06	.03
1991 Leaf	313	.15	.11	.06
1991 Score	292	.08	.06	.03
1991 Studio	87	.15	.11	.06
1991 Topps	710	.08	.06	.03
1991 Topps Stadium Club	248	.25	.20	.10
1991 Upper Deck	167	.12	.09	.05
1992 Bowman	445	.20	.15	.08
1992 Donruss	326	.08	.06	.03
1992 Donruss Triple Play	135	.06	.05	.02
1992 Fleer	205	.06	.05	.02
1992 Fleer Ultra	92	.10	.08	.04
1992 Leaf	362	.15	.11	.06
1992 O-Pee-Chee	347	.06	.05	.02
1992 O-Pee-Chee Premier	46	.15	.11	.06
1992 Pinnacle	68	.10	.08	.04
1992 Score	530	.06	.05	.02
1992 Studio	205	.15	.11	.06
1992 Topps	347	.06	.05	.02
1992 Topps Gold	347	.45	.35	.20
1992 Topps Kids	111	.10	.08	.04
1992 Topps Stadium Club	235	.15	.11	.06
1992 Topps Stadium Club Special Edition	89	.15	.11	.06
1992 Upper Deck	334	.06	.05	.02
1993 Bowman	677	.10	.08	.04
1993 DiamondMarks	(95)	.50	.40	.20
1993 Donruss	283	.08	.06	.03
1993 Donruss Long Ball Leaders	7	2.00	1.50	.80
1993 Donruss Triple Play	128	.10	.08	.04
1993 Fleer	267	.08	.06	.03
1993 Fleer Flair	236	.25	.15	.08
1993 Fleer Ultra	231	.10	.08	.04
1993 Leaf	76	.10	.08	.04
1993 O-Pee-Chee	150	.15	.11	.06
1993 Pinnacle	27	.06	.05	.02
1993 Pinnacle	307	.06	.05	.02
1993 Pinnacle Home Run Club	45	.25	.20	.10
1993 Score	98	.10	.08	.04
1993 Score Select	80	.10	.08	.04
1993 Studio	35	.08	.06	.03
1993 Topps	9	.06	.05	.02
1993 Topps Finest	117	1.00	.70	.40
1993 Topps Finest Refractors	117	20.00	15.00	8.00
1993 Topps Gold	9	.10	.08	.04
1993 Topps Stadium Club	525	.10	.08	.04
1993 Topps Stadium Club First Day Production	525	5.00	3.75	2.00
1993 Upper Deck	50	.15	.11	.06
1993 Upper Deck	74	.08	.06	.03
1993 Upper Deck SP	247	.15	.11	.06
1994 Donruss	443	.07	.05	.03
1994 Donruss Triple Play	253	.05	.04	.02
1994 Fleer	208	.05	.04	.02
1994 Fleer Extra Bases	117	.10	.08	.04
1994 Fleer Flair	75	.20	.15	.08
1994 Fleer Ultra	87	.10	.08	.04
1994 Leaf	269	.10	.08	.04
1994 Leaf Limited	48	1.00	.70	.40
1994 O-Pee-Chee	261	.05	.04	.02
1994 Pacific Crown	355	.05	.04	.02
1994 Pinnacle	206	.10	.08	.04
1994 Pinnacle Artist's Proof	206	3.00	2.25	1.25
1994 Pinnacle Museum Collection	206	1.50	1.25	.60
1994 Score	65	.04	.03	.02
1994 Score Select	261	.10	.08	.04
1994 Sportflics 2000	100	.10	.08	.04
1994 Studio	196	.10	.08	.04
1994 Topps	490	.04	.03	.02
1994 Topps Finest	261	.50	.40	.20
1994 Topps Finest Refractors	261	3.50	2.75	1.50
1994 Topps Gold	490	.15	.11	.06
1994 Topps Stadium Club	224	.10	.08	.04
1994 Topps Stadium Club First Day Production	224	2.50	2.00	1.00
1994 Upper Deck	98	.10	.08	.04
1994 Upper Deck All-Stars Green Foil	14	.75	.60	.30
1994 Upper Deck All-Stars Gold Foil	14	4.00	3.00	1.50
1994 Upper Deck Collector's Choice	486	.05	.04	.02
1994 Upper Deck Electric Diamond	98	.25	.20	.10

Catfish Hunter

Set	Card #	NM	EX	VG
1965 Topps	526 (R)	90.00	45.00	27.00
1966 O-Pee-Chee	36	32.50	16.00	9.75
1966 Topps	36	18.00	9.00	5.50
1967 Topps	369	15.00	7.50	4.50
1968 Topps	385	8.00	4.00	2.50
1969 Topps	235	11.00	8.25	4.50
1970 Topps	565	11.00	5.50	3.25
1971 O-Pee-Chee	45	10.25	5.25	3.00
1971 Topps	45	5.00	2.50	1.50
1972 O-Pee-Chee	330	6.00	3.00	1.75
1972 Topps	330	3.50	1.75	1.00
1973 O-Pee-Chee	235	5.00	2.50	1.50
1973 O-Pee-Chee	344	1.00	.50	.30
1973 Topps	235	4.00	2.00	1.25
1973 Topps	344	1.50	.70	.45
1974 O-Pee-Chee	196	6.25	3.25	2.00
1974 O-Pee-Chee	339	.60	.30	.20
1974 Topps	7	4.00	2.00	1.25
1974 Topps	339	.80	.40	.25
1975 O-Pee-Chee	230	1.50	.70	.45
1975 O-Pee-Chee	310	.75	.40	.25
1975 O-Pee-Chee	311	.55	.30	.15
1975 Topps	230	2.00	1.00	.60
1975 Topps	310	.80	.40	.25
1975 Topps	311	.50	.25	.15
1975 Topps Mini	230	4.00	2.00	1.25
1975 Topps Mini	310	1.25	.60	.40
1975 Topps Mini	311	.80	.40	.25
1976 O-Pee-Chee	100	3.00	1.50	.90
1976 O-Pee-Chee	200	2.00	1.00	.60
1976 O-Pee-Chee	202	5.00	2.50	1.50
1976 Topps	100	3.00	1.50	.90

1976 Topps	200	2.00	1.00	.60
1976 Topps	202	5.00	2.50	1.50
1977 O-Pee-Chee	10	1.50	.70	.45
1977 Topps	280	2.00	1.00	.60
1978 O-Pee-Chee	69	1.50	.70	.45
1978 Topps	460	2.00	1.00	.60
1979 O-Pee-Chee	352	.60	.30	.20
1979 Topps	670	1.25	.60	.40

Set	Card #	MT	NM	EX
1986 Sportflics Decade Greats	63	.30	.25	.12
1988 Pacific Trading Cards Baseball Legends	16	.20	.15	.08
1988 Topps All-Star Glossy Set of 22	11	.25	.20	.10
1989 Pacific Trading Cards Legends II	193	.10	.08	.04
1990 Pacific Legends	68	.15	.11	.06
1992 Pinnacle	587	.10	.08	.04

Monte Irvin

Set	Card #	NM	EX	VG
1951 Bowman	198 (R)	100.00	50.00	30.00
1951 Topps Red Backs	50	40.00	20.00	12.00
1952 Bowman	162	40.00	20.00	12.00
1952 Red Man Tobacco	9N	60.00	30.00	18.00
1952 Topps	26	80.00	40.00	18.50
1953 Bowman Color	51	50.00	25.00	15.00
1953 Topps	62	70.00	35.00	16.00
1954 Red Man Tobacco	5N	60.00	30.00	18.00
1954 Topps	3	35.00	17.50	10.50
1955 Topps	100	30.00	15.00	9.00
1956 Topps	194	32.50	16.00	9.75

Set	Card #	MT	NM	EX
1983 Topps 1952 Reprint Set	26	2.00	1.50	.80
1988 Pacific Trading Cards Baseball Legends	79	.15	.11	.06
1990 Pacific Legends	32	.15	.11	.06
1991 "1953" Topps Archives	62	.50	.40	.20
1994 "1954" Topps Archives	3	.30	.25	.12

* * *

Hank "Bow Wow" Arft's 1949 Bowman card contains his nickname on the front. "I was kind of surprised when I saw it on there 'cause I didn't realize it was coming out on that," he said. "I still didn't mind, though."

* * *

Bo Jackson

Set	Card #	MT	NM	EX
1986 Sportflics Rookies	40	1.00	.70	.40
1986 Topps Traded	50T	2.00	1.50	.80
1987 Donruss	35 (R)	2.50	2.00	1.00
1987 Fleer	369 (R)	6.00	4.50	2.50
1987 Leaf	35	1.00	.70	.40
1987 Sportflics	190	1.00	.70	.40
1987 Topps	170 (R)	1.00	.70	.40
1988 Donruss	220	.25	.20	.10
1988 Fleer	260	.60	.45	.25
1988 Leaf	187	.30	.25	.12
1988 O-Pee-Chee	8	.30	.25	.12
1988 Score	180	.30	.20	.10
1988 Sportflics	148	.60	.45	.25
1988 Topps	750	.30	.25	.12
1988 Topps Big Baseball	49	.60	.45	.25
1989 Bowman	126	.25	.20	.10
1989 Donruss	208	.25	.20	.10
1989 Fleer	285	.25	.20	.10
1989 O-Pee-Chee	84	.35	.25	.14
1989 Score	330	.25	.20	.10
1989 Sportflics	70	1.00	.70	.40
1989 Topps	540	.30	.25	.12
1989 Topps	789	.12	.09	.05
1989 Topps Big Baseball	238	.25	.20	.10
1989 Upper Deck	221	.60	.45	.25
1990 Bowman	378	.20	.15	.08
1990 Bowman Inserts	(4)	.08	.06	.03
1990 Donruss	1	.15	.11	.06
1990 Donruss	61	.25	.20	.12
1990 Donruss	650	.15	.11	.06
1990 Donruss Grand Slammers	12	.25	.15	.10
1990 Donruss MVP	1	.30	.25	.12
1990 Fleer	110	.25	.20	.10
1990 Fleer	635	.10	.08	.04
1990 Leaf	125	2.50	2.00	1.00
1990 O-Pee-Chee	300	.60	.45	.25
1990 Post Cereal	14	.80	.60	.30
1990 Score	280a	.60	.45	.25
1990 Score	280b	1.00	.70	.40
1990 Score	566	.25	.20	.10
1990 Score	687	.20	.15	.08
1990 Score	697	1.50	1.25	.60
1990 Sportflics	200	.75	.60	.30
1990 Topps	300	.20	.15	.08
1990 Topps All-Star Glossy Set of 22	17	.30	.25	.12
1990 Topps All-Star Glossy Set of 60	44	.40	.30	.15
1990 Topps Big Baseball	6	.50	.40	.20
1990 Upper Deck	32	.15	.11	.06
1990 Upper Deck	75	.25	.20	.10
1990 Upper Deck	105	.25	.20	.10
1991 Donruss	632	.15	.11	.06
1991 Fleer	561	.15	.11	.06
1991 Fleer ProVisions	5	.20	.15	.08
1991 Fleer Ultra	149	.25	.20	.10
1991 Fleer Ultra Gold	6	.75	.60	.30
1991 Score	5	.15	.11	.06

1991 Score	412	.15	.11	.06
1991 Score	420	.15	.11	.06
1991 Score	692	.12	.09	.05
1991 Score	773	.25	.20	.10
1991 Score Traded	1	.20	.15	.08
1991 Topps	600	.15	.11	.06
1991 Topps Traded	58	.20	.15	.08
1991 Upper Deck	545	.25	.20	.10
1991 Upper Deck	744	.25	.20	.10
1992 Donruss	470	.15	.11	.06
1992 Donruss Triple Play	164	.25	.20	.10
1992 Fleer	86	.15	.11	.06
1992 O-Pee-Chee	290	.20	.15	.08
1992 Score	361	.15	.11	.06
1992 Score Impact Players	53	.25	.20	.10
1992 Topps	290	.15	.11	.06
1992 Topps Gold	290	2.00	1.50	.80
1992 Topps Kids	103	.20	.15	.08
1992 Upper Deck	555	.15	.11	.06
1993 Bowman	415	.20	.15	.08
1993 DiamondMarks	(80)	.50	.40	.20
1993 Fleer Final Edition	195	.12	.09	.05
1993 Fleer Flair	186	.75	.60	.30
1993 Fleer Ultra	534	.25	.20	.10
1993 Leaf	316	.15	.11	.06
1993 O-Pee-Chee	151	.20	.15	.08
1993 Pinnacle	524	.15	.11	.06
1993 Pinnacle Home Run Club	43	.75	.60	.30
1993 Studio	110	.15	.11	.06
1993 Topps	400	.15	.11	.06
1993 Topps Finest	91	2.00	1.50	.80
1993 Topps Finest Jumbo All-Stars	91	10.00	7.50	4.00
1993 Topps Finest Refractors	91	25.00	18.50	10.00
1993 Topps Gold	400	.30	.25	.12
1993 Topps Stadium Club	495	.25	.20	.10
1993 Topps Stadium Club First Day Production	495	20.00	15.00	8.00
1993 Upper Deck	775	.15	.11	.06
1993 Upper Deck Fun Packs	31	.15	.11	.06
1993 Upper Deck Fun Packs	199	.20	.15	.08
1993 Upper Deck On Deck	15	.75	.60	.30
1993 Upper Deck SP	255	.50	.40	.20
1994 Bowman	535	.10	.08	.04
1994 Donruss	173	.15	.11	.06
1994 Donruss Long Ball Leaders	4	2.00	1.50	.80
1994 Fleer	84	.15	.11	.06
1994 Fleer Extra Bases	36	.15	.11	.06
1994 Fleer Flair	23	.35	.25	.14
1994 Fleer Golden Moments	5	1.50	1.25	.60
1994 Fleer Golden Moments Super	5	7.50	5.50	3.00
1994 Fleer Ultra	329	.15	.11	.06
1994 Fleer Update	18	.20	.15	.08
1994 Leaf	307	.15	.11	.06
1994 O-Pee-Chee	116	.25	.20	.10
1994 Pacific Crown	128	.15	.11	.06
1994 Pinnacle	509	.20	.15	.08
1994 Pinnacle Artist's Proof	509	5.00	3.75	2.00
1994 Pinnacle Museum Collection	509	2.50	2.00	1.00
1994 Pinnacle Tribute	4	2.00	1.50	.80
1994 Score	513	.15	.11	.06
1994 Score Gold Stars	35	3.00	2.25	1.25
1994 Score Rookie & Traded Gold Rush	3	.40	.30	.15
1994 Score Rookie & Traded Changing Places	4	2.00	1.50	.80
1994 Score Rookie and Traded	3	.15	.11	.06
1994 Score Rookie/ Traded Samples	3RT	3.00	2.25	1.25
1994 Score Select	356	.20	.15	.08
1994 Studio	12	.15	.11	.06
1994 Topps	500	.08	.06	.03
1994 Topps Finest	241	.75	.60	.30
1994 Topps Finest Refractors	241	5.00	3.75	2.00
1994 Topps Gold	500	.20	.15	.08
1994 Topps Stadium Club	167	.20	.15	.08
1994 Topps Stadium Club	547	.15	.11	.06
1994 Topps Stadium Club First Day Production	167	5.00	3.75	2.00
1994 Topps Stadium Club First Day Production	547	15.00	11.00	6.00
1994 Topps Traded	90	.10	.08	.04
1994 Upper Deck	117	.15	.11	.06
1994 Upper Deck Collector's Choice	356	.06	.05	.02
1994 Upper Deck Diamond Collection	7W	5.00	3.75	2.00
1994 Upper Deck Electric Diamond	117	.50	.40	.20
1994 Upper Deck Fun Packs	151	.08	.06	.03
1994 Upper Deck SP	24	.25	.20	.10
1994 Upper Deck SP Baseball Die-Cut	24	.40	.30	.15
1994 Upper Deck SP Holoview Blue	15	4.00	3.00	1.50
1994 Upper Deck SP Holoview Red	15	15.00	11.00	6.00

Reggie Jackson

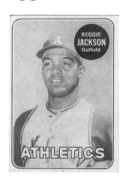

Set	Card #	NM	EX	VG
1969 Topps	260 (R)	425.00	210.00	125.00
1970 O-Pee-Chee	64	2.00	1.00	.60
1970 O-Pee-Chee	66	2.00	1.00	.60
1970 O-Pee-Chee	140	175.00	87.00	52.00
1970 O-Pee-Chee	459	30.00	15.00	9.00
1970 Topps	64	5.00	2.50	1.50
1970 Topps	66	5.00	2.50	1.50
1970 Topps	140	85.00	42.00	25.00
1970 Topps	459	24.00	12.00	7.50
1971 O-Pee-Chee	20	127.50	64.00	38.00
1971 Topps	20	60.00	30.00	18.00
1972 O-Pee-Chee	90	1.00	.50	.30
1972 O-Pee-Chee	435	60.00	30.00	18.00
1972 O-Pee-Chee	436	30.00	15.00	9.00
1972 Topps	90	3.50	1.75	1.00
1972 Topps	435	40.00	20.00	12.00
1972 Topps	436	20.00	10.00	6.00
1973 O-Pee-Chee	255	38.00	19.00	11.50
1973 Topps	255	30.00	15.00	9.00
1974 O-Pee-Chee	130	38.00	19.00	11.50
1974 O-Pee-Chee	202	6.25	3.25	2.00
1974 O-Pee-Chee	203	6.25	3.25	2.00
1974 O-Pee-Chee	338	6.00	3.00	1.75
1974 Topps	130	25.00	12.50	7.50

Set	Card #	MT	NM	EX
1974 Topps	202	5.00	2.50	1.50
1974 Topps	203	5.00	2.50	1.50
1974 Topps	338	5.00	2.50	1.50
1975 O-Pee-Chee	211	6.00	3.00	1.75
1975 O-Pee-Chee	300	30.00	15.00	9.00
1975 Topps	211	6.00	3.00	1.75
1975 Topps	300	25.00	12.50	7.50
1975 Topps Mini	211	7.00	3.50	2.00
1975 Topps Mini	300	30.00	15.00	9.00
1976 O-Pee-Chee	194	2.00	1.00	.60
1976 O-Pee-Chee	500	23.00	11.50	7.00
1976 Topps	194	2.00	1.00	.60
1976 Topps	500	18.00	9.00	5.50
1977 O-Pee-Chee	200	17.00	8.50	5.00
1977 Topps	10	16.00	8.00	4.75
1978 O-Pee-Chee	110	14.50	7.25	4.25
1978 O-Pee-Chee	242	6.25	3.25	2.00
1978 Topps	7	4.00	2.00	1.25
1978 Topps	200	15.00	7.50	4.50
1979 O-Pee-Chee	374	3.25	1.75	1.00
1979 Topps	700	5.00	2.50	1.50
1980 O-Pee-Chee	314	8.50	4.25	2.50
1980 Topps	600	7.00	3.50	2.00
Set	**Card #**	**MT**	**NM**	**EX**
1981 Donruss	228	2.50	2.00	1.00
1981 Donruss	348	2.50	2.00	1.00
1981 Donruss	468	2.50	2.00	1.00
1981 Fleer	79a	4.00	3.00	1.50
1981 Fleer	79b	2.00	1.50	.80
1981 Fleer	650	2.50	2.00	1.00
1981 O-Pee-Chee	370	3.25	2.50	1.25
1981 Topps	2	.90	.70	.35
1981 Topps	400	3.00	2.25	1.25
1982 Donruss	535	2.00	1.50	.80
1982 Donruss	575	2.00	1.50	.80
1982 Fleer	39	2.00	1.50	.80
1982 Fleer	646a	2.00	1.50	.80
1982 Fleer	646b	2.00	1.50	.80
1982 O-Pee-Chee	300	2.75	2.00	1.00
1982 O-Pee-Chee	301	1.00	.70	.40
1982 O-Pee-Chee	377	.40	.30	.15
1982 Topps	300	3.50	2.75	1.50
1982 Topps	301	2.00	1.50	.80
1982 Topps	551	1.00	.70	.40
1982 Topps Traded	47T	15.00	11.00	6.00
1983 Donruss	3	.50	.40	.20
1983 Donruss	115	1.50	1.25	.60
1983 Fleer	93	1.00	.70	.40
1983 Fleer	640	.25	.20	.10
1983 Fleer	645	.30	.25	.12
1983 O-Pee-Chee	56	2.00	1.50	.80
1983 O-Pee-Chee	219	.30	.25	.12
1983 O-Pee-Chee	390	.30	.25	.12
1983 Topps	390	.75	.60	.30
1983 Topps	500	2.00	1.50	.80
1983 Topps	501	.75	.60	.30
1983 Topps	702	.25	.20	.10
1983 Topps All-Star Glossy Set of 40	39	.70	.50	.30
1984 Donruss	57	6.00	4.50	2.50
1984 Fleer	520	1.50	1.25	.60
1984 O-Pee-Chee	100	1.00	.70	.40
1984 Topps	100	1.50	1.25	.60
1984 Topps	711	.30	.25	.12
1984 Topps	712	.20	.15	.08
1984 Topps	713	.20	.15	.08
1985 Donruss	57	1.50	1.25	.60
1985 Fleer	303	2.00	1.50	.80
1985 Fleer	639	.75	.60	.30
1985 Leaf-Donruss	170	1.50	1.25	.60
1985 O-Pee-Chee	200	.85	.60	.35
1985 Topps	200	.80	.60	.30
1985 Topps All-Star Glossy Set of 40	15	.70	.50	.30
1985 Topps All-Star Glossy Set of 22	19	.60	.45	.25
1986 Donruss	377	1.00	.70	.40
1986 Fleer	160	1.25	.90	.50
1986 Leaf	173	1.00	.70	.40
1986 O-Pee-Chee	394	.40	.30	.15
1986 Sportflics	37	1.00	.70	.40
1986 Sportflics	57	.35	.25	.14
1986 Sportflics	61	.25	.20	.10
1986 Sportflics	71	.30	.25	.12
1986 Sportflics	147	.25	.20	.10
1986 Sportflics	150	.20	.15	.08
1986 Sportflics Decade Greats	53	.70	.50	.30
1986 Topps	700	.35	.25	.14
1986 Topps All-Star Glossy Set of 60	2	.70	.50	.30
1987 Donruss	210	.35	.25	.14
1987 Fleer	84	1.00	.70	.40
1987 Fleer Update	49	.60	.45	.25
1987 Leaf	201	.60	.45	.25
1987 O-Pee-Chee	300	.25	.20	.10
1987 Sportflics	44	1.00	.70	.40
1987 Topps	300	.30	.25	.12
1987 Topps	312	.10	.08	.04
1987 Topps All-Star Glossy Set of 60	54	.70	.50	.30
1987 Topps Traded	52T	.50	.40	.20
1988 Fleer	283	.50	.40	.20
1988 Score	500	.20	.15	.08
1988 Score	501	.20	.15	.08
1988 Score	502	.20	.15	.08
1988 Score	503	.20	.15	.08
1988 Score	504	.20	.15	.08
1988 Sportflics	120	1.00	.70	.40
1989 Pacific Trading Cards Legends II	111	.30	.25	.12
1990 Upper Deck Reggie Jackson Heroes	1	3.00	2.25	1.25
1990 Upper Deck Reggie Jackson Heroes	2	3.00	2.25	1.25
1990 Upper Deck Reggie Jackson Heroes	3	3.00	2.25	1.25
1990 Upper Deck Reggie Jackson Heroes	4	3.00	2.25	1.25
1990 Upper Deck Reggie Jackson Heroes	5	3.00	2.25	1.25
1990 Upper Deck Reggie Jackson Heroes	6	3.00	2.25	1.25
1990 Upper Deck Reggie Jackson Heroes	7	3.00	2.25	1.25
1990 Upper Deck Reggie Jackson Heroes	8	3.00	2.25	1.25
1990 Upper Deck Reggie Jackson Heroes	9	3.00	2.25	1.25
1992 Upper Deck Heroes Highlights	5	4.00	3.00	1.50
1993 Upper Deck All-Time Heroes	72	.50	.40	.20
1993 Upper Deck All-Time Heroes	135	.10	.08	.04
1993 Upper Deck All-Time Heroes	165	.10	.08	.04
1993 Upper Deck Fun Packs	28	.15	.11	.06
1993 Upper Deck Heroes of Baseball Previews	2	2.00	1.50	.80
1993 Upper Deck Heroes of Baseball Previews	3	2.00	1.50	.80
1993 Upper Deck Heroes of Baseball Previews	4	3.00	2.25	1.25
1993 Upper Deck Then And Now	16	3.00	2.25	1.25
1993 Upper Deck 5th Anniversary	9	1.00	.75	.40
1993 Upper Deck 5th Anniversary Super	9	4.00	3.00	1.50
1994 Upper Deck All-Stars Green Foil	47	.50	.40	.20
1994 Upper Deck All-Stars Gold Foil	47	2.50	2.00	1.00
1994 Upper Deck All-Time Heroes	9	.25	.20	.10
1994 Upper Deck All-Time Heroes	44	.35	.25	.14
1994 Upper Deck All-Time Heroes	167	.15	.11	.06

Set	Card #	MT	NM	EX
1994 Upper Deck All-Time Heroes	210	.15	.11	.06
1994 Upper Deck Heroes Autographed Inserts	(2)	60.00	45.00	24.00
1994 Upper Deck Heroes Gold	9	.60	.45	.25
1994 Upper Deck Heroes Gold	44	.50	.40	.20
1994 Upper Deck Heroes Gold	167	.75	.60	.30
1994 Upper Deck Heroes Gold	210	.35	.25	.14

Gregg Jefferies

Set	Card #	MT	NM	EX
1988 Donruss	657 (R)	2.00	1.50	.80
1988 Fleer	137 (R)	4.00	3.00	1.50
1988 Leaf	259	2.50	2.00	1.00
1988 Score	645 (R)	1.50	1.25	.60
1989 Bowman	381	.40	.30	.15
1989 Donruss	35	.40	.30	.15
1989 Fleer	38	.40	.30	.15
1989 O-Pee-Chee	233	.25	.20	.10
1989 Score	600	.30	.25	.12
1989 Sportflics	90	.40	.30	.15
1989 Sportflics	223	4.00	3.00	1.50
1989 Topps	233	.30	.25	.12
1989 Topps Big Baseball	253	.60	.45	.25
1989 Topps Glossy Rookies Set of 22	13	.60	.45	.25
1989 Upper Deck	9	1.50	1.25	.60
1990 Bowman	140	.25	.20	.10
1990 Donruss	270	.25	.20	.10
1990 Fleer	207	.20	.15	.08
1990 Leaf	171	4.00	3.00	1.50
1990 O-Pee-Chee	457	.30	.25	.12
1990 Score	468	.25	.20	.10
1990 Sportflics	14	.30	.25	.12
1990 Topps	457	.30	.25	.12
1990 Topps All-Star Glossy Set of 60	60	.20	.15	.08
1990 Topps Big Baseball	57	.15	.11	.06
1990 Topps Glossy Rookies	16	.45	.35	.20
1990 Upper Deck	166	.40	.30	.15
1991 Bowman	481	.08	.06	.03
1991 Donruss	79	.15	.11	.06
1991 Fleer	151	.10	.08	.04
1991 Fleer Ultra	221	.15	.11	.06
1991 Leaf	465	.40	.30	.15
1991 Post Cereal	9	.40	.30	.15
1991 Score	660	.15	.11	.06
1991 Studio	206	.25	.20	.10
1991 Topps	30	.15	.11	.06
1991 Topps Stadium Club	257	1.25	.90	.50
1991 Upper Deck	156	.15	.11	.06
1992 Bowman	13	.75	.60	.30
1992 Donruss	372	.15	.11	.06
1992 Fleer	508	.12	.09	.05
1992 Fleer Ultra	372	.25	.20	.10
1992 Fleer Update	26	.30	.25	.12
1992 Leaf	215	.25	.20	.10
1992 O-Pee-Chee	707	.10	.08	.04
1992 O-Pee-Chee Premier	95	.15	.11	.06
1992 Pinnacle	330	.20	.15	.08
1992 Pinnacle Team 2000	45	.25	.20	.10
1992 Score	192	.10	.08	.04
1992 Score Rookie & Traded	39	.20	.15	.08
1992 Studio	184	.20	.15	.08
1992 Topps	707	.10	.08	.04
1992 Topps Gold	707	.50	.40	.20
1992 Topps Kids	14	.15	.11	.06
1992 Topps Stadium Club	737	.25	.20	.10
1992 Topps Stadium Club National Convention	737	30.00	22.00	12.00
1992 Topps Traded	55	.08	.06	.03
1992 Topps Traded Gold	55	.25	.20	.10
1992 Upper Deck	133	.10	.08	.04
1992 Upper Deck	725	.08	.06	.03
1993 Bowman	544	.10	.08	.04
1993 DiamondMarks	(53)	.35	.25	.14
1993 Donruss	307	.08	.06	.03
1993 Donruss Triple Play	130	.10	.08	.04
1993 Fleer	238	.10	.08	.04
1993 Fleer Final Edition	124	.10	.08	.04
1993 Fleer Flair	121	.35	.25	.14
1993 Fleer Ultra	209	.20	.15	.08
1993 Fleer Ultra	463	.15	.11	.06
1993 Leaf	265	.15	.11	.06
1993 O-Pee-Chee	123	.20	.15	.08
1993 O-Pee-Chee Premier	98	.15	.11	.06
1993 Pinnacle	24	.06	.05	.02
1993 Pinnacle	480	.15	.11	.06
1993 Score	17	.08	.06	.03
1993 Score Select	152	.15	.11	.06
1993 Score Select Rookie/Traded	12	.30	.25	.12
1993 Score The Franchise	7	1.00	.70	.40
1993 Studio	90	.08	.06	.03
1993 Topps	105	.08	.06	.03
1993 Topps Finest	83	2.50	2.00	1.00
1993 Topps Finest Refractors	83	27.50	21.00	11.00
1993 Topps Gold	105	.15	.11	.06
1993 Topps Stadium Club	628	.10	.08	.04
1993 Topps Stadium Club First Day Production	628	15.00	11.00	6.00
1993 Topps Traded	122	.10	.08	.04
1993 Upper Deck	54	.20	.15	.08
1993 Upper Deck	176	.12	.09	.05
1993 Upper Deck	545	.08	.06	.03
1993 Upper Deck	818	.10	.08	.04
1993 Upper Deck Fun Packs	75	.20	.15	.08
1993 Upper Deck SP	75	.20	.15	.08
1994 Bowman	536	.10	.08	.04
1994 Bowman's Best	27	.50	.40	.20
1994 Bowman's Best Refractors	27	4.00	3.00	1.50
1994 Donruss	9	.05	.04	.02
1994 Donruss Diamond Kings	21	1.00	.75	.40
1994 Donruss Diamond Kings Super	21	3.50	2.75	1.50
1994 Donruss MVP's	12	.75	.60	.30
1994 Donruss Special Edition - Gold	9	.40	.30	.15
1994 Donruss Triple Play Nicknames	8	1.50	1.25	.60
1994 Donruss Triple Play	62	.05	.04	.02
1994 Fleer	633	.06	.05	.02
1994 Fleer Extra Bases	359	.10	.08	.04
1994 Fleer Flair	429	.20	.15	.08
1994 Fleer Team Leaders	26	.60	.45	.25
1994 Fleer Ultra	266	.10	.08	.04
1994 Fleer Ultra On-Base Leaders	7	5.00	3.75	2.00
1994 Leaf	56	.10	.08	.04
1994 Leaf Limited	145	1.00	.70	.40

1994 Leaf Limited Gold	2	15.00	11.00	6.00
1994 Leaf MVP Contenders	7a	2.50	2.00	1.00
1994 Leaf MVP Contenders	7b	5.00	3.75	2.00
1994 O-Pee-Chee	77	.05	.04	.02
1994 Pacific Crown	591	.10	.08	.04
1994 Pacific Crown Jewels of the Crown	27	2.50	2.00	1.00
1994 Pinnacle	204	.15	.11	.06
1994 Pinnacle Artist's Proof	204	4.00	3.00	1.50
1994 Pinnacle Museum Collection	204	2.00	1.50	.80
1994 Pinnacle Run Creators	27	1.50	1.25	.60
1994 Post Cereal	28	.35	.25	.14
1994 Score	29	.04	.03	.02
1994 Score Gold Stars	9	3.00	2.25	1.25
1994 Score Select	232	.10	.08	.04
1994 Score The Cycle	5	6.00	4.50	2.50
1994 Sportflics 2000	74	.10	.08	.04
1994 Sportflics 2000 Movers	1	3.00	2.25	1.25
1994 Studio	51	.10	.08	.04
1994 Studio Heritage	7	1.00	.75	.40
1994 Topps	660	.06	.05	.02
1994 Topps Black Gold	35	.50	.40	.20
1994 Topps Finest	92	.50	.40	.20
1994 Topps Finest Refractors	92	6.00	4.50	2.50
1994 Topps Gold	660	.15	.11	.06
1994 Topps Stadium Club	109	.12	.09	.05
1994 Topps Stadium Club	531	.10	.08	.04
1994 Topps Stadium Club First Day Production	109	2.50	2.00	1.00
1994 Topps Stadium Club First Day Production	531	2.50	2.00	1.00
1994 Topps Stadium Club Members Only Baseball	19	.35	.25	.14
1994 Upper Deck	265	.10	.08	.04
1994 Upper Deck All-Stars Green Foil	4	.25	.20	.10
1994 Upper Deck All-Stars Gold Foil	4	1.00	.70	.40
1994 Upper Deck Collector's Choice	148	.05	.04	.02
1994 Upper Deck Electric Diamond	265	.25	.20	.10
1994 Upper Deck Fun Packs	153	.05	.04	.02
1994 Upper Deck SP	63	.15	.11	.06
1994 Upper Deck SP Baseball Die-Cut	63	.25	.20	.10

Fergie Jenkins

Set	Card #	NM	EX	VG
1966 Topps	254 (R)	90.00	45.00	27.00

1967 Topps	333	20.00	10.00	6.00
1968 O-Pee-Chee	9	2.25	1.25	.70
1968 O-Pee-Chee	11	2.25	1.25	.70
1968 Topps	9	3.50	1.75	1.00
1968 Topps	11	4.50	2.25	1.25
1968 Topps	410	20.00	10.00	6.00
1969 O-Pee-Chee	10	8.50	4.25	2.50
1969 O-Pee-Chee	12	2.25	1.25	.70
1969 Topps	10	3.50	1.75	1.00
1969 Topps	12	3.00	1.50	.90
1969 Topps	640	20.00	10.00	6.00
1970 O-Pee-Chee	69	7.50	3.75	2.25
1970 O-Pee-Chee	71	1.75	.90	.50
1970 O-Pee-Chee	240	12.75	6.50	3.75
1970 Topps	69	5.00	2.50	1.50
1970 Topps	71	4.00	2.00	1.25
1970 Topps	240	8.00	4.00	2.50
1971 O-Pee-Chee	70	1.50	.70	.45
1971 O-Pee-Chee	72	7.50	3.75	2.25
1971 O-Pee-Chee	280	14.50	7.25	4.25
1971 Topps	70	3.50	1.75	1.00
1971 Topps	72	3.50	1.75	1.00
1971 Topps	280	8.00	4.00	2.50
1972 O-Pee-Chee	93	5.00	2.50	1.50
1972 O-Pee-Chee	95	1.00	.50	.30
1972 O-Pee-Chee	410	9.25	4.75	2.75
1972 Topps	93	3.50	1.75	1.00
1972 Topps	95	3.00	1.50	.90
1972 Topps	410	6.00	3.00	1.75
1973 O-Pee-Chee	180	6.00	3.00	1.75
1973 Topps	180	4.00	2.00	1.25
1974 O-Pee-Chee	87	5.00	2.50	1.50
1974 Topps	87	4.00	2.00	1.25
1975 O-Pee-Chee	60	4.25	2.25	1.25
1975 O-Pee-Chee	310	.75	.40	.25
1975 Topps	60	4.00	2.00	1.25
1975 Topps	310	.80	.40	.25
1975 Topps Mini	60	3.00	1.50	.90
1975 Topps Mini	310	1.25	.60	.40
1976 O-Pee-Chee	250	4.25	2.25	1.25
1976 Topps	250	3.00	1.50	.90
1976 Topps Traded	250T	3.00	1.50	.90
1977 O-Pee-Chee	187	.75	.40	.25
1977 Topps	430	3.00	1.50	.90
1978 Topps	720	2.00	1.00	.60
1979 Topps	544	1.50	.70	.45
1980 O-Pee-Chee	203	.40	.20	.12
1980 Topps	390	.40	.20	.12

Set	Card #	MT	NM	EX
1981 Donruss	146	.50	.40	.20
1981 Fleer	622	.50	.40	.20
1981 Topps	158	.90	.70	.35
1982 Donruss	643	.15	.11	.06
1982 Fleer	320	.15	.11	.06
1982 O-Pee-Chee	137	.20	.15	.08
1982 Topps	624	.60	.45	.25
1982 Topps Traded	49T	2.00	1.50	.80
1983 Donruss	300	.20	.15	.08
1983 Fleer	498	.15	.11	.06
1983 O-Pee-Chee	230	.15	.11	.06
1983 O-Pee-Chee	231	.12	.09	.05
1983 Topps	51	.15	.11	.06
1983 Topps	230	.60	.45	.25
1983 Topps	231	.20	.15	.08
1984 Donruss	189	1.00	.75	.40
1984 Fleer	494	.60	.45	.25
1984 O-Pee-Chee	343	.30	.25	.12
1984 Topps	456	.15	.11	.06
1984 Topps	483	.20	.15	.08
1984 Topps	706	.30	.25	.12
1988 Pacific Trading Cards Baseball Legends	43	.15	.11	.06
1990 Pacific Senior League	29	.50	.40	.20
1990 Topps Senior League	119	.50	.40	.20
1991 Pacific Senior League	108	.50	.40	.20

1991 Upper Deck Heroes of Baseball	3	15.00	10.00	5.00
1991 Upper Deck Heroes of Baseball	4	15.00	11.00	6.00

Tommy John

Set	Card #	NM	EX	VG
1964 Topps	146 (R)	55.00	27.00	16.50
1965 O-Pee-Chee	208	21.00	10.50	6.25
1965 Topps	208	10.00	5.00	3.00
1966 Topps	486	13.00	6.50	4.00
1967 Topps	609	70.00	35.00	21.00
1968 O-Pee-Chee	72	2.25	1.25	.70
1968 Topps	72	5.00	2.50	1.50
1969 Topps	465	4.00	2.00	1.25
1970 O-Pee-Chee	180	1.75	.90	.50
1970 Topps	180	3.00	1.50	.90
1971 O-Pee-Chee	520	2.50	1.25	.70
1971 Topps	520	4.00	2.00	1.25
1972 O-Pee-Chee	264	1.50	.70	.45
1972 Topps	264	2.00	1.00	.60
1973 O-Pee-Chee	258	1.25	.60	.40
1973 Topps	258	2.00	1.00	.60
1974 O-Pee-Chee	451	1.25	.60	.40
1974 Topps	451	1.00	.50	.30
1975 O-Pee-Chee	47	1.00	.50	.30
1975 Topps	47	1.25	.60	.40
1975 Topps Mini	47	2.50	1.25	.70
1976 O-Pee-Chee	416	1.00	.50	.30
1976 Topps	416	1.00	.50	.30
1977 Topps	128	1.25	.60	.40
1978 Topps	375	.90	.45	.25
1979 O-Pee-Chee	129	.25	.13	.08
1979 Topps	255	.80	.40	.25
1980 O-Pee-Chee	348	.50	.25	.15
1980 Topps	690	.60	.30	.20

Set	Card #	MT	NM	EX
1981 Donruss	107	.20	.15	.08
1981 Fleer	81	.20	.15	.08
1981 O-Pee-Chee	96	.40	.30	.15
1981 Topps	550	.50	.40	.20
1982 Donruss	409	.20	.15	.08
1982 Donruss	558	.15	.11	.06
1982 Fleer	40	.20	.15	.08
1982 O-Pee-Chee	75	.20	.15	.08
1982 Topps	75	.30	.25	.12
1982 Topps	486	.20	.15	.08
1983 Donruss	570	.20	.15	.08
1983 Fleer	95	.20	.15	.08
1983 O-Pee-Chee	144	.12	.09	.05
1983 O-Pee-Chee	196	.20	.15	.08
1983 Topps	735	.25	.20	.10
1983 Topps	736	.12	.09	.05
1984 Donruss	301	.35	.25	.14
1984 Fleer	522	.25	.20	.10
1984 O-Pee-Chee	284	.40	.30	.15
1984 Topps	415	.25	.20	.10
1984 Topps	715	.25	.20	.10
1985 Donruss	423	.25	.20	.10
1985 Fleer	304	.20	.15	.08
1985 O-Pee-Chee	179	.15	.11	.06
1985 Topps	179	.20	.15	.08
1986 Fleer	422	.20	.15	.08
1986 Fleer Update	57	.20	.15	.08
1986 Topps	240	.20	.15	.08
1987 Fleer	102	.10	.08	.04
1987 O-Pee-Chee	236	.12	.09	.05
1987 Topps	236	.15	.11	.06
1988 Donruss	17	.08	.06	.03
1988 Donruss	401	.15	.11	.06
1988 Fleer	211	.15	.11	.06
1988 Leaf	17	.08	.06	.03
1988 Leaf	230	.08	.06	.03
1988 Score	240	.12	.09	.05
1988 Topps	611	.12	.09	.05
1989 Fleer	255	.12	.09	.05
1989 Score	477	.10	.08	.04
1989 Topps	359	.10	.08	.04
1989 Upper Deck	230	.12	.09	.05

Howard Johnson

Set	Card #	MT	NM	EX
1983 Donruss	328 (R)	1.25	.90	.50
1983 Fleer	332 (R)	1.00	.75	.40
1985 Donruss	247	.50	.40	.20
1985 Fleer	12	.40	.30	.15
1985 Fleer Update	62	.75	.60	.30
1985 O-Pee-Chee	192	3.00	2.25	1.25
1985 Topps	192	.25	.20	.10
1985 Topps Traded	64T	.60	.45	.25
1986 Donruss	312	.12	.09	.05
1986 Fleer	85	.20	.15	.08
1986 O-Pee-Chee	304	.40	.30	.15
1986 Topps	751	.15	.11	.06
1987 Donruss	646	.10	.08	.04
1987 Fleer	13	.10	.08	.04
1987 O-Pee-Chee	267	.08	.06	.03
1987 Topps	267	.10	.08	.04
1988 Donruss	569	.08	.06	.03
1988 Fleer	138	.10	.08	.04
1988 Leaf	238	.08	.06	.03
1988 O-Pee-Chee	85	.08	.06	.03
1988 Score	69	.08	.06	.03
1988 Sportflics	138	.15	.11	.06
1988 Sportflics Gamewinners	17	.25	.20	.10
1988 Topps	85	.08	.06	.03
1988 Topps All-Star Glossy Set of 60	52	.20	.15	.08
1988 Topps Big Baseball	129	.08	.06	.03
1989 Donruss	235	.08	.06	.03
1989 Fleer	39	.08	.06	.03
1989 O-Pee-Chee	383	.07	.05	.03
1989 Score	136	.08	.06	.03
1989 Topps	383	.07	.05	.03
1989 Topps All-Star Glossy Set of 60	22	.20	.15	.08

1989 Topps Big Baseball	208	.15	.11	.06
1989 Upper Deck	582	.10	.08	.04
1990 Bowman	133	.10	.08	.04
1990 Donruss	18	.06	.05	.02
1990 Donruss	99	.15	.11	.06
1990 Donruss	654	.08	.06	.03
1990 Donruss MVP	2	.10	.08	.04
1990 Fleer	208	.08	.06	.03
1990 Fleer	639	.10	.08	.04
1990 Fleer All-Stars	4	.30	.25	.12
1990 Leaf	272	.50	.40	.20
1990 O-Pee-Chee	399	.08	.06	.03
1990 O-Pee-Chee	680	.15	.11	.06
1990 Score	124	.07	.05	.03
1990 Sportflics	109	.20	.15	.08
1990 Topps	399	.08	.06	.03
1990 Topps	680	.08	.06	.03
1990 Topps All-Star Glossy Set of 22	4	.15	.11	.06
1990 Topps All-Star Glossy Set of 60	43	.20	.15	.08
1990 Topps Big Baseball	216	.10	.08	.04
1990 Upper Deck	263	.08	.06	.03
1991 Bowman	464	.10	.08	.04
1991 Donruss	454	.06	.05	.02
1991 Fleer	152	.08	.06	.03
1991 Fleer Ultra	222	.10	.07	.04
1991 Leaf	34	.25	.20	.10
1991 Score	185	.07	.05	.03
1991 Studio	207	.20	.15	.08
1991 Topps	470	.07	.05	.03
1991 Topps Stadium Club	86	.30	.25	.12
1991 Topps Stadium Club Members Only	(15)	.25	.20	.10
1991 Upper Deck	124	.12	.09	.05
1992 Bowman	10	.20	.15	.08
1992 Donruss	341	.06	.05	.02
1992 Donruss Elite	15	25.00	18.00	10.00
1992 Donruss Triple Play	236	.12	.09	.05
1992 Fleer	509	.07	.05	.03
1992 Fleer	689	.06	.05	.02
1992 Fleer Team Leaders	2	.75	.60	.30
1992 Fleer Ultra	235	.15	.11	.06
1992 Leaf	132	.05	.04	.02
1992 O-Pee-Chee	590	.10	.08	.04
1992 O-Pee-Chee Premier	42	.15	.11	.06
1992 Pinnacle	15	.15	.11	.06
1992 Post Cereal	28	.30	.25	.12
1992 Score	550	.08	.06	.03
1992 Score	776	.08	.06	.03
1992 Studio	67	.15	.11	.06
1992 Topps	388	.05	.04	.02
1992 Topps	590	.10	.08	.04
1992 Topps Gold	388	.25	.20	.10
1992 Topps Gold	590	.35	.25	.14
1992 Topps Kids	12	.10	.08	.04
1992 Topps Stadium Club	430	.10	.08	.04
1992 Topps Stadium Club	610	.10	.07	.04
1992 Topps Stadium Club East Coast National	610	4.00	3.00	1.50
1992 Topps Stadium Club Special Edition	92	.15	.11	.06
1992 Upper Deck	37	.05	.04	.02
1992 Upper Deck	256	.06	.05	.02
1992 Upper Deck	720	.08	.06	.03
1992 Upper Deck Home Run Heroes	3	.40	.30	.15
1992 Upper Deck MVP Holograms	26	.25	.20	.10
1993 Bowman	130	.10	.08	.04
1993 DiamondMarks	(43)	.50	.40	.20
1993 Donruss	434	.05	.04	.02
1993 Donruss Triple Play	86	.07	.05	.03
1993 Fleer	89	.08	.06	.03
1993 Fleer Flair	93	.25	.15	.08
1993 Fleer Ultra	76	.10	.08	.04
1993 Leaf	39	.10	.08	.04
1993 O-Pee-Chee	166	.15	.11	.06
1993 Pinnacle	389	.06	.05	.02
1993 Pinnacle Home Run Club	44	.35	.25	.14
1993 Pinnacle Slugfest	18	.50	.40	.20
1993 Score	62	.08	.06	.03
1993 Score Select	101	.10	.08	.04
1993 Studio	128	.08	.06	.03
1993 Topps	106	.06	.05	.02
1993 Topps Finest	143	1.00	.70	.40
1993 Topps Finest Refractors	143	20.00	15.00	8.00
1993 Topps Gold	106	.10	.08	.04
1993 Topps Stadium Club	404	.10	.08	.04
1993 Topps Stadium Club First Day Production	404	4.00	3.00	1.50
1993 Upper Deck	484	.08	.06	.03
1993 Upper Deck	676	.08	.06	.03
1993 Upper Deck Fun Packs	127	.15	.11	.06
1993 Upper Deck Iooss Collection	14	.50	.40	.20
1993 Upper Deck Iooss Collection Super	14	3.00	2.25	1.25
1993 Upper Deck SP	151	.15	.11	.06
1993 Upper Deck Then And Now	12	1.50	1.25	.60
1994 Bowman	142	.10	.08	.04
1994 Donruss	487	.10	.08	.04
1994 Donruss Triple Play	227	.05	.04	.02
1994 Fleer	568	.05	.04	.02
1994 Fleer Extra Bases	248	.10	.08	.04
1994 Fleer Ultra	484	.10	.08	.04
1994 Fleer Update	125	.10	.08	.04
1994 Leaf	432	.10	.08	.04
1994 O-Pee-Chee	31	.05	.04	.02
1994 Pacific Crown	407	.05	.04	.02
1994 Pinnacle	518	.10	.08	.04
1994 Pinnacle Artist's Proof	518	3.00	2.25	1.25
1994 Pinnacle Museum Collection	518	1.50	1.25	.60
1994 Score	414	.04	.03	.02
1994 Score Rookie & Traded Gold Rush	63	.25	.20	.10
1994 Score Rookie and Traded	63	.05	.04	.02
1994 Score Select	315	.10	.08	.04
1994 Topps	302	.04	.03	.02
1994 Topps Finest	374	.50	.40	.20
1994 Topps Finest Refractors	374	3.50	2.75	1.50
1994 Topps Gold	302	.15	.11	.06
1994 Topps Stadium Club	640	.10	.08	.04
1994 Topps Stadium Club First Day Production	640	4.00	3.00	1.50
1994 Topps Traded	82	.05	.04	.02
1994 Upper Deck	462	.10	.08	.04
1994 Upper Deck Collector's Choice	530	.05	.04	.02
1994 Upper Deck Electric Diamond	462	.25	.20	.10
1994 Upper Deck Fun Packs	86	.05	.04	.02

* * *

"Sports fans - there are surely millions. But sports collectors - several thousand perhaps - maybe as many as 25,000. Quite likely, however, a good share of that number are still as yet unknown to one another," wrote Editor John Stommen in his initial introduction in the first-ever issue of Sports Collectors Digest, dated Oct. 12, 1973.

* * *

Randy Johnson

Set	Card #	MT	NM	EX
1989 Donruss	42 (R)	.75	.60	.30
1989 Fleer	381 (R)	.90	.70	.35
1989 O-Pee-Chee	186	.08	.06	.03
1989 Score	645 (R)	.75	.50	.25
1989 Score Traded	77T	.60	.45	.25
1989 Sportflics	224	1.50	1.25	.60
1989 Topps	647 (R)	.75	.60	.30
1989 Topps Big Baseball	287	.15	.11	.06
1989 Topps Traded	57T	.75	.60	.30
1989 Upper Deck	25 (R)	2.50	2.00	1.00
1990 Bowman	468	.25	.20	.10
1990 Donruss	379	.12	.09	.05
1990 Fleer	518	.15	.11	.06
1990 Leaf	483	3.50	2.75	1.50
1990 O-Pee-Chee	431	.10	.08	.04
1990 Score	415	.12	.09	.05
1990 Sportflics	64	.20	.15	.08
1990 Topps	431	.10	.08	.04
1990 Upper Deck	563	.25	.20	.10
1991 Bowman	253	.12	.09	.05
1991 Donruss	134	.08	.06	.03
1991 Fleer	455	.10	.08	.04
1991 Fleer Ultra	339	.08	.06	.03
1991 Leaf	319	.15	.11	.06
1991 Score	290	.06	.05	.02
1991 Score	700	.10	.08	.04
1991 Topps	225	.06	.05	.02
1991 Topps Desert Shield	225	2.00	1.50	.80
1991 Upper Deck	376	.10	.08	.04
1992 Bowman	178	.60	.45	.25
1992 Donruss	207	.08	.06	.03
1992 Donruss Diamond Kings	22	.75	.60	.30
1992 Donruss Triple Play	71	.06	.05	.02
1992 Fleer	283	.08	.06	.03
1992 Fleer Smoke 'N Heat	11	1.00	.75	.40
1992 Fleer Ultra	125	.10	.08	.04
1992 Leaf	302	.10	.08	.04
1992 O-Pee-Chee	525	.06	.05	.02
1992 O-Pee-Chee Premier	173	.10	.08	.04
1992 Pinnacle	379	.12	.09	.05
1992 Pinnacle	595	.15	.11	.06
1992 Score	584	.06	.05	.02
1992 Topps	525	.06	.05	.02
1992 Topps Gold	525	.35	.25	.14
1992 Topps Kids	126	.10	.08	.04
1992 Topps Stadium Club	720	.20	.15	.08
1992 Upper Deck	164	.08	.06	.03
1992 Upper Deck MVP Holograms	27	.30	.25	.12
1993 Bowman	431	.20	.15	.08
1993 Donruss	581	.05	.04	.02
1993 Donruss Triple Play	167	.07	.05	.03
1993 Fleer	676	.05	.04	.02
1993 Fleer Flair	272	.35	.25	.14
1993 Fleer Ultra	269	.15	.11	.06
1993 Fleer Ultra Strikeout Kings	3	1.50	1.25	.60
1993 Leaf	380	.15	.11	.06
1993 O-Pee-Chee	140	.30	.25	.12
1993 Pinnacle	41	.06	.05	.02
1993 Score	384	.06	.05	.02
1993 Score Select	118	.08	.06	.03
1993 Score Select Stat Leaders	73	.10	.08	.04
1993 Topps	460	.03	.02	.01
1993 Topps Finest	154	2.00	1.50	.80
1993 Topps Finest Refractors	154	27.50	21.00	11.00
1993 Topps Gold	460	.10	.08	.04
1993 Topps Stadium Club	501	.15	.11	.06
1993 Topps Stadium Club First Day Production	501	5.00	3.75	2.00
1993 Upper Deck	336	.06	.05	.02
1993 Upper Deck	824	.08	.06	.03
1993 Upper Deck Fun Packs	115	.15	.11	.06
1993 Upper Deck SP	132	.15	.11	.06
1994 Bowman	285	.10	.08	.04
1994 Donruss	352	.05	.04	.02
1994 Donruss Special Edition - Gold	352	.30	.25	.12
1994 Donruss Triple Play Medalists	13	1.25	.90	.50
1994 Donruss Triple Play	128	.05	.04	.02
1994 Fleer	290	.08	.06	.03
1994 Fleer All-Stars	12	.35	.25	.14
1994 Fleer Extra Bases	168	.10	.08	.04
1994 Fleer Extra Bases Pitcher's Duel	2M	.40	.30	.15
1994 Fleer Flair	337	.20	.15	.08
1994 Fleer Smoke N' Heat	5	5.00	3.75	2.00
1994 Fleer Ultra	418	.10	.08	.04
1994 Fleer Ultra League Leaders	5	.50	.40	.20
1994 Fleer Ultra Strikeout Kings	1	1.00	.75	.40
1994 Leaf	164	.10	.08	.04
1994 Leaf Limited	67	1.25	.90	.50
1994 O-Pee-Chee	81	.15	.11	.06
1994 Pacific Crown	574	.10	.08	.04
1994 Pacific Crown Jewels of the Crown	7	2.50	2.00	1.00
1994 Pinnacle	278	.10	.08	.04
1994 Pinnacle Artist's Proof	278	3.00	2.25	1.25
1994 Pinnacle Museum Collection	278	2.00	1.50	.80
1994 Pinnacle The Naturals Box Set	10	.25	.20	.10
1994 Pinnacle Tribute	9	2.00	1.50	.80
1994 Score	33	.04	.03	.02
1994 Score Gold Stars	43	3.00	2.25	1.25
1994 Score Select	19	.10	.08	.04
1994 Score Select Crown Contenders	4	5.00	3.75	2.00
1994 Score Select Skills	1	5.00	3.75	2.00
1994 Sportflics 2000	30	.10	.08	.04
1994 Studio	102	.10	.08	.04
1994 Topps	290	.08	.06	.03
1994 Topps Black Gold	10	.25	.20	.10
1994 Topps Finest	213	.75	.60	.30
1994 Topps Finest Refractors	213	4.00	3.00	1.50
1994 Topps Finest Superstars	213	2.50	2.00	1.00
1994 Topps Gold	290	.20	.15	.08
1994 Topps Stadium Club	438	.10	.08	.04
1994 Topps Stadium Club Dugout Dirt	11	.35	.25	.14
1994 Topps Stadium Club First Day Production	438	2.50	2.00	1.00
1994 Topps Stadium Club Members Only Baseball	22	.25	.20	.10
1994 Upper Deck	31	.10	.08	.04
1994 Upper Deck	330	.10	.08	.04
1994 Upper Deck All-Stars Green Foil	20	.25	.20	.10

Set	Card #	MT	NM	EX
1994 Upper Deck All-Stars Gold Foil	20	1.00	.70	.40
1994 Upper Deck Collector's Choice	307	.10	.08	.04
1994 Upper Deck Collector's Choice	357	.05	.04	.02
1994 Upper Deck Electric Diamond	31	.25	.20	.10
1994 Upper Deck Electric Diamond	330	.25	.20	.10
1994 Upper Deck Fun Packs	51	.05	.04	.02
1994 Upper Deck Fun Packs	175	.05	.04	.02
1994 Upper Deck Fun Packs	197	.05	.04	.02
1994 Upper Deck SP	106	.15	.11	.06
1994 Upper Deck SP Baseball Die-Cut	106	.25	.20	.10

Jay Johnstone

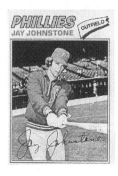

Set	Card #	NM	EX	VG
1967 Topps	213 (R)	2.00	1.00	.60
1968 Topps	389	1.50	.70	.45
1969 O-Pee-Chee	59	2.25	1.25	.70
1969 Topps	59	1.00	.50	.30
1970 O-Pee-Chee	485	2.25	1.25	.70
1970 Topps	485	1.50	.70	.45
1971 O-Pee-Chee	292	1.50	.70	.45
1971 Topps	292	1.00	.50	.30
1972 O-Pee-Chee	233	.75	.40	.25
1972 Topps	233	.75	.40	.25
1975 O-Pee-Chee	242	.55	.30	.15
1975 Topps	242	.30	.15	.09
1975 Topps Mini	242	.60	.30	.20
1976 O-Pee-Chee	114	.35	.20	.11
1976 Topps	114	.25	.13	.08
1977 O-Pee-Chee	226	.30	.15	.09
1977 Topps	415	.20	.10	.06
1978 Topps	675	.20	.10	.06
1979 O-Pee-Chee	287	.25	.13	.08
1979 Topps	558	.20	.10	.06
1980 O-Pee-Chee	15	.15	.08	.05
1980 Topps	31	.20	.10	.06

Set	Card #	MT	NM	EX
1981 Donruss	300	.08	.06	.03
1981 Fleer	128	.08	.06	.03
1981 O-Pee-Chee	372	.12	.09	.05
1981 Topps	372	.10	.08	.04
1982 Donruss	262	.08	.06	.03
1982 Fleer	10	.08	.06	.03
1982 Topps	774	.10	.08	.04
1982 Topps Traded	52T	.20	.15	.08
1983 Donruss	561	.08	.06	.03
1983 Fleer	499	.08	.06	.03
1983 O-Pee-Chee	152	.12	.09	.05
1983 Topps	152	.10	.08	.04
1984 Donruss	540	.12	.09	.05
1984 Fleer	495	.10	.08	.04
1984 Topps	249	.10	.08	.04
1986 Topps	496	.07	.05	.03

Wally Joyner

Set	Card #	MT	NM	EX
1986 Fleer Update	59	1.25	.90	.50
1986 Sportflics Rookies	7	.80	.60	.30
1986 Topps Traded	51T	.75	.60	.30
1987 Donruss	1	.25	.20	.10
1987 Donruss	135 (R)	.60	.45	.25
1987 Donruss Diamond Kings Supers	1	.40	.30	.15
1987 Fleer	86 (R)	1.50	1.25	.60
1987 Fleer	628	.75	.60	.30
1987 Fleer All Stars	23	.30	.25	.12
1987 Leaf	1	.80	.60	.30
1987 Leaf	252	1.00	.70	.40
1987 O-Pee-Chee	80	.40	.30	.15
1987 Sportflics	26	.40	.30	.15
1987 Sportflics	75	.50	.40	.20
1987 Topps	80 (R)	.40	.30	.15
1987 Topps All-Star Glossy Set of 22	13	.30	.25	.12
1987 Topps All-Star Glossy Set of 60	39	.60	.45	.25
1987 Topps Glossy Rookies	7	.90	.70	.35
1988 Donruss	110	.12	.09	.05
1988 Donruss MVP	13	.25	.20	.10
1988 Fleer	493	.10	.08	.04
1988 Fleer	622	.35	.25	.14
1988 Leaf	50	.60	.45	.25
1988 O-Pee-Chee	168	.40	.30	.15
1988 Score	7	.10	.08	.04
1988 Sportflics	75	.50	.40	.20
1988 Topps	381	.12	.09	.05
1988 Topps	420	.10	.08	.04
1988 Topps All-Star Glossy Set of 60	48	.35	.25	.14
1988 Topps Big Baseball	52	.40	.30	.15
1989 Bowman	47	.10	.08	.04
1989 Donruss	52	.10	.08	.04
1989 Donruss MVP	21	.15	.11	.06
1989 Fleer	481	.10	.08	.04
1989 O-Pee-Chee	270	.10	.08	.04
1989 Score	65	.08	.05	.02
1989 Sportflics	2	.40	.30	.15
1989 Topps	270	.06	.05	.02
1989 Topps Big Baseball	201	.15	.11	.06
1989 Upper Deck	573	.10	.08	.04
1989 Upper Deck	668	.08	.06	.03
1990 Bowman	299	.08	.06	.03
1990 Donruss	94	.15	.11	.06
1990 Fleer	136	.10	.08	.04
1990 Leaf	24	.40	.30	.15
1990 O-Pee-Chee	525	.20	.15	.08
1990 Score	120	.15	.11	.06
1990 Sportflics	49	.30	.25	.12
1990 Topps	525	.10	.07	.04

Set	#	MT	NM	EX
1990 Topps Big Baseball	168	.08	.06	.03
1990 Upper Deck	693	.05	.04	.02
1991 Bowman	195	.10	.08	.04
1991 Donruss	677	.06	.05	.02
1991 Fleer	317	.10	.08	.04
1991 Fleer Ultra	48	.15	.11	.06
1991 Leaf	31	.20	.15	.08
1991 Score	470	.12	.09	.05
1991 Score	873	.08	.06	.03
1991 Studio	26	.30	.25	.12
1991 Topps	195	.10	.08	.04
1991 Topps Stadium Club	2	.30	.25	.12
1991 Upper Deck	575	.10	.08	.04
1992 Bowman	435	.40	.30	.15
1992 Donruss	333	.15	.11	.06
1992 Donruss Triple Play Gallery of Stars	2	1.50	1.25	.60
1992 Fleer	62	.10	.08	.04
1992 Fleer Ultra	373	.15	.11	.06
1992 Fleer Update	27	.30	.25	.12
1992 Leaf	438	.15	.11	.06
1992 O-Pee-Chee	629	.10	.08	.04
1992 O-Pee-Chee Premier	61	.15	.11	.06
1992 Pinnacle	284	.15	.11	.06
1992 Pinnacle	537	.12	.09	.05
1992 Post Cereal	4	.30	.25	.12
1992 Score	535	.08	.06	.03
1992 Score Rookie & Traded	13	.08	.06	.03
1992 Studio	185	.20	.15	.08
1992 Topps	629	.10	.08	.04
1992 Topps Gold	629	.35	.25	.14
1992 Topps Kids	95	.10	.08	.04
1992 Topps Stadium Club	122	.20	.15	.08
1992 Topps Stadium Club	710	.20	.15	.08
1992 Topps Stadium Club National Convention	710	15.00	11.00	6.00
1992 Topps Traded	59	.08	.06	.03
1992 Topps Traded Gold	59	.25	.20	.10
1992 Topps Triple Header Photo Balls	(1)	6.00	4.50	2.50
1992 Upper Deck	343	.10	.08	.04
1992 Upper Deck	744	.08	.06	.03
1993 Bowman	645	.10	.08	.04
1993 DiamondMarks	(88)	.25	.20	.10
1993 Donruss	129	.08	.06	.03
1993 Donruss Diamond Kings	8	.75	.60	.30
1993 Donruss Triple Play Action Baseball	25	.15	.11	.06
1993 Donruss Triple Play	153	.12	.09	.05
1993 Fleer	239	.08	.06	.03
1993 Fleer Flair	218	.25	.15	.08
1993 Fleer Ultra	210	.10	.08	.04
1993 Leaf	376	.10	.08	.04
1993 O-Pee-Chee	148	.15	.11	.06
1993 Pinnacle	51	.06	.05	.02
1993 Score	43	.10	.08	.04
1993 Score Select	34	.12	.09	.05
1993 Studio	164	.08	.06	.03
1993 Topps	375	.08	.06	.03
1993 Topps Finest	59	1.00	.70	.40
1993 Topps Finest Refractors	59	20.00	15.00	8.00
1993 Topps Gold	375	.15	.11	.06
1993 Topps Stadium Club	537	.10	.08	.04
1993 Topps Stadium Club First Day Production	537	10.00	7.50	4.00
1993 Upper Deck	54	.20	.15	.08
1993 Upper Deck	252	.08	.06	.03
1993 Upper Deck Fun Packs	184	.15	.11	.06
1993 Upper Deck SP	231	.15	.11	.06
1994 Bowman	443	.10	.08	.04
1994 Donruss	345	.05	.04	.02
1994 Donruss MVP's	21	.75	.60	.30
1994 Donruss Special Edition - Gold	345	.30	.25	.12
1994 Donruss Triple Play	236	.05	.04	.02
1994 Fleer	162	.05	.04	.02
1994 Fleer Extra Bases	93	.10	.08	.04
1994 Fleer Flair	60	.20	.15	.08
1994 Fleer Ultra	365	.10	.08	.04
1994 Leaf	141	.10	.08	.04
1994 Leaf Limited	40	1.00	.70	.40
1994 O-Pee-Chee	91	.05	.04	.02
1994 Pacific Crown	290	.05	.04	.02
1994 Pinnacle	291	.10	.08	.04
1994 Pinnacle Artist's Proof	291	3.00	2.25	1.25
1994 Pinnacle Museum Collection	291	1.50	1.25	.60
1994 Score	67	.04	.03	.02
1994 Score Select	35	.10	.08	.04
1994 Sportflics 2000	23	.10	.08	.04
1994 Studio	186	.10	.08	.04
1994 Topps	275	.04	.03	.02
1994 Topps Finest	176	.50	.40	.20
1994 Topps Finest Refractors	176	3.50	2.75	1.50
1994 Topps Gold	275	.15	.11	.06
1994 Topps Stadium Club	431	.10	.08	.04
1994 Topps Stadium Club First Day Production	431	6.00	4.50	2.50
1994 Upper Deck	169	.10	.08	.04
1994 Upper Deck	287	.10	.08	.04
1994 Upper Deck Collector's Choice	155	.05	.04	.02
◄1994 Upper Deck Electric Diamond	169	.25	.20	.10
1994 Upper Deck Electric Diamond	287	.25	.20	.10
1994 Upper Deck Fun Packs	48	.05	.04	.02
1994 Upper Deck SP	174	.15	.11	.06
1994 Upper Deck SP Baseball Die-Cut	174	.25	.20	.10

Dave Justice

Set	Card #	MT	NM	EX
1990 Donruss	704 (R)	1.50	1.25	.60
1990 Fleer	586 (R)	1.25	.90	.50
1990 Leaf	297 (R)	15.00	11.00	6.00
1990 Score	650 (R)	1.50	1.25	.60
1990 Topps Traded	48T	1.50	1.25	.60
1990 Upper Deck	711 (R)	3.00	2.25	1.25
1991 Bowman	574	.30	.25	.12
1991 Donruss	402	.25	.20	.10
1991 Donruss	548	.40	.30	.15
1991 Donruss	683	.25	.20	.10
1991 Fleer	693	.40	.30	.15
1991 Fleer Ultra	7	.75	.60	.30
1991 Fleer Ultra	394	.30	.25	.12
1991 Leaf	77	1.00	.75	.40
1991 O-Pee-Chee Premier	70	.50	.40	.20
1991 Post Cereal	1	.50	.40	.20
1991 Score	55	.30	.25	.12

1991 Score	861	.15	.10	.05
1991 Score	880	.25	.20	.10
1991 Score Hot Rookies	1	3.00	2.25	1.25
1991 Studio	146	1.00	.75	.40
1991 Topps	329	.30	.25	.12
1991 Topps Glossy Rookies	15	.75	.60	.30
1991 Topps Stadium Club	26	4.00	3.00	1.50
1991 Topps Stadium Club Charter Members	(16)	.60	.45	.25
1991 Upper Deck	363	.75	.60	.30
1992 Bowman	312	3.00	2.25	1.25
1992 Donruss	327	.35	.25	.14
1992 Donruss Diamond Kings	6	3.00	2.00	1.00
1992 Donruss Triple Play Gallery of Stars	9	3.00	2.25	1.25
1992 Donruss Triple Play	217	.30	.25	.14
1992 Fleer	360	.30	.25	.12
1992 Fleer	713	.20	.15	.08
1992 Fleer Ultra	164	.75	.60	.30
1992 Leaf	404	.60	.40	.20
1992 O-Pee-Chee	80	.30	.25	.12
1992 O-Pee-Chee Premier	117	.25	.20	.10
1992 Pinnacle	100	.75	.60	.30
1992 Pinnacle	588	.30	.25	.12
1992 Pinnacle	604	.30	.25	.12
1992 Pinnacle	620	.30	.25	.12
1992 Pinnacle Slugfest	5	2.50	2.00	1.00
1992 Pinnacle Team Pinnacle	10	20.00	15.00	8.00
1992 Pinnacle Team 2000	9	1.50	1.25	.60
1992 Post Cereal	29	.35	.25	.14
1992 Score	4	.30	.25	.12
1992 Score Impact Players	44	.50	.40	.20
1992 Studio	5	.30	.25	.12
1992 Topps	80	.30	.25	.12
1992 Topps Gold	80	1.25	.90	.50
1992 Topps Kids	31	.15	.11	.06
1992 Topps Stadium Club	182	.75	.60	.30
1992 Topps Stadium Club	592	.50	.40	.20
1992 Topps Stadium Club Special Edition	97	.40	.30	.15
1992 Upper Deck	29	.08	.06	.03
1992 Upper Deck	546	.30	.25	.12
1993 Bowman	578	.40	.30	.15
1993 DiamondMarks	(4)	1.00	.70	.40
1993 DiamondMarks Inserts	(4)	15.00	11.00	6.00
1993 Donruss	580	.30	.25	.12
1993 Donruss Elite Dominators	5	100.00	75.00	40.00
1993 Donruss Long Ball Leaders	5	4.00	3.00	1.50
1993 Donruss Masters of the Game	12	2.50	2.00	1.00
1993 Donruss Spirit of the Game	2	2.00	1.50	.80
1993 Donruss Triple Play Action Baseball	29	.15	.11	.06
1993 Donruss Triple Play	249	.12	.09	.05
1993 Fleer	367	.25	.15	.10
1993 Fleer Flair	5	1.50	1.25	.60
1993 Fleer Ultra	306	.50	.40	.20
1993 Leaf	50	.40	.30	.15
1993 Leaf Fasttrack	18	6.00	4.50	2.50
1993 Leaf Gold All-Stars	8	3.00	2.25	1.25
1993 Leaf Update Gold All-Stars	9	2.00	1.50	.80
1993 O-Pee-Chee	180	1.00	.75	.40
1993 Pinnacle	344	.60	.45	.25
1993 Pinnacle Home Run Club	31	.60	.45	.25
1993 Pinnacle Slugfest	15	2.50	2.00	1.00
1993 Score	107	.25	.20	.10
1993 Score Select	39	.50	.40	.20
1993 Studio	173	.50	.40	.20
1993 Topps	170	.25	.20	.10
1993 Topps Finest	1	6.00	4.50	2.50
1993 Topps Finest Refractors	1	80.00	60.00	32.00
1993 Topps Gold	170	.50	.40	.20
1993 Topps Stadium Club	660	.50	.40	.20
1993 Topps Stadium Club First Day Production	660	40.00	30.00	16.00
1993 Upper Deck	366	.25	.20	.10
1993 Upper Deck	460	.25	.20	.10
1993 Upper Deck Fun Packs	64	.20	.15	.08
1993 Upper Deck Home Run Heroes	17	1.50	1.25	.60
1993 Upper Deck SP	13	1.50	1.25	.60
1993 Upper Deck SP Platinum Power	11	11.00	8.25	4.50
1993 Upper Deck 5th Anniversary	7	2.00	1.50	.80
1993 Upper Deck 5th Anniversary Super	7	4.00	3.00	1.50
1994 Bowman	133	.40	.30	.15
1994 Bowman's Best	63	1.50	1.25	.60
1994 Bowman's Best Refractors	63	12.00	9.00	4.75
1994 Donruss	25	.40	.30	.15
1994 Donruss Long Ball Leaders	6	4.00	3.00	1.50
1994 Donruss MVP's	1	1.00	.70	.40
1994 Donruss Special Edition - Gold	25	.60	.45	.25
1994 Donruss Spirit of the Game	8	4.00	3.00	1.50
1994 Donruss Spirit of the Game Super	8	10.00	7.50	4.00
1994 Donruss Triple Play Bomb Squad	5	2.50	2.00	1.00
1994 Donruss Triple Play	45	.25	.20	.10
1994 Fleer	361	.25	.20	.10
1994 Fleer	706	.05	.04	.02
1994 Fleer All-Stars	42	.60	.45	.25
1994 Fleer Extra Bases	202	.50	.40	.20
1994 Fleer Extra Bases Game Breakers	15	.60	.45	.25
1994 Fleer Flair	126	.75	.60	.30
1994 Fleer Flair Outfield Power	7	2.50	2.00	1.00
1994 Fleer Lumber Co.	6	1.00	.75	.40
1994 Fleer Team Leaders	15	1.00	.75	.40
1994 Fleer Ultra	443	.30	.25	.12
1994 Fleer Ultra All-Stars	18	1.00	.75	.40
1994 Fleer Ultra Home Run Kings	8	4.00	3.00	1.50
1994 Fleer Ultra RBI Kings	8	10.00	7.50	4.00
1994 Leaf	263	.40	.30	.15
1994 Leaf Gamers	5	5.00	3.75	2.00
1994 Leaf Gold Stars	3	15.00	11.00	6.00
1994 Leaf Limited	83	3.00	2.25	1.25
1994 Leaf Limited Gold	14	16.00	12.00	6.50
1994 Leaf MVP Contenders	8a	4.00	3.00	1.50
1994 Leaf MVP Contenders	8b	8.00	6.00	3.25
1994 Leaf Power Brokers	2	1.50	1.25	.60
1994 Leaf Slide Show	10	4.00	3.00	1.50
1994 O-Pee-Chee	233	.40	.30	.15
1994 O-Pee-Chee All-Star Redemption Cards	24	.85	.60	.35
1994 O-Pee-Chee Jumbo All-Stars	24	7.00	5.25	2.75
1994 O-Pee-Chee Jumbo All-Stars Factory Set	24	1.75	1.25	.70
1994 Pacific Crown	11	.25	.20	.10
1994 Pacific Crown Homerun Leaders	12	4.00	3.00	1.50
1994 Pinnacle	40	.40	.30	.15
1994 Pinnacle Artist's Proof	40	18.00	12.00	6.50
1994 Pinnacle Museum Collection	40	6.00	4.50	2.50
1994 Pinnacle Power Surge	1	.50	.40	.20

1994 Pinnacle Run Creators	32	5.00	3.75	2.00
1994 Pinnacle Team Pinnacle	8	15.00	11.00	6.00
1994 Pinnacle The Naturals Box Set	5	.50	.40	.20
1994 Pinnacle Tribute	5	3.00	2.25	1.25
1994 Post Cereal	6	.45	.35	.20
1994 Score	422	.30	.25	.12
1994 Score Gold Stars	24	8.00	6.00	3.25
1994 Score Select	236	.50	.40	.20
1994 Score The Cycle	19	12.00	9.00	4.75
1994 Sportflics 2000	6	.50	.40	.20
1994 Sportflics 2000	192	.35	.25	.14
1994 Studio	35	.40	.30	.15
1994 Topps	389	.30	.25	.12
1994 Topps	630	.25	.20	.10
1994 Topps Black Gold	36	1.25	.90	.50
1994 Topps Finest	233	2.00	1.50	.80
1994 Topps Finest Refractors	233	12.00	9.00	4.75
1994 Topps Finest Superstars	233	6.00	4.50	2.50
1994 Topps Gold	389	1.00	.70	.40
1994 Topps Gold	630	.75	.60	.30
1994 Topps Stadium Club	94	.50	.40	.20
1994 Topps Stadium Club	263	.35	.25	.14
1994 Topps Stadium Club	530	.30	.25	.12
1994 Topps Stadium Club Finest	7	3.00	2.25	1.25
1994 Topps Stadium Club First Day Production	94	20.00	15.00	8.00
1994 Topps Stadium Club First Day Production	263	15.00	11.00	6.00
1994 Topps Stadium Club First Day Production	530	12.00	9.00	4.75
1994 Topps Stadium Club Members Only Baseball	5	.45	.35	.20
1994 Upper Deck	267	.25	.20	.10
1994 Upper Deck	375	.35	.25	.14
1994 Upper Deck All-Stars Green Foil	33	.45	.35	.20
1994 Upper Deck All-Stars Gold Foil	33	2.00	1.50	.80
1994 Upper Deck Collector's Choice	156	.25	.20	.10
1994 Upper Deck Collector's Choice	325	.10	.08	.04
1994 Upper Deck Collector's Choice	332	.10	.08	.04
1994 Upper Deck Collector's Choice	636	.10	.08	.04
1994 Upper Deck Diamond Collection	7E	10.00	7.50	4.00
1994 Upper Deck Electric Diamond	267	.75	.60	.30
1994 Upper Deck Electric Diamond	375	1.00	.75	.40
1994 Upper Deck Fun Packs	23	.35	.25	.14
1994 Upper Deck Fun Packs	192	.20	.15	.08
1994 Upper Deck Mickey Mantle's Long Shots	11MM	3.00	2.25	1.25
1994 Upper Deck Next Generation	9	2.50	2.00	1.00
1994 Upper Deck SP	50	.60	.45	.25
1994 Upper Deck SP Baseball Die-Cut	50	1.00	.75	.40
1994 Upper Deck SP Holoview Blue	17	5.00	3.75	2.00
1994 Upper Deck SP Holoview Red	17	40.00	30.00	15.00

Jim Kaat

Set	Card #	NM	EX	VG
1960 Topps	136 (R)	35.00	17.50	10.50
1961 Topps	63	7.50	3.75	2.25
1962 Topps	21	6.00	3.00	1.75
1963 Fleer	22	18.00	9.00	5.50
1963 Post Cereal	10	4.00	2.00	1.25
1963 Topps	10	5.50	2.75	1.75
1963 Topps	165	5.00	2.50	1.50
1964 Topps	567	13.00	6.50	4.00
1965 O-Pee-Chee	62	3.00	1.50	.90
1965 Topps	62	5.00	2.50	1.50
1966 Topps	224	4.00	2.00	1.25
1966 Topps	445	8.00	4.00	2.50
1967 Topps	235	3.00	1.50	.90
1967 Topps	237	3.00	1.50	.90
1967 Topps	300	9.00	4.50	2.75
1968 O-Pee-Chee	67	2.25	1.25	.70
1968 Topps	67	3.00	1.50	.90
1968 Topps	450	6.00	3.00	1.75
1969 Topps	290	4.50	2.25	1.25
1970 O-Pee-Chee	75	1.50	.70	.45
1970 Topps	75	3.00	1.50	.90
1971 O-Pee-Chee	245	1.50	.70	.45
1971 Topps	245	2.50	1.25	.70
1972 Topps	709	9.00	4.50	2.75
1972 Topps	710	6.00	3.00	1.75
1973 O-Pee-Chee	530	3.50	1.75	1.00
1973 Topps	530	4.00	2.00	1.25
1974 O-Pee-Chee	440	1.00	.50	.30
1974 Topps	440	1.25	.60	.40
1975 O-Pee-Chee	243	1.00	.50	.30
1975 Topps	243	1.25	.60	.40
1975 Topps Mini	243	2.00	1.00	.60
1976 O-Pee-Chee	80	.75	.40	.25
1976 Topps	80	.90	.45	.25
1976 Topps Traded	80T	1.00	.50	.30
1977 Topps	638	.80	.40	.25
1978 Topps	715	.60	.30	.20
1979 Topps	136	.60	.30	.20
1980 Topps	250	.50	.25	.15

Set	Card #	MT	NM	EX
1981 Donruss	536	.15	.11	.06
1981 Fleer	536	.15	.11	.06
1981 Topps	563	.30	.25	.12
1982 Donruss	217	.15	.11	.06
1982 Fleer	117	.15	.11	.06
1982 Topps	367	.25	.20	.10
1983 Donruss	343	.15	.11	.06
1983 Fleer	11	.15	.11	.06
1983 O-Pee-Chee	211	.15	.11	.06
1983 O-Pee-Chee	383	.15	.11	.06
1983 Topps	672	.20	.15	.08
1983 Topps	673	.12	.09	.05

* * *

Four years ago: Barry Bonds' 1987 Fleer card (#604) was $12 in July 1991.

* * *

Al Kaline

Eric Karros

Set	Card #	NM	EX	VG
1954 Topps	201 (R)	650.00	325.00	180.00
1955 Bowman	23	110.00	55.00	32.50
1955 Topps	4	165.00	82.00	48.00
1956 Topps	20	90.00	45.00	27.00
1957 Topps	125	65.00	32.00	19.50
1958 Topps	70a	200.00	100.00	60.00
1958 Topps	70b	65.00	32.00	19.50
1958 Topps	304	17.50	8.75	5.25
1959 Home Run Derby	(9)	300.00	150.00	90.00
1959 Topps	34	12.00	6.00	3.50
1959 Topps	360	60.00	30.00	18.00
1959 Topps	463	12.00	6.00	3.50
1959 Topps	562	55.00	27.00	16.50
1960 Post Cereal	(4)	450.00	225.00	135.00
1960 Topps	50	35.00	17.50	10.50
1960 Topps	561	50.00	25.00	15.00
1961 Post Cereal	35a	30.00	15.00	9.00
1961 Post Cereal	35b	30.00	15.00	9.00
1961 Topps	429	40.00	20.00	12.00
1961 Topps	580	90.00	45.00	27.00
1962 Post Cereal	20	10.00	5.00	3.00
1962 Topps	51	8.00	4.00	2.50
1962 Topps	150	35.00	17.50	10.50
1962 Topps	470	20.00	10.00	6.00
1963 Post Cereal	51	10.00	5.00	3.00
1963 Topps	25	30.00	15.00	9.00
1964 Topps	8	11.00	5.50	3.25
1964 Topps	12	8.00	4.00	2.50
1964 Topps	250	32.50	16.00	9.75
1964 Topps	331	130.00	65.00	39.00
1965 O-Pee-Chee	130	30.00	15.00	9.00
1965 Topps	130	27.00	13.50	8.00
1966 Topps	410	22.00	11.00	6.50
1967 O-Pee-Chee	30	21.00	10.50	6.25
1967 Topps	30	15.00	7.50	4.50
1967 Topps	216	7.50	3.75	2.25
1967 Topps	239	12.00	6.00	3.50
1968 O-Pee-Chee	2	12.75	6.50	3.75
1968 Topps	2	8.00	4.00	2.50
1968 Topps	240	20.00	10.00	6.00
1969 Topps	410	18.00	9.00	5.50
1970 Topps	640	50.00	25.00	15.00
1971 O-Pee-Chee	180	25.00	12.50	7.50
1971 Topps	180	15.00	7.50	4.50
1972 Topps	600	20.00	10.00	6.00
1973 O-Pee-Chee	280	7.50	3.75	2.25
1973 Topps	280	8.00	4.00	2.50
1974 O-Pee-Chee	215	7.25	3.75	2.25
1974 Topps	215	8.00	4.00	2.50
1975 O-Pee-Chee	4	4.50	2.25	1.25
1975 Topps	4	2.00	1.00	.60
1975 Topps Mini	4	3.25	1.75	1.00

Set	Card #	MT	NM	EX
1986 Sportflics Decade Greats	51	.30	.25	.12
1988 Pacific Trading Cards Baseball Legends	104	.30	.25	.12

Set	Card #	MT	NM	EX
1991 Bowman	604 (R)	.30	.25	.12
1991 Fleer Ultra	380 (R)	.40	.30	.15
1991 Upper Deck	24 (R)	.50	.40	.20
1992 Bowman	288	.75	.60	.30
1992 Donruss	16 (R)	.25	.20	.10
1992 Fleer	462	.20	.15	.08
1992 Fleer Ultra	508	.40	.30	.15
1992 Fleer Ultra All-Rookies	1	2.50	2.00	1.00
1992 Leaf	293	.20	.15	.08
1992 O-Pee-Chee	194	.30	.25	.12
1992 O-Pee-Chee Premier	63	2.00	1.50	.80
1992 Pinnacle	256	.20	.15	.08
1992 Pinnacle Rookies	24	.40	.30	.15
1992 Pinnacle Team 2000	76	.25	.20	.10
1992 Score	827	.25	.20	.10
1992 Studio	45	.15	.11	.06
1992 Topps	194	.20	.15	.08
1992 Topps Gold	194	.45	.35	.20
1992 Topps Stadium Club	236	.40	.30	.15
1992 Upper Deck	534	.10	.08	.04
1992 Upper Deck Scouting Report	12	1.00	.75	.40
1993 Bowman	14	.15	.11	.06
1993 DiamondMarks	(32)	.50	.40	.20
1993 Donruss	430	.10	.07	.04
1993 Donruss Diamond Kings	30	1.00	.75	.40
1993 Donruss MVP's	8	.75	.60	.30
1993 Donruss Triple Play League Leaders	3	2.50	2.00	1.00
1993 Donruss Triple Play	4	.15	.11	.06
1993 Donruss Triple Play Action Baseball	7	.20	.15	.08
1993 Fleer	64	.08	.06	.03
1993 Fleer Flair	71	.35	.25	.14
1993 Fleer NL Team Leaders	4	2.00	1.50	.80
1993 Fleer Rookie Sensations I	6	1.50	1.25	.60
1993 Fleer Ultra	56	.15	.11	.06
1993 Fleer Ultra Award Winners	20	1.25	.90	.50
1993 Fleer Ultra Performers	4	1.25	.90	.50
1993 Leaf	234	.15	.11	.06
1993 O-Pee-Chee	208	.25	.20	.10
1993 O-Pee-Chee Premier Star Performers	8	.30	.25	.12
1993 Pinnacle	14	.15	.11	.06
1993 Pinnacle Team 2001	26	.75	.60	.30
1993 Post Cereal	6	.35	.25	.14
1993 Score	63	.08	.06	.03
1993 Score	486	.08	.06	.03
1993 Score Select	278	.15	.11	.06
1993 Score Select Chase Rookies	5	8.00	6.00	3.25
1993 Studio	92	.15	.11	.06
1993 Studio Heritage	10	1.00	.70	.40

Set	Card #	NM	EX	VG
1993 Topps	11	.10	.08	.04
1993 Topps Black Gold	9	.30	.25	.12
1993 Topps Finest	32	1.50	1.25	.60
1993 Topps Finest Refractors	32	20.00	15.00	8.00
1993 Topps Gold	11	.20	.15	.08
1993 Topps Stadium Club	292	.15	.11	.06
1993 Topps Stadium Club	528	.15	.11	.06
1993 Topps Stadium Club First Day Production	292	15.00	11.00	6.00
1993 Topps Stadium Club First Day Production	528	20.00	15.00	8.00
1993 Upper Deck	385	.10	.07	.04
1993 Upper Deck	490	.08	.06	.03
1993 Upper Deck Fun Packs	86	.20	.15	.08
1993 Upper Deck Fun Packs	89	.20	.15	.08
1993 Upper Deck Home Run Heroes	19	.75	.60	.30
1993 Upper Deck Iooss Collection	9	.75	.60	.30
1993 Upper Deck Iooss Collection Super	9	4.00	3.00	1.50
1993 Upper Deck On Deck	17	.75	.60	.30
1993 Upper Deck SP	94	.15	.11	.06
1993 Upper Deck 5th Anniversary	10	.75	.60	.30
1993 Upper Deck 5th Anniversary Super	10	3.50	2.75	1.50
1994 Bowman	14	.10	.08	.04
1994 Donruss	338	.10	.08	.04
1994 Donruss Special Edition - Gold	338	.25	.20	.10
1994 Donruss Triple Play	85	.05	.04	.02
1994 Fleer	514	.10	.07	.04
1994 Fleer	713	.50	.40	.20
1994 Fleer Extra Bases	289	.15	.11	.06
1994 Fleer Flair	397	.20	.15	.08
1994 Fleer Ultra	519	.10	.08	.04
1994 Leaf	171	.12	.09	.05
1994 Leaf Limited	118	1.00	.70	.40
1994 O-Pee-Chee	163	.05	.04	.02
1994 Pacific Crown	312	.12	.09	.05
1994 Pinnacle	87	.15	.11	.06
1994 Pinnacle Artist's Proof	87	4.00	3.00	1.50
1994 Pinnacle Museum Collection	87	2.00	1.50	.80
1994 Pinnacle Power Surge	18	.30	.25	.12
1994 Score	26	.10	.07	.04
1994 Score Select	44	.10	.08	.04
1994 Sportflics 2000	5	.10	.08	.04
1994 Studio	69	.10	.08	.04
1994 Topps	115	.10	.08	.04
1994 Topps Finest	356	.50	.40	.20
1994 Topps Finest Refractors	356	4.00	3.00	1.50
1994 Topps Gold	115	.25	.20	.10
1994 Topps Stadium Club	240	.15	.11	.06
1994 Topps Stadium Club First Day Production	240	2.50	2.00	1.00
1994 Upper Deck	208	.10	.08	.04
1994 Upper Deck Collector's Choice	158	.08	.06	.03
1994 Upper Deck Electric Diamond	208	.25	.20	.10
1994 Upper Deck Fun Packs	146	.05	.04	.02
1994 Upper Deck SP	78	.15	.11	.06
1994 Upper Deck SP Baseball Die-Cut	78	.25	.20	.10

George Kell

Set	Card #	NM	EX	VG
1948 Leaf	120 (R)	550.00	275.00	165.00
1949 Bowman	26	60.00	30.00	18.00
1950 Bowman	8	80.00	40.00	24.00
1951 Bowman	46	65.00	32.50	19.50
1952 Bowman	75	45.00	25.00	15.00
1952 Red Man Tobacco	13A	60.00	30.00	18.00
1952 Topps	246	80.00	40.00	18.50
1953 Bowman Color	61	55.00	27.50	16.50
1953 Red Man Tobacco	8A	55.00	27.00	16.50
1953 Topps	138	70.00	35.00	16.00
1954 Bowman	50	30.00	15.00	9.00
1954 Red Heart Dog Food	(12)	40.00	20.00	12.00
1954 Red Man Tobacco	4Aa	80.00	40.00	24.00
1954 Red Man Tobacco	4Ab	90.00	45.00	27.00
1955 Bowman	213	25.00	12.50	7.50
1956 Topps	195	32.50	16.00	9.75
1957 Topps	230	18.00	9.00	5.50
1958 Topps	40	12.50	6.25	3.75

Set	Card #	MT	NM	EX
1983 Topps 1952 Reprint Set	246	2.00	1.50	.80
1986 Sportflics Decade Greats	24	.15	.11	.06
1988 Pacific Trading Cards Baseball Legends	69	.15	.11	.06
1990 Pacific Legends	86	.10	.08	.04
1991 "1953" Topps Archives	138	.50	.40	.20

Harmon Killebrew

Set	Card #	NM	EX	VG
1955 Topps	124 (R)	250.00	125.00	75.00
1956 Topps	164	110.00	55.00	32.50
1958 Topps	288	80.00	40.00	24.00
1959 Home Run Derby	(10)	275.00	137.00	82.00

1959 Topps	515	125.00	62.50	37.50
1960 Post Cereal	(5)	400.00	200.00	120.00
1960 Topps	210	25.00	12.50	7.50
1961 Post Cereal	92a	32.50	16.00	9.75
1961 Post Cereal	92b	32.50	16.00	9.75
1961 Topps	80	22.00	11.00	6.50
1962 Post Cereal	85	10.00	5.00	3.00
1962 Topps	53	60.00	30.00	18.00
1962 Topps	70	18.00	9.00	5.50
1962 Topps	316	16.00	8.00	4.75
1963 Post Cereal	5	12.00	6.00	3.50
1963 Topps	4	11.00	5.50	3.25
1963 Topps	500	110.00	55.00	32.50
1964 Topps	10	5.00	2.50	1.50
1964 Topps	12	8.00	4.00	2.50
1964 Topps	81	9.50	4.75	2.75
1964 Topps	177	20.00	10.00	6.00
1965 O-Pee-Chee	3	30.00	15.00	9.00
1965 O-Pee-Chee	5	30.00	15.00	9.00
1965 Topps	3	20.00	10.00	6.00
1965 Topps	5	30.00	15.00	9.00
1965 Topps	400	30.00	15.00	9.00
1966 O-Pee-Chee	120	25.00	12.50	7.50
1966 Topps	120	20.00	10.00	6.00
1967 Topps	241	4.50	2.25	1.25
1967 Topps	243	6.00	3.00	1.75
1967 Topps	334	4.50	2.25	1.25
1967 Topps	460	40.00	20.00	12.00
1968 O-Pee-Chee	4	13.50	6.75	4.00
1968 O-Pee-Chee	6	10.25	5.25	3.00
1968 Topps	4	8.00	4.00	2.50
1968 Topps	6	8.00	4.00	2.50
1968 Topps	220	12.50	6.25	3.75
1968 Topps	361	5.00	2.50	1.50
1968 Topps	490	125.00	62.50	37.50
1969 Topps	375	20.00	10.00	6.00
1970 O-Pee-Chee	64	2.00	1.00	.60
1970 O-Pee-Chee	66	2.00	1.00	.60
1970 O-Pee-Chee	150	10.25	5.25	3.00
1970 Topps	64	5.00	2.50	1.50
1970 Topps	66	5.00	2.50	1.50
1970 Topps	150	8.00	4.00	2.50
1971 O-Pee-Chee	65	1.50	.70	.45
1971 O-Pee-Chee	550	30.00	15.00	9.00
1971 Topps	65	3.50	1.75	1.00
1971 Topps	550	20.00	10.00	6.00
1972 O-Pee-Chee	51	7.50	3.75	2.25
1972 O-Pee-Chee	52	1.50	.70	.45
1972 O-Pee-Chee	88	1.25	.60	.40
1972 Topps	51	6.00	3.00	1.75
1972 Topps	52	3.00	1.50	.90
1972 Topps	88	3.50	1.75	1.00
1973 O-Pee-Chee	170	6.00	3.00	1.75
1973 Topps	170	5.00	2.50	1.50
1974 O-Pee-Chee	400	6.00	3.00	1.75
1974 Topps	400	5.00	2.50	1.50
1975 O-Pee-Chee	207	2.00	1.00	.60
1975 O-Pee-Chee	640	5.50	2.75	1.75
1975 Topps	207	1.50	.70	.45
1975 Topps	640	5.00	2.50	1.50
1975 Topps Mini	207	2.25	1.25	.70
1975 Topps Mini	640	6.00	3.00	1.75

Set	Card #	MT	NM	EX
1986 Sportflics Decade Greats	48	.30	.25	.12
1988 Pacific Trading Cards Baseball Legends	86	.25	.20	.10
1989 Pacific Trading Cards Legends II	163	.25	.20	.10
1990 Pacific Legends	35	.25	.20	.10
1991 Upper Deck Heroes of Baseball	1	15.00	10.00	5.00
1991 Upper Deck Heroes of Baseball	4	15.00	11.00	6.00

Ralph Kiner

Set	Card #	NM	EX	VG
1948 Bowman	3 (R)	125.00	62.50	37.50
1948 Leaf	91 (R)	180.00	90.00	55.00
1949 Bowman	29	65.00	32.00	19.50
1950 Bowman	33	100.00	50.00	30.00
1951 Topps Red Backs	15	25.00	12.50	7.50
1952 Bowman	11	60.00	30.00	18.00
1952 Red Man Tobacco	12N	60.00	30.00	18.00
1953 Bowman Color	80	60.00	30.00	18.00
1953 Red Man Tobacco	15N	55.00	27.00	16.50
1953 Topps	191	70.00	35.00	16.00
1954 Bowman	45	30.00	15.00	9.00
1954 Red Heart Dog Food	(14)	55.00	27.00	16.50
1955 Bowman	197	40.00	20.00	12.00
1960 Fleer	79	3.50	1.75	1.00
1961-62 Fleer	50	4.00	2.00	1.25
1977 Topps	437	.35	.20	.11

Set	Card #	MT	NM	EX
1986 Sportflics Decade Greats	35	.30	.25	.12
1988 Pacific Trading Cards Baseball Legends	9	.20	.15	.08
1990 Pacific Legends	36	.15	.11	.06
1991 "1953" Topps Archives	191	.50	.40	.20

Dave Kingman

Set	Card #	NM	EX	VG
1972 O-Pee-Chee	147	7.25	3.75	2.25
1972 Topps	147 (R)	5.00	2.50	1.50
1973 O-Pee-Chee	23	1.00	.50	.30
1973 Topps	23	.75	.40	.25
1974 O-Pee-Chee	610	.75	.40	.25
1974 Topps	610	.45	.25	.14
1975 O-Pee-Chee	156	1.00	.50	.30
1975 Topps	156	.45	.25	.14

1975 Topps Mini	156	.90	.45	.25
1976 O-Pee-Chee	40	.75	.40	.25
1976 O-Pee-Chee	193	2.00	1.00	.60
1976 Topps	40	.25	.13	.08
1976 Topps	193	2.00	1.00	.60
1977 O-Pee-Chee	98	.50	.25	.15
1977 Topps	500	.30	.15	.09
1978 Topps	570	.30	.15	.09
1979 O-Pee-Chee	191	.30	.15	.09
1979 Topps	370	.35	.20	.11
1980 O-Pee-Chee	127	.40	.20	.12
1980 Topps	202	.25	.13	.08
1980 Topps	240	.15	.08	.05

Set	Card #	MT	NM	EX
1981 Donruss	553	.12	.09	.05
1981 Fleer	291	.15	.11	.06
1981 O-Pee-Chee	361	.12	.09	.05
1981 Topps	450	.10	.08	.04
1981 Topps Traded	781	.20	.15	.08
1982 Donruss	17	.15	.11	.06
1982 Donruss	182	.12	.09	.05
1982 Fleer	530	.15	.11	.06
1982 O-Pee-Chee	276	.15	.11	.06
1982 Topps	690	.10	.08	.04
1983 Donruss	301	.15	.11	.06
1983 Fleer	548	.15	.11	.06
1983 O-Pee-Chee	160	.15	.11	.06
1983 O-Pee-Chee	161	.12	.09	.05
1983 Topps	160	.10	.08	.04
1983 Topps	161	.10	.08	.04
1983 Topps	702	.25	.20	.10
1984 Donruss	360	.20	.15	.08
1984 Fleer	590	.15	.11	.06
1984 Fleer Update	62	.25	.20	.10
1984 O-Pee-Chee	172	.30	.25	.12
1984 Topps	573	.15	.11	.06
1984 Topps	703	.30	.25	.12
1984 Topps Traded	63T	.25	.20	.10
1985 Donruss	54	.15	.11	.06
1985 Fleer	427	.15	.11	.06
1985 Leaf-Donruss	182	.20	.15	.08
1985 O-Pee-Chee	123	.12	.09	.05
1985 Topps	730	.15	.11	.06
1985 Topps All-Star Glossy Set of 40	5	.25	.20	.10
1986 Donruss	54	.15	.11	.06
1986 Fleer	423	.15	.11	.06
1986 O-Pee-Chee	322	.10	.08	.04
1986 Sportflics	68	.30	.25	.12
1986 Sportflics	116	.15	.11	.06
1986 Sportflics	150	.20	.15	.08
1986 Topps	410	.15	.11	.06
1987 Donruss	425	.12	.09	.05
1987 Fleer	396	.12	.09	.05
1987 O-Pee-Chee	266	.12	.09	.05
1987 Sportflics	178	.15	.11	.06
1987 Topps	709	.10	.08	.04
1989 Pacific Trading Cards Legends II	175	.06	.05	.02
1990 Pacific Legends	87	.10	.08	.04
1990 Pacific Senior League	164	.10	.08	.04
1990 Pacific Senior League	186	.10	.08	.04
1990 Topps Senior League	101	.15	.11	.06

* * *

Pitcher Greg Minton, on memorabilia: "I have a unique bat at home. I hit one home run in my big league career. I hit it with a Duane Kuiper bat. I have it mounted on my wall. Duane's bat has two home runs in it, one for him, and one for me."

* * *

Ted Kluszewski

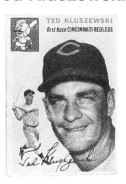

Set	Card #	NM	EX	VG
1948 Leaf	38 (R)	100.00	50.00	30.00
1950 Bowman	62	75.00	37.50	22.00
1951 Bowman	143	30.00	15.00	9.00
1951 Topps Red Backs	39	15.00	7.50	4.50
1952 Topps	29	90.00	45.00	21.00
1953 Bowman Color	62	45.00	22.50	13.50
1953 Red Man Tobacco	6N	32.50	16.00	9.75
1953 Topps	162	45.00	22.00	10.50
1954 Red Heart Dog Food	(13)	40.00	20.00	12.00
1954 Red Man Tobacco	6N	37.50	18.50	11.00
1954 Topps	7	25.00	12.50	7.50
1955 Red Man Tobacco	16N	35.00	17.50	10.50
1955 Topps	120	25.00	12.50	7.50
1956 Topps	25	20.00	10.00	6.00
1957 Topps	165	35.00	17.50	10.50
1958 Topps	178	9.00	4.50	2.75
1958 Topps	321	50.00	25.00	15.00
1959 Topps	17	9.00	4.50	2.75
1959 Topps	35	11.00	5.50	3.25
1960 Topps	505	10.00	5.00	3.00
1961 Post Cereal	31	4.50	2.25	1.25
1961 Topps	65	7.50	3.75	2.25
1962 Post Cereal	82	4.50	2.25	1.25
1973 O-Pee-Chee	296	.75	.40	.25
1973 Topps	296	2.00	1.00	.60
1974 O-Pee-Chee	326	.60	.30	.20
1974 Topps	326	1.50	.70	.45

Set	Card #	MT	NM	EX
1983 Topps 1952 Reprint Set	29	1.50	1.25	.60
1986 Sportflics Decade Greats	38	.25	.20	.10
1988 Pacific Trading Cards Baseball Legends	72	.10	.08	.04
1991 "1953" Topps Archives	162	.35	.25	.14
1994 "1954" Topps Archives	7	.25	.20	.10

* * *

Dealers surveyed at a February 1987 show in Hawaii recorded hobby sales in 1986 of: less than $50,000 (20%); $50,000-$100,000 (4%); $100,000-$200,000 (16%); $200,000-$350,000 (24%); $350,000-$600,000 (24%); $600,000-$1,000,000 (0%); and $1,000,000 or more (12%).

* * *

On the back of Houston Astros' star Lee May's 1973 Topps card (135), where you're supposed to find his career batting average, you'll find .000.

* * *

Chuck Knoblauch

Set	Card #	MT	NM	EX
1990 Bowman	415 (R)	.50	.40	.20
1990 Score	672 (R)	.60	.45	.25
1991 Bowman	330	.20	.15	.08
1991 Donruss	421	.30	.25	.12
1991 Fleer Ultra	382	.50	.40	.20
1991 Fleer Ultra Update	37	1.25	.90	.50
1991 Fleer Update	37	.50	.40	.20
1991 Leaf	396	.50	.40	.20
1991 Score Traded	93	.25	.20	.15
1991 Topps Stadium Club	548	1.50	1.25	.60
1991 Topps Stadium Club Members Only	(16)	.40	.30	.15
1991 Topps Traded	69	.40	.30	.15
1991 Upper Deck	40	.75	.60	.30
1992 Bowman	24	.35	.25	.14
1992 Donruss	390	.08	.06	.03
1992 Donruss Triple Play	171	.12	.09	.05
1992 Fleer	206	.15	.11	.06
1992 Fleer Rookie Sensations	10	3.00	2.25	1.25
1992 Fleer Ultra	93	.25	.20	.10
1992 Fleer Ultra Award Winners	2	1.25	.90	.50
1992 Leaf	230	.20	.15	.08
1992 O-Pee-Chee	23	.10	.08	.04
1992 O-Pee-Chee Premier	35	.25	.20	.10
1992 Pinnacle	119	.15	.11	.06
1992 Pinnacle	285	.15	.11	.06
1992 Pinnacle	307	.10	.07	.04
1992 Pinnacle Team 2000	6	.30	.25	.12
1992 Post Cereal	6	.30	.25	.12
1992 Score	572	.10	.08	.04
1992 Score	792	.10	.08	.04
1992 Score Impact Players	1	.25	.20	.10
1992 Topps	23	.10	.08	.04
1992 Topps Gold	23	.45	.35	.20
1992 Topps Kids	112	.05	.04	.02
1992 Topps Stadium Club	601	.12	.09	.05
1992 Topps Stadium Club	830	.15	.11	.06
1992 Topps Stadium Club East Coast National	601	6.00	4.50	2.50
1992 Topps Stadium Club National Convention	830	15.00	11.00	6.00
1992 Upper Deck	446	.15	.11	.06
1993 Bowman	481	.20	.15	.08
1993 DiamondMarks	(96)	.35	.25	.14
1993 Donruss	415	.12	.09	.05
1993 Donruss Triple Play	48	.10	.08	.04
1993 Fleer	357	.15	.11	.06
1993 Fleer	639	.10	.07	.04
1993 Fleer Flair	237	.40	.30	.15
1993 Fleer Ultra	583	.15	.11	.06
1993 Leaf	98	.15	.11	.06
1993 Leaf Fasttrack	6	2.00	1.50	.80
1993 Leaf Gold All-Stars	5	1.00	.75	.40
1993 O-Pee-Chee	175	.20	.15	.08
1993 Pinnacle	107	.12	.09	.05
1993 Pinnacle Team 2001	4	.50	.40	.20
1993 Score	148	.08	.06	.03
1993 Score Select	36	.12	.09	.05
1993 Studio	109	.12	.09	.05
1993 Topps	250	.08	.06	.03
1993 Topps Finest	76	1.75	1.25	.70
1993 Topps Finest Refractors	76	22.00	16.50	8.75
1993 Topps Gold	250	.15	.11	.06
1993 Topps Stadium Club	314	.15	.11	.06
1993 Topps Stadium Club First Day Production	314	15.00	11.00	6.00
1993 Topps Stadium Club Special Master Photo	(5)	.75	.60	.30
1993 Topps Stadium Club Special	8	.10	.08	.04
1993 Upper Deck	254	.10	.08	.04
1993 Upper Deck Fun Packs	193	.12	.09	.05
1993 Upper Deck SP	248	.12	.09	.05
1994 Bowman	229	.10	.08	.04
1994 Donruss	28	.05	.04	.02
1994 Donruss Special Edition - Gold	28	.25	.20	.10
1994 Donruss Triple Play	254	.05	.04	.02
1994 Fleer	210	.05	.04	.02
1994 Fleer	712	.05	.04	.02
1994 Fleer Extra Bases	118	.15	.11	.06
1994 Fleer Flair	314	.20	.15	.08
1994 Fleer Ultra	89	.10	.08	.04
1994 Leaf	64	.12	.09	.05
1994 Leaf Limited	49	1.50	1.25	.60
1994 O-Pee-Chee	155	.05	.04	.02
1994 Pacific Crown	357	.10	.08	.04
1994 Pinnacle	83	.10	.08	.04
1994 Pinnacle Artist's Proof	83	3.00	2.25	1.25
1994 Pinnacle Museum Collection	83	1.50	1.25	.60
1994 Score	89	.04	.03	.02
1994 Score Select	29	.10	.08	.04
1994 Sportflics 2000	83	.10	.08	.04
1994 Studio	197	.10	.08	.04
1994 Topps	555	.05	.04	.02
1994 Topps Finest	324	.60	.45	.25
1994 Topps Finest Refractors	324	3.50	2.75	1.50
1994 Topps Gold	555	.15	.11	.06
1994 Topps Stadium Club	416	.12	.09	.05
1994 Topps Stadium Club First Day Production	416	2.50	2.00	1.00
1994 Upper Deck	152	.10	.08	.04
1994 Upper Deck Collector's Choice	166	.05	.04	.02
1994 Upper Deck Electric Diamond	152	.25	.20	.10
1994 Upper Deck Fun Packs	147	.05	.04	.02
1994 Upper Deck SP	185	.15	.11	.06
1994 Upper Deck SP Baseball Die-Cut	185	.25	.20	.10

* * *

At the peak of the Billy Ripken 1989 Fleer X-rated card hysteria, SCD received reports of $6 wax packs, $125-wax boxes and $1,800-cases (20 boxes per case). The card itself was selling for between $25-$125.

* * *

Joe Rudi once surprised card show attendees when he informed them that the player being congratulated on his 1973 Topps card (supposedly Rudi) is actually Gene Tenace.

* * *

Sandy Koufax

John Kruk

Set	Card #	NM	EX	VG
1955 Topps	123 (R)	900.00	450.00	250.00
1956 Topps	79	325.00	160.00	95.00
1957 Topps	302	295.00	145.00	85.00
1958 Topps	187	165.00	82.50	48.00
1959 Topps	163	120.00	60.00	36.00
1960 Topps	343	100.00	50.00	30.00
1961 Topps	49	10.00	5.00	3.00
1961 Topps	207	22.00	11.00	6.50
1961 Topps	344	80.00	40.00	24.00
1962 Post Cereal	109a	40.00	20.00	12.00
1962 Post Cereal	109b	25.00	12.50	7.50
1962 Topps	5	115.00	85.00	45.00
1962 Topps	60	10.00	5.00	3.00
1963 Fleer	42	160.00	80.00	47.50
1963 Post Cereal	121	15.00	7.50	4.50
1963 Topps	5	15.00	7.50	4.50
1963 Topps	9	12.00	6.00	3.50
1963 Topps	210	125.00	62.50	37.50
1963 Topps	412	35.00	17.50	10.50
1964 Topps	1	22.00	11.00	5.50
1964 Topps	3	15.00	11.00	6.00
1964 Topps	5	12.00	6.00	3.50
1964 Topps	200	90.00	45.00	27.00
1965 O-Pee-Chee	8	17.00	8.50	5.00
1965 Topps	8	11.00	5.50	3.25
1965 Topps	300	105.00	50.00	30.00
1966 O-Pee-Chee	100	120.00	60.00	36.00
1966 Topps	100	90.00	45.00	26.00
1966 Topps	221	8.00	4.00	2.50
1966 Topps	223	8.00	4.00	2.50
1966 Topps	225	8.00	4.00	2.50
1967 Topps	234	12.00	6.00	3.50
1967 Topps	236	12.00	6.00	3.50
1967 Topps	238	11.00	5.50	3.25
1975 O-Pee-Chee	201	3.00	1.50	.90
1975 Topps	201	1.50	.70	.45

Set	Card #	MT	NM	EX
1990 O-Pee-Chee	665	.07	.05	.03
1990 Topps	665	.07	.05	.03

* * *

Catcher Johnny Oates, about his 1972 Topps Orioles rookie card: "Some kid came up to me and said, 'I paid about a buck for your card the other day, but that's only because Don Baylor's on it.' That's OK, I think Roric Harrison and I both know that having Don on there is a big plus."

* * *

What does reliever Bruce Sutter think of his high ERA of 4.48 in 1985? "I just hope they don't put this season on the back of my baseball card."

* * *

Set	Card #	MT	NM	EX
1986 Fleer Update	61	1.50	1.25	.60
1986 Sportflics Rookies	1	.80	.60	.30
1986 Topps Traded	56T	1.00	.75	.40
1987 Donruss	328 (R)	1.00	.75	.40
1987 Fleer	420 (R)	3.00	2.25	1.25
1987 Leaf	217	2.50	2.00	1.00
1987 Sportflics	61	.30	.25	.12
1987 Topps	123 (R)	.60	.45	.25
1988 Donruss	205	.12	.09	.05
1988 Fleer	589	.10	.08	.04
1988 Leaf	176	.25	.20	.10
1988 O-Pee-Chee	32	.09	.07	.04
1988 Score	36	.12	.08	.04
1988 Sportflics	64	.25	.20	.10
1988 Topps	596	.12	.09	.05
1988 Topps Big Baseball	60	.15	.11	.06
1989 Bowman	460	.03	.02	.01
1989 Donruss	86	.06	.05	.02
1989 Fleer	309	.12	.09	.05
1989 Fleer Update	109	.15	.11	.06
1989 O-Pee-Chee	235	.20	.15	.08
1989 Score	148	.12	.08	.04
1989 Score Traded	70T	.12	.09	.05
1989 Sportflics	184	.15	.11	.06
1989 Topps	235	.10	.08	.04
1989 Topps Big Baseball	216	.05	.04	.02
1989 Topps Traded	63T	.25	.20	.10
1989 Upper Deck	280	.40	.30	.15
1990 Bowman	154	.05	.04	.02
1990 Donruss	160	.05	.04	.02
1990 Fleer	565	.07	.05	.03
1990 Leaf	284	.75	.60	.30
1990 O-Pee-Chee	469	.07	.05	.02
1990 Score	467	.07	.05	.03
1990 Sportflics	124	.10	.08	.04
1990 Topps	469	.07	.05	.02
1990 Topps Big Baseball	214	.15	.11	.06
1990 Upper Deck	668	.12	.09	.05
1991 Bowman	503	.08	.06	.03
1991 Donruss	260	.06	.05	.02
1991 Fleer	402	.06	.05	.02
1991 Fleer Ultra	266	.08	.06	.03
1991 Leaf	278	.20	.15	.08
1991 Score	94	.05	.04	.02
1991 Topps	689	.06	.05	.02
1991 Topps Stadium Club	227	.25	.20	.10
1991 Upper Deck	199	.06	.05	.02
1992 Bowman	541	.08	.06	.03
1992 Donruss	230	.08	.06	.03
1992 Donruss Diamond Kings	12	.60	.45	.25
1992 Donruss Triple Play	38	.12	.09	.05
1992 Fleer	537	.06	.05	.02
1992 Fleer Ultra	246	.15	.11	.06
1992 Leaf	313	.15	.11	.06
1992 O-Pee-Chee	30	.06	.05	.02
1992 O-Pee-Chee Premier	134	.15	.11	.06
1992 Pinnacle	147	.12	.09	.05

Card	#			
1992 Score	235	.08	.06	.03
1992 Studio	76	.15	.11	.06
1992 Topps	30	.06	.05	.02
1992 Topps Gold	30	1.00	.70	.40
1992 Topps Kids	18	.10	.08	.04
1992 Topps Stadium Club	209	.15	.11	.06
1992 Topps Stadium Club Special Edition	100	.25	.20	.10
1992 Upper Deck	38	.05	.04	.02
1992 Upper Deck	326	.08	.06	.03
1992 Upper Deck Home Run Heroes	23	.50	.40	.20
1992 Upper Deck MVP Holograms	28	.35	.25	.14
1993 Bowman	540	.20	.15	.08
1993 DiamondMarks	(48)	.35	.25	.14
1993 Donruss	436	.05	.04	.02
1993 Donruss Triple Play	139	.10	.08	.04
1993 Fleer	104	.08	.06	.03
1993 Fleer Flair	105	.40	.30	.15
1993 Fleer NL Team Leaders	8	2.00	1.50	.80
1993 Fleer Ultra	90	.20	.15	.08
1993 Leaf	366	.15	.11	.06
1993 Leaf Update Gold All-Stars	3	1.00	.75	.40
1993 O-Pee-Chee	216	.20	.15	.08
1993 O-Pee-Chee Premier	76	.15	.11	.06
1993 Pinnacle	8	.08	.06	.03
1993 Pinnacle Slugfest	17	.60	.45	.25
1993 Post Cereal	29	.25	.20	.10
1993 Score	79	.08	.06	.03
1993 Score Select	33	.12	.09	.05
1993 Score Select Stat Leaders	6	.20	.15	.08
1993 Score Select Stat Leaders	53	.15	.11	.06
1993 Studio	183	.15	.11	.06
1993 Studio Heritage	12	1.00	.70	.40
1993 Studio Silhouettes	7	1.00	.70	.40
1993 Topps	340	.08	.06	.03
1993 Topps Finest	38	1.75	1.25	.70
1993 Topps Finest Refractors	38	22.00	16.50	8.75
1993 Topps Full Shot Super	16	3.00	2.25	1.25
1993 Topps Gold	340	.15	.11	.06
1993 Topps Stadium Club	83	.12	.09	.05
1993 Topps Stadium Club First Day Production	83	15.00	11.00	6.00
1993 Topps Stadium Club Special	84	.10	.08	.04
1993 Upper Deck	247	.10	.08	.04
1993 Upper Deck Fun Packs	146	.15	.11	.06
1993 Upper Deck SP	14	.15	.11	.06
1994 Bowman	412	.10	.08	.04
1994 Donruss	7	.08	.06	.03
1994 Donruss Decade Dominators	10	1.25	.90	.50
1994 Donruss Decade Dominators Supers	10	3.50	2.75	1.50
1994 Donruss Diamond Kings	9	1.00	.75	.40
1994 Donruss Diamond Kings Super	9	3.75	2.75	1.50
1994 Donruss Elite	41	15.00	11.00	6.00
1994 Donruss Special Edition - Gold	7	.30	.25	.12
1994 Donruss Triple Play	177	.05	.04	.02
1994 Fleer	594	.08	.06	.03
1994 Fleer All-Stars	44	.30	.25	.12
1994 Fleer Extra Bases	340	.15	.11	.06
1994 Fleer Flair	415	.25	.20	.10
1994 Fleer Ultra	249	.10	.08	.04
1994 Fleer Ultra Phillies Finest	2M	1.50	1.25	.60
1994 Fleer Ultra Phillies Finest	4M	1.50	1.25	.60
1994 Fleer Ultra Phillies Finest	6	1.00	.70	.40
1994 Fleer Ultra Phillies Finest	7	1.00	.70	.40
1994 Fleer Ultra Phillies Finest	8	1.00	.70	.40
1994 Fleer Ultra Phillies Finest	9	1.00	.70	.40
1994 Fleer Ultra Phillies Finest	10	1.00	.70	.40
1994 Fleer Ultra Phillies Finest	16	1.00	.70	.40
1994 Fleer Ultra Phillies Finest	17	1.00	.70	.40
1994 Fleer Ultra Phillies Finest	18	1.00	.70	.40
1994 Fleer Ultra Phillies Finest	19	1.00	.70	.40
1994 Fleer Ultra Phillies Finest	20	1.00	.70	.40
1994 Leaf	347	.15	.11	.06
1994 Leaf Gamers	11	1.50	1.25	.60
1994 Leaf Limited	138	1.25	.90	.50
1994 O-Pee-Chee	257	.10	.08	.04
1994 Pacific Crown	479	.10	.08	.04
1994 Pacific Crown Jewels of the Crown	32	2.50	2.00	1.00
1994 Pinnacle	63	.10	.08	.04
1994 Pinnacle Artist's Proof	63	3.00	2.25	1.25
1994 Pinnacle Museum Collection	63	2.00	1.50	.80
1994 Pinnacle Run Creators	25	1.50	1.25	.60
1994 Score	28	.10	.08	.04
1994 Score Gold Stars	7	3.00	2.25	1.25
1994 Score Select	24	.20	.15	.08
1994 Score Select Promos	24	4.00	3.00	1.50
1994 Sportflics 2000	101	.10	.08	.04
1994 Studio	142	.10	.08	.04
1994 Topps	401	.05	.04	.02
1994 Topps Black Gold	37	.50	.40	.20
1994 Topps Finest	416	.75	.60	.30
1994 Topps Finest Refractors	416	4.00	3.00	1.50
1994 Topps Gold	401	.15	.11	.06
1994 Topps Stadium Club	361	.12	.09	.05
1994 Topps Stadium Club	533	.10	.08	.04
1994 Topps Stadium Club Dugout Dirt	3	.25	.20	.10
1994 Topps Stadium Club First Day Production	361	3.00	2.25	1.25
1994 Topps Stadium Club First Day Production	533	2.50	2.00	1.00
1994 Topps Stadium Club Members Only Baseball	3	.35	.25	.14
1994 Topps Team Stadium Club	226	.14	.14	.14
1994 Topps Team Stadium Club 1st Day Issue	226	.14	.14	.14
1994 Upper Deck	276	.12	.09	.05
1994 Upper Deck	410	.12	.09	.05
1994 Upper Deck All-Stars Green Foil	7	.25	.20	.10
1994 Upper Deck All-Stars Gold Foil	7	1.00	.70	.40
1994 Upper Deck Collector's Choice	168	.10	.08	.04
1994 Upper Deck Collector's Choice	326	.05	.04	.02
1994 Upper Deck Electric Diamond	276	.25	.20	.10
1994 Upper Deck Electric Diamond	410	.25	.20	.10
1994 Upper Deck Fun Packs	120	.07	.05	.03
1994 Upper Deck Fun Packs	214	.08	.06	.03

Set	Card #	MT	NM	EX
1994 Upper Deck Fun Packs	230	.10	.08	.04
1994 Upper Deck SP	138	.20	.15	.08
1994 Upper Deck SP Baseball Die-Cut	138	.25	.20	.10
1994 Upper Deck SP Holoview Blue	22	3.00	2.25	1.25
1994 Upper Deck SP Holoview Red	22	15.00	11.00	6.00

Mark Langston

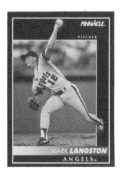

Set	Card #	MT	NM	EX
1984 Fleer Update	70	25.00	18.50	10.00
1984 Topps Traded	70T	8.00	6.00	3.25
1985 Donruss	557 (R)	5.00	3.75	2.00
1985 Fleer	492 (R)	3.00	2.25	1.25
1985 Leaf-Donruss	56	3.25	2.50	1.25
1985 O-Pee-Chee	259	1.75	1.25	.70
1985 Topps	625 (R)	1.50	1.25	.60
1986 Donruss	118	.30	.25	.12
1986 Fleer	467	.30	.25	.12
1986 O-Pee-Chee	198	.12	.09	.05
1986 Topps	495	.20	.15	.08
1987 Donruss	568	.12	.09	.05
1987 Fleer	589	.30	.25	.12
1987 Leaf	55	.10	.08	.04
1987 O-Pee-Chee	215	.10	.08	.04
1987 Sportflics	102	.15	.11	.06
1987 Topps	215	.12	.09	.05
1988 Donruss	20	.06	.05	.02
1988 Donruss	317	.12	.09	.05
1988 Donruss Diamond Kings Supers	20	.35	.25	.14
1988 Fleer	377	.12	.09	.05
1988 Leaf	20	.08	.06	.03
1988 Leaf	123	.10	.08	.04
1988 O-Pee-Chee	80	.09	.07	.04
1988 Score	30	.10	.08	.04
1988 Sportflics	46	.15	.11	.06
1988 Topps	80	.10	.08	.04
1988 Topps Big Baseball	176	.10	.08	.04
1989 Bowman	205	.15	.11	.06
1989 Donruss	227	.10	.08	.04
1989 Fleer	551	.10	.08	.04
1989 Fleer Update	97	.15	.11	.06
1989 O-Pee-Chee	355	.05	.04	.02
1989 Score	161	.08	.06	.03
1989 Score Traded	25T	.12	.09	.05
1989 Sportflics	159	.15	.11	.06
1989 Topps	355	.08	.06	.03
1989 Topps Traded	66T	.25	.20	.10
1989 Upper Deck	526	.15	.11	.06
1990 Bowman	284	.06	.05	.02
1990 Donruss	338	.12	.09	.05
1990 Fleer	352	.10	.07	.04
1990 Fleer Update	78	.08	.06	.03
1990 Leaf	155	.35	.25	.14
1990 O-Pee-Chee	530	.10	.08	.04
1990 Score	401	.15	.11	.06
1990 Score	688	.10	.07	.04
1990 Score Traded	11T	.08	.06	.03
1990 Sportflics	110	.12	.09	.05
1990 Topps	530	.10	.08	.04
1990 Topps Big Baseball	232	.10	.08	.04
1990 Topps Traded	54T	.10	.08	.04
1990 Upper Deck	647	.10	.08	.04
1990 Upper Deck	783	.12	.09	.05
1991 Bowman	202	.08	.06	.03
1991 Donruss	190	.08	.06	.03
1991 Fleer	318	.10	.08	.04
1991 Fleer Ultra	49	.12	.09	.05
1991 Leaf	67	.15	.11	.06
1991 Score	21	.10	.08	.04
1991 Score	411	.10	.08	.04
1991 Score	699	.08	.06	.03
1991 Studio	27	.25	.20	.10
1991 Topps	755	.10	.08	.04
1991 Upper Deck	234	.15	.11	.06
1992 Bowman	520	.40	.30	.15
1992 Donruss	531	.08	.06	.03
1992 Donruss Diamond Kings	20	.50	.40	.20
1992 Donruss Triple Play	36	.08	.06	.03
1992 Fleer	63	.10	.08	.04
1992 Fleer Ultra	327	.15	.11	.06
1992 Fleer Ultra Award Winners	16	.75	.60	.30
1992 Leaf	229	.15	.11	.06
1992 O-Pee-Chee	165	.10	.08	.04
1992 Pinnacle	132	.12	.09	.05
1992 Score	12	.08	.06	.03
1992 Studio	148	.15	.11	.06
1992 Topps	165	.10	.08	.04
1992 Topps Gold	165	.25	.20	.10
1992 Topps Kids	98	.05	.04	.02
1992 Topps Stadium Club	670	.10	.08	.04
1992 Topps Stadium Club Special Edition	101	.15	.11	.06
1992 Upper Deck	305	.10	.08	.04
1993 Bowman	469	.10	.08	.04
1993 Donruss	593	.05	.04	.02
1993 Donruss Triple Play	235	.07	.05	.03
1993 Fleer	194	.08	.06	.03
1993 Fleer Flair	175	.25	.15	.08
1993 Fleer Ultra	166	.10	.08	.04
1993 Fleer Ultra Award Winners	10	1.00	.75	.40
1993 Leaf	324	.10	.08	.04
1993 O-Pee-Chee	232	.15	.11	.06
1993 Pinnacle	56	.06	.05	.02
1993 Score	66	.04	.03	.02
1993 Score Select	52	.12	.09	.05
1993 Score The Franchise	3	1.00	.70	.40
1993 Topps	210	.08	.06	.03
1993 Topps Finest	82	1.00	.70	.40
1993 Topps Finest Refractors	82	20.00	15.00	8.00
1993 Topps Gold	210	.15	.11	.06
1993 Topps Stadium Club	355	.10	.08	.04
1993 Topps Stadium Club First Day Production	355	5.00	3.75	2.00
1993 Topps Stadium Club Special	107	.10	.08	.04
1993 Upper Deck	128	.06	.05	.02
1993 Upper Deck Fun Packs	40	.05	.04	.02
1993 Upper Deck SP	5	.15	.11	.06
1994 Bowman	235	.10	.08	.04
1994 Donruss	31	.05	.04	.02
1994 Donruss Special Edition - Gold	31	.25	.20	.10
1994 Donruss Triple Play	17	.05	.04	.02
1994 Fleer	61	.05	.04	.02
1994 Fleer All-Stars	14	.25	.20	.10
1994 Fleer Extra Bases	37	.10	.08	.04
1994 Fleer Flair	271	.20	.15	.08
1994 Fleer Smoke N' Heat	6	4.00	3.00	1.50
1994 Fleer Ultra	330	.10	.08	.04

1994 Fleer Ultra Award Winners	9	.40	.30	.15
1994 Fleer Ultra Strikeout Kings	2	.75	.60	.30
1994 Leaf	162	.10	.08	.04
1994 Leaf Limited	17	1.00	.70	.40
1994 O-Pee-Chee	175	.05	.04	.02
1994 Pacific Crown	81	.05	.04	.02
1994 Pinnacle	311	.10	.08	.04
1994 Pinnacle Artist's Proof	311	3.00	2.25	1.25
1994 Pinnacle Museum Collection	311	1.50	1.25	.60
1994 Score	71	.04	.03	.02
1994 Score Select	351	.10	.08	.04
1994 Sportflics 2000	38	.10	.08	.04
1994 Studio	13	.10	.08	.04
1994 Topps	665	.04	.03	.02
1994 Topps Finest	24	.50	.40	.20
1994 Topps Finest Refractors	24	3.50	2.75	1.50
1994 Topps Gold	665	.15	.11	.06
1994 Topps Stadium Club	442	.10	.08	.04
1994 Topps Stadium Club First Day Production	442	2.50	2.00	1.00
1994 Topps Stadium Club Members Only Baseball	16	.25	.20	.10
1994 Upper Deck	485	.10	.08	.04
1994 Upper Deck Collector's Choice	169	.05	.04	.02
1994 Upper Deck Electric Diamond	485	.25	.20	.10
1994 Upper Deck Fun Packs	112	.05	.04	.02
1994 Upper Deck SP	25	.15	.11	.06
1994 Upper Deck SP Baseball Die-Cut	25	.25	.20	.10

Barry Larkin

Set	Card #	MT	NM	EX
1986 Sportflics Rookies	34	.75	.60	.30
1987 Donruss	492 (R)	1.50	1.25	.60
1987 Fleer	204 (R)	3.50	2.75	1.50
1987 Topps	648 (R)	.75	.60	.30
1988 Donruss	492	.20	.15	.08
1988 Fleer	239	.20	.15	.08
1988 Leaf	226	.30	.25	.12
1988 O-Pee-Chee	102	.09	.07	.04
1988 Score	72	.20	.15	.08
1988 Topps	102	.12	.09	.05
1988 Topps Big Baseball	74	.15	.11	.06
1989 Bowman	311	.10	.08	.04
1989 Donruss	257	.10	.08	.04
1989 Fleer	164	.15	.11	.06
1989 O-Pee-Chee	363	.10	.08	.04
1989 Score	31	.12	.09	.05
1989 Sportflics	136	.25	.20	.10

1989 Topps	515	.10	.08	.04
1989 Topps Big Baseball	199	.08	.06	.03
1989 Upper Deck	270	.25	.20	.10
1990 Bowman	50	.10	.08	.04
1990 Donruss	71	.12	.09	.05
1990 Fleer	423	.15	.11	.06
1990 Fleer League Standouts	1	.50	.40	.20
1990 Leaf	18	.75	.60	.30
1990 O-Pee-Chee	10	.15	.11	.06
1990 Score	155	.12	.09	.05
1990 Score	689	.12	.09	.05
1990 Sportflics	160	.15	.11	.06
1990 Topps	10	.10	.07	.04
1990 Topps All-Star Glossy Set of 60	5	.15	.11	.06
1990 Topps Big Baseball	189	.15	.11	.06
1990 Upper Deck	167	.12	.09	.05
1991 Bowman	379	.08	.06	.03
1991 Bowman	673	.10	.08	.04
1991 Donruss	5	.06	.05	.02
1991 Donruss	471	.12	.09	.05
1991 Fleer	68	.10	.08	.04
1991 Fleer	711	.15	.11	.06
1991 Fleer All Stars	2	.60	.45	.25
1991 Fleer Ultra	96	.15	.11	.06
1991 Leaf	168	.15	.11	.06
1991 Post Cereal	18	.40	.30	.15
1991 Score	505	.12	.09	.05
1991 Score	666	.08	.06	.03
1991 Score	888	.12	.09	.05
1991 Studio	167	.15	.11	.06
1991 Topps	400	.08	.06	.03
1991 Topps	730	.10	.08	.04
1991 Topps Stadium Club	92	.60	.45	.25
1991 Upper Deck	353	.10	.08	.04
1991 Upper Deck Silver Sluggers	18	.60	.45	.25
1992 Bowman	353	.40	.30	.15
1992 Bowman	694	1.00	.75	.40
1992 Donruss	185	.10	.08	.04
1992 Donruss Triple Play	31	.15	.11	.06
1992 Fleer	411	.10	.08	.04
1992 Fleer	704	.10	.08	.04
1992 Fleer All-Stars	16	.50	.40	.20
1992 Fleer Ultra	191	.20	.15	.08
1992 Fleer Ultra All-Stars	13	.60	.45	.25
1992 Leaf	73	.15	.10	.05
1992 O-Pee-Chee	465	.12	.09	.05
1992 O-Pee-Chee Premier	96	.20	.15	.08
1992 Pinnacle	5	.15	.11	.06
1992 Pinnacle Rookie Idols	9	5.00	3.75	2.00
1992 Pinnacle Team Pinnacle	7	35.00	26.00	14.00
1992 Post Cereal	23	.30	.25	.12
1992 Score	100	.10	.08	.04
1992 Score	775	.08	.06	.03
1992 Score Impact Players	50	.15	.11	.06
1992 Studio	23	.25	.20	.10
1992 Topps	389	.05	.04	.02
1992 Topps	465	.12	.09	.05
1992 Topps Gold	389	.25	.20	.10
1992 Topps Gold	465	1.50	1.25	.60
1992 Topps Kids	37	.10	.08	.04
1992 Topps Stadium Club	100	.15	.11	.06
1992 Topps Stadium Club	596	.15	.11	.06
1992 Topps Stadium Club Special Edition	102	.25	.20	.10
1992 Upper Deck	144	.10	.07	.04
1992 Upper Deck MVP Holograms	29	.30	.25	.12
1993 Bowman	470	.10	.08	.04
1993 DiamondMarks	(13)	.50	.40	.20
1993 Donruss	426	.10	.08	.04
1993 Donruss Elite	23	20.00	15.00	8.00
1993 Donruss Elite Supers	5	10.00	7.50	4.00
1993 Donruss Spirit of the Game	13	1.00	.75	.40

1993 Donruss Triple Play Action Baseball	8	.10	.08	.04
1993 Donruss Triple Play	31	.12	.09	.05
1993 Fleer	394	.10	.08	.04
1993 Fleer All-Stars	4	.75	.60	.30
1993 Fleer Flair	27	.35	.25	.14
1993 Fleer Ultra	30	.20	.15	.08
1993 Fleer Ultra All-Stars	4	1.00	.75	.40
1993 Leaf	311	.10	.08	.04
1993 Leaf Gold All-Stars	14	3.00	2.25	1.25
1993 Leaf Update Gold All-Stars	6	4.00	3.00	1.50
1993 O-Pee-Chee	147	.20	.15	.08
1993 O-Pee-Chee Premier	103	.15	.11	.06
1993 Pinnacle	22	.12	.09	.05
1993 Pinnacle	306	.06	.05	.02
1993 Pinnacle Cooperstown	26	.25	.20	.10
1993 Pinnacle Cooperstown Dufex	26	60.00	45.00	24.00
1993 Post Cereal	28	.30	.25	.12
1993 Score	16	.08	.06	.03
1993 Score Select	23	.15	.11	.06
1993 Score The Franchise	17	1.00	.70	.40
1993 Studio	43	.15	.11	.06
1993 Studio Heritage	7	1.00	.70	.40
1993 Topps	110	.08	.06	.03
1993 Topps	404	.10	.08	.04
1993 Topps Black Gold	11	.30	.25	.12
1993 Topps Finest	114	1.25	.90	.50
1993 Topps Finest Jumbo All-Stars	114	7.00	5.25	2.75
1993 Topps Finest Refractors	114	20.00	15.00	8.00
1993 Topps Full Shot Super	17	3.00	2.25	1.25
1993 Topps Gold	110	.15	.11	.06
1993 Topps Gold	404	.20	.15	.08
1993 Topps Stadium Club	415	.15	.11	.06
1993 Topps Stadium Club First Day Production	415	10.00	7.50	4.00
1993 Upper Deck	245	.10	.07	.04
1993 Upper Deck Clutch Performers	13	.75	.60	.30
1993 Upper Deck Diamond Gallery	22	1.00	.70	.40
1993 Upper Deck Fun Packs	167	.15	.11	.06
1993 Upper Deck Fun Packs	170	.15	.11	.06
1993 Upper Deck Iooss Collection	21	.60	.45	.25
1993 Upper Deck Iooss Collection Super	21	3.50	2.75	1.50
1993 Upper Deck SP	15	.15	.11	.06
1994 Bowman	471	.10	.08	.04
1994 Bowman's Best	95	.50	.40	.20
1994 Bowman's Best Refractors	95	5.00	3.75	2.00
1994 Donruss	45	.05	.04	.02
1994 Donruss Diamond Kings	17	1.00	.75	.40
1994 Donruss Diamond Kings Super	17	3.00	2.25	1.25
1994 Donruss Special Edition - Gold	45	.25	.20	.10
1994 Donruss Triple Play Medalists	8	1.00	.75	.40
1994 Donruss Triple Play	214	.05	.04	.02
1994 Fleer	414	.05	.04	.02
1994 Fleer All-Stars	45	.30	.25	.12
1994 Fleer Extra Bases	233	.15	.11	.06
1994 Fleer Flair	146	.20	.15	.08
1994 Fleer Team Leaders	17	.60	.45	.25
1994 Fleer Ultra	474	.10	.08	.04
1994 Leaf	126	.10	.08	.04
1994 Leaf Limited	95	1.00	.70	.40
1994 Leaf MVP Contenders	11a	2.50	2.00	1.00
1994 Leaf MVP Contenders	11b	5.00	3.75	2.00
1994 O-Pee-Chee	125	.05	.04	.02
1994 Pacific Crown	150	.10	.08	.04
1994 Pinnacle	12	.15	.11	.06
1994 Pinnacle Artist's Proof	12	6.00	4.50	2.50
1994 Pinnacle Museum Collection	12	2.00	1.50	.80
1994 Post Cereal	12	.35	.25	.14
1994 Score	74	.04	.03	.02
1994 Score Dream Team	5	4.00	3.00	1.50
1994 Score Gold Stars	15	2.50	2.00	1.00
1994 Score Select	7	.20	.15	.08
1994 Score Select Skills	2	5.00	3.75	2.00
1994 Sportflics 2000	109	.10	.08	.04
1994 Studio	168	.10	.08	.04
1994 Topps	250	.04	.03	.02
1994 Topps Finest	240	.75	.60	.30
1994 Topps Finest Refractors	240	4.00	3.00	1.50
1994 Topps Finest Superstars	240	3.00	2.25	1.25
1994 Topps Gold	250	.15	.11	.06
1994 Topps Stadium Club	414	.10	.08	.04
1994 Topps Stadium Club First Day Production	414	2.50	2.00	1.00
1994 Upper Deck	269	.12	.09	.05
1994 Upper Deck	385	.10	.08	.04
1994 Upper Deck All-Stars Green Foil	26	.25	.20	.10
1994 Upper Deck All-Stars Gold Foil	26	1.00	.70	.40
1994 Upper Deck Collector's Choice	171	.05	.04	.02
1994 Upper Deck Collector's Choice	349	.05	.04	.02
1994 Upper Deck Diamond Collection	3C	4.00	3.00	1.50
1994 Upper Deck Electric Diamond	269	.25	.20	.10
1994 Upper Deck Electric Diamond	385	.25	.20	.10
1994 Upper Deck Fun Packs	111	.05	.04	.02
1994 Upper Deck SP	159	.15	.11	.06
1994 Upper Deck SP Baseball Die-Cut	159	.25	.20	.10
1994 Upper Deck SP Holoview Blue	23	3.00	2.25	1.25
1994 Upper Deck SP Holoview Red	23	15.00	11.00	6.00
1995 Topps	348	.05	.04	.02

Tommy Lasorda

Set	Card #	NM	EX	VG
1954 Topps	132 (R)	150.00	75.00	45.00
1973 O-Pee-Chee	569	3.50	1.75	1.00
1973 Topps	569	4.00	2.00	1.25
1974 O-Pee-Chee	144	1.25	.60	.40
1974 Topps	144	1.50	.70	.45

1977 Topps	504	2.00	1.00	.60
1978 Topps	189	.50	.25	.15
1979 Topps	526	.60	.30	.20
1980 Topps	302	.60	.30	.20

Set	Card #	MT	NM	EX
1981 Donruss	420	.10	.08	.04
1981 Fleer	116	.10	.08	.04
1981 Topps	679	.35	.25	.14
1982 Donruss	110	.10	.08	.04
1983 Donruss	136	.10	.08	.04
1983 Topps	306	.12	.09	.05
1984 Topps	681	.12	.09	.05
1985 Topps	601	.10	.08	.04
1986 Topps	291	.07	.05	.03
1987 Topps	493	.07	.05	.03
1988 Topps	74	.06	.05	.02
1989 Topps	254	.06	.05	.02
1990 O-Pee-Chee	669	.03	.02	.01
1990 Topps	669	.03	.02	.01
1990 Topps All-Star Glossy Set of 22	1	.12	.09	.05
1991 Topps	789	.04	.03	.02
1992 O-Pee-Chee	261	.04	.03	.02
1992 Topps	261	.04	.03	.02
1992 Topps Gold	261	.25	.20	.10
1992 Topps Gold Winners	261	.15	.11	.06
1994 "1954" Topps Archives	132	.75	.60	.30

Bill Lee

Set	Card #	NM	EX	VG
1970 O-Pee-Chee	279	1.75	.90	.50
1970 Topps	279 (R)	.90	.45	.25
1971 O-Pee-Chee	58	1.50	.70	.45
1971 Topps	58	1.00	.50	.30
1972 Topps	636	2.00	1.00	.60
1973 O-Pee-Chee	224	.75	.40	.25
1973 Topps	224	.40	.20	.12
1974 O-Pee-Chee	118	.60	.30	.20
1974 Topps	118	.30	.15	.09
1975 O-Pee-Chee	128	.55	.30	.15
1975 Topps	128	.35	.20	.11
1975 Topps Mini	128	.60	.30	.20
1976 O-Pee-Chee	396	.35	.20	.11
1976 Topps	396	.25	.13	.08
1977 Topps	503	.20	.10	.06
1978 Topps	295	.20	.10	.06
1979 O-Pee-Chee	237	.25	.13	.08
1979 Topps	455	.15	.08	.05
1980 O-Pee-Chee	53	.15	.08	.05
1980 Topps	97	.15	.08	.05

Set	Card #	MT	NM	EX
1981 Donruss	211	.08	.06	.03
1981 Fleer	157	.08	.06	.03
1981 O-Pee-Chee	371	.12	.09	.05
1981 Topps	633	.10	.08	.04
1982 Donruss	194	.08	.06	.03
1982 Fleer	194	.08	.06	.03

1982 O-Pee-Chee	323	.12	.09	.05
1982 Topps	323	.10	.08	.04
1990 Pacific Senior League	28	.05	.04	.02
1990 Topps Senior League	33	.10	.08	.04
1991 Pacific Senior League	146	.05	.04	.02

Ron LeFlore

Set	Card #	NM	EX	VG
1975 O-Pee-Chee	628	.60	.30	.20
1975 Topps	628 (R)	.80	.40	.25
1975 Topps Mini	628	1.25	.60	.40
1976 O-Pee-Chee	61	.35	.20	.11
1976 Topps	61	.25	.13	.08
1977 O-Pee-Chee	167	.30	.15	.09
1977 Topps	240	.20	.10	.06
1978 O-Pee-Chee	88	.25	.13	.08
1978 Topps	480	.20	.10	.06
1979 O-Pee-Chee	348	.25	.13	.08
1979 Topps	4	.15	.08	.05
1979 Topps	660	.15	.08	.05
1980 O-Pee-Chee	45	.20	.10	.06
1980 Topps	80	.20	.10	.06

Set	Card #	MT	NM	EX
1981 Donruss	576	.08	.06	.03
1981 Fleer	154	.08	.06	.03
1981 O-Pee-Chee	104	.12	.09	.05
1981 Topps	4	1.00	.75	.40
1981 Topps	204	.10	.08	.04
1981 Topps	710	.08	.06	.03
1981 Topps Traded	791	.20	.15	.08
1982 Donruss	165	.08	.06	.03
1982 Fleer	350	.08	.06	.03
1982 O-Pee-Chee	140	.12	.09	.05
1982 Topps	140	.10	.08	.04
1983 Donruss	543	.08	.06	.03
1983 Fleer	246	.08	.06	.03
1983 O-Pee-Chee	297	.12	.09	.05
1983 Topps	560	.10	.08	.04
1990 Pacific Senior League	4	.10	.08	.04
1990 Topps Senior League	111	.10	.08	.04
1991 Pacific Senior League	63	.05	.04	.02

* * *

Graig Nettles, during the height of his 1981 Fleer error card, which was selling for between $10-$20: "I'm saving 'em myself in hopes of putting my kids through college." The card back lists his first name as "Craig."

* * *

Kenny Lofton

Set	Card #	MT	NM	EX
1991 Bowman	565 (R)	1.50	1.25	.60
1991 Upper Deck Final Edition	24	2.00	1.50	.80
1992 Bowman	110	6.00	4.50	2.50
1992 Donruss	5	1.00	.75	.40
1992 Fleer	655	.75	.60	.30
1992 Fleer Ultra	350	1.50	1.25	.60
1992 Fleer Ultra All-Rookies	7	8.00	6.00	3.25
1992 Fleer Update	17	20.00	15.00	8.00
1992 Leaf Gold Rookies	4	5.00	3.75	2.00
1992 O-Pee-Chee	69	.40	.30	.15
1992 O-Pee-Chee Premier	72	.50	.40	.20
1992 Pinnacle	290	.50	.40	.20
1992 Pinnacle	582	1.25	.90	.50
1992 Pinnacle Rookie Idols	7	18.00	13.50	7.25
1992 Pinnacle Rookies	3	2.50	2.00	1.00
1992 Pinnacle Team 2000	35	1.50	1.25	.60
1992 Score	845	.40	.30	.15
1992 Score Hot Rookies	3	20.00	15.00	8.00
1992 Score Impact Players	32	1.25	.90	.50
1992 Score Rookie & Traded	14	9.00	6.75	3.50
1992 Studio	168	.50	.40	.20
1992 Topps	69 (R)	.50	.40	.20
1992 Topps Gold	69 (R)	7.00	5.25	2.75
1992 Topps Stadium Club	695	1.50	1.25	.60
1992 Topps Stadium Club National Convention	695	55.00	41.00	22.00
1992 Topps Traded	66	1.50	1.25	.60
1992 Upper Deck	25 (R)	.50	.40	.20
1992 Upper Deck	766	.50	.40	.20
1992 Upper Deck Scouting Report	15	5.00	3.75	2.00
1993 Bowman	417	.75	.60	.30
1993 DiamondMarks	(79)	.35	.25	.14
1993 Donruss	537	.30	.25	.12
1993 Donruss Spirit of the Game	11	3.00	2.25	1.25
1993 Donruss Triple Play	144	.10	.08	.04
1993 Donruss Triple Play	181	.25	.20	.10
1993 Fleer	218	.30	.25	.12
1993 Fleer	346	.15	.11	.06
1993 Fleer Flair	195	1.50	1.25	.60
1993 Fleer Rookie Sensations I	1	12.00	9.00	4.75
1993 Fleer Ultra	542	.60	.45	.25
1993 Leaf	40	.60	.45	.25
1993 Leaf Fasttrack	3	9.00	6.75	3.50
1993 O-Pee-Chee	251	1.50	1.25	.60
1993 O-Pee-Chee Premier Star Performers	17	.40	.30	.15
1993 Pinnacle	40	.60	.45	.25
1993 Pinnacle Team 2001	18	3.00	2.25	1.25
1993 Score	58	.25	.20	.10
1993 Score Select	275	.40	.30	.15
1993 Score Select Chase Rookies	4	45.00	34.00	18.00
1993 Score Select Stat Leaders	55	.10	.08	.04
1993 Studio	180	.50	.40	.20
1993 Topps	331	.30	.25	.12
1993 Topps Black Gold	36	.60	.45	.25
1993 Topps Finest	43	7.00	5.25	2.75
1993 Topps Finest Refractors	43	70.00	52.00	28.00
1993 Topps Gold	331	.60	.45	.25
1993 Topps Stadium Club	277	.60	.45	.25
1993 Topps Stadium Club First Day Production	277	25.00	18.50	10.00
1993 Upper Deck	262	.30	.25	.12
1993 Upper Deck "Highlights"	11	10.00	7.50	4.00
1993 Upper Deck Fun Packs	109	.30	.25	.12
1993 Upper Deck SP	122	2.00	1.50	.80
1994 Bowman	195	.40	.30	.15
1994 Donruss	39	.50	.40	.20
1994 Donruss Special Edition - Gold	39	.35	.25	.14
1994 Donruss Triple Play	115	.15	.11	.06
1994 Fleer	111	.30	.25	.12
1994 Fleer Extra Bases	60	.50	.40	.20
1994 Fleer Flair	283	1.00	.75	.40
1994 Fleer Flair Hot Glove	4	15.00	11.00	6.00
1994 Fleer League Leaders	4	1.00	.75	.40
1994 Fleer Ultra	45	.50	.40	.20
1994 Fleer Ultra Award Winners	7	1.50	1.25	.60
1994 Fleer Ultra League Leaders	3	2.00	1.50	.80
1994 Fleer Ultra Rising Stars	7	12.00	9.00	4.75
1994 Leaf	350	.40	.30	.15
1994 Leaf Limited	28	4.00	3.00	1.50
1994 O-Pee-Chee	237	.35	.25	.14
1994 O-Pee-Chee All-Star Redemption Cards	25	.75	.60	.30
1994 O-Pee-Chee Jumbo All-Stars	25	6.00	4.50	2.50
1994 O-Pee-Chee Jumbo All-Stars Factory Set	25	1.50	1.25	.60
1994 Pacific Crown	174	.30	.25	.12
1994 Pacific Crown Jewels of the Crown	17	4.00	3.00	1.50
1994 Pinnacle	179	.40	.30	.15
1994 Pinnacle Artist's Proof	179	30.00	22.00	12.00
1994 Pinnacle Museum Collection	179	12.00	9.00	4.75
1994 Pinnacle Run Creators	14	5.00	3.75	2.00
1994 Pinnacle The Naturals Box Set	7	.50	.40	.20
1994 Score	81	.30	.25	.12
1994 Score Gold Stars	41	10.00	7.50	4.00
1994 Score Select	231	.75	.60	.30
1994 Score Select Skills	4	10.00	7.50	4.00
1994 Score The Cycle	2	15.00	11.00	6.00
1994 Sportflics 2000	43	.60	.45	.25
1994 Sportflics 2000 Shakers	1	8.00	6.00	3.25
1994 Studio	93	.50	.40	.20
1994 Topps	149	.25	.20	.10
1994 Topps Black Gold	11	.75	.60	.30
1994 Topps Finest	218	3.00	2.25	1.25
1994 Topps Finest Refractors	218	18.00	13.50	7.25
1994 Topps Finest Superstars	218	10.00	7.50	4.00
1994 Topps Gold	149	.75	.60	.30
1994 Topps Stadium Club	301	.50	.40	.20
1994 Topps Stadium Club First Day Production	301	30.00	22.00	12.00

Set	Card #	MT	NM	EX
1994 Topps Stadium Club Members Only Baseball	27	.25	.20	.10
1994 Topps Traded Finest Inserts	6	.75	.60	.30
1994 Upper Deck	215	.50	.40	.20
1994 Upper Deck All-Stars Green Foil	29	.50	.40	.20
1994 Upper Deck All-Stars Gold Foil	29	2.50	2.00	1.00
1994 Upper Deck Collector's Choice	315	.15	.11	.06
1994 Upper Deck Collector's Choice	565	.15	.11	.06
1994 Upper Deck Electric Diamond	215	1.50	1.25	.60
1994 Upper Deck Fun Packs	107	.20	.15	.08
1994 Upper Deck SP	98	.60	.45	.25
1994 Upper Deck SP Baseball Die-Cut	98	1.00	.75	.40

Set	Card #	MT	NM	EX
1988 Pacific Trading Cards Baseball Legends	39	.10	.08	.04

Jim Lonborg

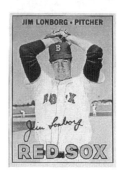

Set	Card #	NM	EX	VG
1965 Topps	573 (R)	22.00	11.00	6.50
1966 O-Pee-Chee	93	2.25	1.25	.70
1966 Topps	93	1.50	.70	.45
1967 Topps	371	3.00	1.50	.90
1968 O-Pee-Chee	10	2.25	1.25	.70
1968 O-Pee-Chee	12	2.25	1.25	.70
1968 Topps	10a	3.50	1.75	1.00
1968 Topps	10b	3.00	1.50	.90
1968 Topps	12	3.00	1.50	.90
1968 Topps	460	2.50	1.25	.70
1969 O-Pee-Chee	109	2.25	1.25	.70
1969 Topps	109	1.25	.60	.40
1970 Topps	665	7.00	3.50	2.00
1971 O-Pee-Chee	577	5.00	2.50	1.50
1971 Topps	577	4.00	2.00	1.25
1972 O-Pee-Chee	255	.75	.40	.25
1972 Topps	255	.90	.45	.25
1973 O-Pee-Chee	3	.75	.40	.25
1973 Topps	3	.50	.25	.15
1974 O-Pee-Chee	342	.60	.30	.20
1974 Topps	342	.30	.15	.09
1975 O-Pee-Chee	94	.55	.30	.15
1975 Topps	94	.35	.20	.11
1975 Topps Mini	94	.75	.40	.25
1976 O-Pee-Chee	271	.35	.20	.11
1976 Topps	271	.25	.13	.08
1977 Topps	569	.20	.10	.06
1978 Topps	52	.20	.10	.06
1979 O-Pee-Chee	233	.25	.13	.08
1979 Topps	446	.20	.10	.06

Mickey Lolich

Set	Card #	NM	EX	VG
1964 Topps	128 (R)	20.00	10.00	6.00
1965 Topps	335	4.50	2.25	1.25
1966 Topps	226	4.00	2.00	1.25
1966 Topps	455	9.00	4.50	2.75
1967 O-Pee-Chee	88	2.25	1.25	.70
1967 Topps	88	4.00	2.00	1.25
1968 Topps	414	2.75	1.50	.80
1969 Topps	270	3.50	1.75	1.00
1970 O-Pee-Chee	72	1.25	.60	.40
1970 Topps	72	3.50	1.75	1.00
1970 Topps	715	7.00	3.50	2.00
1971 O-Pee-Chee	71	1.50	.70	.45
1971 O-Pee-Chee	133	1.50	.70	.45
1971 Topps	71	1.50	.70	.45
1971 Topps	133	1.25	.60	.40
1972 O-Pee-Chee	94	.75	.40	.25
1972 O-Pee-Chee	96	.75	.40	.25
1972 O-Pee-Chee	450	1.75	.90	.50
1972 Topps	94	2.00	1.00	.60
1972 Topps	96	2.00	1.00	.60
1972 Topps	450	1.25	.60	.40
1973 O-Pee-Chee	390	.75	.40	.25
1973 Topps	390	.75	.40	.25
1974 O-Pee-Chee	166	1.50	.70	.45
1974 Topps	9	.60	.30	.20
1975 O-Pee-Chee	245	.55	.30	.15
1975 Topps	245	.40	.20	.12
1975 Topps Mini	245	.80	.40	.25
1976 O-Pee-Chee	3	.35	.20	.11
1976 O-Pee-Chee	385	.40	.20	.12
1976 Topps	3	.35	.20	.11
1976 Topps	385	.40	.20	.12
1976 Topps Traded	385T	.90	.45	.25
1977 Topps	565	.35	.20	.11
1979 Topps	164	.30	.15	.09
1980 Topps	459	.12	.06	.04

Davey Lopes

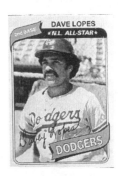

Set	Card #	NM	EX	VG
1973 O-Pee-Chee	609	3.50	1.75	1.00

Sparky Lyle

1973 Topps	609 (R)	4.00	2.00	1.25
1974 O-Pee-Chee	112	.60	.30	.20
1974 Topps	112	.40	.20	.12
1975 O-Pee-Chee	93	.55	.30	.15
1975 Topps	93	.40	.20	.12
1975 Topps Mini	93	.60	.30	.20
1976 O-Pee-Chee	4	.35	.20	.11
1976 O-Pee-Chee	197	2.00	1.00	.60
1976 O-Pee-Chee	660	.35	.20	.11
1976 Topps	4	.25	.13	.08
1976 Topps	197	1.00	.50	.30
1976 Topps	660	.25	.13	.08
1977 O-Pee-Chee	4	.30	.15	.09
1977 O-Pee-Chee	96	.30	.15	.09
1977 Topps	4	.20	.10	.06
1977 Topps	180	.25	.13	.08
1978 O-Pee-Chee	222	.25	.13	.08
1978 Topps	440	.25	.13	.08
1979 O-Pee-Chee	144	.25	.13	.08
1979 Topps	290	.25	.13	.08
1980 O-Pee-Chee	291	.15	.08	.05
1980 Topps	560	.25	.13	.08

Set	Card #	MT	NM	EX
1981 Donruss	416	.10	.08	.04
1981 Fleer	114a	.10	.08	.04
1981 Fleer	114b	1.00	.70	.40
1981 O-Pee-Chee	50	.12	.09	.05
1981 Topps	50	.12	.09	.05
1982 Donruss	327	.10	.08	.04
1982 Fleer	12	.10	.08	.04
1982 O-Pee-Chee	85	.12	.09	.05
1982 O-Pee-Chee	218	.12	.09	.05
1982 O-Pee-Chee	338	.12	.09	.05
1982 Topps	338	.12	.09	.05
1982 Topps	740	.12	.09	.05
1982 Topps	741	.10	.08	.04
1982 Topps Traded	64T	.20	.15	.08
1983 Donruss	339	.10	.08	.04
1983 Fleer	524	.10	.08	.04
1983 O-Pee-Chee	365	.12	.09	.05
1983 Topps	365	.12	.09	.05
1984 Donruss	400	.15	.11	.06
1984 Fleer	453	.10	.08	.04
1984 O-Pee-Chee	17	.20	.15	.08
1984 Topps	669	.10	.08	.04
1984 Topps	714	.10	.08	.04
1985 Donruss	604	.10	.08	.04
1985 Fleer	60	.08	.06	.03
1985 O-Pee-Chee	12	.08	.06	.03
1985 Topps	12	.08	.06	.03
1986 Donruss	9	.10	.08	.04
1986 Donruss	388	.08	.06	.03
1986 Donruss Diamond Kings Supers	9	.20	.15	.08
1986 Fleer	372	.08	.06	.03
1986 Leaf	9	.08	.06	.03
1986 O-Pee-Chee	125	.08	.06	.03
1986 Sportflics	144	.15	.11	.06
1986 Sportflics	194	.10	.08	.04
1986 Topps	125	.07	.05	.03
1987 Donruss	455	.07	.05	.03
1987 Fleer	62	.08	.06	.03
1987 O-Pee-Chee	311	.08	.06	.03
1987 Topps	4	.07	.05	.03
1987 Topps	445	.07	.05	.03
1988 Score	489	.06	.05	.02
1988 Topps	226	.06	.05	.02

Set	Card #	NM	EX	VG
1969 Topps	311 (R)	12.50	6.25	3.75
1970 O-Pee-Chee	116	1.25	.60	.40
1970 Topps	116	1.50	.70	.45
1971 O-Pee-Chee	649	12.00	6.00	3.50
1971 Topps	649	8.00	4.00	2.50
1972 O-Pee-Chee	259	.75	.40	.25
1972 Topps	259	1.00	.50	.30
1973 O-Pee-Chee	68	.75	.40	.25
1973 O-Pee-Chee	394	.75	.40	.25
1973 Topps	68	.75	.40	.25
1973 Topps	394	.40	.20	.12
1974 O-Pee-Chee	66	.60	.30	.20
1974 Topps	66	.30	.15	.09
1975 O-Pee-Chee	485	.55	.30	.15
1975 Topps	485	.30	.15	.09
1975 Topps Mini	485	.60	.30	.20
1976 O-Pee-Chee	545	.35	.20	.11
1976 Topps	545	.25	.13	.08
1977 O-Pee-Chee	89	.30	.15	.09
1977 Topps	598	.35	.20	.11
1978 O-Pee-Chee	214	.25	.13	.08
1978 O-Pee-Chee	237	.25	.13	.08
1978 Topps	2	.25	.13	.08
1978 Topps	35	.30	.15	.09
1979 O-Pee-Chee	188	.25	.13	.08
1979 Topps	365	.30	.15	.09
1980 O-Pee-Chee	62	.15	.08	.05
1980 Topps	115	.15	.08	.05

Set	Card #	MT	NM	EX
1981 Donruss	284	.10	.08	.04
1981 Fleer	17	.10	.08	.04
1981 O-Pee-Chee	337	.12	.09	.05
1981 Topps	719	.12	.09	.05
1982 Donruss	189	.10	.08	.04
1982 Fleer	247	.10	.08	.04
1982 O-Pee-Chee	285	.12	.09	.05
1982 Topps	285	.12	.09	.05
1983 O-Pee-Chee	92	.12	.09	.05
1983 O-Pee-Chee	208	.12	.09	.05
1983 Topps	693	.12	.09	.05
1983 Topps	694	.10	.08	.04
1990 Pacific Legends	93	.05	.04	.02

* * *

Mickey Rivers' favorite card of himself is his '73 Topps, which pictures him with his six-finger glove. The former outfielder later presented the 23-year-old six-fingered baseball glove to a child who was sick in the hospital.

* * *

Between August 1973 and February's final show in 1989, 15,444 shows featuring baseball cards and sports memorabilia were reported in the pages of SCD. By actual count, more than a third of these - 5,235 - were held in 1988. More than a third of all reported shows by December 1987 had been held during that year.

* * *

Fred Lynn

Set	Card #	NM	EX	VG
1975 O-Pee-Chee	622	12.00	6.00	3.50
1975 Topps	622 (R)	10.00	5.00	3.00
1975 Topps Mini	622	15.00	7.50	4.50
1976 O-Pee-Chee	50	1.75	.90	.50
1976 O-Pee-Chee	192	2.00	1.00	.60
1976 O-Pee-Chee	196	.50	.25	.15
1976 Topps	50	2.00	1.00	.60
1976 Topps	192	2.00	1.00	.60
1976 Topps	196	1.00	.50	.30
1977 O-Pee-Chee	163	1.25	.60	.40
1977 Topps	210	1.50	.70	.45
1978 O-Pee-Chee	62	.75	.40	.25
1978 Topps	320	.90	.45	.25
1979 O-Pee-Chee	249	.60	.30	.20
1979 Topps	480	.70	.35	.20
1980 O-Pee-Chee	60	.30	.15	.09
1980 Topps	110	.35	.20	.11
1980 Topps	201	.50	.25	.15

Set	Card #	MT	NM	EX
1981 Donruss	218	.20	.15	.08
1981 Fleer	223	.20	.15	.08
1981 O-Pee-Chee	313	.25	.20	.10
1981 Topps	720	.20	.15	.08
1981 Topps Traded	797	.20	.15	.08
1982 Donruss	367	.20	.15	.08
1982 Fleer	468	.20	.15	.08
1982 Fleer	642	.15	.11	.06
1982 O-Pee-Chee	251	.25	.20	.10
1982 O-Pee-Chee	252	.12	.09	.05
1982 Topps	251	.30	.25	.12
1982 Topps	252	.15	.11	.06
1983 Donruss	241	.20	.15	.08
1983 Fleer	97	.20	.15	.08
1983 O-Pee-Chee	182	.20	.15	.08
1983 O-Pee-Chee	392	.12	.09	.05
1983 Topps	392	.15	.11	.06
1983 Topps	520	.25	.20	.10
1984 Donruss	17a	.35	.25	.14
1984 Donruss	17b	.70	.50	.30
1984 Donruss	108	.35	.25	.14
1984 Fleer	525	.25	.20	.10
1984 Fleer	626	.12	.09	.05
1984 O-Pee-Chee	247	.40	.30	.15
1984 Topps	680	.25	.20	.10
1984 Topps All-Star Glossy Set of 22	7	.25	.20	.10
1985 Donruss	133	.25	.20	.10
1985 Fleer	307	.20	.15	.08
1985 Fleer Update	75	.30	.25	.12
1985 Leaf-Donruss	198	.20	.15	.08
1985 O-Pee-Chee	220	.15	.11	.06
1985 Topps	220	.20	.15	.08
1985 Topps Traded	77T	.30	.25	.12
1986 Donruss	245	.20	.15	.08
1986 Fleer	278	.10	.08	.04
1986 Leaf	120	.10	.08	.04
1986 O-Pee-Chee	55	.12	.09	.05
1986 Sportflics	38	.20	.15	.08
1986 Sportflics	63	.30	.25	.12
1986 Sportflics	71	.30	.25	.12
1986 Sportflics	73	.25	.20	.10
1986 Sportflics	137	.20	.15	.08
1986 Sportflics	150	.20	.15	.08
1986 Sportflics Rookies	46	.40	.30	.15
1986 Topps	55	.15	.11	.06
1987 Donruss	9	.12	.09	.05
1987 Donruss	108	.15	.11	.06
1987 Donruss Diamond Kings Supers	9	.20	.15	.08
1987 Fleer	474	.15	.11	.06
1987 Fleer All Stars	25	.12	.09	.05
1987 Leaf	9	.10	.08	.04
1987 Leaf	83	.10	.08	.04
1987 O-Pee-Chee	370	.10	.08	.04
1987 Sportflics	49	.20	.15	.08
1987 Sportflics	198	.25	.20	.10
1987 Topps	370	.15	.11	.06
1988 Donruss	248	.15	.11	.06
1988 Fleer	566	.15	.11	.06
1988 Leaf	163	.10	.08	.04
1988 Score	42	.10	.08	.04
1988 Sportflics	23	.15	.11	.06
1988 Topps	707	.10	.08	.04
1988 Topps Big Baseball	169	.10	.08	.04
1989 Donruss	563	.10	.08	.04
1989 Fleer	138	.10	.08	.04
1989 O-Pee-Chee	27	.07	.05	.03
1989 Score	126	.10	.08	.04
1989 Sportflics	68	.15	.11	.06
1989 Topps	416	.10	.08	.04
1989 Upper Deck	761	.10	.08	.04
1990 Bowman	216	.05	.04	.02
1990 Bowman Tiffany	216	.20	.15	.08
1990 Fleer	609	.06	.05	.02
1990 Leaf	188	.40	.30	.15
1990 O-Pee-Chee	107	.05	.04	.02
1990 O-Pee-Chee	663	.07	.05	.03
1990 Score	131	.09	.07	.04
1990 Score Traded	20T	.06	.05	.02
1990 Topps	107	.05	.04	.02
1990 Topps	663	.07	.05	.03
1990 Topps Big Baseball	277	.06	.05	.02
1990 Topps Traded	62T	.06	.05	.02
1990 Upper Deck	247	.09	.07	.04
1990 Upper Deck	771	.10	.08	.04
1991 Donruss	673	.05	.04	.02
1991 Fleer	536	.06	.05	.02
1991 Score	554	.05	.04	.02
1991 Topps	586	.05	.04	.02
1991 Upper Deck	273	.08	.06	.03

Greg Maddux

Set	Card #	MT	NM	EX
1987 Donruss	36 (R)	8.00	6.00	3.25
1987 Fleer Update	68	6.00	4.50	2.50
1987 Leaf	36	6.00	4.50	2.50
1987 Topps Traded	70T	4.00	3.00	1.50

Card	#			
1987 Topps Traded Tiffany	70T	12.00	9.00	4.75
1988 Donruss	539	.75	.60	.30
1988 Fleer	423	2.50	2.00	1.00
1988 O-Pee-Chee	361	.60	.45	.25
1988 Topps	361	1.25	.90	.50
1988 Topps Tiffany	361	3.75	2.75	1.50
1989 Bowman	284	.40	.30	.15
1989 Donruss	373	.35	.25	.14
1989 Fleer	431	.40	.30	.15
1989 O-Pee-Chee	240	.10	.08	.04
1989 Score	119	.35	.25	.14
1989 Sportflics	108	.15	.11	.06
1989 Topps	240	.35	.25	.14
1989 Upper Deck	241	2.50	2.00	1.00
1990 Bowman	27	.25	.20	.10
1990 Donruss	158	.25	.20	.10
1990 Fleer	37	.25	.20	.10
1990 Leaf	25	8.00	6.00	3.25
1990 O-Pee-Chee	715	.15	.11	.06
1990 Score	403	.25	.20	.10
1990 Sportflics	211	.15	.11	.06
1990 Topps	715	.25	.20	.10
1990 Topps Big Baseball	204	.08	.06	.03
1990 Upper Deck	213	.50	.40	.20
1991 Bowman	426	.20	.15	.08
1991 Donruss	374	.20	.15	.08
1991 Fleer	426	.20	.15	.08
1991 Fleer Ultra	64	.40	.30	.15
1991 Leaf	127	.40	.30	.15
1991 Score	317	.25	.20	.10
1991 Topps	35	.15	.11	.06
1991 Topps Stadium Club	126	3.00	2.25	1.25
1991 Upper Deck	115	.30	.25	.12
1992 Bowman	148	1.75	1.25	.60
1992 Donruss	520	.20	.15	.08
1992 Donruss Triple Play	19	.12	.09	.05
1992 Fleer	386	.20	.15	.08
1992 Fleer Ultra	178	.15	.11	.06
1992 Fleer Ultra Award Winners	24	3.50	2.75	1.50
1992 Leaf	294	.30	.25	.12
1992 O-Pee-Chee	580	.05	.04	.02
1992 Pinnacle	65	.40	.30	.15
1992 Pinnacle	608	.30	.25	.12
1992 Pinnacle Team 2000	32	.50	.40	.20
1992 Score	269	.25	.20	.10
1992 Score Impact Players	77	.40	.30	.15
1992 Studio	15	.35	.25	.14
1992 Topps	580	.15	.11	.06
1992 Topps Gold	580	2.00	1.50	.80
1992 Topps Stadium Club	665	.40	.30	.15
1992 Topps Stadium Club East Coast National	665	15.00	11.00	6.00
1992 Upper Deck	353	.25	.20	.10
1992 Upper Deck MVP Holograms	30	.75	.60	.30
1993 Bowman	550	.60	.45	.25
1993 Donruss	608	.25	.20	.10
1993 Donruss Elite Dominators	3	65.00	49.00	26.00
1993 Donruss Triple Play League Leaders	2	3.00	2.25	1.25
1993 Donruss Triple Play Gallery	4	2.00	1.50	.80
1993 Fleer	380	.35	.25	.14
1993 Fleer	707	.15	.11	.06
1993 Fleer All-Stars	10	2.50	2.00	1.00
1993 Fleer Final Edition	3	.40	.30	.15
1993 Fleer Flair	7	2.00	1.50	.80
1993 Fleer Ultra	307	.50	.40	.20
1993 Fleer Ultra All-Stars	9	3.00	2.25	1.25
1993 Fleer Ultra Award Winners	1	3.00	2.25	1.25
1993 Fleer Ultra Award Winners	22	3.00	2.25	1.25
1993 Fleer Ultra Performers	6	2.00	1.50	.80
1993 Leaf	326	.40	.30	.15
1993 Leaf Gold All-Stars	19	5.00	3.75	2.00
1993 O-Pee-Chee	135	.75	.60	.30
1993 O-Pee-Chee Premier	126	.25	.20	.10
1993 O-Pee-Chee Premier Star Performers	19	.25	.20	.10
1993 Pinnacle	517	.40	.30	.15
1993 Pinnacle Team Pinnacle	1	12.00	9.00	4.75
1993 Score	484	.15	.11	.06
1993 Score	527	.10	.08	.04
1993 Score	576	.30	.25	.12
1993 Score Select	31	.40	.30	.15
1993 Score Select Aces	4	10.00	7.50	4.00
1993 Score Select Chase Stars	9	7.50	5.50	3.00
1993 Score Select Rookie/ Traded	123	2.00	1.50	.80
1993 Score Select Stat Leaders	66	.10	.08	.04
1993 Score Select Stat Leaders	78	.15	.11	.06
1993 Score Select Stat Leaders	84	.15	.11	.06
1993 Studio	196	.40	.30	.15
1993 Topps	183	.25	.20	.10
1993 Topps	409	.10	.08	.04
1993 Topps Black Gold	12	.60	.45	.25
1993 Topps Finest	85	7.00	5.25	2.75
1993 Topps Finest Jumbo All-Stars	85	15.00	11.00	6.00
1993 Topps Finest Refractors	85	70.00	52.00	28.00
1993 Topps Gold	183	.50	.40	.20
1993 Topps Gold	409	.20	.15	.08
1993 Topps Stadium Club	2	.50	.40	.20
1993 Topps Stadium Club	665	.40	.30	.15
1993 Topps Stadium Club	750	.20	.15	.08
1993 Topps Stadium Club First Day Production	2	15.00	11.00	6.00
1993 Topps Stadium Club First Day Production	665	20.00	15.00	8.00
1993 Topps Stadium Club First Day Production	750	20.00	15.00	8.00
1993 Topps Stadium Club Master Photos	(27)	2.00	1.50	.80
1993 Topps Stadium Club Members Only	(14)	.75	.60	.30
1993 Topps Stadium Club Special	126	.30	.25	.12
1993 Topps Traded	54	.20	.15	.08
1993 Upper Deck	472	.15	.11	.06
1993 Upper Deck	488	.10	.08	.04
1993 Upper Deck	535	.20	.15	.08
1993 Upper Deck Fun Packs	65	.15	.11	.06
1993 Upper Deck SP	59	2.00	1.50	.80
1994 Bowman	245	.40	.30	.15
1994 Bowman's Best	101	1.50	1.25	.60
1994 Bowman's Best	36	2.50	2.00	1.00
1994 Bowman's Best Refractors	101	5.00	3.75	2.00
1994 Bowman's Best Refractors	36	10.00	7.50	4.00
1994 Donruss	380	.40	.30	.15
1994 Donruss Award Winners Supers	2	3.00	2.25	1.25
1994 Donruss Special Edition - Gold	380	.50	.40	.20
1994 Donruss Triple Play Promos	10	3.00	2.25	1.25
1994 Donruss Triple Play Medalists	14	1.50	1.25	.60
1994 Donruss Triple Play	46	.25	.20	.10
1994 Fleer	365	.40	.30	.15
1994 Fleer Atlantic	16	.50	.40	.20
1994 Fleer Award Winners	4	1.50	1.25	.60
1994 Fleer Extra Bases	208	.40	.30	.15
1994 Fleer Extra Bases Game Breakers	16	.75	.60	.30

1994 Fleer Extra Bases Pitcher's Duel	7M	1.00	.75	.40
1994 Fleer Flair	130	1.00	.75	.40
1994 Fleer Flair Hot Glove	5	15.00	11.00	6.00
1994 Fleer League Leaders	12	1.25	.90	.50
1994 Fleer Smoke N' Heat	7	15.00	11.00	6.00
1994 Fleer Ultra	447	.40	.30	.15
1994 Fleer Ultra All-Stars	20	1.25	.90	.50
1994 Fleer Ultra Award Winners	18	1.25	.90	.50
1994 Fleer Ultra Award Winners	23	1.25	.90	.50
1994 Fleer Ultra Strikeout Kings	3	2.50	2.00	1.00
1994 Leaf	94	.40	.30	.15
1994 Leaf Gold Stars	8	25.00	18.00	10.00
1994 Leaf Limited	87	3.50	2.75	1.50
1994 Leaf Limited Gold	18	25.00	18.00	10.00
1994 Leaf Statistical Standouts	5	2.00	1.50	.80
1994 O-Pee-Chee	101	.40	.30	.15
1994 O-Pee-Chee All-Star Redemption Cards	22	.75	.60	.30
1994 O-Pee-Chee Jumbo All-Stars	22	7.00	5.25	2.75
1994 O-Pee-Chee Jumbo All-Stars Factory Set	22	1.25	.90	.50
1994 Pacific Crown	15	.40	.30	.15
1994 Pacific Crown	656	.25	.20	.10
1994 Pacific Crown Jewels of the Crown	30	4.00	3.00	1.50
1994 Pinnacle	11	.40	.30	.15
1994 Pinnacle Artist's Proof	11	20.00	15.00	8.00
1994 Pinnacle Museum Collection	11	8.00	6.00	3.25
1994 Pinnacle Team Pinnacle	9	15.00	11.00	6.00
1994 Pinnacle The Naturals Box Set	15	.50	.40	.20
1994 Pinnacle Tribute	12	4.00	3.00	1.50
1994 Score	524	.25	.20	.10
1994 Score	634	.10	.08	.04
1994 Score Select	2	.60	.45	.25
1994 Score Select Crown Contenders	2	10.00	7.50	4.00
1994 Sportflics 2000	53	.40	.30	.15
1994 Sportflics 2000	193	.25	.20	.10
1994 Sportflics 2000 Promos	193	2.00	1.50	.80
1994 Studio	39	.50	.40	.20
1994 Studio Gold Stars	8	30.00	22.00	12.00
1994 Studio Silver Stars	8	15.00	11.00	6.00
1994 Topps	392	.15	.11	.06
1994 Topps	499	.20	.15	.08
1994 Topps Black Gold	38	1.00	.75	.40
1994 Topps Finest	209	2.50	2.00	1.00
1994 Topps Finest Refractors	209	15.00	11.00	6.00
1994 Topps Finest Superstars	209	8.00	6.00	3.25
1994 Topps Gold	392	.45	.35	.20
1994 Topps Gold	499	.60	.45	.25
1994 Topps Stadium Club	544	.40	.30	.15
1994 Topps Stadium Club	716	.25	.20	.10
1994 Topps Stadium Club First Day Production	544	6.00	4.50	2.50
1994 Topps Stadium Club First Day Production	716	12.00	9.00	4.75
1994 Topps Stadium Club Members Only Baseball	42	.25	.20	.10
1994 Topps Traded Finest Inserts	1	1.00	.75	.40
1994 Upper Deck	320	.50	.40	.20
1994 Upper Deck All-Stars Green Foil	18	.25	.20	.10
1994 Upper Deck All-Stars Gold Foil	18	1.00	.70	.40
1994 Upper Deck Collector's Choice	183	.25	.20	.12
1994 Upper Deck Electric Diamond	320	1.00	.75	.40
1994 Upper Deck Fun Packs	131	.25	.20	.10
1994 Upper Deck Fun Packs	184	.15	.11	.06
1994 Upper Deck Fun Packs	207	1.25	.90	.50
1994 Upper Deck SP	54	.75	.60	.30
1994 Upper Deck SP Baseball Die-Cut	54	1.50	1.25	.60

Bill Madlock

Set	Card #	NM	EX	VG
1974 O-Pee-Chee	600	6.00	3.00	1.75
1974 Topps	600 (R)	5.00	2.50	1.50
1975 O-Pee-Chee	104	1.25	.60	.40
1975 Topps	104	1.25	.60	.40
1975 Topps Mini	104	1.00	.50	.30
1976 O-Pee-Chee	191	.50	.25	.15
1976 O-Pee-Chee	640	.75	.40	.25
1976 Topps	191	1.00	.50	.30
1976 Topps	640	.50	.25	.15
1977 O-Pee-Chee	1	6.00	3.00	1.75
1977 O-Pee-Chee	56	.50	.25	.15
1977 Topps	1	5.00	2.50	1.50
1977 Topps	250	.40	.20	.12
1978 O-Pee-Chee	89	.40	.20	.12
1978 Topps	410	.50	.25	.15
1979 O-Pee-Chee	96	.30	.15	.09
1979 Topps	195	.40	.20	.12
1980 O-Pee-Chee	30	.30	.15	.09
1980 Topps	55	.20	.10	.06

Set	Card #	MT	NM	EX
1981 Donruss	252	.12	.09	.05
1981 Fleer	381	.12	.09	.05
1981 O-Pee-Chee	137	.20	.15	.08
1981 Topps	715	.15	.11	.06
1982 Donruss	653	.12	.09	.05
1982 Fleer	485	.12	.09	.05
1982 O-Pee-Chee	365	.15	.11	.06
1982 Topps	161	.10	.08	.04
1982 Topps	365	.10	.08	.04
1982 Topps	696	.15	.11	.06
1983 Donruss	311	.12	.09	.05
1983 Fleer	309	.12	.09	.05
1983 O-Pee-Chee	335	.15	.11	.06
1983 Topps	291	.15	.11	.06
1983 Topps	645	.15	.11	.06
1983 Topps All-Star Glossy Set of 40	26	.20	.15	.08
1984 Donruss	20a	.30	.25	.12
1984 Donruss	20b	.60	.45	.25
1984 Donruss	113	.20	.15	.08
1984 Fleer	253	.12	.09	.05
1984 O-Pee-Chee	250	.30	.25	.12
1984 Topps	131	.50	.40	.20

Set	Card #			
1984 Topps	250	.12	.09	.05
1984 Topps	696	.15	.11	.06
1984 Topps	701	.35	.25	.14
1984 Topps All-Star Glossy Set of 40	19	.20	.15	.08
1985 Donruss	200	.15	.11	.06
1985 Fleer	468	.12	.09	.05
1985 Leaf-Donruss	185	.08	.06	.03
1985 O-Pee-Chee	157	.10	.08	.04
1985 Topps	560	.12	.09	.05
1986 Donruss	617	.12	.09	.05
1986 Fleer	135	.12	.09	.05
1986 Leaf	238	.08	.06	.03
1986 O-Pee-Chee	47	.10	.08	.04
1986 Sportflics	58	.60	.45	.25
1986 Sportflics	88	.15	.11	.06
1986 Sportflics	131	.10	.08	.04
1986 Sportflics	181	.70	.50	.30
1986 Topps	470	.12	.09	.05
1987 Donruss	155a	.12	.09	.05
1987 Donruss	155b	.70	.50	.30
1987 Fleer	445	.12	.09	.05
1987 Fleer Update	69	.15	.11	.06
1987 Leaf	120	.08	.06	.03
1987 O-Pee-Chee	276	.08	.06	.03
1987 Sportflics	130	.15	.11	.06
1987 Topps	734	.10	.08	.04
1987 Topps Traded	71T	.15	.11	.06
1988 Donruss	496	.10	.08	.04
1988 Fleer	63	.10	.08	.04
1988 Leaf	232	.08	.06	.03
1988 O-Pee-Chee	145	.08	.06	.03
1988 Score	445	.08	.06	.03
1988 Score Glossy	445	.40	.30	.15
1988 Sportflics	123	.15	.11	.06
1988 Topps	145	.08	.06	.03
1990 Pacific Senior League	214	.10	.08	.04
1990 Topps Senior League	71	.15	.11	.06

Mickey Mantle

Set	Card #	NM	EX	VG
1951 Bowman	253 (R)	8000.	4000.	2200.
1952 Bowman	101	2400.	1200.	725.00
1952 Topps	311a	18000.	9000.	4140.
1952 Topps	311b	18000.	9000.	4140.
1953 Bowman Color	44	450.00	225.00	125.00
1953 Bowman Color	59	2500.	1250.	650.00
1953 Topps	82	3000.	1500.	690.00
1954 Bowman	65	925.00	460.00	275.00
1954 Red Heart Dog Food	(18)	550.00	275.00	165.00
1955 Bowman	202	550.00	275.00	140.00
1956 Topps	135	975.00	475.00	275.00
1957 Topps	95	1000.	500.00	250.00
1957 Topps	407	325.00	160.00	95.00
1958 Topps	150	650.00	275.00	175.00
1958 Topps	418	180.00	90.00	55.00
1958 Topps	487	115.00	57.00	34.00

1959 Home Run Derby	(12)	1200.	600.00	360.00
1959 Topps	10	450.00	200.00	120.00
1959 Topps	461	60.00	30.00	18.00
1959 Topps	564	280.00	140.00	84.00
1960 Post Cereal	(7)	1500.	750.00	450.00
1960 Topps	160	50.00	25.00	15.00
1960 Topps	350	400.00	200.00	120.00
1960 Topps	563	250.00	125.00	75.00
1961 Post Cereal	4a	125.00	62.00	37.00
1961 Post Cereal	4b	125.00	62.00	37.00
1961 Topps	44	50.00	25.00	15.00
1961 Topps	300	375.00	185.00	110.00
1961 Topps	475	125.00	62.00	37.00
1961 Topps	578	400.00	200.00	120.00
1962 Post Cereal	5a	100.00	50.00	30.00
1962 Post Cereal	5b	90.00	45.00	27.00
1962 Topps	18	125.00	62.50	37.50
1962 Topps	53	60.00	30.00	18.00
1962 Topps	200	500.00	250.00	130.00
1962 Topps	318	60.00	30.00	18.00
1962 Topps	471	145.00	72.00	43.00
1963 Post Cereal	15	325.00	162.00	97.00
1963 Topps	2	27.00	13.50	8.00
1963 Topps	173	80.00	40.00	24.00
1963 Topps	200	430.00	215.00	130.00
1964 Topps	50	275.00	135.00	82.50
1964 Topps	331	130.00	65.00	39.00
1965 O-Pee-Chee	3	30.00	15.00	9.00
1965 O-Pee-Chee	5	30.00	15.00	9.00
1965 Topps	3	20.00	10.00	6.00
1965 Topps	5	30.00	15.00	9.00
1965 Topps	350	475.00	240.00	140.00
1966 O-Pee-Chee	50	275.00	137.00	82.00
1966 Topps	50	200.00	100.00	60.00
1967 O-Pee-Chee	103	13.50	6.75	4.00
1967 O-Pee-Chee	150	320.00	160.00	96.00
1967 Topps	103a	15.00	7.50	4.50
1967 Topps	103b	10.00	5.00	3.00
1967 Topps	150	235.00	120.00	72.50
1968 Topps	280	225.00	110.00	66.00
1968 Topps	490	125.00	62.50	37.50
1969 Topps	412	9.00	4.50	2.75
1969 Topps	500a	750.00	375.00	225.00
1969 Topps	500b	250.00	125.00	75.00
1975 O-Pee-Chee	194	6.75	3.50	2.00
1975 O-Pee-Chee	195	12.75	6.50	3.75
1975 O-Pee-Chee	200	6.75	3.50	2.00
1975 Topps	194	6.00	3.00	1.75
1975 Topps	195	10.00	5.00	3.00
1975 Topps	200	6.00	3.00	1.75
1975 Topps Mini	194	9.00	4.50	2.75
1975 Topps Mini	195	10.00	5.00	3.00
1975 Topps Mini	200	9.00	4.50	2.75

Set	Card #	MT	NM	EX
1983 Topps 1952 Reprint Set	311	30.00	22.00	12.00
1986 Sportflics Decade Greats	26	3.50	2.75	1.50
1991 "1953" Topps Archives Promos	(6)	45.00	34.00	18.00
1991 "1953" Topps Archives	82	15.00	11.00	6.00
1992 Score The Franchise	2	12.00	9.00	4.75
1992 Score The Franchise	4	9.00	6.75	3.50
1993 Score Select Triple Crown	1	75.00	56.00	30.00

* * *

Hank Aaron's 1957 Topps card shows him batting left-handed. Topps reversed the negative when it printed the card, making the right-handed hitter a lefty. The card was not corrected, so there's no additional premium.

* * *

Juan Marichal

Set	Card #	NM	EX	VG
1961 Topps	417 (R)	125.00	62.50	37.50
1962 Post Cereal	140	80.00	40.00	24.00
1962 Topps	505	35.00	17.50	10.50
1963 Post Cereal	109	9.00	4.50	2.75
1963 Topps	440	30.00	15.00	9.00
1964 Topps	3	15.00	11.00	6.00
1964 Topps	280	13.00	6.50	4.00
1965 O-Pee-Chee	10	2.75	1.50	.80
1965 O-Pee-Chee	50	12.75	6.50	3.75
1965 Topps	10	6.00	3.00	1.75
1965 Topps	50	12.00	6.00	3.50
1966 Topps	221	8.00	4.00	2.50
1966 Topps	420	8.00	4.00	2.50
1967 Topps	234	12.00	6.00	3.50
1967 Topps	236	12.00	6.00	3.50
1967 Topps	454a	12.00	6.00	3.50
1967 Topps	454b	12.00	6.00	3.50
1967 Topps	500	18.00	9.00	5.50
1968 O-Pee-Chee	107	2.50	1.25	.70
1968 Topps	107	3.50	1.75	1.00
1968 Topps	205	8.00	4.00	2.50
1969 O-Pee-Chee	10	8.50	4.25	2.50
1969 Topps	10	3.50	1.75	1.00
1969 Topps	370	7.00	3.50	2.00
1969 Topps	572	15.00	7.50	4.50
1970 O-Pee-Chee	67	7.50	3.75	2.25
1970 O-Pee-Chee	69	7.50	3.75	2.25
1970 O-Pee-Chee	210	7.50	3.75	2.25
1970 O-Pee-Chee	466	3.00	1.50	.90
1970 Topps	67	4.00	2.00	1.25
1970 Topps	69	5.00	2.50	1.50
1970 Topps	210	8.00	4.00	2.50
1970 Topps	466	5.00	2.50	1.50
1971 O-Pee-Chee	325	5.00	2.50	1.50
1971 Topps	325	6.00	3.00	1.75
1972 Topps	567	6.00	3.00	1.75
1972 Topps	568	3.00	1.50	.90
1973 O-Pee-Chee	480	2.50	1.25	.70
1973 Topps	480	6.00	3.00	1.75
1974 O-Pee-Chee	330	1.75	.90	.50
1974 Topps	330	4.00	2.00	1.25
1974 Topps Traded	330T	3.00	2.25	1.25

Set	Card #	MT	NM	EX
1986 Sportflics Decade Greats	46	.25	.20	.10
1988 Pacific Trading Cards Baseball Legends	54	.20	.15	.08
1991 Topps All-Star Glossy Set of 22	22	.20	.15	.08

* * *

If you're sending a card to your favorite player for him to autograph, always include an SASE so he can return your item to you. But don't send a card that you can't afford to lose if he doesn't respond.

* * *

Roger Maris

Set	Card #	NM	EX	VG
1958 Topps	47 (R)	430.00	215.00	125.00
1959 Topps	202	100.00	50.00	30.00
1960 Topps	377	90.00	45.00	27.00
1960 Topps	565	90.00	45.00	27.00
1961 Post Cereal	7a	35.00	17.50	10.50
1961 Post Cereal	7b	35.00	17.50	10.50
1961 Topps	2	160.00	80.00	48.00
1961 Topps	44	50.00	25.00	15.00
1961 Topps	478	45.00	22.50	13.50
1961 Topps	576	130.00	65.00	40.00
1962 Post Cereal	6a	20.00	10.00	6.00
1962 Post Cereal	6b	15.00	7.50	4.50
1962 Topps	1	200.00	100.00	60.00
1962 Topps	53	60.00	30.00	18.00
1962 Topps	313	25.00	12.50	7.50
1962 Topps	401	40.00	20.00	12.00
1963 Post Cereal	16	150.00	75.00	45.00
1963 Topps	4	11.00	5.50	3.25
1963 Topps	120	45.00	22.00	13.50
1964 Topps	225	65.00	32.00	19.50
1964 Topps	331	130.00	65.00	39.00
1965 O-Pee-Chee	155	72.00	36.00	22.00
1965 Topps	155	55.00	27.00	16.50
1966 Topps	365	55.00	27.00	16.50
1967 O-Pee-Chee	45	55.00	27.00	16.50
1967 Topps	45a	35.00	17.50	10.50
1967 Topps	45b	500.00	250.00	150.00
1968 Topps	330	32.00	16.00	10.00
1975 O-Pee-Chee	198	3.00	1.50	.90
1975 O-Pee-Chee	199	3.00	1.50	.90
1975 Topps	198	1.25	.60	.40
1975 Topps	199	1.50	.70	.45
1975 Topps Mini	198	1.75	.90	.50
1975 Topps Mini	199	2.25	1.25	.70
1979 Topps	413	1.00	.50	.30

Set	Card #	MT	NM	EX
1986 Topps	405	.20	.15	.08
1988 Pacific Trading Cards Baseball Legends	89	.30	.25	.12

* * *

Joe Pepitone played in only three games for the Atlanta Braves before he decided to hang up his cleats for good. "Hank (Aaron) asked me if he could have my pair of spikes, which I gave him. I think he hit his 714th or 715th home run wearing my old pair of baseball shoes. I'm very proud of that," he said.

* * *

Four years ago: Nolan Ryan's 1971 Topps card (#513) was $150 in July 1991.

* * *

Billy Martin

Eddie Mathews

Set	Card #	NM	EX	VG
1952 Topps	175 (R)	300.00	150.00	69.00
1953 Bowman Color	93	200.00	100.00	60.00
1953 Bowman Color	118	225.00	112.50	67.50
1953 Topps	86	110.00	55.00	25.00
1954 Bowman	145a	35.00	17.50	10.50
1954 Bowman	145b	45.00	22.50	13.50
1954 Red Heart Dog Food	(19)	55.00	27.00	16.50
1954 Topps	13	75.00	37.00	22.00
1956 Topps	181	85.00	42.00	25.00
1957 Topps	62	45.00	22.00	13.50
1958 Topps	271	12.00	6.00	3.50
1959 Topps	295	12.50	6.25	3.75
1960 Topps	173	9.50	4.75	2.75
1961 Post Cereal	190a	4.50	2.25	1.25
1961 Post Cereal	190b	9.00	4.50	2.75
1961 Topps	89	12.00	6.00	3.50
1962 Post Cereal	84	4.50	2.25	1.25
1962 Topps	208	8.00	4.00	2.50
1969 Topps	547	5.00	2.50	1.50
1971 O-Pee-Chee	208	1.50	.70	.45
1971 Topps	208	3.50	1.75	1.00
1972 O-Pee-Chee	33	1.25	.60	.40
1972 O-Pee-Chee	34	.75	.40	.25
1972 Topps	33	4.50	2.25	1.25
1972 Topps	34	1.50	.70	.45
1973 O-Pee-Chee	323	1.00	.50	.30
1973 Topps	323	1.50	.70	.45
1974 O-Pee-Chee	379	.75	.40	.25
1974 Topps	379	1.00	.50	.30
1975 O-Pee-Chee	511	.60	.30	.20
1975 Topps	511	2.00	1.00	.60
1975 Topps Mini	511	1.25	.60	.40
1976 O-Pee-Chee	17	1.00	.50	.30
1976 Topps	17	1.25	.60	.40
1977 Topps	387	2.00	1.00	.60
1978 Topps	721	.50	.25	.15

Set	Card #	MT	NM	EX
1981 Donruss	479	.12	.09	.05
1981 Fleer	581	.12	.09	.05
1981 Topps	671	.30	.25	.12
1982 Donruss	491	.12	.09	.05
1983 Donruss	575	.12	.09	.05
1983 Topps	156	.12	.09	.05
1983 Topps Traded	66T	.20	.15	.08
1983 Topps 1952 Reprint Set	175	1.25	.90	.50
1984 Topps	81	.12	.09	.05
1985 Topps Traded	78T	.20	.15	.08
1986 Topps	651	.12	.09	.05
1991 "1953" Topps Archives	86	.35	.25	.14
1994 "1954" Topps Archives	13	.35	.25	.14

Set	Card #	NM	EX	VG
1952 Topps	407 (R)	3000.	1300.	800.00
1953 Bowman Color	97	200.00	100.00	60.00
1953 Topps	37	90.00	45.00	21.00
1954 Bowman	64	60.00	30.00	18.00
1954 Red Man Tobacco	23N	70.00	35.00	21.00
1954 Topps	30	75.00	37.50	22.00
1955 Bowman	103	55.00	27.00	16.50
1955 Topps	155	90.00	45.00	27.00
1956 Topps	107	50.00	25.00	15.00
1957 Topps	250	40.00	20.00	12.00
1958 Topps	351	30.00	15.00	9.00
1958 Topps	440	30.00	15.00	9.00
1958 Topps	480	12.50	6.25	3.75
1959 Home Run Derby	(13)	275.00	137.00	82.00
1959 Topps	212	60.00	30.00	18.00
1959 Topps	450	30.00	15.00	9.00
1960 Post Cereal	(6)	400.00	200.00	120.00
1960 Topps	420	28.00	14.00	8.50
1960 Topps	558	30.00	15.00	9.00
1961 Post Cereal	106	40.00	20.00	12.00
1961 Topps	43	9.00	4.50	2.75
1961 Topps	120	26.00	13.00	8.00
1962 Post Cereal	147	10.00	5.00	3.00
1962 Topps	30	20.00	10.00	6.00
1963 Post Cereal	151	10.00	5.00	3.00
1963 Topps	275	20.00	10.00	6.00
1964 Topps	35	20.00	10.00	6.00
1965 Topps	500	32.50	16.00	9.75
1966 Topps	200	18.00	9.00	5.50
1967 O-Pee-Chee	166	17.00	8.50	5.00
1967 Topps	166	10.00	5.00	3.00
1968 O-Pee-Chee	58	17.00	8.50	5.00
1968 Topps	58	10.00	5.00	3.00
1973 O-Pee-Chee	237	1.00	.50	.30
1973 Topps	237a	2.00	1.00	.60
1973 Topps	237b	2.00	1.00	.60
1974 O-Pee-Chee	634	.75	.40	.25
1974 Topps	634	1.50	.70	.45

Set	Card #	MT	NM	EX
1983 Topps 1952 Reprint Set	407	6.00	4.50	2.50
1986 Sportflics Decade Greats	34	.30	.25	.12
1989 Pacific Trading Cards Legends II	116	.25	.20	.10
1990 Pacific Legends	66	.25	.20	.10
1991 "1953" Topps Archives	37	1.00	.70	.40
1994 "1954" Topps Archives	30	.30	.25	.12

* * *

Usually, the best time to buy a player's card is in the off season, when the hype and media attention he's generated during the season, which helps drive prices up, has died down.

* * *

Don Mattingly

Set	Card #	MT	NM	EX
1984 Donruss	248 (R)	55.00	41.00	22.00
1984 Fleer	131 (R)	32.00	24.00	13.00
1984 O-Pee-Chee	8	13.50	10.00	5.50
1984 Topps	8 (R)	14.00	10.50	5.50
1985 Donruss	7	3.50	2.75	1.50
1985 Donruss	295	8.00	6.00	3.25
1985 Donruss	651a	4.00	3.00	1.50
1985 Donruss	651b	6.00	4.50	2.50
1985 Donruss Diamond Kings Supers	7	3.00	2.25	1.25
1985 Fleer	133	9.00	6.75	3.50
1985 Leaf-Donruss	7	2.75	2.00	1.00
1985 Leaf-Donruss	140	3.25	2.50	1.25
1985 O-Pee-Chee	324	3.00	2.25	1.25
1985 Topps	665	3.00	2.25	1.25
1985 Topps All-Star Glossy Set of 40	27	2.00	1.50	.80
1986 Donruss	173	4.00	3.00	1.50
1986 Fleer	109	2.50	2.00	1.00
1986 Fleer	627	1.25	.90	.50
1986 Fleer	639	1.00	.70	.40
1986 Fleer All Stars	1	5.00	3.75	2.00
1986 Leaf	103	2.50	2.00	1.00
1986 O-Pee-Chee	180	.85	.60	.35
1986 Sportflics	2	2.00	1.50	.80
1986 Sportflics	54	1.25	.90	.50
1986 Sportflics	75	1.50	1.25	.60
1986 Sportflics	176	1.00	.70	.40
1986 Sportflics	179	1.25	.90	.50
1986 Sportflics	180	1.25	.90	.50
1986 Sportflics	183	1.25	.90	.50
1986 Sportflics	184	1.50	1.25	.60
1986 Sportflics Decade Greats	65	1.25	.90	.50
1986 Topps	180	1.00	.75	.40
1986 Topps	712	.40	.30	.15
1986 Topps All-Star Glossy Set of 60	31	3.00	2.25	1.25
1987 Donruss	52	1.00	.70	.40
1987 Fleer	104	2.00	1.50	.80
1987 Fleer	638	.75	.60	.30
1987 Fleer All Stars	1	3.00	1.50	.80
1987 Fleer All Stars	26	.90	.70	.35
1987 Leaf	150	.85	.60	.35
1987 O-Pee-Chee	229	.40	.30	.15
1987 Sportflics	1	2.00	1.50	.80
1987 Sportflics	75	.50	.40	.20
1987 Sportflics	159	1.25	.90	.50
1987 Topps	406	.25	.20	.10
1987 Topps	500	.50	.40	.20
1987 Topps	606a	1.25	.90	.50
1987 Topps	606b	.25	.20	.10
1987 Topps All-Star Glossy Set of 60	1	2.00	1.50	.80
1988 Donruss	217	.30	.25	.12
1988 Donruss MVP	21	.50	.40	.20
1988 Fleer	214	.60	.45	.25
1988 Fleer Headliners	1	2.00	1.50	.80
1988 Leaf	177	.30	.25	.12
1988 O-Pee-Chee	300	.30	.25	.12
1988 Score	1	.40	.30	.15
1988 Score	650	.20	.15	.08
1988 Score	658	.30	.25	.12
1988 Sportflics	1	1.00	.70	.40
1988 Sportflics	222	.50	.40	.20
1988 Sportflics Gamewinners	1	2.00	1.50	.80
1988 Topps	2	.15	.11	.06
1988 Topps	300	.40	.30	.15
1988 Topps	386	.15	.11	.06
1988 Topps All-Star Glossy Set of 22	2	1.00	.70	.40
1988 Topps All-Star Glossy Set of 60	11	2.00	1.50	.80
1988 Topps Big Baseball	229	1.00	.70	.40
1989 Bowman	176	.30	.25	.12
1989 Donruss	26	.20	.15	.08
1989 Donruss	74	.30	.25	.12
1989 Fleer	258	.35	.25	.14
1989 O-Pee-Chee	26	.45	.35	.20
1989 Score	100	.25	.20	.10
1989 Sportflics	50	.80	.60	.30
1989 Topps	397	.20	.15	.08
1989 Topps	700	.25	.20	.10
1989 Topps All-Star Glossy Set of 60	51	.90	.70	.35
1989 Topps Big Baseball	50	1.50	1.25	.60
1989 Upper Deck	200	1.50	1.25	.60
1989 Upper Deck	693	.20	.15	.08
1990 Bowman	443	.35	.25	.14
1990 Donruss	190	.25	.20	.10
1990 Fleer	447	.25	.20	.10
1990 Fleer	626	.20	.15	.08
1990 Fleer League Standouts	3	1.00	.70	.40
1990 Leaf	69	4.00	3.00	1.50
1990 O-Pee-Chee	200	.40	.30	.15
1990 Post Cereal	1	.80	.60	.30
1990 Score	1	.25	.20	.10
1990 Sportflics	150	.80	.60	.30
1990 Topps	200	.25	.20	.10
1990 Topps All-Star Glossy Set of 60	11	.80	.60	.30
1990 Topps Big Baseball	85	.60	.45	.25
1990 Upper Deck	191	.40	.30	.15
1991 Bowman	178	.25	.20	.10
1991 Donruss	107	.25	.20	.10
1991 Fleer	673	.25	.20	.10
1991 Fleer ProVisions	11	.75	.60	.30
1991 Fleer Ultra	239	.60	.45	.25
1991 Leaf	425	.50	.40	.20
1991 O-Pee-Chee Premier	77	.40	.30	.15
1991 Post Cereal	29	.80	.60	.30
1991 Score	23	.30	.25	.12
1991 Score	856	.12	.06	.03
1991 Studio	97	.50	.40	.20
1991 Topps	100a	.60	.45	.25
1991 Topps	100b	.15	.11	.06
1991 Topps Stadium Club	21	2.00	1.50	.80
1991 Upper Deck	354	.40	.30	.15
1992 Bowman	340	2.00	1.50	.80
1992 Donruss	596	.25	.20	.10
1992 Donruss Triple Play	159	.20	.15	.08
1992 Fleer	237	.30	.25	.12
1992 Fleer Team Leaders	1	10.00	7.50	4.00
1992 Fleer Ultra	105	.50	.40	.20
1992 Fleer Ultra Award Winners	19	4.00	3.00	1.50
1992 Leaf	57	.25	.15	.08
1992 O-Pee-Chee	300	.15	.11	.06
1992 O-Pee-Chee Premier	92	.40	.30	.15
1992 Pinnacle	23	.50	.40	.20
1992 Pinnacle	584	.20	.15	.08
1992 Post Cereal	3	.45	.35	.20
1992 Score	23	.25	.20	.10
1992 Studio	216	.40	.30	.15
1992 Studio Heritage	5	2.50	2.00	1.00
1992 Topps	300	.40	.30	.15
1992 Topps Gold	300	5.00	3.75	2.00
1992 Topps Kids	84	.20	.15	.08

1992 Topps Stadium Club	420	.75	.60	.30
1992 Upper Deck	356	.35	.25	.14
1992 Upper Deck MVP Holograms	33	.75	.60	.30
1993 Bowman	595	.75	.60	.30
1993 Donruss	609	.40	.30	.15
1993 Donruss Elite	24	90.00	67.00	36.00
1993 Donruss Elite Dominators	6	250.00	187.00	100.00
1993 Donruss Elite Dominators	6	100.00	75.00	40.00
1993 Donruss Elite Supers	6	25.00	18.50	10.00
1993 Donruss MVP's	5	2.00	1.50	.80
1993 Donruss Triple Play Action Baseball	19	.15	.11	.06
1993 Donruss Triple Play	120	.50	.40	.20
1993 Fleer	281	.40	.30	.15
1993 Fleer Flair	249	3.00	2.25	1.25
1993 Fleer Ultra	244	1.00	.75	.40
1993 Fleer Ultra Award Winners	12	5.00	3.75	2.00
1993 Leaf	237	1.00	.75	.40
1993 Leaf Gold All-Stars	2	3.00	2.25	1.25
1993 O-Pee-Chee	103	1.00	.70	.40
1993 O-Pee-Chee Premier	46	.40	.30	.15
1993 Pinnacle	23	1.00	.75	.40
1993 Pinnacle	470	.40	.30	.15
1993 Pinnacle Cooperstown	14	.45	.35	.20
1993 Pinnacle Cooperstown Dufex	14	100.00	75.00	40.00
1993 Pinnacle Slugfest	23	4.00	3.00	1.50
1993 Post Cereal	12	.75	.60	.30
1993 Score	23	.50	.40	.20
1993 Score Select	24	.75	.60	.30
1993 Score Select Stat Leaders	14	.25	.20	.10
1993 Score The Franchise	10	10.00	7.50	4.00
1993 Studio	193	.75	.60	.30
1993 Topps	32	.25	.20	.10
1993 Topps Finest	98	13.00	9.75	5.25
1993 Topps Finest Jumbo All-Stars	98	32.00	24.00	13.00
1993 Topps Finest Refractors	98	250.00	185.00	100.00
1993 Topps Gold	32	.50	.40	.20
1993 Topps Stadium Club	557	.60	.45	.25
1993 Topps Stadium Club First Day Production	557	60.00	45.00	24.00
1993 Topps Stadium Club II Inserts	2	4.00	3.00	1.50
1993 Upper Deck	47	.20	.15	.08
1993 Upper Deck	134	.40	.30	.15
1993 Upper Deck Clutch Performers	14	1.75	1.25	.70
1993 Upper Deck Diamond Gallery	28	3.00	2.25	1.25
1993 Upper Deck Fun Packs	208	.35	.25	.14
1993 Upper Deck Iooss Collection	26	1.50	1.25	.60
1993 Upper Deck Iooss Collection Super	26	4.00	3.00	1.50
1993 Upper Deck SP	265	4.00	3.00	1.50
1993 Upper Deck Then And Now	13	4.00	3.00	1.50
1994 Bowman	25	.75	.60	.30
1994 Bowman	386	.75	.60	.30
1994 Bowman's Best	45	4.00	3.00	1.50
1994 Bowman's Best Refractors	45	35.00	26.00	14.00
1994 Donruss	340	.60	.45	.25
1994 Donruss Anniversary-1984	8	7.00	5.25	2.75
1994 Donruss Diamond Kings	16	4.00	3.00	1.50
1994 Donruss Diamond Kings Super	16	4.00	3.00	1.50
1994 Donruss MVP's	24	3.00	2.25	1.25
1994 Donruss Special Edition - Gold	340	1.50	1.25	.60
1994 Donruss Spirit of the Game	9	6.00	4.50	2.50
1994 Donruss Spirit of the Game Super	9	12.00	9.00	4.75
1994 Donruss Triple Play Promos	9	4.00	3.00	1.50
1994 Donruss Triple Play	276	.40	.30	.15
1994 Fleer	239	.50	.40	.20
1994 Fleer Extra Bases	133	.60	.45	.25
1994 Fleer Extra Bases Game Breakers	17	1.50	1.25	.60
1994 Fleer Flair	84	2.00	1.50	.80
1994 Fleer Flair Hot Glove	6	25.00	18.00	10.00
1994 Fleer Flair Infield Power	4	7.00	5.25	2.75
1994 Fleer Team Leaders	10	2.00	1.50	.80
1994 Fleer Ultra	397	.75	.60	.30
1994 Fleer Ultra Award Winners	2	2.00	1.50	.80
1994 Fleer Update Diamond Tribute	6	1.00	.75	.40
1994 Leaf	121	.75	.60	.30
1994 Leaf Gamers	4	10.00	7.50	4.00
1994 Leaf Gold Stars	6	35.00	26.00	14.00
1994 Leaf Limited	56	10.00	7.50	4.00
1994 O-Pee-Chee	54	.75	.60	.30
1994 Pacific Crown	430	.75	.60	.30
1994 Pacific Crown Jewels of the Crown	10	7.00	5.50	3.50
1994 Pinnacle	23	.75	.60	.30
1994 Pinnacle Artist's Proof	23	75.00	56.00	30.00
1994 Pinnacle Museum Collection	23	20.00	15.00	8.00
1994 Post Cereal	2	.60	.45	.25
1994 Score	23	.50	.40	.20
1994 Score Dream Team	3	25.00	18.00	10.00
1994 Score Gold Stars	49	15.00	11.00	6.00
1994 Score Select	23	1.00	.70	.40
1994 Sportflics 2000	127	.75	.60	.30
1994 Sportflics 2000 Movers	9	15.00	11.00	6.00
1994 Studio	215	.75	.60	.30
1994 Studio Gold Stars	10	40.00	30.00	15.00
1994 Studio Heritage	4	3.00	2.25	1.25
1994 Studio Silver Stars	10	20.00	15.00	8.00
1994 Topps	600	.40	.30	.15
1994 Topps Finest	392	5.00	3.75	2.00
1994 Topps Finest Refractors	392	45.00	34.00	18.00
1994 Topps Gold	600	1.50	1.25	.60
1994 Topps Stadium Club	195	.75	.60	.30
1994 Topps Stadium Club First Day Production	195	40.00	30.00	15.00
1994 Upper Deck	90	.75	.60	.30
1994 Upper Deck	290	.40	.30	.15
1994 Upper Deck All-Stars Green Foil	8	.75	.60	.30
1994 Upper Deck All-Stars Gold Foil	8	4.00	3.00	1.50
1994 Upper Deck Collector's Choice	192	.25	.20	.10
1994 Upper Deck Collector's Choice	355	.10	.08	.04
1994 Upper Deck Diamond Collection	8E	12.00	9.00	4.75
1994 Upper Deck Electric Diamond	90	3.00	2.25	1.25
1994 Upper Deck Electric Diamond	290	2.00	1.50	.80
1994 Upper Deck Fun Packs	123	.40	.30	.15
1994 Upper Deck Fun Packs	200	2.50	2.00	1.00
1994 Upper Deck SP	198	1.50	1.25	.60
1994 Upper Deck SP Baseball Die-Cut	198	4.00	3.00	1.50
1994 Upper Deck SP Holoview Blue	25	10.00	7.50	4.00

1994 Upper Deck SP Holoview Red	25	75.00	56.00	30.00
1994 Upper Deck SP Insert	4	10.00	7.50	4.00

Willie Mays

Set	Card #	NM	EX	VG
1951 Bowman	305 (R)	3000.	1200.	725.00
1952 Bowman	218	1200.	600.00	360.00
1952 Red Man Tobacco	15N	175.00	87.00	52.00
1952 Topps	261	2650.	1325.	609.00
1953 Topps	244	2500.	1250.	575.00
1954 Bowman	89	350.00	175.00	105.00
1954 Red Man Tobacco	25N	150.00	75.00	45.00
1954 Topps	90	495.00	245.00	145.00
1955 Bowman	184	200.00	100.00	60.00
1955 Red Man Tobacco	7N	150.00	75.00	45.00
1955 Topps	194	400.00	200.00	120.00
1956 Topps	130	325.00	160.00	95.00
1957 Topps	10	175.00	85.00	50.00
1958 Topps	5	180.00	90.00	55.00
1958 Topps	436	65.00	32.00	19.50
1958 Topps	486	50.00	25.00	15.00
1959 Home Run Derby	(14)	450.00	225.00	135.00
1959 Topps	50	130.00	65.00	40.00
1959 Topps	317	40.00	20.00	12.00
1959 Topps	464	25.00	12.50	7.50
1959 Topps	563	115.00	57.50	33.00
1960 Topps	7	19.00	9.50	5.75
1960 Topps	200	95.00	47.00	28.00
1960 Topps	564	120.00	60.00	35.00
1961 Post Cereal	145a	35.00	17.50	10.50
1961 Post Cereal	145b	35.00	17.50	10.50
1961 Topps	41	11.00	5.50	3.25
1961 Topps	150	115.00	57.50	33.00
1961 Topps	482	40.00	20.00	12.00
1961 Topps	579	140.00	70.00	42.00
1962 Post Cereal	142	35.00	17.50	10.50
1962 Topps	18	125.00	62.50	37.50
1962 Topps	54	12.00	6.00	3.50
1962 Topps	300	120.00	60.00	35.00
1962 Topps	395	40.00	20.00	12.00
1963 Fleer	5	175.00	87.00	50.00
1963 Post Cereal	106	25.00	12.50	7.50
1963 Topps	3	26.00	13.00	7.75
1963 Topps	138	45.00	22.50	13.50
1963 Topps	300	145.00	72.50	45.00
1964 Topps	9	25.00	12.50	7.50
1964 Topps	150	100.00	45.00	25.00
1964 Topps	306	22.00	11.00	6.50
1964 Topps	423	130.00	65.00	39.00
1965 O-Pee-Chee	4	12.75	6.50	3.75
1965 O-Pee-Chee	6	3.50	1.75	1.00
1965 O-Pee-Chee	250	150.00	75.00	45.00
1965 Topps	4	15.00	7.50	4.50
1965 Topps	6	12.00	6.00	3.50
1965 Topps	250	90.00	45.00	27.00
1966 O-Pee-Chee	1	210.00	105.00	63.00
1966 Topps	1	125.00	62.00	37.00
1966 Topps	215	22.00	11.00	6.50
1966 Topps	217	7.50	3.75	2.25
1966 Topps	219	8.00	4.00	2.50
1967 O-Pee-Chee	191	12.75	6.50	3.75
1967 Topps	191a	12.00	6.00	3.50
1967 Topps	191b	12.00	6.00	3.50
1967 Topps	200	80.00	40.00	24.00
1967 Topps	244	12.00	6.00	3.50
1967 Topps	423	25.00	12.50	7.50
1968 O-Pee-Chee	50	95.00	47.00	28.00
1968 Topps	50	62.50	31.00	19.00
1968 Topps	490	125.00	62.50	37.50
1969 O-Pee-Chee	190	75.00	37.00	22.00
1969 Topps	190	55.00	27.00	16.50
1970 Topps	600	65.00	32.00	19.50
1971 O-Pee-Chee	600	127.50	64.00	38.00
1971 Topps	600	90.00	45.00	27.00
1972 O-Pee-Chee	49	32.00	16.00	9.50
1972 O-Pee-Chee	50	15.00	7.50	4.50
1972 Topps	49	25.00	12.50	7.50
1972 Topps	50	15.00	7.50	4.50
1973 O-Pee-Chee	1	38.00	19.00	11.50
1973 O-Pee-Chee	305	42.50	21.00	12.50
1973 Topps	1	35.00	17.50	10.50
1973 Topps	305	35.00	17.50	10.50
1975 O-Pee-Chee	192	5.00	2.50	1.50
1975 O-Pee-Chee	203	5.00	2.50	1.50
1975 Topps	192	2.00	1.00	.60
1975 Topps	203	1.50	.70	.45
1975 Topps Mini	192	2.25	1.25	.70
1975 Topps Mini	203	1.75	.90	.50

Set	Card #	MT	NM	EX
1983 Topps 1952 Reprint Set	261	11.00	8.25	4.50
1986 Sportflics Decade Greats	50	1.00	.70	.40
1986 Sportflics Rookies	46	.40	.30	.15
1986 Topps	403	.20	.15	.08
1988 Pacific Trading Cards Baseball Legends	24	.50	.40	.20
1989 Bowman Inserts	(7)	.25	.20	.10
1991 "1953" Topps Archives Promos	(7)	24.00	18.00	9.50
1991 "1953" Topps Archives	244	.25	.20	.10
1994 "1954" Topps Archives	90	2.00	1.50	.80

Bill Mazeroski

Set	Card #	NM	EX	VG
1957 Topps	24 (R)	70.00	35.00	21.00
1958 Topps	238	16.00	8.00	4.75
1959 Topps	415	9.00	4.50	2.75
1959 Topps	555	27.50	13.50	8.25
1960 Topps	55	5.00	2.50	1.50
1961 Post Cereal	128a	3.75	2.00	1.25

1961 Post Cereal	128b	3.75	2.00	1.25
1961 Topps	430	47.50	24.00	14.00
1961 Topps	571	40.00	20.00	12.00
1962 Post Cereal	170	5.00	2.50	1.50
1962 Topps	353	8.00	4.00	2.50
1962 Topps	391	7.50	3.75	2.25
1963 Fleer	59	25.00	12.50	7.50
1963 Post Cereal	138	5.00	2.50	1.50
1963 Topps	323	8.00	4.00	2.50
1964 Topps	570	13.00	6.50	4.00
1965 O-Pee-Chee	95	2.75	1.50	.80
1965 Topps	95	7.00	3.50	2.00
1966 Topps	210	4.25	2.25	1.25
1967 Topps	510	13.00	6.50	4.00
1968 Topps	390	4.00	2.00	1.25
1969 Topps	335	2.50	1.25	.70
1970 O-Pee-Chee	440	1.75	.90	.50
1970 Topps	440	3.00	1.50	.90
1971 O-Pee-Chee	110	1.50	.70	.45
1971 Topps	110	2.50	1.25	.70
1972 Topps	760	12.00	6.00	3.50
1973 O-Pee-Chee	517	1.25	.60	.40
1973 Topps	517a	2.00	1.00	.60
1973 Topps	517b	.70	.35	.20
1974 O-Pee-Chee	489	.60	.30	.20
1974 Topps	489	.75	.40	.25

Set	Card #	MT	NM	EX
1988 Pacific Trading Cards Baseball Legends	60	.10	.08	.04
1990 Pacific Legends	39	.15	.11	.06

Willie McCovey

Set	Card #	NM	EX	VG
1960 Topps	316 (R)	150.00	75.00	45.00
1960 Topps	554	45.00	22.50	13.50
1961 Post Cereal	147a	7.00	3.50	2.00
1961 Post Cereal	147b	30.00	15.00	9.00
1961 Topps	517	45.00	22.00	13.50
1962 Post Cereal	131	80.00	40.00	24.00
1962 Topps	544	120.00	60.00	36.00
1963 Post Cereal	112	10.00	5.00	3.00
1963 Topps	490	125.00	62.50	36.00
1964 Topps	9	25.00	12.50	7.50
1964 Topps	41	5.00	2.50	1.50
1964 Topps	350	22.50	11.00	6.75
1965 O-Pee-Chee	176	23.00	11.50	7.00
1965 Topps	176	17.00	8.50	5.00
1966 Topps	217	7.50	3.75	2.25
1966 Topps	550	115.00	57.00	34.00
1967 Topps	423	25.00	12.50	7.50
1967 Topps	480	30.00	15.00	9.00
1968 O-Pee-Chee	5	10.25	5.25	3.00
1968 Topps	5	8.00	4.00	2.50
1968 Topps	290	10.00	5.00	3.00
1969 O-Pee-Chee	4	8.50	4.25	2.50
1969 O-Pee-Chee	6	8.50	4.25	2.50
1969 Topps	4	4.00	2.00	1.25

1969 Topps	6	4.00	2.00	1.25
1969 Topps	416	3.50	1.75	1.00
1969 Topps	440a	120.00	60.00	36.00
1969 Topps	440b	16.00	8.00	4.75
1969 Topps	572	15.00	7.50	4.50
1970 O-Pee-Chee	63	1.75	.90	.50
1970 O-Pee-Chee	65	2.25	1.25	.70
1970 O-Pee-Chee	250	12.75	6.50	3.75
1970 O-Pee-Chee	450	2.50	1.25	.70
1970 Topps	63	3.75	2.00	1.25
1970 Topps	65	5.00	2.50	1.50
1970 Topps	250	8.00	4.00	2.50
1970 Topps	450	5.00	2.50	1.50
1971 O-Pee-Chee	50	12.75	6.50	3.75
1971 Topps	50	7.00	3.50	2.00
1972 O-Pee-Chee	280	8.00	4.00	2.50
1972 Topps	280	6.00	3.00	1.75
1973 O-Pee-Chee	410	6.75	3.50	2.00
1973 Topps	410	6.00	3.00	1.75
1974 O-Pee-Chee	250	6.75	3.50	2.00
1974 Topps	250a	25.00	12.50	7.50
1974 Topps	250b	5.00	2.50	1.50
1975 O-Pee-Chee	207	2.00	1.00	.60
1975 O-Pee-Chee	450	5.50	2.75	1.75
1975 Topps	207	1.50	.70	.45
1975 Topps	450	4.00	2.00	1.25
1975 Topps Mini	207	2.25	1.25	.70
1975 Topps Mini	450	7.00	3.50	2.00
1976 O-Pee-Chee	520	4.25	2.25	1.25
1976 Topps	520	3.00	1.50	.90
1977 Topps	547	3.00	1.50	.90
1978 O-Pee-Chee	185	1.75	.90	.50
1978 O-Pee-Chee	238	.60	.30	.20
1978 Topps	3	.70	.35	.20
1978 Topps	34	3.00	1.50	.90
1979 O-Pee-Chee	107	1.25	.60	.40
1979 Topps	215	2.00	1.00	.60
1980 O-Pee-Chee	176	1.25	.60	.40
1980 Topps	2	.50	.25	.15
1980 Topps	335	1.50	.70	.45

Set	Card #	MT	NM	EX
1981 Fleer	434	.60	.45	.25
1985 Topps All-Star Glossy Set of 22	11	.40	.30	.15
1986 Sportflics Decade Greats	48	.30	.25	.12

Ben McDonald

Set	Card #	MT	NM	EX
1990 Bowman	243 (R)	.50	.40	.20
1990 Donruss	32 (R)	.40	.30	.15
1990 Fleer	180 (R)	.40	.30	.15
1990 Leaf	249	3.50	2.75	1.50
1990 O-Pee-Chee	774	.40	.30	.15
1990 Score	680 (R)	.60	.45	.25
1990 Topps	774 (R)	.40	.30	.15

1990 Topps Big Baseball	228	.50	.40	.20
1990 Topps Traded	70T	.60	.45	.25
1990 Upper Deck	54a (R)	15.00	11.00	6.00
1990 Upper Deck	54b (R)	1.25	.90	.50
1991 Bowman	86	.12	.09	.05
1991 Donruss	485	.10	.08	.04
1991 Fleer	481	.10	.08	.04
1991 Fleer Ultra	19	.15	.11	.06
1991 Leaf	117	.25	.20	.10
1991 Score	645	.10	.08	.04
1991 Studio	6	.30	.25	.12
1991 Topps	497	.12	.09	.05
1991 Topps Glossy Rookies	18	.30	.25	.12
1991 Upper Deck	446	.15	.11	.06
1992 Bowman	359	.40	.30	.15
1992 Donruss	436	.10	.08	.04
1992 Donruss Triple Play	105	.15	.11	.06
1992 Fleer	14	.10	.08	.04
1992 Fleer Ultra	303	.30	.25	.12
1992 Leaf	145	.30	.25	.12
1992 O-Pee-Chee	540	.12	.09	.05
1992 Pinnacle	44	.25	.20	.10
1992 Pinnacle Team 2000	41	.15	.11	.06
1992 Score	658	.10	.08	.04
1992 Score Impact Players	81	.15	.11	.06
1992 Studio	126	.15	.11	.06
1992 Topps	540	.12	.09	.05
1992 Topps Gold	540	.35	.25	.14
1992 Topps Kids	64	.05	.04	.02
1992 Upper Deck	93	.05	.04	.02
1992 Upper Deck	163	.20	.15	.08
1993 Bowman	437	.20	.15	.08
1993 Donruss	249	.08	.06	.03
1993 Donruss Triple Play	145	.07	.05	.03
1993 Fleer	169	.08	.06	.03
1993 Fleer Flair	152	.25	.15	.08
1993 Fleer Ultra	142	.10	.08	.04
1993 Leaf	1	.10	.08	.04
1993 O-Pee-Chee	254	.20	.15	.08
1993 Pinnacle	72	.06	.05	.02
1993 Score	202	.10	.08	.04
1993 Score Select	224	.25	.20	.10
1993 Topps Finest	65	1.00	.70	.40
1993 Topps Finest Refractors	65	20.00	15.00	8.00
1993 Topps Gold	218	.15	.11	.06
1993 Topps Stadium Club	259	.30	.25	.12
1993 Topps Stadium Club First Day Production	259	5.00	3.75	2.00
1993 Upper Deck	276	.08	.06	.03
1993 Upper Deck Fun Packs	133	.05	.04	.02
1993 Upper Deck SP	158	.12	.09	.05
1994 Bowman	459	.15	.11	.06
1994 Bowman's Best	22	.50	.40	.20
1994 Bowman's Best Refractors	22	2.00	1.50	.80
1994 Donruss	158	.10	.08	.04
1994 Donruss Triple Play	155	.05	.04	.02
1994 Fleer	8	.05	.04	.02
1994 Fleer Extra Bases	7	.15	.11	.06
1994 Fleer Extra Bases Game Breakers	18	.25	.20	.10
1994 Fleer Extra Bases Pitcher's Duel	2M	.40	.30	.15
1994 Fleer Flair	4	.30	.25	.12
1994 Fleer Ultra	3	.10	.08	.04
1994 Leaf	127	.15	.11	.06
1994 Leaf Limited	2	1.50	1.25	.60
1994 O-Pee-Chee	122	.08	.06	.03
1994 Pacific Crown	35	.10	.08	.04
1994 Pinnacle	184	.10	.08	.04
1994 Pinnacle Artist's Proof	184	3.00	2.25	1.25
1994 Pinnacle Museum Collection	184	1.50	1.25	.60
1994 Score	111	.04	.03	.02
1994 Score Select	117	.20	.15	.08

1994 Sportflics 2000	11	.20	.15	.08
1994 Studio	124	.15	.11	.06
1994 Topps	636	.05	.04	.02
1994 Topps Finest	161	.75	.60	.30
1994 Topps Finest Refractors	161	3.50	2.75	1.50
1994 Topps Gold	636	.15	.11	.06
1994 Topps Stadium Club	413	.12	.09	.05
1994 Topps Stadium Club First Day Production	413	2.50	2.00	1.00
1994 Upper Deck	456	.15	.11	.06
1994 Upper Deck Collector's Choice	195	.05	.04	.02
1994 Upper Deck Electric Diamond	456	.35	.25	.14
1994 Upper Deck SP	123	.20	.15	.08
1994 Upper Deck SP Baseball Die-Cut	123	.25	.20	.10

Jack McDowell

Set	Card #	MT	NM	EX
1988 Donruss	47 (R)	1.00	.75	.40
1988 Fleer	407 (R)	2.50	2.00	1.00
1988 Leaf	47	1.50	1.25	.60
1988 Score Traded	85T	10.00	7.50	4.00
1988 Score Traded/ Rookie Glossy	85T	40.00	30.00	16.00
1988 Topps Traded	68T	1.50	1.25	.60
1989 Bowman	61	.25	.20	.10
1989 Donruss	531	.25	.20	.10
1989 Fleer	504	.25	.20	.10
1989 O-Pee-Chee	143	.08	.06	.03
1989 Score	289	.40	.30	.15
1989 Topps	486	.30	.25	.12
1989 Upper Deck	530	1.00	.75	.40
1990 Bowman	305	.15	.11	.06
1990 Topps Traded	71T	.20	.15	.08
1990 Upper Deck	625	.30	.25	.12
1991 Bowman	352	.10	.08	.04
1991 Donruss	57	.06	.05	.02
1991 Fleer	129	.06	.05	.02
1991 Fleer Ultra	78	.12	.09	.05
1991 Leaf	340	.15	.11	.06
1991 Score	27	.08	.06	.03
1991 Studio	36	.25	.20	.10
1991 Topps	219	.06	.05	.02
1991 Topps Stadium Club	87	1.00	.75	.40
1991 Upper Deck	323	.12	.09	.05
1992 Bowman	371	.50	.40	.20
1992 Bowman	605	.50	.40	.20
1992 Donruss	352	.10	.08	.04
1992 Donruss Triple Play	129	.08	.06	.03
1992 Fleer	89	.08	.06	.03
1992 Fleer Smoke 'N Heat	2	1.25	.90	.50
1992 Fleer Ultra	40	.15	.11	.06
1992 Fleer Ultra All-Stars	10	.75	.60	.30
1992 Leaf	422	.15	.11	.06

1992 O-Pee-Chee	11	.08	.06	.03
1992 Pinnacle	107	.30	.25	.12
1992 Pinnacle	291	.15	.11	.06
1992 Pinnacle	607	.20	.15	.08
1992 Score	62	.08	.06	.03
1992 Score Impact Players	73	.15	.11	.06
1992 Topps	11	.08	.06	.03
1992 Topps Gold	11	.40	.30	.15
1992 Topps Stadium Club	52	.20	.15	.08
1992 Topps Stadium Club Special Edition	114	.25	.20	.10
1992 Upper Deck	553	.08	.06	.03
1992 Upper Deck MVP Holograms	34	.35	.25	.14
1993 Bowman	527	.20	.15	.08
1993 Donruss	433	.08	.06	.03
1993 Donruss Triple Play	158	.10	.08	.04
1993 Fleer	207	.10	.08	.04
1993 Fleer All-Stars	12	.75	.60	.30
1993 Fleer Flair	188	.40	.30	.15
1993 Fleer Ultra	176	.20	.15	.08
1993 Leaf	400	.15	.11	.06
1993 O-Pee-Chee	264	.20	.15	.08
1993 Pinnacle	80	.06	.05	.02
1993 Score	70	.08	.06	.03
1993 Score Select	196	.15	.11	.06
1993 Score Select Aces	3	3.00	2.25	1.25
1993 Score Select Stat Leaders	61	.10	.08	.04
1993 Score Select Stat Leaders	86	.10	.08	.04
1993 Studio	200	.15	.11	.06
1993 Topps	344	.08	.06	.03
1993 Topps Black Gold	38	.35	.25	.14
1993 Topps Finest	172	2.00	1.50	.80
1993 Topps Finest Refractors	172	25.00	18.50	10.00
1993 Topps Gold	344	.15	.11	.06
1993 Topps Stadium Club	75	.15	.11	.06
1993 Topps Stadium Club First Day Production	75	15.00	11.00	6.00
1993 Topps Stadium Club Members Only	(15)	.50	.40	.20
1993 Topps Stadium Club Special	157	.10	.08	.04
1993 Upper Deck	357	.20	.15	.08
1993 Upper Deck Fun Packs	200	.15	.11	.06
1993 Upper Deck SP	258	.25	.20	.10
1994 Bowman	455	.15	.11	.06
1994 Bowman's Best	23	.50	.40	.20
1994 Bowman's Best Refractors	23	2.00	1.50	.80
1994 Donruss	20	.10	.08	.04
1994 Donruss Award Winners Supers	7	3.00	2.25	1.25
1994 Donruss Elite	47	15.00	11.00	6.00
1994 Donruss Special Edition - Gold	20	.30	.25	.12
1994 Donruss Triple Play Medalists	13	1.25	.90	.50
1994 Donruss Triple Play	267	.10	.07	.04
1994 Fleer	89	.10	.07	.04
1994 Fleer	708	.05	.04	.02
1994 Fleer All-Stars	15	.30	.25	.12
1994 Fleer Award Winners	3	1.00	.70	.40
1994 Fleer Extra Bases	51	.20	.15	.08
1994 Fleer Extra Bases Pitcher's Duel	1M	1.00	.75	.40
1994 Fleer Flair	280	.40	.30	.15
1994 Fleer League Leaders	5	.35	.25	.14
1994 Fleer ProVisions	7	.35	.25	.14
1994 Fleer Ultra	339	.12	.09	.05
1994 Fleer Ultra All-Stars	10	.50	.40	.20
1994 Fleer Ultra Award Winners	22	.60	.45	.25
1994 Fleer Ultra League Leaders	4	.60	.45	.25
1994 Leaf	125	.12	.09	.05
1994 Leaf Gold Stars	15	10.00	7.50	4.00
1994 Leaf Limited	22	1.50	1.25	.60
1994 O-Pee-Chee	173	.20	.15	.08
1994 O-Pee-Chee All-Star Redemption Cards	14	.35	.25	.14
1994 O-Pee-Chee Jumbo All-Stars	14	5.00	3.75	2.00
1994 O-Pee-Chee Jumbo All-Stars Factory Set	14	1.00	.75	.40
1994 Pacific Crown	134	.15	.11	.06
1994 Pacific Crown	657	.10	.08	.04
1994 Pinnacle	57	.15	.11	.06
1994 Pinnacle Artist's Proof	57	4.00	3.00	1.50
1994 Pinnacle Museum Collection	57	2.00	1.50	.80
1994 Pinnacle Team Pinnacle	9	15.00	11.00	6.00
1994 Post Cereal	7	.25	.20	.10
1994 Score	6	.10	.08	.04
1994 Score	633	.06	.05	.02
1994 Score Gold Stars	39	2.50	2.00	1.00
1994 Score Select	97	.20	.15	.08
1994 Sportflics 2000	92	.25	.20	.10
1994 Sportflics 2000	184	.10	.08	.04
1994 Studio	207	.10	.08	.04
1994 Topps	392	.15	.11	.06
1994 Topps	515	.06	.05	.02
1994 Topps Black Gold	12	.35	.25	.14
1994 Topps Finest	226	.75	.60	.30
1994 Topps Finest Refractors	226	4.00	3.00	1.50
1994 Topps Finest Superstars	226	2.50	2.00	1.00
1994 Topps Gold	392	.45	.35	.20
1994 Topps Gold	515	.15	.11	.06
1994 Topps Stadium Club	24	.15	.11	.06
1994 Topps Stadium Club Dugout Dirt	5	.25	.20	.10
1994 Topps Stadium Club First Day Production	24	6.00	4.50	2.50
1994 Topps Stadium Club Members Only Baseball	21	.25	.20	.10
1994 Upper Deck	395	.15	.11	.06
1994 Upper Deck All-Stars Green Foil	42	.25	.20	.10
1994 Upper Deck All-Stars Gold Foil	42	1.00	.70	.40
1994 Upper Deck Collector's Choice	306	.10	.08	.04
1994 Upper Deck Collector's Choice	309	.10	.08	.04
1994 Upper Deck Collector's Choice	445	.08	.06	.03
1994 Upper Deck Electric Diamond	395	.35	.25	.14
1994 Upper Deck Fun Packs	129	.08	.06	.03
1994 Upper Deck SP	192	.20	.15	.08
1994 Upper Deck SP Baseball Die-Cut	192	.25	.20	.10

* * *

U.L. Washington of the Kansas City Royals gained extra attention during the 1980 playoffs and World Series for keeping a toothpick in his mouth. At a Cincinnati show shortly after the Series, a dealer offered the toothpicks as souvenirs for $7.50, but was doing so with tongue in cheek.

* * *

Cards of defensive standouts and pitchers (especially relief pitchers) receive less collector interest than do those of home run hitters or batting champs.

* * *

Tug McGraw

Fred McGriff

Set	Card #	NM	EX	VG
1965 Topps	533 (R)	28.00	14.00	8.50
1966 O-Pee-Chee	124	2.50	1.25	.70
1966 Topps	124	3.00	1.50	.90
1967 Topps	348	2.50	1.25	.70
1968 Topps	236	1.50	.70	.45
1969 Topps	601	2.50	1.25	.70
1970 O-Pee-Chee	26	1.25	.60	.40
1970 Topps	26	.90	.45	.25
1971 O-Pee-Chee	618	5.00	2.50	1.50
1971 Topps	618	3.50	1.75	1.00
1972 O-Pee-Chee	163	1.00	.50	.30
1972 O-Pee-Chee	164	.75	.40	.25
1972 Topps	163	.75	.40	.25
1972 Topps	164	.75	.40	.25
1973 O-Pee-Chee	30	.75	.40	.25
1973 Topps	30	.40	.20	.12
1974 O-Pee-Chee	265	.60	.30	.20
1974 Topps	265	.30	.15	.09
1975 O-Pee-Chee	67	.55	.30	.15
1975 Topps	67	.35	.20	.11
1975 Topps Mini	67	.60	.30	.20
1976 O-Pee-Chee	565	.35	.20	.11
1976 Topps	565	.25	.13	.08
1977 O-Pee-Chee	142	.30	.15	.09
1977 Topps	164	.20	.10	.06
1978 Topps	446	.20	.10	.06
1979 O-Pee-Chee	176	.25	.13	.08
1979 Topps	345	.30	.15	.09
1980 O-Pee-Chee	346	.20	.10	.06
1980 Topps	655	.15	.08	.05

Set	Card #	MT	NM	EX
1981 Donruss	273	.10	.08	.04
1981 Fleer	7a	.50	.40	.20
1981 Fleer	7b	.12	.09	.05
1981 Fleer	657	.25	.20	.10
1981 Topps	40	.10	.08	.04
1982 Donruss	420	.12	.09	.05
1982 Fleer	251	.12	.09	.05
1982 O-Pee-Chee	250	.12	.09	.05
1982 Topps	250	.15	.11	.06
1983 Donruss	371	.12	.09	.05
1983 Fleer	166	.12	.09	.05
1983 O-Pee-Chee	166	.12	.09	.05
1983 O-Pee-Chee	187	.12	.09	.05
1983 Topps	510	.15	.11	.06
1983 Topps	511	.10	.08	.04
1984 Donruss	547	.20	.15	.08
1984 Fleer	42	.12	.09	.05
1984 O-Pee-Chee	161	.25	.20	.10
1984 Topps	709	.12	.09	.05
1984 Topps	728	.12	.09	.05
1985 Fleer	261	.10	.08	.04
1985 Topps	157	.10	.08	.04

Set	Card #	MT	NM	EX
1986 Donruss	28 (R)	35.00	26.00	14.00
1986 Leaf	28	27.00	20.00	11.00
1987 Donruss	621	4.00	3.00	1.50
1987 Fleer Update	75	4.00	3.00	1.50
1987 Sportflics Rookies	12	2.00	1.50	.80
1987 Topps Traded	74T	3.00	2.25	1.25
1988 Donruss	195	.40	.30	.15
1988 Fleer	118	2.50	2.00	1.00
1988 O-Pee-Chee	395	.50	.40	.20
1988 Score	107	.40	.25	.15
1988 Sportflics	168	.50	.40	.20
1988 Topps	463	.50	.40	.20
1988 Topps	729	.10	.08	.04
1989 Bowman	253	.35	.25	.14
1989 Donruss	16	.15	.11	.06
1989 Donruss	70	.30	.25	.12
1989 Donruss MVP	19	.25	.20	.10
1989 Fleer	240	.35	.25	.14
1989 O-Pee-Chee	258	.20	.15	.08
1989 Score	6	.35	.25	.14
1989 Sportflics	14	.50	.40	.20
1989 Topps	745	.15	.11	.06
1989 Topps Big Baseball	15	.15	.11	.06
1989 Upper Deck	572	1.25	.90	.50
1989 Upper Deck	671	.15	.11	.06
1990 Bowman	513	.08	.06	.03
1990 Donruss	188	.25	.20	.10
1990 Donruss Grand Slammers	9	.40	.30	.15
1990 Fleer	89	.25	.20	.10
1990 Leaf	132	3.00	2.25	1.25
1990 O-Pee-Chee	295	.25	.20	.10
1990 O-Pee-Chee	385	.20	.15	.08
1990 Score	271	.25	.20	.10
1990 Sportflics	13	.40	.30	.15
1990 Topps	295	.25	.20	.10
1990 Topps	385	.15	.11	.06
1990 Topps All-Star Glossy Set of 60	55	.20	.15	.08
1990 Topps Big Baseball	134	.20	.15	.08
1990 Upper Deck	108	.35	.25	.14
1991 Bowman	659	.20	.15	.08
1991 Donruss	261	.20	.15	.08
1991 Donruss	389	.15	.11	.06
1991 Fleer	180	.20	.15	.08
1991 Fleer Ultra	308	.50	.40	.20
1991 Fleer Update	125	.20	.15	.08
1991 Leaf	342	.40	.30	.15
1991 O-Pee-Chee Premier	79	.30	.25	.12
1991 Score	404	.15	.08	.04
1991 Score	480	.20	.15	.05
1991 Score Traded	58	.20	.15	.08
1991 Studio	247	.30	.25	.12
1991 Topps	140	.15	.11	.06
1991 Topps Stadium Club	357	1.50	1.25	.60
1991 Upper Deck	565	.25	.20	.10
1991 Upper Deck	775	.25	.20	.10
1992 Bowman	650	1.75	1.25	.70

Set	#			
1992 Donruss	283	.15	.11	.06
1992 Donruss Diamond Kings	26	2.00	1.50	.80
1992 Donruss Triple Play	87	.15	.11	.06
1992 Fleer	614	.15	.11	.06
1992 Fleer Ultra	282	.50	.40	.20
1992 Leaf	274	.25	.20	.10
1992 O-Pee-Chee	660	.10	.08	.04
1992 O-Pee-Chee Premier	166	.25	.20	.10
1992 Pinnacle	112	.35	.25	.14
1992 Score	7	.15	.11	.06
1992 Score Impact Players	56	.35	.25	.14
1992 Studio	106	.25	.20	.10
1992 Topps	660	.15	.11	.06
1992 Topps Gold	660	.50	.40	.20
1992 Topps Kids	55	.10	.08	.04
1992 Topps Stadium Club	580	.60	.45	.25
1992 Upper Deck	33	.05	.04	.02
1992 Upper Deck	344	.15	.11	.06
1992 Upper Deck Home Run Heroes	10	1.00	.75	.40
1992 Upper Deck MVP Holograms	35	.50	.40	.20
1993 Bowman	686	.50	.40	.20
1993 DiamondMarks	(59)	.60	.45	.25
1993 Donruss	390	.20	.15	.08
1993 Donruss Elite	19	40.00	30.00	15.00
1993 Donruss Elite Dominators	2	65.00	49.00	26.00
1993 Donruss Elite Supers	1	15.00	11.00	6.00
1993 Donruss Long Ball Leaders	2	5.00	3.75	2.00
1993 Donruss Masters of the Game	4	3.00	2.25	1.25
1993 Donruss Spirit of the Game	12	1.50	1.25	.60
1993 Donruss Triple Play League Leaders	4	9.00	6.75	3.50
1993 Donruss Triple Play Nicknames	10	3.00	2.25	1.25
1993 Donruss Triple Play	95	.12	.09	.05
1993 Fleer	143	.20	.15	.08
1993 Fleer	349	.12	.09	.05
1993 Fleer All-Stars	1	2.50	2.00	1.00
1993 Fleer Flair	8	1.25	.90	.50
1993 Fleer Ultra	119	.40	.25	.12
1993 Fleer Ultra Home Run Kings	4	3.00	2.25	1.20
1993 Leaf	46	.50	.40	.20
1993 Leaf Gold All-Stars	2	3.00	2.25	1.25
1993 O-Pee-Chee	255	.60	.45	.25
1993 O-Pee-Chee Premier Star Performers	2	.35	.25	.14
1993 Pinnacle	71	.35	.25	.14
1993 Pinnacle Home Run Club	2	.50	.40	.20
1993 Pinnacle Slugfest	5	2.00	1.50	.80
1993 Pinnacle Team Pinnacle	4	45.00	32.50	18.00
1993 Post Cereal	5	.30	.25	.12
1993 Score	44	.20	.15	.08
1993 Score	528	.08	.06	.03
1993 Score Select	19	.25	.20	.10
1993 Score Select Chase Stars	1	7.00	5.50	3.00
1993 Score Select Rookie/Traded	5	1.00	.75	.40
1993 Score Select Stat Leaders	28	.20	.15	.08
1993 Score Select Stat Leaders	36	.20	.15	.08
1993 Score Select Stat Leaders	48	.20	.15	.08
1993 Studio	157	.30	.25	.12
1993 Topps	30	.20	.15	.08
1993 Topps	401	.40	.30	.15
1993 Topps Black Gold	13	.75	.60	.30
1993 Topps Finest	106	6.00	4.50	2.50
1993 Topps Finest Jumbo All-Stars	106	20.00	15.00	8.00
1993 Topps Finest Refractors	106	60.00	45.00	24.00
1993 Topps Full Shot Super	21	4.00	3.00	1.50
1993 Topps Gold	30	.40	.30	.15
1993 Topps Gold	401	.90	.70	.35
1993 Topps Stadium Club	510	.40	.30	.15
1993 Topps Stadium Club	594	.25	.20	.10
1993 Topps Stadium Club First Day Production	510	15.00	11.00	6.00
1993 Topps Stadium Club First Day Production	594	15.00	11.00	6.00
1993 Topps Stadium Club Special	78	.25	.20	.10
1993 Topps Traded	88	.20	.15	.08
1993 Upper Deck	496	.15	.11	.06
1993 Upper Deck	577	.20	.15	.08
1993 Upper Deck Clutch Performers	15	1.50	1.25	.60
1993 Upper Deck Fun Packs All-Star Scratch-Off	1	5.00	3.75	2.00
1993 Upper Deck Fun Packs	136	.20	.15	.08
1993 Upper Deck Fun Packs	139	.20	.15	.08
1993 Upper Deck Home Run Heroes	4	1.00	.75	.40
1993 Upper Deck Iooss Collection	16	1.50	1.25	.60
1993 Upper Deck Iooss Collection Super	16	3.50	2.75	1.50
1993 Upper Deck SP	60	1.00	.75	.40
1993 Upper Deck SP Platinum Power	12	10.00	7.50	4.00
1993 Upper Deck Triple Crown	5	2.50	2.00	1.00
1994 Bowman	405	.40	.30	.15
1994 Bowman's Best	92	2.00	1.50	.80
1994 Bowman's Best	15	2.00	1.50	.80
1994 Bowman's Best Refractors	92	6.00	4.50	2.50
1994 Bowman's Best Refractors	15	10.00	7.50	4.00
1994 Donruss	342	.30	.25	.12
1994 Donruss Decade Dominators	3	2.50	2.00	1.00
1994 Donruss Decade Dominators Supers	3	4.00	3.00	1.50
1994 Donruss Special Edition - Gold	342	.40	.30	.15
1994 Donruss Triple Play Medalists	4	2.50	2.00	1.00
1994 Donruss Triple Play Bomb Squad	6	2.00	1.50	.80
1994 Donruss Triple Play	47	.20	.15	.08
1994 Fleer	366	.20	.15	.08
1994 Fleer	706	.05	.04	.02
1994 Fleer Extra Bases	209	.35	.25	.14
1994 Fleer Extra Bases Game Breakers	19	.40	.30	.15
1994 Fleer Flair	131	.75	.60	.30
1994 Fleer Flair Hot Numbers	4	8.00	6.00	3.25
1994 Fleer Flair Infield Power	5	2.00	1.50	.80
1994 Fleer Golden Moments	8	1.50	1.25	.60
1994 Fleer Golden Moments Super	8	7.50	5.50	3.00
1994 Fleer Lumber Co.	7	1.00	.75	.40
1994 Fleer Ultra	154	.30	.25	.12
1994 Fleer Ultra All-Stars	12	1.00	.75	.40
1994 Fleer Ultra Home Run Kings	10	4.00	3.00	1.50
1994 Fleer Update Diamond Tribute	7	.60	.45	.25
1994 Leaf	345	.30	.25	.12
1994 Leaf Clean-Up Crew	9	5.00	3.75	2.00
1994 Leaf Gold Stars	14	15.00	11.00	6.00

1994 Leaf Limited	88	3.00	2.25	1.25
1994 Leaf MVP Contenders	10a	4.00	3.00	1.50
1994 Leaf MVP Contenders	10b	8.00	6.00	3.25
1994 Leaf Power Brokers	8	1.50	1.25	.60
1994 O-Pee-Chee	13	.25	.20	.10
1994 O-Pee-Chee All-Star Redemption Cards	13	.85	.60	.35
1994 O-Pee-Chee Jumbo All-Stars	13	8.00	6.00	3.25
1994 O-Pee-Chee Jumbo All-Stars Factory Set	13	2.00	1.50	.80
1994 Pacific Crown	16	.25	.20	.10
1994 Pacific Crown Homerun Leaders	14	3.50	2.75	1.50
1994 Pinnacle	384	.40	.30	.15
1994 Pinnacle Artist's Proof	384	12.50	9.50	5.00
1994 Pinnacle Museum Collection	384	8.00	6.00	3.25
1994 Pinnacle Run Creators	26	4.00	3.00	1.50
1994 Pinnacle The Naturals Box Set	13	.40	.30	.15
1994 Score	82	.25	.20	.10
1994 Score Gold Stars	18	7.50	5.25	2.75
1994 Score Select	68	.10	.08	.04
1994 Sportflics 2000	32	.40	.30	.15
1994 Sportflics 2000	185	.25	.20	.10
1994 Studio	40	.25	.20	.10
1994 Topps	384	.40	.30	.15
1994 Topps	565	.15	.11	.06
1994 Topps Black Gold	39	.75	.60	.30
1994 Topps Finest	224	2.00	1.50	.80
1994 Topps Finest Refractors	224	12.00	9.00	4.50
1994 Topps Finest Superstars	224	6.00	4.50	2.50
1994 Topps Gold	384	1.50	1.25	.60
1994 Topps Gold	565	.45	.35	.20
1994 Topps Stadium Club	180	.15	.11	.06
1994 Topps Stadium Club	264	.20	.15	.08
1994 Topps Stadium Club	665	.35	.25	.14
1994 Topps Stadium Club First Day Production	180	8.00	6.00	3.25
1994 Topps Stadium Club First Day Production	264	12.00	9.00	4.75
1994 Topps Stadium Club First Day Production	665	15.00	11.00	6.00
1994 Topps Stadium Club Members Only Baseball	30	.45	.35	.20
1994 Upper Deck	225	.35	.25	.14
1994 Upper Deck All-Stars Green Foil	11	.25	.20	.10
1994 Upper Deck All-Stars Gold Foil	11	1.00	.70	.40
1994 Upper Deck Collector's Choice	197	.20	.15	.08
1994 Upper Deck Electric Diamond	225	2.00	1.50	.80
1994 Upper Deck Fun Packs	27	.20	.15	.08
1994 Upper Deck Fun Packs	186	.15	.11	.06
1994 Upper Deck Mickey Mantle's Long Shots	12MM	2.00	1.50	.80
1994 Upper Deck SP	55	.40	.30	.15
1994 Upper Deck SP Baseball Die-Cut	55	.75	.60	.30

Mark McGwire

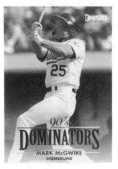

Set	Card #	MT	NM	EX
1985 Topps	401 (R)	9.00	6.75	3.50
1987 Donruss	46	2.00	1.50	.80
1987 Donruss Rookies	1	2.00	1.50	.80
1987 Fleer Update	76	2.50	2.00	1.00
1987 Leaf	46	3.50	2.75	1.50
1987 Sportflics Rookie Discs	2	3.00	2.25	1.25
1987 Topps	366	.75	.60	.30
1988 Donruss	1	.20	.15	.08
1988 Donruss	256	.25	.20	.10
1988 Donruss Diamond Kings Supers	1	.70	.50	.30
1988 Donruss MVP	23	.40	.30	.15
1988 Fleer	286	.75	.60	.30
1988 Fleer	624	.50	.40	.20
1988 Fleer	629	.35	.25	.14
1988 Fleer	633	.15	.11	.06
1988 Fleer Headliners	2	.75	.60	.30
1988 Leaf	1	.30	.25	.12
1988 Leaf	194	.30	.25	.12
1988 O-Pee-Chee	394	.30	.25	.12
1988 Score	5	.25	.20	.10
1988 Score	648	.20	.15	.08
1988 Score	659	.15	.11	.06
1988 Sportflics	100	.50	.40	.20
1988 Sportflics	221	.50	.40	.20
1988 Sportflics Gamewinners	2	.80	.60	.30
1988 Topps	3a	.40	.30	.15
1988 Topps	3b	.15	.11	.06
1988 Topps	580	.25	.20	.10
1988 Topps	759	.30	.25	.12
1988 Topps All-Star Glossy Set of 60	39	.50	.40	.20
1988 Topps Big Baseball	179	.40	.30	.15
1989 Bowman	197	.25	.20	.10
1989 Donruss	95	.25	.20	.10
1989 Donruss Grand Slammers	7	.30	.25	.12
1989 Fleer	17	.20	.15	.08
1989 Fleer	634	.30	.25	.12
1989 O-Pee-Chee	70	.15	.11	.06
1989 O-Pee-Chee	174	.15	.11	.06
1989 Score	3	.25	.20	.10
1989 Sportflics	200	.50	.40	.20
1989 Topps	70	.25	.20	.10
1989 Topps All-Star Glossy Set of 22	2	.15	.11	.06
1989 Topps All-Star Glossy Set of 60	41	.35	.25	.14
1989 Topps Big Baseball	34	1.00	.70	.40
1989 Upper Deck	300	.50	.40	.20
1990 Bowman	454	.15	.11	.06
1990 Donruss	185	.15	.11	.06
1990 Donruss	697	.09	.07	.04
1990 Donruss Grand Slammers	4	.30	.25	.12
1990 Fleer	15	.15	.11	.06
1990 Fleer	638	.10	.08	.04

Set	#			
1990 Fleer MVP	25	.40	.30	.15
1990 Leaf	62	1.50	1.25	.60
1990 O-Pee-Chee	690	.30	.25	.12
1990 Post Cereal	12	.40	.30	.15
1990 Score	385	.20	.15	.08
1990 Sportflics	141	.60	.45	.25
1990 Topps	690	.20	.15	.08
1990 Topps All-Star Glossy Set of 22	13	.30	.25	.12
1990 Topps All-Star Glossy Set of 60	42	.35	.25	.14
1990 Topps Big Baseball	28	.50	.40	.20
1990 Upper Deck	171	.15	.11	.06
1991 Bowman	234	.15	.11	.06
1991 Donruss	56	.10	.08	.04
1991 Donruss	105	.15	.11	.06
1991 Donruss Grand Slammers	11	.20	.15	.08
1991 Fleer	17a	.10	.08	.04
1991 Fleer	17b	.10	.08	.04
1991 Fleer ProVisions	4	.20	.15	.08
1991 Fleer Ultra	251	.20	.15	.08
1991 Leaf	487	.25	.20	.10
1991 Post Cereal	2	.40	.30	.15
1991 Score	324	.10	.08	.04
1991 Studio	106	.25	.20	.10
1991 Topps	270a	.15	.11	.06
1991 Topps	270b	.15	.11	.06
1991 Topps All-Star Glossy Set of 22	2	.30	.25	.12
1991 Upper Deck	174	.25	.20	.10
1992 Bowman	384	.75	.60	.30
1992 Bowman	620	.75	.60	.30
1992 Donruss	348	.12	.09	.05
1992 Donruss Triple Play	231	.05	.04	.02
1992 Donruss Triple Play	262	.15	.10	.05
1992 Fleer	262	.15	.11	.06
1992 Fleer Ultra	115	.35	.25	.14
1992 Fleer Ultra All-Stars	1	.75	.60	.30
1992 Leaf	16	.25	.15	.08
1992 O-Pee-Chee	450	.12	.09	.05
1992 O-Pee-Chee Premier	99	.30	.25	.12
1992 Pinnacle	217	.20	.15	.08
1992 Pinnacle Slugfest	2	1.50	1.25	.60
1992 Score	20	.10	.07	.04
1992 Studio	226	.25	.20	.10
1992 Topps	450	.12	.09	.05
1992 Topps Gold	450	1.25	.90	.50
1992 Topps Kids	121	.20	.15	.08
1992 Topps Stadium Club	475	.20	.15	.08
1992 Upper Deck	153	.15	.11	.06
1993 Bowman	161	.15	.11	.06
1993 DiamondMarks	(104)	.50	.40	.20
1993 Donruss	479	.10	.08	.04
1993 Donruss Diamond Kings	18	1.00	.75	.40
1993 Donruss Elite	33	20.00	15.00	8.00
1993 Donruss Elite Supers	15	12.00	9.00	4.75
1993 Donruss Long Ball Leaders	4	2.00	1.50	.80
1993 Donruss MVP's	19	1.00	.70	.40
1993 Donruss Triple Play Action Baseball	23	.15	.11	.06
1993 Donruss Triple Play	68	.10	.08	.04
1993 Donruss Triple Play	87	.15	.11	.06
1993 Donruss Triple Play	245	.15	.11	.06
1993 Fleer	296	.08	.06	.03
1993 Fleer	710	.10	.08	.04
1993 Fleer AL Team Leaders	2	1.25	.90	.50
1993 Fleer Flair	261	.40	.30	.15
1993 Fleer Ultra	609	.15	.11	.06
1993 Fleer Ultra All-Stars	12	1.00	.75	.40
1993 Fleer Ultra Home Run Kings	2	1.50	1.25	.60
1993 Leaf	323	.15	.11	.06
1993 Leaf Gold All-Stars	11	1.50	1.25	.60
1993 O-Pee-Chee	201	.25	.20	.10
1993 O-Pee-Chee Premier Star Performers	16	.25	.20	.10
1993 Pinnacle	58	.15	.11	.06
1993 Pinnacle Cooperstown	30	.35	.25	.14
1993 Pinnacle Cooperstown Dufex	30	60.00	45.00	24.00
1993 Pinnacle Home Run Club	8	.75	.60	.30
1993 Pinnacle Slugfest	2	.75	.60	.30
1993 Post Cereal	19	.35	.25	.14
1993 Score	557	.10	.08	.04
1993 Score Select	16	.15	.11	.06
1993 Score Select Stat Leaders	26	.20	.15	.08
1993 Score Select Stat Leaders	43	.40	.30	.15
1993 Studio	141	.15	.11	.06
1993 Studio Heritage	4	1.00	.75	.40
1993 Studio Superstars on Canvas	3	1.00	.70	.40
1993 Topps	100	.10	.08	.04
1993 Topps Black Gold	39	.35	.25	.14
1993 Topps Finest	92	1.50	1.25	.60
1993 Topps Finest Jumbo All-Stars	92	8.00	6.00	3.25
1993 Topps Finest Refractors	92	25.00	18.50	10.00
1993 Topps Gold	100	.20	.15	.08
1993 Topps Stadium Club	478	.15	.11	.06
1993 Topps Stadium Club	595	.15	.11	.06
1993 Topps Stadium Club First Day Production	478	15.00	11.00	6.00
1993 Topps Stadium Club First Day Production	595	15.00	11.00	6.00
1993 Topps Stadium Club II Inserts	1	4.50	3.50	1.75
1993 Topps Stadium Club Master Photos	(20)	2.50	2.00	1.00
1993 Topps Stadium Club Special	153	.15	.11	.06
1993 Upper Deck	49	.12	.09	.05
1993 Upper Deck	420	.05	.04	.02
1993 Upper Deck	493	.10	.08	.04
1993 Upper Deck	566	.12	.09	.05
1993 Upper Deck	814	.10	.08	.04
1993 Upper Deck Diamond Gallery	3	.60	.45	.25
1993 Upper Deck Fun Packs All-Star Scratch-Off	3	2.50	2.00	1.00
1993 Upper Deck Fun Packs	17	.10	.08	.04
1993 Upper Deck Fun Packs	48	.25	.20	.10
1993 Upper Deck Fun Packs	51	.20	.15	.08
1993 Upper Deck Future Heroes	60	1.00	.70	.40
1993 Upper Deck Home Run Heroes	2	.60	.45	.25
1993 Upper Deck Iooss Collection	3	.60	.45	.25
1993 Upper Deck Iooss Collection Super	3	5.00	3.75	2.00
1993 Upper Deck On Deck	18	.75	.60	.30
1993 Upper Deck SP	41	.20	.15	.08
1993 Upper Deck SP Platinum Power	13	5.00	3.75	2.00
1994 Bowman	(192)	.15	.11	.06
1994 Donruss	335	.15	.11	.06
1994 Donruss Decade Dominators	10	1.25	.90	.50
1994 Donruss Decade Dominators Supers	10	5.00	3.75	2.00
1994 Donruss Special Edition - Gold	335	.30	.25	.12
1994 Donruss Triple Play	5	.05	.04	.02
1994 Donruss Triple Play Nicknames	7	1.75	1.25	.70
1994 Fleer	268	.10	.08	.04
1994 Fleer Extra Bases	153	.15	.11	.06

1994 Fleer Flair	94	.30	.25	.12
1994 Fleer Team Leaders	11	.75	.60	.30
1994 Fleer Ultra	111	.15	.11	.06
1994 Leaf	391	.15	.11	.06
1994 Leaf Limited	61	1.25	.90	.50
1994 O-Pee-Chee	74	.15	.11	.06
1994 Pacific Crown	456	.12	.09	.05
1994 Pinnacle	300	.20	.15	.08
1994 Pinnacle Artist's Proof	300	5.00	3.75	2.00
1994 Pinnacle Museum Collection	300	2.50	2.00	1.00
1994 Score	550	.15	.11	.06
1994 Score Select	57	.25	.20	.10
1994 Sportflics 2000	4	.25	.20	.10
1994 Studio	4	.15	.11	.06
1994 Topps	340	.10	.08	.04
1994 Topps Finest	78	.75	.60	.30
1994 Topps Finest Refractors	78	10.00	7.50	4.00
1994 Topps Gold	340	.25	.20	.10
1994 Topps Stadium Club	358	.15	.11	.06
1994 Topps Stadium Club First Day Production	358	10.00	7.50	4.00
1994 Upper Deck	67	.15	.11	.06
1994 Upper Deck Collector's Choice	330	.05	.04	.02
1994 Upper Deck Collector's Choice	525	.07	.05	.03
1994 Upper Deck Diamond Collection	8W	5.00	3.75	2.00
1994 Upper Deck Electric Diamond	67	.50	.40	.20
1994 Upper Deck Fun Packs	125	.10	.08	.04
1994 Upper Deck Mickey Mantle's Long Shots	13MM	1.50	1.25	.60
1994 Upper Deck SP	36	.25	.20	.10
1994 Upper Deck SP Baseball Die-Cut	36	.30	.25	.12
1994 Upper Deck SP Holoview Blue	26	3.00	2.25	1.25
1994 Upper Deck SP Holoview Red	26	15.00	11.00	6.00

Denny McLain

Set	Card #	NM	EX	VG
1965 O-Pee-Chee	236	32.50	16.00	9.75
1965 Topps	236 (R)	27.00	13.50	8.00
1966 Topps	226	4.00	2.00	1.25
1966 Topps	540	40.00	20.00	12.00
1967 Topps	235	3.00	1.50	.90
1967 Topps	420	7.50	3.75	2.25
1968 O-Pee-Chee	40	15.00	7.50	4.50
1968 Topps	40	3.00	1.50	.90
1969 O-Pee-Chee	9	2.25	1.25	.70
1969 O-Pee-Chee	11	2.25	1.25	.70
1969 O-Pee-Chee	57	2.25	1.25	.70
1969 O-Pee-Chee	150	2.25	1.25	.70
1969 Topps	9	2.50	1.25	.70
1969 Topps	11	2.50	1.25	.70
1969 Topps	57	3.00	1.50	.90
1969 Topps	150	2.00	1.00	.60
1969 Topps	433	1.50	.70	.45
1970 O-Pee-Chee	70	1.25	.60	.40
1970 O-Pee-Chee	400	1.75	.90	.50
1970 O-Pee-Chee	467	3.00	1.50	.90
1970 Topps	70	3.50	1.75	1.00
1970 Topps	400	2.50	1.25	.70
1970 Topps	467	1.50	.70	.45
1971 O-Pee-Chee	750	12.00	6.00	3.50
1971 Topps	750	15.00	7.50	4.50
1972 O-Pee-Chee	210	1.00	.50	.30
1972 Topps	210	1.00	.50	.30
1972 Topps	753	10.00	5.00	3.00
1973 O-Pee-Chee	630	3.50	1.75	1.00
1973 Topps	630	3.00	1.50	.90
1975 O-Pee-Chee	206	2.00	1.00	.60
1975 Topps	206	1.25	.60	.40
1975 Topps Mini	206	1.75	.90	.50

Dave McNally

Set	Card #	NM	EX	VG
1963 Topps	562 (R)	20.00	10.00	6.00
1964 Topps	161	2.50	1.25	.70
1965 O-Pee-Chee	249	6.25	3.25	2.00
1965 Topps	249	2.50	1.25	.70
1966 O-Pee-Chee	193	2.50	1.25	.70
1966 Topps	193	2.00	1.00	.60
1967 Topps	382	3.00	1.50	.90
1968 Topps	478	2.50	1.25	.70
1969 O-Pee-Chee	7	2.25	1.25	.70
1969 O-Pee-Chee	9	2.25	1.25	.70
1969 Topps	7	2.00	1.00	.60
1969 Topps	9	2.50	1.25	.70
1969 Topps	340	1.00	.50	.30
1969 Topps	532	3.00	1.50	.90
1970 O-Pee-Chee	20	1.00	.50	.30
1970 O-Pee-Chee	70	1.25	.60	.40
1970 Topps	20	.90	.45	.25
1970 Topps	70	3.50	1.75	1.00
1971 O-Pee-Chee	69	1.50	.70	.45
1971 O-Pee-Chee	320	1.50	.70	.45
1971 Topps	69	1.50	.70	.45
1971 Topps	320	1.00	.50	.30
1972 O-Pee-Chee	344	1.25	.60	.40
1972 O-Pee-Chee	490	1.75	.90	.50
1972 Topps	344	.75	.40	.25
1972 Topps	490	1.00	.50	.30
1973 O-Pee-Chee	600	3.50	1.75	1.00
1973 Topps	600	2.00	1.00	.60
1974 O-Pee-Chee	235	.60	.30	.20
1974 Topps	235	.30	.15	.09
1975 O-Pee-Chee	26	.55	.30	.15
1975 Topps	26	.35	.20	.11
1975 Topps Mini	26	.60	.30	.20

Set	Card #	MT	NM	EX
1988 Pacific Trading Cards Baseball Legends	38	.06	.05	.02

Minnie Minoso

Set	Card #	NM	EX	VG
1952 Bowman	5 (R)	90.00	45.00	27.00
1952 Red Man Tobacco	15A	30.00	15.00	9.00
1952 Topps	195 (R)	125.00	62.00	29.00
1953 Bowman Color	36	35.00	17.50	10.50
1953 Topps	66	40.00	20.00	9.25
1954 Bowman	38a	12.00	6.00	3.60
1954 Bowman	38b	12.00	6.00	3.60
1954 Red Heart Dog Food	(22)	35.00	17.50	10.50
1954 Red Man Tobacco	7A	30.00	15.00	9.00
1955 Bowman	25	15.00	7.50	4.50
1955 Red Man Tobacco	24A	30.00	15.00	9.00
1956 Topps	125	20.00	10.00	6.00
1957 Topps	138	11.00	5.50	3.25
1958 Topps	295	9.00	4.50	2.75
1959 Topps	80	8.00	4.00	2.50
1959 Topps	166	12.00	6.00	3.50
1960 Topps	365	4.50	2.25	1.25
1961 Post Cereal	25a	3.75	2.00	1.25
1961 Post Cereal	25b	3.75	2.00	1.25
1961 Topps	42	6.00	3.00	1.75
1961 Topps	380	6.00	3.00	1.75
1962 Post Cereal	51	4.50	2.25	1.25
1962 Topps	28	5.00	2.50	1.50
1963 Topps	190	4.00	2.00	1.25
1964 Topps	538	11.00	5.50	3.25
1977 O-Pee-Chee	262	.30	.15	.09
1977 Topps	232	.35	.20	.11

Set	Card #	MT	NM	EX
1983 Topps 1952 Reprint Set	195	.60	.45	.25
1988 Pacific Trading Cards Baseball Legends	51	.10	.08	.04
1991 "1953" Topps Archives	66	.35	.25	.14

Kevin Mitchell

Set	Card #	MT	NM	EX
1986 Fleer Update	76	1.50	1.25	.60

Set	Card #	NM	EX	VG
1986 Sportflics Rookies	49	.60	.45	.25
1986 Topps Traded	74T	.75	.60	.30
1987 Donruss	599 (R)	1.50	1.25	.60
1987 Fleer	17 (R)	2.00	1.50	.80
1987 Fleer Update	82	.60	.45	.25
1987 Leaf	170	1.00	.70	.40
1987 O-Pee-Chee	307	.50	.40	.20
1987 Sportflics	144	.20	.15	.08
1987 Topps	653 (R)	.60	.45	.25
1987 Topps All-Star Glossy Set of 60	50	.25	.20	.10
1987 Topps Traded	81T	.25	.20	.10
1988 Donruss	66	.10	.08	.04
1988 Fleer	92	.20	.15	.08
1988 Leaf	87	.08	.06	.03
1988 O-Pee-Chee	387	.08	.06	.03
1988 Score	481	.15	.11	.06
1988 Topps	261	.10	.08	.04
1988 Topps	497	.12	.09	.05
1988 Topps Big Baseball	57	.08	.06	.03
1989 Bowman	474	.12	.09	.05
1989 Donruss	485	.15	.11	.06
1989 Fleer	336	.10	.08	.04
1989 O-Pee-Chee	189	.07	.05	.03
1989 Score	39	.08	.05	.02
1989 Sportflics	142	.10	.08	.04
1989 Topps	189	.10	.08	.04
1989 Topps Big Baseball	129	.15	.11	.06
1989 Upper Deck	163	.15	.11	.06
1990 Bowman	232	.10	.07	.04
1990 Bowman Inserts	(6)	.08	.06	.03
1990 Donruss	11	.06	.05	.02
1990 Donruss	98	.10	.08	.04
1990 Donruss	715	.09	.07	.04
1990 Donruss MVP	11	.20	.15	.08
1990 Fleer	65	.10	.08	.04
1990 Fleer	637	.10	.08	.04
1990 Leaf	120	.50	.40	.20
1990 O-Pee-Chee	401	.10	.08	.04
1990 O-Pee-Chee	500	.35	.25	.14
1990 Post Cereal	15	.40	.30	.15
1990 Score	343	.08	.06	.03
1990 Sportflics	1	.20	.15	.08
1990 Topps	401	.10	.08	.04
1990 Topps	500	.15	.11	.06
1990 Topps All-Star Glossy Set of 22	6	.20	.15	.08
1990 Topps All-Star Glossy Set of 60	21	.30	.25	.12
1990 Topps Big Baseball	137	.30	.25	.12
1990 Upper Deck	117	.12	.09	.05
1991 Bowman	636	.10	.08	.04
1991 Donruss	255	.08	.06	.03
1991 Donruss	407	.10	.08	.04
1991 Donruss	438	.10	.08	.04
1991 Fleer	267	.08	.06	.03
1991 Fleer Ultra	326	.15	.11	.06
1991 Leaf	85	.30	.25	.12
1991 O-Pee-Chee Premier	81	.10	.08	.04
1991 Post Cereal	24	.40	.30	.15
1991 Score	406	.10	.08	.04
1991 Score	451	.15	.11	.06
1991 Studio	257	.15	.11	.06
1991 Topps	40	.20	.15	.08
1991 Topps All-Star Glossy Set of 22	17	.10	.08	.04
1991 Upper Deck	247	.12	.09	.05
1992 Bowman	276	.40	.30	.15
1992 Donruss	583	.08	.06	.03
1992 Fleer	644	.12	.09	.05
1992 Fleer Ultra	434	.25	.20	.10
1992 Fleer Update	56	.20	.15	.08
1992 Leaf	185	.10	.08	.04
1992 O-Pee-Chee	180	.10	.08	.04
1992 O-Pee-Chee Premier	97	.15	.11	.06
1992 Pinnacle	393	.10	.08	.04
1992 Score	640	.08	.06	.03
1992 Score Rookie & Traded	18	.08	.06	.03
1992 Studio	237	.15	.11	.06
1992 Topps	180	.10	.08	.04

1992 Topps Gold	180	.35	.25	.14
1992 Topps Kids	59	.05	.04	.02
1992 Topps Stadium Club	215	.15	.11	.06
1992 Topps Stadium Club	765	.20	.15	.08
1992 Topps Stadium Club East Coast National	765	5.00	3.75	2.00
1992 Topps Traded	74	.08	.06	.03
1992 Upper Deck	80	.10	.08	.04
1992 Upper Deck	266	.08	.06	.03
1992 Upper Deck	735	.08	.06	.03
1993 Bowman	386	.10	.08	.04
1993 DiamondMarks	(14)	.25	.20	.10
1993 Donruss	157	.08	.06	.03
1993 Fleer	396	.06	.05	.02
1993 Fleer Final Edition	17	.05	.04	.02
1993 Fleer Flair	28	.25	.15	.08
1993 Fleer Ultra	331	.12	.09	.05
1993 Leaf	321	.10	.08	.04
1993 O-Pee-Chee	252	.15	.11	.06
1993 Pinnacle	551	.06	.05	.02
1993 Pinnacle Home Run Club	23	.25	.20	.10
1993 Pinnacle Slugfest	21	.60	.45	.25
1993 Score	407	.08	.06	.03
1993 Score Select	108	.12	.09	.05
1993 Score Select Rookie/Traded	29	.25	.20	.10
1993 Studio	162	.08	.06	.03
1993 Topps	217	.08	.06	.03
1993 Topps Finest	136	1.00	.70	.40
1993 Topps Finest Refractors	136	20.00	15.00	8.00
1993 Topps Gold	217	.15	.11	.06
1993 Topps Stadium Club	694	.10	.08	.04
1993 Topps Stadium Club First Day Production	694	8.00	6.00	3.25
1993 Topps Traded	112	.05	.04	.02
1993 Upper Deck	55	.50	.40	.20
1993 Upper Deck	213	.08	.06	.03
1993 Upper Deck	646	.08	.06	.03
1993 Upper Deck Fun Packs	171	.15	.11	.06
1993 Upper Deck SP	210	.15	.11	.06
1994 Bowman	514	.10	.08	.04
1994 Bowman's Best	33	.50	.40	.20
1994 Bowman's Best Refractors	33	2.00	1.50	.80
1994 Donruss	377	.06	.05	.02
1994 Donruss Special Edition - Gold	377	.25	.20	.10
1994 Donruss Triple Play	215	.05	.04	.02
1994 Fleer	416	.05	.04	.02
1994 Fleer Extra Bases	234	.15	.11	.06
1994 Fleer Flair	368	.20	.15	.08
1994 Fleer Ultra	173	.12	.09	.05
1994 Leaf	370	.10	.08	.04
1994 Leaf Limited	96	1.00	.70	.40
1994 O-Pee-Chee	29	.05	.04	.02
1994 Pacific Crown	152	.05	.04	.02
1994 Pinnacle	70	.10	.08	.04
1994 Pinnacle Artist's Proof	70	3.00	2.25	1.25
1994 Pinnacle Museum Collection	70	1.50	1.25	.60
1994 Score	24	.04	.03	.02
1994 Score Select	112	.20	.15	.08
1994 Sportflics 2000	126	.10	.08	.04
1994 Studio	169	.10	.08	.04
1994 Topps	335	.04	.03	.02
1994 Topps Finest	323	.50	.40	.20
1994 Topps Finest Refractors	323	3.50	2.75	1.50
1994 Topps Gold	335	.15	.11	.06
1994 Topps Stadium Club	422	.10	.08	.04
1994 Topps Stadium Club First Day Production	422	2.50	2.00	1.00
1994 Upper Deck	58	.10	.08	.04
1994 Upper Deck Collector's Choice	470	.05	.04	.02
1994 Upper Deck Electric Diamond	58	.25	.20	.10
1994 Upper Deck SP	160	.15	.11	.06
1994 Upper Deck SP Baseball Die-Cut	160	.25	.20	.10

Johnny Mize

Set	Card #	NM	EX	VG
1941 Double Play	39	.10	.10	.10
1941 Double Play	99	.10	.10	.10
1948 Bowman	4	100.00	50.00	30.00
1948 Leaf	46	90.00	45.00	27.00
1949 Bowman	85a	65.00	32.50	19.50
1949 Bowman	85b	125.00	62.00	37.00
1950 Bowman	139	60.00	30.00	18.00
1951 Bowman	50	55.00	27.00	16.50
1951 Topps Blue Backs	50	60.00	30.00	18.00
1952 Bowman	145	50.00	30.00	15.00
1952 Topps	129	80.00	40.00	18.50
1953 Bowman Black & White	15	110.00	55.00	33.00
1953 Red Man Tobacco	18A	55.00	27.00	16.50
1953 Topps	77	70.00	35.00	16.00
1960 Fleer	38	3.50	1.75	1.00
1961-62 Fleer	63	4.00	2.00	1.25
1973 Topps 1953 Reprints	8	65.00	32.00	19.50

Set	Card #	MT	NM	EX
1983 Topps 1952 Reprint Set	129	2.00	1.50	.80
1986 Sportflics Decade Greats	24	.15	.11	.06
1988 Pacific Trading Cards Baseball Legends	63	.15	.11	.06
1989 Pacific Trading Cards Legends II	180	.15	.11	.06
1991 "1953" Topps Archives	77	.75	.60	.30

* * *

Four years ago: Paul Molitor's 1978 Topps rookie card (#707) was $50 in July 1991. He shares the card with Alan Trammell.

* * *

Pitcher Nolan Ryan's 1989 Upper Deck baseball card shows him throwing a football. He's doing an exercise that strengthens the arm by working different muscles.

* * *

Paul Molitor

Set	Card #	NM	EX	VG
1978 Topps	707 (R)	100.00	50.00	30.00
1979 O-Pee-Chee	8	34.00	17.00	10.00
1979 Topps	24	35.00	17.50	10.50
1980 O-Pee-Chee	211	15.00	7.50	4.50
1980 Topps	406	17.00	8.50	5.00

Set	Card #	MT	NM	EX
1981 Donruss	203	3.00	2.25	1.25
1981 Fleer	515	3.50	2.75	1.50
1981 O-Pee-Chee	300	5.50	4.25	2.25
1981 Topps	300	5.00	3.75	2.00
1982 Donruss	78	3.00	2.25	1.25
1982 Fleer	148	3.00	2.25	1.25
1982 O-Pee-Chee	195	5.00	3.75	2.00
1982 Topps	195	4.00	3.00	1.50
1983 Donruss	484	1.50	1.25	.60
1983 Fleer	40	2.50	2.00	1.00
1983 O-Pee-Chee	371	3.00	2.25	1.25
1983 Topps	630	3.00	2.25	1.25
1984 Donruss	107	8.00	6.00	3.25
1984 Fleer	207	5.00	3.75	2.00
1984 O-Pee-Chee	60	1.75	1.25	.70
1984 Topps	60	2.00	1.50	.80
1985 Donruss	359	3.00	2.25	1.25
1985 Fleer	588	3.00	2.25	1.25
1985 O-Pee-Chee	395	1.25	.90	.50
1985 Topps	522	1.00	.75	.40
1986 Donruss	124	2.00	1.50	.80
1986 Fleer	495	1.75	1.25	.70
1986 Leaf	70	1.50	1.25	.60
1986 O-Pee-Chee	267	.60	.45	.25
1986 Sportflics	39	.60	.45	.25
1986 Sportflics	128	.20	.15	.08
1986 Topps	267	.75	.60	.30
1987 Donruss	117	.75	.60	.30
1987 Fleer	350	1.00	.70	.40
1987 Leaf	71	.40	.30	.15
1987 O-Pee-Chee	184	.10	.08	.04
1987 Sportflics	54	.60	.45	.25
1987 Topps	56	.15	.11	.06
1987 Topps	741	.25	.20	.10
1988 Donruss	7	.15	.11	.06
1988 Donruss	249	.30	.25	.12
1988 Donruss Diamond Kings Supers	7	.50	.40	.20
1988 Donruss MVP	3	.35	.25	.14
1988 Fleer	169	.40	.30	.15
1988 Fleer All Stars	12	1.00	.70	.40
1988 Leaf	7	.10	.08	.04
1988 Leaf	168	.12	.09	.05
1988 O-Pee-Chee	231	.09	.07	.04
1988 Score	340	.30	.25	.12
1988 Score	660	.15	.11	.06
1988 Sportflics	79	.75	.60	.30
1988 Sportflics	221	.50	.40	.20
1988 Topps	465	.30	.25	.12
1988 Topps All-Star Glossy Set of 60	57	.40	.30	.15
1988 Topps Big Baseball	1	.20	.15	.08
1989 Bowman	140	.25	.20	.10
1989 Donruss	291	.25	.20	.10
1989 Donruss MVP	9	.25	.20	.10
1989 Fleer	193	.25	.20	.10
1989 Fleer All-Stars	8	1.00	.75	.40
1989 O-Pee-Chee	110	.35	.25	.14
1989 Score	565	.20	.12	.06
1989 Sportflics	209	.40	.30	.15
1989 Topps	110	.20	.15	.08
1989 Topps All-Star Glossy Set of 22	3	.15	.11	.06
1989 Topps All-Star Glossy Set of 60	43	.30	.25	.12
1989 Topps Big Baseball	330	.15	.11	.06
1989 Upper Deck	525	.75	.60	.30
1989 Upper Deck	673	.20	.15	.08
1990 Bowman	399	.08	.06	.03
1990 Donruss	103	.20	.15	.08
1990 Donruss MVP	15	.20	.15	.08
1990 Fleer	330	.20	.15	.08
1990 Leaf	242	2.50	2.00	1.00
1990 O-Pee-Chee	360	.09	.07	.04
1990 Score	460	.20	.15	.08
1990 Sportflics	183	.12	.09	.05
1990 Topps	360	.20	.15	.08
1990 Topps Big Baseball	103	.12	.09	.05
1990 Upper Deck	254	.35	.25	.14
1991 Bowman	32	.15	.11	.06
1991 Donruss	85	.15	.11	.06
1991 Fleer	591	.15	.11	.06
1991 Fleer Ultra	178	.25	.20	.10
1991 Leaf	302	.40	.30	.15
1991 O-Pee-Chee Premier	82	.25	.20	.10
1991 Score	49	.15	.11	.06
1991 Studio	73	.50	.40	.20
1991 Topps	95	.15	.11	.06
1991 Topps Stadium Club	245	1.75	1.25	.70
1991 Topps Stadium Club Members Only	(19)	.50	.40	.20
1991 Upper Deck	324	.20	.15	.08
1992 Bowman	375	1.50	1.25	.60
1992 Bowman	645	4.00	3.00	1.50
1992 Donruss	51	.15	.11	.06
1992 Donruss Diamond Kings	1	2.00	1.50	.80
1992 Donruss Triple Play	254	.12	.09	.05
1992 Fleer	182	.15	.11	.06
1992 Fleer	702	.06	.05	.02
1992 Fleer Ultra	81	.30	.25	.12
1992 Leaf	238	.25	.15	.08
1992 O-Pee-Chee	600	.10	.08	.04
1992 O-Pee-Chee Premier	141	.20	.15	.08
1992 Pinnacle	8	.30	.25	.12
1992 Post Cereal	17	.35	.25	.14
1992 Score	61	.20	.15	.08
1992 Studio	194	.30	.25	.12
1992 Studio Heritage	11	2.00	1.50	.80
1992 Topps	600	.15	.11	.06
1992 Topps Gold	600	1.50	1.25	.60
1992 Topps Kids	81	.15	.11	.06
1992 Topps Stadium Club	230	.35	.25	.14
1992 Topps Stadium Club Special Edition	122	.40	.30	.15
1992 Upper Deck	423	.15	.11	.06
1992 Upper Deck MVP Holograms	36	.60	.45	.25
1993 Bowman	167	.50	.40	.20
1993 Donruss	75	.25	.20	.10
1993 Donruss Elite	22	40.00	30.00	15.00
1993 Donruss Elite Dominators	18	200.00	150.00	80.00
1993 Donruss Elite Dominators	18	100.00	75.00	40.00
1993 Donruss Elite Supers	4	25.00	18.50	10.00
1993 Donruss MVP's	4	1.50	1.25	.60
1993 Donruss Triple Play Gallery	6	2.50	2.00	1.00
1993 Donruss Triple Play	97	.25	.20	.10
1993 Fleer	254	.20	.15	.08
1993 Fleer Final Edition	5DT	.60	.45	.25

Card	#			
1993 Fleer Final Edition	295	.30	.25	.12
1993 Fleer Flair	292	1.25	.90	.50
1993 Fleer Ultra	645	.30	.25	.12
1993 Leaf	262	.35	.25	.14
1993 Leaf Update Gold All-Stars	10	1.50	1.25	.60
1993 O-Pee-Chee	237	.60	.45	.25
1993 O-Pee-Chee Premier	124	.20	.15	.08
1993 Pinnacle	428	.35	.25	.14
1993 Pinnacle	481	.20	.15	.08
1993 Pinnacle Cooperstown	23	.30	.25	.12
1993 Pinnacle Cooperstown Dufex	23	75.00	56.00	30.00
1993 Post Cereal	16	.40	.30	.15
1993 Score	598	.20	.15	.08
1993 Score Select	42	.25	.20	.10
1993 Score Select Chase Stars	23	8.00	6.00	3.25
1993 Score Select Rookie/ Traded	16	1.00	.75	.40
1993 Score Select Stat Leaders	9	.25	.20	.10
1993 Studio	172	.25	.20	.10
1993 Topps	207	.15	.11	.06
1993 Topps Finest	70	5.00	3.75	2.00
1993 Topps Finest Refractors	70	50.00	37.00	20.00
1993 Topps Gold	207	.30	.25	.12
1993 Topps Stadium Club	627	.35	.25	.14
1993 Topps Stadium Club First Day Production	627	20.00	15.00	8.00
1993 Topps Stadium Club Members Only	(16)	1.50	1.25	.60
1993 Topps Stadium Club Special	131	.25	.20	.10
1993 Topps Traded	48	.20	.15	.08
1993 Upper Deck	43	.15	.11	.06
1993 Upper Deck	333	.20	.15	.08
1993 Upper Deck	705	.20	.15	.08
1993 Upper Deck Fun Packs	58	.25	.20	.10
1993 Upper Deck Iooss Collection	6	1.00	.75	.40
1993 Upper Deck Iooss Collection Super	6	4.00	3.00	1.50
1993 Upper Deck SP	50	1.50	1.25	.60
1994 Bowman	281	.30	.25	.12
1994 Bowman's Best	1	2.00	1.50	.80
1994 Bowman's Best Refractors	1	12.00	9.00	4.75
1994 Donruss	24	.30	.25	.12
1994 Donruss Award Winners Supers	10	4.50	3.50	1.75
1994 Donruss Decade Dominators	3	1.50	1.25	.60
1994 Donruss Decade Dominators Supers	3	5.00	3.75	2.00
1994 Donruss Special Edition - Gold	24	.50	.40	.20
1994 Donruss Triple Play Promos	5	4.00	3.00	1.50
1994 Donruss Triple Play Medalists	15	1.50	1.25	.60
1994 Donruss Triple Play	35	.20	.15	.08
1994 Fleer	338	.30	.25	.12
1994 Fleer	707	.10	.08	.04
1994 Fleer All-Stars	16	.50	.40	.20
1994 Fleer Extra Bases	192	.40	.30	.15
1994 Fleer Extra Bases	192a	3.00	2.25	1.25
1994 Fleer Extra Bases Game Breakers	20	.40	.30	.15
1994 Fleer Flair	119	.75	.60	.30
1994 Fleer Flair Hot Numbers	5	8.00	6.00	3.25
1994 Fleer Team Leaders	14	.75	.60	.30
1994 Fleer Ultra	140	.30	.25	.12
1994 Fleer Ultra Award Winners	21	1.00	.75	.40
1994 Fleer Ultra Career Achievement Awards	2	2.00	1.50	.80
1994 Fleer Ultra Hitting Machines	7	1.00	.75	.40
1994 Fleer Ultra On-Base Leaders	9	9.00	6.75	3.50
1994 Leaf	395	.50	.40	.20
1994 Leaf Gold Stars	10	20.00	15.00	8.00
1994 Leaf Limited	78	3.00	2.25	1.25
1994 Leaf MVP Contenders	8a	4.00	3.00	1.50
1994 Leaf MVP Contenders	8b	8.00	6.00	3.25
1994 O-Pee-Chee	1	.25	.20	.10
1994 O-Pee-Chee All-Star Redemption Cards	2	.75	.60	.30
1994 O-Pee-Chee Jumbo All-Stars	2	8.00	6.00	3.25
1994 O-Pee-Chee Jumbo All-Stars Factory Set	2	2.50	2.00	1.00
1994 O-Pee-Chee Toronto Blue Jays	3	6.00	4.50	2.50
1994 Pacific Crown	648	.30	.25	.12
1994 Pacific Crown Jewels of the Crown	4	4.00	3.00	1.50
1994 Pinnacle	27	.35	.25	.14
1994 Pinnacle Artist's Proof	27	20.00	15.00	8.00
1994 Pinnacle Museum Collection	27	7.00	5.25	2.75
1994 Pinnacle Run Creators	4	3.00	2.25	1.25
1994 Pinnacle Tribute	1	3.00	2.25	1.25
1994 Score	427	.25	.20	.10
1994 Score Gold Stars	57	8.00	6.00	3.25
1994 Score Select	3	.50	.40	.20
1994 Score Select MVP	1	25.00	18.00	10.00
1994 Score The Cycle	3	12.00	9.00	4.75
1994 Sportflics Commemoratives	1	40.00	30.00	16.00
1994 Sportflics 2000	106	.40	.30	.15
1994 Studio	29	.30	.25	.12
1994 Topps	540	.20	.15	.08
1994 Topps	609	.10	.08	.04
1994 Topps Black Gold	13	.75	.60	.30
1994 Topps Finest	239	2.00	1.50	.80
1994 Topps Finest Refractors	239	12.00	9.00	4.75
1994 Topps Finest Superstars	239	6.00	4.50	2.50
1994 Topps Gold	540	.60	.45	.25
1994 Topps Gold	609	.25	.20	.10
1994 Topps Stadium Club	526	.25	.20	.10
1994 Topps Stadium Club	645	.35	.25	.14
1994 Topps Stadium Club First Day Production	526	10.00	7.50	4.00
1994 Topps Stadium Club First Day Production	645	15.00	11.00	6.00
1994 Topps Stadium Club Members Only Baseball	4	.45	.35	.20
1994 Upper Deck	294	.30	.25	.12
1994 Upper Deck	470	.40	.30	.15
1994 Upper Deck All-Stars Green Foil	16	.50	.40	.20
1994 Upper Deck All-Stars Gold Foil	16	2.50	2.00	1.00
1994 Upper Deck Collector's Choice	208	.20	.15	.08
1994 Upper Deck Electric Diamond	294	.75	.60	.30
1994 Upper Deck Electric Diamond	470	1.00	.75	.40
1994 Upper Deck Fun Packs	150	.25	.20	.10
1994 Upper Deck SP	44	.40	.30	.15
1994 Upper Deck SP Baseball Die-Cut	44	.75	.60	.30

Raul Mondesi

Set	Card #	MT	NM	EX
1991 Bowman	593 (R)	2.50	2.00	1.00
1992 Bowman	64	18.00	13.50	7.25
1992 Donruss Rookies	83	2.50	2.00	1.00
1992 Leaf Gold Rookies	16	12.00	9.00	4.75
1992 Upper Deck	60 (R)	2.00	1.50	.80
1993 Bowman	353	2.50	2.00	1.00
1993 Bowman	618	2.50	2.00	1.00
1993 Fleer Final Edition	82	1.50	1.25	.60
1993 Fleer Ultra	402	2.00	1.50	.80
1993 Leaf	473	2.50	2.00	1.00
1993 Upper Deck SP	96	7.50	5.50	3.00
1994 Bowman	538	1.00	.75	.40
1994 Bowman's Best	99	4.00	3.00	1.50
1994 Bowman's Best	86	4.00	3.00	1.50
1994 Bowman's Best Refractors	99	15.00	11.00	6.00
1994 Bowman's Best Refractors	86	30.00	22.00	12.00
1994 Donruss	313	1.00	.75	.40
1994 Donruss Triple Play	288	.75	.60	.30
1994 Fleer	518	1.00	.75	.40
1994 Fleer Extra Bases	291	1.00	.75	.40
1994 Fleer Extra Bases Rookie Standouts	13	2.00	1.50	.80
1994 Fleer Flair	179	2.00	1.50	.80
1994 Fleer Flair Wave of the Future	6	12.00	9.00	4.75
1994 Fleer Ultra	216	1.00	.75	.40
1994 Fleer Ultra All-Rookie Team	7	4.00	3.00	1.50
1994 Fleer Ultra All-Rookie Team Supers	7	12.00	9.00	4.75
1994 Leaf	93	1.00	.75	.40
1994 O-Pee-Chee	(199)	1.00	.75	.40
1994 O-Pee-Chee Hot Prospects	4	6.00	4.50	2.50
1994 Pacific Crown	316	.75	.60	.30
1994 Pinnacle	242	1.00	.75	.40
1994 Pinnacle Artist's Proof	242	60.00	45.00	25.00
1994 Pinnacle Museum Collection	242	20.00	15.00	8.00
1994 Score	618	.75	.60	.30
1994 Score Boys of Summer	47	16.00	12.00	6.50
1994 Score Rookie & Traded Super Rookies	4	10.00	7.50	4.00
1994 Score Rookie & Traded Gold Rush	82	3.50	2.75	1.50
1994 Score Rookie and Traded	82	1.00	.75	.40
1994 Score Select	183	1.00	.75	.40
1994 Score Select Rookie Surge	17	35.00	26.00	14.00
1994 Sportflics 2000	162	1.25	.90	.50
1994 Studio	70	1.00	.75	.40
1994 Topps	783	.60	.45	.25
1994 Topps Finest	74	4.00	3.00	1.50
1994 Topps Finest Refractors	74	50.00	38.00	20.00
1994 Topps Gold	783	2.50	2.00	1.00
1994 Topps Stadium Club	390	1.00	.75	.40
1994 Topps Stadium Club First Day Production	390	40.00	30.00	15.00
1994 Topps Traded Finest Inserts	4	1.50	1.25	.60
1994 Upper Deck	59	1.00	.75	.40
1994 Upper Deck Collector's Choice	209	1.00	.75	.40
1994 Upper Deck Electric Diamond	59	6.00	4.50	2.50
1994 Upper Deck Fun Packs	143	1.50	1.25	.60
1994 Upper Deck Next Generation	12	6.00	4.50	2.50
1994 Upper Deck SP	79	1.75	1.25	.70
1994 Upper Deck SP Baseball Die-Cut	79	2.50	2.00	1.00
1994 Upper Deck SP Holoview Blue	27	10.00	7.50	4.00
1994 Upper Deck SP Holoview Red	27	60.00	45.00	25.00

Joe Leonard Morgan

Set	Card #	NM	EX	VG
1965 O-Pee-Chee	16	135.00	67.00	40.00
1965 Topps	16 (R)	65.00	32.00	19.50
1966 O-Pee-Chee	195	38.00	19.00	11.50
1966 Topps	195	27.00	13.50	8.25
1967 Topps	337	18.00	9.00	5.50
1968 O-Pee-Chee	144	21.00	10.50	6.25
1968 Topps	144	12.50	6.25	3.75
1968 Topps	364	3.00	1.50	.90
1969 O-Pee-Chee	35	17.00	8.50	5.00
1969 Topps	35	8.00	4.00	2.50
1970 O-Pee-Chee	537	3.00	1.50	.90
1970 Topps	537	10.00	5.00	3.00
1971 O-Pee-Chee	264	12.75	6.50	3.75
1971 Topps	264	10.00	5.00	3.00
1972 O-Pee-Chee	132	6.25	3.25	2.00
1972 Topps	132	5.00	2.50	1.50
1972 Topps	752	30.00	15.00	9.00
1973 O-Pee-Chee	230	6.75	3.50	2.00
1973 Topps	230	5.00	2.50	1.50
1974 O-Pee-Chee	85	7.25	3.75	2.25
1974 O-Pee-Chee	333	1.50	.70	.45
1974 Topps	85	6.00	3.00	1.75
1974 Topps	333	3.00	1.50	.90
1975 O-Pee-Chee	180	7.50	3.75	2.25
1975 Topps	180	5.00	2.50	1.50
1975 Topps Mini	180	10.00	5.00	3.00
1976 O-Pee-Chee	197	2.00	1.00	.60
1976 O-Pee-Chee	420	6.75	3.50	2.00
1976 Topps	197	1.00	.50	.30
1976 Topps	420	6.00	3.00	1.75
1977 O-Pee-Chee	220	5.00	2.50	1.50
1977 Topps	100	6.00	3.00	1.75
1977 Topps	411	1.50	.70	.45

Set	Card #			
1978 O-Pee-Chee	160	3.50	1.75	1.00
1978 Topps	300	3.00	1.50	.90
1979 O-Pee-Chee	5	3.00	1.50	.90
1979 Topps	20	.40	.20	.12
1980 O-Pee-Chee	342	3.00	1.50	.90
1980 Topps	650	2.00	1.00	.60

Set	Card #	MT	NM	EX
1981 Donruss	18	.60	.45	.25
1981 Fleer	78	.70	.50	.30
1981 Topps	560	.90	.70	.35
1981 Topps Traded	807	3.00	2.25	1.25
1982 Donruss	312	.50	.40	.20
1982 Fleer	397	.50	.40	.20
1982 O-Pee-Chee	146	.15	.11	.06
1982 O-Pee-Chee	208	.30	.25	.12
1982 Topps	754	.70	.50	.30
1982 Topps	755	.20	.15	.08
1983 Donruss	24	.30	.25	.12
1983 Donruss	438	.40	.30	.15
1983 Donruss	648	.15	.11	.06
1983 Fleer	270	.50	.40	.20
1983 O-Pee-Chee	81	.30	.25	.12
1983 O-Pee-Chee	264	.12	.09	.05
1983 Topps	171	.15	.11	.06
1983 Topps	603	.60	.45	.25
1983 Topps	604	.15	.11	.06
1983 Topps Traded	77T	3.00	2.25	1.25
1984 Donruss	355	1.00	.75	.40
1984 Fleer	43	.60	.45	.25
1984 Fleer	636	.50	.40	.20
1984 Fleer Update	80	6.00	4.50	2.50
1984 O-Pee-Chee	210	.50	.40	.20
1984 Topps	210	.30	.25	.12
1984 Topps	705	.12	.09	.05
1984 Topps Traded	82T	3.00	2.25	1.25
1985 Donruss	584	.25	.20	.10
1985 Fleer	431	.40	.30	.15
1985 Leaf-Donruss	28	.20	.15	.08
1985 O-Pee-Chee	352	.15	.11	.06
1985 Topps	5	.15	.11	.06
1985 Topps	352	.30	.25	.12
1986 Sportflics Decade Greats	56	.25	.20	.10
1989 Score	660	.06	.05	.02
1992 Upper Deck Bench/ Morgan Heroes	40	.50	.40	.20
1992 Upper Deck Bench/ Morgan Heroes	41	.50	.40	.20
1992 Upper Deck Bench/ Morgan Heroes	42	.50	.40	.20
1992 Upper Deck Bench/ Morgan Heroes	43	.75	.60	.30
1992 Upper Deck Bench/ Morgan Heroes	44	.75	.60	.30
1992 Upper Deck Bench/ Morgan Heroes	45	.75	.60	.30

Jack Morris

JACK MORRIS

Set	Card #	NM	EX	VG
1978 Topps	703 (R)	6.00	3.00	1.75

1979 Topps	251	3.00	1.50	.90
1980 Topps	371	1.25	.60	.40

Set	Card #	MT	NM	EX
1981 Donruss	127	.60	.45	.25
1981 Fleer	475	.75	.60	.30
1981 O-Pee-Chee	284	.50	.40	.20
1981 Topps	572	.75	.60	.30
1982 Donruss	107	.50	.40	.20
1982 Fleer	274	.30	.25	.12
1982 O-Pee-Chee	47	.20	.15	.08
1982 O-Pee-Chee	108	2.25	1.75	.90
1982 Topps	165	.20	.15	.08
1982 Topps	450	.60	.45	.25
1982 Topps	556	.20	.15	.08
1983 Donruss	5	.30	.25	.12
1983 Donruss	107	.60	.45	.25
1983 Fleer	336	.40	.30	.15
1983 O-Pee-Chee	65	1.50	1.25	.60
1983 Topps	65	.50	.40	.20
1984 Donruss	415	1.00	.75	.40
1984 Fleer	87	1.00	.75	.40
1984 O-Pee-Chee	195	1.00	.70	.40
1984 Topps	136	.25	.20	.10
1984 Topps	195	.30	.25	.12
1984 Topps	666	.15	.11	.06
1984 Topps All-Star Glossy Set of 40	10	.30	.25	.12
1985 Donruss	415	.25	.20	.10
1985 Fleer	18	.20	.15	.08
1985 Fleer	643	.15	.11	.06
1985 Leaf-Donruss	142	.15	.11	.06
1985 O-Pee-Chee	382	.20	.15	.08
1985 Topps	610	.12	.09	.05
1985 Topps All-Star Glossy Set of 40	26	.30	.25	.12
1986 Donruss	105	.25	.20	.10
1986 Fleer	232	.12	.09	.05
1986 Leaf	38	.50	.40	.20
1986 O-Pee-Chee	270	.15	.11	.06
1986 Sportflics	117	.15	.11	.06
1986 Sportflics	141	.20	.15	.08
1986 Topps	270	.10	.07	.04
1986 Topps All-Star Glossy Set of 22	10	.30	.25	.12
1987 Donruss	13	.10	.08	.04
1987 Donruss	173	.15	.11	.06
1987 Donruss Diamond Kings Supers	13	.20	.15	.08
1987 Fleer	158	.15	.11	.06
1987 Fleer All Stars	28	.15	.11	.06
1987 Leaf	13	.30	.25	.12
1987 Leaf	135	.25	.20	.10
1987 O-Pee-Chee	376	.15	.11	.06
1987 Sportflics	87	.20	.15	.08
1987 Sportflics	111	.25	.20	.10
1987 Topps	778	.10	.07	.04
1987 Topps All-Star Glossy Set of 60	47	.25	.20	.10
1988 Donruss	127	.12	.09	.05
1988 Fleer	64	.10	.08	.04
1988 Fleer	626	.10	.08	.04
1988 Leaf	85	.20	.15	.08
1988 O-Pee-Chee	340	.12	.09	.05
1988 Score	545	.10	.08	.04
1988 Sportflics	176	.20	.15	.08
1988 Topps	340	.10	.08	.04
1988 Topps All-Star Glossy Set of 60	17	.20	.15	.08
1988 Topps Big Baseball	170	.12	.09	.05
1989 Bowman	93	.03	.02	.01
1989 Donruss	234	.10	.08	.04
1989 Fleer	139	.12	.09	.05
1989 O-Pee-Chee	266	.07	.05	.03
1989 Score	250	.12	.09	.05
1989 Sportflics	5	.20	.15	.08
1989 Topps	645	.12	.09	.05
1989 Topps Big Baseball	61	.05	.04	.02
1989 Upper Deck	352	.15	.11	.06
1990 Donruss	639a	.25	.20	.10
1990 Donruss	639b	.08	.06	.03

1990 Fleer	610	.07	.05	.02
1990 Leaf	482	.35	.25	.14
1990 O-Pee-Chee	555	.07	.05	.03
1990 Score	203	.08	.06	.03
1990 Topps	555	.07	.05	.03
1990 Upper Deck	573	.09	.07	.04
1991 Bowman	319	.08	.06	.03
1991 Donruss	492	.06	.05	.02
1991 Fleer	343	.08	.06	.03
1991 Fleer Ultra Update	39	.20	.15	.08
1991 Fleer Update	39	.10	.08	.04
1991 Leaf	294	.15	.11	.06
1991 O-Pee-Chee Premier	84	.08	.06	.03
1991 Score	114	.08	.06	.03
1991 Score Traded	74	.08	.06	.03
1991 Studio	89	.20	.15	.08
1991 Topps	75	.08	.06	.03
1991 Topps Stadium Club	447	.30	.25	.12
1991 Topps Stadium Club Members Only	(20)	.25	.20	.10
1991 Topps Traded	82	.08	.06	.03
1991 Upper Deck	336	.08	.06	.03
1991 Upper Deck	736	.10	.07	.04
1991 Upper Deck Final Edition	80	.10	.07	.04
1992 Bowman	16	.40	.30	.15
1992 Donruss	25	.07	.05	.03
1992 Donruss	216	.08	.06	.03
1992 Donruss Triple Play Gallery of Stars	3	1.00	.70	.40
1992 Fleer	211	.08	.06	.03
1992 Fleer Ultra	452	.20	.15	.08
1992 Fleer Ultra Award Winners	1	.75	.60	.30
1992 Fleer Update	66	.20	.15	.08
1992 Leaf	425	.08	.06	.03
1992 O-Pee-Chee	235	.08	.06	.03
1992 O-Pee-Chee Premier	79	.20	.15	.08
1992 Pinnacle	483	.12	.09	.05
1992 Pinnacle	585	.20	.15	.08
1992 Score	652	.06	.05	.02
1992 Score	798	.06	.05	.02
1992 Score Rookie & Traded	15	.10	.08	.04
1992 Studio	257	.15	.11	.06
1992 Topps	235	.08	.06	.03
1992 Topps Gold	235	.35	.25	.14
1992 Topps Stadium Club	640	.10	.08	.04
1992 Topps Stadium Club Members Only	(7)	.25	.20	.10
1992 Topps Stadium Club Special Edition	125	.15	.11	.06
1992 Topps Stadium Club Special Edition	126	.15	.11	.06
1992 Topps Traded	77	.08	.06	.03
1992 Topps Traded Gold	77	.15	.11	.06
1992 Upper Deck	315	.10	.08	.04
1992 Upper Deck	732	.05	.04	.02
1993 Bowman	463	.10	.08	.04
1993 Donruss	351	.08	.06	.03
1993 Donruss Triple Play	160	.07	.05	.03
1993 Fleer	347	.07	.05	.03
1993 Fleer	697	.05	.04	.02
1993 Fleer Ultra	290	.10	.08	.04
1993 Leaf	113	.10	.08	.04
1993 O-Pee-Chee	179	.15	.11	.06
1993 Pinnacle	57	.06	.05	.02
1993 Pinnacle	472	.06	.05	.02
1993 Score	37	.04	.03	.02
1993 Score	508	.04	.03	.02
1993 Score Select	158	.15	.11	.06
1993 Score Select Aces	5	3.00	2.25	1.25
1993 Topps	185	.08	.06	.03
1993 Topps Gold	185	.15	.11	.06
1993 Topps Stadium Club	356	.10	.08	.04
1993 Topps Stadium Club First Day Production	356	8.00	6.00	3.25
1993 Upper Deck	164	.10	.08	.04
1993 Upper Deck Fun Packs	59	.12	.09	.05
1993 Upper Deck SP	51	.15	.11	.06
1994 Fleer	339	.05	.04	.02
1994 Fleer Extra Bases	63	.10	.08	.04
1994 Fleer Flair	285	.20	.15	.08
1994 Fleer Ultra	345	.10	.08	.04
1994 Fleer Update	33	.10	.08	.04
1994 Leaf	401	.10	.08	.04
1994 Pacific Crown	649	.05	.04	.02
1994 Pinnacle	532	.10	.08	.04
1994 Pinnacle Artist's Proof	532	3.00	2.25	1.25
1994 Pinnacle Museum Collection	532	1.50	1.25	.60
1994 Score	453	.04	.03	.02
1994 Score Rookie & Traded Gold Rush	21	.25	.20	.10
1994 Score Rookie and Traded	21	.05	.04	.02
1994 Score Select	289	.10	.08	.04
1994 Topps Stadium Club	556	.10	.08	.04
1994 Topps Stadium Club First Day Production	556	3.00	2.25	1.25
1994 Topps Traded	36	.05	.04	.02
1994 Upper Deck	331	.10	.08	.04
1994 Upper Deck Collector's Choice	542	.05	.04	.02
1994 Upper Deck Electric Diamond	331	.25	.20	.10

Thurman Munson

Set	Card #	NM	EX	VG
1970 O-Pee-Chee	189	105.00	52.00	31.00
1970 Topps	189 (R)	85.00	42.00	25.00
1971 O-Pee-Chee	5	50.00	25.00	15.00
1971 Topps	5	30.00	15.00	9.00
1972 O-Pee-Chee	441	25.00	12.50	7.50
1972 O-Pee-Chee	442	12.75	6.50	3.75
1972 Topps	441	15.00	7.50	4.50
1972 Topps	442	7.00	3.50	2.00
1973 O-Pee-Chee	142	12.75	6.50	3.75
1973 Topps	142	10.00	5.00	3.00
1974 O-Pee-Chee	340	12.00	6.00	3.50
1974 Topps	340	5.00	2.50	1.50
1975 O-Pee-Chee	20	10.25	5.25	3.00
1975 Topps	20	7.00	3.50	2.00
1975 Topps Mini	20	10.00	5.00	3.00
1976 O-Pee-Chee	192	2.00	1.00	.60
1976 O-Pee-Chee	650	8.50	4.25	2.50
1976 Topps	192	2.00	1.00	.60
1976 Topps	650	6.00	3.00	1.75
1977 O-Pee-Chee	30	6.00	3.00	1.75
1977 Topps	170	5.00	2.50	1.50
1978 O-Pee-Chee	200	5.00	2.50	1.50
1978 Topps	60	5.00	2.50	1.50
1979 O-Pee-Chee	157	3.50	1.75	1.00
1979 Topps	310	4.00	2.00	1.25

Set	Card #	MT	NM	EX
1986 Sportflics Decade Greats	62	.25	.20	.10
1988 Pacific Trading Cards Baseball Legends	34	.20	.15	.08
1992 Pinnacle Rookie Idols	10	7.50	5.50	3.00

Bobby Murcer

Set	Card #	NM	EX	VG
1966 Topps	469 (R)	30.00	15.00	9.00
1967 O-Pee-Chee	93	2.25	1.25	.70
1967 Topps	93 (R)	3.50	1.75	1.00
1969 Topps	657	3.00	1.50	.90
1970 O-Pee-Chee	333	1.75	.90	.50
1970 Topps	333	.90	.45	.25
1971 O-Pee-Chee	635	5.00	2.50	1.50
1971 Topps	635	4.00	2.00	1.25
1972 O-Pee-Chee	86	.75	.40	.25
1972 Topps	86	2.00	1.00	.60
1972 Topps	699	6.00	3.00	1.75
1972 Topps	700	6.00	3.00	1.75
1973 O-Pee-Chee	240	.75	.40	.25
1973 O-Pee-Chee	343	.75	.40	.25
1973 Topps	240	.60	.30	.20
1973 Topps	343	.40	.20	.12
1974 O-Pee-Chee	90	.60	.30	.20
1974 O-Pee-Chee	336	2.00	1.00	.60
1974 Topps	90	.40	.20	.12
1974 Topps	336	2.50	1.25	.70
1975 O-Pee-Chee	350	.55	.30	.15
1975 Topps	350	.30	.15	.09
1975 Topps Mini	350	.60	.30	.20
1976 O-Pee-Chee	470	.40	.20	.12
1976 Topps	470	.25	.13	.08
1977 O-Pee-Chee	83	.30	.15	.09
1977 Topps	40	.30	.15	.09
1978 O-Pee-Chee	95	.25	.13	.08
1978 Topps	590	.20	.10	.06
1979 O-Pee-Chee	63	.25	.13	.08
1979 Topps	135	.25	.13	.08
1980 O-Pee-Chee	190	.20	.10	.06
1980 Topps	365	.25	.13	.08

Set	Card #	MT	NM	EX
1981 Donruss	111	.10	.08	.04
1981 Fleer	94	.10	.08	.04
1981 O-Pee-Chee	253	.12	.09	.05
1981 Topps	602	.15	.11	.06
1982 Donruss	486	.10	.08	.04
1982 Fleer	44	.10	.08	.04
1982 Topps	208	.10	.08	.04
1983 Donruss	261	.10	.08	.04
1983 Fleer	390	.10	.08	.04
1983 O-Pee-Chee	122	.12	.09	.05
1983 O-Pee-Chee	304	.12	.09	.05
1983 Topps	782	.12	.09	.05
1983 Topps	783	.10	.08	.04

Set	Card #	MT	NM	EX
1989 Pacific Trading Cards Legends II	196	.06	.05	.02

Dale Murphy

Set	Card #	NM	EX	VG
1977 Topps	476	20.00	10.00	6.00
1978 Topps	708 (R)	10.00	5.00	3.00
1979 O-Pee-Chee	15	5.50	2.75	1.75
1979 Topps	39	6.00	3.00	1.75
1980 O-Pee-Chee	143	3.50	1.75	1.00
1980 Topps	274	3.00	1.50	.90

Set	Card #	MT	NM	EX
1981 Donruss	437	.75	.60	.30
1981 Fleer	243	.75	.60	.30
1981 O-Pee-Chee	118	2.25	1.75	.90
1981 Topps	504	.90	.70	.35
1982 Donruss	299	.75	.60	.30
1982 Fleer	443	.75	.60	.30
1982 O-Pee-Chee	391	1.75	1.25	.70
1982 Topps	668	1.25	.90	.50
1983 Donruss	12	.30	.25	.12
1983 Donruss	47	.70	.50	.30
1983 Fleer	142	.75	.60	.30
1983 O-Pee-Chee	21	.60	.45	.25
1983 O-Pee-Chee	23	1.25	.90	.50
1983 Topps	401	.20	.15	.08
1983 Topps	502	.25	.20	.10
1983 Topps	703	.35	.25	.14
1983 Topps	760	.75	.60	.30
1983 Topps All-Star Glossy Set of 40	16	.60	.45	.25
1984 Donruss	66	2.00	1.50	.80
1984 Fleer	186	.75	.60	.30
1984 O-Pee-Chee	150	1.25	.90	.50
1984 O-Pee-Chee	391	.60	.45	.25
1984 Topps	126	.25	.20	.10
1984 Topps	133	.40	.30	.15
1984 Topps	150	.40	.30	.15
1984 Topps	391	.20	.15	.08
1984 Topps All-Star Glossy Set of 22	19	.80	.60	.30
1984 Topps All-Star Glossy Set of 40	31	.50	.40	.20
1985 Donruss	66	.60	.45	.25
1985 Fleer	335	.50	.40	.20
1985 Leaf-Donruss	222	.40	.30	.15
1985 O-Pee-Chee	320	.50	.40	.20
1985 Topps	320	.20	.15	.08
1985 Topps	716	.15	.11	.06
1985 Topps All-Star Glossy Set of 40	1	1.00	.70	.40
1985 Topps All-Star Glossy Set of 22	7	.40	.30	.15
1986 Donruss	66	.35	.25	.14
1986 Fleer	522	.30	.25	.12
1986 Fleer	635	.30	.25	.12
1986 Fleer	640	.30	.25	.12
1986 Leaf	60	.40	.30	.15
1986 Sportflics	5	.50	.40	.20

1986 Sportflics	62	.50	.40	.20
1986 Sportflics	179	1.25	.90	.50
1986 Sportflics	183	1.25	.90	.50
1986 Sportflics Decade Greats	67	.80	.60	.30
1986 Topps	456	.15	.11	.06
1986 Topps	600	.12	.09	.05
1986 Topps	705	.10	.08	.04
1986 Topps All-Star Glossy Set of 22	18	.80	.60	.30
1986 Topps All-Star Glossy Set of 60	37	.90	.70	.35
1987 Donruss	3	.12	.09	.05
1987 Donruss	78	.10	.08	.04
1987 Donruss Diamond Kings Supers	3	.40	.30	.15
1987 Fleer	522	.25	.20	.10
1987 Fleer All Stars	29	.30	.25	.12
1987 Leaf	3	.30	.25	.12
1987 Leaf	141	.30	.25	.12
1987 O-Pee-Chee	359	.35	.25	.14
1987 Sportflics	3	.50	.40	.20
1987 Sportflics	155	.30	.25	.12
1987 Sportflics	159	1.25	.90	.50
1987 Topps	490	.12	.09	.05
1987 Topps All-Star Glossy Set of 60	6	.60	.45	.25
1987 Topps All-Star Glossy Set of 22	7	.30	.25	.12
1988 Donruss	78	.10	.08	.04
1988 Donruss MVP	14	.35	.25	.14
1988 Fleer	544	.12	.09	.05
1988 Fleer	639	.15	.11	.06
1988 Leaf	83	.30	.25	.12
1988 O-Pee-Chee	90	.25	.20	.10
1988 Score	450	.10	.08	.04
1988 Sportflics	170	.50	.40	.20
1988 Topps	90	.10	.08	.04
1988 Topps	549	.08	.06	.03
1988 Topps All-Star Glossy Set of 60	26	.60	.45	.25
1988 Topps Big Baseball	14	.30	.25	.12
1989 Bowman	276	.10	.08	.04
1989 Donruss	104	.08	.06	.03
1989 Fleer	596	.10	.08	.04
1989 O-Pee-Chee	210	.20	.15	.08
1989 Score	30	.10	.06	.03
1989 Sportflics	110	.40	.30	.15
1989 Topps	210	.10	.08	.04
1989 Topps Big Baseball	172	.08	.06	.03
1989 Upper Deck	357a	35.00	25.00	14.00
1989 Upper Deck	357b	.20	.15	.08
1989 Upper Deck	672	.08	.06	.03
1990 Bowman	19	.10	.08	.04
1990 Donruss	168	.07	.05	.03
1990 Fleer	591	.10	.07	.04
1990 Fleer	623	.08	.06	.03
1990 Fleer Update	46	.30	.25	.12
1990 Leaf	243	.35	.25	.14
1990 O-Pee-Chee	750	.10	.08	.04
1990 Post Cereal	18	.60	.45	.25
1990 Score	66	.12	.09	.05
1990 Score Traded	31T	.10	.08	.04
1990 Sportflics	189	.12	.09	.05
1990 Topps	750	.10	.08	.04
1990 Topps Big Baseball	40	.12	.09	.05
1990 Upper Deck	533	.10	.08	.04
1991 Bowman	486	.08	.06	.03
1991 Donruss	484	.10	.08	.04
1991 Fleer	409	.10	.08	.04
1991 Fleer Ultra	270	.10	.08	.04
1991 Leaf	412	.15	.11	.06
1991 O-Pee-Chee Premier	85	.08	.06	.03
1991 Score	650	.12	.09	.05
1991 Studio	220	.20	.15	.08
1991 Topps	545	.10	.08	.04
1991 Topps Stadium Club	243	.25	.20	.10
1991 Upper Deck	447	.10	.07	.04
1992 Bowman	684	.20	.15	.08
1992 Donruss	146	.08	.06	.03
1992 Donruss Triple Play	158	.08	.06	.03

1992 Donruss Triple Play	260	.08	.06	.03
1992 Fleer	541	.12	.09	.05
1992 Fleer Ultra	249	.10	.08	.04
1992 Leaf	527	.12	.09	.05
1992 O-Pee-Chee	680	.08	.06	.03
1992 Pinnacle	124	.15	.11	.06
1992 Pinnacle	284	.15	.11	.06
1992 Score	80	.08	.06	.03
1992 Studio	79	.20	.15	.08
1992 Topps	680	.08	.06	.03
1992 Topps Gold	680	.75	.60	.30
1992 Topps Stadium Club	280	.25	.20	.10
1992 Upper Deck	127	.10	.08	.04
1993 Donruss	646	.05	.04	.02
1993 Fleer	496	.05	.04	.02
1993 Fleer Ultra	353	.10	.08	.04
1993 Pinnacle	503	.06	.05	.02
1993 Pinnacle Cooperstown	5	.30	.25	.12
1993 Pinnacle Cooperstown Dufex	5	35.00	26.00	14.00
1993 Score	597	.20	.15	.08
1993 Score Select	103	.12	.09	.05
1993 Topps	445	.04	.03	.02
1993 Topps Gold	445	.10	.08	.04
1993 Topps Stadium Club	572	.10	.08	.04
1993 Topps Stadium Club First Day Production	572	12.00	9.00	4.75
1993 Upper Deck	32	.10	.08	.04
1993 Upper Deck	706	.12	.09	.05

Eddie Murray

Set	Card #	NM	EX	VG
1978 O-Pee-Chee	154	75.00	37.00	22.00
1978 Topps	36 (R)	85.00	42.00	25.00
1979 O-Pee-Chee	338	25.00	12.50	7.50
1979 Topps	640	25.00	12.50	7.50
1980 O-Pee-Chee	88	12.75	6.50	3.75
1980 Topps	160	15.00	7.50	4.50

Set	Card #	MT	NM	EX
1981 Donruss	112	4.00	3.00	1.50
1981 Fleer	184	4.00	3.00	1.50
1981 O-Pee-Chee	39	4.00	3.00	1.50
1981 Topps	490	5.00	3.75	2.00
1982 Donruss	483	2.00	1.50	.80
1982 Fleer	174	.80	.60	.30
1982 O-Pee-Chee	390	2.75	2.00	1.00
1982 Topps	162	.25	.20	.10
1982 Topps	163	.50	.40	.20
1982 Topps	390	1.25	.90	.50
1982 Topps	426	.25	.20	.10
1983 Donruss	405	.80	.60	.30
1983 Fleer	67	1.50	1.25	.60
1983 O-Pee-Chee	141	2.25	1.75	.90
1983 Topps	21	.25	.20	.10
1983 Topps	530	2.00	1.50	.80

1983 Topps All-Star Glossy Set of 40	37	.60	.45	.25
1984 Donruss	22a	2.00	1.50	.80
1984 Donruss	22b	4.00	3.00	1.50
1984 Donruss	47	6.00	4.50	2.50
1984 Fleer	14	3.00	2.25	1.25
1984 O-Pee-Chee	240	1.25	.90	.50
1984 O-Pee-Chee	291	.50	.40	.20
1984 Topps	240	1.00	.75	.40
1984 Topps	397	.40	.30	.15
1984 Topps All-Star Glossy Set of 40	4	.60	.45	.25
1985 Donruss	47	2.00	1.50	.80
1985 Fleer	184	2.00	1.50	.80
1985 Leaf-Donruss	203	1.75	1.25	.70
1985 O-Pee-Chee	221	.40	.30	.15
1985 Topps	700	.75	.60	.30
1985 Topps	701	.30	.25	.12
1985 Topps All-Star Glossy Set of 40	28	.60	.45	.25
1986 Donruss	88	1.00	.70	.40
1986 Fleer	282	1.00	.70	.40
1986 Leaf	83	.30	.25	.12
1986 O-Pee-Chee	30	.35	.25	.14
1986 Sportflics	4	.60	.45	.25
1986 Sportflics	73	.25	.20	.10
1986 Sportflics	145	.15	.11	.06
1986 Sportflics Decade Greats	70	.60	.45	.25
1986 Sportflics Rookies	48	.60	.45	.25
1986 Topps	30	.40	.30	.15
1986 Topps All-Star Glossy Set of 22	2	.50	.40	.20
1986 Topps All-Star Glossy Set of 60	33	.60	.45	.25
1987 Donruss	48	.50	.40	.20
1987 Fleer	476	.75	.60	.30
1987 Fleer	636	.20	.15	.08
1987 Leaf	110	.40	.30	.15
1987 O-Pee-Chee	120	.25	.20	.10
1987 Sportflics	6	.50	.40	.20
1987 Sportflics	75	.50	.40	.20
1987 Sportflics	159	1.25	.90	.50
1987 Topps	120	.40	.30	.15
1987 Topps All-Star Glossy Set of 60	12	.60	.45	.25
1988 Donruss	231	.20	.15	.08
1988 Fleer	567	.35	.25	.14
1988 Leaf	172	.25	.20	.10
1988 O-Pee-Chee	4	.20	.15	.08
1988 Score	18	.25	.20	.10
1988 Sportflics	59	.40	.30	.15
1988 Topps	4a	.25	.20	.10
1988 Topps	4b	.10	.08	.04
1988 Topps	51	.30	.25	.12
1988 Topps	495	.25	.20	.10
1989 Bowman	346	.15	.11	.06
1989 Donruss	96	.20	.15	.08
1989 Donruss Traded	12	.30	.25	.12
1989 Fleer	611	.20	.15	.08
1989 Fleer Update	92	.20	.15	.08
1989 O-Pee-Chee	148	.20	.15	.08
1989 Score	94	.20	.15	.08
1989 Score Traded	31T	.15	.11	.06
1989 Sportflics	147	.40	.30	.15
1989 Topps	625	.15	.11	.06
1989 Topps Big Baseball	319	.10	.08	.04
1989 Topps Traded	87T	.30	.25	.12
1989 Upper Deck	275	.40	.30	.15
1989 Upper Deck	763	.50	.40	.20
1990 Bowman	101	.08	.06	.03
1990 Donruss	77	.15	.11	.06
1990 Fleer	404	.10	.08	.04
1990 Leaf	181	.80	.60	.30
1990 O-Pee-Chee	305	.15	.11	.06
1990 Score	80	.12	.09	.05
1990 Topps	305	.15	.11	.06
1990 Topps Big Baseball	29	.15	.11	.06
1990 Upper Deck	277	.15	.11	.06
1991 Bowman	376	.08	.06	.03
1991 Bowman	614	.10	.07	.04
1991 Donruss	405	.10	.08	.04
1991 Donruss	502	.12	.09	.05
1991 Fleer	214	.08	.06	.03
1991 Fleer Ultra	166	.12	.09	.05
1991 Leaf	126	.15	.11	.06
1991 O-Pee-Chee Premier	86	.15	.11	.06
1991 Score	310	.10	.08	.04
1991 Studio	185	.15	.11	.06
1991 Topps	397	.08	.06	.03
1991 Topps	590	.10	.08	.04
1991 Topps Stadium Club	177	.60	.45	.25
1991 Upper Deck	237	.20	.15	.08
1991 Upper Deck Silver Sluggers	6	.60	.45	.25
1992 Bowman	433	.08	.06	.03
1992 Donruss	392	.10	.08	.04
1992 Fleer	466	.10	.07	.04
1992 Fleer Ultra	532	.25	.20	.10
1992 Leaf	396	.15	.11	.06
1992 O-Pee-Chee	780	.10	.08	.04
1992 O-Pee-Chee Premier	193	.15	.11	.06
1992 Pinnacle	424	.20	.15	.08
1992 Score	195	.12	.09	.05
1992 Score Rookie & Traded	11	.40	.30	.15
1992 Studio	68	.15	.11	.06
1992 Topps	780	.10	.08	.04
1992 Topps Gold	780	.60	.45	.25
1992 Topps Kids	50	.15	.11	.06
1992 Topps Stadium Club	795	.20	.15	.08
1992 Topps Stadium Club Members Only	(8)	.40	.30	.15
1992 Topps Stadium Club Special Edition	128	.30	.25	.12
1992 Topps Traded	79	.08	.06	.03
1992 Upper Deck	32	.05	.04	.02
1992 Upper Deck	265	.15	.11	.06
1992 Upper Deck	728	.12	.09	.05
1992 Upper Deck	753	.08	.06	.03
1993 Bowman	454	.10	.08	.04
1993 Donruss	278	.08	.06	.03
1993 Donruss Diamond Kings	25	1.00	.75	.40
1993 Donruss Elite	21	20.00	15.00	8.00
1993 Donruss Elite Supers	3	8.00	6.00	3.25
1993 Donruss MVP's	10	.75	.60	.30
1993 Donruss Triple Play	41	.10	.08	.04
1993 Fleer	91	.10	.08	.04
1993 Fleer Flair	94	.35	.25	.14
1993 Fleer Ultra	78	.15	.11	.06
1993 Leaf	167	.15	.11	.06
1993 Leaf Heading for the Hall	4	2.50	2.00	1.00
1993 O-Pee-Chee	280	.25	.20	.10
1993 Pinnacle	18	.15	.11	.06
1993 Pinnacle	292	.06	.05	.02
1993 Pinnacle Cooperstown	27	.25	.20	.10
1993 Pinnacle Cooperstown Dufex	27	60.00	45.00	24.00
1993 Pinnacle Home Run Club	35	.50	.40	.20
1993 Score	77	.12	.09	.05
1993 Score Select	29	.12	.09	.05
1993 Topps	430	.03	.02	.01
1993 Topps Finest	122	2.00	1.50	.80
1993 Topps Finest Refractors	122	25.00	18.50	10.00
1993 Topps Gold	430	.10	.08	.04
1993 Topps Stadium Club	50	.15	.11	.06
1993 Topps Stadium Club First Day Production	50	30.00	22.00	12.00
1993 Topps Stadium Club Members Only	(17)	.75	.60	.30
1993 Upper Deck	115	.10	.08	.04
1993 Upper Deck	484	.08	.06	.03
1993 Upper Deck "Highlights"	13	2.00	1.50	.80

1993 Upper Deck Fun Packs	128	.15	.11	.06
1993 Upper Deck SP	152	.15	.11	.06
1993 Upper Deck Then And Now	14	2.00	1.50	.80
1994 Bowman	467	.15	.11	.06
1994 Bowman's Best	2	.75	.60	.30
1994 Bowman's Best Refractors	2	6.00	4.50	2.50
1994 Donruss	386	.10	.08	.04
1994 Donruss Triple Play	117	.08	.06	.03
1994 Fleer	573	.08	.06	.03
1994 Fleer Extra Bases	64	.15	.11	.06
1994 Fleer Flair	286	.30	.25	.12
1994 Fleer Ultra	346	.12	.09	.05
1994 Fleer Update	34	.15	.11	.06
1994 Fleer Update Diamond Tribute	8	.40	.30	.15
1994 Leaf	313	.15	.11	.06
1994 Leaf Limited	29	1.50	1.25	.60
1994 O-Pee-Chee	184	.15	.11	.06
1994 Pacific Crown	413	.10	.08	.04
1994 Pinnacle	495	.15	.11	.06
1994 Pinnacle Artist's Proof	495	5.00	3.75	2.00
1994 Pinnacle Museum Collection	495	2.00	1.50	.80
1994 Score	36	.04	.03	.02
1994 Score Rookie & Traded Gold Rush	5	.35	.25	.14
1994 Score Rookie and Traded	5	.10	.08	.04
1994 Score Rookie/ Traded Samples	5RT	3.00	2.25	1.25
1994 Score Select	329	.20	.15	.08
1994 Studio	94	.15	.11	.06
1994 Topps	65	.08	.06	.03
1994 Topps Finest	317	.75	.60	.30
1994 Topps Finest Refractors	317	4.50	3.50	1.75
1994 Topps Gold	65	.20	.15	.08
1994 Topps Stadium Club	542	.15	.11	.06
1994 Topps Stadium Club	674	.15	.11	.06
1994 Topps Stadium Club First Day Production	542	15.00	11.00	6.00
1994 Topps Stadium Club First Day Production	674	15.00	11.00	6.00
1994 Topps Traded	60	.08	.06	.03
1994 Upper Deck Collector's Choice	595	.08	.06	.03
1994 Upper Deck Fun Packs	85	.05	.04	.02
1994 Upper Deck SP	100	.20	.15	.08
1994 Upper Deck SP Baseball Die-Cut	100	.35	.25	.14

Stan Musial

Set	Card #	NM	EX	VG
1948 Bowman	36 (R)	750.00	375.00	220.00

Set	Card #	MT	NM	EX
1948 Leaf	4 (R)	675.00	340.00	200.00
1949 Bowman	24	500.00	250.00	150.00
1952 Bowman	196	450.00	225.00	135.00
1952 Red Man Tobacco	16N	175.00	87.00	52.00
1953 Bowman Color	32	525.00	260.00	152.00
1953 Red Man Tobacco	26N	150.00	75.00	45.00
1954 Red Heart Dog Food	(23)	400.00	200.00	120.00
1958 Topps	476	30.00	15.00	9.00
1959 Topps	150	120.00	60.00	36.00
1959 Topps	470	18.00	9.00	5.50
1960 Topps	250	100.00	50.00	30.00
1961 Topps	290	90.00	45.00	27.00
1962 Topps	50	90.00	45.00	27.00
1962 Topps	317	25.00	12.50	7.50
1963 Topps	1	35.00	17.50	10.50
1963 Topps	138	45.00	22.50	13.50
1963 Topps	250	85.00	42.00	25.00

Set	Card #	MT	NM	EX
1986 Sportflics Decade Greats	30	1.00	.70	.40
1988 Pacific Trading Cards Baseball Legends	6	.50	.40	.20
1988 Topps	665	.12	.09	.05
1992 Score The Franchise	1	8.00	6.00	3.25
1992 Score The Franchise	4	9.00	6.75	3.50

Charles Nagy

Set	Card #	MT	NM	EX
1988 Topps Traded	74T	.75	.60	.30
1989 Bowman	73 (R)	.25	.20	.10
1989 Topps Big Baseball	217	.25	.20	.10
1990 Score	611	.25	.20	.10
1991 Bowman	65	.12	.09	.05
1991 Donruss	592	.12	.09	.05
1991 Fleer Ultra Update	20	.75	.60	.30
1991 Fleer Update	20	.25	.20	.10
1991 Score	75	.08	.06	.03
1991 Topps	466	.10	.08	.04
1991 Topps Stadium Club	472	.40	.30	.15
1991 Upper Deck	19	.15	.11	.06
1992 Bowman	203	.40	.30	.15
1992 Bowman	566	.50	.40	.20
1992 Donruss	315	.10	.08	.04
1992 Fleer	118	.08	.06	.03
1992 Fleer Ultra	351	.20	.15	.08
1992 Leaf	115	.10	.08	.04
1992 O-Pee-Chee	299	.06	.05	.02
1992 O-Pee-Chee Premier	138	.15	.11	.06
1992 Pinnacle	383	.15	.11	.06
1992 Pinnacle	609	.12	.09	.05
1992 Pinnacle Team 2000	19	.10	.08	.04
1992 Score	330	.10	.08	.04
1992 Score Impact Players	19	.15	.11	.06
1992 Topps	299	.06	.05	.02
1992 Topps Gold	299	.25	.20	.10
1992 Topps Stadium Club	389	.10	.08	.04

1992 Upper Deck	178	.08	.06	.03
1992 Upper Deck MVP Holograms	37	.25	.20	.10
1993 Bowman	149	.10	.08	.04
1993 Donruss	141	.08	.06	.03
1993 Donruss Triple Play	49	.05	.04	.02
1993 Fleer	219	.15	.11	.06
1993 Fleer Ultra	189	.15	.11	.06
1993 Leaf	171	.10	.08	.04
1993 O-Pee-Chee	278	.15	.11	.06
1993 Pinnacle	65	.06	.05	.02
1993 Pinnacle Team 2001	22	.50	.40	.20
1993 Score	29	.04	.03	.02
1993 Score	538	.04	.03	.02
1993 Score Gold Dream Team	7	.50	.40	.20
1993 Score Select	70	.20	.15	.08
1993 Score Select Aces	12	3.00	2.25	1.25
1993 Studio	203	.08	.06	.03
1993 Topps	730	.03	.02	.01
1993 Topps Finest	58	1.00	.70	.40
1993 Topps Finest Refractors	58	20.00	15.00	8.00
1993 Topps Gold	730	.10	.08	.04
1993 Topps Stadium Club	551	.10	.08	.04
1993 Topps Stadium Club First Day Production	551	10.00	7.50	4.00
1993 Topps Stadium Club Special	88	.10	.08	.04
1993 Upper Deck	243	.10	.07	.04
1993 Upper Deck Fun Packs	110	.05	.04	.02
1993 Upper Deck SP	125	.15	.11	.06
1994 Bowman	251	.10	.08	.04
1994 Donruss	239	.05	.04	.02
1994 Donruss Triple Play	118	.05	.04	.02
1994 Fleer	115	.05	.04	.02
1994 Fleer Extra Bases	65	.10	.08	.04
1994 Fleer Flair	42	.20	.15	.08
1994 Fleer Ultra	348	.10	.08	.04
1994 Leaf	297	.10	.08	.04
1994 O-Pee-Chee	254	.05	.04	.02
1994 Pacific Crown	179	.05	.04	.02
1994 Pinnacle	385	.10	.08	.04
1994 Pinnacle Artist's Proof	385	3.00	2.25	1.25
1994 Pinnacle Museum Collection	385	1.50	1.25	.60
1994 Score	333	.04	.03	.02
1994 Score Select	264	.10	.08	.04
1994 Sportflics 2000	130	.10	.08	.04
1994 Topps	330	.04	.03	.02
1994 Topps Finest	104	.50	.40	.20
1994 Topps Finest Refractors	104	3.50	2.75	1.50
1994 Topps Gold	330	.15	.11	.06
1994 Topps Stadium Club	478	.10	.08	.04
1994 Topps Stadium Club First Day Production	478	2.50	2.00	1.00
1994 Upper Deck	394	.10	.08	.04
1994 Upper Deck Collector's Choice	578	.05	.04	.02
1994 Upper Deck Electric Diamond	394	.25	.20	.10

* * *

Rip Sewell, on throwing his famous blooper pitch:
"Whitey Kurowski on the Cardinals wouldn't swing at
it. When I threw it to him he wouldn't swing at it. He'd
spit at it. He'd spit tobacco juice at it.
He hated that thing."

* * *

Four years ago: Lou Whitaker's 1978 Topps rookie
card (#704) was $12 in July 1991.

* * *

Graig Nettles

Set	Card #	NM	EX	VG
1969 O-Pee-Chee	99	30.00	15.00	9.00
1969 Topps	99a (R)	18.00	9.00	5.50
1969 Topps	99b (R)	18.00	9.00	5.50
1970 O-Pee-Chee	491	7.50	3.75	2.25
1970 Topps	491	3.00	1.50	.90
1971 O-Pee-Chee	324	1.75	.90	.50
1971 Topps	324	2.00	1.00	.60
1972 Topps	590	3.00	1.50	.90
1973 O-Pee-Chee	498	1.50	.70	.45
1973 Topps	498	1.00	.50	.30
1974 O-Pee-Chee	251	1.25	.60	.40
1974 Topps	251	.30	.15	.09
1975 O-Pee-Chee	160	1.25	.60	.40
1975 Topps	160	.45	.25	.14
1976 O-Pee-Chee	169	1.00	.50	.30
1976 Topps	169	1.00	.50	.30
1977 O-Pee-Chee	2	3.00	1.50	.90
1977 O-Pee-Chee	217	.75	.40	.25
1977 Topps	2	1.50	.70	.45
1977 Topps	20	.45	.25	.14
1978 O-Pee-Chee	10	.25	.13	.08
1978 Topps	250	.30	.15	.09
1979 O-Pee-Chee	240	.40	.20	.12
1979 Topps	460	.25	.13	.08
1980 O-Pee-Chee	359	.30	.15	.09
1980 Topps	710	.15	.08	.05

Set	Card #	MT	NM	EX
1981 Donruss	105	.15	.11	.06
1981 Fleer	87a	10.00	7.50	4.00
1981 Fleer	87b	.30	.25	.12
1981 O-Pee-Chee	365	.12	.09	.05
1981 Topps	365	.12	.09	.05
1982 Donruss	335	.15	.11	.06
1982 Fleer	46	.15	.11	.06
1982 O-Pee-Chee	21	.12	.09	.05
1982 O-Pee-Chee	62	.15	.11	.06
1982 Topps	505	.15	.11	.06
1982 Topps	506	.12	.09	.05
1983 Donruss	83	.15	.11	.06
1983 Fleer	391	.15	.11	.06
1983 O-Pee-Chee	207	.12	.09	.05
1983 O-Pee-Chee	293	.15	.11	.06
1983 Topps	635	.20	.15	.08
1983 Topps	636	.12	.09	.05
1984 Donruss	518	.35	.25	.14
1984 Fleer	135	.20	.15	.08
1984 Fleer Update	82	1.00	.70	.40
1984 O-Pee-Chee	175	.25	.20	.10
1984 Topps	175	.20	.15	.08
1984 Topps	712	.20	.15	.08
1984 Topps	713	.20	.15	.08
1985 Donruss	234	.20	.15	.08
1985 Fleer	42	.15	.11	.06
1985 Leaf-Donruss	177	.20	.15	.08
1985 O-Pee-Chee	35	.12	.09	.05
1985 Topps	35	.15	.11	.06
1986 Donruss	478	.15	.11	.06
1986 Fleer	332	.15	.11	.06

Set	Card #			
1986 O-Pee-Chee	151	.10	.08	.04
1986 Sportflics	91	.15	.11	.06
1986 Topps	450	.15	.11	.06
1986 Topps All-Star Glossy Set of 22	15	.20	.15	.08
1987 Fleer	426	.12	.09	.05
1987 O-Pee-Chee	205	.08	.06	.03
1987 Topps	205	.10	.08	.04
1987 Topps Traded	85T	.12	.09	.05
1988 Score	440	.08	.06	.03
1988 Score Traded	25T	.20	.15	.08
1988 Score Traded/ Rookie Glossy	25T	.80	.60	.30
1988 Topps	574	.08	.06	.03
1989 Score	277	.10	.08	.04
1990 Pacific Senior League	115	.10	.08	.04
1990 Pacific Senior League	132	.10	.08	.04
1990 Pacific Senior League	158	.10	.08	.04
1990 Topps Senior League	25	.15	.11	.06

Phil Niekro

PHIL NIEKRO

Set	Card #	NM	EX	VG
1964 Topps	541 (R)	160.00	80.00	47.50
1965 Topps	461	45.00	22.00	13.50
1966 O-Pee-Chee	28	21.00	10.50	6.25
1966 Topps	28	15.00	7.50	4.50
1967 Topps	456	12.00	6.00	3.50
1968 O-Pee-Chee	7	2.25	1.25	.70
1968 Topps	7	3.50	1.75	1.00
1968 Topps	257	5.00	2.50	1.50
1969 Topps	355	7.00	3.50	2.00
1970 O-Pee-Chee	69	7.50	3.75	2.25
1970 O-Pee-Chee	160	2.50	1.25	.70
1970 Topps	69	5.00	2.50	1.50
1970 Topps	160	3.50	1.75	1.00
1971 O-Pee-Chee	30	2.25	1.25	.70
1971 Topps	30	3.25	1.75	1.00
1972 Topps	620	6.00	3.00	1.75
1973 O-Pee-Chee	503	5.00	2.50	1.50
1973 Topps	503	5.00	2.50	1.50
1974 O-Pee-Chee	29	1.50	.70	.45
1974 Topps	29	2.00	1.00	.60
1975 O-Pee-Chee	130	1.50	.70	.45
1975 O-Pee-Chee	310	.75	.40	.25
1975 Topps	130	1.50	.70	.45
1975 Topps	310	.80	.40	.25
1975 Topps Mini	130	4.00	2.00	1.25
1975 Topps Mini	310	1.25	.60	.40
1976 O-Pee-Chee	435	1.75	.90	.50
1976 Topps	435	1.50	.70	.45
1977 O-Pee-Chee	43	1.25	.60	.40
1977 Topps	615	1.50	.70	.45
1978 O-Pee-Chee	6	3.75	2.00	1.25
1978 O-Pee-Chee	155	1.00	.50	.30
1978 Topps	10	1.25	.60	.40
1978 Topps	206	2.50	1.25	.70
1979 O-Pee-Chee	313	1.75	.90	.50
1979 Topps	595	1.25	.60	.40
1980 O-Pee-Chee	130	.75	.40	.25
1980 Topps	205	.40	.20	.12
1980 Topps	245	.80	.40	.25

Set	Card #	MT	NM	EX
1981 Donruss	328	.30	.25	.12
1981 Fleer	242	.30	.25	.12
1981 O-Pee-Chee	201	.12	.09	.05
1981 Topps	387	.80	.60	.30
1982 Donruss	10	.30	.25	.12
1982 Donruss	475	.30	.25	.12
1982 Fleer	444	.30	.25	.12
1982 O-Pee-Chee	185	.40	.30	.15
1982 Topps	185	.50	.40	.20
1983 Donruss	97	.30	.25	.12
1983 Donruss	613	.15	.11	.06
1983 Fleer	143	.30	.25	.12
1983 O-Pee-Chee	94	.30	.25	.12
1983 O-Pee-Chee	316	.15	.11	.06
1983 Topps	410	.40	.30	.15
1983 Topps	411	.20	.15	.08
1983 Topps	502	.25	.20	.10
1984 Donruss	188	1.00	.75	.40
1984 Fleer	187	.30	.25	.12
1984 Fleer Update	83	4.00	3.00	1.50
1984 O-Pee-Chee	29	.50	.40	.20
1984 Topps	650	.30	.25	.12
1984 Topps Traded	84T	2.00	1.50	.80
1985 Donruss	458	.30	.25	.12
1985 Fleer	138	.25	.20	.10
1985 Leaf-Donruss	138	.20	.15	.08
1985 O-Pee-Chee	40	.20	.15	.08
1985 Topps	40	.25	.20	.10
1985 Topps All-Star Glossy Set of 40	32	.35	.25	.14
1986 Donruss	580	.30	.25	.12
1986 Donruss	645	.15	.11	.06
1986 Fleer	112	.25	.20	.10
1986 Fleer	630	.15	.11	.06
1986 Fleer Update	81	.25	.20	.10
1986 Leaf	243	.10	.08	.04
1986 O-Pee-Chee	246	.20	.15	.08
1986 Sportflics	53	.15	.11	.06
1986 Sportflics	135	.25	.20	.10
1986 Sportflics	163	.25	.20	.10
1986 Sportflics	182	1.50	1.25	.60
1986 Topps	204	.08	.06	.03
1986 Topps	790	.12	.09	.05
1986 Topps Traded	77T	.20	.15	.08
1987 Donruss	465	.15	.11	.06
1987 Fleer	254	.20	.15	.08
1987 Fleer	626	.12	.09	.05
1987 Leaf	181	.15	.11	.06
1987 O-Pee-Chee	6	.15	.11	.06
1987 Sportflics	147	.25	.20	.10
1987 Topps	11	.07	.05	.03
1987 Topps	694	.10	.08	.04
1988 Score	555	.15	.11	.06
1988 Topps	5	.10	.08	.04
1989 Pacific Trading Cards Legends II	212	.10	.08	.04
1990 Pacific Legends	96	.15	.11	.06

* * *

The Dec. 18, 1992, Sports Collectors Digest puts Michael Jordan at the top of the list for collective value for all his cards. His 59 cards total $3,135, based mainly on his $1,200 1984-85 Star Co. rookie card. Trailers include George Mikan, one card, 1948 Bowman, at $3,000; Bill Russell, three cards, at $2,440; Wilt Chamberlain, 18 cards, at $2,270.50; and Kareem Abdul-Jabbar, 53 cards, at $1,680.50.

* * *

Blue Moon Odom

Set	Card #	NM	EX	VG
1965 Topps	526 (R)	90.00	45.00	27.00
1967 Topps	282	2.50	1.25	.70
1968 Topps	501	2.50	1.25	.70
1969 O-Pee-Chee	195	2.25	1.25	.70
1969 Topps	195	1.00	.50	.30
1970 O-Pee-Chee	55	1.00	.50	.30
1970 Topps	55	.90	.45	.25
1971 O-Pee-Chee	523	2.50	1.25	.70
1971 Topps	523	2.00	1.00	.60
1972 Topps	557	2.00	1.00	.60
1972 Topps	558	2.00	1.00	.60
1973 O-Pee-Chee	315	.75	.40	.25
1973 Topps	315	.40	.20	.12
1974 O-Pee-Chee	461	.60	.30	.20
1974 Topps	461	.30	.15	.09
1975 O-Pee-Chee	69	.55	.30	.15
1975 Topps	69	.35	.20	.11
1976 O-Pee-Chee	651	.35	.20	.11
1976 Topps	651	.25	.13	.08

Ben Oglivie

Set	Card #	NM	EX	VG
1972 Topps	761 (R)	20.00	10.00	6.00
1973 O-Pee-Chee	388	.75	.40	.25
1973 Topps	388	.40	.20	.12
1975 O-Pee-Chee	344	.55	.30	.15
1975 Topps	344	.30	.15	.09
1975 Topps Mini	344	.60	.30	.20
1976 O-Pee-Chee	659	.35	.20	.11
1976 Topps	659	.25	.13	.08
1977 O-Pee-Chee	236	.30	.15	.09
1977 Topps	122	.20	.10	.06
1978 Topps	286	.20	.10	.06
1979 Topps	519	.20	.10	.06
1980 Topps	53	.20	.10	.06

Set	Card #	MT	NM	EX
1981 Donruss	446	.08	.06	.03
1981 Fleer	508	.08	.06	.03
1981 O-Pee-Chee	340	.12	.09	.05
1981 Topps	2	.90	.70	.35
1981 Topps	415	.10	.08	.04
1982 Donruss	484	.08	.06	.03
1982 Fleer	151	.08	.06	.03
1982 O-Pee-Chee	280	.12	.09	.05
1982 Topps	280	.10	.08	.04
1983 Donruss	384	.08	.06	.03
1983 Fleer	43	.08	.06	.03
1983 Fleer	640	.25	.20	.10
1983 O-Pee-Chee	91	.12	.09	.05
1983 Topps	750	.10	.08	.04
1984 Donruss	229	.12	.09	.05
1984 Fleer	210	.10	.08	.04
1984 O-Pee-Chee	190	.20	.15	.08
1984 Topps	190	.10	.08	.04
1985 Donruss	333	.10	.08	.04
1985 Fleer	590	.08	.06	.03
1985 Leaf-Donruss	123	.08	.06	.03
1985 O-Pee-Chee	332	.08	.06	.03
1985 Topps	681	.08	.06	.03
1986 Donruss	333	.08	.06	.03
1986 Fleer	497	.08	.06	.03
1986 Leaf	199	.08	.06	.03
1986 O-Pee-Chee	372	.08	.06	.03
1986 Topps	372	.07	.05	.03
1987 Donruss	419	.07	.05	.03
1987 Fleer	353	.08	.06	.03
1987 Topps	586	.07	.05	.03

John Olerud

Set	Card #	MT	NM	EX
1990 Bowman	510 (R)	1.00	.75	.40
1990 Donruss	711 (R)	1.00	.75	.40
1990 Fleer Update	128	1.00	.75	.40
1990 Leaf	237	8.00	6.00	3.25
1990 Score	589 (R)	1.00	.75	.40
1990 Topps Big Baseball	199	.50	.40	.20
1990 Topps Traded	83T	.75	.60	.30
1990 Upper Deck	56 (R)	1.50	1.25	.60
1991 Bowman	7	.25	.20	.10
1991 Donruss	530	.25	.20	.10
1991 Fleer	183	.25	.20	.10
1991 Fleer Ultra	367	.50	.40	.20
1991 Leaf	125	.40	.30	.15
1991 O-Pee-Chee Premier	92	.35	.25	.14
1991 Score	625	.25	.20	.10
1991 Score	860	.20	.15	.08
1991 Score Rising Star	100	.30	.25	.12
1991 Studio	136	.50	.40	.20
1991 Topps	168	.25	.20	.10
1991 Topps Glossy Rookies	24	.50	.40	.20
1991 Topps Stadium Club	482	2.00	1.50	.80
1991 Upper Deck	145	.40	.30	.15

Card	#			
1992 Bowman	644	2.00	1.50	.80
1992 Donruss	98	.20	.15	.08
1992 Donruss Triple Play	110	.25	.15	.06
1992 Fleer	339	.25	.20	.10
1992 Fleer Ultra	151	.50	.40	.20
1992 Leaf	60	.40	.30	.15
1992 O-Pee-Chee	777	.12	.09	.05
1992 Pinnacle	78	.30	.25	.12
1992 Pinnacle Team 2000	65	.35	.25	.14
1992 Score	345	.25	.20	.10
1992 Score Impact Players	41	.30	.25	.12
1992 Studio	258	.25	.20	.10
1992 Topps	777	.15	.11	.06
1992 Topps Gold	777	.60	.45	.25
1992 Topps Gold Winners	777	.30	.25	.12
1992 Topps Stadium Club	531	.25	.20	.10
1992 Upper Deck	375	.25	.20	.10
1993 Bowman	659	.20	.15	.08
1993 DiamondMarks Inserts	(5)	15.00	11.00	6.00
1993 Donruss	483	.15	.11	.06
1993 Donruss Elite Dominators	9	100.00	75.00	40.00
1993 Donruss Triple Play	222	.15	.11	.06
1993 Fleer	339	.15	.11	.06
1993 Fleer Flair	293	.40	.30	.15
1993 Fleer Ultra	291	.25	.20	.10
1993 Leaf	47	.25	.20	.10
1993 Leaf Update Gold All-Stars	3	1.00	.75	.40
1993 O-Pee-Chee	188	.35	.25	.14
1993 O-Pee-Chee Premier	52	.30	.25	.12
1993 O-Pee-Chee World Champs	12	.50	.40	.20
1993 Pinnacle	86	.25	.20	.10
1993 Pinnacle Home Run Club	29	.50	.40	.20
1993 Score	68	.15	.11	.06
1993 Score Select	124	.25	.20	.10
1993 Studio	195	.25	.20	.10
1993 Topps	240	.20	.15	.08
1993 Topps Finest	13	3.00	2.25	1.25
1993 Topps Finest Refractors	13	50.00	38.00	20.00
1993 Topps Full Shot Super	10	4.00	3.00	1.50
1993 Topps Gold	240	.40	.30	.15
1993 Topps Stadium Club	649	.25	.20	.10
1993 Topps Stadium Club First Day Production	649	20.00	15.00	8.00
1993 Upper Deck	344	.15	.11	.06
1993 Upper Deck Fun Packs	60	.20	.15	.08
1993 Upper Deck SP	6	.75	.60	.30
1994 Bowman	169	.20	.15	.08
1994 Bowman's Best	110	1.50	1.25	.60
1994 Bowman's Best	62	1.00	.70	.40
1994 Bowman's Best Refractors	110	5.00	3.75	2.00
1994 Bowman's Best Refractors	62	5.00	3.75	2.00
1994 Donruss	354	.20	.15	.08
1994 Donruss Diamond Kings	24	1.25	.90	.50
1994 Donruss Diamond Kings Super	24	3.75	2.75	1.50
1994 Donruss Elite	43	15.00	11.00	6.00
1994 Donruss MVP's	28	1.00	.75	.40
1994 Donruss Special Edition - Gold	354	.40	.30	.15
1994 Donruss Spirit of the Game	1	3.00	2.25	1.25
1994 Donruss Spirit of the Game Super	1	10.00	7.50	4.00
1994 Donruss Triple Play Medalists	3	5.00	3.75	2.00
1994 Donruss Triple Play Nicknames	5	3.00	2.25	1.25
1994 Donruss Triple Play	36	.15	.11	.06
1994 Fleer	340	.15	.11	.06
1994 Fleer	707	.10	.08	.04
1994 Fleer All-Stars	19	.35	.25	.14
1994 Fleer Extra Bases	193	.35	.25	.14
1994 Fleer Extra Bases Game Breakers	21	.35	.25	.14
1994 Fleer Flair	120	.50	.40	.20
1994 Fleer Flair Hot Numbers	6	6.00	4.50	2.50
1994 Fleer League Leaders	1	.35	.25	.14
1994 Fleer ProVisions	2	.40	.30	.15
1994 Fleer Ultra	141	.15	.11	.06
1994 Fleer Ultra All-Stars	9	.60	.45	.25
1994 Fleer Ultra Hitting Machines	8	1.00	.75	.40
1994 Fleer Ultra League Leaders	1	.60	.45	.25
1994 Fleer Ultra On-Base Leaders	10	7.00	5.25	2.75
1994 Fleer Ultra Rising Stars	8	5.00	3.75	2.00
1994 Leaf	378	.20	.15	.08
1994 Leaf Gold Stars	12	10.00	7.50	4.00
1994 Leaf Limited	79	1.50	1.25	.60
1994 O-Pee-Chee	130	.15	.11	.06
1994 O-Pee-Chee All-Star Redemption Cards	16	.85	.60	.35
1994 O-Pee-Chee Jumbo All-Stars	16	8.00	6.00	3.25
1994 O-Pee-Chee Jumbo All-Stars Factory Set	16	1.25	.90	.50
1994 O-Pee-Chee Toronto Blue Jays	5	4.00	3.00	1.50
1994 Pacific Crown	650	.15	.11	.06
1994 Pacific Crown Jewels of the Crown	6	3.00	2.25	1.25
1994 Pinnacle	5	.20	.15	.08
1994 Pinnacle Artist's Proof	5	15.00	11.00	6.00
1994 Pinnacle Museum Collection	5	6.00	4.50	2.50
1994 Pinnacle Run Creators	1	2.00	1.50	.80
1994 Pinnacle The Naturals Box Set	24	.35	.25	.14
1994 Post Cereal	24	.35	.25	.14
1994 Score	2	.15	.11	.06
1994 Score Gold Stars	37	4.00	3.00	1.50
1994 Score Select	239	.25	.20	.10
1994 Score Select Crown Contenders	8	6.00	4.50	2.50
1994 Score The Cycle	6	8.00	6.00	3.25
1994 Sportflics 2000	75	.35	.25	.14
1994 Studio	30	.25	.20	.10
1994 Topps	10	.10	.08	.04
1994 Topps Black Gold	15	.75	.60	.30
1994 Topps Finest	221	1.00	.75	.40
1994 Topps Finest Refractors	221	6.00	4.50	2.50
1994 Topps Finest Superstars	221	4.00	3.00	1.50
1994 Topps Gold	10	.45	.35	.20
1994 Topps Stadium Club	228	.20	.15	.08
1994 Topps Stadium Club First Day Production	228	15.00	11.00	6.00
1994 Topps Stadium Club Members Only Baseball	9	.35	.25	.14
1994 Upper Deck	48	.15	.11	.06
1994 Upper Deck	99	.25	.20	.10
1994 Upper Deck All-Stars Green Foil	24	.25	.20	.10
1994 Upper Deck All-Stars Gold Foil	24	1.00	.70	.40
1994 Upper Deck Collector's Choice	600	.15	.11	.06
1994 Upper Deck Electric Diamond	48	1.00	.75	.40
1994 Upper Deck Electric Diamond	99	1.25	.90	.50

1994 Upper Deck Fun Packs	99	.25	.20	.10
1994 Upper Deck SP	45	.40	.30	.15
1994 Upper Deck SP Baseball Die-Cut	45	.60	.45	.25

Al Oliver

Tony Oliva

Set	Card #	NM	EX	VG
1963 Topps	228	45.00	22.00	13.50
1964 Topps	116	15.00	7.50	4.50
1965 O-Pee-Chee	1	21.00	10.50	6.25
1965 Topps	1	15.00	7.50	4.50
1965 Topps	340	15.00	7.50	4.50
1966 Topps	216	8.00	4.00	2.50
1966 Topps	220	5.00	2.50	1.50
1966 Topps	450	9.00	4.50	2.75
1967 O-Pee-Chee	50	2.25	1.25	.70
1967 Topps	50	4.00	2.00	1.25
1967 Topps	239	12.00	6.00	3.50
1968 O-Pee-Chee	165	2.25	1.25	.70
1968 Topps	165	2.50	1.25	.70
1968 Topps	371	3.50	1.75	1.00
1968 Topps	480	35.00	17.50	10.50
1969 O-Pee-Chee	1	17.00	8.50	5.00
1969 Topps	1	8.00	4.00	2.50
1969 Topps	427	1.50	.70	.45
1969 Topps	582a	3.50	1.75	1.00
1969 Topps	582b	2.50	1.25	.70
1969 Topps	600	4.50	2.25	1.25
1970 O-Pee-Chee	62	1.75	.90	.50
1970 O-Pee-Chee	510	2.25	1.25	.70
1970 Topps	62	3.50	1.75	1.00
1970 Topps	510	2.50	1.25	.70
1971 O-Pee-Chee	61	1.50	.70	.45
1971 O-Pee-Chee	290	1.50	.70	.45
1971 Topps	61	3.50	1.75	1.00
1971 Topps	290	1.50	.70	.45
1972 O-Pee-Chee	86	.75	.40	.25
1972 O-Pee-Chee	400	1.75	.90	.50
1972 Topps	86	2.00	1.00	.60
1972 Topps	400	1.50	.70	.45
1973 O-Pee-Chee	80	1.00	.50	.30
1973 Topps	80	.75	.40	.25
1974 O-Pee-Chee	190	.75	.40	.25
1974 Topps	190	.50	.25	.15
1975 O-Pee-Chee	325	.75	.40	.25
1975 Topps	325	.45	.25	.14
1975 Topps Mini	325	2.50	1.25	.70
1976 O-Pee-Chee	35	.50	.25	.15
1976 Topps	35	.40	.20	.12

Set	Card #	MT	NM	EX
1988 Pacific Trading Cards Baseball Legends	59	.10	.08	.04
1989 Topps	665	.06	.05	.02

Set	Card #	NM	EX	VG
1969 O-Pee-Chee	82	17.00	8.50	5.00
1969 Topps	82 (R)	11.00	5.50	3.25
1970 O-Pee-Chee	166	2.50	1.25	.70
1970 Topps	166	2.50	1.25	.70
1971 O-Pee-Chee	388	1.50	.70	.45
1971 Topps	388	1.50	.70	.45
1972 Topps	575	3.00	1.50	.90
1973 O-Pee-Chee	225	1.00	.50	.30
1973 Topps	225	.75	.40	.25
1974 O-Pee-Chee	52	1.00	.50	.30
1974 Topps	52	.75	.40	.25
1975 O-Pee-Chee	555	.75	.40	.25
1975 Topps	555	.60	.30	.20
1976 O-Pee-Chee	620	.60	.30	.20
1976 Topps	620	.40	.20	.12
1977 O-Pee-Chee	203	.60	.30	.20
1977 Topps	130	.60	.30	.20
1978 O-Pee-Chee	97	.75	.40	.25
1978 Topps	430	.40	.20	.12
1979 O-Pee-Chee	204	.25	.13	.08
1979 Topps	391	.40	.20	.12
1980 O-Pee-Chee	136	.30	.15	.09
1980 Topps	260	.20	.10	.06

Set	Card #	MT	NM	EX
1981 Donruss	387	.15	.11	.06
1981 Fleer	626	.15	.11	.06
1981 O-Pee-Chee	70	.12	.09	.05
1981 Topps	70	.15	.11	.06
1982 Donruss	116	.15	.11	.06
1982 Fleer	326	.15	.11	.06
1982 O-Pee-Chee	22	.12	.09	.05
1982 O-Pee-Chee	326	.15	.11	.06
1982 Topps	36	.12	.09	.05
1982 Topps	590	.20	.15	.08
1982 Topps	591	.10	.08	.04
1982 Topps Traded	83T	.30	.25	.12
1983 Donruss	140	.15	.11	.06
1983 Fleer	290	.15	.11	.06
1983 O-Pee-Chee	5	.12	.09	.05
1983 O-Pee-Chee	311	.15	.11	.06
1983 Topps	111	.15	.11	.06
1983 Topps	420	.20	.15	.08
1983 Topps	421	.12	.09	.05
1983 Topps	701	.15	.11	.06
1983 Topps	703	.35	.25	.14
1983 Topps All-Star Glossy Set of 40	30	.20	.15	.08
1984 Donruss	9a	.35	.25	.14
1984 Donruss	9b	.70	.50	.30
1984 Donruss	177	.30	.25	.12
1984 Fleer	280	.20	.15	.08
1984 Fleer	632	.10	.08	.04
1984 Fleer Update	85	.80	.60	.30
1984 O-Pee-Chee	307	.25	.20	.10
1984 Topps	516	.12	.09	.05
1984 Topps	620	.20	.15	.08
1984 Topps	704	.15	.11	.06

Set	Card #	NM/MT	EX	VG
1984 Topps All-Star Glossy Set of 22	13	.25	.20	.10
1984 Topps All-Star Glossy Set of 40	21	.20	.15	.08
1984 Topps Traded	87T	.30	.25	.12
1985 Donruss	598	.15	.11	.06
1985 Fleer	262	.12	.09	.05
1985 Fleer Update	84	.25	.20	.10
1985 Leaf-Donruss	67	.20	.15	.08
1985 O-Pee-Chee	130	.10	.08	.04
1985 Topps	130	.12	.09	.05
1985 Topps Traded	88T	.15	.11	.06
1986 Donruss	485	.12	.09	.05
1986 Fleer	69	.10	.08	.04
1986 O-Pee-Chee	114	.10	.08	.04
1986 Sportflics	126	.15	.11	.06
1986 Sportflics	140	.20	.15	.08
1986 Sportflics	164	.15	.11	.06
1986 Topps	775	.10	.08	.04
1990 Pacific Senior League	142	.15	.11	.06
1990 Topps Senior League	36	.15	.11	.06

Set	Card #	NM/MT	EX	VG
1981 O-Pee-Chee	288	.12	.09	.05
1981 Topps	585	.10	.08	.04
1982 Donruss	70	.08	.06	.03
1982 Fleer	419	.08	.06	.03
1982 O-Pee-Chee	162	.12	.09	.05
1982 O-Pee-Chee	350	.12	.09	.05
1982 Topps	725	.10	.08	.04
1982 Topps	726	.10	.08	.04
1983 Donruss	364	.08	.06	.03
1983 Fleer	120	.08	.06	.03
1983 O-Pee-Chee	75	.12	.09	.05
1983 Topps	75	.10	.08	.04
1984 Fleer	351	.12	.09	.05
1984 Fleer Update	87	.25	.20	.10
1984 O-Pee-Chee	53	.20	.15	.08
1984 Topps	655	.10	.08	.04
1984 Topps Traded	89T	.25	.20	.10
1990 Pacific Senior League	83	.05	.04	.02
1990 Topps Senior League	81	.10	.08	.04
1991 Pacific Senior League	26	.05	.04	.02

Amos Otis

Set	Card #	NM	EX	VG
1969 O-Pee-Chee	31	2.25	1.25	.70
1969 Topps	31 (R)	1.50	.70	.45
1970 O-Pee-Chee	354	1.75	.90	.50
1970 Topps	354	.90	.45	.25
1971 O-Pee-Chee	610	5.00	2.50	1.50
1971 Topps	610	3.50	1.75	1.00
1972 O-Pee-Chee	10	.75	.40	.25
1972 Topps	10	.75	.40	.25
1973 O-Pee-Chee	510	1.25	.60	.40
1973 Topps	510	.70	.35	.20
1974 O-Pee-Chee	65	.60	.30	.20
1974 O-Pee-Chee	337	.60	.30	.20
1974 Topps	65	.30	.15	.09
1974 Topps	337	.40	.20	.12
1975 O-Pee-Chee	520	.55	.30	.15
1975 Topps	520	.30	.15	.09
1975 Topps Mini	520	.40	.20	.12
1976 O-Pee-Chee	198	.40	.20	.12
1976 O-Pee-Chee	510	.35	.20	.11
1976 Topps	198	1.00	.50	.30
1976 Topps	510	.25	.13	.08
1977 O-Pee-Chee	141	.30	.15	.09
1977 Topps	290	.20	.10	.06
1978 O-Pee-Chee	16	.25	.13	.08
1978 Topps	490	.20	.10	.06
1979 O-Pee-Chee	185	.25	.13	.08
1979 Topps	360	.20	.10	.06
1980 O-Pee-Chee	72	.15	.08	.05
1980 Topps	130	.20	.10	.06

Set	Card #	MT	NM	EX
1981 Donruss	104	.08	.06	.03
1981 Fleer	32a	.50	.40	.20
1981 Fleer	32b	.10	.08	.04
1981 Fleer	483	.70	.50	.30

Satchel Paige

Set	Card #	NM	EX	VG
1948 Leaf	8 (R)	2400.	1200.	720.00
1949 Bowman	224 (R)	1200.	600.00	350.00
1953 Topps	220	395.00	197.00	91.00
1973 Topps 1953 Reprints	1	225.00	112.00	67.00

Set	Card #	MT	NM	EX
1991 "1953" Topps Archives Promos	(9)	24.00	18.00	9.50
1991 "1953" Topps Archives	220	4.00	3.00	1.50
1992 Score	882	.20	.15	.08

Rafael Palmeiro

Set	Card #	MT	NM	EX
1987 Donruss	43 (R)	4.00	3.00	1.50

1987 Leaf	43	4.50	3.50	1.75
1987 Sportflics	158	1.25	.90	.50
1987 Sportflics Rookie Prospects	2	2.00	1.50	.80
1987 Sportflics Rookies	32	1.50	1.25	.60
1987 Topps	634 (R)	1.00	.75	.40
1987 Topps Glossy Rookies	12	1.00	.70	.40
1988 Donruss	324	.30	.25	.12
1988 Fleer	429	1.50	1.25	.60
1988 O-Pee-Chee	186	.40	.30	.15
1988 Score	186	.35	.25	.14
1988 Topps	186	.35	.25	.14
1989 Bowman	237	.25	.20	.10
1989 Donruss	49	.25	.20	.10
1989 Donruss Traded	6	.30	.25	.12
1989 Fleer	434	.25	.20	.10
1989 Fleer	631	.40	.30	.15
1989 Fleer Update	66	.25	.20	.10
1989 O-Pee-Chee	310	.10	.08	.04
1989 Score	199	.25	.20	.10
1989 Score Traded	1T	.25	.20	.10
1989 Sportflics	30	.20	.15	.08
1989 Topps	310	.20	.15	.08
1989 Topps Big Baseball	257	.05	.04	.02
1989 Topps Traded	93T	.30	.25	.12
1989 Upper Deck	235	.75	.60	.30
1989 Upper Deck	772	1.00	.75	.40
1990 Bowman	496	.10	.07	.04
1990 Donruss	225	.12	.09	.05
1990 Fleer	308	.07	.05	.02
1990 Leaf	100	2.50	2.00	1.00
1990 O-Pee-Chee	755	.10	.07	.04
1990 Score	405	.15	.07	.04
1990 Sportflics	9	.10	.08	.04
1990 Topps	755	.10	.07	.04
1990 Topps Big Baseball	127	.12	.09	.05
1990 Upper Deck	335	.25	.20	.10
1991 Bowman	286	.12	.09	.05
1991 Donruss	19	.05	.04	.02
1991 Donruss	394	.10	.08	.04
1991 Donruss	521	.12	.09	.05
1991 Fleer	295	.08	.06	.03
1991 Fleer Ultra	350	.30	.25	.12
1991 Leaf	347	.25	.20	.10
1991 Score	216	.10	.08	.04
1991 Topps	295	.15	.11	.06
1991 Topps Stadium Club	502	1.50	1.25	.60
1991 Upper Deck	474	.12	.09	.05
1992 Bowman	610	.08	.06	.03
1992 Donruss	46	.10	.08	.04
1992 Donruss Triple Play	183	.12	.09	.05
1992 Fleer	311	.10	.08	.04
1992 Fleer All-Stars	17	1.25	.90	.50
1992 Fleer Team Leaders	12	3.50	2.75	1.50
1992 Fleer Ultra	136	.40	.30	.15
1992 Leaf	296	.15	.11	.06
1992 O-Pee-Chee	55	.10	.08	.04
1992 Pinnacle	35	.25	.20	.10
1992 Score	55	.08	.06	.03
1992 Score Impact Players	68	.30	.25	.12
1992 Topps	55	.10	.08	.04
1992 Topps Gold	55	1.25	.90	.50
1992 Topps Kids	130	.10	.08	.04
1992 Topps Stadium Club	516	.25	.20	.10
1992 Topps Stadium Club Special Edition	138	.25	.20	.10
1992 Upper Deck	223	.12	.09	.05
1993 Bowman	137	.20	.15	.08
1993 Donruss	365	.15	.11	.06
1993 Donruss Triple Play	71	.20	.15	.08
1993 Fleer	687	.15	.11	.06
1993 Fleer Flair	283	.60	.45	.25
1993 Fleer Ultra	281	.15	.11	.06
1993 Leaf	49	.15	.11	.06
1993 O-Pee-Chee	171	.20	.15	.08
1993 Pinnacle	220	.06	.05	.02
1993 Score	74	.10	.08	.04
1993 Score Select	162	.15	.11	.06
1993 Topps	305	.15	.11	.06
1993 Topps Finest	52	3.00	2.25	1.25
1993 Topps Finest Refractors	52	35.00	26.00	14.00
1993 Topps Gold	305	.30	.25	.12
1993 Topps Stadium Club	115	.20	.15	.08
1993 Topps Stadium Club First Day Production	115	15.00	11.00	6.00
1993 Topps Stadium Club Team Sets	26	.40	.30	.15
1993 Upper Deck	52	.25	.20	.10
1993 Upper Deck	574	.10	.08	.04
1993 Upper Deck Fun Packs	157	.20	.15	.08
1993 Upper Deck SP	196	.60	.45	.25
1994 Bowman	515	.25	.20	.10
1994 Bowman's Best	51	1.00	.70	.40
1994 Bowman's Best Refractors	51	5.00	3.75	2.00
1994 Donruss	26	.15	.11	.06
1994 Donruss Special Edition - Gold	26	.30	.25	.12
1994 Donruss Triple Play Medalists	3	5.00	3.75	2.00
1994 Donruss Triple Play	158	.05	.04	.02
1994 Fleer	313	.15	.11	.06
1994 Fleer	710	.25	.20	.10
1994 Fleer Extra Bases	11	.20	.15	.08
1994 Fleer Flair	257	.30	.25	.12
1994 Fleer Flair Infield Power	6	1.25	.90	.50
1994 Fleer League Leaders	3	.50	.40	.20
1994 Fleer Lumber Co.	8	.75	.60	.30
1994 Fleer Ultra	308	.20	.15	.08
1994 Fleer Ultra Home Run Kings	5	3.00	2.25	1.25
1994 Fleer Ultra League Leaders	2	.60	.45	.25
1994 Fleer Update	5	.20	.15	.08
1994 Leaf	289	.15	.11	.06
1994 Leaf Limited	4	1.50	1.25	.60
1994 Leaf MVP Contenders	9a	2.50	2.00	1.00
1994 Leaf MVP Contenders	9b	5.00	3.75	2.00
1994 O-Pee-Chee	25	.15	.11	.06
1994 Pacific Crown	622	.10	.08	.04
1994 Pacific Crown All Latino All-Star Team	3	1.50	1.25	.60
1994 Pacific Crown Homerun Leaders	5	2.00	1.50	.80
1994 Pacific Crown Jewels of the Crown	3	3.00	2.25	1.25
1994 Pinnacle	493	.15	.11	.06
1994 Pinnacle Artist's Proof	493	5.00	3.75	2.00
1994 Pinnacle Museum Collection	493	3.00	2.25	1.25
1994 Pinnacle Run Creators	5	2.50	2.00	1.00
1994 Score	495	.12	.09	.05
1994 Score Gold Stars	59	3.00	2.25	1.25
1994 Score Rookie & Traded Changing Places	2	3.00	2.25	1.25
1994 Score Rookie & Traded Gold Rush	8	.60	.45	.25
1994 Score Rookie and Traded	8	.25	.20	.10
1994 Score Rookie/ Traded Samples	2CP	2.00	1.50	.80
1994 Score Select	317	.15	.11	.06
1994 Sportflics 2000	144	.10	.08	.04
1994 Topps	470	.05	.04	.02
1994 Topps Black Gold	16	.60	.45	.25
1994 Topps Finest	227	1.00	.75	.40
1994 Topps Finest Refractors	227	6.00	4.50	2.50
1994 Topps Finest Superstars	227	3.50	2.75	1.50
1994 Topps Gold	470	.15	.11	.06

1994 Topps Stadium Club	208	.15	.11	.06
1994 Topps Stadium Club	265	.12	.09	.05
1994 Topps Stadium Club	557	.20	.15	.08
1994 Topps Stadium Club First Day Production	208	12.00	9.00	4.75
1994 Topps Stadium Club First Day Production	265	8.00	6.00	3.25
1994 Topps Stadium Club First Day Production	557	15.00	11.00	6.00
1994 Topps Stadium Club Members Only Baseball	6	.45	.35	.20
1994 Topps Traded	76	.10	.08	.04
1994 Upper Deck	34	.12	.09	.05
1994 Upper Deck	340	.20	.15	.08
1994 Upper Deck Collector's Choice	605	.06	.05	.02
1994 Upper Deck Electric Diamond	34	.50	.40	.20
1994 Upper Deck Electric Diamond	340	.50	.40	.20
1994 Upper Deck Fun Packs	154	.07	.05	.03
1994 Upper Deck SP	125	.35	.25	.14
1994 Upper Deck SP Baseball Die-Cut	125	.50	.40	.20

Jim Palmer

Set	Card #	NM	EX	VG
1966 O-Pee-Chee	126	240.00	120.00	72.00
1966 Topps	126 (R)	140.00	70.00	42.00
1967 Topps	475	85.00	42.00	25.00
1968 Topps	575	45.00	22.00	13.50
1969 Topps	573	35.00	17.50	10.50
1970 O-Pee-Chee	68	1.50	.70	.45
1970 O-Pee-Chee	449	25.00	12.50	7.50
1970 Topps	68	3.50	1.75	1.00
1970 Topps	449	16.00	8.00	4.75
1971 O-Pee-Chee	67	1.50	.70	.45
1971 O-Pee-Chee	570	42.50	21.00	12.50
1971 Topps	67	1.50	.70	.45
1971 Topps	570	30.00	15.00	9.00
1972 O-Pee-Chee	92	1.00	.50	.30
1972 O-Pee-Chee	270	17.00	8.50	5.00
1972 Topps	92	3.00	1.50	.90
1972 Topps	270	10.00	5.00	3.00
1973 O-Pee-Chee	160	13.50	6.75	4.00
1973 O-Pee-Chee	341	1.00	.50	.30
1973 Topps	160	10.00	5.00	3.00
1973 Topps	341	2.00	1.00	.60
1974 O-Pee-Chee	40	12.75	6.50	3.75
1974 O-Pee-Chee	206	6.25	3.25	2.00
1974 Topps	40	9.00	4.50	2.75
1974 Topps	206	2.00	1.00	.60
1975 O-Pee-Chee	335	10.25	5.25	3.00
1975 Topps	335	8.00	4.00	2.50

1976 O-Pee-Chee	200	2.00	1.00	.60
1976 O-Pee-Chee	202	5.00	2.50	1.50
1976 O-Pee-Chee	450	8.00	4.00	2.50
1976 Topps	200	2.00	1.00	.60
1976 Topps	202	5.00	2.50	1.50
1976 Topps	450	6.00	3.00	1.75
1977 O-Pee-Chee	5	2.00	1.00	.60
1977 O-Pee-Chee	80	7.25	3.75	2.25
1977 Topps	5	.80	.40	.25
1977 Topps	600	4.00	2.00	1.25
1978 O-Pee-Chee	5	.50	.25	.15
1978 O-Pee-Chee	179	5.00	2.50	1.50
1978 Topps	160	4.00	2.00	1.25
1978 Topps	205	1.50	.70	.45
1979 O-Pee-Chee	174	4.00	2.00	1.25
1979 Topps	340	4.00	2.00	1.25
1980 O-Pee-Chee	310	3.25	1.75	1.00
1980 Topps	590	3.00	1.50	.90

Set	Card #	MT	NM	EX
1981 Donruss	353	1.00	.75	.40
1981 Donruss	473	.80	.60	.30
1981 Fleer	169	1.00	.70	.40
1981 O-Pee-Chee	210	2.25	1.75	.90
1981 Topps	210	2.00	1.50	.80
1982 Donruss	231	.70	.50	.30
1982 Fleer	175	.60	.45	.25
1982 O-Pee-Chee	80	1.25	.90	.50
1982 O-Pee-Chee	81	.25	.20	.10
1982 Topps	80	1.00	.70	.40
1982 Topps	81	.30	.25	.12
1983 Donruss	4	.40	.30	.15
1983 Donruss	77	.80	.60	.30
1983 Fleer	69	.50	.40	.20
1983 O-Pee-Chee	299	1.50	1.25	.60
1983 O-Pee-Chee	328	.15	.11	.06
1983 Topps	21	.25	.20	.10
1983 Topps	490	1.00	.70	.40
1983 Topps	491	.20	.15	.08
1983 Topps All-Star Glossy Set of 40	19	.40	.30	.15
1984 Donruss	576	4.00	3.00	1.50
1984 Fleer	16	1.75	1.25	.70
1984 O-Pee-Chee	194	1.00	.70	.40
1984 Topps	715	.25	.20	.10
1984 Topps	717	.15	.11	.06
1984 Topps	750	1.00	.70	.40
1986 Sportflics Decade Greats	58	.30	.25	.12

Dave Parker

Set	Card #	NM	EX	VG
1974 O-Pee-Chee	252	25.00	12.50	7.50
1974 Topps	252 (R)	20.00	10.00	6.00
1975 O-Pee-Chee	29	6.00	3.00	1.75
1975 Topps	29	8.00	4.00	2.50
1976 O-Pee-Chee	185	7.00	3.50	2.00
1976 Topps	185	3.00	1.50	.90
1977 O-Pee-Chee	242	3.00	1.50	.90

Set	Card #	MT	NM	EX
1977 Topps	270	4.00	2.00	1.25
1978 O-Pee-Chee	1	.75	.40	.25
1978 O-Pee-Chee	60	1.75	.90	.50
1978 Topps	201	1.00	.50	.30
1978 Topps	560	2.00	1.00	.60
1979 O-Pee-Chee	223	1.75	.90	.50
1979 Topps	1	3.00	1.50	.90
1979 Topps	430	2.00	1.00	.60
1980 O-Pee-Chee	163	.75	.40	.25
1980 Topps	310	1.00	.50	.30
Set	Card #	MT	NM	EX
1981 Donruss	136	.45	.35	.20
1981 Fleer	360	.30	.25	.12
1981 O-Pee-Chee	178	.50	.40	.20
1981 Topps	640	.60	.45	.25
1982 Donruss	12	.30	.25	.12
1982 Donruss	95	.30	.25	.12
1982 Fleer	489	.30	.25	.12
1982 Fleer	638	.25	.20	.10
1982 O-Pee-Chee	40	.25	.20	.10
1982 O-Pee-Chee	41	.12	.09	.05
1982 O-Pee-Chee	343	.15	.11	.06
1982 Topps	40	.35	.25	.14
1982 Topps	41	.15	.11	.06
1982 Topps	343	.20	.15	.08
1983 Donruss	473	.40	.30	.15
1983 Fleer	315	.30	.25	.12
1983 O-Pee-Chee	205	.30	.25	.12
1983 Topps	205	.40	.30	.15
1984 Donruss	288	.50	.40	.20
1984 Fleer	258	.30	.25	.12
1984 Fleer Update	89	4.00	3.00	1.50
1984 O-Pee-Chee	31	.50	.40	.20
1984 Topps	701	.35	.25	.14
1984 Topps	775	.30	.25	.12
1984 Topps Traded	90T	3.00	2.25	1.25
1985 Donruss	62	.35	.25	.14
1985 Fleer	544	.25	.20	.10
1985 Leaf-Donruss	169	.20	.15	.08
1985 O-Pee-Chee	175	.20	.15	.08
1985 Topps	175	.25	.20	.10
1986 Donruss	203	.15	.11	.06
1986 Fleer	184	.20	.15	.08
1986 Fleer	640	.30	.25	.12
1986 Leaf	135	.15	.11	.06
1986 O-Pee-Chee	287	.12	.09	.05
1986 Sportflics	23	.60	.45	.25
1986 Sportflics	58	.60	.45	.25
1986 Sportflics	181	.70	.50	.30
1986 Sportflics	183	1.25	.90	.50
1986 Topps	595	.15	.11	.06
1986 Topps All-Star Glossy Set of 60	13	.25	.20	.10
1987 Donruss	388	.25	.20	.10
1987 Fleer	208	.20	.15	.08
1987 Fleer	639	.12	.09	.05
1987 Leaf	79	.15	.11	.06
1987 O-Pee-Chee	352	.12	.09	.05
1987 Sportflics	35	.40	.30	.15
1987 Sportflics	117	.25	.20	.10
1987 Topps	600	.10	.08	.04
1987 Topps	691	.10	.08	.04
1987 Topps All-Star Glossy Set of 60	17	.40	.30	.15
1988 Donruss	388	.08	.06	.03
1988 Fleer	243	.10	.08	.04
1988 Fleer Update	55	.12	.09	.05
1988 O-Pee-Chee	315	.09	.07	.04
1988 Score	17	.12	.09	.05
1988 Score Traded	50T	.25	.20	.10
1988 Score Traded/ Rookie Glossy	50T	1.00	.70	.40
1988 Sportflics	101	.60	.45	.25
1988 Topps	315	.12	.09	.05
1988 Topps All-Star Glossy Set of 60	34	.25	.20	.10
1988 Topps Big Baseball	242	.20	.15	.08
1988 Topps Traded	81T	.12	.09	.05
1989 Bowman	202	.05	.04	.02
1989 Donruss	150	.12	.09	.05

Set	Card #	MT	NM	EX
1989 Fleer	19	.12	.09	.05
1989 O-Pee-Chee	199	.12	.09	.05
1989 Score	108	.10	.08	.04
1989 Sportflics	49	.15	.11	.06
1989 Topps	475	.10	.08	.04
1989 Topps Big Baseball	144	.05	.04	.02
1989 Upper Deck	605	.12	.09	.05
1990 Bowman	398	.10	.08	.04
1990 Donruss	328	.09	.07	.04
1990 Fleer	18	.12	.09	.05
1990 Fleer Update	106	.20	.15	.08
1990 Leaf	190	.50	.40	.20
1990 O-Pee-Chee	45	.09	.07	.04
1990 Score	135	.10	.08	.04
1990 Score Traded	12T	.15	.11	.06
1990 Topps	45	.09	.07	.04
1990 Topps Big Baseball	227	.12	.09	.05
1990 Topps Traded	86T	.15	.11	.06
1990 Upper Deck	192	.12	.09	.05
1990 Upper Deck	766	.15	.11	.06
1991 Bowman	199	.08	.06	.03
1991 Bowman	375	.08	.06	.03
1991 Donruss	6	.05	.04	.02
1991 Donruss	142	.10	.08	.04
1991 Donruss	390	.10	.08	.04
1991 Fleer	593	.12	.09	.05
1991 Fleer Ultra Update	10	.25	.20	.10
1991 Fleer Update	10	.35	.25	.14
1991 Leaf	334	.10	.08	.04
1991 O-Pee-Chee Premier	94	.06	.05	.02
1991 Score	484	.08	.06	.03
1991 Topps	235	.10	.08	.04
1991 Topps Stadium Club	75	.25	.20	.10
1991 Topps Traded	89	.08	.06	.03
1991 Upper Deck	274	.10	.07	.04
1991 Upper Deck	733	.10	.07	.04
1991 Upper Deck Silver Sluggers	14	.50	.40	.20
1992 Upper Deck	522	.10	.08	.04

Tony Perez

Set	Card #	NM	EX	VG
1965 Topps	581	105.00	52.50	30.00
1966 O-Pee-Chee	72	38.00	19.00	11.50
1966 Topps	72	25.00	12.50	7.50
1967 Topps	476	60.00	30.00	18.00
1968 O-Pee-Chee	130	17.00	8.50	5.00
1968 Topps	130	8.00	4.00	2.50
1969 Topps	295	9.00	4.50	2.75
1970 O-Pee-Chee	63	1.75	.90	.50
1970 O-Pee-Chee	380	11.00	5.50	3.25
1970 Topps	63	3.75	2.00	1.25
1970 Topps	380	3.00	1.50	.90
1971 O-Pee-Chee	64	1.50	.70	.45
1971 O-Pee-Chee	66	1.50	.70	.45
1971 O-Pee-Chee	580	17.00	8.50	5.00
1971 Topps	64	3.50	1.75	1.00
1971 Topps	66	3.50	1.75	1.00

	Card #			
1971 Topps	580	12.00	6.00	3.50
1972 O-Pee-Chee	80	6.00	3.00	1.75
1972 Topps	80	4.00	2.00	1.25
1973 O-Pee-Chee	275	1.25	.60	.40
1973 Topps	275	3.00	1.50	.90
1974 O-Pee-Chee	230	1.00	.50	.30
1974 Topps	230	1.25	.60	.40
1975 O-Pee-Chee	560	.75	.40	.25
1975 Topps	560	2.00	1.00	.60
1975 Topps Mini	560	4.00	2.00	1.25
1976 O-Pee-Chee	195	2.00	1.00	.60
1976 O-Pee-Chee	325	.60	.30	.20
1976 Topps	195	2.00	1.00	.60
1976 Topps	325	1.50	.70	.45
1977 O-Pee-Chee	135	.75	.40	.25
1977 Topps	655	1.50	.70	.45
1978 O-Pee-Chee	90	.25	.13	.08
1978 Topps	15	.25	.13	.08
1979 O-Pee-Chee	261	.50	.25	.15
1979 Topps	495	.40	.20	.12
1980 O-Pee-Chee	69	.50	.25	.15
1980 Topps	125	.30	.15	.09

Set	Card #	MT	NM	EX
1981 Donruss	334	.20	.15	.08
1981 Fleer	241	.20	.15	.08
1981 O-Pee-Chee	231	.25	.20	.10
1981 Topps	575	.35	.25	.14
1982 Donruss	408	.20	.15	.08
1982 Fleer	302	.20	.15	.08
1982 O-Pee-Chee	255	.25	.20	.10
1982 O-Pee-Chee	256	.12	.09	.05
1982 Topps	255	.30	.25	.12
1982 Topps	256	.15	.11	.06
1983 Donruss	578	.20	.15	.08
1983 Fleer	191	.20	.15	.08
1983 O-Pee-Chee	74	.12	.09	.05
1983 O-Pee-Chee	355	.20	.15	.08
1983 Topps	715	.25	.20	.10
1983 Topps	716	.12	.09	.05
1983 Topps Traded	85T	1.00	.75	.40
1984 Donruss	503	.75	.60	.30
1984 Fleer	44	.20	.15	.08
1984 Fleer	636	.50	.40	.20
1984 Fleer Update	91	7.00	5.25	2.75
1984 O-Pee-Chee	385	.30	.25	.12
1984 Topps	385	.20	.15	.08
1984 Topps	702	.35	.25	.14
1984 Topps	703	.30	.25	.12
1984 Topps	704	.15	.11	.06
1984 Topps Traded	91T	1.50	1.25	.60
1985 Fleer	546	.15	.11	.06
1985 O-Pee-Chee	212	.15	.11	.06
1985 Topps	675	.15	.11	.06
1986 Donruss	15	.15	.11	.06
1986 Donruss	428	.15	.11	.06
1986 Donruss Diamond Kings Supers	15	.25	.20	.10
1986 Fleer	186	.15	.11	.06
1986 Leaf	15	.10	.08	.04
1986 O-Pee-Chee	85	.10	.08	.04
1986 Sportflics	138	.50	.40	.20
1986 Topps	85	.15	.11	.06
1986 Topps	205	.10	.08	.04
1987 Fleer	209	.15	.11	.06
1993 Topps	503	.03	.02	.01
1993 Topps Gold	503	.10	.08	.04

* * *

Lou Piniella appears on three Topps multiplayer rookie cards - a 1964 Senators Rookie Stars card, a 1968 Indians Rookie Stars card and a 1969 Pilots Rookie Stars card. But he won his American League Rookie of the Year Award in 1969 as a Kansas City Royal.

* * *

Gaylord Perry

Set	Card #	NM	EX	VG
1962 Topps	199 (R)	95.00	47.00	28.00
1963 Topps	169	25.00	12.50	7.50
1964 Topps	468	40.00	20.00	12.00
1965 O-Pee-Chee	193	25.00	12.50	7.50
1965 Topps	193	16.50	8.25	5.00
1966 Topps	598	200.00	100.00	60.00
1967 Topps	236	12.00	6.00	3.50
1967 Topps	320	14.00	7.00	4.25
1968 O-Pee-Chee	11	2.25	1.25	.70
1968 O-Pee-Chee	85	13.50	6.75	4.00
1968 Topps	11	4.50	2.25	1.25
1968 Topps	85	9.00	4.50	2.75
1969 Topps	485a	125.00	62.00	37.00
1969 Topps	485b	9.00	4.50	2.75
1970 Topps	560	9.00	4.50	2.75
1971 O-Pee-Chee	70	1.50	.70	.45
1971 O-Pee-Chee	140	10.25	5.25	3.00
1971 Topps	70	3.50	1.75	1.00
1971 Topps	140	6.00	3.00	1.75
1972 O-Pee-Chee	285	9.25	4.75	2.75
1972 Topps	285	6.00	3.00	1.75
1973 O-Pee-Chee	66	1.00	.50	.30
1973 O-Pee-Chee	346	1.00	.50	.30
1973 O-Pee-Chee	400	6.00	3.00	1.75
1973 Topps	66	2.00	1.00	.60
1973 Topps	346	1.50	.70	.45
1973 Topps	400	6.00	3.00	1.75
1974 O-Pee-Chee	35	5.00	2.50	1.50
1974 Topps	35	4.00	2.00	1.25
1975 O-Pee-Chee	530	2.00	1.00	.60
1975 Topps	530	3.00	1.50	.90
1975 Topps Mini	530	6.00	3.00	1.75
1976 O-Pee-Chee	55	3.00	1.50	.90
1976 O-Pee-Chee	204	.50	.25	.15
1976 Topps	55	3.00	1.50	.90
1976 Topps	204	1.00	.50	.30
1977 O-Pee-Chee	149	1.50	.70	.45
1977 Topps	152	3.00	1.50	.90
1978 Topps	686	2.00	1.00	.60
1979 O-Pee-Chee	161	1.25	.60	.40
1979 Topps	5	.30	.15	.09
1979 Topps	321	2.00	1.00	.60
1980 O-Pee-Chee	148	.75	.40	.25
1980 Topps	280	1.50	.70	.45

Set	Card #	MT	NM	EX
1981 Donruss	471	.50	.40	.20
1981 Fleer	91	.60	.45	.25
1981 Topps	582	.70	.50	.30
1981 Topps Traded	812	2.50	2.00	1.00
1982 Donruss	543	.40	.30	.15
1982 Fleer	445	.40	.30	.15
1982 O-Pee-Chee	115	.30	.25	.12
1982 Topps	115	.50	.40	.20
1982 Topps Traded	88T	2.00	1.50	.80
1983 Donruss	307	.40	.30	.15
1983 Fleer	483	.40	.30	.15
1983 Fleer	630	.15	.11	.06
1983 O-Pee-Chee	96	.30	.25	.12

Set	Card #			
1983 O-Pee-Chee	159	.15	.11	.06
1983 Topps	463	.40	.30	.15
1983 Topps	464	.20	.15	.08
1984 Donruss	A	5.00	3.75	2.00
1984 Fleer	352	.60	.45	.25
1984 Fleer	638	.30	.25	.12
1984 Fleer	641	.15	.11	.06
1984 Topps	4	1.00	.75	.40
1984 Topps	6	.40	.30	.15
1989 Pacific Trading Cards Legends II	152	.10	.08	.04
1990 Pacific Legends	43	.20	.15	.08
1991 Upper Deck Heroes of Baseball	2	15.00	10.00	5.00
1991 Upper Deck Heroes of Baseball	4	15.00	11.00	6.00
1992 Upper Deck Heroes Highlights	6	2.00	1.50	.80

Rico Petrocelli

Set	Card #	NM	EX	VG
1965 O-Pee-Chee	74	2.75	1.50	.80
1965 Topps	74 (R)	7.00	3.50	2.00
1966 Topps	298	3.00	1.50	.90
1967 Topps	528	9.00	4.50	2.75
1968 Topps	430	1.50	.70	.45
1969 O-Pee-Chee	215	2.25	1.25	.70
1969 Topps	215	1.25	.60	.40
1970 O-Pee-Chee	457	1.75	.90	.50
1970 Topps	457	1.50	.70	.45
1970 Topps	680	7.00	3.50	2.00
1971 O-Pee-Chee	340	1.50	.70	.45
1971 Topps	340	1.00	.50	.30
1972 O-Pee-Chee	30	.75	.40	.25
1972 Topps	30	.90	.45	.25
1973 O-Pee-Chee	365	.75	.40	.25
1973 Topps	365	.40	.20	.12
1974 O-Pee-Chee	609	.60	.30	.20
1974 Topps	609	.30	.15	.09
1975 O-Pee-Chee	356	.55	.30	.15
1975 Topps	356	.15	.15	.15
1976 O-Pee-Chee	445	.35	.20	.11
1976 Topps	445	.25	.13	.08
1977 Topps	111	.20	.10	.06

Set	Card #	MT	NM	EX
1990 Pacific Legends	64	.05	.04	.02

* * *

Tim Raines' 1989 Topps card uses his nickname "Rock" on the front of the card instead of his first name. A 1989 glossy Topps version uses the initial R. (for Rock) on the front.

* * *

Mike Piazza

Set	Card #	MT	NM	EX
1992 Bowman	461 (R)	32.00	24.00	13.00
1992 Fleer Update	92	75.00	56.00	30.00
1993 Bowman	646	3.00	2.25	1.25
1993 DiamondMarks	(34)	3.00	2.25	1.25
1993 Donruss	209	1.50	1.25	.60
1993 Donruss Elite Dominators	8	150.00	112.00	60.00
1993 Donruss Triple Play	55	2.00	1.50	.80
1993 Fleer Flair	75	8.00	6.00	3.25
1993 Fleer Flair Wave of the Future	12	17.00	12.50	6.75
1993 Fleer Major League Prospects I	13	15.00	11.00	6.00
1993 Fleer Ultra	60	3.00	2.25	1.25
1993 Fleer Ultra All-Rookies	7	12.00	9.00	4.75
1993 Leaf	35	3.00	2.25	1.25
1993 Leaf Update Gold Rookies	4	30.00	22.00	12.00
1993 O-Pee-Chee	314	6.00	4.50	2.50
1993 O-Pee-Chee Premier	26	2.50	2.00	1.00
1993 Pinnacle	252	3.00	2.25	1.25
1993 Pinnacle Home Run Club	26	2.00	1.50	.80
1993 Pinnacle Rookie Team Pinnacle	3	75.00	56.00	30.00
1993 Score	286 (R)	1.50	1.25	.60
1993 Score Boys of Summer	5	30.00	22.00	12.00
1993 Score Select	347	2.50	2.00	1.00
1993 Score Select All-Star Rookies	5	90.00	67.00	36.00
1993 Score Select Rookie/ Traded Inserts	2ROY	90.00	67.00	36.00
1993 Studio	201	2.00	1.50	.80
1993 Studio Silhouettes	9	6.00	4.50	2.50
1993 Topps	701	2.00	1.50	.80
1993 Topps Finest	199	28.00	21.00	11.00
1993 Topps Finest Refractors	199	320.00	240.00	130.00
1993 Topps Full Shot Super	6	6.00	4.50	2.50
1993 Topps Gold	701	5.00	3.75	2.00
1993 Topps Stadium Club	585	3.00	2.25	1.25
1993 Topps Stadium Club First Day Production	585	125.00	94.00	50.00
1993 Topps Stadium Club Members Only	(18)	1.00	.70	.40
1993 Topps Stadium Club Members Only	(19)	1.00	.70	.40
1993 Topps Traded	24	2.50	2.00	1.00
1993 Upper Deck	2 (R)	2.00	1.50	.80
1993 Upper Deck Diamond Gallery	34	3.50	2.75	1.50
1993 Upper Deck Fun Packs	6	2.00	1.50	.80
1993 Upper Deck SP	98	12.00	9.00	4.75

1993 Upper Deck SP Platinum Power	15	35.00	26.00	14.00
1994 Bowman	387	1.50	1.25	.60
1994 Bowman	510	1.50	1.25	.60
1994 Bowman's Best	104	3.00	2.25	1.25
1994 Bowman's Best	81	4.00	3.00	1.50
1994 Bowman's Best Refractors	104	10.00	7.50	4.00
1994 Bowman's Best Refractors	81	40.00	30.00	16.00
1994 Donruss	2	1.50	1.25	.60
1994 Donruss Award Winners Supers	3	6.00	4.50	2.50
1994 Donruss Diamond Kings	15	5.00	3.75	2.00
1994 Donruss Diamond Kings Super	15	6.00	4.50	2.50
1994 Donruss Elite	46	50.00	38.00	20.00
1994 Donruss Long Ball Leaders	7	10.00	7.50	4.00
1994 Donruss MVP's	7	3.50	2.75	1.50
1994 Donruss Special Edition - Gold	2	1.50	1.25	.60
1994 Donruss Spirit of the Game	4	8.00	6.00	3.25
1994 Donruss Spirit of the Game Super	4	18.00	13.50	7.25
1994 Donruss Triple Play Promos	6	4.00	3.00	1.50
1994 Donruss Triple Play	88	.75	.60	.30
1994 Fleer	520	1.00	.75	.40
1994 Fleer	713	.50	.40	.20
1994 Fleer All-Stars	47	2.00	1.50	.80
1994 Fleer Award Winners	6	2.50	2.00	1.00
1994 Fleer Extra Bases	294	1.25	.90	.50
1994 Fleer Extra Bases Game Breakers	22	2.00	1.50	.80
1994 Fleer Extra Bases Second Year Stars	16	2.00	1.50	.80
1994 Fleer Flair	182	2.50	2.00	1.00
1994 Fleer Flair Hot Numbers	7	28.00	21.00	11.00
1994 Fleer Flair Infield Power	7	8.00	6.00	3.25
1994 Fleer ProVisions	8	2.00	1.50	.80
1994 Fleer Rookie Sensations	14	8.00	6.00	3.25
1994 Fleer Team Leaders	21	2.50	2.00	1.00
1994 Fleer Ultra	218	1.50	1.25	.60
1994 Fleer Ultra All-Stars	11	3.00	2.25	1.25
1994 Fleer Ultra Award Winners	25	3.00	2.25	1.25
1994 Fleer Ultra Hitting Machines	9	3.00	2.25	1.25
1994 Fleer Ultra Home Run Kings	12	12.00	9.00	4.75
1994 Fleer Ultra Rising Stars	9	25.00	18.00	10.00
1994 Fleer Ultra RBI Kings	10	28.00	21.00	11.00
1994 Fleer Ultra Second Year Standouts	9	9.00	6.75	3.50
1994 Leaf	436	1.50	1.25	.60
1994 Leaf Gamers	12	12.00	9.00	4.75
1994 Leaf Limited	120	10.00	7.50	4.00
1994 Leaf Limited Gold	16	50.00	38.00	20.00
1994 Leaf MVP Contenders	12a	12.00	9.00	4.75
1994 Leaf MVP Contenders	12b	24.00	18.00	9.50
1994 Leaf Power Brokers	6	4.00	3.00	1.50
1994 Leaf Slide Show	2	10.00	7.50	4.00
1994 Leaf Statistical Standouts	4	4.00	3.00	1.50
1994 O-Pee-Chee	147	1.50	1.25	.60
1994 O-Pee-Chee All-Star Redemption Cards	9	2.00	1.50	.80
1994 O-Pee-Chee Diamond Dynamos	1	20.00	15.00	8.00
1994 O-Pee-Chee Jumbo All-Stars	9	35.00	26.00	14.00
1994 O-Pee-Chee Jumbo All-Stars Factory Set	9	3.50	2.75	1.50
1994 Pacific Crown	318	1.00	.75	.40
1994 Pacific Crown	658	.75	.60	.30
1994 Pacific Crown Homerun Leaders	16	9.00	6.75	3.50
1994 Pacific Crown Jewels of the Crown	29	10.00	7.50	4.00
1994 Pinnacle	28	1.50	1.25	.60
1994 Pinnacle Artist's Proof	28	90.00	67.00	36.00
1994 Pinnacle Museum Collection	28	30.00	22.00	12.00
1994 Pinnacle New Generation	2	.75	.60	.30
1994 Pinnacle Power Surge	17	.75	.60	.30
1994 Pinnacle Run Creators	28	12.00	9.00	4.75
1994 Pinnacle Team Pinnacle	5	25.00	18.00	10.00
1994 Pinnacle The Naturals Box Set	19	1.25	.90	.50
1994 Pinnacle Tribute	7	10.00	7.50	4.00
1994 Post Cereal	1	.50	.40	.20
1994 Score	476	.75	.60	.30
1994 Score	636	.40	.30	.15
1994 Score Boys of Summer	6	20.00	15.00	8.00
1994 Score Gold Stars	13	24.00	18.00	9.50
1994 Score Select	4	1.75	1.25	.70
1994 Score Select Crown Contenders	9	20.00	15.00	8.00
1994 Sportflics 2000	67	2.00	1.50	.80
1994 Sportflics 2000	189	1.00	.75	.40
1994 Sportflics 2000 Shakers	11	15.00	11.00	6.00
1994 Studio	72	1.50	1.25	.60
1994 Studio Editor's Choice	8	10.00	7.50	4.00
1994 Studio Gold Stars	6	60.00	45.00	24.00
1994 Studio Silver Stars	6	30.00	22.00	12.00
1994 Topps	1	1.00	.75	.40
1994 Topps	391	.35	.25	.14
1994 Topps Black Gold	41	2.00	1.50	.80
1994 Topps Finest	1	6.00	4.50	2.50
1994 Topps Finest Refractors	1	60.00	45.00	24.00
1994 Topps Finest Superstars	1	20.00	15.00	8.00
1994 Topps Gold	1	5.00	3.75	2.00
1994 Topps Gold	391	1.25	.90	.50
1994 Topps Stadium Club	140	1.50	1.25	.60
1994 Topps Stadium Club	266	.75	.60	.30
1994 Topps Stadium Club Dugout Dirt	1	1.75	1.25	.70
1994 Topps Stadium Club Finest	8	4.00	3.00	1.50
1994 Topps Stadium Club First Day Production	140	60.00	45.00	24.00
1994 Topps Stadium Club First Day Production	266	25.00	18.00	10.00
1994 Topps Stadium Club Members Only Baseball	28	.60	.45	.25
1994 Topps Traded Finest Inserts	2	1.50	1.25	.60
1994 Upper Deck	33	1.00	.75	.40
1994 Upper Deck	47	1.00	.75	.40
1994 Upper Deck	273	.75	.60	.30
1994 Upper Deck	500	1.25	.90	.50
1994 Upper Deck All-Stars Green Foil	31	.75	.60	.30
1994 Upper Deck All-Stars Gold Foil	31	4.00	3.00	1.50
1994 Upper Deck Collector's Choice	310	1.00	.75	.40
1994 Upper Deck Collector's Choice	318	.15	.11	.06

Set	Card #	NM	EX	VG
1994 Upper Deck Collector's Choice	336	.25	.20	.10
1994 Upper Deck Collector's Choice	400	.75	.60	.30
1994 Upper Deck Collector's Choice	637	.40	.30	.15
1994 Upper Deck Diamond Collection	9W	25.00	18.00	10.00
1994 Upper Deck Electric Diamond	33	4.00	3.00	1.50
1994 Upper Deck Electric Diamond	47	7.50	5.50	3.00
1994 Upper Deck Electric Diamond	273	3.00	2.25	1.25
1994 Upper Deck Electric Diamond	500	4.00	3.00	1.50
1994 Upper Deck Fun Packs	31	1.50	1.25	.60
1994 Upper Deck Fun Packs	185	.75	.60	.30
1994 Upper Deck Fun Packs	203	2.00	1.50	.80
1994 Upper Deck Fun Packs	208	.75	.60	.30
1994 Upper Deck Fun Packs	220	.75	.60	.30
1994 Upper Deck Fun Packs	231	.75	.60	.30
1994 Upper Deck Fun Packs	238	.35	.25	.14
1994 Upper Deck Mickey Mantle's Long Shots	15MM	7.50	5.50	2.75
1994 Upper Deck Next Generation	13	9.00	6.75	3.50
1994 Upper Deck SP	80	2.50	2.00	1.00
1994 Upper Deck SP Baseball Die-Cut	80	3.50	2.75	1.50
1994 Upper Deck SP Holoview Blue	29	12.00	9.75	4.50
1994 Upper Deck SP Holoview Red	29	90.00	67.00	36.00
1994 Upper Deck SP Insert	4	16.00	12.00	6.50

Jimmy Piersall

Set	Card #	NM	EX	VG
1951 Bowman	306 (R)	100.00	50.00	30.00
1952 Bowman	189	20.00	10.00	6.00
1953 Bowman Black & White	36	50.00	25.00	15.00
1954 Bowman	66b	80.00	40.00	24.00
1954 Bowman	210	15.00	7.50	4.50
1954 Red Man Tobacco	11A	30.00	15.00	9.00
1955 Bowman	16	10.00	5.00	3.00
1955 Red Man Tobacco	21A	30.00	15.00	9.00
1956 Topps	143	12.00	6.00	3.50
1957 Topps	75	10.00	5.00	3.00
1958 Topps	280	8.00	4.00	2.50
1959 Topps	355	4.00	2.00	1.25
1960 Topps	159	4.50	2.25	1.25

Set	Card #	NM	EX	VG
1961 Topps	345	4.00	2.00	1.25
1962 Topps	51	8.00	4.00	2.50
1962 Topps	90	4.00	2.00	1.25
1963 Topps	443	6.00	3.00	1.75
1964 Topps	586	10.00	5.00	3.00
1965 O-Pee-Chee	172	2.75	1.50	.80
1965 Topps	172	2.50	1.25	.70
1966 Topps	565	35.00	17.50	10.50
1967 Topps	584	20.00	10.00	6.00

Set	Card #	MT	NM	EX
1989 Pacific Trading Cards Legends II	182	.06	.05	.02
1990 Pacific Legends	44	.10	.08	.04
1991 "1953" Topps Archives	286	.25	.20	.10

Lou Piniella

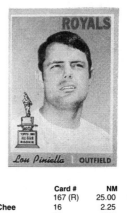

Set	Card #	NM	EX	VG
1964 Topps	167 (R)	25.00	12.50	7.50
1968 O-Pee-Chee	16	2.25	1.25	.70
1968 Topps	16	3.50	1.75	1.00
1969 Topps	394	2.00	1.00	.60
1970 O-Pee-Chee	321	1.75	.90	.50
1970 Topps	321	1.50	.70	.45
1971 O-Pee-Chee	35	1.50	.70	.45
1971 Topps	35	1.00	.50	.30
1972 O-Pee-Chee	491	1.75	.90	.50
1972 Topps	491	1.00	.50	.30
1972 Topps	580	2.50	1.25	.70
1973 O-Pee-Chee	140	.75	.40	.25
1973 Topps	140	.60	.30	.20
1974 O-Pee-Chee	390	.60	.30	.20
1974 Topps	390	.30	.15	.09
1974 Topps Traded	390T	1.00	.70	.40
1975 O-Pee-Chee	217	.55	.30	.15
1975 Topps	217	.30	.15	.09
1975 Topps Mini	217	.80	.40	.25
1976 O-Pee-Chee	453	.50	.25	.15
1976 Topps	453	.25	.13	.08
1977 Topps	96	.30	.15	.09
1978 O-Pee-Chee	82	.30	.15	.09
1978 Topps	159	.35	.20	.11
1979 O-Pee-Chee	342	.25	.13	.08
1979 Topps	648	.35	.20	.11
1980 O-Pee-Chee	120	.25	.13	.08
1980 Topps	225	.15	.08	.05

Set	Card #	MT	NM	EX
1981 Donruss	109	.12	.09	.05
1981 Fleer	85	.12	.09	.05
1981 O-Pee-Chee	306	.12	.09	.05
1981 Topps	724	.20	.15	.08
1982 Donruss	135	.15	.11	.06
1982 Fleer	48	.12	.09	.05
1982 O-Pee-Chee	236	.12	.09	.05
1982 Topps	538	.15	.11	.06
1983 Donruss	335	.12	.09	.05
1983 Fleer	392	.12	.09	.05
1983 O-Pee-Chee	307	.12	.09	.05

Set		Card #	NM	EX	VG
1983 Topps		307	.15	.11	.06
1984 Donruss		274	.20	.15	.08
1984 Fleer		136	.15	.11	.06
1984 O-Pee-Chee		351	.25	.20	.10
1984 Topps		408	.15	.11	.06
1986 Topps Traded		86T	.12	.09	.05
1987 Topps		168	.07	.05	.03
1988 Topps		44	.06	.05	.02
1990 Pacific Legends		99	.05	.04	.02
1990 Topps Traded		96T	.05	.04	.02
1991 Topps		669	.04	.03	.02
1992 O-Pee-Chee		321	.03	.02	.01
1992 Topps		321	.03	.02	.01
1992 Topps Gold		321	.25	.20	.10
1993 Topps		512	.03	.02	.01
1993 Topps Gold		512	.10	.08	.04

Vada Pinson

Set	Card #	NM	EX	VG
1958 Topps	420 (R)	30.00	15.00	9.00
1959 Topps	448	7.50	3.75	2.25
1960 Topps	32	5.50	2.75	1.50
1960 Topps	176	4.50	2.25	1.25
1961 Post Cereal	181a	3.75	2.00	1.25
1961 Post Cereal	181b	3.75	2.00	1.25
1961 Topps	25	8.00	4.00	2.50
1961 Topps	110	6.00	3.00	1.75
1962 Post Cereal	121	3.50	1.75	1.00
1962 Topps	52	10.00	5.00	3.00
1962 Topps	80	5.00	2.50	1.50
1963 Fleer	34	15.00	7.50	4.50
1963 Post Cereal	130	3.50	1.75	1.00
1963 Topps	265	5.00	2.50	1.50
1964 Topps	80	3.50	1.75	1.00
1964 Topps	162	3.50	1.75	1.00
1965 Topps	355	6.00	3.00	1.75
1966 O-Pee-Chee	180	2.50	1.25	.70
1966 Topps	180	2.50	1.25	.70
1967 Topps	550	18.00	9.00	5.50
1968 O-Pee-Chee	90	2.25	1.25	.70
1968 Topps	90	3.00	1.50	.90
1969 O-Pee-Chee	160	2.25	1.25	.70
1969 Topps	160	2.00	1.00	.60
1970 O-Pee-Chee	445	1.75	.90	.50
1970 Topps	445	2.00	1.00	.60
1971 O-Pee-Chee	275	1.50	.70	.45
1971 Topps	275	2.00	1.00	.60
1972 O-Pee-Chee	135	.75	.40	.25
1972 Topps	135	1.00	.50	.30
1973 O-Pee-Chee	75	.75	.40	.25
1973 Topps	75	.75	.40	.25
1974 O-Pee-Chee	490	.60	.30	.20
1974 Topps	490	.60	.30	.20
1975 O-Pee-Chee	295	.55	.30	.15
1975 Topps	295	.45	.25	.14
1975 Topps Mini	295	1.50	.70	.45
1976 O-Pee-Chee	415	.40	.20	.12
1976 Topps	415	.40	.20	.12
1977 Topps	597	1.25	.60	.40

Set	Card #	MT	NM	EX
1982 Donruss	445	.08	.06	.03

Boog Powell

Set	Card #	NM	EX	VG
1962 Topps	99 (R)	30.00	15.00	9.00
1963 Topps	398	25.00	12.50	7.50
1964 Topps	89	6.00	3.00	1.75
1965 O-Pee-Chee	3	30.00	15.00	9.00
1965 Topps	3	20.00	10.00	6.00
1965 Topps	560	21.00	10.50	6.25
1966 O-Pee-Chee	167	2.50	1.25	.70
1966 Topps	167	4.00	2.00	1.25
1967 Topps	230	3.00	1.50	.90
1967 Topps	241	4.50	2.25	1.25
1967 Topps	243	6.00	3.00	1.75
1967 Topps	521	13.00	6.50	4.00
1968 Topps	381	3.00	1.50	.90
1969 O-Pee-Chee	15	2.25	1.25	.70
1969 Topps	15	2.00	1.00	.60
1970 O-Pee-Chee	64	2.00	1.00	.60
1970 O-Pee-Chee	410	1.75	.90	.50
1970 O-Pee-Chee	451	1.75	.90	.50
1970 Topps	64	5.00	2.50	1.50
1970 Topps	410	2.50	1.25	.70
1970 Topps	451	1.50	.70	.45
1971 O-Pee-Chee	63	1.50	.70	.45
1971 O-Pee-Chee	700	23.00	11.50	7.00
1971 Topps	63	1.50	.70	.45
1971 Topps	700	12.00	6.00	3.50
1972 O-Pee-Chee	250	1.00	.50	.30
1972 Topps	250	1.25	.60	.40
1973 O-Pee-Chee	325	.75	.40	.25
1973 Topps	325	.75	.40	.25
1974 O-Pee-Chee	460	.75	.40	.25
1974 Topps	460	.75	.40	.25
1975 O-Pee-Chee	208	3.00	1.50	.90
1975 O-Pee-Chee	625	.60	.30	.20
1975 Topps	208	1.25	.60	.40
1975 Topps	625	.45	.25	.14
1975 Topps Mini	208	1.75	.90	.50
1975 Topps Mini	625	2.00	1.00	.60
1976 O-Pee-Chee	45	.40	.20	.12
1976 Topps	45	.25	.13	.08
1977 Topps	206	.50	.25	.15

Set	Card #	MT	NM	EX
1990 Pacific Legends	46	.10	.08	.04

* * *

Pittsburgh Pirates star Andy Van Slyke's favorite baseball card is his 1984 Topps rookie card, #206. "They got the swing with which I hit a home run off Tom Seaver," says Van Slyke.

* * *

Kirby Puckett

Set	Card #	MT	NM	EX
1984 Fleer Update	93	360.00	270.00	145.00
1985 Donruss	438 (R)	45.00	34.00	18.00
1985 Fleer	286 (R)	45.00	34.00	18.00
1985 Leaf-Donruss	107	42.50	32.00	17.00
1985 O-Pee-Chee	10	17.00	12.50	6.75
1985 Topps	536 (R)	21.00	15.50	8.50
1986 Donruss	72	10.00	7.50	4.00
1986 Fleer	401	10.00	7.50	4.00
1986 Leaf	69	8.50	6.50	3.50
1986 O-Pee-Chee	329	3.25	2.50	1.25
1986 Sportflics	93	2.00	1.50	.80
1986 Topps	329	4.00	3.00	1.50
1987 Donruss	19	.60	.45	.25
1987 Donruss	149	2.00	1.50	.80
1987 Donruss Diamond Kings Supers	19	.90	.70	.35
1987 Fleer	549	4.00	3.00	1.50
1987 Fleer	633	.75	.60	.30
1987 Fleer All Stars	5	6.00	4.00	2.00
1987 Fleer All Stars	32	.70	.50	.30
1987 Leaf	19	.80	.60	.30
1987 Leaf	56	1.75	1.25	.70
1987 O-Pee-Chee	82	1.00	.70	.40
1987 Sportflics	7	.90	.70	.35
1987 Sportflics	198	.25	.20	.10
1987 Topps	450	1.00	.70	.40
1987 Topps	611	.40	.30	.15
1987 Topps All-Star Glossy Set of 22	19	.40	.30	.15
1987 Topps All-Star Glossy Set of 60	57	.60	.45	.25
1988 Donruss	368	.50	.40	.20
1988 Donruss MVP	15	.40	.30	.15
1988 Fleer	19	.75	.60	.30
1988 Fleer	638	.20	.15	.08
1988 Leaf	144	.40	.30	.15
1988 O-Pee-Chee	120	.40	.30	.15
1988 Score	24	.40	.25	.15
1988 Score	653	.30	.25	.12
1988 Sportflics	8	1.00	.70	.40
1988 Sportflics	180	.25	.20	.10
1988 Topps	120	.40	.30	.15
1988 Topps	391	.20	.15	.08
1988 Topps All-Star Glossy Set of 60	27	.50	.40	.20
1988 Topps Big Baseball	36	.40	.30	.15
1989 Bowman	162	.40	.30	.15
1989 Donruss	182	.40	.30	.15
1989 Donruss MVP	1	.35	.25	.14
1989 Fleer	124	.40	.30	.15
1989 O-Pee-Chee	132	.45	.35	.20
1989 Score	20	.35	.25	.14
1989 Sportflics	156	.40	.30	.15
1989 Topps	403	.20	.15	.08
1989 Topps	650	.35	.25	.14
1989 Topps All-Star Glossy Set of 60	1	.50	.40	.20
1989 Topps Big Baseball	167	.25	.20	.10
1989 Upper Deck	376	1.50	1.25	.60
1990 Bowman	424	.40	.30	.15
1990 Donruss	269	.30	.25	.12
1990 Donruss	683	.20	.15	.08
1990 Donruss MVP	8	.30	.25	.12
1990 Fleer	383	.30	.25	.12
1990 Fleer	635	.10	.08	.04
1990 Fleer All-Stars	7	1.00	.70	.40
1990 Leaf	123	4.00	3.00	1.50
1990 O-Pee-Chee	391	.20	.15	.08
1990 O-Pee-Chee	700	.25	.20	.10
1990 Post Cereal	3	.60	.45	.25
1990 Score	400	.30	.25	.12
1990 Score	690	.25	.20	.10
1990 Sportflics	11	.40	.30	.15
1990 Topps	391	.20	.15	.08
1990 Topps	700	.25	.20	.10
1990 Topps All-Star Glossy Set of 22	18	.35	.25	.14
1990 Topps All-Star Glossy Set of 60	48	.35	.25	.14
1990 Topps Big Baseball	2	.25	.20	.10
1990 Upper Deck	48	.20	.15	.08
1990 Upper Deck	236	.75	.60	.30
1991 Bowman	320	.25	.20	.10
1991 Donruss	490	.25	.20	.10
1991 Fleer	623	.25	.20	.10
1991 Fleer ProVisions	1	.40	.30	.15
1991 Leaf	208	.75	.60	.30
1991 O-Pee-Chee Premier	96	.50	.40	.20
1991 Post Cereal	28	.60	.45	.25
1991 Score	200	.25	.20	.10
1991 Score	855	.12	.06	.03
1991 Score	891	.40	.30	.15
1991 Studio	90	.60	.45	.25
1991 Topps	300	.20	.15	.08
1991 Upper Deck	544	.35	.25	.14
1992 Bowman	80	3.00	2.25	1.25
1992 Donruss	617	.25	.20	.12
1992 Donruss Elite	17	85.00	64.00	34.00
1992 Donruss Triple Play	202	.25	.15	.08
1992 Fleer	217	.15	.11	.06
1992 Fleer	704	.10	.08	.04
1992 Fleer All-Stars	22	3.00	2.25	1.25
1992 Fleer Team Leaders	5	10.00	7.50	4.00
1992 Fleer Ultra	97	1.00	.70	.40
1992 Fleer Ultra All-Stars	8	4.00	3.00	1.50
1992 Fleer Ultra Award Winners	23	5.00	3.75	2.00
1992 Leaf	98	.50	.30	.15
1992 O-Pee-Chee	575	.15	.11	.06
1992 O-Pee-Chee Premier	102	.50	.40	.20
1992 Pinnacle	20	.60	.45	.25
1992 Pinnacle	289	.40	.30	.15
1992 Pinnacle Slugfest	13	4.00	3.00	1.50
1992 Post Cereal	7	.40	.30	.15
1992 Score	600	.25	.20	.10
1992 Score	796	.15	.11	.06
1992 Score	886	.30	.25	.12
1992 Score Factory Inserts	6	.50	.40	.20
1992 Studio	209	.50	.40	.20
1992 Studio Heritage	14	2.50	2.00	1.00
1992 Topps	575	.35	.25	.14
1992 Topps Gold	575	3.50	2.75	1.50
1992 Topps Kids	109	.20	.15	.08
1992 Topps Stadium Club	500	1.00	.75	.40
1992 Topps Stadium Club Special Edition	144	.60	.45	.25
1992 Topps Stadium Club Special Edition	145	.60	.45	.25
1992 Upper Deck	254	.25	.20	.10
1992 Upper Deck MVP Holograms	41	.75	.60	.30
1993 Bowman	325	1.00	.75	.40
1993 DiamondMarks	(97)	.60	.45	.25
1993 Donruss	607	.40	.30	.15
1993 Donruss Diamond Kings	4	4.00	3.00	1.50
1993 Donruss Masters of the Game	13	3.00	2.25	1.25
1993 Donruss MVP's	18	3.50	2.75	1.50

Card	Number			
1993 Donruss Triple Play Action Baseball	20	.20	.15	.08
1993 Donruss Triple Play	260	.35	.25	.14
1993 Fleer	273	.40	.30	.15
1993 Fleer	355	.15	.11	.06
1993 Fleer All-Stars	9	4.00	3.00	1.50
1993 Fleer AL Team Leaders	1	15.00	11.00	6.00
1993 Fleer Flair	242	3.00	2.25	1.25
1993 Fleer Ultra	236	1.00	.75	.40
1993 Fleer Ultra All-Stars	18	5.00	3.75	2.00
1993 Fleer Ultra Award Winners	17	5.00	3.75	2.00
1993 Leaf	378	1.00	.75	.40
1993 Leaf Gold All-Stars	17	3.00	2.25	1.25
1993 Leaf Heading for the Hall	9	6.00	4.50	2.50
1993 Leaf Update Gold All-Stars	7	7.50	5.75	3.00
1993 O-Pee-Chee	306	1.50	1.25	.60
1993 O-Pee-Chee Premier Star Performers	11	.60	.45	.25
1993 Pinnacle	426	1.00	.75	.40
1993 Pinnacle Cooperstown	12	.35	.25	.14
1993 Pinnacle Cooperstown Dufex	12	100.00	75.00	40.00
1993 Pinnacle Slugfest	16	5.00	3.75	2.00
1993 Pinnacle Team Pinnacle	9	15.00	11.00	6.00
1993 Post Cereal	3	.75	.60	.30
1993 Score	505	.25	.20	.10
1993 Score	533	.25	.20	.10
1993 Score	550	.25	.20	.10
1993 Score	606	.40	.30	.15
1993 Score Gold Dream Team	2	2.00	1.50	.75
1993 Score Select	4	.75	.60	.30
1993 Score Select Chase Stars	18	15.00	11.00	6.00
1993 Score Select Stat Leaders	2	.50	.40	.20
1993 Score Select Stat Leaders	7	.50	.40	.20
1993 Score The Franchise	9	10.00	7.50	4.00
1993 Studio	214	1.00	.75	.40
1993 Topps	200	.35	.25	.14
1993 Topps	406	.15	.11	.06
1993 Topps Black Gold	40	1.00	.75	.40
1993 Topps Finest	112	13.00	9.75	5.25
1993 Topps Finest Jumbo All-Stars	112	30.00	22.00	12.00
1993 Topps Finest Refractors	112	250.00	185.00	100.00
1993 Topps Gold	200	.75	.60	.30
1993 Topps Gold	406	.30	.25	.12
1993 Topps Stadium Club	283	.75	.60	.30
1993 Topps Stadium Club	597	.40	.30	.15
1993 Topps Stadium Club First Day Production	283	75.00	56.00	30.00
1993 Topps Stadium Club First Day Production	597	50.00	37.00	20.00
1993 Topps Stadium Club Master Photos	(6)	4.00	3.00	1.50
1993 Topps Stadium Club Members Only	(20)	2.00	1.50	.80
1993 Topps Stadium Club Special Master Photo	(7)	1.25	.90	.50
1993 Topps Stadium Club Special	28	.50	.40	.20
1993 Upper Deck	34	.25	.20	.10
1993 Upper Deck	50	.15	.11	.06
1993 Upper Deck	565	.25	.20	.10
1993 Upper Deck Clutch Performers	17	2.00	1.50	.00
1993 Upper Deck Diamond Gallery	26	3.00	2.25	1.25
1993 Upper Deck Fun Packs All-Star Scratch-Off	9	2.00	1.50	.80
1993 Upper Deck Fun Packs	191	.25	.20	.10
1993 Upper Deck Fun Packs	195	.40	.30	.15
1993 Upper Deck Future Heroes	61	2.00	1.50	.80
1993 Upper Deck Home Run Heroes	24	2.00	1.50	.80
1993 Upper Deck Iooss Collection	24	2.00	1.50	.80
1993 Upper Deck Iooss Collection Super	24	4.00	3.00	1.50
1993 Upper Deck On Deck	19	1.50	1.25	.60
1993 Upper Deck SP	7	4.00	3.00	1.50
1993 Upper Deck Triple Crown	6	4.50	3.50	1.75
1994 Bowman	460	.75	.60	.30
1994 Bowman's Best	75	4.50	3.50	1.75
1994 Bowman's Best Refractors	75	35.00	26.00	14.00
1994 Donruss	343	.75	.60	.30
1994 Donruss Award Winners Supers	5	4.50	3.50	1.75
1994 Donruss Decade Dominators	5	3.00	2.25	1.25
1994 Donruss Decade Dominators Supers	5	5.00	3.75	2.00
1994 Donruss MVP's	23	3.00	2.25	1.25
1994 Donruss Special Edition - Gold	343	1.50	1.25	.60
1994 Donruss Triple Play Medalists	11	5.00	3.75	2.00
1994 Donruss Triple Play	258	.40	.30	.15
1994 Fleer	217	.60	.45	.25
1994 Fleer	712	.05	.04	.02
1994 Fleer All-Stars	20	1.50	1.25	.60
1994 Fleer Extra Bases	123	.60	.45	.25
1994 Fleer Extra Bases Game Breakers	23	1.50	1.25	.60
1994 Fleer Flair	77	2.50	2.00	1.00
1994 Fleer Flair Hot Glove	7	25.00	18.00	10.00
1994 Fleer Flair Outfield Power	8	7.00	5.25	2.75
1994 Fleer Team Leaders	9	2.00	1.50	.80
1994 Fleer Ultra	391	.75	.60	.30
1994 Fleer Update Diamond Tribute	9	1.25	.90	.50
1994 Leaf	294	1.00	.75	.40
1994 Leaf Gamers	9	10.00	7.50	4.00
1994 Leaf Limited	51	10.00	7.50	4.00
1994 Leaf Limited Gold	9	40.00	30.00	15.00
1994 Leaf MVP Contenders	10a	10.00	7.50	4.00
1994 Leaf MVP Contenders	10b	20.00	15.00	8.00
1994 O-Pee-Chee	93	1.00	.70	.40
1994 O-Pee-Chee All-Star Redemption Cards	17	1.25	.90	.50
1994 O-Pee-Chee Jumbo All-Stars	17	15.00	11.00	6.00
1994 O-Pee-Chee Jumbo All-Stars Factory Set	17	2.50	2.00	1.00
1994 Pacific Crown	365	.75	.60	.30
1994 Pacific Crown Jewels of the Crown	11	9.00	6.75	3.50
1994 Pinnacle	21	1.00	.70	.40
1994 Pinnacle Artist's Proof	21	75.00	56.00	30.00
1994 Pinnacle Museum Collection	21	25.00	18.00	10.00
1994 Pinnacle Run Creators	20	8.00	6.00	3.25
1994 Pinnacle The Naturals Box Set	11	1.00	.75	.40
1994 Post Cereal	4	.60	.45	.25
1994 Score	21	.50	.40	.20
1994 Score Gold Stars	52	20.00	15.00	8.00
1994 Score Select	17	1.00	.70	.40
1994 Sportflics 2000	42	1.00	.75	.40

1994 Sportflics 2000 Movers	4	15.00	11.00	6.00
1994 Studio	200	.75	.60	.30
1994 Topps	100	.50	.40	.20
1994 Topps	607	.25	.20	.10
1994 Topps Black Gold	17	1.25	.90	.50
1994 Topps Finest	204	5.00	3.75	2.00
1994 Topps Finest Refractors	204	45.00	34.00	18.00
1994 Topps Finest Superstars	204	20.00	15.00	8.00
1994 Topps Gold	100	2.00	1.50	.80
1994 Topps Gold	607	.75	.60	.30
1994 Topps Stadium Club	359	.75	.60	.30
1994 Topps Stadium Club First Day Production	359	30.00	22.00	12.00
1994 Upper Deck	289	.75	.60	.30
1994 Upper Deck	325	.75	.60	.30
1994 Upper Deck All-Stars Green Foil	14	.75	.60	.30
1994 Upper Deck All-Stars Gold Foil	14	4.00	3.00	1.50
1994 Upper Deck Collector's Choice	319	.10	.07	.04
1994 Upper Deck Collector's Choice	353	.15	.11	.06
1994 Upper Deck Collector's Choice	425	.25	.20	.10
1994 Upper Deck Collector's Choice	638	.25	.20	.10
1994 Upper Deck Diamond Collection	4C	20.00	15.00	8.00
1994 Upper Deck Electric Diamond	289	3.00	2.25	1.25
1994 Upper Deck Electric Diamond	325	2.50	2.00	1.00
1994 Upper Deck Fun Packs	34	.60	.45	.25
1994 Upper Deck Fun Packs	206	1.50	1.25	.60
1994 Upper Deck Fun Packs	232	.30	.25	.12
1994 Upper Deck Next Generation	14	6.00	4.50	2.50
1994 Upper Deck SP	186	1.50	1.25	.60
1994 Upper Deck SP Baseball Die-Cut	186	4.00	3.00	1.50
1994 Upper Deck SP Holoview Blue	30	9.00	6.75	3.50
1994 Upper Deck SP Holoview Red	30	80.00	60.00	32.00
1994 Upper Deck SP Insert	3	12.00	9.00	4.75

Tim Raines

Set	Card #	MT	NM	EX
1981 Donruss	538 (R)	6.00	4.50	2.50
1981 O-Pee-Chee	136	7.25	5.50	3.00
1981 Topps	479	9.00	6.75	3.50

1981 Topps Traded	816	12.00	9.00	4.75
1982 Donruss	214	1.50	1.25	.60
1982 Fleer	202	1.50	1.25	.60
1982 O-Pee-Chee	70	2.50	2.00	1.00
1982 Topps	3	.30	.25	.12
1982 Topps	70	1.00	.70	.40
1982 Topps	164	.90	.70	.35
1983 Donruss	540	.35	.25	.14
1983 Fleer	292	.35	.25	.14
1983 O-Pee-Chee	227	.40	.30	.15
1983 O-Pee-Chee	352	.30	.25	.12
1983 Topps	403	.25	.20	.10
1983 Topps	595	.60	.45	.25
1983 Topps	704	.35	.25	.14
1984 Donruss	299	1.50	1.25	.60
1984 Fleer	281	1.00	.70	.40
1984 Fleer	631	.20	.15	.08
1984 O-Pee-Chee	370	.60	.45	.25
1984 O-Pee-Chee	390	.40	.30	.15
1984 Topps	134	.30	.25	.12
1984 Topps	370	.50	.40	.20
1984 Topps	390	.25	.20	.10
1984 Topps All-Star Glossy Set of 22	17	.35	.25	.14
1984 Topps All-Star Glossy Set of 40	37	.35	.25	.14
1985 Donruss	299	.50	.40	.20
1985 Fleer	405	.35	.25	.14
1985 Leaf-Donruss	218	.35	.25	.14
1985 Leaf-Donruss	252	.80	.60	.30
1985 O-Pee-Chee	277	.30	.25	.12
1985 Topps	630	.20	.15	.08
1986 Donruss	177	.40	.30	.15
1986 Fleer	256	.35	.25	.14
1986 Fleer	632	.25	.20	.10
1986 Leaf	108	1.00	.70	.40
1986 O-Pee-Chee	280	.25	.20	.10
1986 Sportflics	11	.20	.15	.08
1986 Sportflics	127	.25	.20	.10
1986 Sportflics	144	.15	.11	.06
1986 Sportflics Decade Greats	74	.30	.25	.12
1986 Topps	280	.12	.09	.05
1986 Topps All-Star Glossy Set of 60	15	.50	.40	.20
1987 Donruss	56	.30	.25	.12
1987 Fleer	328	.30	.25	.12
1987 Fleer	642	.12	.09	.05
1987 Fleer All Stars	12	.75	.60	.30
1987 Fleer All Stars	34	.25	.20	.10
1987 Leaf	149	.50	.40	.20
1987 O-Pee-Chee	30	.20	.15	.08
1987 Sportflics	34	.20	.15	.08
1987 Sportflics	152	.20	.15	.08
1987 Sportflics	197	.80	.60	.30
1987 Sportflics	199	.35	.25	.14
1987 Topps	30	.12	.09	.05
1987 Topps All-Star Glossy Set of 60	48	.30	.25	.12
1988 Donruss	2	.08	.06	.03
1988 Donruss	345	.08	.06	.03
1988 Donruss Diamond Kings Supers	2	.30	.25	.12
1988 Donruss MVP	18	.25	.20	.10
1988 Fleer	193	.10	.08	.04
1988 Fleer	631	.20	.15	.08
1988 Leaf	2	.20	.15	.08
1988 Leaf	114	.20	.15	.08
1988 Leaf	211	.50	.40	.20
1988 O-Pee-Chee	243	.20	.15	.08
1988 Score	3	.08	.06	.03
1988 Score	649	.10	.08	.04
1988 Sportflics	2	.35	.25	.14
1988 Topps	403	.12	.09	.05
1988 Topps	720	.10	.08	.04
1988 Topps All-Star Glossy Set of 60	12	.25	.20	.10
1988 Topps Big Baseball	116	.25	.20	.10
1989 Bowman	369	.08	.06	.03
1989 Donruss	97	.08	.06	.03
1989 Fleer	391	.08	.06	.03

1989 O-Pee-Chee	87	.40	.30	.15
1989 Score	40	.08	.05	.02
1989 Sportflics	150	.35	.25	.14
1989 Topps	81	.08	.06	.03
1989 Topps	560	.08	.06	.03
1989 Topps All-Star Glossy Set of 60	53	.20	.15	.08
1989 Topps Big Baseball	73	.08	.06	.03
1989 Upper Deck	402	.15	.11	.06
1990 Bowman	118	.08	.06	.03
1990 Donruss	216	.09	.07	.04
1990 Donruss MVP	7	.10	.08	.04
1990 Fleer	359	.10	.08	.04
1990 Leaf	212	.35	.25	.14
1990 O-Pee-Chee	180	.10	.08	.04
1990 Score	409	.10	.08	.04
1990 Sportflics	69	.12	.09	.05
1990 Topps	180	.10	.08	.04
1990 Topps All-Star Glossy Set of 60	38	.15	.11	.06
1990 Topps Big Baseball	154	.15	.11	.06
1990 Upper Deck	177	.12	.09	.05
1991 Bowman	362	.08	.06	.03
1991 Donruss	457	.08	.06	.03
1991 Fleer	244	.08	.06	.03
1991 Fleer Ultra	81	.10	.08	.04
1991 Fleer Update	15	.15	.11	.06
1991 Leaf	413	.15	.11	.06
1991 O-Pee-Chee Premier	97	.08	.06	.03
1991 Score	35	.12	.09	.05
1991 Score Traded	10	.15	.11	.06
1991 Studio	37	.25	.20	.10
1991 Topps	360	.15	.11	.06
1991 Topps Traded	94	.12	.09	.05
1991 Upper Deck	143	.12	.09	.05
1991 Upper Deck	773	.15	.11	.06
1992 Bowman	204	.20	.15	.08
1992 Donruss	312	.10	.08	.04
1992 Donruss Triple Play	107	.06	.05	.02
1992 Fleer	97	.10	.08	.04
1992 Fleer Ultra	43	.15	.11	.06
1992 Leaf	37	.15	.11	.06
1992 O-Pee-Chee	426	.10	.08	.04
1992 Pinnacle	178	.15	.11	.06
1992 Pinnacle	605	.15	.11	.06
1992 Score	635	.06	.05	.02
1992 Studio	156	.15	.11	.06
1992 Topps	426	.10	.08	.04
1992 Topps Gold	426	.40	.30	.15
1992 Topps Kids	104	.10	.08	.04
1992 Topps Stadium Club	426	.20	.15	.08
1992 Upper Deck	575	.10	.08	.04
1993 Bowman	499	.10	.08	.04
1993 Donruss	565	.05	.04	.02
1993 Donruss Triple Play	108	.12	.09	.05
1993 Fleer	209	.08	.06	.03
1993 Fleer Ultra	178	.10	.08	.04
1993 Leaf	420	.10	.08	.04
1993 O-Pee-Chee	290	.15	.11	.06
1993 Pinnacle	53	.06	.05	.02
1993 Score	658	.08	.06	.03
1993 Score Select	236	.12	.09	.05
1993 Studio	215	.12	.09	.05
1993 Topps Finest	183	1.00	.70	.40
1993 Topps Finest Refractors	183	20.00	15.00	8.00
1993 Topps Gold	675	.10	.08	.04
1993 Topps Stadium Club	43	.12	.09	.05
1993 Topps Stadium Club First Day Production	43	5.00	3.75	2.00
1993 Upper Deck	597	.08	.06	.03
1993 Upper Deck Fun Packs	201	.15	.11	.06
1993 Upper Deck SP	259	.15	.11	.06
1994 Bowman	127	.10	.08	.04
1994 Donruss	220	.05	.04	.02
1994 Donruss	258	.05	.04	.02
1994 Donruss Triple Play	268	.05	.04	.02
1994 Fleer	93	.05	.04	.02
1994 Fleer Extra Bases	52	.10	.08	.04

1994 Fleer Flair	35	.20	.15	.08
1994 Fleer Ultra	340	.10	.08	.04
1994 Leaf	116	.10	.08	.04
1994 Leaf Limited	23	1.00	.70	.40
1994 O-Pee-Chee	228	.05	.04	.02
1994 Pacific Crown	136	.05	.04	.02
1994 Pinnacle	462	.10	.08	.04
1994 Pinnacle Artist's Proof	462	3.00	2.25	1.25
1994 Pinnacle Museum Collection	462	1.50	1.25	.60
1994 Score	379	.05	.04	.02
1994 Score Select	92	.10	.08	.04
1994 Studio	208	.10	.08	.04
1994 Topps	243	.04	.03	.02
1994 Topps Finest	192	.50	.40	.20
1994 Topps Finest Refractors	192	3.50	2.75	1.50
1994 Topps Gold	243	.15	.11	.06
1994 Topps Stadium Club	350	.12	.09	.05
1994 Topps Stadium Club	525	.10	.08	.04
1994 Topps Stadium Club First Day Production	350	2.50	2.00	1.00
1994 Topps Stadium Club First Day Production	525	2.50	2.00	1.00
1994 Upper Deck	254	.12	.09	.05
1994 Upper Deck All-Stars Green Foil	42	.25	.20	.10
1994 Upper Deck All-Stars Gold Foil	42	1.00	.70	.40
1994 Upper Deck Collector's Choice	385	.05	.04	.02
1994 Upper Deck Electric Diamond	254	.25	.20	.10

Willie Randolph

Set	Card #	NM	EX	VG
1976 O-Pee-Chee	592	8.50	4.25	2.50
1976 Topps	592	5.00	2.50	1.50
1976 Topps Traded	592T	2.00	1.00	.60
1977 O-Pee-Chee	110	.40	.20	.12
1977 Topps	359	.60	.30	.20
1978 O-Pee-Chee	228	.25	.13	.08
1978 Topps	620	.30	.15	.09
1979 O-Pee-Chee	125	.25	.13	.08
1979 Topps	250	.30	.15	.09
1980 O-Pee-Chee	239	.15	.08	.05
1980 Topps	460	.15	.08	.05

Set	Card #	MT	NM	EX
1981 Donruss	345	.10	.08	.04
1981 Fleer	109	.10	.08	.04
1981 O-Pee-Chee	60	.12	.09	.05
1981 Topps	60	.15	.11	.06
1982 Donruss	461	.10	.08	.04
1982 Fleer	49	.10	.08	.04
1982 O-Pee-Chee	37	.12	.09	.05
1982 O-Pee-Chee	159	.12	.09	.05

1982 O-Pee-Chee	213	.12	.09	.05
1982 Topps	548	.12	.09	.05
1982 Topps	569	.15	.11	.06
1982 Topps	570	.10	.08	.04
1983 Donruss	283	.10	.08	.04
1983 Fleer	393	.10	.08	.04
1983 O-Pee-Chee	140	.12	.09	.05
1983 Topps	140	.12	.09	.05
1984 Donruss	417	.20	.15	.08
1984 Fleer	137	.12	.09	.05
1984 O-Pee-Chee	360	.20	.15	.08
1984 Topps	360	.12	.09	.05
1985 Donruss	92	.12	.09	.05
1985 Fleer	140	.10	.08	.04
1985 Leaf-Donruss	83	.08	.06	.03
1985 O-Pee-Chee	8	.08	.06	.03
1985 Topps	765	.10	.08	.04
1986 Donruss	16	.12	.09	.05
1986 Donruss	92	.10	.08	.04
1986 Donruss Diamond Kings Supers	16	.25	.20	.10
1986 Fleer	115	.10	.08	.04
1986 Leaf	16	.08	.06	.03
1986 O-Pee-Chee	332	.08	.06	.03
1986 Topps	276	.07	.05	.03
1986 Topps	455	.10	.08	.04
1987 Donruss	154	.10	.08	.04
1987 Fleer	109	.10	.08	.04
1987 Fleer All Stars	35	.07	.05	.03
1987 Leaf	58	.08	.06	.03
1987 O-Pee-Chee	377	.08	.06	.03
1987 Topps	701	.07	.05	.03
1988 Donruss	228	.07	.05	.03
1988 Fleer	218	.08	.06	.03
1988 Leaf	162	.08	.06	.03
1988 O-Pee-Chee	210	.08	.06	.03
1988 Score	266	.06	.05	.02
1988 Sportflics	47	.10	.08	.04
1988 Sportflics Gamewinners	6	.20	.15	.08
1988 Topps	210	.06	.05	.02
1988 Topps	387	.06	.05	.02
1988 Topps	459	.08	.06	.03
1988 Topps All-Star Glossy Set of 22	3	.15	.11	.06
1988 Topps All-Star Glossy Set of 60	42	.15	.11	.06
1988 Topps Big Baseball	76	.08	.06	.03
1989 Bowman	344	.03	.02	.01
1989 Donruss	395	.06	.05	.02
1989 Fleer	265	.07	.05	.03
1989 Fleer Update	93	.06	.05	.02
1989 O-Pee-Chee	244	.05	.04	.02
1989 Score	45	.06	.05	.02
1989 Score Traded	41T	.08	.06	.03
1989 Topps	519	.03	.02	.01
1989 Topps	635	.06	.05	.02
1989 Topps Big Baseball	244	.05	.04	.02
1989 Topps Traded	100T	.10	.08	.04
1989 Upper Deck	237	.08	.06	.03
1989 Upper Deck	777	.10	.08	.04
1990 Bowman	90	.06	.05	.02
1990 Donruss	19	.08	.06	.03
1990 Donruss	250	.07	.05	.03
1990 Donruss Diamond Kings Supers	19	.10	.08	.04
1990 Fleer	406	.08	.06	.03
1990 Leaf	345	.25	.20	.10
1990 O-Pee-Chee	25	.08	.06	.03
1990 Score	395	.09	.07	.04
1990 Score Traded	51T	.08	.06	.03
1990 Sportflics	175	.10	.08	.04
1990 Topps	25	.08	.06	.03
1990 Topps Big Baseball	43	.06	.05	.02
1990 Topps Traded	100T	.08	.06	.03
1990 Upper Deck	183	.10	.08	.04
1990 Upper Deck	704	.12	.09	.05
1991 Bowman	46	.06	.05	.02
1991 Donruss	217	.06	.05	.02
1991 Donruss	766	.05	.04	.02
1991 Fleer	22	.06	.05	.02
1991 Fleer Ultra Update	32	.15	.11	.06
1991 Fleer Update	33	.08	.06	.03
1991 Leaf	419	.10	.08	.04
1991 Score	194	.06	.05	.02
1991 Score Traded	35	.08	.06	.03
1991 Studio	74	.12	.09	.05
1991 Topps	525	.06	.05	.02
1991 Topps Stadium Club	545	.20	.15	.08
1991 Topps Traded	95	.06	.05	.02
1991 Upper Deck	421	.08	.06	.03
1991 Upper Deck	720	.12	.09	.05
1992 Bowman	681	.20	.15	.08
1992 Donruss	625	.05	.04	.02
1992 Fleer	186	.05	.04	.02
1992 Fleer Ultra	536	.10	.08	.04
1992 Leaf	240	.10	.08	.04
1992 O-Pee-Chee	116	.05	.04	.02
1992 O-Pee-Chee Premier	67	.10	.08	.04
1992 Pinnacle	382	.12	.09	.05
1992 Score	30	.05	.04	.02
1992 Score Rookie & Traded	35	.06	.05	.02
1992 Topps	116	.05	.04	.02
1992 Topps Gold	116	.25	.20	.10
1992 Topps Stadium Club	890	.15	.11	.06
1992 Topps Traded	90	.06	.05	.02
1992 Upper Deck	211	.05	.04	.02
1992 Upper Deck	795	.06	.05	.02
1993 Donruss	644	.05	.04	.02
1993 Fleer	479	.06	.05	.02
1993 Score	613	.04	.03	.02
1993 Score Select	195	.08	.06	.03
1993 Topps	324	.06	.05	.02
1993 Topps Gold	324	.10	.08	.04
1993 Upper Deck	419	.06	.05	.02

Pee Wee Reese

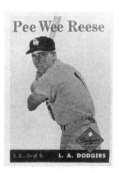

Set	Card #	NM	EX	VG
1941 Double Play	23	.02	.02	.02
1941 Play Ball	54	750.00	325.00	187.00
1949 Bowman	36	200.00	100.00	60.00
1950 Bowman	21	210.00	105.00	62.50
1951 Bowman	80	140.00	70.00	42.50
1952 Bowman	8	80.00	40.00	24.00
1952 Red Man Tobacco	17N	85.00	42.00	25.00
1952 Topps	333	1200.	600.00	276.00
1953 Bowman Color	33	450.00	225.00	135.00
1953 Red Man Tobacco	10N	75.00	37.00	22.00
1953 Topps	76	150.00	75.00	34.00
1954 Topps	58	60.00	30.00	18.00
1954 Red Man Tobacco	15N	90.00	45.00	27.00
1955 Bowman	37	60.00	30.00	18.00
1955 Red Man Tobacco	17N	75.00	37.00	22.00
1956 Topps	260	110.00	55.00	32.50
1957 Topps	30	60.00	30.00	18.00
1958 Topps	375	55.00	27.00	16.50

Set	Card #	MT	NM	EX
1983 Topps 1952 Reprint Set	333	9.00	6.75	3.50

1986 Sportflics Decade Greats	21	.40	.30	.15
1988 Pacific Trading Cards Baseball Legends	21	.25	.20	.10
1991 "1953" Topps Archives	76	2.00	1.50	.80

Jim Rice

Set	Card #	NM	EX	VG
1975 O-Pee-Chee	616	18.00	9.00	5.50
1975 Topps	616 (R)	15.00	7.50	4.50
1975 Topps Mini	616	50.00	25.00	15.00
1976 O-Pee-Chee	340	4.50	2.25	1.25
1976 Topps	340	6.00	3.00	1.75
1977 O-Pee-Chee	62	4.25	2.25	1.25
1977 Topps	60	4.00	2.00	1.25
1978 O-Pee-Chee	2	.25	.13	.08
1978 O-Pee-Chee	163	5.00	2.50	1.50
1978 Topps	202	.25	.13	.08
1978 Topps	670	2.00	1.00	.60
1979 O-Pee-Chee	210	3.50	1.75	1.00
1979 Topps	2	.30	.15	.09
1979 Topps	3	.30	.15	.09
1979 Topps	400	1.00	.50	.30
1980 O-Pee-Chee	112	2.00	1.00	.60
1980 Topps	200	1.00	.50	.30

Set	Card #	MT	NM	EX
1981 Donruss	338	.30	.25	.12
1981 Fleer	222	.30	.25	.12
1981 O-Pee-Chee	68	.75	.60	.30
1981 Topps	500	.35	.25	.14
1982 Donruss	200	.30	.25	.12
1982 Fleer	305	.25	.20	.10
1982 O-Pee-Chee	366	.75	.60	.30
1982 Topps	750	.35	.25	.14
1983 Donruss	208	.30	.25	.12
1983 Fleer	194	.20	.15	.08
1983 O-Pee-Chee	30	.60	.45	.25
1983 Topps	30	.20	.15	.08
1983 Topps	381	.15	.11	.06
1984 Donruss	50	.50	.40	.20
1984 Fleer	408	.40	.30	.15
1984 O-Pee-Chee	184	.60	.45	.25
1984 O-Pee-Chee	364	.50	.40	.20
1984 Topps	132	.50	.40	.20
1984 Topps	133	.40	.30	.15
1984 Topps	401	.30	.25	.12
1984 Topps	550	.20	.15	.08
1984 Topps All-Star Glossy Set of 22	6	.25	.20	.10
1984 Topps All-Star Glossy Set of 40	22	.25	.20	.10
1985 Donruss	15	.20	.15	.08
1985 Donruss	50	.30	.25	.12
1985 Donruss Diamond Kings Supers	15	.35	.25	.14
1985 Fleer	168	.20	.15	.08
1985 Leaf-Donruss	15	.30	.25	.12
1985 O-Pee-Chee	150	.30	.25	.12
1985 Topps	150	.15	.11	.06
1985 Topps All-Star Glossy Set of 40	6	.35	.25	.14
1986 Donruss	213	.20	.15	.08
1986 Fleer	358	.12	.09	.05
1986 Leaf	146	.30	.25	.12
1986 O-Pee-Chee	320	.25	.20	.10
1986 Sportflics	17	.30	.25	.12
1986 Sportflics	52	.35	.25	.14
1986 Sportflics	61	.25	.20	.10
1986 Sportflics	139	.30	.25	.12
1986 Sportflics	146	.25	.20	.10
1986 Sportflics Decade Greats	57	.40	.30	.15
1986 Topps	320	.08	.06	.03
1986 Topps All-Star Glossy Set of 22	6	.30	.25	.12
1986 Topps All-Star Glossy Set of 60	36	.50	.40	.20
1987 Donruss	92	.12	.09	.05
1987 Fleer	41	.20	.15	.08
1987 Fleer	633	.75	.60	.30
1987 Fleer Headliners	6	.30	.25	.12
1987 Leaf	247	.20	.15	.08
1987 O-Pee-Chee	146	.20	.15	.08
1987 Sportflics	80	.50	.40	.20
1987 Sportflics	97	.20	.15	.08
1987 Topps	480	.12	.09	.05
1987 Topps	610	.15	.11	.06
1987 Topps All-Star Glossy Set of 60	42	.25	.20	.10
1988 Donruss	399	.08	.06	.03
1988 Fleer	361	.10	.08	.04
1988 Leaf	215	.20	.15	.08
1988 O-Pee-Chee	61	.15	.11	.06
1988 Score	14	.08	.06	.03
1988 Sportflics	158	.15	.11	.06
1988 Topps	662	.08	.06	.03
1988 Topps	675	.08	.06	.03
1988 Topps Big Baseball	181	.10	.08	.04
1989 Bowman	33	.10	.08	.04
1989 Donruss	122	.08	.06	.03
1989 Fleer	97	.08	.06	.03
1989 O-Pee-Chee	245	.08	.06	.03
1989 Score	85	.08	.05	.02
1989 Sportflics	173	.30	.25	.12
1989 Topps	245	.10	.08	.04
1989 Topps Big Baseball	18	.05	.04	.02
1989 Upper Deck	413	.10	.08	.04
1990 O-Pee-Chee	785	.07	.05	.03
1990 Topps	785	.07	.05	.03
1990 Upper Deck	373	.08	.06	.03
1991 Pacific Senior League	148	.20	.15	.08

Bobby Richardson

Set	Card #	NM	EX	VG
1957 Topps	286 (R)	100.00	50.00	30.00
1958 Topps	101a	45.00	22.00	13.50
1958 Topps	101b	19.00	9.50	5.75

1959 Topps	76	17.50	8.75	5.25
1959 Topps	237	9.00	4.50	2.75
1960 Topps	405	8.00	4.00	2.50
1961 Post Cereal	8a	4.50	2.25	1.25
1961 Post Cereal	8b	4.50	2.25	1.25
1961 Topps	180	9.00	4.50	2.75
1962 Post Cereal	2	4.50	2.25	1.25
1962 Topps	65	6.00	3.00	1.75
1963 Fleer	25	20.00	10.00	6.00
1963 Post Cereal	13	4.00	2.00	1.25
1963 Topps	173	80.00	40.00	24.00
1963 Topps	420	11.00	5.50	3.25
1964 Topps	190	7.50	3.75	2.25
1965 O-Pee-Chee	115	2.75	1.50	.80
1965 Topps	115	5.00	2.50	1.50
1966 Topps	490	12.00	6.00	3.50

Set	Card #	MT	NM	EX
1988 Pacific Trading Cards Baseball Legends	74	.15	.11	.06
1990 Pacific Legends	100	.10	.08	.04

Cal Ripken Jr.

Set	Card #	MT	NM	EX
1982 Donruss	405 (R)	45.00	34.00	18.00
1982 Fleer	176 (R)	48.00	36.00	19.00
1982 Topps	21 (R)	75.00	56.00	30.00
1982 Topps Traded	98T	235.00	176.00	94.00
1983 Donruss	279	16.00	12.00	6.50
1983 Fleer	70	16.00	12.00	6.50
1983 O-Pee-Chee	163	18.00	13.50	7.25
1983 Topps	163	20.00	15.00	8.00
1984 Donruss	106	32.00	24.00	13.00
1984 Fleer	17	20.00	15.00	8.00
1984 O-Pee-Chee	2	5.50	4.25	2.25
1984 O-Pee-Chee	363	1.75	1.25	.70
1984 Topps	400	2.00	1.50	.80
1984 Topps	426	1.00	.75	.40
1984 Topps	490	6.00	4.50	2.50
1985 Donruss	14	4.50	3.50	1.75
1985 Donruss	169	10.00	7.50	4.00
1985 Donruss Diamond Kings Supers	14	4.00	3.00	1.50
1985 Fleer	187	10.00	7.50	4.00
1985 Fleer	626	3.50	2.75	1.50
1985 Fleer	641	4.00	3.00	1.50
1985 Leaf-Donruss	14	4.25	3.25	1.75
1985 O-Pee-Chee	30	3.25	2.50	1.25
1985 Topps	30	4.00	3.00	1.50
1985 Topps	704	2.00	1.50	.80
1985 Topps All-Star Glossy Set of 22	16	.60	.45	.25
1985 Topps All-Star Glossy Set of 40	24	.75	.60	.30
1986 Donruss	210	5.00	3.75	2.00
1986 Fleer	284	5.00	3.75	2.00
1986 Fleer	633	1.00	.70	.40
1986 Fleer All Stars	5	8.00	6.00	3.25
1986 Leaf	142	4.25	3.25	1.75
1986 O-Pee-Chee	340	2.00	1.50	.80

1986 Sportflics	8	2.00	1.50	.80
1986 Sportflics	54	1.25	.90	.50
1986 Sportflics	57	.35	.25	.14
1986 Sportflics	69	1.00	.70	.40
1986 Sportflics	73	.25	.20	.10
1986 Sportflics	128	.20	.15	.08
1986 Sportflics Decade Greats	73	.30	.25	.12
1986 Sportflics Rookies	48	.60	.45	.25
1986 Topps	340	2.50	2.00	1.00
1986 Topps	715	1.00	.75	.40
1986 Topps All-Star Glossy Set of 22	5	.60	.45	.25
1986 Topps All-Star Glossy Set of 60	14	.70	.50	.30
1987 Donruss	89	2.00	1.50	.80
1987 Fleer	478	3.50	2.75	1.50
1987 Fleer All Stars	36	1.00	.70	.40
1987 Leaf	98	1.25	.90	.50
1987 O-Pee-Chee	312	.75	.60	.30
1987 Sportflics	9	3.00	2.25	1.25
1987 Sportflics	113	.25	.20	.10
1987 Topps	609	.60	.45	.25
1987 Topps	784	1.00	.75	.40
1987 Topps All-Star Glossy Set of 22	16	.50	.40	.20
1987 Topps All-Star Glossy Set of 60	37	1.50	1.25	.60
1988 Donruss	26	.35	.25	.14
1988 Donruss	171	.50	.40	.20
1988 Donruss	625	.30	.25	.12
1988 Donruss Diamond Kings Supers	26	2.00	1.50	.80
1988 Donruss MVP	1	.50	.40	.20
1988 Fleer	570	1.00	.70	.40
1988 Fleer	635	.30	.25	.12
1988 Fleer	640	.50	.40	.20
1988 Leaf	26	1.00	.70	.40
1988 Leaf	100	.40	.30	.15
1988 O-Pee-Chee	74	.50	.40	.20
1988 Score	550	.60	.45	.25
1988 Score	651	.25	.20	.10
1988 Sportflics	152	1.50	1.25	.60
1988 Topps	51	.30	.25	.12
1988 Topps	650	.50	.40	.20
1988 Topps All-Star Glossy Set of 22	5	.75	.60	.30
1988 Topps All-Star Glossy Set of 60	6	.70	.50	.30
1988 Topps Big Baseball	62	.45	.35	.20
1989 Bowman	9	.50	.40	.20
1989 Bowman	260	.20	.15	.08
1989 Donruss	51	.40	.30	.15
1989 Donruss MVP	15	.60	.45	.25
1989 Fleer	617	.40	.30	.15
1989 O-Pee-Chee	250	.60	.45	.25
1989 Score	15	.50	.40	.20
1989 Sportflics	66	.60	.45	.25
1989 Topps	250	.50	.40	.20
1989 Topps All-Star Glossy Set of 22	5	.25	.20	.10
1989 Topps All-Star Glossy Set of 60	47	.50	.40	.20
1989 Topps Big Baseball	286	.30	.25	.12
1989 Upper Deck	467	2.00	1.50	.80
1989 Upper Deck	682	.40	.30	.15
1990 Bowman	255	.40	.30	.15
1990 Donruss	96	.35	.25	.14
1990 Donruss	676	.25	.20	.10
1990 Donruss MVP	18	.30	.25	.12
1990 Fleer	187	.40	.30	.15
1990 Fleer	624a	3.00	2.25	1.25
1990 Fleer	624b	.25	.20	.10
1990 Fleer	634	.10	.08	.04
1990 Fleer All-Stars	8	1.50	1.00	.50
1990 Leaf	197	5.00	3.75	2.00
1990 O-Pee-Chee	8	.15	.11	.06
1990 O-Pee-Chee	388	.15	.11	.06
1990 O-Pee-Chee	570	.35	.25	.14
1990 Post Cereal	21	1.00	.70	.40
1990 Score	2	.40	.30	.15

Card	#			
1990 Sportflics	100	.80	.60	.30
1990 Topps	8	.20	.15	.08
1990 Topps	388	.25	.20	.10
1990 Topps	570	.35	.25	.14
1990 Topps All-Star Glossy Set of 22	16	.40	.30	.15
1990 Topps All-Star Glossy Set of 60	51	.70	.50	.30
1990 Topps Big Baseball	327	.35	.25	.14
1990 Upper Deck	266	.60	.45	.25
1991 Bowman	104	.30	.25	.12
1991 Donruss	52	.20	.15	.08
1991 Donruss	223	.40	.30	.15
1991 Fleer	490	.40	.30	.15
1991 Fleer Ultra	24	.75	.60	.30
1991 Leaf	430	.75	.60	.30
1991 O-Pee-Chee Premier	100	1.00	.75	.40
1991 Post Cereal	19	1.00	.70	.40
1991 Score	95	.40	.30	.15
1991 Score	849	.12	.09	.05
1991 Studio	9	.75	.60	.30
1991 Topps	5	.10	.08	.04
1991 Topps	150	.35	.25	.14
1991 Topps All-Star Glossy Set of 22	5	.50	.40	.20
1991 Topps Stadium Club	430	4.00	3.00	1.50
1991 Topps Stadium Club Members Only	(25)	1.00	.70	.40
1991 Upper Deck	347	.50	.40	.20
1991 Upper Deck Final Edition	85	.50	.40	.20
1992 Bowman	400	4.00	3.00	1.50
1992 Donruss	22	.20	.15	.08
1992 Donruss	35	.30	.25	.12
1992 Donruss Diamond Kings	5	4.00	3.00	1.50
1992 Donruss Elite	----	350.00	260.00	140.00
1992 Donruss Triple Play Gallery of Stars	11	5.00	3.75	2.00
1992 Donruss Triple Play	199	.25	.15	.08
1992 Donruss Triple Play	253	.25	.15	.06
1992 Fleer	26	.50	.40	.20
1992 Fleer	703	.15	.11	.06
1992 Fleer	711	.25	.20	.10
1992 Fleer All-Stars	20	4.00	3.00	1.50
1992 Fleer Lumber Co.	7	5.00	3.75	2.00
1992 Fleer Team Leaders	17	16.00	12.00	6.50
1992 Fleer Ultra	11	1.00	.70	.40
1992 Fleer Ultra All-Stars	3	4.00	3.00	1.50
1992 Fleer Ultra Award Winners	5	5.00	3.75	2.00
1992 Fleer Ultra Award Winners	21a	5.00	3.75	2.00
1992 Fleer Ultra Award Winners	21b	5.00	3.75	2.00
1992 Leaf	52	.75	.60	.30
1992 O-Pee-Chee	40	.20	.15	.08
1992 O-Pee-Chee Premier	137	.75	.60	.30
1992 Pinnacle	200	1.00	.70	.40
1992 Pinnacle Rookie Idols	11	20.00	15.00	8.00
1992 Pinnacle Slugfest	14	5.00	3.75	2.00
1992 Pinnacle Team Pinnacle	7	35.00	26.00	14.00
1992 Post Cereal	9	.75	.60	.30
1992 Score	433	.20	.15	.08
1992 Score	540	.30	.25	.12
1992 Score	788	.20	.15	.08
1992 Score	794	.15	.11	.06
1992 Score	884	.35	.25	.14
1992 Studio	129	.75	.60	.30
1992 Studio Heritage	7	3.50	2.75	1.50
1992 Topps	40	.40	.30	.15
1992 Topps	400	.20	.15	.08
1992 Topps Gold	40	10.00	7.50	4.00
1992 Topps Gold	400	2.00	1.50	.80
1992 Topps Kids	63	.25	.20	.10
1992 Topps Stadium Club	1	1.00	70	.40
1992 Topps Stadium Club	595	.50	.40	.20
1992 Topps Stadium Club Master Photos	(10)	7.50	5.75	3.00
1992 Topps Stadium Club Special Edition	154	.75	.60	.30
1992 Upper Deck	82	.15	.11	.06
1992 Upper Deck	165	.40	.30	.15
1992 Upper Deck	645	.25	.20	.10
1992 Upper Deck FanFest	36	1.00	.70	.40
1992 Upper Deck Home Run Heroes	4	2.00	1.50	.80
1992 Upper Deck MVP Holograms	1	.25	.20	.10
1992 Upper Deck MVP Holograms	44	1.50	1.25	.60
1993 Bowman	225	1.50	1.25	.60
1993 DiamondMarks	(67)	2.00	1.50	.80
1993 Donruss	559	.75	.60	.30
1993 Donruss Elite Dominators	19	150.00	112.00	60.00
1993 Donruss Masters of the Game	6	5.00	3.75	2.00
1993 Donruss MVP's	14	5.00	3.75	2.00
1993 Donruss Triple Play	3	.50	.40	.20
1993 Donruss Triple Play Action Baseball	17	.25	.20	.10
1993 Fleer	551	.75	.60	.30
1993 Fleer Flair	157	4.50	3.50	1.75
1993 Fleer Ultra	501	1.50	1.25	.60
1993 Fleer Ultra All-Stars	14	8.00	6.00	3.25
1993 Fleer Ultra Award Winners	15	8.00	6.00	3.25
1993 Leaf	431	1.50	1.25	.60
1993 Leaf Gold All-Stars	14	3.00	2.25	1.25
1993 Leaf Heading for the Hall	5	7.00	5.25	2.75
1993 Leaf Update Gold All-Stars	6	4.00	3.00	1.50
1993 O-Pee-Chee	352	2.00	1.50	.80
1993 O-Pee-Chee Premier	125	.70	.50	.30
1993 Pinnacle	20	1.50	1.25	.60
1993 Pinnacle	305	.60	.45	.25
1993 Pinnacle	471	.75	.60	.30
1993 Pinnacle Cooperstown	17	.50	.40	.20
1993 Pinnacle Cooperstown Dufex	17	150.00	112.00	60.00
1993 Pinnacle Home Run Club	47	3.00	2.25	1.25
1993 Post Cereal	9	.80	.60	.30
1993 Score	6	.75	.60	.30
1993 Score Select	18	1.50	1.25	.60
1993 Score Select Chase Stars	15	28.00	21.00	11.00
1993 Score The Franchise	1	15.00	11.00	6.00
1993 Studio	80	1.50	1.25	.60
1993 Topps	300	.75	.60	.30
1993 Topps Finest	96	22.00	16.50	8.75
1993 Topps Finest Jumbo All-Stars	96	45.00	34.00	18.00
1993 Topps Finest Refractors	96	800.00	600.00	320.00
1993 Topps Full Shot Super	11	9.00	6.75	3.50
1993 Topps Gold	300	1.75	1.25	.70
1993 Topps Stadium Club	40	1.50	1.25	.60
1993 Topps Stadium Club First Day Production	40	100.00	75.00	40.00
1993 Topps Stadium Club Master Photos	(7)	6.00	4.50	2.50
1993 Topps Stadium Club Special	141	.75	.60	.30
1993 Upper Deck	36	.30	.25	.12
1993 Upper Deck	44	.20	.15	.08
1993 Upper Deck	585	.75	.60	.30
1993 Upper Deck Diamond Gallery	16	4.00	3.00	1.50
1993 Upper Deck Fun Packs All-Star Scratch-Off	6	4.00	3.00	1.50
1993 Upper Deck Fun Packs	32	.25	.20	.10
1993 Upper Deck Fun Packs	130	.25	.20	.10

Set	Card #	NM	EX	VG
1993 Upper Deck Fun Packs	135	.75	.60	.30
1993 Upper Deck Fun Packs	218	.50	.40	.20
1993 Upper Deck Iooss Collection	15	2.50	2.00	1.00
1993 Upper Deck Iooss Collection Super	15	6.00	4.50	2.50
1993 Upper Deck SP	8	6.00	4.50	2.50
1993 Upper Deck Then And Now	4	6.00	4.50	2.00
1993 Upper Deck Triple Crown	7	5.00	3.75	2.00
1994 Bowman	75	1.50	1.25	.60
1994 Bowman's Best	94	3.00	2.25	1.25
1994 Bowman's Best	71	6.00	4.50	2.50
1994 Bowman's Best Refractors	94	10.00	7.50	4.00
1994 Bowman's Best Refractors	71	65.00	49.00	26.00
1994 Donruss	40	1.50	1.25	.60
1994 Donruss	140	.05	.04	.02
1994 Donruss Anniversary-1984	6	10.00	7.50	4.00
1994 Donruss MVP's	15	6.00	4.50	2.50
1994 Donruss Special Edition - Gold	40	2.00	1.50	.80
1994 Donruss Triple Play Nicknames	6	6.00	4.50	2.50
1994 Donruss Triple Play Medalists	7	2.50	2.00	1.00
1994 Donruss Triple Play	159	.60	.45	.25
1994 Fleer	19	1.50	1.25	.60
1994 Fleer All-Stars	21	2.00	1.50	.80
1994 Fleer Extra Bases	12	1.25	.90	.50
1994 Fleer Extra Bases Game Breakers	24	2.50	2.00	1.00
1994 Fleer Flair	8	3.00	2.25	1.25
1994 Fleer Flair Hot Glove	8	40.00	30.00	15.00
1994 Fleer Flair Hot Numbers	8	35.00	26.00	14.00
1994 Fleer Flair Infield Power	8	9.00	6.75	3.50
1994 Fleer Team Leaders	1	3.00	2.25	1.25
1994 Fleer Ultra	9	1.50	1.25	.60
1994 Fleer Ultra All-Stars	4	3.00	2.25	1.25
1994 Fleer Ultra Career Achievement Awards	3	6.00	4.50	2.50
1994 Fleer Update Diamond Tribute	10	2.00	1.50	.80
1994 Leaf	1	1.50	1.25	.60
1994 Leaf Limited	5	12.00	9.00	4.75
1994 Leaf Limited Gold	7	50.00	38.00	20.00
1994 Leaf MVP Contenders	11a	15.00	11.00	6.00
1994 Leaf MVP Contenders	11b	30.00	22.00	12.00
1994 Leaf Statistical Standouts	10	5.00	3.75	2.00
1994 O-Pee-Chee	185	1.25	.90	.50
1994 O-Pee-Chee All-Star Redemption Cards	15	1.50	1.25	.60
1994 O-Pee-Chee Jumbo All-Stars	15	15.00	11.00	6.00
1994 O-Pee-Chee Jumbo All-Stars Factory Set	15	3.50	2.75	1.50
1994 Pacific Crown	44	1.00	.75	.40
1994 Pacific Crown Jewels of the Crown	15	10.00	7.50	4.00
1994 Pinnacle	50	1.50	1.25	.60
1994 Pinnacle Artist's Proof	50	100.00	75.00	40.00
1994 Pinnacle Museum Collection	50	40.00	30.00	15.00
1994 Pinnacle Team Pinnacle	4	40.00	30.00	15.00
1994 Pinnacle The Naturals Box Set	23	1.50	1.25	.60
1994 Pinnacle Tribute	13	10.00	7.50	4.00
1994 Post Cereal	25	.75	.60	.30
1994 Score	85	1.00	.75	.40
1994 Score Gold Stars	36	30.00	22.00	12.00
1994 Score Select	249	1.50	1.25	.60
1994 Score Select Salute	1	120.00	90.00	47.50
1994 Sportflics 2000	69	2.00	1.50	.80
1994 Sportflics 2000	179	.60	.45	.25
1994 Studio	127	1.25	.90	.50
1994 Studio Gold Stars	7	50.00	38.00	20.00
1994 Studio Silver Stars	7	25.00	18.00	10.00
1994 Topps	200	.75	.60	.30
1994 Topps	387	.20	.15	.08
1994 Topps	604	.30	.25	.12
1994 Topps Black Gold	18	1.25	.90	.50
1994 Topps Finest	235	10.00	7.50	4.00
1994 Topps Finest Refractors	235	80.00	60.00	32.00
1994 Topps Finest Superstars	235	22.00	16.50	8.75
1994 Topps Gold	200	3.00	2.25	1.25
1994 Topps Gold	387	.60	.45	.25
1994 Topps Gold	604	1.00	.70	.40
1994 Topps Stadium Club	373	1.50	1.25	.60
1994 Topps Stadium Club Dugout Dirt	4	2.00	1.50	.80
1994 Topps Stadium Club First Day Production	373	60.00	45.00	24.00
1994 Upper Deck	281	1.00	.75	.40
1994 Upper Deck	425	1.50	1.25	.60
1994 Upper Deck All-Stars Green Foil	15	1.00	.70	.40
1994 Upper Deck All-Stars Gold Foil	15	5.00	3.75	2.00
1994 Upper Deck Collector's Choice	240	.60	.45	.25
1994 Upper Deck Collector's Choice	343	.20	.15	.08
1994 Upper Deck Diamond Collection	9E	20.00	15.00	8.00
1994 Upper Deck Electric Diamond	281	2.50	2.00	1.00
1994 Upper Deck Electric Diamond	425	4.00	3.00	1.50
1994 Upper Deck Fun Packs	108	.75	.60	.30
1994 Upper Deck Fun Packs	180	.40	.30	.15
1994 Upper Deck Fun Packs	219	.90	.70	.35
1994 Upper Deck SP	126	2.50	2.00	1.00
1994 Upper Deck SP Baseball Die-Cut	126	7.00	5.25	2.75
1994 Upper Deck SP Holoview Blue	32	18.00	13.50	7.25
1994 Upper Deck SP Holoview Red	32	110.00	80.00	40.00
1994 Upper Deck SP Insert	5	18.00	13.50	7.25

Mickey Rivers

Set	Card #	NM	EX	VG
1972 O-Pee-Chee	272	1.25	.60	.40

1972 Topps	272 (R)	1.00	.50	.30
1973 O-Pee-Chee	597	3.50	1.75	1.00
1973 Topps	597	2.00	1.00	.60
1974 O-Pee-Chee	76	.60	.30	.20
1974 Topps	76	.30	.15	.09
1975 O-Pee-Chee	164	.55	.30	.15
1975 Topps	164	.30	.15	.09
1975 Topps Mini	164	.60	.30	.20
1976 O-Pee-Chee	85	.35	.20	.11
1976 O-Pee-Chee	198	.40	.20	.12
1976 Topps	85	.25	.13	.08
1976 Topps	198	1.00	.50	.30
1976 Topps Traded	85T	.25	.13	.08
1977 O-Pee-Chee	69	.30	.15	.09
1977 Topps	305	.20	.10	.06
1978 O-Pee-Chee	182	.25	.13	.08
1978 Topps	690	.25	.13	.08
1979 O-Pee-Chee	24	.25	.13	.08
1979 Topps	60	.20	.10	.06
1980 O-Pee-Chee	251	.15	.08	.05
1980 Topps	485	.20	.10	.06

Set	Card #	MT	NM	EX
1981 Donruss	496	.08	.06	.03
1981 Fleer	617	.08	.06	.03
1981 O-Pee-Chee	145	.12	.09	.05
1981 Topps	145	.10	.08	.04
1982 Donruss	242	.08	.06	.03
1982 Fleer	328	.08	.06	.03
1982 O-Pee-Chee	51	.12	.09	.05
1982 O-Pee-Chee	356	.12	.09	.05
1982 Topps	704	.10	.08	.04
1982 Topps	705	.10	.08	.04
1983 Donruss	394	.08	.06	.03
1983 Fleer	576	.08	.06	.03
1983 O-Pee-Chee	224	.12	.09	.05
1983 Topps	224	.10	.08	.04
1984 Donruss	465	.12	.09	.05
1984 Fleer	425	.10	.08	.04
1984 O-Pee-Chee	269	.20	.15	.08
1984 Topps	504	.10	.08	.04
1985 Donruss	465	.10	.08	.04
1985 Fleer	565	.08	.06	.03
1985 Leaf-Donruss	35	.08	.06	.03
1985 O-Pee-Chee	371	.08	.06	.03
1985 Topps	371	.08	.06	.03
1990 Pacific Senior League	163	.05	.04	.02
1990 Topps Senior League	115	.10	.08	.04

Phil Rizzuto

Set	Card #	NM	EX	VG
1948 Bowman	8	260.00	130.00	80.00
1949 Bowman	98a	125.00	62.50	37.50
1949 Bowman	98b	170.00	85.00	50.00
1950 Bowman	11	155.00	77.50	46.00
1951 Bowman	26	120.00	60.00	35.00
1951 Topps Red Backs	5	45.00	22.50	13.50

1952 Bowman	52	90.00	45.00	27.00
1952 Topps	11	140.00	70.00	32.00
1953 Bowman Color	9	110.00	55.00	33.00
1953 Bowman Color	93	200.00	100.00	60.00
1953 Red Man Tobacco	10A	65.00	32.00	19.50
1953 Topps	114	150.00	75.00	34.00
1954 Bowman	1	125.00	62.50	37.50
1954 Red Man Tobacco	17A	75.00	37.00	22.00
1954 Topps	17	60.00	30.00	18.00
1955 Bowman	10	60.00	30.00	18.00
1955 Topps	189	140.00	70.00	42.00
1956 Topps	113	65.00	32.00	19.50
1956 Topps Pins	(41)	40.00	20.00	12.00
1961 Topps	471	15.00	7.50	4.50

Set	Card #	MT	NM	EX
1983 Topps 1952 Reprint Set	11	4.00	3.00	1.50
1986 Sportflics Decade Greats	22	.30	.25	.12
1988 Pacific Trading Cards Baseball Legends	10	.20	.15	.08
1990 Pacific Legends	101	.20	.15	.08
1991 "1953" Topps Archives	114	2.00	1.50	.80
1994 "1954" Topps Archives	17	.40	.30	.15

Robin Roberts

Set	Card #	NM	EX	VG
1949 Bowman	46 (R)	240.00	120.00	72.50
1950 Bowman	32	150.00	75.00	45.00
1951 Bowman	3	80.00	40.00	25.00
1952 Bowman	4	55.00	27.00	16.50
1952 Red Man Tobacco	18N	60.00	30.00	18.00
1952 Topps	59	110.00	55.00	25.00
1953 Bowman Color	65	60.00	30.00	18.00
1953 Red Man Tobacco	11N	55.00	27.00	16.50
1954 Bowman	95	35.00	17.50	10.50
1954 Red Man Tobacco	18N	60.00	30.00	18.00
1955 Bowman	171	30.00	15.00	9.00
1956 Topps	180	35.00	17.50	10.50
1957 Topps	15	24.00	12.00	7.25
1958 Topps	90	23.00	11.50	7.00
1959 Topps	156	7.00	3.50	2.00
1959 Topps	352	14.00	7.00	4.25
1960 Topps	264	14.00	7.00	4.25
1961 Post Cereal	117a	9.00	4.50	2.75
1961 Post Cereal	117b	9.00	4.50	2.75
1961 Topps	20	12.00	6.00	3.50
1962 Post Cereal	198	10.00	5.00	3.00
1962 Topps	243	15.00	7.50	4.50
1963 Post Cereal	66	7.50	3.75	2.25
1963 Topps	6	6.50	3.25	2.00
1963 Topps	125	10.00	5.00	3.00
1964 Topps	285	10.00	5.00	3.00
1965 O-Pee-Chee	15	10.25	5.25	3.00
1965 Topps	15	9.00	4.50	2.75
1966 Topps	530	42.00	21.00	12.50

Set	Card #	MT	NM	EX
1983 Topps 1952 Reprint Set	59	2.00	1.50	.80
1988 Pacific Trading Cards Baseball Legends	15	.20	.15	.08
1990 Pacific Legends	47	.15	.11	.06
1991 "1953" Topps Archives	288	.50	.40	.20

Brooks Robinson

Set	Card #	NM	EX	VG
1957 Topps	328 (R)	325.00	160.00	95.00
1958 Topps	307	100.00	50.00	30.00
1959 Topps	439	42.50	21.00	12.50
1960 Leaf	27	40.00	20.00	12.00
1960 Topps	28	45.00	22.00	13.50
1961 Post Cereal	75a	35.00	17.50	10.50
1961 Post Cereal	75b	35.00	17.50	10.50
1961 Topps	10	30.00	15.00	9.00
1961 Topps	572	65.00	32.00	19.50
1962 Post Cereal	29	10.00	5.00	3.00
1962 Topps	45	30.00	15.00	9.00
1962 Topps	468	20.00	10.00	6.00
1963 Fleer	4	60.00	30.00	18.00
1963 Post Cereal	59	10.00	5.00	3.00
1963 Topps	345	60.00	30.00	18.00
1964 Topps	230	35.00	17.50	10.50
1965 O-Pee-Chee	1	21.00	10.50	6.25
1965 O-Pee-Chee	5	30.00	15.00	9.00
1965 O-Pee-Chee	150	32.50	16.00	9.75
1965 Topps	1	15.00	7.50	4.50
1965 Topps	5	30.00	15.00	9.00
1965 Topps	150	22.00	11.00	6.50
1966 Topps	390	30.00	15.00	9.00
1967 O-Pee-Chee	1	25.00	12.50	7.50
1967 Topps	1	20.00	10.00	6.00
1967 Topps	531	12.00	6.00	3.50
1967 Topps	600	225.00	112.00	67.00
1968 O-Pee-Chee	20	30.00	15.00	9.00
1968 Topps	20	20.00	10.00	6.00
1968 Topps	365	6.00	3.00	1.75
1968 Topps	530	10.00	5.00	3.00
1969 Topps	421	6.00	3.00	1.75
1969 Topps	504	4.00	2.00	1.25
1969 Topps	550	20.00	10.00	6.00
1970 O-Pee-Chee	230	15.00	7.50	4.50
1970 O-Pee-Chee	455	2.50	1.25	.70
1970 Topps	230	12.00	6.00	3.50
1970 Topps	455	8.00	4.00	2.50
1971 Topps	300	20.00	10.00	6.00
1972 O-Pee-Chee	498	1.75	.90	.50
1972 Topps	498	2.00	1.00	.60
1972 Topps	550	20.00	10.00	6.00
1973 O-Pee-Chee	90	7.50	3.75	2.25
1973 Topps	90	7.50	3.75	2.25
1974 O-Pee-Chee	160	7.25	3.75	2.25
1974 O-Pee-Chee	334	1.00	.50	.30
1974 Topps	160	9.00	4.50	2.75

Set	Card #	MT	NM	EX
1974 Topps	334	3.00	1.50	.90
1975 O-Pee-Chee	50	6.25	3.25	2.00
1975 O-Pee-Chee	202	2.00	1.00	.60
1975 Topps	50	6.00	3.00	1.75
1975 Topps	202	1.25	.60	.40
1975 Topps Mini	50	10.00	5.00	3.00
1975 Topps Mini	202	1.75	.90	.50
1976 O-Pee-Chee	95	6.00	3.00	1.75
1976 Topps	95	5.00	2.50	1.50
1977 Topps	285	6.00	3.00	1.75
1978 O-Pee-Chee	239	1.00	.50	.30
1978 Topps	4	2.00	1.00	.60

Set	Card #	MT	NM	EX
1986 Sportflics Decade Greats	45	.50	.40	.20
1988 Pacific Trading Cards Baseball Legends	3	.30	.25	.12
1989 Pacific Trading Cards Legends II	129	.30	.25	.12
1990 Pacific Legends	102	.20	.15	.08

Frank Robinson

Set	Card #	NM	EX	VG
1957 Topps	35 (R)	200.00	100.00	55.00
1958 Topps	285	85.00	42.00	25.00
1958 Topps	386	12.00	6.00	3.50
1958 Topps	484	25.00	12.50	7.50
1959 Home Run Derby	(16)	275.00	137.00	82.00
1959 Topps	435	35.00	17.50	10.50
1960 Topps	352	9.00	4.50	2.75
1960 Topps	490	45.00	22.50	13.50
1961 Post Cereal	182a	30.00	15.00	9.00
1961 Post Cereal	182b	30.00	15.00	9.00
1961 Topps	25	8.00	4.00	2.50
1961 Topps	360	35.00	17.50	10.50
1961 Topps	581	75.00	37.00	22.00
1962 Post Cereal	122	25.00	12.50	7.50
1962 Topps	54	12.00	6.00	3.50
1962 Topps	350	48.00	24.00	14.00
1962 Topps	396	18.00	9.00	5.50
1963 Post Cereal	131a	10.00	5.00	3.00
1963 Post Cereal	131b	15.00	7.50	4.50
1963 Topps	1	35.00	17.50	10.50
1963 Topps	3	26.00	13.00	7.75
1963 Topps	400	45.00	22.50	13.50
1964 Topps	260	27.50	13.50	8.25
1965 O-Pee-Chee	120	32.50	16.00	9.75
1965 Topps	120	30.00	15.00	9.00
1966 Topps	219	8.00	4.00	2.50
1966 Topps	310	30.00	15.00	9.00
1967 O-Pee-Chee	1	25.00	12.50	7.50
1967 O-Pee-Chee	62	11.00	5.50	3.25
1967 O-Pee-Chee	100	21.00	10.50	6.25
1967 Topps	1	20.00	10.00	6.00
1967 Topps	100	16.00	8.00	4.75
1967 Topps	239	12.00	6.00	3.50
1967 Topps	241	4.50	2.25	1.25

1967 Topps	243	6.00	3.00	1.75
1968 O-Pee-Chee	2	12.75	6.50	3.75
1968 O-Pee-Chee	4	13.50	6.75	4.00
1968 Topps	2	8.00	4.00	2.50
1968 Topps	4	8.00	4.00	2.50
1968 Topps	373	8.00	4.00	2.50
1968 Topps	454	4.00	2.00	1.25
1968 Topps	500	25.00	12.50	7.50
1968 Topps	530	10.00	5.00	3.00
1969 Topps	250	25.00	12.50	7.50
1970 O-Pee-Chee	463	8.50	4.25	2.50
1970 Topps	463	8.00	4.00	2.50
1970 Topps	700	60.00	30.00	18.00
1971 O-Pee-Chee	640	50.00	25.00	15.00
1971 Topps	640	35.00	17.50	10.50
1972 O-Pee-Chee	88	1.25	.60	.40
1972 O-Pee-Chee	100	6.75	3.50	2.00
1972 Topps	88	3.50	1.75	1.00
1972 Topps	100	6.00	3.00	1.75
1972 Topps	754	35.00	17.50	10.50
1973 O-Pee-Chee	175	6.75	3.50	2.00
1973 Topps	175	7.50	3.75	2.25
1974 O-Pee-Chee	55	6.75	3.50	2.00
1974 Topps	55	7.00	3.50	2.00
1975 O-Pee-Chee	199	3.00	1.50	.90
1975 O-Pee-Chee	204	4.00	2.00	1.25
1975 O-Pee-Chee	331	.60	.30	.20
1975 O-Pee-Chee	580	5.00	2.50	1.50
1975 Topps	199	1.50	.70	.45
1975 Topps	204	2.00	1.00	.60
1975 Topps	331	2.00	1.00	.60
1975 Topps	580	6.00	3.00	1.75
1975 Topps Mini	199	2.25	1.25	.70
1975 Topps Mini	204	2.25	1.25	.70
1975 Topps Mini	331	1.25	.60	.40
1975 Topps Mini	580	7.00	3.50	2.00
1976 O-Pee-Chee	477	.60	.30	.20
1976 Topps	477	.80	.40	.25
1977 Topps	18	2.00	1.00	.60

Set	Card #	MT	NM	EX
1982 Donruss	424	.15	.11	.06
1983 Donruss	564	.12	.09	.05
1983 Donruss	648	.15	.11	.06
1983 Topps	576	.12	.09	.05
1984 Topps	171	.12	.09	.05
1986 Sportflics Decade Greats	41	.30	.25	.12
1986 Topps	404	.15	.11	.06
1988 Topps Traded	96T	.15	.11	.06
1989 Topps	774	.08	.06	.03
1990 O-Pee-Chee	381	.03	.02	.01
1990 Topps	381	.03	.02	.01
1991 Topps	639	.05	.04	.02

Jackie Robinson

Set	Card #	NM	EX	VG
1948 Leaf	79 (R)	900.00	450.00	240.00
1949 Bowman	50 (R)	1000.	500.00	300.00

1950 Bowman	22	675.00	325.00	200.00
1952 Topps	312a	1450.	725.00	333.00
1952 Topps	312b	1450.	725.00	333.00
1953 Topps	1	525.00	262.00	121.00
1954 Topps	10	225.00	110.00	65.00
1955 Topps	50	225.00	110.00	65.00
1956 Topps	30	160.00	80.00	45.00
1973 Topps 1953 Reprints	2	150.00	75.00	45.00

Set	Card #	MT	NM	EX
1983 Topps 1952 Reprint Set	312	15.00	11.00	6.00
1986 Sportflics Decade Greats	28	1.00	.70	.40
1988 Pacific Trading Cards Baseball Legends	40	.50	.40	.20
1991 "1953" Topps Archives	1	4.00	3.00	1.50
1991 "1953" Topps Archives Promos	(8)	24.00	18.00	9.50
1994 "1954" Topps Archives	10	1.00	.70	.40

Pete Rose

Set	Card #	NM	EX	VG
1963 Topps	537	920.00	460.00	276.00
1964 Topps	125	145.00	72.00	43.00
1965 O-Pee-Chee	207	235.00	117.00	70.00
1965 Topps	207	135.00	65.00	40.00
1966 O-Pee-Chee	30	55.00	27.00	16.50
1966 Topps	30	40.00	20.00	12.00
1967 Topps	430	60.00	30.00	18.00
1968 Topps	230	32.00	16.00	9.50
1969 O-Pee-Chee	2	8.50	4.25	2.50
1969 O-Pee-Chee	120	42.50	21.00	12.50
1969 Topps	2	4.00	2.00	1.25
1969 Topps	120	30.00	15.00	9.00
1969 Topps	424	12.00	6.00	3.50
1970 O-Pee-Chee	61	8.50	4.25	2.50
1970 O-Pee-Chee	458	15.00	7.50	4.50
1970 Topps	61	7.00	3.50	2.00
1970 Topps	458	12.00	6.00	3.50
1970 Topps	580	60.00	30.00	18.00
1971 O-Pee-Chee	100	50.00	25.00	15.00
1971 Topps	100	35.00	17.50	10.50
1972 Topps	559	35.00	17.50	10.50
1972 Topps	560	18.00	9.00	5.00
1973 O-Pee-Chee	130	18.00	9.00	5.50
1973 Topps	130	20.00	10.00	6.00
1974 O-Pee-Chee	201	6.75	3.50	2.00
1974 O-Pee-Chee	300	15.00	7.50	4.50
1974 O-Pee-Chee	336	2.00	1.00	.60
1974 Topps	201	4.00	2.00	1.25
1974 Topps	300	15.00	7.50	4.50
1974 Topps	336	2.50	1.25	.70
1975 O-Pee-Chee	211	6.00	3.00	1.75
1975 O-Pee-Chee	320	17.00	8.50	5.00
1975 Topps	211	6.00	3.00	1.75

1975 Topps	320	20.00	10.00	6.00
1975 Topps Mini	211	7.00	3.50	2.00
1975 Topps Mini	320	25.00	12.50	7.50
1976 O-Pee-Chee	240	12.75	6.50	3.75
1976 Topps	240	12.00	6.00	3.50
1977 O-Pee-Chee	240	8.50	4.25	2.50
1977 Topps	450	9.00	4.50	2.75
1978 O-Pee-Chee	100	4.50	2.25	1.25
1978 O-Pee-Chee	240	3.25	1.75	1.00
1978 Topps	5	3.00	1.50	.90
1978 Topps	20	5.00	2.50	1.50
1979 O-Pee-Chee	343	5.00	2.50	1.50
1979 Topps	204	1.50	.70	.45
1979 Topps	650	5.00	2.50	1.50
1980 O-Pee-Chee	282	4.25	2.25	1.25
1980 Topps	4	2.00	1.00	.60
1980 Topps	540	4.00	2.00	1.25

Set	Card #	MT	NM	EX
1981 Donruss	131a	2.25	1.75	.90
1981 Donruss	131b	1.25	.90	.50
1981 Donruss	251	2.00	1.50	.80
1981 Donruss	371	1.50	1.25	.60
1981 Fleer	1	2.00	1.50	.80
1981 Fleer	645a	2.00	1.50	.80
1981 Fleer	645b	2.00	1.50	.80
1981 O-Pee-Chee	180	3.00	2.25	1.25
1981 Topps	180	3.00	2.25	1.25
1981 Topps	205	1.25	.90	.50
1982 Donruss	1	2.00	1.50	.80
1982 Donruss	168	1.50	1.25	.60
1982 Donruss	585	1.00	.75	.40
1982 Fleer	256	1.00	.70	.40
1982 Fleer	640	1.50	1.25	.60
1982 O-Pee-Chee	24	1.00	.70	.40
1982 O-Pee-Chee	337	.75	.60	.30
1982 O-Pee-Chee	361	2.25	1.75	.90
1982 Topps	4	.75	.60	.30
1982 Topps	337	1.00	.70	.40
1982 Topps	636	.50	.40	.20
1982 Topps	780	2.25	1.75	.90
1982 Topps	781	1.00	.70	.40
1983 Donruss	42	1.50	1.25	.60
1983 Fleer	171	1.50	1.25	.60
1983 Fleer	634	.40	.30	.15
1983 O-Pee-Chee	100	2.00	1.50	.80
1983 O-Pee-Chee	101	.70	.50	.30
1983 O-Pee-Chee	373	.60	.45	.25
1983 Topps	100	1.75	1.25	.70
1983 Topps	101	.80	.60	.30
1983 Topps	397	.75	.60	.30
1983 Topps All-Star Glossy Set of 40	14	.90	.70	.35
1984 Donruss	61	4.00	3.00	1.50
1984 Fleer	46	3.00	2.25	1.25
1984 Fleer	636	.50	.40	.20
1984 Fleer Update	102	30.00	22.00	12.00
1984 O-Pee-Chee	300	1.00	.70	.40
1984 Topps	300	1.00	.70	.40
1984 Topps	701	.35	.25	.14
1984 Topps	702	.35	.25	.14
1984 Topps All-Star Glossy Set of 40	1	1.25	.90	.50
1984 Topps Traded	103T	8.00	6.00	3.25
1985 Donruss	254	1.75	1.25	.70
1985 Donruss	641	2.00	1.50	.80
1985 Fleer	550	2.00	1.50	.80
1985 Fleer	640	.75	.60	.30
1985 Leaf-Donruss	144	2.00	1.50	.80
1985 O-Pee-Chee	116	.75	.60	.30
1985 Topps	6	.60	.45	.25
1985 Topps	547	.60	.45	.25
1985 Topps	600	.60	.45	.25
1985 Topps All-Star Glossy Set of 40	10	1.25	.90	.50
1986 Donruss	62	1.00	.70	.40
1986 Donruss	644	.50	.40	.20
1986 Donruss	653	1.00	.70	.40
1986 Donruss All-Stars	34	.60	.45	.25
1986 Fleer	191	.70	.50	.30
1986 Fleer	628	.50	.40	.20

1986 Fleer	638	.50	.40	.20
1986 Leaf	53	1.00	.70	.40
1986 Leaf	209	.30	.25	.12
1986 Leaf	260	1.00	.70	.40
1986 O-Pee-Chee	1	1.00	.70	.40
1986 Sportflics	50	1.50	1.25	.60
1986 Sportflics	51	.70	.50	.30
1986 Sportflics	56	.80	.60	.30
1986 Sportflics	58	.60	.45	.25
1986 Sportflics	69	1.00	.70	.40
1986 Sportflics	130	.50	.40	.20
1986 Sportflics	138	.50	.40	.20
1986 Sportflics	181	.70	.50	.30
1986 Sportflics	182	1.50	1.25	.60
1986 Sportflics Decade Greats	60	1.25	.90	.50
1986 Sportflics Rookies	46	.40	.30	.15
1986 Topps	1	.90	.70	.35
1986 Topps	2	.30	.25	.12
1986 Topps	3	.30	.25	.12
1986 Topps	4	.30	.25	.12
1986 Topps	5	.30	.25	.12
1986 Topps	6	.30	.25	.12
1986 Topps	7	.30	.25	.12
1986 Topps	206	.50	.40	.20
1986 Topps	741	.40	.30	.15
1986 Topps All-Star Glossy Set of 60	51	1.25	.90	.50
1987 Donruss	186	.60	.45	.25
1987 Fleer	213	.60	.45	.25
1987 Fleer All Stars	37	.50	.40	.20
1987 Leaf	129	.50	.40	.20
1987 O-Pee-Chee	200	.50	.40	.20
1987 Sportflics	25	1.00	.70	.40
1987 Topps	200	.40	.30	.15
1987 Topps	281	.10	.08	.04
1987 Topps	393	.25	.20	.10
1987 Topps All-Star Glossy Set of 60	41	.80	.60	.30
1988 Topps	475	.20	.15	.08
1989 Topps	505	.20	.15	.08

Joe Rudi

Set	Card #	NM	EX	VG
1969 Topps	587 (R)	2.00	1.00	.60
1970 O-Pee-Chee	102	1.00	.50	.30
1970 Topps	102	.90	.45	.25
1971 O-Pee-Chee	407	2.50	1.25	.70
1971 Topps	407	2.00	1.00	.60
1972 O-Pee-Chee	209	.75	.40	.25
1972 Topps	209	.75	.40	.25
1973 O-Pee-Chee	360	.75	.40	.25
1973 Topps	360	.40	.20	.12
1974 O-Pee-Chee	264	.60	.30	.20
1974 Topps	264	.30	.15	.09
1975 O-Pee-Chee	45	.55	.30	.15
1975 Topps	45	.40	.20	.12
1976 O-Pee-Chee	475	.35	.20	.11

1976 Topps	475	.25	.13	.08
1977 O-Pee-Chee	206	.30	.15	.09
1977 Topps	155	.25	.13	.08
1978 O-Pee-Chee	28	.25	.13	.08
1978 Topps	635	.20	.10	.06
1979 O-Pee-Chee	134	.25	.13	.08
1979 Topps	267	.20	.10	.06
1980 O-Pee-Chee	289	.15	.08	.05
1980 Topps	556	.20	.10	.06

Set	Card #	MT	NM	EX
1981 Donruss	174	.10	.08	.04
1981 Fleer	272	.10	.08	.04
1981 O-Pee-Chee	362	.12	.09	.05
1981 Topps	701	.12	.09	.05
1981 Topps Traded	826	.20	.15	.08
1982 Donruss	586	.10	.08	.04
1982 Fleer	306	.10	.08	.04
1982 O-Pee-Chee	388	.12	.09	.05
1982 Topps	388	.12	.09	.05
1982 Topps Traded	102T	.20	.15	.08
1983 Donruss	287	.10	.08	.04
1983 Fleer	532	.10	.08	.04
1983 Topps	87	.12	.09	.05

Babe Ruth

Set	Card #	NM	EX	VG
1933 Goudey	53	6000.	2850.	1350.
1933 Goudey	144	4500.	2200.	1275.
1933 Goudey	149	5500.	2750.	1300.
1933 Goudey	181	5500.	2200.	1500.
1935 Goudey	(16)	1900.	950.00	570.00
1948 Leaf	3	2500.	1250.	750.00
1960 Fleer	3	85.00	40.00	24.00
1961-62 Fleer	75	85.00	40.00	24.00
1962 Topps	135	15.00	7.50	4.50
1962 Topps	136	15.00	7.50	4.50
1962 Topps	137	15.00	7.50	4.50
1962 Topps	138	17.50	8.75	5.25
1962 Topps	139c	20.00	10.00	6.00
1962 Topps	140	32.00	16.00	9.50
1962 Topps	141	12.00	6.00	3.50
1962 Topps	142	12.00	6.00	3.50
1962 Topps	143	12.00	6.00	3.50
1962 Topps	144	12.00	6.00	3.50
1972 Topps	626	2.00	1.00	.60
1973 O-Pee-Chee	1	38.00	19.00	11.50
1973 O-Pee-Chee	474	13.50	6.75	4.00
1973 Topps	1	35.00	17.50	10.50
1973 Topps	474	12.00	6.00	3.50
1976 O-Pee-Chee	345	12.75	6.50	3.75
1976 Topps	345	10.00	5.00	3.00

Set	Card #	MT	NM	EX
1986 Sportflics Decade Greats	1	3.50	2.75	1.50
1989 Pacific Trading Cards Legends II	176	1.00	.70	.40
1992 Score	879	.40	.30	.15

Nolan Ryan

Set	Card #	NM	EX	VG
1968 O-Pee-Chee	177	2000.	1000.	600.00
1968 Topps	177 (R)	1200.	600.00	350.00
1969 Topps	533	450.00	225.00	135.00
1970 Topps	712	500.00	250.00	150.00
1971 O-Pee-Chee	513	315.00	157.00	94.00
1971 Topps	513	250.00	125.00	75.00
1972 Topps	595	250.00	125.00	75.00
1973 O-Pee-Chee	67	23.00	11.50	7.00
1973 O-Pee-Chee	220	105.00	52.00	31.00
1973 Topps	67	18.00	9.00	5.50
1973 Topps	220	95.00	47.00	28.00
1974 O-Pee-Chee	20	90.00	45.00	27.00
1974 O-Pee-Chee	207	22.00	11.00	6.50
1974 Topps	20	80.00	40.00	24.00
1974 Topps	207	15.00	7.50	4.50
1975 O-Pee-Chee	5	30.00	15.00	9.00
1975 O-Pee-Chee	7	8.50	4.25	2.50
1975 O-Pee-Chee	312	18.00	9.00	5.50
1975 O-Pee-Chee	500	90.00	45.00	27.00
1975 Topps	5	30.00	15.00	9.00
1975 Topps	7	1.00	.50	.30
1975 Topps	312	9.00	4.50	2.75
1975 Topps	500	85.00	42.00	25.00
1975 Topps Mini	5	15.00	7.50	4.50
1975 Topps Mini	7	.60	.30	.20
1975 Topps Mini	312	2.50	1.25	.70
1975 Topps Mini	500	90.00	45.00	27.00
1976 O-Pee-Chee	330	75.00	37.00	22.00
1976 Topps	330	70.00	35.00	21.00
1977 O-Pee-Chee	6	15.00	7.50	4.50
1977 O-Pee-Chee	65	55.00	27.00	16.50
1977 O-Pee-Chee	264	18.00	9.00	5.50
1977 Topps	6	9.00	4.50	2.75
1977 Topps	234	20.00	10.00	6.00
1977 Topps	650	45.00	22.00	13.50
1978 O-Pee-Chee	6	3.75	2.00	1.25
1978 O-Pee-Chee	105	42.50	21.00	12.50
1978 O-Pee-Chee	241	15.00	7.50	4.50
1978 Topps	6	15.00	7.50	4.50
1978 Topps	206	2.50	1.25	.70
1978 Topps	400	40.00	20.00	12.00
1979 O-Pee-Chee	51	32.00	16.00	9.50
1979 Topps	6	4.00	2.00	1.25
1979 Topps	115	32.00	16.00	9.50
1979 Topps	417	4.00	2.00	1.25
1980 O-Pee-Chee	303	21.00	10.50	6.25
1980 Topps	206	3.00	1.50	.90
1980 Topps	580	20.00	10.00	6.00

Set	Card #	MT	NM	EX
1981 Donruss	260	8.00	6.00	3.25
1981 Fleer	57	8.00	6.00	3.25
1981 O-Pee-Chee	240	11.00	8.25	4.50
1981 Topps	240	12.00	9.00	4.75
1982 Donruss	13	4.00	3.00	1.50
1982 Donruss	419	9.00	6.75	3.50
1982 Fleer	229	9.00	6.75	3.50
1982 O-Pee-Chee	90	12.00	9.00	4.75
1982 Topps	5	3.00	2.25	1.25

Set	Number			
1982 Topps	66	.50	.40	.20
1982 Topps	90	12.00	9.00	4.75
1982 Topps	167	1.50	1.25	.60
1983 Donruss	118	8.50	6.50	3.50
1983 Fleer	463	8.00	6.00	3.25
1983 O-Pee-Chee	360	10.25	7.75	4.00
1983 O-Pee-Chee	361	5.00	3.75	2.00
1983 Topps	360	12.00	9.00	4.75
1983 Topps	361	5.00	3.75	2.00
1983 Topps All-Star Glossy Set of 40	28	1.00	.70	.40
1984 Donruss	60	30.00	22.00	12.00
1984 Fleer	239	20.00	15.00	8.00
1984 O-Pee-Chee	66	6.00	4.50	2.50
1984 Topps	4	1.00	.75	.40
1984 Topps	66	.25	.20	.10
1984 Topps	470	7.00	5.25	2.75
1984 Topps	707	.35	.25	.14
1984 Topps All-Star Glossy Set of 40	15	1.50	1.25	.60
1985 Donruss	60	10.00	7.50	4.00
1985 Fleer	359	10.00	7.50	4.00
1985 Leaf-Donruss	216	8.50	6.50	3.50
1985 O-Pee-Chee	63	4.00	3.00	1.50
1985 Topps	7	1.50	1.25	.60
1985 Topps	760	5.00	3.75	2.00
1986 Donruss	258	6.00	4.50	2.50
1986 Fleer	310	6.00	4.50	2.50
1986 Leaf	132	5.00	3.75	2.00
1986 O-Pee-Chee	100	2.50	2.00	1.00
1986 Sportflics	43	2.00	1.50	.80
1986 Sportflics	141	.20	.15	.08
1986 Sportflics	143	1.25	.90	.50
1986 Sportflics	182	1.50	1.25	.60
1986 Sportflics Decade Greats	63	.30	.25	.12
1986 Topps	100	3.00	2.25	1.25
1986 Topps All-Star Glossy Set of 60	45	.50	.40	.20
1987 Donruss	138	2.50	2.00	1.00
1987 Fleer	67	4.00	3.00	1.50
1987 Fleer All Stars	38	1.50	1.25	.60
1987 Leaf	257	2.25	1.75	.90
1987 O-Pee-Chee	155	1.00	.70	.40
1987 Sportflics	125	2.00	1.50	.80
1987 Topps	757	1.25	.90	.50
1988 Donruss	61	.60	.45	.25
1988 Fleer	455	1.50	1.25	.60
1988 Leaf	77	.75	.60	.30
1988 O-Pee-Chee	250	.75	.60	.30
1988 Score	575	.60	.45	.25
1988 Sportflics	39	2.00	1.50	.80
1988 Topps	6	.40	.30	.15
1988 Topps	250	.70	.50	.30
1988 Topps	661	.35	.25	.14
1988 Topps Big Baseball	29	1.25	.90	.50
1989 Bowman	225	.75	.60	.30
1989 Donruss	154	.75	.60	.30
1989 Donruss Traded	19	1.50	1.25	.60
1989 Fleer	368	.75	.60	.30
1989 Fleer Update	67	1.75	1.25	.70
1989 O-Pee-Chee	366	.90	.70	.35
1989 Score	300	.60	.45	.25
1989 Score Traded	2T	1.50	1.25	.60
1989 Sportflics	115	1.00	.70	.40
1989 Topps	530	.50	.40	.20
1989 Topps Traded	106T	1.50	1.25	.60
1989 Upper Deck	145	4.00	3.00	1.50
1989 Upper Deck	669	.60	.45	.25
1989 Upper Deck	774	4.00	3.00	1.50
1990 Bowman	486	.50	.40	.20
1990 Donruss	166	.60	.45	.25
1990 Donruss	659a	2.50	2.00	1.00
1990 Donruss	659b	.50	.40	.20
1990 Donruss	665a	2.50	2.00	1.00
1990 Donruss	665b	.50	.40	.20
1990 Donruss	665c	1.00	.70	.40
1990 Fleer	313	.60	.45	.25
1990 Fleer	636	.10	.08	.04
1990 Fleer Update	131	.70	.50	.30
1990 Leaf	21	7.00	5.25	2.75
1990 Leaf	265	6.00	4.50	2.50
1990 O-Pee-Chee	1	.35	.25	.14
1990 O-Pee-Chee	2	.20	.15	.08
1990 O-Pee-Chee	3	.20	.15	.08
1990 O-Pee-Chee	4	.20	.15	.08
1990 O-Pee-Chee	5	.20	.15	.08
1990 Post Cereal	11	1.50	1.25	.60
1990 Score	250	.60	.45	.25
1990 Score	696	.60	.45	.25
1990 Sportflics	8	1.00	.70	.40
1990 Topps	1	.50	.40	.20
1990 Topps	2	.20	.15	.08
1990 Topps	3	.20	.15	.08
1990 Topps	4	.20	.15	.08
1990 Topps	5	.20	.15	.08
1990 Topps All-Star Glossy Set of 60	2	.90	.70	.35
1990 Topps Big Baseball	171	.50	.40	.20
1990 Upper Deck	34	1.00	.75	.40
1990 Upper Deck	544	1.25	.90	.50
1990 Upper Deck	734a	2.00	1.50	.80
1990 Upper Deck	734b	8.00	6.00	3.25
1991 Bowman	280	.50	.40	.20
1991 Donruss	89	.40	.30	.15
1991 Donruss Elite	----	300.00	220.00	120.00
1991 Fleer	302	.40	.30	.15
1991 Fleer Ultra	355	1.50	1.25	.60
1991 Fleer Ultra	395	.60	.45	.25
1991 Leaf	423	2.50	2.00	1.00
1991 Leaf Gold Rookies	25	3.00	2.25	1.25
1991 O-Pee-Chee Premier	102	1.25	.90	.50
1991 Post Cereal	17	1.50	1.25	.60
1991 Score	4	.50	.40	.20
1991 Score	417	.35	.25	.14
1991 Score	686	.30	.25	.12
1991 Score	701	.30	.25	.12
1991 Score Cooperstown	7	3.00	2.25	1.25
1991 Studio	128	1.25	.90	.50
1991 Topps	1	.40	.30	.15
1991 Topps	6	.25	.20	.10
1991 Topps Stadium Club	200	15.00	11.00	6.00
1991 Topps Stadium Club Charter Members	(24)	2.50	2.00	1.00
1991 Topps Stadium Club Charter Members	(25)	2.50	2.00	1.00
1991 Topps Stadium Club Members Only	(26)	2.00	1.50	.80
1991 Topps Stadium Club Members Only	(27)	2.00	1.50	.80
1991 Topps Stadium Club Nolan Ryan Bronze	----	12.00	9.00	4.75
1991 Upper Deck	345	.75	.60	.30
1991 Upper Deck	----	4.00	3.00	1.50
1992 Bowman	222	8.00	6.00	3.25
1992 Donruss	154	.40	.30	.15
1992 Donruss	555	.20	.15	.08
1992 Donruss	707	.75	.60	.30
1992 Donruss Triple Play	22	.40	.30	.15
1992 Fleer	320	.35	.25	.14
1992 Fleer	682	.20	.15	.08
1992 Fleer	710	.75	.60	.30
1992 Fleer Smoke 'N Heat	5	6.00	4.50	2.50
1992 Fleer Ultra	141	3.00	2.25	1.25
1992 Fleer Ultra	300	.15	.11	.06
1992 Leaf	41	1.25	.90	.50
1992 Leaf Gold Previews	25	12.00	9.00	4.75
1992 O-Pee-Chee	1	.50	.40	.20
1992 O-Pee-Chee	4	.10	.08	.04
1992 O-Pee-Chee Premier	81	.60	.45	.25
1992 Pinnacle	50	2.00	1.50	.80
1992 Pinnacle	281	.15	.11	.06
1992 Pinnacle	294	1.00	.70	.40
1992 Pinnacle	618	.75	.60	.30
1992 Pinnacle Rookie Idols	12	30.00	22.00	12.00
1992 Post Cereal	27	.80	.60	.30
1992 Score	2	.75	.60	.30
1992 Score	425	.30	.25	.12

Set	Card #			
1992 Studio	248	1.50	1.25	.60
1992 Topps	1	.75	.60	.30
1992 Topps	4	.40	.30	.15
1992 Topps Gold	1	15.00	11.00	6.00
1992 Topps Gold	4	4.50	3.50	1.75
1992 Topps Kids	127	.35	.25	.14
1992 Topps Stadium Club	605	1.50	1.25	.60
1992 Topps Stadium Club	770	3.00	2.25	1.25
1992 Topps Stadium Club East Coast National	605	60.00	45.00	24.00
1992 Topps Stadium Club Master Photos	(11)	9.00	6.75	3.50
1992 Upper Deck	92	.40	.30	.15
1992 Upper Deck	655	.60	.45	.25
1992 Upper Deck MVP Holograms	45	2.00	1.50	.80
1993 Bowman	405	4.00	3.00	1.50
1993 DiamondMarks	(114)	3.00	2.25	1.25
1993 DiamondMarks Inserts	(6)	30.00	22.00	12.00
1993 Donruss	423	1.00	.75	.40
1993 Donruss Elite Dominators	10	425.00	319.00	170.00
1993 Donruss Elite Dominators	10	275.00	206.00	110.00
1993 Donruss Elite Supers	20	60.00	45.00	24.00
1993 Donruss Masters of the Game	2	6.00	4.50	2.50
1993 Donruss Triple Play Nicknames	7	7.50	5.75	3.00
1993 Donruss Triple Play	96	.75	.60	.30
1993 Fleer	690	.60	.45	.25
1993 Fleer Final Edition	6DT	4.50	3.50	1.75
1993 Fleer Flair	286	7.50	5.50	3.00
1993 Fleer Ultra	636	2.50	2.00	1.00
1993 Fleer Ultra Strikeout Kings	4	10.00	7.50	4.00
1993 Leaf	115	2.00	1.50	.80
1993 Leaf Gold All-Stars	19	5.00	3.75	2.00
1993 Leaf Heading for the Hall	1	12.00	9.00	4.75
1993 O-Pee-Chee	229	5.00	3.75	2.00
1993 O-Pee-Chee Premier Star Performers	20	2.00	1.50	.80
1993 Pinnacle	75	2.50	2.00	1.00
1993 Pinnacle	290	1.00	.75	.40
1993 Pinnacle Cooperstown	1	1.00	.75	.40
1993 Pinnacle Cooperstown Dufex	1	400.00	300.00	160.00
1993 Pinnacle Tribute	6	10.00	7.50	4.00
1993 Pinnacle Tribute	7	10.00	7.50	4.00
1993 Pinnacle Tribute	8	10.00	7.50	4.00
1993 Pinnacle Tribute	9	10.00	7.50	4.00
1993 Pinnacle Tribute	10	10.00	7.50	4.00
1993 Post Cereal	20	1.00	.70	.40
1993 Score	59	1.00	.75	.40
1993 Score Select	90	1.50	1.25	.60
1993 Score Select Rookie/ Traded Inserts	1NR	150.00	110.00	60.00
1993 Studio	71	2.00	1.50	.80
1993 Studio Silhouettes	10	7.00	5.25	2.75
1993 Topps	700	1.00	.75	.40
1993 Topps Finest	107	40.00	30.00	15.00
1993 Topps Finest Jumbo All-Stars	107	85.00	60.00	45.00
1993 Topps Finest Promos	107	75.00	56.00	30.00
1993 Topps Finest Refractors	107	800.00	600.00	320.00
1993 Topps Gold	700	3.00	2.25	1.25
1993 Topps Stadium Club	353	2.00	1.50	.80
1993 Topps Stadium Club First Day Production	353	300.00	225.00	120.00
1993 Topps Stadium Club Master Photos	(21)	7.00	5.25	2.75
1993 Upper Deck	37	.50	.40	.20
1993 Upper Deck	155	1.00	.75	.40

Set	Card #			
1993 Upper Deck "Highlights"	17	32.00	24.00	13.00
1993 Upper Deck Diamond Gallery	30	5.00	3.75	2.00
1993 Upper Deck Fun Packs	18	2.00	1.50	.80
1993 Upper Deck Fun Packs	26	.75	.60	.30
1993 Upper Deck Fun Packs	33	.60	.45	.25
1993 Upper Deck Fun Packs	160	1.00	.70	.40
1993 Upper Deck Fun Packs	214	.60	.45	.25
1993 Upper Deck Iooss Collection	19	4.00	3.00	1.50
1993 Upper Deck Iooss Collection Super	19	7.50	5.75	3.00
1993 Upper Deck On Deck	20	4.50	3.50	1.75
1993 Upper Deck SP	198	8.00	6.00	3.25
1993 Upper Deck Then And Now	5	9.00	6.75	3.50
1993 Upper Deck 5th Anniversary	5	4.00	3.00	1.50
1993 Upper Deck 5th Anniversary Super	5	7.50	5.75	3.00
1994 Donruss	1	2.50	2.00	1.00
1994 Donruss Anniversary-1984	5	15.00	11.00	6.00
1994 Donruss Special Edition - Gold	1	4.00	3.00	1.50
1994 Fleer	321	1.50	1.25	.60
1994 Fleer Golden Moments	7	4.00	3.00	1.50
1994 Fleer Golden Moments Super	7	12.50	9.50	5.00
1994 Fleer Smoke N' Heat	10	40.00	30.00	15.00
1994 Topps	34	1.00	.75	.40
1994 Topps Gold	34	4.00	3.00	1.50
1994 Topps Stadium Club	34	2.00	1.50	.80
1994 Topps Stadium Club First Day Production	34	150.00	110.00	60.00
1994 Upper Deck Collector's Choice	249	.75	.60	.30
1994 Upper Deck Collector's Choice	320	.15	.11	.06

Bret Saberhagen

Set	Card #	MT	NM	EX
1984 Fleer Update	103	25.00	18.50	10.00
1984 Topps Traded	104T	7.50	5.50	3.00
1985 Donruss	222 (R)	2.50	2.00	1.00
1985 Fleer	212 (R)	2.50	2.00	1.00
1985 O-Pee-Chee	23	1.00	.70	.40
1985 Topps	23 (R)	1.25	.90	.50
1986 Donruss	11	.25	.20	.10
1986 Donruss	100	.60	.45	.25
1986 Donruss Diamond Kings Supers	11	.60	.45	.25

Card	#			
1986 Fleer	19	.40	.30	.15
1986 Leaf	11	.20	.15	.08
1986 O-Pee-Chee	249	.25	.20	.10
1986 Sportflics	10	.15	.11	.06
1986 Sportflics	176	1.00	.70	.40
1986 Sportflics	185	.60	.45	.25
1986 Sportflics	186	.40	.30	.15
1986 Topps	487	.25	.20	.10
1986 Topps	720	.15	.11	.06
1986 Topps All-Star Glossy Set of 60	27	.30	.25	.12
1987 Donruss	132	.12	.09	.05
1987 Fleer	379	.20	.15	.08
1987 Leaf	261	.15	.11	.06
1987 O-Pee-Chee	140	.15	.11	.06
1987 Sportflics	145	.25	.20	.10
1987 Topps	140	.15	.11	.06
1988 Donruss	96	.08	.06	.03
1988 Fleer	268	.10	.08	.04
1988 Fleer	626	.10	.08	.04
1988 Leaf	68	.15	.11	.06
1988 O-Pee-Chee	5	.12	.09	.05
1988 Score	89	.10	.08	.04
1988 Sportflics	15	.20	.15	.08
1988 Topps	141	.12	.09	.05
1988 Topps	540	.10	.08	.04
1988 Topps All-Star Glossy Set of 22	10	.25	.20	.10
1988 Topps Big Baseball	94	.12	.09	.05
1989 Bowman	111	.10	.08	.04
1989 Donruss	144	.12	.09	.05
1989 Fleer	291	.15	.11	.06
1989 O-Pee-Chee	157	.08	.06	.03
1989 Score	251	.12	.09	.05
1989 Sportflics	109	.20	.15	.08
1989 Topps	750	.12	.09	.05
1989 Topps Big Baseball	6	.12	.09	.05
1989 Upper Deck	37	.15	.11	.06
1990 Bowman	364	.10	.08	.04
1990 Bowman Inserts	(9)	.08	.06	.03
1990 Donruss	89	.08	.06	.03
1990 Fleer	116	.10	.08	.04
1990 Leaf	72	.30	.25	.12
1990 O-Pee-Chee	350	.10	.08	.04
1990 O-Pee-Chee	393	.10	.08	.04
1990 Score	195a	.25	.20	.10
1990 Score	195b	.30	.25	.12
1990 Sportflics	94	.15	.11	.06
1990 Topps	350	.10	.08	.04
1990 Topps	393	.10	.08	.04
1990 Topps All-Star Glossy Set of 60	13	.20	.15	.08
1990 Topps Big Baseball	21	.15	.11	.06
1990 Upper Deck	326	.08	.06	.03
1991 Bowman	291	.08	.06	.03
1991 Donruss	88	.10	.08	.04
1991 Fleer	567	.10	.08	.04
1991 Fleer Ultra	154	.10	.08	.04
1991 Leaf	118	.15	.11	.06
1991 Score	6	.12	.09	.05
1991 Studio	69	.15	.11	.06
1991 Topps	280	.08	.06	.03
1991 Topps Stadium Club	38	.30	.25	.12
1991 Topps Stadium Club Members Only	(28)	.25	.20	.10
1991 Upper Deck	435	.12	.09	.05
1992 Bowman	586	.40	.30	.15
1992 Donruss	128	.10	.08	.04
1992 Donruss	434	.08	.06	.03
1992 Fleer	167	.08	.06	.03
1992 Fleer Ultra	537	.10	.08	.04
1992 Leaf	376	.15	.11	.06
1992 O-Pee-Chee	75	.08	.06	.03
1992 O-Pee-Chee Premier	82	.15	.11	.06
1992 Pinnacle	442	.10	.08	.04
1992 Score	6	.08	.06	.03
1992 Score	786	.06	.05	.02
1992 Score Rookie & Traded	20	.08	.06	.03
1992 Studio	69	.15	.11	.06
1992 Topps	75	.08	.06	.03
1992 Topps Gold	75	.35	.25	.14
1992 Topps Kids	107	.05	.04	.02
1992 Topps Stadium Club	755	.15	.11	.06
1992 Topps Traded	97	.08	.06	.03
1992 Topps Traded Gold	97	.25	.20	.10
1992 Upper Deck	233	.06	.05	.02
1992 Upper Deck	751	.05	.04	.02
1993 Bowman	510	.10	.08	.04
1993 Donruss	222	.08	.06	.03
1993 Donruss Triple Play	124	.07	.05	.03
1993 Fleer	93	.08	.06	.03
1993 Fleer Flair	96	.25	.15	.08
1993 Fleer Ultra	79	.10	.08	.04
1993 Leaf	93	.10	.08	.04
1993 O-Pee-Chee	302	.15	.11	.06
1993 Pinnacle	185	.06	.05	.02
1993 Score	115	.08	.06	.03
1993 Score Select	123	.12	.09	.05
1993 Studio	112	.08	.06	.03
1993 Topps	600	.03	.02	.01
1993 Topps Finest	53	1.00	.70	.40
1993 Topps Finest Refractors	53	20.00	15.00	8.00
1993 Topps Gold	600	.10	.08	.04
1993 Topps Stadium Club	335	.10	.08	.04
1993 Topps Stadium Club First Day Production	335	5.00	3.75	2.00
1993 Upper Deck	282	.08	.06	.03
1993 Upper Deck Fun Packs	129	.12	.09	.05
1993 Upper Deck SP	153	.15	.11	.06
1994 Bowman	16	.10	.08	.04
1994 Donruss	298	.05	.04	.02
1994 Donruss Triple Play	148	.05	.04	.02
1994 Fleer	576	.05	.04	.02
1994 Fleer Extra Bases	323	.10	.08	.04
1994 Fleer Extra Bases Pitcher's Duel	8M	.40	.30	.15
1994 Fleer Flair	409	.20	.15	.08
1994 Fleer Ultra	534	.10	.08	.04
1994 Leaf	437	.10	.08	.04
1994 Leaf Limited	132	1.00	.70	.40
1994 O-Pee-Chee	46	.05	.04	.02
1994 Pacific Crown	416	.05	.04	.02
1994 Pinnacle	203	.10	.08	.04
1994 Pinnacle Artist's Proof	203	3.00	2.25	1.25
1994 Pinnacle Museum Collection	203	1.50	1.25	.60
1994 Score	92	.04	.03	.02
1994 Score Select	101	.10	.08	.04
1994 Studio	119	.10	.08	.04
1994 Topps	245	.04	.03	.02
1994 Topps Finest	419	.50	.40	.20
1994 Topps Finest Refractors	419	3.50	2.75	1.50
1994 Topps Gold	245	.15	.11	.06
1994 Topps Stadium Club	368	.10	.08	.04
1994 Topps Stadium Club First Day Production	368	2.50	2.00	1.00
1994 Upper Deck	428	.10	.08	.04
1994 Upper Deck Collector's Choice	250	.05	.04	.02
1994 Upper Deck Electric Diamond	428	.25	.20	.10
1994 Upper Deck SP	120	.15	.11	.06
1994 Upper Deck SP Baseball Die-Cut	120	.25	.20	.10

* * *

When buying a card that is in a holder, ask the owner to take it out of its case. The case could be hiding creases, or scratches, which may appear to be on the case but are really on the card.

* * *

Ryne Sandberg

Set	Card #	MT	NM	EX
1983 Donruss	277 (R)	40.00	30.00	16.00
1983 Fleer	507 (R)	30.00	22.00	12.00
1983 O-Pee-Chee	83	42.50	32.00	17.00
1983 Topps	83 (R)	45.00	34.00	18.00
1984 Donruss	311	25.00	18.50	10.00
1984 Fleer	504	18.00	13.50	7.25
1984 O-Pee-Chee	64	6.25	4.75	2.50
1984 Topps	596	7.00	5.50	3.00
1985 Donruss	1	4.00	3.00	1.50
1985 Donruss	67	10.00	7.50	4.00
1985 Donruss Diamond Kings Supers	1	4.00	3.00	1.50
1985 Fleer	65	8.00	6.00	3.25
1985 Fleer	630	2.00	1.50	.80
1985 Leaf-Donruss	1	3.00	2.25	1.25
1985 O-Pee-Chee	296	3.25	2.50	1.25
1985 Topps	460	3.00	2.25	1.25
1985 Topps	713	1.00	.70	.40
1985 Topps All-Star Glossy Set of 22	3	.50	.40	.20
1985 Topps All-Star Glossy Set of 40	21	.75	.60	.30
1986 Donruss	67	4.50	3.50	1.75
1986 Fleer	378	4.00	3.00	1.50
1986 Leaf	62	4.25	3.25	1.75
1986 O-Pee-Chee	19	1.75	1.25	.70
1986 Sportflics	20	2.00	1.50	.80
1986 Sportflics	51	.70	.50	.30
1986 Sportflics	127	.25	.20	.10
1986 Topps	690	2.00	1.50	.80
1986 Topps All-Star Glossy Set of 60	34	.40	.30	.15
1987 Donruss	77	2.50	2.00	1.00
1987 Fleer	572	3.00	2.25	1.25
1987 Fleer	639	.12	.09	.05
1987 Leaf	234	1.25	.90	.50
1987 O-Pee-Chee	143	.85	.60	.35
1987 Sportflics	8	3.00	2.25	1.25
1987 Sportflics	116	.15	.11	.06
1987 Sportflics	197	.80	.60	.30
1987 Topps	680	1.00	.70	.40
1987 Topps All-Star Glossy Set of 22	3	.50	.40	.20
1988 Donruss	242	.40	.30	.15
1988 Fleer	431	1.00	.70	.40
1988 Fleer	628	.35	.25	.14
1988 Leaf	207	.40	.30	.15
1988 O-Pee-Chee	10	.40	.30	.15
1988 Score	26	.40	.30	.15
1988 Sportflics	12	1.50	1.25	.60
1988 Topps	10	.50	.40	.20
1988 Topps All-Star Glossy Set of 22	14	.75	.60	.30
1988 Topps All-Star Glossy Set of 60	14	.70	.50	.30
1988 Topps Big Baseball	16	.45	.35	.20
1989 Bowman	290	.40	.30	.15
1989 Donruss	105	.40	.30	.15
1989 Fleer	437	.40	.30	.15
1989 O-Pee-Chee	360	.60	.45	.25
1989 Score	35	.40	.30	.15
1989 Sportflics	201	.80	.60	.30
1989 Topps	360	.30	.25	.12
1989 Topps	387	.15	.11	.06
1989 Topps All-Star Glossy Set of 22	14	.25	.20	.10
1989 Topps All-Star Glossy Set of 60	34	.75	.60	.30
1989 Topps Big Baseball	212	.35	.25	.14
1989 Upper Deck	120	1.50	1.25	.60
1989 Upper Deck	675	.30	.25	.12
1990 Bowman	30	.40	.30	.15
1990 Donruss	105	.25	.20	.10
1990 Donruss	692	.25	.20	.10
1990 Donruss MVP	10	.30	.25	.12
1990 Fleer	40	.30	.25	.12
1990 Fleer	625	.25	.20	.10
1990 Fleer	639	.10	.08	.04
1990 Leaf	98	4.00	3.00	1.50
1990 O-Pee-Chee	210	.30	.25	.12
1990 O-Pee-Chee	398	.20	.15	.08
1990 Post Cereal	9	1.00	.70	.40
1990 Score	90	.30	.25	.12
1990 Score	561a	10.00	7.50	4.00
1990 Score	561b	.25	.20	.10
1990 Score	691	.25	.20	.10
1990 Sportflics	54	.80	.60	.30
1990 Topps	210	.30	.25	.12
1990 Topps	398	.20	.15	.08
1990 Topps All-Star Glossy Set of 60	1	.70	.50	.30
1990 Topps All-Star Glossy Set of 22	3	.40	.30	.15
1990 Topps Big Baseball	75	.40	.30	.15
1990 Upper Deck	324	.60	.45	.25
1991 Bowman	377	.25	.20	.10
1991 Bowman	416	.25	.20	.10
1991 Donruss	14	.15	.11	.06
1991 Donruss	404	.20	.15	.05
1991 Donruss	433	.10	.08	.04
1991 Donruss	504	.20	.15	.08
1991 Fleer	431	.25	.20	.10
1991 Fleer	709	.15	.11	.06
1991 Fleer	713	.15	.11	.06
1991 Fleer All Stars	1	2.50	2.00	1.00
1991 Fleer ProVisions	3F	1.00	.70	.40
1991 Fleer Ultra	66	.75	.60	.30
1991 Fleer Ultra Gold	10	1.50	1.25	.60
1991 Leaf	207	.75	.60	.30
1991 O-Pee-Chee Premier	103	.75	.60	.30
1991 Post Cereal	16	1.00	.70	.40
1991 Score	3	.30	.25	.12
1991 Score	665	.15	.11	.06
1991 Score	815	.20	.15	.08
1991 Score	862	.15	.11	.06
1991 Studio	158	.75	.60	.30
1991 Topps	7	.15	.11	.06
1991 Topps	398	.10	.08	.04
1991 Topps	740	.20	.15	.08
1991 Topps All-Star Glossy Set of 22	14	.50	.40	.20
1991 Topps Stadium Club	230	3.50	2.75	1.50
1991 Upper Deck	132	.40	.30	.15
1991 Upper Deck Final Edition	79	.40	.30	.15
1991 Upper Deck Final Edition	93	.30	.25	.12
1991 Upper Deck Silver Sluggers	8	3.00	2.25	1.25
1992 Bowman	300	2.50	2.00	1.00
1992 Donruss	429	.15	.11	.06
1992 Donruss	576	.20	.15	.08
1992 Donruss Triple Play	102	.05	.04	.02
1992 Donruss Triple Play	229	.20	.15	.08
1992 Fleer	389	.25	.20	.10
1992 Fleer All-Stars	14	3.00	2.00	1.00
1992 Fleer Lumber Co.	4	4.00	3.00	1.50
1992 Fleer Ultra	181	1.00	.70	.40
1992 Fleer Ultra All-Stars	12	3.50	2.50	1.25

Card	No.			
1992 Fleer Ultra Award Winners	25	5.00	3.75	2.00
1992 Leaf	317	.50	.30	.15
1992 O-Pee-Chee	110	.20	.15	.08
1992 O-Pee-Chee Premier	34	.30	.25	.12
1992 Pinnacle	10	.75	.60	.30
1992 Pinnacle	617	.40	.30	.15
1992 Pinnacle Rookie Idols	13	18.00	13.50	7.00
1992 Pinnacle Slugfest	9	4.00	3.00	1.50
1992 Pinnacle Team Pinnacle	5	30.00	22.00	12.00
1992 Post Cereal	2	.75	.60	.30
1992 Score	200	.25	.20	.10
1992 Score	442	.25	.20	.10
1992 Score	774	.15	.11	.06
1992 Studio	18	.50	.40	.20
1992 Studio Heritage	1	3.00	2.25	1.25
1992 Topps	110	.35	.25	.14
1992 Topps	387	.10	.08	.04
1992 Topps Gold	110	9.00	6.75	3.50
1992 Topps Gold	387	2.00	1.50	.80
1992 Topps Kids	1	.25	.20	.10
1992 Topps Stadium Club	50	1.00	.70	.40
1992 Topps Stadium Club	600	.60	.45	.25
1992 Topps Stadium Club Special Edition	162	.75	.60	.30
1992 Upper Deck	145	.25	.20	.10
1992 Upper Deck MVP Holograms	46	1.00	.75	.40
1993 Bowman	200	.75	.60	.30
1993 DiamondMarks	(10)	2.00	1.50	.80
1993 Donruss	344	.40	.30	.15
1993 Donruss Diamond Kings	2	4.00	3.00	1.50
1993 Donruss Elite	20	90.00	67.00	36.00
1993 Donruss Elite Dominators	1	125.00	94.00	50.00
1993 Donruss Elite Supers	2	30.00	22.00	12.00
1993 Donruss Long Ball Leaders	15	10.00	7.50	4.00
1993 Donruss Masters of the Game	5	5.00	3.75	2.00
1993 Donruss MVP's	22	3.00	2.25	1.25
1993 Donruss Spirit of the Game	14	5.00	3.75	2.00
1993 Donruss Triple Play Nicknames	3	3.50	2.75	1.50
1993 Donruss Triple Play Action Baseball	4	.25	.20	.10
1993 Donruss Triple Play	10	.40	.30	.15
1993 Fleer	25	.40	.30	.15
1993 Fleer	356	.15	.11	.06
1993 Fleer Flair	20	3.00	2.25	1.25
1993 Fleer NL Team Leaders	6	12.00	9.00	4.75
1993 Fleer Ultra	320	1.00	.75	.40
1993 Fleer Ultra All-Stars	3	5.00	3.75	2.00
1993 Leaf	224	1.00	.75	.40
1993 Leaf Gold All-Stars	4	4.00	3.00	1.50
1993 Leaf Heading for the Hall	8	6.00	4.50	2.50
1993 Leaf Update Gold All-Stars	4	4.00	3.00	1.50
1993 O-Pee-Chee	274	1.50	1.25	.60
1993 O-Pee-Chee Premier Star Performers	4	.60	.45	.25
1993 Pinnacle	15	1.00	.75	.40
1993 Pinnacle Cooperstown	8	.50	.40	.20
1993 Pinnacle Cooperstown Dufex	8	150.00	112.00	60.00
1993 Pinnacle Home Run Club	12	3.00	2.25	1.25
1993 Pinnacle Slugfest	27	4.00	3.00	1.50
1993 Post Cereal	13	.80	.60	.30
1993 Score	4	.40	.30	.15
1993 Score	530	.25	.20	.10
1993 Score Select	97	.75	.60	.30
1993 Score Select Chase Stars	2	15.00	11.00	6.00
1993 Score Select Stat Leaders	11	.40	.30	.15
1993 Score The Franchise	16	10.00	7.50	4.00
1993 Studio	176	1.00	.75	.40
1993 Topps	3	.30	.25	.12
1993 Topps	402	.15	.11	.06
1993 Topps Black Gold	17	.90	.70	.35
1993 Topps Finest	105	13.00	9.75	5.25
1993 Topps Finest Jumbo All-Stars	105	45.00	30.00	20.00
1993 Topps Finest Refractors	105	250.00	185.00	100.00
1993 Topps Gold	3	.60	.45	.25
1993 Topps Gold	402	.30	.25	.12
1993 Topps Stadium Club	366	1.00	.75	.40
1993 Topps Stadium Club	600	.50	.40	.20
1993 Topps Stadium Club First Day Production	366	45.00	34.00	18.00
1993 Topps Stadium Club First Day Production	600	45.00	34.00	18.00
1993 Topps Stadium Club II Inserts	3	10.00	7.50	4.00
1993 Topps Stadium Club Special Master Photo	(9)	2.00	1.50	.80
1993 Topps Stadium Club Special	44	.30	.25	.12
1993 Upper Deck	38	.25	.20	.10
1993 Upper Deck	175	.35	.25	.14
1993 Upper Deck	483	.15	.11	.06
1993 Upper Deck	735	.06	.05	.02
1993 Upper Deck Clutch Performers	18	2.00	1.50	.80
1993 Upper Deck Diamond Gallery	8	4.00	3.00	1.50
1993 Upper Deck Fun Packs All-Star Scratch-Off	4	3.00	2.25	1.25
1993 Upper Deck Fun Packs	19	.75	.60	.30
1993 Upper Deck Fun Packs	80	.25	.20	.10
1993 Upper Deck Fun Packs	84	.75	.60	.30
1993 Upper Deck Home Run Heroes	11	2.00	1.50	.80
1993 Upper Deck On Deck	22	2.00	1.50	.80
1993 Upper Deck SP	17	4.00	3.00	1.50
1993 Upper Deck SP Platinum Power	17	25.00	18.00	10.00
1993 Upper Deck Then And Now	6	5.00	3.75	2.00
1994 Bowman	250	.75	.60	.30
1994 Bowman	388	.75	.60	.30
1994 Donruss	18	.75	.60	.30
1994 Donruss	110	.05	.04	.02
1994 Donruss Anniversary-1984	9	7.00	5.25	2.75
1994 Donruss Special Edition - Gold	18	1.00	.75	.40
1994 Donruss Triple Play Nicknames	2	4.00	3.00	1.50
1994 Donruss Triple Play Medalists	6	2.00	1.50	.80
1994 Donruss Triple Play	77	.35	.25	.14
1994 Fleer	396	.60	.45	.25
1994 Fleer All-Stars	48	1.50	1.25	.60
1994 Fleer Flair	141	2.50	2.00	1.00
1994 Fleer Flair Hot Numbers	9	20.00	15.00	8.00
1994 Fleer Team Leaders	16	2.00	1.50	.80
1994 Fleer Ultra	166	.75	.60	.30
1994 Fleer Ultra All-Stars	13	2.00	1.50	.80
1994 Fleer Ultra Career Achievement Awards	4	5.00	3.75	2.00
1994 Leaf	425	1.00	.75	.40
1994 Leaf Slide Show	4	7.50	5.50	3.00
1994 O-Pee-Chee	16	.75	.60	.30

Deion Sanders

1994 O-Pee-Chee All-Star Redemption Cards	7	1.50	1.25	.60
1994 O-Pee-Chee Jumbo All-Stars	7	15.00	11.00	6.00
1994 O-Pee-Chee Jumbo All-Stars Factory Set	7	3.00	2.25	1.25
1994 Pacific Crown	109	.60	.45	.25
1994 Pacific Crown Jewels of the Crown	26	7.00	5.50	3.00
1994 Pinnacle	6	1.00	.70	.40
1994 Pinnacle Artist's Proof	6	75.00	60.00	30.00
1994 Pinnacle Museum Collection	6	20.00	15.00	8.00
1994 Pinnacle The Naturals Box Set	14	1.00	.75	.40
1994 Score	20	.50	.40	.20
1994 Score Select	32	1.00	.70	.40
1994 Sportflics 2000	45	1.00	.75	.40
1994 Sportflics 2000 Movers	2	15.00	11.00	6.00
1994 Studio	63	.75	.60	.30
1994 Studio Heritage	5	3.00	2.25	1.25
1994 Topps	300	.40	.30	.15
1994 Topps	602	.10	.08	.04
1994 Topps Finest	210	5.00	3.75	2.00
1994 Topps Finest Refractors	210	45.00	30.00	15.00
1994 Topps Finest Superstars	210	15.00	11.00	6.00
1994 Topps Gold	300	1.50	1.25	.60
1994 Topps Gold	602	.25	.20	.10
1994 Topps Stadium Club	397	.60	.45	.25
1994 Topps Stadium Club	719	.40	.30	.15
1994 Topps Stadium Club First Day Production	397	45.00	34.00	18.00
1994 Topps Stadium Club First Day Production	719	20.00	15.00	8.00
1994 Upper Deck	92	.75	.60	.30
1994 Upper Deck All-Stars Green Foil	5	1.00	.70	.40
1994 Upper Deck All-Stars Gold Foil	5	5.00	3.75	2.00
1994 Upper Deck Collector's Choice	335	.10	.08	.04
1994 Upper Deck Collector's Choice	555	.20	.15	.08
1994 Upper Deck Diamond Collection	6C	20.00	15.00	8.00
1994 Upper Deck Electric Diamond	92	4.00	3.00	1.50
1994 Upper Deck Fun Packs	60	.40	.30	.15
1994 Upper Deck SP	71	1.50	1.25	.60
1994 Upper Deck SP Baseball Die-Cut	71	4.00	3.00	1.50

* * *

Milwaukee Brewer outfielder Gorman Thomas, about his favorite T-shirt: "There's a favorite T-shirt that I wear that I save only for the second half of the season. It says, "Stormin' Gorman" and "Bambi's No. 1 Bomber." I've had it since '78 and it's in threads. It has been resewed 15 or 20 times."

* * *

Basketball star Terry Porter, about his 1989 Starting Lineup Kenner figure of himself: "(Laughs) Huh? I've never seen this one! Geez, is this supposed to be me? This guy has too much hair!"

* * *

Set	Card #	MT	NM	EX
1989 Fleer Update	53	3.50	2.75	1.50
1989 Topps Traded	110T	2.50	2.00	1.00
1990 Donruss	427 (R)	.75	.60	.30
1990 Fleer	454 (R)	.75	.60	.30
1990 Leaf	359	8.00	6.00	3.25
1990 O-Pee-Chee	61	.35	.25	.14
1990 Score	586 (R)	.75	.60	.30
1990 Sportflics	221	.70	.50	.30
1990 Topps	61 (R)	.60	.45	.25
1990 Upper Deck	13 (R)	2.50	2.00	1.00
1991 Bowman	588	.25	.20	.10
1991 Leaf	436	.75	.60	.30
1991 Score Traded	34	.50	.40	.20
1991 Topps Stadium Club	442	3.50	2.75	1.50
1991 Upper Deck	352	.50	.40	.20
1991 Upper Deck	743	.40	.30	.15
1992 Bowman	160	2.00	1.50	.80
1992 Donruss	564	.08	.06	.03
1992 Donruss Triple Play	186	.20	.15	.08
1992 Fleer	338	.40	.30	.15
1992 Fleer Ultra	464	.75	.60	.30
1992 Fleer Ultra All-Stars	17	3.00	2.25	1.25
1992 Leaf	448	.50	.40	.20
1992 O-Pee-Chee	645	.12	.09	.05
1992 O-Pee-Chee Premier	91	.40	.30	.15
1992 Pinnacle	170	.50	.40	.20
1992 Pinnacle Team 2000	31	1.00	.75	.40
1992 Score	571	.10	.08	.04
1992 Studio	9	.40	.30	.15
1992 Topps	645	.15	.11	.06
1992 Topps Gold	645	.50	.40	.20
1992 Topps Stadium Club	15	.50	.40	.20
1992 Topps Stadium Club Master Photos	(12)	3.50	2.75	1.50
1992 Upper Deck	247	.25	.20	.10
1993 Bowman	438	.50	.40	.20
1993 DiamondMarks	(6)	1.00	.70	.40
1993 Donruss	158	.30	.25	.12
1993 Donruss Masters of the Game	16	3.00	2.25	1.25
1993 Donruss Triple Play Nicknames	8	2.00	1.50	.80
1993 Donruss Triple Play Action Baseball	9	.20	.15	.08
1993 Donruss Triple Play	162	.15	.11	.06
1993 Fleer	13	.30	.25	.12
1993 Fleer Flair	10	1.50	1.25	.60
1993 Fleer Ultra	12	.40	.30	.15
1993 Leaf	222	.60	.45	.25
1993 O-Pee-Chee	372	.75	.60	.30
1993 O-Pee-Chee Premier Star Performers	10	.20	.15	.08
1993 Pinnacle	4	.40	.30	.15
1993 Score	123	.30	.25	.12
1993 Score Select	84	.50	.40	.20
1993 Score Select Stat Leaders	22	.20	.15	.08
1993 Topps	795	.03	.02	.01
1993 Topps Finest	141	7.00	5.25	2.75

1993 Topps Finest Refractors	141	50.00	37.00	20.00
1993 Topps Gold	795	.10	.08	.04
1993 Topps Stadium Club	408	.50	.40	.20
1993 Topps Stadium Club First Day Production	408	15.00	11.00	6.00
1993 Upper Deck	166	.30	.25	.12
1993 Upper Deck Fun Packs	34	.15	.11	.06
1993 Upper Deck Fun Packs	67	.20	.15	.08
1993 Upper Deck Fun Packs	219	.35	.25	.14
1993 Upper Deck SP	62	2.00	1.50	.80
1994 Bowman	301	.40	.30	.15
1994 Bowman's Best	38	2.00	1.50	.80
1994 Bowman's Best Refractors	38	10.00	7.50	4.00
1994 Donruss	430	.40	.30	.15
1994 Donruss Triple Play	49	.10	.07	.04
1994 Fleer	373	.25	.20	.10
1994 Fleer Extra Bases	239	.25	.20	.10
1994 Fleer Flair	371	.75	.60	.30
1994 Fleer Ultra	156	.40	.30	.15
1994 Fleer Update	121	.50	.40	.20
1994 Leaf	101	.40	.30	.15
1994 Leaf Limited	98	3.50	2.75	1.50
1994 Leaf MVP Contenders	13a	5.00	3.75	2.00
1994 Leaf MVP Contenders	13b	10.00	7.50	4.00
1994 O-Pee-Chee	118	.25	.20	.10
1994 Pacific Crown	21	.25	.20	.10
1994 Pinnacle	174	.40	.30	.15
1994 Pinnacle Artist's Proof	174	10.00	7.50	4.00
1994 Pinnacle Museum Collection	174	4.00	3.00	1.50
1994 Score	496	.30	.25	.12
1994 Score Gold Stars	6	9.00	6.75	3.50
1994 Score Rookie & Traded Changing Places	10	4.00	3.00	1.50
1994 Score Rookie & Traded Gold Rush	57	1.00	.75	.40
1994 Score Rookie and Traded	57	.35	.25	.14
1994 Score Select	305	.50	.40	.20
1994 Sportflics 2000	108	.40	.30	.15
1994 Studio	172	.10	.08	.04
1994 Topps	375	.25	.20	.10
1994 Topps Finest	22	2.00	1.50	.80
1994 Topps Finest Refractors	22	15.00	11.00	6.00
1994 Topps Gold	375	.60	.45	.25
1994 Topps Stadium Club	472	.40	.30	.15
1994 Topps Stadium Club First Day Production	472	12.00	9.00	4.75
1994 Upper Deck	85	.40	.30	.15
1994 Upper Deck Collector's Choice	575	.15	.11	.06
1994 Upper Deck Electric Diamond	85	1.00	.75	.40
1994 Upper Deck Fun Packs	164	.40	.30	.15
1994 Upper Deck SP	162	.60	.45	.25
1994 Upper Deck SP Baseball Die-Cut	162	1.50	1.25	.60

* * *

Scottie Pippen, on the first time he saw himself on a basketball card, his 1988-89 Fleer rookie card: "It was really neat. You always look forward to the opportunity to be on your first card. Once you get on one, you think it's the neatest thing."

* * *

Ron Santo

Set	Card #	NM	EX	VG
1961 Bazooka	3	15.00	7.50	4.50
1961 Post Cereal	196a	4.50	2.25	1.25
1961 Post Cereal	196b	4.50	2.25	1.25
1961 Topps	35 (R)	60.00	30.00	18.00
1962 Bazooka	(34)	15.00	7.50	4.50
1962 Post Cereal	184	3.50	1.75	1.00
1962 Topps	170	14.00	7.00	4.25
1963 Fleer	32	20.00	10.00	6.00
1963 Post Cereal	170	3.50	1.75	1.00
1963 Topps	252	4.50	2.25	1.25
1964 Topps	375	7.00	3.50	2.00
1965 Bazooka	28	10.00	5.00	3.00
1965 O-Pee-Chee	6	3.50	1.75	1.00
1965 O-Pee-Chee	110	2.75	1.50	.80
1965 Topps	6	12.00	6.00	3.50
1965 Topps	110	4.50	2.25	1.25
1966 Topps	39	10.00	5.00	3.00
1966 Topps	290	5.00	2.50	1.50
1967 Bazooka	39	10.00	5.00	3.00
1967 O-Pee-Chee	70	2.25	1.25	.70
1967 Topps	70	2.00	1.00	.60
1968 Bazooka	(24)	8.00	4.00	2.25
1968 Bazooka	(60)	8.00	4.00	2.25
1968 O-Pee-Chee	5	10.25	5.25	3.00
1968 Topps	5	8.00	4.00	2.50
1968 Topps	235	4.00	2.00	1.25
1968 Topps	366	3.50	1.75	1.00
1969 O-Pee-Chee	4	8.50	4.25	2.50
1969 Topps	4	4.00	2.00	1.25
1969 Topps	420	1.50	.70	.45
1969 Topps	570	2.00	1.00	.60
1970 O-Pee-Chee	63	1.75	.90	.50
1970 O-Pee-Chee	454	1.75	.90	.50
1970 Topps	63	3.75	2.00	1.25
1970 Topps	454	1.50	.70	.45
1970 Topps	670	7.50	3.75	2.25
1971 O-Pee-Chee	220	1.50	.70	.45
1971 Topps	220	2.50	1.25	.70
1972 Topps	555	3.00	1.50	.90
1972 Topps	556	2.00	1.00	.60
1973 O-Pee-Chee	115	.75	.40	.25
1973 Topps	115	.75	.40	.25
1974 O-Pee-Chee	270	.60	.30	.20
1974 O-Pee-Chee	334	1.00	.50	.30
1974 Topps	270	.50	.25	.15
1974 Topps	334	3.00	1.50	.90
1974 Topps Traded	270T	2.00	1.50	.80
1975 O-Pee-Chee	35	.55	.30	.15
1975 Topps	35	.50	.25	.15
1975 Topps Mini	35	.80	.40	.25

Set	Card #	MT	NM	EX
1988 Pacific Trading Cards Baseball Legends	97	.10	.08	.04
1990 Pacific Legends	48	.15	.11	.06

Mike Schmidt

Mike Schmidt

Set	Card #	NM	EX	VG
1973 O-Pee-Chee	615	535.00	267.00	160.00
1973 Topps	615 (R)	450.00	225.00	135.00
1974 O-Pee-Chee	283	105.00	52.00	31.00
1974 Topps	283	75.00	37.00	22.00
1975 O-Pee-Chee	70	65.00	32.00	19.50
1975 O-Pee-Chee	307	4.00	2.00	1.25
1975 Topps	70	65.00	32.00	19.50
1975 Topps	307	.90	.45	.25
1975 Topps Mini	70	60.00	30.00	18.00
1975 Topps Mini	307	1.25	.60	.40
1976 O-Pee-Chee	193	2.00	1.00	.60
1976 O-Pee-Chee	480	34.00	17.00	10.00
1976 Topps	193	2.00	1.00	.60
1976 Topps	480	30.00	15.00	9.00
1977 O-Pee-Chee	2	3.00	1.50	.90
1977 O-Pee-Chee	245	20.50	10.00	6.25
1977 Topps	2	1.50	.70	.45
1977 Topps	140	15.00	7.50	4.50
1978 O-Pee-Chee	225	17.00	8.50	5.00
1978 Topps	360	15.00	7.50	4.50
1979 O-Pee-Chee	323	8.50	4.25	2.50
1979 Topps	610	10.00	5.00	3.00
1980 O-Pee-Chee	141	4.25	2.25	1.25
1980 Topps	270	4.00	2.00	1.25

Set	Card #	MT	NM	EX
1981 Donruss	11	2.50	2.00	1.00
1981 Donruss	590	1.00	.70	.40
1981 Fleer	5a	2.00	1.50	.80
1981 Fleer	5b	2.00	1.50	.80
1981 Fleer	640	2.00	1.50	.80
1981 Fleer	645a	2.00	1.50	.80
1981 Fleer	645b	2.00	1.50	.80
1981 O-Pee-Chee	207	2.50	2.00	1.00
1981 Topps	2	.90	.70	.35
1981 Topps	3	.30	.25	.12
1981 Topps	206	1.50	1.25	.60
1981 Topps	540	4.00	3.00	1.50
1982 Donruss	294	2.50	2.00	1.00
1982 Donruss	585	1.00	.75	.40
1982 Fleer	258	2.00	1.50	.80
1982 Fleer	637	.40	.30	.15
1982 Fleer	641	.50	.40	.20
1982 O-Pee-Chee	100	3.00	2.25	1.25
1982 O-Pee-Chee	101	1.50	1.25	.60
1982 O-Pee-Chee	339	.40	.30	.15
1982 Topps	100	3.00	2.25	1.25
1982 Topps	101	1.25	.90	.50
1982 Topps	162	.25	.20	.10
1982 Topps	163	.50	.40	.20
1982 Topps	339	1.00	.75	.40
1983 Donruss	168	2.00	1.50	.80
1983 Fleer	173	2.00	1.50	.80
1983 O-Pee-Chee	300	2.50	2.00	1.00
1983 O-Pee-Chee	301	1.50	1.25	.60
1983 O-Pee-Chee	342	.40	.30	.15
1983 Topps	300	3.50	2.75	1.50
1983 Topps	301	1.00	.70	.40
1983 Topps	399	1.00	.75	.40

Set	Card #			
1983 Topps All-Star Glossy Set of 40	8	.80	.60	.30
1984 Donruss	23a	4.00	3.00	1.50
1984 Donruss	23b	5.00	3.75	2.00
1984 Donruss	183	15.00	11.00	6.00
1984 Fleer	48	8.00	6.00	3.25
1984 O-Pee-Chee	361	2.25	1.75	.90
1984 O-Pee-Chee	388	.60	.45	.25
1984 Topps	132	.50	.40	.20
1984 Topps	388	.50	.40	.20
1984 Topps	700	2.50	2.00	1.00
1984 Topps	703	.30	.25	.12
1984 Topps All-Star Glossy Set of 22	15	.80	.60	.30
1984 Topps All-Star Glossy Set of 40	39	1.00	.70	.40
1985 Donruss	61	4.00	3.00	1.50
1985 Fleer	265	5.00	3.75	2.00
1985 Fleer	627	1.50	1.25	.60
1985 Fleer	630	2.00	1.50	.80
1985 Leaf-Donruss	205	4.25	3.25	1.75
1985 O-Pee-Chee	67	1.25	.90	.50
1985 Topps	500	1.50	1.25	.60
1985 Topps	714	.50	.40	.20
1985 Topps All-Star Glossy Set of 22	4	.60	.45	.25
1985 Topps All-Star Glossy Set of 40	23	1.00	.70	.40
1986 Donruss	61	2.00	1.50	.80
1986 Fleer	450	2.00	1.50	.80
1986 Leaf	51	2.25	1.75	.90
1986 O-Pee-Chee	200	.85	.60	.35
1986 Sportflics	44	1.25	.90	.50
1986 Sportflics	62	.50	.40	.20
1986 Sportflics	68	.30	.25	.12
1986 Sportflics	139	.30	.25	.12
1986 Sportflics	148	.20	.15	.08
1986 Sportflics Decade Greats	55	.70	.50	.30
1986 Topps	200	1.00	.70	.40
1986 Topps All-Star Glossy Set of 60	17	.90	.70	.35
1987 Donruss	139	1.00	.70	.40
1987 Fleer	187	1.00	.75	.40
1987 Fleer All Stars	6	3.00	1.50	.80
1987 Fleer All Stars	40	.40	.30	.15
1987 Leaf	122	.85	.60	.35
1987 O-Pee-Chee	396	.50	.40	.20
1987 Sportflics	30	1.00	.70	.40
1987 Sportflics	115	.35	.25	.14
1987 Sportflics	156	.30	.25	.12
1987 Topps	430	.40	.30	.15
1987 Topps	597	.20	.15	.08
1987 Topps All-Star Glossy Set of 22	4	.70	.50	.30
1987 Topps All-Star Glossy Set of 60	28	.90	.70	.35
1988 Donruss	330	.30	.25	.12
1988 Donruss MVP	4	.35	.25	.14
1988 Fleer	315	.50	.40	.20
1988 Fleer	636	.25	.20	.10
1988 Leaf	124	.50	.40	.20
1988 O-Pee-Chee	321	.30	.25	.12
1988 Score	16	.40	.30	.15
1988 Score	657	.20	.15	.08
1988 Sportflics	35	1.00	.70	.40
1988 Sportflics	180	.25	.20	.10
1988 Sportflics Gamewinners	21	1.00	.70	.40
1988 Topps	600	.40	.30	.15
1988 Topps All-Star Glossy Set of 60	3	.70	.50	.30
1988 Topps All-Star Glossy Set of 22	15	.60	.45	.25
1988 Topps Big Baseball	88	.60	.45	.25
1989 Bowman	402	.30	.25	.12
1989 Donruss	193	.25	.20	.10
1989 Fleer	582	.25	.20	.10
1989 O-Pee-Chee	100	.45	.35	.20
1989 Score	149	.30	.25	.12
1989 Sportflics	21	.60	.45	.25

1989 Topps	100	.25	.20	.10
1989 Topps Big Baseball	220	.30	.25	.12
1989 Upper Deck	406	1.50	1.25	.60
1989 Upper Deck	684	.25	.20	.10
1990 Donruss	643	.25	.20	.10
1990 O-Pee-Chee	662	.07	.05	.03
1990 Topps	662	.07	.05	.03
1990 Upper Deck	20	.50	.40	.20

1983 Topps 1952 Reprint Set	91	2.00	1.50	.80
1988 Topps	351	.06	.05	.02
1990 Topps Traded	113T	.05	.04	.02
1991 "1953" Topps Archives	78	.50	.40	.20

Red Schoendienst

Set	Card #	NM	EX	VG
1948 Bowman	38 (R)	125.00	62.50	37.50
1949 Bowman	111	65.00	32.50	19.50
1950 Bowman	71	80.00	40.00	24.00
1951 Bowman	10	65.00	32.00	20.00
1951 Topps Blue Backs	6	60.00	30.00	18.00
1952 Bowman	30	55.00	27.50	16.50
1952 Red Man Tobacco	19N	35.00	17.50	10.50
1952 Topps	91	80.00	40.00	18.50
1953 Bowman Color	101	80.00	40.00	25.00
1953 Red Man Tobacco	12N	55.00	27.00	16.50
1953 Topps	78	70.00	35.00	16.00
1954 Bowman	110	30.00	15.00	9.00
1954 Red Heart Dog Food	(27)	40.00	20.00	12.00
1954 Red Man Tobacco	10N	37.50	18.50	11.00
1955 Bowman	29	25.00	12.50	7.50
1955 Red Man Tobacco	18N	35.00	17.50	10.50
1956 Topps	165	25.00	12.50	7.50
1957 Topps	154	18.00	9.00	5.50
1958 Topps	190	16.00	8.00	4.75
1959 Topps	480	13.00	6.50	4.00
1960 Topps	335	10.00	5.00	3.00
1961 Post Cereal	111	7.50	3.75	2.25
1961 Topps	505	11.00	5.50	3.25
1962 Topps	575	35.00	17.50	10.50
1965 Topps	556	15.00	7.50	4.50
1966 O-Pee-Chee	76	2.25	1.25	.70
1966 Topps	76	5.00	2.50	1.50
1967 Topps	512	15.00	7.50	4.50
1968 Topps	294	4.00	2.00	1.25
1969 Topps	462	3.00	1.50	.90
1970 O-Pee-Chee	346	1.75	.90	.50
1970 Topps	346	1.75	.90	.50
1971 O-Pee-Chee	239	1.50	.70	.45
1971 Topps	239	3.50	1.75	1.00
1972 O-Pee-Chee	67	.75	.40	.25
1972 Topps	67	3.00	1.50	.90
1973 O-Pee-Chee	497	1.25	.60	.40
1973 Topps	497	1.25	.60	.40
1974 O-Pee-Chee	236	.60	.30	.20
1974 Topps	236	.75	.40	.25
1975 O-Pee-Chee	246	.60	.30	.20
1975 Topps	246	2.00	1.00	.60
1975 Topps Mini	246	1.25	.60	.40
1976 O-Pee-Chee	581	.60	.30	.20
1976 Topps	581	.80	.40	.25

Set	Card #	MT	NM	EX
1981 Donruss	431	.15	.11	.06

Tom Seaver

Set	Card #	NM	EX	VG
1967 Topps	581 (R)	850.00	425.00	250.00
1968 O-Pee-Chee	45	235.00	117.00	70.00
1968 Topps	45	100.00	50.00	30.00
1969 Topps	480	75.00	37.00	22.00
1970 O-Pee-Chee	69	7.50	3.75	2.25
1970 O-Pee-Chee	300	85.00	42.00	25.00
1970 Topps	69	5.00	2.50	1.50
1970 Topps	300	55.00	27.00	16.50
1971 O-Pee-Chee	68	1.50	.70	.45
1971 O-Pee-Chee	72	7.50	3.75	2.25
1971 O-Pee-Chee	160	63.00	31.00	19.00
1971 Topps	68	1.50	.70	.45
1971 Topps	72	3.50	1.75	1.00
1971 Topps	160	45.00	22.00	13.50
1972 O-Pee-Chee	91	1.00	.50	.30
1972 O-Pee-Chee	93	5.00	2.50	1.50
1972 O-Pee-Chee	95	1.00	.50	.30
1972 O-Pee-Chee	347	5.00	2.50	1.50
1972 O-Pee-Chee	445	42.50	21.00	12.50
1972 O-Pee-Chee	446	21.00	10.50	6.25
1972 Topps	91	3.00	1.50	.90
1972 Topps	93	3.50	1.75	1.00
1972 Topps	95	3.00	1.50	.90
1972 Topps	347	4.00	2.00	1.25
1972 Topps	445	24.00	12.00	7.25
1972 Topps	446	10.00	5.00	3.00
1973 O-Pee-Chee	350	25.00	12.50	7.50
1973 Topps	350	20.00	10.00	6.00
1974 O-Pee-Chee	80	20.00	10.00	6.00
1974 O-Pee-Chee	206	6.25	3.25	2.00
1974 O-Pee-Chee	207	22.00	11.00	6.50
1974 Topps	80	15.00	7.50	4.50
1974 Topps	206	2.00	1.00	.60
1974 Topps	207	15.00	7.50	4.50
1975 O-Pee-Chee	370	18.00	9.00	5.50
1975 Topps	370	15.00	7.50	4.50
1975 Topps Mini	370	20.00	10.00	6.00
1976 O-Pee-Chee	5	5.00	2.50	1.50
1976 O-Pee-Chee	199	2.00	1.00	.60
1976 O-Pee-Chee	201	2.00	1.00	.60
1976 O-Pee-Chee	203	2.00	1.00	.60
1976 O-Pee-Chee	600	17.00	8.50	5.00
1976 Topps	5	4.00	2.00	1.25
1976 Topps	199	2.00	1.00	.60
1976 Topps	201	2.00	1.00	.60
1976 Topps	203	1.50	.75	.45
1976 Topps	600	12.00	6.00	3.50
1977 O-Pee-Chee	6	15.00	7.50	4.50
1977 O-Pee-Chee	205	10.25	5.25	3.00
1977 Topps	6	9.00	4.50	2.75

		MT	NM	EX
1977 Topps	150	9.00	4.50	2.75
1978 O-Pee-Chee	120	6.75	3.50	2.00
1978 Topps	450	8.00	4.00	2.50
1979 O-Pee-Chee	44	3.25	1.75	1.00
1979 Topps	100	4.00	2.00	1.25
1980 O-Pee-Chee	260	4.25	2.25	1.25
1980 Topps	500	3.00	1.50	.90

Set	Card #	MT	NM	EX
1981 Donruss	422	2.00	1.50	.80
1981 Donruss	425	2.00	1.50	.80
1981 Fleer	200	2.00	1.50	.80
1981 O-Pee-Chee	220	2.50	2.00	1.00
1981 Topps	220	3.00	2.25	1.25
1982 Donruss	16	.80	.60	.30
1982 Donruss	148	1.50	1.25	.60
1982 Donruss	628	.80	.60	.30
1982 Fleer	82	.90	.70	.35
1982 Fleer	634	.30	.25	.12
1982 Fleer	645	.25	.20	.10
1982 O-Pee-Chee	30	2.00	1.50	.80
1982 O-Pee-Chee	31	1.00	.70	.40
1982 O-Pee-Chee	346	.30	.25	.12
1982 Topps	30	2.00	1.50	.80
1982 Topps	31	1.00	.70	.40
1982 Topps	165	.20	.15	.08
1982 Topps	346	.75	.60	.30
1982 Topps	756	.30	.25	.12
1983 Donruss	122	1.50	1.25	.60
1983 Fleer	601	1.00	.70	.40
1983 O-Pee-Chee	52	1.75	1.25	.70
1983 O-Pee-Chee	354	1.00	.70	.40
1983 Topps	580	2.00	1.50	.80
1983 Topps	581	.50	.40	.20
1984 Donruss	116	6.00	4.50	2.50
1984 Fleer	595	4.00	3.00	1.50
1984 Fleer Update	106	25.00	18.50	10.00
1984 O-Pee-Chee	261	1.25	.90	.50
1984 Topps	246	.25	.20	.10
1984 Topps	706	.30	.25	.12
1984 Topps	707	.35	.25	.14
1984 Topps	708	.25	.20	.10
1984 Topps	740	1.50	1.25	.60
1985 Donruss	424a	3.00	2.25	1.25
1985 Donruss	424b	30.00	22.00	12.00
1985 Fleer	526	1.25	.90	.50
1985 Leaf-Donruss	101	.80	.60	.30
1985 O-Pee-Chee	1	.25	.20	.10
1985 Topps	670	.40	.30	.15
1986 Donruss	609a	1.00	.70	.40
1986 Donruss	609b	3.00	2.25	1.25
1986 Fleer	216	1.00	.70	.40
1986 Fleer	630	.15	.11	.06
1986 Leaf	234	1.00	.70	.40
1986 O-Pee-Chee	390	.25	.20	.10
1986 Sportflics	25	.75	.60	.30
1986 Sportflics	60	.20	.15	.08
1986 Sportflics	67	.15	.11	.06
1986 Sportflics	70	.25	.20	.10
1986 Sportflics	134	.15	.11	.06
1986 Sportflics	135	.25	.20	.10
1986 Sportflics	142	.15	.11	.06
1986 Sportflics	182	1.50	1.25	.60
1986 Sportflics Decade Greats	52	.60	.45	.25
1986 Sportflics Rookies	47	.40	.30	.15
1986 Topps	390	.40	.30	.15
1986 Topps	402	.15	.11	.06
1986 Topps All-Star Glossy Set of 60	22	.50	.40	.20
1987 Donruss	375	.40	.30	.15
1987 Fleer	45	.75	.60	.30
1987 Leaf	263	1.00	.70	.40
1987 O-Pee-Chee	49	.20	.15	.08
1987 Sportflics	28	.75	.60	.30
1987 Topps	306	.07	.05	.03
1987 Topps	425	.30	.25	.12

Gary Sheffield

Set	Card #	MT	NM	EX
1989 Bowman	142	1.00	.75	.40
1989 Donruss	31 (R)	1.00	.75	.40
1989 Fleer	196 (R)	1.00	.75	.40
1989 Score	625 (R)	1.00	.75	.40
1989 Sportflics	41	.60	.45	.25
1989 Sportflics	223	4.00	3.00	1.50
1989 Topps	343 (R)	1.00	.75	.40
1989 Topps Glossy Rookies Set of 22	20	.30	.25	.12
1989 Upper Deck	13a (R)	5.00	3.75	2.00
1989 Upper Deck	13b (R)	5.00	3.75	2.00
1990 Bowman	391	.12	.09	.05
1990 Donruss	501	.25	.20	.10
1990 Fleer	336	.25	.20	.10
1990 Leaf	157	4.00	3.00	1.50
1990 O-Pee-Chee	718	.25	.20	.10
1990 Score	97	.25	.20	.10
1990 Sportflics	52	.15	.11	.06
1990 Topps	718	.25	.20	.10
1990 Topps Big Baseball	163	.25	.20	.10
1990 Topps Glossy Rookies	25	.35	.25	.14
1990 Upper Deck	157	.35	.25	.14
1991 Bowman	52	.10	.08	.04
1991 Donruss	751	.10	.08	.04
1991 Fleer	596	.10	.08	.04
1991 Fleer Ultra	180	.20	.15	.08
1991 Leaf	173	.25	.20	.10
1991 Post Cereal	15	.40	.30	.15
1991 Score	473	.10	.08	.04
1991 Studio	76	.35	.25	.14
1991 Topps	68	.15	.11	.06
1991 Topps Stadium Club	95	2.00	1.50	.80
1991 Upper Deck	266	.20	.15	.08
1992 Bowman	214	.60	.45	.25
1992 Donruss	192	.15	.11	.06
1992 Donruss Triple Play	53	.15	.11	.06
1992 Fleer	188	.10	.08	.04
1992 Fleer Ultra	83	.35	.25	.14
1992 Fleer Ultra	582	.30	.25	.12
1992 Fleer Ultra All-Stars	14	.60	.45	.25
1992 Fleer Update	125	1.50	1.25	.60
1992 Leaf	446	.25	.20	.10
1992 O-Pee-Chee	695	.12	.09	.05
1992 Pinnacle	235	.25	.20	.10
1992 Pinnacle Team 2000	59	.35	.25	.14
1992 Score	589	.15	.11	.06
1992 Score Rookie & Traded	1	.25	.20	.10
1992 Studio	108	.20	.15	.08
1992 Topps	695	.12	.09	.05
1992 Topps Gold	695	.60	.45	.25
1992 Topps Stadium Club	309	.25	.20	.10
1992 Topps Stadium Club	766	.25	.20	.10
1992 Topps Stadium Club East Coast National	766	7.50	5.75	3.00
1992 Topps Stadium Club Members Only	(6)	.35	.25	.14

1992 Topps Traded	105	.15	.11	.06
1992 Topps Traded Gold	105	.35	.25	.14
1992 Upper Deck	84	.10	.08	.04
1992 Upper Deck	234	.10	.08	.04
1992 Upper Deck	745	.15	.11	.06
1993 Bowman	490	.15	.11	.06
1993 DiamondMarks	(60)	.50	.40	.20
1993 Donruss	444	.15	.11	.06
1993 Donruss Diamond Kings	21	1.00	.75	.40
1993 Donruss Elite	28	20.00	15.00	8.00
1993 Donruss Elite Supers	10	12.00	9.00	4.75
1993 Donruss Long Ball Leaders	16	2.00	1.50	.80
1993 Donruss Masters of the Game	3	2.00	1.50	.80
1993 Donruss MVP's	26	1.00	.75	.40
1993 Donruss Spirit of the Game	12	1.50	1.25	.60
1993 Donruss Triple Play	6	.15	.11	.06
1993 Donruss Triple Play Action Baseball	10	.10	.08	.04
1993 Fleer	147	.10	.08	.04
1993 Fleer	351	.10	.08	.04
1993 Fleer	356	.15	.11	.06
1993 Fleer	704	.10	.08	.04
1993 Fleer All-Stars	3	.75	.60	.30
1993 Fleer Final Edition	71	.10	.08	.04
1993 Fleer Flair	54	.35	.25	.14
1993 Fleer NL Team Leaders	5	2.00	1.50	.80
1993 Fleer ProVisions I	3	1.00	.75	.40
1993 Fleer Ultra	122	.20	.15	.08
1993 Fleer Ultra All-Stars	5	1.00	.75	.40
1993 Fleer Ultra Award Winners	25	1.00	.75	.40
1993 Fleer Ultra Home Run Kings	8	1.50	1.25	.60
1993 Fleer Ultra Performers	8	1.00	.75	.40
1993 Leaf	307	.15	.11	.06
1993 Leaf Gold All-Stars	15	1.25	.90	.50
1993 Leaf Update Gold All-Stars	5	1.00	.75	.40
1993 O-Pee-Chee	317	.20	.15	.08
1993 O-Pee-Chee Premier Star Performers	6	.30	.25	.12
1993 Pinnacle	1	.15	.11	.06
1993 Pinnacle	300	.08	.06	.03
1993 Pinnacle Home Run Club	6	.50	.40	.20
1993 Pinnacle Slugfest	7	1.00	.75	.40
1993 Pinnacle Team Pinnacle	6	6.00	4.50	2.50
1993 Post Cereal	11	.30	.25	.12
1993 Score	2	.10	.08	.04
1993 Score	531	.06	.05	.03
1993 Score	534	.06	.05	.02
1993 Score Gold Dream Team	3	.75	.60	.30
1993 Score Select	41	.15	.11	.06
1993 Score Select Chase Stars	4	2.50	2.00	1.00
1993 Score Select Rookie/ Traded	4	.35	.25	.14
1993 Score Select Stat Leaders	4	.15	.11	.06
1993 Score Select Stat Leaders	30	.20	.15	.08
1993 Score Select Stat Leaders	47	.20	.15	.08
1993 Score The Franchise	25	1.50	1.25	.60
1993 Studio	207	.15	.11	.06
1993 Topps	140	.10	.08	.04
1993 Topps	403	.03	.02	.01
1993 Topps Black Gold	18	.30	.25	.12
1993 Topps Finest	31	3.00	2.25	1.25
1993 Topps Finest Refractors	31	30.00	22.00	12.00
1993 Topps Full Shot Super	18	4.00	3.00	1.50
1993 Topps Gold	140	.20	.15	.08
1993 Topps Gold	403	.10	.08	.04
1993 Topps Stadium Club	300	.15	.11	.06
1993 Topps Stadium Club	618	.15	.11	.06
1993 Topps Stadium Club First Day Production	300	15.00	11.00	6.00
1993 Topps Stadium Club First Day Production	618	20.00	15.00	8.00
1993 Topps Stadium Club Special Master Photo	(10)	.75	.60	.30
1993 Topps Stadium Club Special	17	.15	.11	.06
1993 Topps Traded	51	.10	.08	.04
1993 Upper Deck	222	.10	.08	.04
1993 Upper Deck	474	.20	.15	.08
1993 Upper Deck	492	.10	.08	.04
1993 Upper Deck	494	.10	.08	.04
1993 Upper Deck	828	.10	.08	.04
1993 Upper Deck Fun Packs	20	.25	.20	.10
1993 Upper Deck Fun Packs	25	.05	.04	.02
1993 Upper Deck Fun Packs	141	.20	.15	.08
1993 Upper Deck SP	18	.35	.25	.14
1993 Upper Deck SP Platinum Power	18	5.00	3.75	2.00
1993 Upper Deck Triple Crown	8	1.50	1.25	.60
1993 Upper Deck 5th Anniversary	2	1.00	.75	.40
1993 Upper Deck 5th Anniversary Super	2	3.00	2.25	1.25
1994 Bowman	290	.10	.08	.04
1994 Bowman's Best	13	.50	.40	.20
1994 Bowman's Best Refractors	13	2.00	1.50	.80
1994 Donruss	5	.15	.11	.06
1994 Donruss Diamond Kings	25	1.25	.90	.50
1994 Donruss Diamond Kings Super	25	3.75	2.75	1.50
1994 Donruss Special Edition - Gold	5	.35	.25	.14
1994 Donruss Triple Play Nicknames	3	1.75	1.25	.70
1994 Donruss Triple Play Medalists	10	1.50	1.25	.60
1994 Donruss Triple Play	140	.05	.04	.02
1994 Fleer	477	.10	.07	.04
1994 Fleer All-Stars	49	.40	.30	.15
1994 Fleer Extra Bases	266	.15	.11	.06
1994 Fleer Extra Bases Game Breakers	26	.25	.20	.10
1994 Fleer Flair	166	.35	.25	.14
1994 Fleer Team Leaders	19	.60	.45	.25
1994 Fleer Ultra	199	.15	.11	.06
1994 Leaf	319	.15	.11	.06
1994 Leaf Limited	109	1.50	1.25	.60
1994 Leaf MVP Contenders	1b	5.00	3.75	2.00
1994 O-Pee-Chee	45	.10	.08	.04
1994 Pacific Crown	250	.15	.11	.06
1994 Pinnacle	88	.15	.11	.06
1994 Pinnacle Artist's Proof	88	3.50	2.75	1.50
1994 Pinnacle Museum Collection	88	2.50	2.00	1.00
1994 Pinnacle Power Surge	15	.30	.25	.12
1994 Pinnacle The Naturals Box Set	18	.25	.20	.10
1994 Post Cereal	5	.40	.30	.15
1994 Score	100	.10	.08	.04
1994 Score Gold Stars	20	3.00	2.25	1.25
1994 Score Select	256	.20	.15	.08
1994 Sportflics 2000	28	.15	.11	.06
1994 Studio	112	.15	.11	.06
1994 Topps	560	.06	.05	.02

Set	Card #	MT	NM	EX
1994 Topps Finest	225	.75	.60	.30
1994 Topps Finest Refractors	225	4.00	3.00	1.50
1994 Topps Finest Superstars	225	2.50	2.00	1.00
1994 Topps Gold	560	.15	.11	.06
1994 Topps Stadium Club	4	.25	.20	.10
1994 Topps Stadium Club	180	.15	.11	.06
1994 Topps Stadium Club First Day Production	4	7.00	5.25	2.75
1994 Topps Stadium Club First Day Production	180	8.00	6.00	3.25
1994 Upper Deck	50	.12	.09	.05
1994 Upper Deck	271	.12	.09	.05
1994 Upper Deck	475	.12	.09	.05
1994 Upper Deck All-Stars Green Foil	3	.25	.20	.10
1994 Upper Deck All-Stars Gold Foil	3	1.00	.70	.40
1994 Upper Deck Collector's Choice	257	.10	.08	.04
1994 Upper Deck Collector's Choice	341	.10	.08	.04
1994 Upper Deck Diamond Collection	10E	5.00	3.75	2.00
1994 Upper Deck Electric Diamond	50	.25	.20	.10
1994 Upper Deck Electric Diamond	271	.25	.20	.10
1994 Upper Deck Electric Diamond	475	.25	.20	.10
1994 Upper Deck Fun Packs	10	.05	.04	.02
1994 Upper Deck Next Generation	18	1.50	1.25	.60
1994 Upper Deck SP	114	.20	.15	.08
1994 Upper Deck SP Baseball Die-Cut	114	.25	.20	.10
1994 Upper Deck SP Holoview Blue	35	3.00	2.25	1.25
1994 Upper Deck SP Holoview Red	35	15.00	11.00	6.00

Ruben Sierra

Set	Card #	MT	NM	EX
1986 Fleer Update	105	4.00	3.00	1.50
1986 Sportflics Rookies	16	1.50	1.25	.60
1987 Donruss	346 (R)	3.50	2.75	1.50
1987 Fleer	138 (R)	7.50	5.75	3.00
1987 Leaf	225	3.25	2.50	1.25
1987 Topps	6	.25	.20	.10
1987 Topps	261 (R)	.75	.60	.30
1987 Topps Glossy Rookies	15	.90	.70	.35
1988 Donruss	223	.25	.20	.10
1988 Fleer	479	.75	.60	.30
1988 Leaf	206	.30	.25	.12
1988 O-Pee-Chee	319	.30	.25	.12
1988 Score	113	.30	.20	.10
1988 Sportflics	113	.50	.40	.20
1988 Topps	771	.15	.11	.06
1988 Topps All-Star Glossy Set of 60	4	.40	.30	.15
1989 Bowman	235	.25	.20	.10
1989 Donruss	48	.25	.20	.10
1989 Fleer	532	.25	.20	.10
1989 O-Pee-Chee	53	.15	.11	.06
1989 Score	43	.25	.20	.10
1989 Sportflics	189	.35	.25	.14
1989 Topps	53	.25	.20	.10
1989 Topps Big Baseball	82	.20	.15	.08
1989 Upper Deck	416	.50	.40	.20
1989 Upper Deck	686	.08	.06	.03
1990 Bowman	490	.10	.07	.04
1990 Donruss	3a	1.00	.70	.40
1990 Donruss	3b	.10	.08	.04
1990 Donruss	174	.12	.09	.05
1990 Donruss	673	.09	.07	.04
1990 Donruss Diamond Kings Supers	3	.35	.25	.14
1990 Fleer	314	.12	.09	.05
1990 Fleer All-Stars	11	.35	.25	.14
1990 Leaf	257	1.25	.90	.50
1990 O-Pee-Chee	185	.20	.15	.08
1990 O-Pee-Chee	390	.15	.11	.06
1990 Score	420	.15	.11	.06
1990 Sportflics	188	.40	.30	.15
1990 Topps	185	.20	.15	.08
1990 Topps	390	.10	.07	.04
1990 Topps All-Star Glossy Set of 22	19	.25	.20	.10
1990 Topps All-Star Glossy Set of 60	26	.25	.20	.10
1990 Topps Big Baseball	175	.20	.15	.08
1990 Upper Deck	355	.20	.15	.08
1991 Bowman	283	.15	.11	.06
1991 Donruss	567	.15	.11	.06
1991 Fleer	303	.12	.09	.05
1991 Fleer ProVisions	3	.20	.15	.08
1991 Fleer Ultra	356	.20	.15	.08
1991 Leaf	97	.15	.11	.06
1991 O-Pee-Chee Premier	109	.10	.08	.04
1991 Score	495	.12	.09	.05
1991 Score	859	.10	.08	.04
1991 Studio	129	.15	.11	.06
1991 Topps	535	.12	.09	.05
1991 Topps Stadium Club	123	.75	.60	.30
1991 Upper Deck	455	.15	.11	.06
1992 Bowman	225	.50	.40	.20
1992 Donruss	298	.08	.06	.03
1992 Donruss Triple Play	238	.10	.08	.04
1992 Fleer	321	.12	.09	.05
1992 Fleer Ultra	142	.25	.20	.10
1992 Fleer Update	51	.40	.30	.15
1992 Leaf	383	.15	.10	.05
1992 O-Pee-Chee	700	.15	.11	.06
1992 O-Pee-Chee Premier	66	.30	.25	.12
1992 Pinnacle	14	.15	.11	.06
1992 Pinnacle	616	.15	.11	.06
1992 Pinnacle Slugfest	10	1.00	.75	.40
1992 Pinnacle Team Pinnacle	10	20.00	15.00	8.00
1992 Score	437	.10	.08	.04
1992 Score	490	.15	.11	.06
1992 Score Impact Players	46	.15	.11	.06
1992 Score Rookie & Traded	63	.15	.11	.06
1992 Studio	249	.15	.11	.06
1992 Studio Preview	1	2.50	2.00	1.00
1992 Topps	403	.10	.08	.04
1992 Topps	700	.10	.08	.04
1992 Topps Gold	403	.25	.20	.10
1992 Topps Gold	700	.45	.35	.20
1992 Topps Kids	128	.15	.11	.06
1992 Topps Stadium Club	387	.15	.11	.06
1992 Topps Stadium Club Special Edition	172	.25	.20	.10
1992 Upper Deck	176	.10	.08	.04

1992 Upper Deck MVP Holograms	48	.35	.25	.14
1993 Bowman	245	.10	.08	.04
1993 DiamondMarks	(105)	.40	.30	.15
1993 Donruss	637	.12	.09	.05
1993 Donruss Triple Play	60	.15	.11	.06
1993 Fleer	298	.10	.08	.04
1993 Fleer Flair	262	.40	.30	.15
1993 Fleer Ultra	613	.15	.11	.06
1993 Leaf	29	.15	.11	.06
1993 O-Pee-Chee	243	.20	.15	.08
1993 Pinnacle	200	.15	.11	.06
1993 Pinnacle Home Run Club	46	.35	.25	.14
1993 Pinnacle Slugfest	12	.75	.60	.30
1993 Score	608	.10	.08	.04
1993 Score Select	366	.15	.11	.06
1993 Studio	113	.12	.09	.05
1993 Topps	440	.10	.08	.04
1993 Topps Finest	158	1.50	1.25	.60
1993 Topps Finest Refractors	158	25.00	18.50	10.00
1993 Topps Gold	440	.20	.15	.08
1993 Topps Stadium Club	580	.20	.15	.08
1993 Topps Stadium Club First Day Production	580	15.00	11.00	6.00
1993 Topps Stadium Club Master Photos	(22)	1.50	1.25	.60
1993 Topps Stadium Club Special	47	.10	.08	.04
1993 Upper Deck	49	.12	.09	.05
1993 Upper Deck	145	.10	.07	.04
1993 Upper Deck Fun Packs	52	.15	.11	.06
1993 Upper Deck SP	43	.20	.15	.08
1994 Bowman	24	.15	.11	.06
1994 Bowman's Best	57	.50	.40	.20
1994 Bowman's Best Refractors	57	4.00	3.00	1.50
1994 Donruss	33	.08	.06	.03
1994 Donruss Diamond Kings	18	1.00	.75	.40
1994 Donruss Diamond Kings Super	18	3.50	2.75	1.50
1994 Donruss MVP's	25	.50	.40	.20
1994 Donruss Special Edition - Gold	33	.35	.25	.14
1994 Donruss Triple Play	8	.05	.04	.02
1994 Fleer	273	.08	.06	.03
1994 Fleer Extra Bases	155	.15	.11	.06
1994 Fleer Flair	333	.30	.25	.12
1994 Fleer Ultra	409	.12	.09	.05
1994 Leaf	67	.12	.09	.05
1994 O-Pee-Chee	195	.05	.04	.02
1994 Pacific Crown	462	.15	.11	.06
1994 Pacific Crown All Latino All-Star Team	9	1.50	1.25	.60
1994 Pinnacle	61	.15	.11	.06
1994 Pinnacle Artist's Proof	61	4.00	3.00	1.50
1994 Pinnacle Museum Collection	61	2.00	1.50	.80
1994 Score	409	.08	.06	.03
1994 Score Select	45	.20	.15	.08
1994 Sportflics 2000	73	.10	.08	.04
1994 Studio	6	.10	.08	.04
1994 Topps	680	.05	.04	.02
1994 Topps Finest	371	.75	.60	.30
1994 Topps Finest Refractors	371	4.50	3.50	1.75
1994 Topps Gold	680	.15	.11	.06
1994 Topps Stadium Club	307	.15	.11	.06
1994 Topps Stadium Club	536	.12	.09	.05
1994 Topps Stadium Club First Day Production	307	4.00	3.00	1.50
1994 Topps Stadium Club First Day Production	536	2.50	2.00	1.00
1994 Upper Deck	380	.12	.09	.05

1994 Upper Deck All-Stars Green Foil	2	.25	.20	.10
1994 Upper Deck All-Stars Gold Foil	2	1.00	.70	.40
1994 Upper Deck Collector's Choice	258	.10	.08	.04
1994 Upper Deck Electric Diamond	380	.25	.20	.10
1994 Upper Deck Fun Packs	141	.07	.05	.03
1994 Upper Deck SP	37	.20	.15	.08
1994 Upper Deck SP Baseball Die-Cut	37	.25	.20	.10

Ted Simmons

Set	Card #	NM	EX	VG
1971 O-Pee-Chee	117	25.00	12.50	7.50
1971 Topps	117 (R)	20.00	10.00	6.00
1972 O-Pee-Chee	154	1.25	.60	.40
1972 Topps	154	1.00	.50	.30
1973 O-Pee-Chee	85	1.00	.50	.30
1973 Topps	85	1.50	.70	.45
1974 O-Pee-Chee	260	.75	.40	.25
1974 Topps	260	.50	.25	.15
1975 O-Pee-Chee	75	.60	.30	.20
1975 Topps	75	.35	.20	.11
1975 Topps Mini	75	.60	.30	.20
1976 O-Pee-Chee	191	.50	.25	.15
1976 O-Pee-Chee	290	.60	.30	.20
1976 Topps	191	1.00	.50	.30
1976 Topps	290	.25	.13	.08
1977 O-Pee-Chee	196	.50	.25	.15
1977 Topps	470	.35	.20	.11
1978 O-Pee-Chee	150	.40	.20	.12
1978 Topps	380	.40	.20	.12
1979 O-Pee-Chee	267	.30	.15	.09
1979 Topps	510	.20	.10	.06
1980 O-Pee-Chee	47	.30	.15	.09
1980 Topps	85	.15	.08	.05

Set	Card #	MT	NM	EX
1981 Donruss	308	.12	.09	.05
1981 Fleer	528	.12	.09	.05
1981 O-Pee-Chee	352	.20	.15	.08
1981 Topps	705	.25	.20	.10
1982 Donruss	106	.12	.09	.05
1982 Fleer	152	.12	.09	.05
1982 O-Pee-Chee	150	.20	.15	.08
1982 Topps	150	.10	.08	.04
1983 Donruss	332	.12	.09	.05
1983 Fleer	45	.08	.06	.03
1983 O-Pee-Chee	33	.12	.09	.05
1983 O-Pee-Chee	284	.15	.11	.06
1983 Topps	450	.15	.11	.06
1983 Topps	451	.08	.06	.03
1984 Donruss	473	.20	.15	.08
1984 Fleer	213	.15	.11	.06
1984 O-Pee-Chee	94	.30	.25	.12
1984 O-Pee-Chee	122	.30	.25	.12

1984 Topps	404	.15	.11	.06
1984 Topps	630	.15	.11	.06
1984 Topps	713	.20	.15	.08
1984 Topps	726	.12	.09	.05
1984 Topps All-Star Glossy Set of 22	9	.25	.20	.10
1984 Topps All-Star Glossy Set of 40	18	.20	.15	.08
1985 Donruss	414	.15	.11	.06
1985 Fleer	596	.12	.09	.05
1985 Leaf-Donruss	104	.20	.15	.08
1985 O-Pee-Chee	318	.12	.09	.05
1985 Topps	318	.12	.09	.05
1986 Donruss	292	.12	.09	.05
1986 Fleer	503	.12	.09	.05
1986 Leaf	167	.10	.08	.04
1986 Sportflics	196	.15	.11	.06
1986 Sportflics Decade Greats	62	.25	.20	.10
1986 Topps	237	.12	.09	.05
1986 Topps Traded	102T	.20	.15	.08
1987 Donruss	537	.12	.09	.05
1987 Fleer	528	.12	.09	.05
1987 Topps	516	.10	.08	.04
1988 Donruss	560	.10	.08	.04
1988 Fleer	549	.10	.08	.04
1988 Score	285	.08	.06	.03
1988 Topps	791	.08	.06	.03
1989 Fleer	599	.10	.08	.04
1989 Score	611	.08	.06	.03
1989 Upper Deck	570	.10	.08	.04

Set	Card #	MT	NM	EX
1981 Donruss	115	.10	.08	.04
1981 Fleer	188	.10	.08	.04
1981 O-Pee-Chee	281	.12	.09	.05
1981 Topps	570	.12	.09	.05
1982 Donruss	24	.10	.08	.04
1982 Donruss	105	.10	.08	.04
1982 Fleer	179	.10	.08	.04
1982 O-Pee-Chee	2	.12	.09	.05
1982 O-Pee-Chee	290	.12	.09	.05
1982 Topps	290	.12	.09	.05
1982 Topps	552	.12	.09	.05
1983 Donruss	257	.10	.08	.04
1983 Fleer	73	.10	.08	.04
1983 O-Pee-Chee	85	.12	.09	.05
1983 Topps	85	.12	.09	.05
1984 Donruss	610	.20	.15	.08
1984 Fleer	21	.12	.09	.05
1984 O-Pee-Chee	165	.20	.15	.08
1984 Topps	165	.12	.09	.05
1985 Fleer	191	.08	.06	.03
1985 O-Pee-Chee	326	.08	.06	.03
1985 Topps	755	.08	.06	.03

Moose Skowron

Set	Card #	NM	EX	VG
1954 Topps	239 (R)	90.00	45.00	27.00
1955 Bowman	160 (R)	22.00	11.00	6.50
1955 Topps	22	15.00	7.50	4.50
1956 Topps	61	12.50	6.25	3.75
1957 Topps	135	13.50	6.75	4.00
1958 Topps	240	10.00	5.00	3.00
1958 Topps	477	6.00	3.00	1.75
1959 Topps	90	25.00	12.50	7.50
1959 Topps	554	24.00	12.00	7.25
1960 Topps	370	7.00	3.50	2.00
1960 Topps	553	18.00	9.00	5.50
1961 Post Cereal	3a	3.75	2.00	1.25
1961 Post Cereal	3b	3.75	2.00	1.25
1961 Topps	42	6.00	3.00	1.75
1961 Topps	371	45.00	22.50	13.50
1961 Topps	568	35.00	17.50	10.50
1962 Post Cereal	1	5.00	2.50	1.50
1962 Topps	110	5.00	2.50	1.50
1963 Post Cereal	12	3.50	1.75	1.00
1963 Topps	180	4.50	2.25	1.25
1964 Topps	445	7.00	3.50	2.00
1965 O-Pee-Chee	70	2.75	1.50	.80
1965 Topps	70	2.50	1.25	.70
1966 Topps	199	2.50	1.25	.70
1966 Topps	590	35.00	17.50	10.50
1967 Topps	357	3.50	1.75	1.00

Set	Card #	MT	NM	EX
1988 Pacific Trading Cards Baseball Legends	82	.10	.08	.04
1994 "1954" Topps Archives	239	.45	.35	.20

Ken Singleton

Ken Singleton
OUTFIELD

Set	Card #	NM	EX	VG
1971 O-Pee-Chee	16	1.50	.70	.45
1971 Topps	16 (R)	3.50	1.75	1.00
1972 O-Pee-Chee	425	1.75	.90	.50
1972 O-Pee-Chee	426	1.75	.90	.50
1972 Topps	425	1.00	.50	.30
1972 Topps	426	1.00	.50	.30
1973 O-Pee-Chee	232	.75	.40	.25
1973 Topps	232	.40	.20	.12
1974 O-Pee-Chee	25	.60	.30	.20
1974 Topps	25	.30	.15	.09
1975 O-Pee-Chee	125	.55	.30	.15
1975 Topps	125	.35	.20	.11
1975 Topps Mini	125	.60	.30	.20
1976 O-Pee-Chee	175	.35	.20	.11
1976 Topps	175	.25	.13	.08
1977 O-Pee-Chee	19	.30	.15	.09
1977 Topps	445	.25	.13	.08
1978 O-Pee-Chee	80	.25	.13	.08
1978 Topps	65	.20	.10	.06
1979 O-Pee-Chee	324	.25	.13	.08
1979 Topps	615	.20	.10	.06
1980 O-Pee-Chee	178	.20	.10	.06
1980 Topps	340	.20	.10	.06

Enos Slaughter

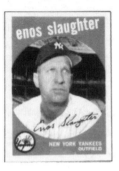

Set	Card #	NM	EX	VG
1941 Double Play	40	110.00	55.00	32.50
1948 Bowman	17	90.00	45.00	27.00
1949 Bowman	65	60.00	30.00	18.00
1950 Bowman	35	90.00	45.00	27.00
1951 Bowman	58	55.00	27.00	16.50
1951 Topps Blue Backs	30	60.00	30.00	18.00
1952 Bowman	232	90.00	45.00	25.00
1952 Red Man Tobacco	20N	60.00	30.00	18.00
1952 Topps	65	100.00	50.00	23.00
1953 Bowman Color	81	50.00	25.00	15.00
1953 Red Man Tobacco	13N	55.00	27.00	16.50
1953 Topps	41	80.00	40.00	18.50
1954 Bowman	62	35.00	17.50	10.50
1954 Red Heart Dog Food	(28)	40.00	20.00	12.00
1954 Red Man Tobacco	19Na	110.00	55.00	33.00
1955 Bowman	60	30.00	15.00	9.00
1956 Topps	109	35.00	17.50	10.50
1957 Topps	215	20.00	10.00	6.00
1958 Topps	142	22.00	11.00	6.50
1959 Topps	155	16.00	8.00	4.75

Set	Card #	MT	NM	EX
1983 Topps 1952 Reprint Set	65	2.00	1.50	.80
1986 Sportflics Decade Greats	18	.25	.20	.10
1988 Pacific Trading Cards Baseball Legends	84	.20	.15	.08
1989 Pacific Trading Cards Legends II	137	.25	.20	.10
1990 Pacific Legends	50	.20	.15	.08
1991 "1953" Topps Archives	41	.50	.40	.20

Lee Smith

Set	Card #	MT	NM	EX
1982 Donruss	252 (R)	9.00	6.75	3.50

1982 Fleer	603a (R)	12.00	9.00	4.75
1982 Fleer	603b (R)	9.00	6.75	3.50
1982 Topps	452 (R)	9.00	6.75	3.50
1983 Donruss	403	1.75	1.25	.70
1983 Fleer	508	1.50	1.25	.60
1983 Topps	699	2.50	2.00	1.00
1984 Donruss	289	3.00	2.25	1.25
1984 Fleer	505	.15	.11	.06
1984 O-Pee-Chee	176	.20	.15	.08
1984 Topps	176	.15	.11	.06
1985 Donruss	311	1.00	.70	.40
1985 Fleer	67	.10	.08	.04
1985 Leaf-Donruss	128	.08	.06	.03
1985 O-Pee-Chee	43	.10	.08	.04
1985 Topps	511	.10	.08	.04
1986 Donruss	144	.10	.08	.04
1986 Fleer	380	.50	.40	.20
1986 Leaf	64	.08	.06	.03
1986 O-Pee-Chee	355	.08	.06	.03
1986 Sportflics	45	.15	.11	.06
1986 Sportflics	55	.10	.08	.04
1986 Topps	355	.10	.08	.04
1986 Topps	636	.07	.05	.03
1987 Donruss	292	.15	.11	.06
1987 Fleer	574	.10	.08	.04
1987 Leaf	80	.08	.06	.03
1987 O-Pee-Chee	23	.08	.06	.03
1987 Sportflics	104	.25	.20	.10
1987 Topps	23	.10	.08	.04
1988 Donruss	292	.10	.08	.04
1988 Fleer	433	.10	.08	.04
1988 Fleer Update	8	.20	.15	.08
1988 O-Pee-Chee	240	.08	.06	.03
1988 Score	31	.08	.06	.03
1988 Score Traded	20T	.50	.40	.20
1988 Score Traded/ Rookie Glossy	20T	2.00	1.50	.80
1988 Sportflics	179	.10	.08	.04
1988 Topps	240	.08	.06	.03
1988 Topps All-Star Glossy Set of 60	56	.25	.20	.10
1988 Topps Traded	110T	.10	.08	.04
1989 Bowman	19	.03	.02	.01
1989 Donruss	66	.08	.06	.03
1989 Fleer	99	.10	.08	.04
1989 O-Pee-Chee	149	.08	.06	.03
1989 Score	150	.08	.06	.03
1989 Sportflics	148	.10	.08	.03
1989 Topps	760	.08	.06	.03
1989 Upper Deck	521	.10	.08	.04
1990 Bowman	263	.06	.05	.02
1990 Donruss	110	.05	.04	.02
1990 Fleer	287	.05	.04	.02
1990 Fleer Update	53	.08	.06	.03
1990 Leaf	524	.40	.30	.15
1990 O-Pee-Chee	495	.06	.05	.02
1990 Score	37	.06	.05	.02
1990 Score Traded	48T	.08	.06	.03
1990 Topps	495	.06	.05	.02
1990 Topps Traded	118T	.08	.06	.03
1990 Upper Deck	393	.08	.06	.03
1991 Bowman	387	.06	.05	.02
1991 Donruss	169	.08	.06	.03
1991 Donruss	403	.05	.04	.02
1991 Fleer	645	.08	.06	.03
1991 Fleer Ultra	295	.08	.06	.03
1991 Leaf	44	.10	.08	.04
1991 Score	81	.08	.06	.03
1991 Studio	237	.15	.11	.06
1991 Topps	660	.06	.05	.02
1991 Topps Stadium Club	42	.25	.20	.10
1991 Upper Deck	348	.08	.06	.03
1992 Bowman	505	.08	.06	.03
1992 Donruss	112	.08	.06	.03
1992 Donruss Triple Play	62	.08	.06	.03
1992 Fleer	591	.06	.05	.02
1992 Fleer	697	.05	.04	.02
1992 Fleer All-Stars	8	.40	.30	.15
1992 Fleer Smoke 'N Heat	1	.50	.40	.20
1992 Fleer Ultra	270	.10	.08	.04
1992 Leaf	254	.15	.11	.06

Set	Card #			
1992 O-Pee-Chee	565	.05	.04	.02
1992 O-Pee-Chee Premier	190	.12	.09	.05
1992 Pinnacle	195	.12	.09	.05
1992 Score	630	.06	.05	.02
1992 Score	781	.06	.05	.02
1992 Studio	97	.15	.11	.06
1992 Topps	396	.08	.06	.03
1992 Topps	565	.05	.04	.02
1992 Topps Gold	396	.25	.20	.10
1992 Topps Gold	565	.35	.25	.14
1992 Topps Kids	28	.05	.04	.02
1992 Topps Stadium Club	180	.15	.11	.06
1992 Topps Stadium Club Special Edition	174	.30	.25	.12
1992 Upper Deck	376	.08	.06	.03
1992 Upper Deck MVP Holograms	49	.25	.20	.10
1993 Bowman	600	.10	.08	.04
1993 Donruss	548	.05	.04	.02
1993 Donruss Triple Play	83	.07	.05	.03
1993 Fleer	133	.06	.05	.02
1993 Fleer All-Stars	12	.75	.60	.30
1993 Fleer Final Edition	7DT	.20	.15	.08
1993 Fleer Flair	127	.25	.15	.08
1993 Fleer Ultra	112	.10	.08	.04
1993 Fleer Ultra All-Stars	10	.75	.60	.30
1993 Leaf	154	.10	.08	.04
1993 O-Pee-Chee	324	.15	.11	.06
1993 Pinnacle	416	.06	.05	.02
1993 Score	103	.08	.06	.03
1993 Score	529	.04	.03	.02
1993 Score Select	83	.10	.08	.04
1993 Score Select Chase Stars	12	2.50	2.00	1.00
1993 Score Select Rookie/Traded	31	.25	.20	.10
1993 Score Select Stat Leaders	70	.15	.11	.06
1993 Studio	147	.08	.06	.03
1993 Topps	12	.06	.05	.02
1993 Topps	411	.03	.02	.01
1993 Topps Black Gold	19	.25	.20	.10
1993 Topps Finest	95	1.00	.70	.40
1993 Topps Finest Jumbo All-Stars	95	7.00	5.25	2.75
1993 Topps Finest Refractors	95	20.00	15.00	8.00
1993 Topps Gold	12	.10	.08	.04
1993 Topps Gold	411	.10	.08	.04
1993 Topps Stadium Club	462	.10	.08	.04
1993 Topps Stadium Club First Day Production	462	7.00	5.25	2.75
1993 Topps Stadium Club Members Only	(24)	.50	.40	.20
1993 Topps Stadium Club Special	128	.10	.08	.04
1993 Upper Deck	82	.08	.06	.03
1993 Upper Deck Fun Packs	77	.12	.09	.05
1993 Upper Deck SP	78	.15	.11	.06
1994 Bowman	299	.10	.08	.04
1994 Bowman's Best	5	.50	.40	.20
1994 Bowman's Best Refractors	5	2.00	1.50	.80
1994 Donruss	650	.08	.06	.03
1994 Fleer	246	.05	.04	.02
1994 Fleer Extra Bases	14	.10	.08	.04
1994 Fleer Flair	258	.20	.15	.08
1994 Fleer Ultra	310	.10	.08	.04
1994 Fleer Update	8	.10	.08	.04
1994 Leaf	357	.12	.09	.05
1994 Leaf Limited	6	1.00	.70	.40
1994 Pacific Crown	436	.05	.04	.02
1994 Pinnacle	499	.10	.08	.04
1994 Pinnacle Artist's Proof	499	3.00	2.25	1.25
1994 Pinnacle Museum Collection	499	1.50	1.25	.60
1994 Pinnacle Tribute	18	2.00	1.50	.80
1994 Score	245	.04	.03	.02
1994 Score	627	.04	.03	.02
1994 Score Rookie & Traded Gold Rush	2	.25	.20	.10
1994 Score Rookie & Traded Changing Places	8	1.50	1.25	.60
1994 Score Rookie and Traded	2	.05	.04	.02
1994 Score Rookie/Traded Samples	1RT	2.00	1.50	.80
1994 Score Select	217	.10	.08	.04
1994 Studio	128	.10	.08	.04
1994 Topps	110	.04	.03	.02
1994 Topps Finest	351	.50	.40	.20
1994 Topps Finest Refractors	351	3.50	2.75	1.50
1994 Topps Gold	110	.15	.11	.06
1994 Topps Stadium Club	543a	.10	.08	.04
1994 Topps Stadium Club	605	.10	.08	.04
1994 Topps Stadium Club First Day Production	543a	10.00	7.50	4.00
1994 Topps Stadium Club First Day Production	605	10.00	7.50	4.00
1994 Topps Traded	100	.05	.04	.02
1994 Upper Deck	505	.10	.08	.04
1994 Upper Deck Collector's Choice	260	.05	.04	.02
1994 Upper Deck Collector's Choice	556	.05	.04	.02
1994 Upper Deck Electric Diamond	505	.25	.20	.10
1994 Upper Deck SP	127	.15	.11	.06
1994 Upper Deck SP Baseball Die-Cut	127	.25	.20	.10

Ozzie Smith

Set	Card #	NM	EX	VG
1979 O-Pee-Chee	52	85.00	42.00	25.00
1979 Topps	116 (R)	90.00	45.00	27.00
1980 O-Pee-Chee	205	21.00	10.50	6.25
1980 Topps	393	20.00	10.00	6.00

Set	Card #	MT	NM	EX
1981 Donruss	1	3.00	2.25	1.25
1981 Fleer	488	3.00	2.25	1.25
1981 O-Pee-Chee	254	4.25	3.25	1.75
1981 Topps	207	2.00	1.50	.80
1981 Topps	254	6.00	4.50	2.50
1982 Donruss	21	1.50	1.25	.60
1982 Donruss	94	3.00	2.25	1.25
1982 Fleer	582	1.75	1.25	.70
1982 O-Pee-Chee	95	2.75	2.00	1.00
1982 Topps	95	2.75	2.00	1.00
1983 Donruss	120	2.00	1.50	.80
1983 Fleer	22	2.50	2.00	1.00
1983 Fleer	636	.10	.08	.04
1983 O-Pee-Chee	14	2.25	1.75	.90
1983 Topps	540	2.00	1.50	.80

Year / Set	#			
1984 Donruss	59	6.00	4.50	2.50
1984 Donruss	625	.75	.60	.30
1984 Fleer	336	3.00	2.25	1.25
1984 O-Pee-Chee	130	1.00	.70	.40
1984 O-Pee-Chee	389	.20	.15	.08
1984 Topps	130	1.50	1.25	.60
1984 Topps	389	.50	.40	.20
1984 Topps All-Star Glossy Set of 22	16	.50	.40	.20
1984 Topps All-Star Glossy Set of 40	17	.45	.35	.20
1985 Donruss	59	2.50	2.00	1.00
1985 Fleer	240	2.00	1.50	.80
1985 Fleer	631	.25	.20	.10
1985 Leaf-Donruss	60	.15	.11	.06
1985 O-Pee-Chee	191	1.00	.70	.40
1985 Topps	605	.75	.60	.30
1985 Topps	715	.25	.20	.10
1985 Topps All-Star Glossy Set of 22	5	.30	.25	.12
1986 Donruss	59	1.00	.70	.40
1986 Fleer	46	1.00	.70	.40
1986 Leaf	47	.15	.11	.06
1986 O-Pee-Chee	297	.12	.09	.05
1986 Sportflics	121	.25	.20	.10
1986 Topps	704	.15	.11	.06
1986 Topps	730	.40	.30	.15
1986 Topps All-Star Glossy Set of 22	16	.30	.25	.12
1986 Topps All-Star Glossy Set of 60	46	.25	.20	.10
1987 Donruss	5	.20	.15	.08
1987 Donruss	60	.50	.40	.20
1987 Donruss Diamond Kings Supers	5	.60	.45	.25
1987 Fleer	308	1.00	.75	.40
1987 Fleer All Stars	41	.12	.09	.05
1987 Leaf	5	.30	.25	.12
1987 Leaf	108	.15	.11	.06
1987 O-Pee-Chee	107	.12	.09	.05
1987 Sportflics	79	.15	.11	.06
1987 Sportflics	142	.35	.25	.14
1987 Topps	181	.07	.05	.03
1987 Topps	598	.07	.05	.03
1987 Topps	749	.25	.20	.10
1987 Topps All-Star Glossy Set of 22	5	.30	.25	.12
1987 Topps All-Star Glossy Set of 60	23	.40	.30	.15
1988 Donruss	263	.15	.11	.06
1988 Donruss MVP	22	.30	.25	.12
1988 Fleer	47	.40	.30	.15
1988 Fleer	628	.35	.25	.14
1988 Leaf	115	.12	.09	.05
1988 O-Pee-Chee	38	.09	.07	.04
1988 Score	12	.15	.11	.06
1988 Sportflics	68	.40	.30	.15
1988 Topps	400	.10	.08	.04
1988 Topps	460	.20	.15	.08
1988 Topps All-Star Glossy Set of 22	16	.35	.25	.14
1988 Topps All-Star Glossy Set of 60	47	.35	.25	.14
1988 Topps Big Baseball	228	.20	.15	.08
1989 Bowman	436	.25	.20	.10
1989 Donruss	63	.20	.15	.08
1989 Donruss MVP	14	.30	.25	.12
1989 Fleer	463	.25	.20	.10
1989 O-Pee-Chee	230	.30	.25	.12
1989 Score	80	.25	.20	.10
1989 Sportflics	105	.20	.15	.08
1989 Topps	230	.25	.20	.10
1989 Topps	389	.12	.09	.05
1989 Topps All-Star Glossy Set of 22	16	.10	.08	.04
1989 Topps All-Star Glossy Set of 60	42	.25	.20	.10
1989 Topps Big Baseball	110	.08	.06	.03
1989 Upper Deck	265	.75	.60	.30
1989 Upper Deck	674	.08	.06	.03
1990 Bowman	195	.10	.08	.04
1990 Donruss	201	.10	.08	.04
1990 Donruss	710	.10	.08	.04
1990 Fleer	260	.25	.20	.10
1990 Leaf	142	1.50	1.25	.60
1990 O-Pee-Chee	400	.15	.11	.06
1990 O-Pee-Chee	590	.10	.08	.04
1990 Post Cereal	6	.50	.40	.20
1990 Score	285	.25	.20	.10
1990 Topps	400	.15	.11	.06
1990 Topps	590	.10	.08	.04
1990 Topps All-Star Glossy Set of 22	5	.20	.15	.08
1990 Topps All-Star Glossy Set of 60	16	.25	.20	.10
1990 Upper Deck	225	.25	.20	.10
1991 Bowman	398	.20	.15	.08
1991 Donruss	240	.20	.15	.08
1991 Donruss	437	.10	.08	.04
1991 Fleer	646	.10	.08	.04
1991 Fleer Ultra	296	.30	.25	.12
1991 Leaf	80	.25	.20	.10
1991 O-Pee-Chee Premier	112	.25	.20	.10
1991 Score	825	.10	.08	.04
1991 Studio	238	.25	.20	.10
1991 Topps	130	.08	.06	.03
1991 Topps All-Star Glossy Set of 22	16	.30	.25	.12
1991 Topps Stadium Club	154	.70	.50	.30
1991 Upper Deck	162	.30	.25	.12
1991 Upper Deck Final Edition	95	.15	.11	.06
1992 Bowman	675	1.00	.70	.40
1992 Donruss	423	.10	.08	.04
1992 Donruss	432	.08	.06	.03
1992 Donruss Triple Play	244	.15	.11	.06
1992 Fleer	592	.15	.11	.06
1992 Fleer Ultra	271	.40	.30	.15
1992 Fleer Ultra Award Winners	9	2.50	2.00	1.00
1992 Leaf	400	.25	.20	.10
1992 O-Pee-Chee	760	.10	.08	.04
1992 O-Pee-Chee Premier	84	.20	.15	.08
1992 Pinnacle	6	.30	.25	.12
1992 Pinnacle	285	.15	.11	.06
1992 Pinnacle Rookie Idols	15	8.00	6.00	3.25
1992 Post Cereal	8	.40	.30	.15
1992 Score	590	.15	.11	.06
1992 Score Factory Inserts	9	1.50	1.25	.60
1992 Studio	98	.30	.25	.12
1992 Studio Preview	20	4.00	3.00	1.50
1992 Topps	760	.25	.20	.10
1992 Topps Gold	760	1.50	1.25	.60
1992 Topps Kids	25	.20	.15	.08
1992 Topps Stadium Club	680	.40	.30	.15
1992 Topps Stadium Club Members Only	(9)	.75	.60	.30
1992 Topps Stadium Club Members Only	(10)	.75	.60	.30
1992 Topps Stadium Club National Convention	680	35.00	26.00	14.00
1992 Topps Stadium Club Special Edition	175	.35	.25	.14
1992 Upper Deck	177	.20	.15	.08
1992 Upper Deck	716	.15	.11	.06
1993 Bowman	460	.40	.30	.15
1993 DiamondMarks	(55)	.60	.45	.25
1993 Donruss	520	.25	.20	.10
1993 Donruss Triple Play Action Baseball	3	.20	.15	.08
1993 Donruss Triple Play Nicknames	9	2.00	1.50	.80
1993 Donruss Triple Play	122	.15	.11	.06
1993 Fleer Final Edition	8DT	.40	.30	.15
1993 Fleer Final Edition	131	.25	.20	.10
1993 Fleer Flair	128	1.00	.70	.40
1993 Fleer Ultra	113	.40	.30	.15
1993 Fleer Ultra Award Winners	6	3.00	2.25	1.25

1993 Leaf	328	.40	.30	.15
1993 Leaf Heading for the Hall	10	3.00	2.25	1.25
1993 O-Pee-Chee	313	.90	.70	.35
1993 Pinnacle	329	.35	.25	.14
1993 Pinnacle Cooperstown	9	.30	.25	.12
1993 Pinnacle Cooperstown Dufex	9	60.00	45.00	24.00
1993 Pinnacle Team Pinnacle	7	10.00	7.50	4.00
1993 Post Cereal	26	.50	.40	.20
1993 Score	522	.08	.06	.03
1993 Score	532	.06	.05	.02
1993 Score	562	.25	.20	.10
1993 Score Gold Dream Team	1	1.00	.60	.30
1993 Score Select	15	.25	.20	.10
1993 Score Select Chase Stars	3	9.00	6.75	3.50
1993 Studio	217	.35	.25	.14
1993 Studio Heritage	6	2.00	1.50	.80
1993 Topps	40	.15	.11	.06
1993 Topps Black Gold	20	.40	.30	.15
1993 Topps Finest	28	6.00	4.50	2.50
1993 Topps Finest Refractors	28	75.00	60.00	30.00
1993 Topps Gold	40	.30	.25	.12
1993 Topps Stadium Club	548	.30	.25	.12
1993 Topps Stadium Club First Day Production	548	35.00	26.00	14.00
1993 Topps Stadium Club Special	147	.15	.11	.06
1993 Upper Deck	146	.10	.07	.04
1993 Upper Deck Diamond Gallery	31	3.00	2.25	1.25
1993 Upper Deck Fun Packs All-Star Scratch-Off	6	4.00	3.00	1.50
1993 Upper Deck Fun Packs	35	.05	.04	.02
1993 Upper Deck Fun Packs	74	.20	.15	.08
1993 Upper Deck Fun Packs	78	.20	.15	.08
1993 Upper Deck Fun Packs	215	.10	.08	.04
1993 Upper Deck Iooss Collection	7	1.00	.75	.40
1993 Upper Deck Iooss Collection Super	7	4.00	3.00	1.50
1993 Upper Deck SP	79	1.25	.90	.50
1993 Upper Deck Then And Now	7	2.00	1.50	.80
1994 Bowman	424	.25	.20	.10
1994 Bowman's Best	3	2.00	1.50	.80
1994 Bowman's Best Refractors	3	12.00	9.00	4.75
1994 Donruss	35	.30	.25	.12
1994 Donruss Special Edition - Gold	35	.35	.25	.14
1994 Donruss Triple Play	66	.20	.15	.08
1994 Fleer	646	.25	.20	.10
1994 Fleer Extra Bases	363	.35	.25	.14
1994 Fleer Flair	228	1.00	.75	.40
1994 Fleer ProVisions	5	.50	.40	.20
1994 Fleer Ultra	567	.40	.30	.15
1994 Leaf	409	.40	.30	.15
1994 Leaf Limited	147	3.00	2.25	1.25
1994 Leaf Limited Gold	8	20.00	15.00	8.00
1994 O-Pee-Chee	181	.30	.25	.12
1994 Pacific Crown	604	.25	.20	.10
1994 Pinnacle	389	.25	.20	.10
1994 Pinnacle Artist's Proof	389	15.00	11.00	6.00
1994 Pinnacle Museum Collection	389	5.00	3.75	2.00
1994 Pinnacle Tribute	10	3.50	2.75	1.50
1994 Score	384	.25	.20	.10
1994 Score Select	30	.50	.40	.20
1994 Sportflics 2000	41	.40	.30	.15
1994 Studio	54	.30	.25	.12
1994 Topps	320	.15	.11	.06
1994 Topps Finest	136	2.00	1.50	.80
1994 Topps Finest Refractors	136	18.00	12.00	6.50
1994 Topps Gold	320	.45	.35	.20
1994 Topps Stadium Club	417	.25	.20	.10
1994 Topps Stadium Club	541	.25	.20	.10
1994 Topps Stadium Club First Day Production	417	25.00	18.50	10.00
1994 Topps Stadium Club First Day Production	541	25.00	18.50	10.00
1994 Upper Deck	278	.15	.11	.06
1994 Upper Deck	360	.40	.30	.15
1994 Upper Deck Collector's Choice	334	.05	.04	.02
1994 Upper Deck Collector's Choice	545	.10	.08	.04
1994 Upper Deck Diamond Collection	7C	10.00	7.50	4.00
1994 Upper Deck Electric Diamond	278	.50	.40	.20
1994 Upper Deck Electric Diamond	360	.50	.40	.20
1994 Upper Deck Fun Packs	101	.15	.11	.06
1994 Upper Deck SP	65	.40	.30	.15
1994 Upper Deck SP Baseball Die-Cut	65	1.00	.75	.40
1994 Upper Deck SP Holoview Blue	36	4.00	3.00	1.50
1994 Upper Deck SP Holoview Red	36	40.00	30.00	15.00

Reggie Smith

Set	Card #	NM	EX	VG
1967 Topps	314 (R)	7.50	3.75	2.25
1968 O-Pee-Chee	61	2.25	1.25	.70
1968 Topps	61	2.50	1.25	.70
1969 Topps	660	2.50	1.25	.70
1970 O-Pee-Chee	62	1.75	.90	.50
1970 O-Pee-Chee	215	1.00	.50	.30
1970 Topps	62	3.50	1.75	1.00
1970 Topps	215	1.00	.50	.30
1971 O-Pee-Chee	305	1.50	.70	.45
1971 Topps	305	1.50	.70	.45
1972 O-Pee-Chee	88	1.25	.60	.40
1972 Topps	88	3.50	1.75	1.00
1972 Topps	565	2.00	1.00	.60
1972 Topps	566	2.00	1.00	.60
1973 O-Pee-Chee	40	.75	.40	.25
1973 Topps	40	.40	.20	.12
1974 O-Pee-Chee	285	.60	.30	.20
1974 Topps	285	.30	.15	.09
1975 O-Pee-Chee	490	.55	.30	.15
1975 Topps	490	.30	.15	.09
1975 Topps Mini	490	.60	.30	.20

Set	Card #			
1976 O-Pee-Chee	215	.35	.20	.11
1976 Topps	215	.25	.13	.08
1977 O-Pee-Chee	223	.30	.15	.09
1977 Topps	345	.25	.13	.08
1978 O-Pee-Chee	57	.25	.13	.08
1978 Topps	168	.25	.13	.08
1979 O-Pee-Chee	243	.25	.13	.08
1979 Topps	465	.25	.13	.08
1980 O-Pee-Chee	350	.20	.10	.06
1980 Topps	695	.20	.10	.06

Set	Card #	MT	NM	EX
1981 Donruss	59	.10	.08	.04
1981 Fleer	111	.10	.08	.04
1981 O-Pee-Chee	75	.12	.09	.05
1981 Topps	75	.15	.11	.06
1982 Donruss	488	.10	.08	.04
1982 Fleer	23	.10	.08	.04
1982 O-Pee-Chee	5	.12	.09	.05
1982 O-Pee-Chee	228	.12	.09	.05
1982 Topps	545	.15	.11	.06
1982 Topps	546	.10	.08	.04
1982 Topps Traded	110T	.20	.15	.08
1983 Donruss	611	.10	.08	.04
1983 Fleer	272	.10	.08	.04
1983 O-Pee-Chee	282	.12	.09	.05
1983 O-Pee-Chee	283	.12	.09	.05
1983 Topps	282	.12	.09	.05
1983 Topps	283	.10	.08	.04

Duke Snider

Set	Card #	NM	EX	VG
1949 Bowman	226	950.00	475.00	275.00
1950 Bowman	77	250.00	125.00	75.00
1951 Bowman	32	240.00	120.00	72.50
1951 Topps Red Backs	38	50.00	25.00	15.00
1952 Bowman	116	180.00	90.00	55.00
1952 Red Man Tobacco	21N	115.00	57.00	34.00
1952 Topps	37	275.00	137.00	63.00
1953 Bowman Color	117	575.00	275.00	165.00
1953 Red Man Tobacco	14N	100.00	50.00	30.00
1954 Bowman	170	160.00	80.00	47.50
1954 Red Heart Dog Food	(29)	125.00	62.00	37.00
1954 Red Man Tobacco	16N	100.00	50.00	30.00
1954 Topps	32	110.00	55.00	32.50
1955 Red Man Tobacco	19N	100.00	50.00	30.00
1955 Topps	210	350.00	175.00	100.00
1956 Topps	150	110.00	55.00	32.50
1957 Topps	170	90.00	45.00	27.00
1957 Topps	400	175.00	85.00	50.00
1958 Topps	88	65.00	32.00	19.50
1958 Topps	314	17.50	8.75	5.25
1958 Topps	436	65.00	32.00	19.50
1959 Home Run Derby	(18)	400.00	200.00	120.00
1959 Topps	20	60.00	30.00	18.00
1959 Topps	468	15.00	7.50	4.50
1960 Leaf	37	50.00	25.00	15.00
1960 Topps	493	40.00	20.00	12.00
1961 Post Cereal	167a	8.00	4.00	2.50

Set	Card #	NM	EX	VG
1961 Post Cereal	167b	30.00	15.00	9.00
1961 Topps	443	35.00	17.50	10.50
1962 Post Cereal	114	12.00	6.00	3.50
1962 Topps	500	42.50	21.00	12.50
1963 Post Cereal	118	10.00	5.00	3.00
1963 Topps	68	16.50	8.25	5.00
1963 Topps	550	65.00	32.00	19.50
1964 Topps	155	25.00	12.50	7.50

Set	Card #	MT	NM	EX
1983 Topps 1952 Reprint Set	37	4.00	3.00	1.50
1986 Sportflics Decade Greats	32	.70	.50	.30
1988 Pacific Trading Cards Baseball Legends	55	.30	.25	.12
1989 Bowman Inserts	(10)	.15	.11	.06
1991 "1953" Topps Archives	327	1.50	1.25	.60
1994 "1954" Topps Archives	32	.60	.45	.25

Warren Spahn

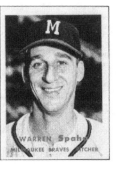

Set	Card #	NM	EX	VG
1948 Bowman	18 (R)	300.00	150.00	90.00
1948 Leaf	32 (R)	300.00	150.00	90.00
1949 Bowman	33	150.00	75.00	45.00
1950 Bowman	19	200.00	100.00	60.00
1951 Bowman	134	115.00	55.00	35.00
1951 Topps Red Backs	30	45.00	22.50	13.50
1952 Bowman	156	80.00	40.00	24.00
1952 Red Man Tobacco	22N	60.00	30.00	18.00
1952 Topps	33	250.00	125.00	57.00
1953 Bowman Color	99	175.00	87.50	52.50
1953 Red Man Tobacco	19N	60.00	30.00	18.00
1953 Topps	147	140.00	70.00	32.00
1954 Red Heart Dog Food	(30)	60.00	30.00	18.00
1954 Red Man Tobacco	11N	75.00	37.00	22.00
1954 Topps	20	75.00	37.50	22.00
1955 Red Man Tobacco	10N	60.00	30.00	18.00
1955 Topps	31	75.00	37.50	22.00
1956 Topps	10	65.00	32.00	19.50
1957 Topps	90	50.00	25.00	15.00
1958 Topps	270	45.00	22.00	13.50
1958 Topps	494	16.00	8.00	4.75
1959 Topps	40	50.00	25.00	15.00
1959 Topps	571	40.00	20.00	12.00
1960 Topps	230	9.00	4.50	2.75
1960 Topps	445	40.00	20.00	12.00
1961 Post Cereal	101a	21.00	10.50	6.25
1961 Post Cereal	101b	12.00	6.00	3.50
1961 Topps	47	6.00	3.00	1.75
1961 Topps	200	30.00	15.00	9.00
1961 Topps	589	120.00	60.00	36.00
1962 Topps	56	8.00	4.00	2.50
1962 Topps	58	8.00	4.00	2.50
1962 Topps	100	30.00	15.00	9.00
1962 Topps	312	8.00	4.00	2.50
1962 Topps	399	15.00	7.50	4.50

Set	Card #		
1963 Fleer	45	50.00	20.00	12.00
1963 Topps	320	32.50	16.00	9.75
1964 Topps	3	15.00	11.00	6.00
1964 Topps	400	40.00	20.00	12.00
1965 O-Pee-Chee	205	38.00	19.00	11.50
1965 Topps	205	20.00	10.00	6.00
1973 O-Pee-Chee	449	1.25	.60	.40
1973 Topps	449a	1.50	.70	.45
1973 Topps	449b	2.00	1.00	.60

Set	Card #	MT	NM	EX
1983 Topps 1952 Reprint Set	33	2.50	2.00	1.00
1986 Sportflics Decade Greats	27	.30	.25	.12
1988 Pacific Trading Cards Baseball Legends	109	.25	.20	.10
1990 Pacific Legends	51	.35	.25	.14
1991 "1953" Topps Archives	147	1.00	.70	.40
1994 "1954" Topps Archives	20	.30	.25	.12

Willie Stargell

Set	Card #	NM	EX	VG
1963 Topps	553 (R)	160.00	80.00	47.50
1964 Topps	342	35.00	17.50	10.50
1965 Topps	377	20.00	10.00	6.00
1966 O-Pee-Chee	99	2.25	1.25	.70
1966 Topps	99	5.00	2.50	1.50
1966 Topps	255	18.00	9.00	5.50
1967 O-Pee-Chee	140	25.00	12.50	7.50
1967 Topps	140	20.00	10.00	6.00
1967 Topps	266	5.00	2.50	1.50
1968 O-Pee-Chee	86	17.00	8.50	5.00
1968 Topps	86	8.00	4.00	2.50
1969 Topps	545	10.00	5.00	3.00
1970 O-Pee-Chee	470	12.75	6.50	3.75
1970 Topps	470	7.00	3.50	2.00
1971 O-Pee-Chee	230	12.75	6.50	3.75
1971 Topps	230	8.00	4.00	2.50
1972 O-Pee-Chee	87	1.25	.60	.40
1972 O-Pee-Chee	89	1.25	.60	.40
1972 O-Pee-Chee	343	1.25	.60	.40
1972 O-Pee-Chee	447	8.50	4.25	2.50
1972 O-Pee-Chee	448	1.75	.90	.50
1972 Topps	87	4.50	2.25	1.25
1972 Topps	89	4.50	2.25	1.25
1972 Topps	343	1.50	.70	.45
1972 Topps	447	5.00	2.50	1.50
1972 Topps	448	2.50	1.25	.75
1973 O-Pee-Chee	370	6.00	3.00	1.75
1973 Topps	370	6.00	3.00	1.75
1974 O-Pee-Chee	100	5.50	2.75	1.75
1974 O-Pee-Chee	202	6.25	3.25	2.00
1974 O-Pee-Chee	203	6.25	3.25	2.00
1974 Topps	100	6.00	3.00	1.75
1974 Topps	202	5.00	2.50	1.50
1974 Topps	203	5.00	2.50	1.50

1975 O-Pee-Chee	100	2.00	1.00	.60
1975 Topps	100	5.00	2.50	1.50
1976 O-Pee-Chee	270	2.25	1.25	.70
1976 Topps	270	3.00	1.50	.90
1977 O-Pee-Chee	25	2.25	1.25	.70
1977 Topps	460	4.00	2.00	1.25
1978 Topps	510	3.00	1.50	.90
1979 O-Pee-Chee	22	1.75	.90	.50
1979 Topps	55	2.00	1.00	.60
1980 O-Pee-Chee	319	1.25	.60	.40
1980 Topps	610	1.50	.70	.45

Set	Card #	MT	NM	EX
1981 Donruss	12	.80	.60	.30
1981 Donruss	132	.60	.45	.25
1981 Fleer	363	.40	.30	.15
1981 O-Pee-Chee	127	.75	.60	.30
1981 Topps	380	1.00	.70	.40
1982 Donruss	639	.40	.30	.15
1982 Fleer	499	.40	.30	.15
1982 O-Pee-Chee	188	.30	.25	.12
1982 O-Pee-Chee	372	.60	.45	.25
1982 Topps	715	.80	.60	.30
1982 Topps	716	.30	.25	.12
1983 Donruss	8	.25	.20	.10
1983 Donruss	610	.40	.30	.15
1983 Fleer	324	.40	.30	.15
1983 Fleer	634	.40	.30	.15
1989 Topps All-Star Glossy Set of 22	22	.10	.08	.04
1991 Donruss	702	.10	.08	.04

Dave Stewart

Set	Card #	MT	NM	EX
1982 Donruss	410 (R)	3.00	2.25	1.25
1982 Fleer	24 (R)	3.00	2.25	1.25
1982 Topps	213 (R)	4.00	3.00	1.50
1983 Donruss	588	.75	.60	.30
1983 Fleer	222	.60	.45	.25
1983 Topps	532	.75	.60	.30
1984 Donruss	343	.50	.40	.20
1984 Fleer	430	.15	.11	.06
1984 O-Pee-Chee	352	.25	.20	.10
1984 Topps	352	.30	.25	.12
1985 Donruss	343	.15	.11	.06
1985 Fleer	569	.12	.09	.05
1985 Topps	723	.12	.09	.05
1986 Donruss	619	.12	.09	.05
1986 Fleer	453	.12	.09	.05
1986 Topps	689	.12	.09	.05
1987 Donruss	648	.10	.08	.04
1987 Fleer	406	.25	.20	.10
1987 Topps	14	.12	.09	.05
1988 Donruss	472	.10	.08	.04
1988 Fleer	295	.10	.08	.04
1988 Leaf	217	.08	.06	.03
1988 O-Pee-Chee	353	.08	.06	.03
1988 Score	458	.08	.06	.03
1988 Sportflics	162	.10	.08	.04

1988 Topps	476	.08	.06	.03
1988 Topps All-Star Glossy Set of 60	33	.25	.20	.10
1989 Bowman	188	.08	.06	.03
1989 Donruss	214	.08	.06	.03
1989 Fleer	23	.10	.08	.04
1989 O-Pee-Chee	145	.10	.08	.04
1989 Score	32	.08	.06	.03
1989 Score	582	.10	.06	.03
1989 Sportflics	23	.10	.08	.04
1989 Topps	145	.08	.06	.03
1989 Topps All-Star Glossy Set of 60	45	.15	.11	.06
1989 Topps Big Baseball	101	.10	.08	.04
1989 Upper Deck	185	.10	.08	.04
1990 Bowman	449	.08	.06	.03
1990 Donruss	6	.12	.09	.05
1990 Donruss	150	.07	.05	.03
1990 Donruss	703	.08	.06	.03
1990 Donruss Diamond Kings Supers	6	.20	.15	.08
1990 Donruss MVP	3	.08	.06	.03
1990 Fleer	21	.10	.08	.06
1990 Leaf	81	.35	.25	.14
1990 O-Pee-Chee	270	.08	.06	.03
1990 Score	410	.09	.07	.04
1990 Sportflics	194	.12	.09	.05
1990 Topps	270	.08	.06	.03
1990 Topps All-Star Glossy Set of 60	4	.15	.11	.06
1990 Topps All-Star Glossy Set of 22	21	.15	.11	.06
1990 Topps Big Baseball	64	.12	.09	.05
1990 Upper Deck	272	.09	.07	.04
1991 Bowman	225	.10	.08	.04
1991 Donruss	102	.08	.06	.03
1991 Fleer	25	.10	.08	.04
1991 Fleer ProVisions	4F	.40	.30	.15
1991 Fleer Ultra	254	.10	.08	.04
1991 Leaf	417	.10	.08	.04
1991 O-Pee-Chee Premier	115	.05	.04	.02
1991 Score	150	.12	.09	.05
1991 Score	702	.08	.06	.03
1991 Score	883	.10	.08	.04
1991 Studio	107	.20	.15	.08
1991 Topps	580	.12	.09	.05
1991 Topps Stadium Club	1	.40	.30	.15
1991 Topps Stadium Club Charter Members	(27)	.25	.20	.10
1991 Upper Deck	127	.12	.09	.05
1992 Bowman	280	.20	.15	.08
1992 Donruss	225	.08	.06	.03
1992 Fleer	268	.08	.06	.03
1992 Fleer Ultra	117	.15	.11	.06
1992 Leaf	258	.15	.11	.06
1992 O-Pee-Chee	410	.08	.06	.03
1992 Pinnacle	157	.12	.09	.05
1992 Score	580	.06	.05	.02
1992 Studio	230	.15	.11	.06
1992 Topps	410	.08	.06	.03
1992 Topps Gold	410	.35	.25	.14
1992 Topps Kids	117	.10	.08	.04
1992 Upper Deck	547	.10	.08	.04
1993 DiamondMarks	(120)	.25	.20	.10
1993 Donruss	611	.05	.04	.02
1993 Fleer	669	.05	.04	.02
1993 Fleer Final Edition	296	.05	.04	.02
1993 Fleer Flair	295	.25	.15	.08
1993 Fleer Ultra	647	.10	.08	.04
1993 Leaf	294	.10	.08	.04
1993 O-Pee-Chee	294	.15	.11	.06
1993 O-Pee-Chee Premier	45	.10	.08	.04
1993 Pinnacle	442	.06	.05	.02
1993 Score	656	.08	.06	.03
1993 Score Select	240	.12	.09	.05
1993 Score Select Rookie/ Traded	24	.25	.20	.10
1993 Topps	290	.08	.06	.03
1993 Topps Gold	290	.15	.11	.06
1993 Topps Stadium Club	629	.10	.08	.04
1993 Topps Stadium Club First Day Production	629	5.00	3.75	2.00
1993 Topps Stadium Club Members Only	(25)	.50	.40	.20
1993 Topps Traded	114	.05	.04	.02
1993 Upper Deck	39	.10	.08	.04
1993 Upper Deck	546	.08	.06	.03
1994 Bowman	113	.10	.08	.04
1994 Donruss	257	.05	.04	.02
1994 Fleer	343	.05	.04	.02
1994 Fleer Extra Bases	195	.10	.08	.04
1994 Fleer Flair	121	.20	.15	.08
1994 Fleer Ultra	143	.10	.08	.04
1994 Leaf	308	.10	.08	.04
1994 O-Pee-Chee	12	.05	.04	.02
1994 Pacific Crown	652	.05	.04	.02
1994 Pinnacle	374	.10	.08	.04
1994 Pinnacle Artist's Proof	374	3.00	2.25	1.25
1994 Pinnacle Museum Collection	374	1.50	1.25	.60
1994 Score	133	.04	.03	.02
1994 Score Select	165	.10	.08	.04
1994 Topps	455	.05	.04	.02
1994 Topps Finest	134	.50	.40	.20
1994 Topps Finest Refractors	134	3.50	2.75	1.50
1994 Topps Gold	455	.15	.11	.06
1994 Topps Stadium Club	317	.10	.08	.04
1994 Topps Stadium Club First Day Production	317	2.50	2.00	1.00
1994 Upper Deck	89	.10	.08	.04
1994 Upper Deck Collector's Choice	371	.05	.04	.02
1994 Upper Deck Electric Diamond	89	.25	.20	.10

Don Sutton

Set	Card #	NM	EX	VG
1966 Topps	288 (R)	90.00	45.00	27.00
1967 Topps	445	24.00	12.00	7.25
1968 O-Pee-Chee	103	17.00	8.50	5.00
1968 Topps	103	8.00	4.00	2.50
1969 O-Pee-Chee	216	10.25	5.25	3.00
1969 Topps	216	4.00	2.00	1.25
1970 Topps	622	7.00	3.50	2.00
1971 O-Pee-Chee	361	10.25	5.25	3.00
1971 Topps	361	3.50	1.75	1.00
1972 Topps	530	4.00	2.00	1.25
1973 O-Pee-Chee	10	1.20	.60	.35
1973 Topps	10	2.00	1.00	.60
1974 O-Pee-Chee	220	1.25	.60	.40
1974 Topps	220	2.00	1.00	.60
1975 O-Pee-Chee	220	2.00	1.00	.60
1975 Topps	220	1.50	.70	.45
1975 Topps Mini	220	3.00	1.50	.90

1976 O-Pee-Chee	530	1.25	.60	.40
1976 Topps	530	1.50	.70	.45
1977 O-Pee-Chee	24	1.25	.60	.40
1977 Topps	620	1.50	.70	.45
1978 O-Pee-Chee	96	1.00	.50	.30
1978 Topps	310	2.00	1.00	.60
1979 O-Pee-Chee	80	1.75	.90	.50
1979 Topps	170	1.25	.60	.40
1980 O-Pee-Chee	228	.75	.40	.25
1980 Topps	440	1.00	.50	.30

Set	Card #	MT	NM	EX
1981 Donruss	58	.25	.20	.10
1981 Fleer	112	.30	.25	.12
1981 Topps	7	.15	.11	.06
1981 Topps	605	.70	.50	.30
1981 Topps Traded	839	1.50	1.25	.60
1982 Donruss	443	.30	.25	.12
1982 Fleer	234	.30	.25	.12
1982 O-Pee-Chee	305	.40	.30	.15
1982 O-Pee-Chee	306	.20	.15	.08
1982 Topps	305	.50	.40	.20
1982 Topps	306	.25	.20	.10
1983 Donruss	531a	.30	.25	.12
1983 Donruss	531b	.30	.25	.12
1983 Fleer	47	.30	.25	.12
1983 O-Pee-Chee	145	.30	.25	.12
1983 O-Pee-Chee	146	.15	.11	.06
1983 Topps	145	.40	.30	.15
1983 Topps	146	.20	.15	.08
1984 Donruss	414	1.00	.70	.40
1984 Fleer	215	.30	.25	.12
1984 O-Pee-Chee	35	.50	.40	.20
1984 Topps	35	.20	.15	.08
1984 Topps	715	.25	.20	.10
1984 Topps	716	.15	.11	.06
1985 Donruss	16	.30	.25	.12
1985 Donruss	107	.35	.25	.14
1985 Donruss Diamond Kings Supers	16	.30	.25	.12
1985 Fleer	598	.30	.25	.12
1985 Fleer Update	115	.60	.45	.25
1985 Leaf-Donruss	16	.20	.15	.08
1985 O-Pee-Chee	172	.20	.15	.08
1985 Topps	10	.20	.15	.08
1985 Topps	729	.20	.15	.08
1985 Topps Traded	116T	.60	.45	.25
1986 Donruss	611	.25	.20	.10
1986 Fleer	170	.25	.20	.10
1986 Leaf	236	.20	.15	.08
1986 O-Pee-Chee	335	.20	.15	.08
1986 Sportflics	135	.25	.20	.10
1986 Sportflics	175	.25	.20	.10
1986 Topps	335	.20	.15	.08
1987 Donruss	181	.20	.15	.08
1987 Fleer	93	.15	.11	.06
1987 Fleer	626	.12	.09	.05
1987 Leaf	153	.15	.11	.06
1987 O-Pee-Chee	259	.12	.09	.05
1987 Sportflics	99	.40	.30	.15
1987 Sportflics	156	.30	.25	.12
1987 Topps	673	.10	.07	.04
1988 Donruss	407	.10	.08	.04
1988 Fleer	505	.12	.09	.05
1988 Score	105	.12	.09	.05
1988 Sportflics	213	.20	.15	.08
1988 Topps	575	.12	.09	.05
1989 Score	400	.08	.05	.02

* * *

Buffalo Bills running back Thurman Thomas, on card collecting: "I know the value of one card - my rookie card," he said. "That's the one everyone is looking for. The guys in the locker room always ask me, when my card goes up, if I have any extra rookie cards I can give them."

* * *

Mickey Tettleton

Set	Card #	MT	NM	EX
1985 Fleer Update	119	7.00	5.25	2.75
1985 Topps Traded	120T	7.00	5.25	2.75
1986 Donruss	345 (R)	2.50	2.00	1.00
1986 Fleer	432 (R)	2.50	2.00	1.00
1986 Topps	457 (R)	.75	.60	.30
1987 Donruss	349	.10	.08	.04
1987 Fleer	407	.25	.20	.10
1987 Topps	456	.07	.05	.03
1987 Topps	649	.20	.15	.08
1988 Donruss	103	.10	.08	.04
1988 Score	269	.10	.08	.04
1988 Score Traded	31T	.60	.45	.25
1988 Score Traded/ Rookie Glossy	31T	2.50	2.00	1.00
1988 Topps	143	.12	.09	.05
1988 Topps Traded	120T	.15	.11	.06
1989 Donruss	401	.08	.06	.03
1989 Fleer	623	.15	.11	.06
1989 Score	358	.03	.02	.01
1989 Topps	521	.03	.02	.01
1989 Topps Big Baseball	198	.08	.06	.03
1989 Upper Deck	553	.15	.11	.06
1990 Bowman	254	.06	.05	.02
1990 Donruss	5	.12	.09	.05
1990 Donruss	169	.08	.06	.03
1990 Donruss Diamond Kings Supers	5	.10	.08	.04
1990 Fleer	190	.08	.06	.03
1990 Fleer All-Stars	12	.20	.15	.08
1990 Leaf	65	.50	.40	.20
1990 O-Pee-Chee	275	.07	.05	.03
1990 Score	322	.09	.07	.04
1990 Sportflics	171	.12	.09	.05
1990 Topps	275	.07	.05	.03
1990 Topps All-Star Glossy Set of 60	57	.15	.11	.06
1990 Upper Deck	297	.10	.08	.04
1991 Bowman	140	.06	.05	.02
1991 Donruss	597	.08	.06	.03
1991 Fleer	494	.06	.05	.02
1991 Fleer Ultra Update	24	.25	.20	.10
1991 Fleer Update	24	.08	.06	.03
1991 Leaf	322	.15	.11	.06
1991 Score	270	.05	.04	.02
1991 Score Traded	25	.08	.06	.03
1991 Studio	58	.20	.15	.08
1991 Topps	385	.05	.04	.02
1991 Topps Stadium Club	412	.25	.20	.10
1991 Topps Traded	119	.06	.05	.02
1991 Upper Deck	296	.06	.05	.02
1991 Upper Deck	729	.12	.09	.05
1992 Bowman	117	.20	.15	.08
1992 Donruss	85	.08	.06	.03
1992 Donruss Triple Play	44	.08	.06	.03
1992 Fleer	147	.06	.05	.02
1992 Fleer All-Stars	9	.50	.40	.20
1992 Fleer Lumber Co.	2	1.00	.60	.30
1992 Fleer Ultra	63	.15	.11	.06
1992 Fleer Ultra All-Stars	5	.50	.40	.20

Set	Card #	MT	NM	EX
1992 Leaf	285	.15	.11	.06
1992 O-Pee-Chee	29	.05	.04	.02
1992 Pinnacle	226	.15	.11	.06
1992 Score	134	.08	.06	.03
1992 Studio	178	.15	.11	.06
1992 Topps	29	.05	.04	.02
1992 Topps Gold	29	.50	.40	.20
1992 Topps Stadium Club	195	.15	.11	.06
1992 Upper Deck	251	.06	.05	.02
1993 Bowman	615	.10	.08	.04
1993 DiamondMarks	(74)	.25	.20	.10
1993 Donruss	13	.08	.06	.03
1993 Donruss Spirit of the Game	10	1.50	1.25	.60
1993 Donruss Triple Play	92	.10	.08	.04
1993 Fleer	234	.08	.06	.03
1993 Fleer Flair	208	.25	.15	.08
1993 Fleer Ultra	554	.10	.08	.04
1993 Leaf	213	.10	.08	.04
1993 O-Pee-Chee	334	.15	.11	.06
1993 Pinnacle	52	.06	.05	.02
1993 Pinnacle Home Run Club	18	.25	.20	.10
1993 Pinnacle Slugfest	22	.50	.40	.20
1993 Score	60	.04	.03	.02
1993 Score Select	60	.10	.08	.04
1993 Studio	138	.08	.06	.03
1993 Topps	135	.08	.06	.03
1993 Topps Black Gold	41	.25	.20	.10
1993 Topps Finest	80	1.00	.70	.40
1993 Topps Finest Refractors	80	20.00	15.00	8.00
1993 Topps Gold	135	.15	.11	.06
1993 Topps Stadium Club	31	.12	.09	.05
1993 Topps Stadium Club First Day Production	31	15.00	11.00	6.00
1993 Upper Deck	46	.12	.09	.05
1993 Upper Deck	86	.08	.06	.03
1993 Upper Deck SP	240	.15	.11	.06
1994 Bowman	125	.10	.08	.04
1994 Donruss	44	.05	.04	.02
1994 Donruss Triple Play Medalists	1	1.00	.75	.40
1994 Donruss Triple Play	248	.05	.04	.02
1994 Fleer	143	.05	.04	.02
1994 Fleer Extra Bases	80	.10	.08	.04
1994 Fleer Flair	295	.20	.15	.08
1994 Fleer Ultra	356	.10	.08	.04
1994 Leaf	279	.10	.08	.04
1994 Leaf Limited	33	1.00	.70	.40
1994 O-Pee-Chee	32	.05	.04	.02
1994 Pacific Crown	229	.05	.04	.02
1994 Pacific Crown Homerun Leaders	8	2.00	1.50	.80
1994 Pinnacle	67	.10	.08	.04
1994 Pinnacle Artist's Proof	67	3.00	2.25	1.25
1994 Pinnacle Museum Collection	67	1.50	1.25	.60
1994 Pinnacle Run Creators	19	1.50	1.25	.60
1994 Score	51	.04	.03	.02
1994 Score Select	331	.10	.08	.04
1994 Sportflics 2000	131	.10	.08	.04
1994 Studio	193	.10	.08	.04
1994 Topps	495	.04	.03	.02
1994 Topps Finest	281	.50	.40	.20
1994 Topps Finest Refractors	281	3.50	2.75	1.50
1994 Topps Gold	495	.15	.11	.06
1994 Topps Stadium Club	192	.10	.08	.04
1994 Topps Stadium Club First Day Production	192	2.50	2.00	1.00
1994 Upper Deck	301	.10	.08	.04
1994 Upper Deck Collector's Choice	275	.05	.04	.02
1994 Upper Deck Electric Diamond	301	.25	.20	.10
1994 Upper Deck Fun Packs	20	.05	.04	.02
1994 Upper Deck SP	180	.15	.11	.06
1994 Upper Deck SP Baseball Die-Cut	180	.25	.20	.10

Frank Thomas

Set	Card #	MT	NM	EX
1990 Bowman	320	3.50	2.75	1.50
1990 Fleer Update	87	4.00	3.00	1.50
1990 Leaf	300	75.00	56.00	30.00
1990 O-Pee-Chee	414	3.00	2.25	1.25
1990 Score	663 (R)	7.00	5.25	2.75
1990 Score Traded	86T	7.00	5.25	2.75
1990 Topps	414a (R)	400.00	300.00	150.00
1990 Topps	414b (R)	4.00	3.00	1.50
1991 Bowman	366	2.00	1.50	.80
1991 Donruss	477	1.50	1.25	.60
1991 Fleer	138	1.50	1.25	.60
1991 Fleer Ultra	85	6.00	4.50	2.50
1991 Leaf	281	5.00	3.75	2.00
1991 O-Pee-Chee Premier	121	3.50	2.75	1.50
1991 Score	840	1.25	.90	.50
1991 Score	874	.75	.45	.25
1991 Score Hot Rookies	4	10.00	7.50	4.00
1991 Studio	40	5.00	3.75	2.00
1991 Topps	79	1.25	.90	.50
1991 Topps Stadium Club	57	25.00	18.00	10.00
1991 Upper Deck	246	4.00	3.00	1.50
1992 Bowman	114	17.00	12.50	6.75
1992 Bowman	551	35.00	26.00	14.00
1992 Donruss	592	1.50	1.25	.60
1992 Donruss Diamond Kings	8	10.00	7.50	4.00
1992 Donruss Elite	18	175.00	125.00	60.00
1992 Donruss Triple Play Gallery of Stars	12	7.00	5.25	2.75
1992 Donruss Triple Play	206	1.25	.90	.50
1992 Fleer	100	1.50	1.25	.60
1992 Fleer	712	1.00	.70	.40
1992 Fleer All-Stars	11	9.00	6.00	3.25
1992 Fleer Rookie Sensations	1	35.00	26.00	14.00
1992 Fleer Ultra	44	5.00	3.75	2.00
1992 Fleer Ultra All-Stars	9	10.00	7.50	4.00
1992 Fleer 7-Eleven	2	1.00	.70	.40
1992 Leaf	349	3.50	2.25	1.25
1992 O-Pee-Chee	555	.90	.70	.35
1992 O-Pee-Chee Premier	59	1.50	1.25	.60
1992 Pinnacle	1	4.00	3.00	1.50
1992 Pinnacle Slugfest	11	10.00	7.50	4.00
1992 Pinnacle Team Pinnacle	4	50.00	37.00	20.00
1992 Pinnacle Team 2000	3	6.00	4.50	2.25
1992 Post Cereal	24	.80	.60	.30
1992 Score	505	1.25	.90	.50
1992 Score	893	1.00	.75	.40
1992 Score Impact Players	43	4.00	3.00	1.50

Set	#			
1992 Studio	159	3.00	2.25	1.25
1992 Topps	555	1.50	1.25	.60
1992 Topps Gold	555	15.00	11.00	6.00
1992 Topps Kids	99	.35	.25	.14
1992 Topps Stadium Club	301	6.00	4.50	2.50
1992 Topps Stadium Club	591	2.75	2.00	1.00
1992 Topps Stadium Club Master Photos	(15)	8.00	6.00	3.25
1992 Upper Deck	87	.20	.15	.08
1992 Upper Deck	166	1.50	1.25	.60
1992 Upper Deck	----	5.00	3.75	2.00
1992 Upper Deck Home Run Heroes	8	5.00	3.75	2.00
1992 Upper Deck MVP Holograms	52	3.50	2.75	1.50
1993 Bowman	555	4.00	3.00	1.50
1993 DiamondMarks	(81)	3.00	2.25	1.25
1993 DiamondMarks Inserts	(7)	20.00	15.00	8.00
1993 Donruss	7	1.50	1.25	.60
1993 Donruss Elite Dominators	13	225.00	169.00	90.00
1993 Donruss Elite Supers	19	60.00	45.00	24.00
1993 Donruss Long Ball Leaders	10	20.00	15.00	8.00
1993 Donruss Masters of the Game	1	6.00	4.50	2.50
1993 Donruss MVP's	2	8.00	6.00	3.25
1993 Donruss Spirit of the Game	6	2.50	2.00	1.00
1993 Donruss Spirit of the Game	18	10.00	7.50	4.00
1993 Donruss Triple Play Nicknames	1	8.00	6.00	3.25
1993 Donruss Triple Play Action Baseball	21	.40	.30	.15
1993 Donruss Triple Play	26	1.50	1.25	.60
1993 Donruss Triple Play	77	.75	.60	.30
1993 Fleer	210	1.50	1.25	.60
1993 Fleer	714	.40	.30	.15
1993 Fleer All-Stars	1	10.00	7.50	4.00
1993 Fleer AL Team Leaders	5	40.00	30.00	15.00
1993 Fleer Flair	189	10.00	7.50	4.00
1993 Fleer Golden Moments II	(3)	7.00	5.25	2.75
1993 Fleer Ultra	181	4.00	3.00	1.50
1993 Fleer Ultra All-Stars	19	14.00	10.50	5.50
1993 Fleer Ultra Performers	10	7.50	5.50	3.00
1993 Leaf	195	4.00	3.00	1.50
1993 Leaf	----	300.00	225.00	125.00
1993 Leaf Fasttrack	1	30.00	22.00	12.00
1993 Leaf Gold All-Stars	12	8.00	6.00	3.25
1993 O-Pee-Chee	362	6.00	4.50	2.50
1993 O-Pee-Chee Premier Star Performers	1	3.00	2.25	1.25
1993 Pinnacle	108	3.50	2.75	1.50
1993 Pinnacle Cooperstown	24	1.00	.75	.40
1993 Pinnacle Cooperstown Dufex	24	400.00	300.00	160.00
1993 Pinnacle Home Run Club	17	3.00	2.25	1.25
1993 Pinnacle Slugfest	9	15.00	11.00	6.00
1993 Pinnacle Team Pinnacle	4	45.00	32.50	18.00
1993 Post Cereal	14	1.00	.70	.40
1993 Score	3	1.75	1.25	.70
1993 Score	510	.75	.60	.30
1993 Score	541	.75	.60	.30
1993 Score Gold Dream Team	10	5.00	3.00	1.50
1993 Score Select	6	3.50	2.75	1.50
1993 Score Select Stat Leaders	3	1.25	.90	.50
1993 Score Select Stat Leaders	13	.75	.60	.30
1993 Score Select Stat Leaders	33	1.25	.90	.50
1993 Score Select Stat Leaders	38	1.25	.90	.50
1993 Score Select Stat Leaders	45	1.25	.90	.50
1993 Score Select Stat Leaders	49	1.25	.90	.50
1993 Score The Franchise	4	30.00	22.00	12.00
1993 Studio	139	3.00	2.25	1.25
1993 Studio Heritage	8	12.00	9.00	4.75
1993 Studio Silhouettes	1	10.00	7.50	4.00
1993 Studio Superstars on Canvas	6	12.00	9.00	4.75
1993 Topps	150	1.50	1.25	.60
1993 Topps	401	.40	.30	.15
1993 Topps Black Gold	42	3.50	2.75	1.50
1993 Topps Finest	102	35.00	26.00	14.00
1993 Topps Finest Jumbo All-Stars	102	80.00	60.00	45.00
1993 Topps Finest Refractors	102	700.00	520.00	280.00
1993 Topps Full Shot Super	1	12.00	9.00	4.75
1993 Topps Gold	150	4.00	3.00	1.50
1993 Topps Gold	401	.90	.70	.35
1993 Topps Stadium Club	200	3.50	2.75	1.50
1993 Topps Stadium Club	746	2.00	1.50	.80
1993 Topps Stadium Club First Day Production	200	185.00	139.00	74.00
1993 Topps Stadium Club First Day Production	746	75.00	56.00	30.00
1993 Topps Stadium Club II Inserts	3	10.00	7.50	4.00
1993 Topps Stadium Club Members Only	(26)	4.00	3.00	1.50
1993 Upper Deck	51	.50	.40	.20
1993 Upper Deck	105	.10	.07	.04
1993 Upper Deck	555	2.00	1.50	.80
1993 Upper Deck All-Time Heroes	118	.10	.08	.04
1993 Upper Deck Clutch Performers	20	8.00	6.00	3.25
1993 Upper Deck Diamond Gallery	27	7.00	5.25	2.75
1993 Upper Deck Fun Packs All-Star Scratch-Off	1	5.00	3.75	2.00
1993 Upper Deck Fun Packs	21	3.00	2.25	1.25
1993 Upper Deck Fun Packs	27	1.00	.75	.40
1993 Upper Deck Fun Packs	36	1.00	.75	.40
1993 Upper Deck Fun Packs	197	1.00	.75	.40
1993 Upper Deck Fun Packs	202	2.00	1.50	.80
1993 Upper Deck Fun Packs	225	.50	.40	.20
1993 Upper Deck Future Heroes	62	6.00	4.50	2.50
1993 Upper Deck Iooss Collection	25	5.00	3.75	2.00
1993 Upper Deck Iooss Collection Super	25	7.50	5.75	3.00
1993 Upper Deck On Deck	24	6.00	4.50	2.50
1993 Upper Deck SP	260	14.00	10.50	5.50
1993 Upper Deck SP Jumbos	260	25.00	18.50	10.00
1993 Upper Deck SP Platinum Power	19	60.00	45.00	24.00
1993 Upper Deck Triple Crown	9	10.00	7.50	4.00
1993 Upper Deck 5th Anniversary	14	7.00	5.25	2.75
1993 Upper Deck 5th Anniversary Super	14	7.50	5.75	3.00
1994 Bowman	15	3.00	2.25	1.25
1994 Bowman's Best	91	8.00	6.00	3.25
1994 Bowman's Best	55	10.00	7.50	4.00

Card	No.			
1994 Bowman's Best Refractors	91	35.00	26.00	14.00
1994 Bowman's Best Refractors	55	100.00	75.00	40.00
1994 Donruss	341	3.00	2.25	1.25
1994 Donruss Award Winners Supers	6	12.00	9.00	4.75
1994 Donruss Decade Dominators	2	10.00	7.50	4.00
1994 Donruss Decade Dominators Supers	2	8.00	6.00	3.25
1994 Donruss Diamond Kings	28	10.00	7.50	4.00
1994 Donruss Diamond Kings Super	28	7.50	5.75	3.00
1994 Donruss Elite	37	100.00	75.00	40.00
1994 Donruss Long Ball Leaders	8	20.00	15.00	8.00
1994 Donruss MVP's	18	8.00	6.00	3.25
1994 Donruss Special Edition - Gold	341	5.00	3.75	2.00
1994 Donruss Spirit of the Game	6	15.00	11.00	6.00
1994 Donruss Spirit of the Game Super	6	25.00	18.50	10.00
1994 Donruss Triple Play Bomb Squad	1	10.00	7.50	4.00
1994 Donruss Triple Play Promos	2	7.50	5.75	3.00
1994 Donruss Triple Play Medalists	3	5.00	3.75	2.00
1994 Donruss Triple Play	269	1.50	1.25	.60
1994 Fleer	96	2.50	2.00	1.00
1994 Fleer All-Stars	23	4.00	3.00	1.50
1994 Fleer Award Winners	1	6.00	4.50	2.50
1994 Fleer Extra Bases	53	2.50	2.00	1.00
1994 Fleer Extra Bases Game Breakers	27	4.00	3.00	1.50
1994 Fleer Flair	36	6.00	4.50	2.50
1994 Fleer Flair Hot Numbers	10	60.00	45.00	25.00
1994 Fleer Flair Infield Power	9	15.00	11.00	6.00
1994 Fleer Golden Moments	9	6.00	4.50	2.50
1994 Fleer Golden Moments Super	9	15.00	11.00	6.00
1994 Fleer Lumber Co.	9	6.00	4.50	2.50
1994 Fleer Team Leaders	4	5.00	3.75	2.00
1994 Fleer Ultra	39	3.00	2.25	1.25
1994 Fleer Ultra All-Stars	2	6.00	4.50	2.50
1994 Fleer Ultra Award Winners	19	6.00	4.50	2.50
1994 Fleer Ultra Hitting Machines	10	6.00	4.50	2.50
1994 Fleer Ultra Home Run Kings	3	22.00	16.50	8.75
1994 Fleer Ultra On-Base Leaders	12	60.00	45.00	24.00
1994 Fleer Ultra RBI Kings	2	60.00	45.00	24.00
1994 Leaf	400	3.00	2.25	1.25
1994 Leaf Gamers	7	25.00	18.00	10.00
1994 Leaf Gold Stars	11	80.00	60.00	32.00
1994 Leaf Limited	24	20.00	15.00	8.00
1994 Leaf Limited Gold	1	95.00	71.00	38.00
1994 Leaf MVP Contenders	12a	60.00	45.00	24.00
1994 Leaf MVP Contenders	12b	125.00	95.00	50.00
1994 Leaf Power Brokers	1	10.00	7.50	4.00
1994 Leaf Slide Show	1	20.00	15.00	8.00
1994 Leaf Statistical Standouts	1	10.00	7.50	4.00
1994 Leaf 5th Anniversary	300	5.00	3.75	2.00
1994 O-Pee-Chee	127	3.00	2.25	1.25
1994 O-Pee-Chee All-Star Redemption Cards	1	3.50	2.75	1.50
1994 O-Pee-Chee Jumbo All-Stars	1	40.00	30.00	15.00
1994 O-Pee-Chee Jumbo All-Stars Factory Set	1	6.00	4.50	2.50
1994 Pacific Crown	138	2.50	2.00	1.00
1994 Pacific Crown	660	1.50	1.25	.60
1994 Pacific Crown Homerun Leaders	3	18.00	13.50	7.25
1994 Pacific Crown Jewels of the Crown	13	18.00	13.50	7.25
1994 Pinnacle	1	3.00	2.25	1.25
1994 Pinnacle Artist's Proof	1	180.00	135.00	75.00
1994 Pinnacle Museum Collection	1	65.00	49.00	26.00
1994 Pinnacle Power Surge	6	1.50	1.25	.60
1994 Pinnacle Run Creators	2	20.00	15.00	8.00
1994 Pinnacle Team Pinnacle	1	70.00	52.00	28.00
1994 Pinnacle The Naturals Box Set	1	2.50	2.00	1.00
1994 Pinnacle Tribute	14	20.00	15.00	8.00
1994 Post Cereal	21	.80	.60	.30
1994 Score	41	1.50	1.25	.60
1994 Score	631	1.00	.75	.40
1994 Score Gold Stars	45	45.00	34.00	18.00
1994 Score Select	6	3.50	2.75	1.50
1994 Score Select Crown Contenders	5	40.00	30.00	15.00
1994 Score The Cycle	18	60.00	45.00	24.00
1994 Sportflics 2000	70	4.00	3.00	1.50
1994 Sportflics 2000	176	2.50	2.00	1.00
1994 Studio	209	3.50	2.75	1.50
1994 Studio Editor's Choice	2	18.00	13.50	7.25
1994 Studio Gold Stars	3	100.00	75.00	40.00
1994 Studio Heritage	2	8.00	6.00	3.25
1994 Studio Silver Stars	3	50.00	38.00	20.00
1994 Topps	270	1.50	1.25	.60
1994 Topps	384	.40	.30	.15
1994 Topps	601	.75	.60	.30
1994 Topps Black Gold	21	4.00	3.00	1.50
1994 Topps Finest	203	14.00	10.50	5.50
1994 Topps Finest Bronze	3	12.50	9.50	5.00
1994 Topps Finest Refractors	203	150.00	110.00	60.00
1994 Topps Finest Superstars	203	50.00	38.00	20.00
1994 Topps Gold	270	6.00	4.50	2.50
1994 Topps Gold	384	1.50	1.25	.60
1994 Topps Gold	601	3.00	2.25	1.25
1994 Topps Stadium Club	267	1.50	1.25	.60
1994 Topps Stadium Club	285	3.00	2.25	1.25
1994 Topps Stadium Club	528	1.50	1.25	.60
1994 Topps Stadium Club	718	1.25	.90	.50
1994 Topps Stadium Club Dugout Dirt	9	4.00	3.00	1.50
1994 Topps Stadium Club Finest	10	10.00	7.50	4.00
1994 Topps Stadium Club First Day Production	267	50.00	37.00	20.00
1994 Topps Stadium Club First Day Production	285	90.00	67.00	36.00
1994 Topps Stadium Club First Day Production	528	55.00	41.00	22.00
1994 Topps Stadium Club First Day Production	718	35.00	26.00	14.00
1994 Topps Stadium Club Members Only Baseball	29	4.00	3.00	1.50
1994 Topps Traded Finest Inserts	7	3.50	2.75	1.50
1994 Upper Deck	55	2.00	1.50	.80
1994 Upper Deck	284	2.00	1.50	.80
1994 Upper Deck	300	3.00	2.25	1.25
1994 Upper Deck All-Stars Green Foil	40	2.00	1.50	.80
1994 Upper Deck All-Stars Gold Foil	40	10.00	7.50	4.00

Set	Card #			
1994 Upper Deck All-Time Heroes	126	.50	.40	.20
1994 Upper Deck All-Time Heroes	218	.50	.40	.20
1994 Upper Deck Collector's Choice	327	.25	.20	.10
1994 Upper Deck Collector's Choice	354	.50	.40	.20
1994 Upper Deck Collector's Choice	500	1.50	1.25	.60
1994 Upper Deck Collector's Choice	640	.75	.60	.30
1994 Upper Deck Diamond Collection	8C	50.00	37.00	20.00
1994 Upper Deck Electric Diamond	55	12.00	9.00	4.75
1994 Upper Deck Electric Diamond	284	12.00	9.00	4.75
1994 Upper Deck Electric Diamond	300	7.00	5.25	2.75
1994 Upper Deck Fun Packs	35	2.50	2.00	1.00
1994 Upper Deck Fun Packs	177	1.00	.70	.40
1994 Upper Deck Fun Packs	195	1.00	.70	.40
1994 Upper Deck Fun Packs	204	2.50	2.00	1.00
1994 Upper Deck Fun Packs	210	1.00	.70	.40
1994 Upper Deck Fun Packs	236	.50	.40	.20
1994 Upper Deck Heroes Gold	126	.15	.11	.06
1994 Upper Deck Heroes Gold	218	.15	.11	.06
1994 Upper Deck Mickey Mantle's Long Shots	18MM	20.00	15.00	8.00
1994 Upper Deck SP	193	5.00	3.75	2.00
1994 Upper Deck SP Baseball Die-Cut	193	15.00	11.00	6.00
1994 Upper Deck SP Insert	5	32.00	24.00	13.00

Luis Tiant

Set	Card #	NM	EX	VG
1965 O-Pee-Chee	145	21.00	10.50	6.25
1965 Topps	145 (R)	17.50	8.75	5.25
1966 Topps	285	4.00	2.00	1.25
1967 Topps	377	4.00	2.00	1.25
1968 Topps	532	2.50	1.25	.70
1969 O-Pee-Chee	7	2.25	1.25	.70
1969 O-Pee-Chee	9	2.25	1.25	.70
1969 O-Pee-Chee	11	2.25	1.25	.70
1969 Topps	7	2.00	1.00	.60
1969 Topps	9	2.50	1.25	.70
1969 Topps	11	2.50	1.25	.70
1969 Topps	560	2.50	1.25	.70
1970 O-Pee-Chee	231	1.00	.50	.30
1970 Topps	231	1.25	.60	.40

Set	Card #			
1971 O-Pee-Chee	95	1.50	.70	.45
1971 Topps	95	1.50	.70	.45
1973 O-Pee-Chee	65	.75	.40	.25
1973 O-Pee-Chee	270	.75	.40	.25
1973 Topps	65	2.00	1.00	.60
1973 Topps	270	.75	.40	.25
1974 O-Pee-Chee	167	.60	.30	.20
1974 Topps	167	.50	.25	.15
1975 O-Pee-Chee	430	.55	.30	.15
1975 Topps	430	.40	.20	.12
1975 Topps Mini	430	.80	.40	.25
1976 O-Pee-Chee	130	.40	.20	.12
1976 Topps	130	.40	.20	.12
1977 O-Pee-Chee	87	.40	.20	.12
1977 Topps	258	.35	.20	.11
1978 O-Pee-Chee	124	.25	.13	.08
1978 Topps	345	.35	.20	.11
1979 O-Pee-Chee	299	.30	.15	.09
1979 Topps	575	.20	.10	.06
1980 O-Pee-Chee	19	.25	.13	.08
1980 Topps	35	.15	.08	.05

Set	Card #	MT	NM	EX
1981 Donruss	231	.12	.09	.05
1981 Fleer	82	.12	.09	.05
1981 Topps	627	.10	.08	.04
1982 O-Pee-Chee	160	.15	.11	.06
1982 Topps	160	.10	.08	.04
1983 Donruss	542	.12	.09	.05
1983 O-Pee-Chee	179	.12	.09	.05
1983 Topps	178	.15	.11	.06
1983 Topps	179	.10	.08	.04

Joe Torre

Set	Card #	NM	EX	VG
1962 Post Cereal	152	4.50	2.25	1.25
1962 Topps	218 (R)	24.00	12.00	7.25
1962 Topps	351	5.00	2.50	1.50
1963 Post Cereal	156	4.00	2.00	1.25
1963 Topps	347	9.00	4.50	2.75
1964 Topps	70	2.50	1.25	.70
1965 O-Pee-Chee	200	6.25	3.25	2.00
1965 Topps	200	4.50	2.25	1.25
1966 O-Pee-Chee	130	2.50	1.25	.70
1966 Topps	130	2.25	1.25	.70
1967 Topps	350	2.50	1.25	.70
1968 O-Pee-Chee	30	2.25	1.25	.70
1968 Topps	30	1.50	.70	.45
1969 Topps	460	1.00	.50	.30
1970 O-Pee-Chee	190	1.25	.60	.40
1970 Topps	190	.90	.45	.25
1971 O-Pee-Chee	62	1.50	.70	.45
1971 O-Pee-Chee	370	1.50	.70	.45
1971 Topps	62	1.50	.70	.45
1971 Topps	370	1.00	.50	.30
1972 O-Pee-Chee	85	.75	.40	.25
1972 O-Pee-Chee	87	1.25	.60	.40
1972 O-Pee-Chee	341	1.25	.60	.40
1972 O-Pee-Chee	500	1.75	.90	.50

1972 Topps	85	2.00	1.00	.60
1972 Topps	87	4.50	2.25	1.25
1972 Topps	341	.75	.40	.25
1972 Topps	500	1.00	.50	.30
1973 O-Pee-Chee	450	1.25	.60	.40
1973 Topps	450	.70	.35	.20
1974 O-Pee-Chee	15	.75	.40	.25
1974 Topps	15	.30	.15	.09
1975 O-Pee-Chee	209	.55	.30	.15
1975 O-Pee-Chee	565	.55	.30	.15
1975 Topps	209	.50	.25	.15
1975 Topps	565	.70	.35	.20
1975 Topps Mini	209	.80	.40	.25
1975 Topps Mini	565	1.00	.50	.30
1976 O-Pee-Chee	585	.40	.20	.12
1976 Topps	585	.25	.13	.08
1977 Topps	425	.20	.10	.06
1978 Topps	109	.20	.10	.06
1979 Topps	82	.60	.30	.20
1980 Topps	259	.60	.30	.20

Set	Card #	MT	NM	EX
1981 Donruss	506	.10	.08	.04
1981 Fleer	325	.08	.06	.03
1981 Topps	681	.30	.25	.12
1983 Donruss	628	.08	.06	.03
1983 Topps	126	.10	.08	.04
1984 Topps	502	.08	.06	.03
1985 Topps	438	.08	.06	.03
1986 Sportflics Decade Greats	49	.15	.11	.06
1990 Pacific Legends	107	.10	.08	.04
1991 Topps	351	.03	.02	.01
1992 O-Pee-Chee	549	.03	.02	.01
1992 Topps	549	.03	.02	.01
1992 Topps Gold	549	.25	.20	.10
1993 Topps	512	.03	.02	.01
1993 Topps Gold	512	.10	.08	.04

Alan Trammell

Set	Card #	NM	EX	VG
1978 Topps	707 (R)	100.00	50.00	30.00
1979 O-Pee-Chee	184	15.00	7.50	4.50
1979 Topps	358	10.00	5.00	3.00
1980 O-Pee-Chee	123	6.25	3.25	2.00
1980 Topps	232	4.00	2.00	1.25

Set	Card #	MT	NM	EX
1981 Donruss	5	1.00	.75	.40
1981 Fleer	461	1.25	.90	.50
1981 O-Pee-Chee	133	1.50	1.25	.60
1981 Topps	709	1.50	1.25	.60
1982 Donruss	5a	1.50	1.25	.60
1982 Donruss	5b	.40	.30	.15
1982 Donruss	76a	2.00	1.50	.80
1982 Donruss	76b	.60	.45	.25
1982 Fleer	283	.75	.60	.30
1982 O-Pee-Chee	381	.12	.09	.05
1982 Topps	475	.60	.45	.25
1983 Donruss	207	.40	.30	.15

1983 Fleer	344	.75	.60	.30
1983 O-Pee-Chee	95	.40	.30	.15
1983 Topps	95	1.00	.75	.40
1984 Donruss	293	2.00	1.50	.80
1984 Fleer	91	1.00	.70	.40
1984 O-Pee-Chee	88	.60	.45	.25
1984 Topps	510	.40	.30	.15
1985 Donruss	171	.40	.30	.15
1985 Fleer	23	.50	.40	.20
1985 Leaf-Donruss	158	.25	.20	.10
1985 O-Pee-Chee	181	.30	.25	.12
1985 Topps	690	.25	.20	.10
1985 Topps All-Star Glossy Set of 40	16	.35	.25	.14
1986 Donruss	171	.35	.25	.14
1986 Fleer	241	.30	.25	.12
1986 Fleer	633	1.00	.70	.40
1986 Leaf	101	.25	.20	.10
1986 O-Pee-Chee	130	.25	.20	.10
1986 Sportflics	147	.25	.20	.10
1986 Sportflics	172	.30	.25	.12
1986 Topps	130	.15	.11	.06
1987 Donruss	127	.25	.20	.10
1987 Fleer	167	.25	.20	.10
1987 Leaf	126	.20	.15	.08
1987 O-Pee-Chee	209	.20	.15	.08
1987 Sportflics	188	.30	.25	.12
1987 Topps	687	.12	.09	.05
1988 Donruss	4	.08	.06	.03
1988 Donruss	230	.08	.06	.03
1988 Donruss Diamond Kings Supers	4	.30	.25	.12
1988 Donruss MVP	11	.25	.20	.10
1988 Fleer	74	.10	.08	.04
1988 Fleer	635	.30	.25	.12
1988 Fleer All Stars	9	.40	.30	.15
1988 Leaf	4	.20	.15	.08
1988 Leaf	167	.15	.11	.06
1988 O-Pee-Chee	320	.12	.09	.05
1988 Score	37	.08	.06	.03
1988 Score	651	.25	.20	.10
1988 Sportflics	25	.25	.20	.10
1988 Topps	320	.10	.08	.04
1988 Topps	389	.08	.06	.03
1988 Topps	429	.08	.06	.03
1988 Topps All-Star Glossy Set of 60	37	.30	.25	.12
1988 Topps Big Baseball	8	.15	.11	.06
1989 Bowman	105	.05	.04	.02
1989 Donruss	180	.08	.06	.03
1989 Donruss MVP	17	.25	.20	.10
1989 Fleer	148	.08	.06	.03
1989 O-Pee-Chee	49	.05	.04	.02
1989 Score	110	.15	.11	.06
1989 Sportflics	215	.30	.25	.12
1989 Topps	400	.08	.06	.03
1989 Topps	770	.08	.06	.03
1989 Topps All-Star Glossy Set of 60	25	.20	.15	.08
1989 Topps Big Baseball	123	.15	.11	.06
1989 Upper Deck	290	.10	.08	.04
1989 Upper Deck	690	.08	.06	.03
1990 Bowman	353	.08	.06	.03
1990 Donruss	90	.10	.08	.04
1990 Donruss MVP	26	.10	.08	.04
1990 Fleer	617	.09	.07	.04
1990 Leaf	218	.40	.30	.15
1990 O-Pee-Chee	440	.09	.07	.04
1990 Post Cereal	28	.40	.30	.15
1990 Score	9	.09	.07	.04
1990 Sportflics	154	.10	.08	.04
1990 Topps	440	.09	.07	.04
1990 Topps Big Baseball	190	.10	.08	.04
1990 Upper Deck	554	.10	.08	.04
1991 Bowman	154	.08	.06	.03
1991 Bowman	370	.08	.06	.03
1991 Donruss	118	.08	.06	.03
1991 Fleer	355	.08	.06	.03
1991 Fleer Ultra	129	.15	.11	.06
1991 Leaf	351	.15	.11	.06
1991 O-Pee-Chee Premier	123	.08	.06	.03

1991 Score	40	.08	.06	.03
1991 Score	852	.08	.06	.03
1991 Studio	59	.25	.20	.10
1991 Topps	275	.10	.08	.04
1991 Topps	389	.06	.05	.02
1991 Topps Stadium Club	63	.40	.30	.15
1991 Upper Deck	223	.12	.09	.05
1991 Upper Deck Silver Sluggers	2	.50	.40	.20
1992 Bowman	690	.20	.15	.08
1992 Donruss	164	.10	.08	.04
1992 Donruss Triple Play	176	.08	.06	.03
1992 Fleer	148	.10	.08	.04
1992 Fleer Ultra	64	.15	.11	.06
1992 Leaf	172	.12	.09	.05
1992 O-Pee-Chee	120	.10	.08	.04
1992 O-Pee-Chee Premier	31	.20	.15	.08
1992 Pinnacle	113	.12	.09	.05
1992 Pinnacle Rookie Idols	17	6.00	4.50	2.50
1992 Score	515	.08	.06	.03
1992 Studio	179	.20	.15	.08
1992 Topps	120	.10	.08	.04
1992 Topps Gold	120	.90	.70	.35
1992 Topps Kids	75	.15	.11	.06
1992 Topps Stadium Club	850	.15	.11	.06
1992 Topps Stadium Club National Convention	850	35.00	26.00	14.00
1992 Upper Deck	273	.10	.08	.04
1993 Bowman	391	.10	.08	.04
1993 DiamondMarks	(75)	.50	.40	.20
1993 Donruss	655	.05	.04	.02
1993 Donruss Triple Play	191	.20	.15	.08
1993 Fleer	613	.05	.04	.02
1993 Fleer Flair	209	.25	.15	.08
1993 Fleer Ultra	204	.10	.08	.04
1993 Leaf	421	.10	.08	.04
1993 O-Pee-Chee	360	.15	.11	.06
1993 Pinnacle	353	.06	.05	.02
1993 Score	313	.04	.03	.02
1993 Score Select	230	.10	.08	.04
1993 Topps	660	.03	.02	.01
1993 Topps Finest	18	1.00	.70	.40
1993 Topps Finest Refractors	18	20.00	15.00	8.00
1993 Topps Gold	660	.10	.08	.04
1993 Topps Stadium Club	416	.10	.08	.04
1993 Topps Stadium Club First Day Production	416	15.00	11.00	6.00
1993 Upper Deck	532	.10	.08	.04
1993 Upper Deck SP	241	.15	.11	.06
1994 Bowman	509	.10	.08	.04
1994 Donruss	280	.05	.04	.02
1994 Donruss Triple Play Medalists	7	2.50	2.00	1.00
1994 Donruss Triple Play	249	.05	.04	.02
1994 Fleer	144	.05	.04	.02
1994 Fleer	709	.05	.04	.02
1994 Fleer Extra Bases	81	.10	.08	.04
1994 Fleer Flair	53	.20	.15	.08
1994 Fleer Ultra	357	.12	.09	.05
1994 Leaf	120	.10	.08	.04
1994 Leaf Limited	34	1.00	.70	.40
1994 O-Pee-Chee	72	.05	.04	.02
1994 Pacific Crown	230	.05	.04	.02
1994 Pinnacle	429	.10	.08	.04
1994 Pinnacle Artist's Proof	429	3.00	2.25	1.25
1994 Pinnacle Museum Collection	429	1.50	1.25	.60
1994 Score	337	.06	.05	.02
1994 Score Select	285	.10	.08	.04
1994 Sportflics 2000	93	.10	.08	.04
1994 Studio	194	.10	.08	.04
1994 Topps	75	.04	.03	.02
1994 Topps Finest	159	.50	.40	.20
1994 Topps Finest Promos	159	2.50	2.00	1.00

1994 Topps Finest Refractors	159	3.50	2.75	1.50
1994 Topps Gold	75	.15	.11	.06
1994 Topps Stadium Club	331	.10	.08	.04
1994 Topps Stadium Club First Day Production	331	2.50	2.00	1.00
1994 Upper Deck	201	.10	.08	.04
1994 Upper Deck Collector's Choice	474	.05	.04	.02
1994 Upper Deck Electric Diamond	201	.25	.20	.10
1994 Upper Deck Fun Packs	103	.05	.04	.02
1994 Upper Deck SP	181	.15	.11	.06
1994 Upper Deck SP Baseball Die-Cut	181	.25	.20	.10

Bob Uecker

Set	Card #	NM	EX	VG
1962 Topps	594 (R)	80.00	40.00	24.00
1963 Topps	126	12.50	6.25	3.75
1964 Topps	543	35.00	17.50	10.50
1965 Topps	519	20.00	10.00	6.00
1966 O-Pee-Chee	91	18.00	9.00	5.50
1966 Topps	91a	65.00	32.00	19.50
1966 Topps	91b	15.00	7.50	4.50
1967 Topps	326	20.00	10.00	6.00

Fernando Valenzuela

Set	Card #	MT	NM	EX
1981 Fleer	140 (R)	1.50	1.25	.60
1981 Topps	302	2.50	2.00	1.00
1981 Topps Traded	850	2.00	1.50	.80
1982 Donruss	462	.25	.20	.10
1982 Fleer	27	.35	.25	.14
1982 Fleer	635	.30	.25	.12

1982 Fleer	636a	1.00	.70	.40
1982 Fleer	636b	.50	.40	.20
1982 O-Pee-Chee	334	1.25	.90	.50
1982 Topps	6	.30	.25	.12
1982 Topps	166	.20	.15	.08
1982 Topps	345	.20	.15	.08
1982 Topps	510	.40	.30	.15
1983 Donruss	1	.20	.15	.08
1983 Donruss	284	.30	.25	.12
1983 Fleer	224	.10	.08	.04
1983 O-Pee-Chee	40	.25	.20	.10
1983 Topps	40	.25	.20	.10
1983 Topps	681	.25	.20	.10
1983 Topps All-Star Glossy Set of 40	10	.25	.20	.10
1984 Donruss	52	.40	.30	.15
1984 Fleer	115	.15	.11	.06
1984 O-Pee-Chee	220	.60	.45	.25
1984 Topps	220	.20	.15	.08
1985 Donruss	52	.25	.20	.10
1985 Fleer	387	.10	.08	.04
1985 Leaf-Donruss	184	.20	.15	.08
1985 O-Pee-Chee	357	.30	.25	.12
1985 Topps	440	.08	.06	.03
1986 Donruss	215	.35	.25	.14
1986 Fleer	145	.10	.08	.04
1986 Fleer	641	.40	.30	.15
1986 Leaf	91	.20	.15	.08
1986 O-Pee-Chee	178	.20	.15	.08
1986 Sportflics	12	.15	.11	.06
1986 Sportflics	60	.20	.15	.08
1986 Sportflics	72	.15	.11	.06
1986 Sportflics	132	.15	.11	.06
1986 Sportflics	143	1.25	.90	.50
1986 Sportflics Decade Greats	66	.30	.25	.12
1986 Sportflics Rookies	47	.40	.30	.15
1986 Topps	207	.08	.06	.03
1986 Topps	401	.15	.11	.06
1986 Topps	630	.08	.06	.03
1986 Topps All-Star Glossy Set of 60	3	.35	.25	.14
1987 Donruss	94	.08	.06	.03
1987 Fleer	457	.10	.08	.04
1987 Fleer	631	.10	.08	.04
1987 Fleer All Stars	10	.30	.20	.10
1987 Fleer All Stars	43	.20	.15	.08
1987 Leaf	148	.15	.11	.06
1987 O-Pee-Chee	273	.20	.15	.08
1987 Sportflics	119	.15	.11	.06
1987 Sportflics	120	.25	.20	.10
1987 Sportflics	150	.15	.11	.06
1987 Topps	410	.08	.06	.03
1987 Topps	604	.12	.09	.05
1987 Topps All-Star Glossy Set of 22	11	.30	.25	.12
1987 Topps All-Star Glossy Set of 60	53	.25	.20	.10
1988 Donruss	53	.06	.05	.02
1988 Fleer	528	.08	.06	.03
1988 Leaf	61	.15	.11	.06
1988 O-Pee-Chee	52	.12	.09	.05
1988 Score	600	.08	.06	.03
1988 Sportflics	40	.15	.11	.06
1988 Topps	489	.08	.06	.03
1988 Topps	780	.15	.11	.06
1988 Topps Big Baseball	18	.15	.11	.06
1989 Bowman	337	.05	.04	.02
1989 Donruss	250	.08	.06	.03
1989 Fleer	76	.08	.06	.03
1989 O-Pee-Chee	150	.07	.05	.03
1989 Score	437	.15	.11	.06
1989 Sportflics	124	.25	.20	.10
1989 Topps	150	.06	.05	.02
1989 Upper Deck	656	.08	.06	.03
1990 Donruss	625	.07	.05	.03
1990 Fleer	409	.07	.05	.03
1990 Fleer	622	.08	.06	.03
1990 Leaf	68	.40	.30	.15
1990 O-Pee-Chee	340	.06	.05	.02
1990 Score	54	.09	.07	.04

1990 Topps	340	.06	.05	.02
1990 Upper Deck	445	.09	.07	.04
1991 Donruss	127	.08	.06	.03
1991 Fleer	222	.06	.05	.02
1991 Score	449	.08	.06	.03
1991 Score	703	.06	.05	.02
1991 Topps	80a	.25	.20	.10
1991 Topps	80b	.12	.09	.05
1991 Topps Stadium Club	90	.30	.25	.12
1991 Topps Stadium Club Charter Members	(30)	.25	.20	.10
1991 Upper Deck	175	.10	.08	.04
1993 Fleer Final Edition	166	.05	.04	.02
1993 Fleer Flair	159	.25	.15	.08
1993 Fleer Ultra	503	.10	.08	.04
1993 Leaf	472	.15	.11	.06
1993 O-Pee-Chee Premier	47	.10	.08	.04
1993 Topps Stadium Club	661	.10	.08	.04
1993 Topps Stadium Club First Day Production	661	5.00	3.75	2.00
1993 Upper Deck	550	.06	.05	.02
1994 Donruss	408	.05	.04	.02
1994 Fleer	22	.05	.04	.02
1994 Fleer Flair	418	.20	.15	.08
1994 Fleer Update	171	.10	.08	.04
1994 Pacific Crown	46	.05	.04	.02
1994 Pacific Crown Jewels of the Crown	14	2.50	2.00	1.00
1994 Score	190	.04	.03	.02
1994 Topps	175	.04	.03	.02
1994 Topps Gold	175	.15	.11	.06
1994 Topps Stadium Club	69	.10	.08	.04
1994 Topps Stadium Club First Day Production	69	2.50	2.00	1.00

Andy Van Slyke

Set	Card #	MT	NM	EX
1984 Donruss	83 (R)	3.50	2.75	1.50
1984 Fleer	339 (R)	3.00	2.25	1.25
1984 Topps	206 (R)	1.50	1.25	.60
1985 Donruss	327	.75	.60	.30
1985 Fleer	242	1.00	.75	.40
1985 O-Pee-Chee	341	.10	.08	.04
1985 Topps	551	.25	.20	.10
1986 Donruss	412	.15	.11	.06
1986 Fleer	48	.60	.45	.25
1986 O-Pee-Chee	33	.12	.09	.05
1986 Topps	683	.10	.08	.04
1987 Donruss	417	.25	.20	.10
1987 Fleer	311	.40	.30	.15
1987 Fleer Update	121	.20	.15	.08
1987 O-Pee-Chee	33	.10	.08	.04
1987 Topps	33	.12	.09	.05
1987 Topps Traded	124T	.20	.15	.08
1988 Donruss	18	.10	.08	.04
1988 Donruss	291	.10	.08	.04

Set	#			
1988 Donruss Diamond Kings Supers	18	.25	.20	.10
1988 Donruss MVP	8	.15	.11	.06
1988 Fleer	341	.08	.06	.03
1988 Leaf	18	.10	.08	.04
1988 Leaf	102	.10	.08	.04
1988 O-Pee-Chee	142	.08	.06	.03
1988 Score	416	.10	.08	.04
1988 Sportflics	109	.15	.11	.06
1988 Topps	142	.10	.08	.04
1988 Topps Big Baseball	184	.10	.08	.04
1989 Bowman	424	.10	.08	.04
1989 Donruss	54	.08	.06	.03
1989 Donruss MVP	10	.15	.11	.06
1989 Fleer	222	.10	.08	.04
1989 O-Pee-Chee	350	.07	.05	.03
1989 Score	174	.12	.09	.05
1989 Sportflics	166	.15	.11	.06
1989 Topps	350	.12	.09	.05
1989 Topps	392	.08	.06	.03
1989 Topps All-Star Glossy Set of 60	4	.20	.15	.08
1989 Topps Big Baseball	255	.08	.06	.03
1989 Upper Deck	537	.15	.11	.06
1989 Upper Deck	685	.08	.06	.03
1990 Bowman	171	.08	.06	.03
1990 Donruss	244	.07	.05	.03
1990 Fleer	481	.09	.07	.04
1990 Leaf	117	.35	.25	.14
1990 O-Pee-Chee	775	.08	.06	.03
1990 Score	440	.10	.08	.04
1990 Sportflics	101	.12	.09	.05
1990 Topps	775	.08	.06	.03
1990 Topps Big Baseball	217	.08	.06	.03
1990 Upper Deck	536	.15	.11	.06
1991 Bowman	529	.08	.06	.03
1991 Donruss	552	.08	.06	.03
1991 Fleer	53	.08	.06	.03
1991 Fleer Ultra	287	.10	.08	.04
1991 Leaf	310	.15	.11	.06
1991 Score	475	.08	.06	.03
1991 Score	698	.08	.06	.03
1991 Studio	230	.15	.11	.06
1991 Topps	425	.08	.06	.03
1991 Topps Stadium Club	118	.30	.25	.12
1991 Upper Deck	256	.10	.07	.04
1992 Bowman	35	.20	.15	.08
1992 Donruss	383	.08	.06	.03
1992 Donruss Triple Play	6	.08	.06	.03
1992 Donruss Triple Play	148	.08	.06	.03
1992 Fleer	570	.06	.05	.02
1992 Fleer Ultra	262	.15	.11	.06
1992 Fleer Ultra Award Winners	10	.75	.60	.30
1992 Leaf	43	.15	.11	.06
1992 O-Pee-Chee	545	.08	.06	.03
1992 Pinnacle	9	.12	.09	.05
1992 Score	655	.08	.06	.03
1992 Studio	89	.10	.08	.04
1992 Studio Heritage	10	1.00	.70	.40
1992 Topps	545	.08	.06	.03
1992 Topps Gold	545	.35	.25	.14
1992 Topps Kids	23	.10	.08	.04
1992 Topps Stadium Club	232	.15	.11	.06
1992 Topps Stadium Club Special Edition	189	.15	.11	.06
1992 Upper Deck	132	.12	.09	.05
1992 Upper Deck	711	.06	.05	.02
1992 Upper Deck	715	.08	.06	.03
1993 Bowman	218	.10	.08	.04
1993 DiamondMarks	(52)	.25	.20	.10
1993 Donruss	414	.05	.04	.02
1993 Donruss Diamond Kings	9	.75	.60	.30
1993 Donruss Elite	32	20.00	15.00	8.00
1993 Donruss Elite Supers	14	6.00	4.50	2.50
1993 Donruss Triple Play Action Baseball	1	.10	.08	.04
1993 Donruss Triple Play	8	.10	.08	.04
1993 Fleer	122	.08	.06	.03
1993 Fleer All-Stars	8	.75	.60	.30
1993 Fleer Atlantic	24	.25	.20	.10
1993 Fleer Flair	117	.35	.25	.14
1993 Fleer NL Team Leaders	10	1.50	1.25	.60
1993 Fleer ProVisions II	1	.75	.60	.30
1993 Fleer Ultra	103	.10	.08	.04
1993 Fleer Ultra Award Winners	8	1.25	.90	.50
1993 Leaf	79	.10	.08	.04
1993 Leaf Gold All-Stars	7	8.00	6.00	3.25
1993 O-Pee-Chee	355	.15	.11	.06
1993 O-Pee-Chee Premier	88	.15	.11	.06
1993 Pinnacle	19	.06	.05	.02
1993 Pinnacle Team Pinnacle	9	15.00	11.00	6.00
1993 Post Cereal	27	.30	.25	.12
1993 Score	12	.08	.06	.03
1993 Score	524	.04	.03	.02
1993 Score	535	.04	.03	.02
1993 Score Gold Dream Team	4	.50	.40	.20
1993 Score Select	35	.12	.09	.05
1993 Score Select Chase Stars	6	2.50	2.00	1.00
1993 Score Select Stat Leaders	5	.10	.08	.04
1993 Score Select Stat Leaders	10	.10	.08	.04
1993 Score Select Stat Leaders	16	.10	.08	.04
1993 Score Select Stat Leaders	24	.10	.08	.04
1993 Score Select Stat Leaders	42	.10	.08	.04
1993 Score The Franchise	23	1.00	.70	.40
1993 Studio	132	.12	.09	.05
1993 Topps	275	.08	.06	.03
1993 Topps	405	.40	.30	.15
1993 Topps Black Gold	21	.25	.20	.10
1993 Topps Finest	185	1.00	.75	.40
1993 Topps Finest Refractors	185	20.00	15.00	8.00
1993 Topps Gold	275	.15	.11	.06
1993 Topps Gold	405	.90	.70	.35
1993 Topps Stadium Club	294	.15	.11	.06
1993 Topps Stadium Club	394	.10	.08	.04
1993 Topps Stadium Club First Day Production	294	8.00	6.00	3.25
1993 Topps Stadium Club First Day Production	394	4.00	3.00	1.50
1993 Topps Stadium Club Special	14	.15	.11	.06
1993 Upper Deck	124	.08	.06	.03
1993 Upper Deck Diamond Gallery	19	.75	.60	.30
1993 Upper Deck Fun Packs	148	.15	.11	.06
1993 Upper Deck Fun Packs	151	.15	.11	.06
1993 Upper Deck Iooss Collection	18	.60	.45	.25
1993 Upper Deck Iooss Collection Super	18	3.00	2.25	1.25
1993 Upper Deck On Deck	25	.50	.40	.20
1993 Upper Deck SP	188	.12	.09	.05
1994 Bowman	50	.10	.08	.04
1994 Bowman's Best	77	.50	.40	.20
1994 Bowman's Best Refractors	77	2.00	1.50	.80
1994 Donruss	375	.05	.04	.02
1994 Donruss Special Edition - Gold	375	.25	.20	.10
1994 Donruss Triple Play Medalists	12	3.00	2.25	1.25
1994 Donruss Triple Play	189	.05	.04	.02
1994 Fleer	622	.05	.04	.02
1994 Fleer Extra Bases	352	.10	.08	.04
1994 Fleer Flair	426	.20	.15	.08
1994 Fleer Ultra	559	.10	.08	.04

Set	Card #	MT	NM	EX
1994 Leaf	411	.10	.08	.04
1994 Leaf Limited	143	1.00	.70	.40
1994 O-Pee-Chee	86	.05	.04	.02
1994 Pacific Crown	509	.10	.08	.04
1994 Pinnacle	16	.10	.08	.04
1994 Pinnacle Artist's Proof	16	3.00	2.25	1.25
1994 Pinnacle Museum Collection	16	1.50	1.25	.60
1994 Score	18	.04	.03	.02
1994 Score Dream Team	8	4.00	3.00	1.50
1994 Score Gold Stars	19	2.00	1.50	.80
1994 Score Select	129	.10	.08	.04
1994 Sportflics 2000	76	.10	.08	.04
1994 Studio	150	.10	.08	.04
1994 Topps	650	.04	.03	.02
1994 Topps Finest	408	.50	.40	.20
1994 Topps Finest Refractors	408	3.50	2.75	1.50
1994 Topps Gold	650	.15	.11	.06
1994 Topps Stadium Club	687	.10	.08	.04
1994 Topps Stadium Club First Day Production	687	3.00	2.25	1.25
1994 Upper Deck	83	.10	.08	.04
1994 Upper Deck All-Stars Green Foil	27	.25	.20	.10
1994 Upper Deck All-Stars Gold Foil	27	1.00	.70	.40
1994 Upper Deck Collector's Choice	280	.05	.04	.02
1994 Upper Deck Collector's Choice	346	.05	.04	.02
1994 Upper Deck Diamond Collection	9C	4.00	3.00	1.50
1994 Upper Deck Electric Diamond	83	.25	.20	.10
1994 Upper Deck Fun Packs	18	.05	.04	.02
1994 Upper Deck SP	144	.15	.11	.06
1994 Upper Deck SP Baseball Die-Cut	144	.25	.20	.10
1994 Upper Deck SP Holoview Blue	38	3.00	2.25	1.25
1994 Upper Deck SP Holoview Red	38	10.00	7.50	4.00

Greg Vaughn

Set	Card #	MT	NM	EX
1989 Fleer Update	41	1.00	.75	.40
1990 Bowman	396	.25	.20	.10
1990 Donruss	37 (R)	.30	.25	.12
1990 Fleer	339 (R)	.20	.15	.08
1990 Leaf	111	2.00	1.50	.80
1990 O-Pee-Chee	57 (R)	.60	.45	.25
1990 Score	585 (R)	.30	.25	.12
1990 Sportflics	135	.20	.15	.08
1990 Topps	57 (R)	.35	.25	.14
1990 Upper Deck	25 (R)	.60	.45	.25

Set	Card #	MT	NM	EX
1991 Bowman	33	.10	.08	.04
1991 Donruss	478	.10	.08	.04
1991 Fleer	599	.12	.09	.05
1991 Fleer Ultra	183	.20	.15	.08
1991 Score	528	.10	.08	.06
1991 Studio	79	.15	.11	.06
1991 Topps	347	.10	.08	.04
1991 Topps Glossy Rookies	30	.30	.25	.12
1991 Topps Stadium Club	135	1.00	.75	.40
1991 Upper Deck	526	.15	.11	.06
1992 Bowman	496	.40	.30	.15
1992 Donruss	224	.10	.08	.04
1992 Donruss Triple Play	122	.12	.09	.05
1992 Fleer	192	.08	.06	.03
1992 Fleer Ultra	86	.25	.20	.10
1992 Leaf	276	.15	.11	.06
1992 O-Pee-Chee	572	.12	.09	.05
1992 Pinnacle	92	.15	.11	.06
1992 Score	639	.08	.06	.03
1992 Studio	198	.10	.08	.04
1992 Topps	572	.12	.09	.05
1992 Topps Gold	572	.25	.20	.10
1992 Topps Kids	83	.05	.04	.02
1992 Upper Deck	97	.05	.04	.02
1992 Upper Deck	232	.10	.08	.04
1992 Upper Deck Home Run Heroes	20	.50	.40	.20
1993 Bowman	295	.10	.08	.04
1993 Donruss	103	.08	.06	.03
1993 Donruss Triple Play	150	.07	.05	.03
1993 Fleer	258	.06	.05	.02
1993 Fleer Flair	231	.40	.30	.15
1993 Fleer Ultra	225	.15	.11	.06
1993 Leaf	56	.10	.08	.04
1993 O-Pee-Chee	373	.40	.30	.15
1993 Pinnacle	318	.15	.11	.06
1993 Pinnacle Home Run Club	30	.25	.20	.10
1993 Score	160	.08	.06	.03
1993 Score Select	222	.10	.08	.04
1993 Studio	197	.12	.09	.05
1993 Topps	153	.06	.05	.02
1993 Topps Gold	153	.10	.08	.04
1993 Topps Stadium Club	122	.25	.20	.10
1993 Topps Stadium Club First Day Production	122	8.00	6.00	3.25
1993 Upper Deck	563	.08	.06	.03
1993 Upper Deck Fun Packs	72	.05	.04	.02
1993 Upper Deck Home Run Heroes	15	.50	.40	.20
1993 Upper Deck SP	71	.15	.11	.06
1994 Bowman	449	.10	.08	.04
1994 Bowman's Best	29	.50	.40	.20
1994 Bowman's Best Refractors	29	2.00	1.50	.80
1994 Donruss	339	.08	.06	.03
1994 Donruss Diamond Kings	20	1.00	.75	.40
1994 Donruss Diamond Kings Super	20	3.00	2.25	1.25
1994 Donruss MVP's	22	.75	.60	.30
1994 Donruss Special Edition - Gold	339	.25	.20	.10
1994 Donruss Triple Play	59	.05	.04	.02
1994 Fleer	195	.05	.04	.02
1994 Fleer All-Stars	24	.25	.20	.10
1994 Fleer Extra Bases	109	.15	.11	.06
1994 Fleer Flair	309	.20	.15	.08
1994 Fleer Team Leaders	8	.50	.40	.20
1994 Fleer Ultra	378	.12	.09	.05
1994 Leaf	321	.10	.08	.04
1994 Leaf Limited	47	1.00	.70	.40
1994 Pacific Crown	347	.10	.08	.04
1994 Pinnacle	37	.12	.09	.05
1994 Pinnacle Artist's Proof	37	3.00	2.25	1.25
1994 Pinnacle Museum Collection	37	1.75	1.25	.70

		MT	NM	EX
1994 Pinnacle Run Creators	16	1.50	1.25	.60
1994 Score	49	.04	.03	.02
1994 Score Gold Stars	47	2.00	1.50	.80
1994 Score Select	303	.10	.08	.04
1994 Sportflics 2000	103	.10	.08	.04
1994 Studio	48	.10	.08	.04
1994 Topps	225	.04	.03	.02
1994 Topps Finest	89	.50	.40	.20
1994 Topps Finest Refractors	89	3.50	2.75	1.50
1994 Topps Gold	225	.15	.11	.06
1994 Topps Stadium Club	378	.12	.09	.05
1994 Topps Stadium Club First Day Production	378	2.50	2.00	1.00
1994 Upper Deck	288	.10	.08	.04
1994 Upper Deck	445	.10	.08	.04
1994 Upper Deck All-Stars Green Foil	9	.25	.20	.10
1994 Upper Deck All-Stars Gold Foil	9	1.00	.70	.40
1994 Upper Deck Collector's Choice	585	.05	.04	.02
1994 Upper Deck Electric Diamond	288	.25	.20	.10
1994 Upper Deck Electric Diamond	445	.25	.20	.10
1994 Upper Deck Fun Packs	144	.05	.04	.02
1994 Upper Deck SP	61	.15	.11	.06
1994 Upper Deck SP Baseball Die-Cut	61	.25	.20	.10

Robin Ventura

Set	Card #	MT	NM	EX
1988 Topps Traded	124T	4.00	3.00	1.50
1989 Bowman	65 (R)	1.00	.75	.40
1989 Fleer Update	23	1.50	1.25	.60
1989 Topps	764 (R)	1.00	.70	.40
1989 Topps Big Baseball	65	.80	.60	.30
1990 Bowman	311	.35	.25	.14
1990 Donruss	28	.60	.45	.25
1990 Fleer	550	.60	.45	.25
1990 Fleer Soaring Stars	4	1.50	1.25	.60
1990 Leaf	167	5.00	3.75	2.00
1990 O-Pee-Chee	121	.60	.45	.25
1990 Score	595	.50	.40	.20
1990 Sportflics	222	.30	.25	.12
1990 Topps	121	.25	.20	.10
1990 Upper Deck	21	1.50	1.25	.60
1991 Bowman	358	.15	.11	.06
1991 Donruss	315	.15	.11	.06
1991 Fleer	139	.15	.11	.06
1991 Fleer Ultra	86	.40	.30	.15
1991 Leaf	271	.50	.40	.20
1991 Score	320	.20	.15	.10
1991 Topps	461	.15	.11	.06
1991 Topps Glossy Rookies	31	.45	.35	.20
1991 Topps Stadium Club	274	2.50	2.00	1.00
1991 Upper Deck	263	.30	.25	.12
1992 Bowman	275	1.00	.75	.40
1992 Bowman	655	2.75	2.00	1.00
1992 Donruss	145	.25	.20	.10
1992 Donruss Triple Play	17	.15	.10	.05
1992 Fleer	101	.20	.15	.08
1992 Fleer All-Stars	19	.75	.60	.30
1992 Fleer Ultra	343	.40	.30	.15
1992 Fleer Ultra Award Winners	15	1.00	.75	.40
1992 Leaf	17	.25	.15	.08
1992 O-Pee-Chee	255	.15	.11	.06
1992 O-Pee-Chee Premier	132	.40	.30	.15
1992 Pinnacle	121	.30	.25	.12
1992 Pinnacle	286	.25	.20	.10
1992 Pinnacle Team Pinnacle	6	18.00	13.50	7.25
1992 Pinnacle Team 2000	43	.40	.30	.15
1992 Score	122	.15	.11	.06
1992 Score Impact Players	42	.25	.20	.10
1992 Studio	160	.25	.20	.10
1992 Topps	255	.15	.11	.06
1992 Topps Gold	255	.80	.60	.30
1992 Topps Kids	102	.10	.08	.04
1992 Topps Stadium Club	70	.25	.20	.10
1992 Upper Deck	263	.15	.11	.06
1993 Bowman	667	.15	.11	.06
1993 DiamondMarks	(82)	.40	.30	.15
1993 Donruss	535	.12	.09	.05
1993 Donruss Diamond Kings	10	1.00	.75	.40
1993 Donruss Triple Play	179	.12	.09	.05
1993 Fleer	211	.12	.09	.05
1993 Fleer	716	.10	.08	.04
1993 Fleer Flair	190	.50	.40	.20
1993 Fleer Ultra	537	.25	.20	.10
1993 Fleer Ultra Award Winners	14	1.50	1.25	.60
1993 Leaf	439	.15	.11	.06
1993 Leaf Fasttrack	14	2.50	2.00	1.00
1993 Leaf Gold All-Stars	6	1.50	1.25	.60
1993 O-Pee-Chee	387	.20	.15	.08
1993 Pinnacle	28	.15	.11	.06
1993 Pinnacle Home Run Club	24	.35	.25	.14
1993 Score	41	.15	.11	.06
1993 Score Select	30	.15	.11	.06
1993 Studio	78	.15	.11	.06
1993 Topps	770	.03	.02	.01
1993 Topps Black Gold	43	.40	.30	.15
1993 Topps Finest	93	2.00	1.50	.80
1993 Topps Finest Jumbo All-Stars	93	10.00	7.50	4.00
1993 Topps Finest Refractors	93	35.00	26.00	14.00
1993 Topps Gold	770	.10	.08	.04
1993 Topps Stadium Club	295	.20	.15	.08
1993 Topps Stadium Club	387	.25	.20	.10
1993 Topps Stadium Club First Day Production	295	15.00	11.00	6.00
1993 Topps Stadium Club First Day Production	387	20.00	15.00	8.00
1993 Topps Stadium Club Special	111	.30	.25	.12
1993 Upper Deck	51	.50	.40	.20
1993 Upper Deck	263	.15	.11	.06
1993 Upper Deck	838	.10	.08	.04
1993 Upper Deck Fun Packs All-Star Scratch-Off	5	1.00	.70	.40
1993 Upper Deck Fun Packs	203	.20	.15	.08
1993 Upper Deck SP	261	.40	.30	.15
1994 Bowman	294	.10	.08	.04
1994 Bowman	295	.10	.08	.04

1994 Bowman's Best	30	.75	.60	.30
1994 Bowman's Best Refractors	30	4.00	3.00	1.50
1994 Donruss	23	.15	.11	.06
1994 Donruss Special Edition - Gold	23	.25	.20	.10
1994 Donruss Triple Play Medalists	9	1.50	1.25	.60
1994 Donruss Triple Play	270	.10	.07	.04
1994 Fleer	97	.15	.11	.06
1994 Fleer Extra Bases	54	.15	.11	.06
1994 Fleer Flair	281	.40	.30	.15
1994 Fleer Ultra	341	.15	.11	.06
1994 Fleer Ultra All-Stars	5	.75	.60	.30
1994 Fleer Ultra Award Winners	4	.50	.40	.20
1994 Leaf	26	.20	.15	.08
1994 Leaf Limited	25	1.50	1.25	.60
1994 O-Pee-Chee	33	.10	.08	.04
1994 Pacific Crown	140	.15	.11	.06
1994 Pinnacle	29	.15	.11	.06
1994 Pinnacle Artist's Proof	29	5.00	3.75	2.00
1994 Pinnacle Museum Collection	29	2.00	1.50	.80
1994 Pinnacle Power Surge	9	.35	.25	.14
1994 Score	347	.08	.06	.03
1994 Score Select	41	.15	.11	.06
1994 Sportflics 2000	66	.25	.20	.10
1994 Studio	210	.15	.11	.06
1994 Topps	90	.10	.08	.04
1994 Topps Black Gold	22	.40	.30	.15
1994 Topps Finest	202	.75	.60	.30
1994 Topps Finest Refractors	202	6.00	4.50	2.50
1994 Topps Finest Superstars	202	4.00	3.00	1.50
1994 Topps Gold	90	.25	.20	.10
1994 Topps Stadium Club	315	.20	.15	.08
1994 Topps Stadium Club First Day Production	315	6.00	4.50	2.50
1994 Upper Deck	263	.20	.15	.08
1994 Upper Deck Collector's Choice	282	.15	.11	.06
1994 Upper Deck Electric Diamond	263	.50	.40	.20
1994 Upper Deck Fun Packs	163	.10	.08	.04
1994 Upper Deck SP	194	.25	.20	.10
1994 Upper Deck SP Baseball Die-Cut	194	.35	.25	.14

Honus Wagner

WAGNER, PITTSBURG

Set	Card #	NM	EX	VG
1908 E102 "Set of 25"	(27)	1500.	750.00	360.00
1908 E102 "Set of 25"	(28)	1500.	750.00	360.00
1909-11 American Caramel Co. (E90-1)	(111)	1500.	750.00	450.00
1909-11 American Caramel Co. (E90-1)	(112)	1500.	750.00	450.00
1909 E101 "Set of 50"	(47)	1000.	500.00	230.00
1909 E101 "Set of 50"	(48)	1000.	500.00	230.00
1909-11 T206 White Border	(486)	230.00	230.00	230.00
1910 American Caramel Co. Pirates (E90-2)	(10)	2000.	1000.	600.00
1910 American Caramel Co. (E91, Set C)	(30)	600.00	300.00	180.00
1910 E98 "Set of 30"	(5)	2000.	1000.	560.00
1914 Cracker Jack	68	3000.	1080.	660.00
1915 American Caramel (E106)	(45)	3000.	1250.	500.00
1915 American Caramel (E106)	(46)	3000.	1250.	500.00
1915 Cracker Jack	68	2250.	1260.	765.00
1936 National Chicle Co. "Fine Pens" (R313)	(104)	80.00	40.00	24.00
1940 Play Ball	168	275.00	107.00	52.00
1948 Leaf	70	250.00	125.00	75.00
1960 Fleer	62	10.00	5.00	3.00
1961-62 Fleer	150	35.00	17.50	10.50
1976 O-Pee-Chee	344	4.25	2.25	1.25
1976 Topps	344	1.25	.60	.40

Set	Card #	MT	NM	EX
1989 Pacific Trading Cards Legends II	211	1.00	.70	.40
1992 Score	880	.20	.15	.08
1993 Cracker Jack Anniversary	(12)	.75	.55	.30

Lou Whitaker

Set	Card #	NM	EX	VG
1978 Topps	704 (R)	25.00	12.50	7.50
1979 O-Pee-Chee	55	10.25	5.25	3.00
1979 Topps	123	7.50	3.75	2.25
1980 O-Pee-Chee	187	5.00	2.50	1.50
1980 Topps	358	3.00	1.50	.90

Set	Card #	MT	NM	EX
1981 Donruss	365	.75	.60	.30
1981 Fleer	463	.75	.60	.30
1981 O-Pee-Chee	234	.40	.30	.15
1981 Topps	234	1.00	.75	.40
1982 Donruss	454	.60	.45	.25
1982 Fleer	284	.40	.30	.15
1982 O-Pee-Chee	39	.25	.20	.10
1982 Topps	39	.40	.30	.15
1983 Donruss	333	.40	.30	.15
1983 Fleer	348	.60	.45	.25
1983 O-Pee-Chee	66	.30	.25	.12
1983 Topps	509	.40	.30	.15
1984 Donruss	227	1.50	1.25	.60
1984 Fleer	92	.75	.60	.30
1984 O-Pee-Chee	181	.50	.40	.20
1984 O-Pee-Chee	211	.25	.20	.10
1984 Topps	398	.20	.15	.08
1984 Topps	666	.15	.11	.06

1984 Topps	695	.40	.30	.15
1984 Topps All-Star Glossy Set of 40	30	.30	.25	.12
1985 Donruss	5	.30	.25	.12
1985 Donruss	293	.40	.30	.15
1985 Donruss Diamond Kings Supers	5	.30	.25	.12
1985 Fleer	24	.50	.40	.20
1985 Leaf-Donruss	5	.20	.15	.08
1985 O-Pee-Chee	108	.20	.15	.08
1985 Topps	480	.25	.20	.10
1985 Topps All-Star Glossy Set of 22	14	.30	.25	.12
1986 Donruss	49	.30	.25	.12
1986 Fleer	242	.30	.25	.12
1986 Leaf	33	.15	.11	.06
1986 O-Pee-Chee	20	.15	.11	.06
1986 Sportflics	48	.20	.15	.08
1986 Sportflics	74	.20	.15	.08
1986 Sportflics Decade Greats	73	.30	.25	.12
1986 Sportflics Rookies	48	.60	.45	.25
1986 Topps	20	.12	.09	.05
1986 Topps All-Star Glossy Set of 22	3	.30	.25	.12
1987 Donruss	107	.25	.20	.10
1987 Fleer	168	.15	.11	.06
1987 Leaf	78	.15	.11	.06
1987 O-Pee-Chee	106	.15	.11	.06
1987 Sportflics	112	.10	.08	.04
1987 Sportflics	137	.20	.15	.08
1987 Topps	661	.15	.11	.06
1987 Topps All-Star Glossy Set of 60	7	.30	.25	.12
1987 Topps All-Star Glossy Set of 22	14	.25	.20	.10
1988 Donruss	173	.08	.06	.03
1988 Fleer	75	.10	.08	.04
1988 Leaf	169	.12	.09	.05
1988 O-Pee-Chee	179	.09	.07	.04
1988 Score	56	.08	.06	.03
1988 Sportflics	30	.20	.15	.08
1988 Topps	770	.10	.08	.04
1989 Bowman	103	.08	.06	.03
1989 Donruss	298	.08	.06	.03
1989 Fleer	151	.08	.06	.03
1989 O-Pee-Chee	320	.07	.05	.03
1989 Score	230	.15	.11	.06
1989 Sportflics	18	.25	.20	.10
1989 Topps	320	.15	.11	.06
1989 Topps Big Baseball	22	.05	.04	.02
1989 Upper Deck	451	.15	.11	.06
1990 Bowman	356	.08	.06	.03
1990 Donruss	16	.08	.06	.03
1990 Donruss	298	.08	.06	.03
1990 Donruss Diamond Kings Supers	16	.15	.11	.06
1990 Fleer	619	.09	.07	.04
1990 Leaf	34	.35	.25	.14
1990 O-Pee-Chee	280	.07	.05	.03
1990 Score	75	.09	.07	.04
1990 Sportflics	103	.10	.08	.04
1990 Topps	280	.07	.05	.03
1990 Topps Big Baseball	130	.10	.08	.04
1990 Upper Deck	327	.10	.08	.04
1991 Bowman	150	.06	.05	.02
1991 Donruss	174	.08	.06	.03
1991 Fleer	357	.08	.06	.03
1991 Fleer Ultra	130	.08	.06	.03
1991 Leaf	120	.10	.08	.04
1991 Score	297	.08	.06	.03
1991 Studio	60	.20	.15	.08
1991 Topps	145	.08	.06	.03
1991 Topps Stadium Club	101	.25	.20	.10
1991 Upper Deck	367	.10	.08	.04
1992 Bowman	630	.08	.06	.03
1992 Donruss	285	.08	.06	.03
1992 Donruss Triple Play	117	.06	.05	.02
1992 Fleer	149	.08	.06	.03
1992 Fleer Ultra	65	.15	.11	.06
1992 Leaf	391	.12	.09	.05
1992 O-Pee-Chee	570	.06	.05	.02
1992 Pinnacle	29	.10	.08	.04
1992 Score	255	.08	.06	.03
1992 Studio	180	.15	.11	.06
1992 Topps	570	.06	.05	.02
1992 Topps Gold	570	.35	.25	.14
1992 Topps Kids	77	.10	.08	.04
1992 Topps Stadium Club	550	.15	.11	.06
1992 Upper Deck	516	.08	.06	.03
1993 Bowman	11	.10	.08	.04
1993 Donruss	686	.05	.04	.02
1993 Donruss Triple Play	224	.10	.08	.04
1993 Fleer	614	.05	.04	.02
1993 Fleer Flair	211	.25	.15	.08
1993 Fleer Ultra	555	.10	.08	.04
1993 Leaf	148	.10	.08	.04
1993 O-Pee-Chee	389	.15	.11	.06
1993 Pinnacle	509	.06	.05	.02
1993 Score	596	.10	.08	.04
1993 Score Select	112	.10	.08	.04
1993 Studio	76	.08	.06	.03
1993 Topps	160	.06	.05	.02
1993 Topps Finest	2	1.00	.70	.40
1993 Topps Finest Refractors	2	20.00	15.00	8.00
1993 Topps Gold	160	.10	.08	.04
1993 Topps Stadium Club	135	.10	.08	.04
1993 Topps Stadium Club First Day Production	135	7.00	5.25	2.75
1993 Upper Deck	273	.08	.06	.03
1993 Upper Deck Fun Packs	190	.15	.11	.06
1993 Upper Deck SP	243	.15	.11	.06
1994 Bowman	237	.10	.08	.04
1994 Donruss	360	.05	.04	.02
1994 Donruss Special Edition - Gold	360	.25	.20	.10
1994 Donruss Triple Play Medalists	5	2.50	2.00	1.00
1994 Donruss Triple Play	250	.05	.04	.02
1994 Fleer	146	.05	.04	.02
1994 Fleer	709	.05	.04	.02
1994 Fleer Extra Bases	82	.10	.08	.04
1994 Fleer Flair	296	.20	.15	.08
1994 Fleer Ultra	60	.10	.08	.04
1994 Leaf	80	.10	.08	.04
1994 Leaf Limited	35	1.00	.70	.40
1994 O-Pee-Chee	172	.05	.04	.02
1994 Pacific Crown	232	.05	.04	.02
1994 Pinnacle	281	.10	.08	.04
1994 Pinnacle Artist's Proof	281	3.00	2.25	1.25
1994 Pinnacle Museum Collection	281	1.50	1.25	.60
1994 Score	79	.04	.03	.02
1994 Score Select	323	.10	.08	.04
1994 Studio	195	.10	.08	.04
1994 Topps	410	.04	.03	.02
1994 Topps Finest	364	.50	.40	.20
1994 Topps Finest Refractors	364	3.50	2.75	1.50
1994 Topps Gold	410	.15	.11	.06
1994 Topps Stadium Club	443	.10	.08	.04
1994 Topps Stadium Club First Day Production	443	4.00	3.00	1.50
1994 Upper Deck	414	.10	.08	.04
1994 Upper Deck Collector's Choice	291	.05	.04	.02
1994 Upper Deck Electric Diamond	414	.25	.20	.10

* * *

When selling cards to a dealer, generally expect to be offered as little as 10 percent of the price guide value for commons, and from 50 to 80 percent of the price guide value for stars and rookies.

* * *

Billy Williams

Matt Williams

Set	Card #	NM	EX	VG
1961 Topps	141 (R)	75.00	37.50	22.00
1962 Topps	288	28.00	14.00	8.50
1963 Post Cereal	172	110.00	55.00	33.00
1963 Topps	353	25.00	12.50	7.50
1964 Topps	175	15.00	7.50	4.50
1965 O-Pee-Chee	4	12.75	6.50	3.75
1965 O-Pee-Chee	220	21.00	10.50	6.25
1965 Topps	4	15.00	7.50	4.50
1965 Topps	220	12.50	6.25	3.75
1966 Topps	217	7.50	3.75	2.25
1966 Topps	580	80.00	40.00	24.00
1967 Topps	315	12.00	6.00	3.50
1968 O-Pee-Chee	37	12.75	6.50	3.75
1968 Topps	37	7.00	3.50	2.00
1969 O-Pee-Chee	4	8.50	4.25	2.50
1969 Topps	4	4.00	2.00	1.25
1969 Topps	450	6.00	3.00	1.75
1970 O-Pee-Chee	170	8.50	4.25	2.50
1970 Topps	170	6.00	3.00	1.75
1971 O-Pee-Chee	64	1.50	.70	.45
1971 O-Pee-Chee	66	1.50	.70	.45
1971 O-Pee-Chee	350	3.00	1.50	.90
1971 Topps	64	3.50	1.75	1.00
1971 Topps	66	3.50	1.75	1.00
1971 Topps	350	8.00	4.00	2.50
1972 O-Pee-Chee	439	1.75	.90	.50
1972 O-Pee-Chee	440	1.75	.90	.50
1972 Topps	439	6.00	3.00	1.75
1972 Topps	440	3.00	1.50	.90
1973 O-Pee-Chee	61	1.25	.60	.40
1973 O-Pee-Chee	200	1.75	.90	.50
1973 Topps	61	2.25	1.25	.70
1973 Topps	200	4.00	2.00	1.25
1974 O-Pee-Chee	110	1.75	.90	.50
1974 O-Pee-Chee	338	6.00	3.00	1.75
1974 Topps	110	6.00	3.00	1.75
1974 Topps	338	5.00	2.50	1.50
1975 O-Pee-Chee	545	2.00	1.00	.60
1975 Topps	545	3.00	1.50	.90
1975 Topps Mini	545	6.00	3.00	1.75
1976 O-Pee-Chee	525	1.75	.90	.50
1976 Topps	525	2.25	1.25	.70

Set	Card #	MT	NM	EX
1986 Sportflics Decade Greats	51	.30	.25	.12
1988 Pacific Trading Cards Baseball Legends	90	.20	.15	.08
1989 Pacific Trading Cards Legends II	184	.25	.20	.10
1990 Pacific Legends	58	.20	.15	.08

* * *

Four years ago: Dwight Gooden's 1985 Donruss
card (#190) was $15 in July 1991.

* * *

Set	Card #	MT	NM	EX
1987 Fleer Update	129	5.00	3.75	2.00
1987 Sportflics Rookies	25	.90	.70	.35
1987 Topps Traded	129T	3.00	2.25	1.25
1988 Donruss	628 (R)	2.50	2.00	1.00
1988 Fleer	101 (R)	6.00	4.50	2.50
1988 Score	118 (R)	2.00	1.50	.80
1988 Topps	372 (R)	2.00	1.50	.80
1989 Donruss	594	.40	.30	.15
1989 Fleer	346	.40	.30	.15
1989 Score	612	.30	.25	.12
1989 Topps	628	.25	.20	.10
1989 Upper Deck	247	2.00	1.50	.80
1990 Bowman	238	.25	.20	.10
1990 Donruss	348	.25	.20	.10
1990 Donruss Grand Slammers	1	.25	.20	.10
1990 Fleer	75	.25	.20	.10
1990 Leaf	94	4.00	3.00	1.50
1990 O-Pee-Chee	41	.15	.11	.06
1990 Score	503	.25	.20	.10
1990 Sportflics	70	.20	.15	.08
1990 Topps	41	.20	.15	.08
1990 Topps Big Baseball	96	.15	.11	.06
1990 Upper Deck	577	.40	.30	.15
1991 Bowman	378	.10	.08	.04
1991 Bowman	618	.08	.06	.03
1991 Donruss	18	.12	.09	.05
1991 Donruss	685	.20	.15	.08
1991 Donruss Elite	8	70.00	52.00	28.00
1991 Donruss Grand Slammers	8	.20	.15	.08
1991 Fleer	276	.20	.15	.08
1991 Fleer All Stars	3	.60	.45	.25
1991 Fleer Ultra	331	.40	.30	.15
1991 Leaf	93	.30	.25	.12
1991 Score	189	.20	.15	.08
1991 Score	667	.10	.06	.03
1991 Score	689	.10	.08	.04
1991 Studio	259	.30	.25	.12
1991 Topps	190	.15	.11	.06
1991 Topps	399	.10	.08	.04
1991 Topps Stadium Club	295	1.75	1.25	.70
1991 Upper Deck	157	.25	.20	.10
1991 Upper Deck Silver Sluggers	13	1.50	1.25	.60
1992 Bowman	175	1.25	.90	.50
1992 Bowman	579	2.00	1.50	.80
1992 Donruss	135	.15	.11	.06
1992 Donruss Triple Play	4	.15	.11	.06
1992 Fleer	650	.15	.11	.06
1992 Fleer Lumber Co.	6	1.50	.90	.50
1992 Fleer Ultra	296	.50	.40	.20
1992 Fleer Ultra Award Winners	13	2.50	2.00	1.00
1992 Leaf	373	.20	.15	.06
1992 O-Pee-Chee	445	.12	.09	.05
1992 O-Pee-Chee Premier	144	.15	.11	.06
1992 Pinnacle	28	.25	.20	.10

Card	#			
1992 Pinnacle Team Pinnacle	6	18.00	13.50	7.25
1992 Score	230	.20	.15	.08
1992 Score Impact Players	62	.30	.25	.12
1992 Studio	120	.25	.20	.10
1992 Topps	445	.20	.15	.08
1992 Topps Gold	445	1.00	.70	.40
1992 Topps Kids	60	.10	.08	.04
1992 Topps Stadium Club	582	.60	.45	.25
1992 Upper Deck	154	.15	.11	.06
1992 Upper Deck Home Run Heroes	5	.75	.60	.30
1993 Bowman	56	.40	.30	.15
1993 DiamondMarks	(64)	.60	.45	.25
1993 Donruss	182	.20	.15	.08
1993 Donruss Triple Play	171	.12	.09	.05
1993 Fleer	540	.25	.20	.10
1993 Fleer Flair	148	1.00	.75	.40
1993 Fleer Ultra	490	.25	.20	.10
1993 Leaf	158	.30	.25	.12
1993 O-Pee-Chee	348	.60	.45	.25
1993 Pinnacle	67	.35	.25	.14
1993 Pinnacle Home Run Club	22	.35	.25	.14
1993 Score	46	.10	.08	.04
1993 Studio	66	.40	.30	.15
1993 Topps	225	.25	.20	.10
1993 Topps Finest	25	7.00	5.25	2.75
1993 Topps Finest Refractors	25	60.00	45.00	25.00
1993 Topps Gold	225	.50	.40	.20
1993 Topps Stadium Club	287	.30	.25	.12
1993 Topps Stadium Club First Day Production	287	15.00	11.00	6.00
1993 Upper Deck	143	.20	.15	.08
1993 Upper Deck	471	.20	.15	.08
1993 Upper Deck	476	.20	.15	.08
1993 Upper Deck Fun Packs	104	.20	.15	.08
1993 Upper Deck Home Run Heroes	21	1.00	.75	.40
1993 Upper Deck SP	117	1.50	1.25	.60
1993 Upper Deck SP Platinum Power	20	12.00	9.00	4.75
1994 Bowman	79	.30	.25	.12
1994 Bowman's Best	93	1.50	1.25	.60
1994 Bowman's Best	8	2.00	1.50	.80
1994 Bowman's Best Refractors	93	5.00	3.75	2.00
1994 Bowman's Best Refractors	8	10.00	7.50	4.00
1994 Donruss	370	.05	.04	.02
1994 Donruss Decade Dominators	4	2.50	2.00	1.00
1994 Donruss Decade Dominators Supers	4	4.00	3.00	1.50
1994 Donruss Special Edition - Gold	370	.25	.20	.10
1994 Donruss Triple Play Bomb Squad	10	2.00	1.50	.80
1994 Donruss Triple Play	110	.10	.08	.04
1994 Fleer	704	.10	.08	.04
1994 Fleer Extra Bases	395	.25	.20	.10
1994 Fleer Extra Bases Game Breakers	29	.50	.40	.20
1994 Fleer Flair	448	.50	.40	.20
1994 Fleer Flair Hot Glove	10	15.00	11.00	6.00
1994 Fleer Flair Infield Power	10	3.00	2.25	1.25
1994 Fleer Lumber Co.	10	1.00	.75	.40
1994 Fleer ProVisions	3	.50	.40	.20
1994 Fleer Ultra	296	.35	.25	.14
1994 Fleer Ultra All-Stars	15	1.00	.75	.40
1994 Fleer Ultra Award Winners	13	1.00	.75	.40
1994 Fleer Ultra Home Run Kings	9	4.00	3.00	1.50
1994 Fleer Ultra RBI Kings	11	8.00	6.00	3.25
1994 Leaf	334	.35	.25	.14
1994 Leaf Clean-Up Crew	10	6.00	4.50	2.50
1994 Leaf Limited	160	3.00	2.25	1.25
1994 Leaf Limited Gold	6	25.00	18.00	10.00
1994 Leaf MVP Contenders	14a	5.00	3.75	2.00
1994 Leaf MVP Contenders	14b	10.00	7.50	4.00
1994 O-Pee-Chee	80	.30	.25	.12
1994 Pacific Crown	559	.10	.08	.04
1994 Pacific Crown Homerun Leaders	13	4.00	3.00	1.50
1994 Pinnacle	298	.25	.20	.10
1994 Pinnacle Artist's Proof	298	14.00	10.50	5.50
1994 Pinnacle Museum Collection	298	10.00	7.50	4.00
1994 Pinnacle Run Creators	39	2.00	1.50	.80
1994 Pinnacle Team Pinnacle	3	12.00	9.00	4.75
1994 Pinnacle The Naturals Box Set	16	.50	.40	.20
1994 Score	94	.20	.15	.08
1994 Score Dream Team	6	12.00	9.00	4.75
1994 Score Gold Stars	10	10.00	7.50	4.00
1994 Score Select	269	.40	.30	.15
1994 Score The Cycle	20	18.00	13.50	7.25
1994 Sportflics 2000	139	.10	.08	.04
1994 Sportflics 2000	187	.25	.20	.10
1994 Studio	89	.50	.40	.20
1994 Topps	386	.10	.08	.04
1994 Topps	550	.05	.04	.02
1994 Topps Black Gold	44	.50	.40	.20
1994 Topps Finest	214	1.75	1.25	.70
1994 Topps Finest Refractors	214	7.50	5.50	3.00
1994 Topps Finest Superstars	214	6.00	4.50	2.50
1994 Topps Gold	386	.25	.20	.10
1994 Topps Gold	550	.15	.11	.06
1994 Topps Stadium Club	268	.12	.09	.05
1994 Topps Stadium Club	419	.40	.30	.15
1994 Topps Stadium Club	717	.25	.20	.10
1994 Topps Stadium Club First Day Production	268	7.00	5.25	2.75
1994 Topps Stadium Club First Day Production	419	15.00	11.00	6.00
1994 Topps Stadium Club First Day Production	717	12.00	9.00	4.75
1994 Topps Stadium Club Members Only Baseball	8	.45	.35	.20
1994 Topps Traded Finest Inserts	3	.60	.45	.25
1994 Upper Deck	36	.20	.15	.08
1994 Upper Deck	490	.25	.20	.10
1994 Upper Deck All-Stars Green Foil	6	.50	.40	.20
1994 Upper Deck All-Stars Gold Foil	6	2.50	2.00	1.00
1994 Upper Deck Collector's Choice	299	.08	.06	.03
1994 Upper Deck Electric Diamond	36	.35	.25	.14
1994 Upper Deck Electric Diamond	490	.50	.40	.20
1994 Upper Deck Fun Packs	90	.05	.04	.02
1994 Upper Deck Fun Packs	188	.10	.08	.04
1994 Upper Deck Mickey Mantle's Long Shots	20MM	3.00	2.25	1.25
1994 Upper Deck SP	95	.60	.45	.25
1994 Upper Deck SP Baseball Die-Cut	95	1.00	.75	.40

Ted Williams

Set	Card #	NM	EX	VG
1939 Play Ball	92a	1800.	900.00	540.00
1939 Play Ball	92b	2000.	1000.	600.00
1940 Play Ball	27	1800.	702.00	342.00
1941 Double Play	57	342.00	342.00	342.00
1941 Double Play	81	342.00	342.00	342.00
1941 Play Ball	14	2000.	940.00	500.00
1948 Leaf	76	875.00	435.00	250.00
1950 Bowman	98	750.00	350.00	210.00
1951 Bowman	165	600.00	250.00	150.00
1952 Red Man Tobacco	23A	175.00	87.00	52.00
1954 Bowman	66a	4250.	2100.	1200.
1954 Topps	1	600.00	200.00	125.00
1954 Topps	250	700.00	225.00	110.00
1955 Topps	2	325.00	160.00	95.00
1956 Topps	5	275.00	135.00	80.00
1957 Topps	1	395.00	175.00	100.00
1958 Topps	1	350.00	175.00	100.00
1958 Topps	321	50.00	25.00	15.00
1958 Topps	485	60.00	30.00	18.00
1960 Fleer	72	60.00	30.00	18.00
1961-62 Fleer	152	65.00	32.00	19.50
1969 Topps	539	3.25	1.75	1.00
1969 Topps	650	12.00	6.00	3.50
1970 O-Pee-Chee	211	12.00	6.00	3.50
1970 Topps	211	12.00	6.00	3.50
1971 O-Pee-Chee	380	10.25	5.25	3.00
1971 Topps	380	10.00	5.00	3.00
1972 O-Pee-Chee	510	10.25	5.25	3.00
1972 Topps	510	10.00	5.00	3.00
1976 O-Pee-Chee	347	10.25	5.25	3.00
1976 Topps	347	7.50	3.75	2.25

Set	Card #	MT	NM	EX
1986 Sportflics Decade Greats	25	1.25	.90	.50
1988 Pacific Trading Cards Baseball Legends	50	.50	.40	.20
1989 Bowman Inserts	(11)	.25	.20	.10
1989 Pacific Trading Cards Legends II	154	.40	.30	.15
1990 Pacific Legends	59	.50	.40	.20
1991 "1953" Topps Archives	319	6.00	4.50	2.50

* * *

Hall of Famer Don Maynard, on why he retired from football: "Well, one day I came home and my wife had used my helmet as a planter."

* * *

Four years ago: Tim Raines' 1981 Topps rookie card (#470) was $9 in July 1991.

* * *

Maury Wills

Set	Card #	NM	EX	VG
1961 Post Cereal	164a	6.00	3.00	1.75
1961 Post Cereal	164b	6.00	3.00	1.75
1962 Post Cereal	104	5.00	2.50	1.50
1963 Fleer	43	80.00	40.00	24.00
1963 Post Cereal	115	4.00	2.00	1.25
1967 Topps	570 (R)	80.00	40.00	24.00
1968 O-Pee-Chee	175	2.50	1.25	.70
1968 Topps	175	2.50	1.25	.70
1969 O-Pee-Chee	45	2.25	1.25	.70
1969 Topps	45	2.00	1.00	.60
1970 Topps	595	4.00	2.00	1.25
1971 O-Pee-Chee	385	1.50	.70	.45
1971 Topps	385	1.25	.60	.40
1972 O-Pee-Chee	437	1.75	.90	.50
1972 O-Pee-Chee	438	1.75	.90	.50
1972 Topps	437	1.50	.70	.45
1972 Topps	438	1.00	.50	.30
1975 O-Pee-Chee	200	6.75	3.50	2.00
1975 Topps	200	6.00	3.00	1.75
1975 Topps Mini	200	9.00	4.50	2.75
1977 Topps	435	.35	.20	.11

Set	Card #	MT	NM	EX
1981 Fleer	595	.10	.08	.04
1981 Topps	672	.25	.20	.10
1987 Topps	315	.07	.05	.03

Dave Winfield

Set	Card #	NM	EX	VG
1974 O-Pee-Chee	456	250.00	125.00	75.00
1974 Topps	456 (R)	200.00	100.00	60.00
1975 O-Pee-Chee	61	75.00	37.00	22.00
1975 Topps	61	70.00	35.00	21.00
1976 O-Pee-Chee	160	42.50	21.00	12.50
1976 Topps	160	45.00	22.00	13.50
1977 O-Pee-Chee	156	30.00	15.00	9.00
1977 Topps	390	25.00	12.50	7.50

1978 O-Pee-Chee	78	25.00	12.50	7.50
1978 Topps	530	24.00	12.00	7.25
1979 O-Pee-Chee	11	17.00	8.50	5.00
1979 Topps	30	15.00	7.50	4.50
1980 O-Pee-Chee	122	12.00	6.00	3.50
1980 Topps	203	.50	.25	.15
1980 Topps	230	10.00	5.00	3.00

Set	Card #	MT	NM	EX
1981 Donruss	364	3.00	2.25	1.25
1981 Fleer	484	3.00	2.25	1.25
1981 Topps	370	5.00	3.75	2.00
1981 Topps Traded	855	13.00	9.75	5.25
1982 Donruss	18	1.00	.75	.40
1982 Donruss	31	2.50	2.00	1.00
1982 Donruss	575	2.00	1.50	.80
1982 Fleer	56	2.50	2.00	1.00
1982 Fleer	646a	2.00	1.50	.80
1982 Fleer	646b	2.00	1.50	.80
1982 O-Pee-Chee	76	.20	.15	.08
1982 O-Pee-Chee	352	3.75	2.75	1.50
1982 Topps	553	.90	.70	.35
1982 Topps	600	4.00	3.00	1.50
1983 Donruss	409	3.00	2.25	1.25
1983 Fleer	398	2.50	2.00	1.00
1983 Fleer	633	.25	.20	.10
1983 O-Pee-Chee	258	3.25	2.50	1.25
1983 Topps	770	2.50	2.00	1.00
1983 Topps All-Star Glossy Set of 40	7	.60	.45	.25
1984 Donruss	51	11.00	8.25	4.50
1984 Fleer	143	8.00	6.00	3.25
1984 O-Pee-Chee	266	1.75	1.25	.70
1984 O-Pee-Chee	378	.60	.45	.25
1984 Topps	402	.30	.25	.12
1984 Topps	460	2.00	1.50	.80
1984 Topps All-Star Glossy Set of 22	8	.50	.40	.20
1984 Topps All-Star Glossy Set of 40	16	.60	.45	.25
1985 Donruss	51	4.50	3.50	1.75
1985 Donruss	651a	4.00	3.00	1.50
1985 Donruss	651b	6.00	4.50	2.50
1985 Fleer	146	4.00	3.00	1.50
1985 Fleer	629	1.00	.70	.40
1985 Leaf-Donruss	127	3.25	2.50	1.25
1985 Leaf-Donruss	140	3.25	2.50	1.25
1985 O-Pee-Chee	180	1.25	.90	.50
1985 Topps	180	1.25	.90	.50
1985 Topps	705	.50	.40	.20
1985 Topps All-Star Glossy Set of 40	14	.60	.45	.25
1985 Topps All-Star Glossy Set of 22	17	.50	.40	.20
1986 Donruss	248	1.50	1.25	.60
1986 Fleer	121	1.50	1.25	.60
1986 Leaf	125	1.00	.70	.40
1986 O-Pee-Chee	70	.50	.40	.20
1986 Sportflics	49	.60	.45	.25
1986 Sportflics Decade Greats	74	.30	.25	.12
1986 Topps	70	.60	.45	.25
1986 Topps	717	.20	.15	.08
1986 Topps All-Star Glossy Set of 22	8	.50	.40	.20
1986 Topps All-Star Glossy Set of 60	42	.50	.40	.20
1987 Donruss	20	.25	.20	.10
1987 Donruss	105	.60	.45	.25
1987 Donruss Diamond Kings Supers	20	.50	.40	.20
1987 Fleer	120	1.00	.70	.40
1987 Leaf	20	.80	.60	.30
1987 Leaf	70	1.00	.70	.40
1987 O-Pee-Chee	36	.20	.15	.08
1987 Sportflics	41	.90	.70	.35
1987 Sportflics	153	.25	.20	.10
1987 Topps	770	.35	.25	.14
1987 Topps All-Star Glossy Set of 22	17	.40	.30	.15
1988 Donruss	298	.35	.25	.14

1988 Fleer	226	.50	.40	.20
1988 Leaf	116	.25	.20	.10
1988 O-Pee-Chee	89	.15	.11	.06
1988 Score	55	.35	.25	.14
1988 Sportflics	7	.75	.60	.30
1988 Sportflics Gamewinners	7	.80	.60	.30
1988 Topps	392	.15	.11	.06
1988 Topps	459	.08	.06	.03
1988 Topps	510	.20	.15	.08
1988 Topps All-Star Glossy Set of 22	8	.40	.30	.15
1988 Topps All-Star Glossy Set of 60	46	.50	.40	.20
1988 Topps Big Baseball	24	.45	.35	.20
1989 Bowman	179	.25	.20	.10
1989 Donruss	159	.25	.20	.10
1989 Donruss Grand Slammers	6	.40	.30	.15
1989 Donruss MVP	11	.25	.20	.10
1989 Fleer	274	.30	.25	.12
1989 O-Pee-Chee	260	.40	.30	.15
1989 Score	50	.25	.20	.10
1989 Sportflics	24	.35	.25	.14
1989 Topps	260	.25	.20	.10
1989 Topps	407	.12	.09	.05
1989 Topps All-Star Glossy Set of 22	8	.15	.11	.06
1989 Topps All-Star Glossy Set of 60	21	.40	.30	.15
1989 Topps Big Baseball	314	.20	.15	.08
1989 Upper Deck	349	.75	.60	.30
1990 Bowman	432	.20	.15	.08
1990 Donruss	551	.20	.15	.08
1990 Fleer	458	.15	.11	.06
1990 Fleer Update	81	.20	.15	.08
1990 Leaf	426	1.50	1.25	.60
1990 O-Pee-Chee	380	.15	.11	.06
1990 Score	307	.20	.15	.08
1990 Score Traded	1T	.20	.15	.08
1990 Sportflics	87	.15	.11	.06
1990 Topps	380	.15	.11	.06
1990 Topps Big Baseball	20	.12	.09	.05
1990 Topps Traded	130T	.20	.15	.08
1990 Upper Deck	337	.30	.25	.12
1990 Upper Deck	745	.25	.20	.10
1991 Bowman	210	.15	.11	.06
1991 Donruss	468	.12	.09	.05
1991 Fleer	329	.12	.09	.05
1991 Fleer Ultra	54	.35	.25	.14
1991 Leaf	499	.40	.30	.15
1991 O-Pee-Chee Premier	130	.15	.11	.06
1991 Score	83	.12	.09	.05
1991 Studio	30	.25	.20	.10
1991 Topps	630	.10	.08	.04
1991 Topps Stadium Club	263	1.00	.70	.40
1991 Topps Stadium Club Members Only	(30)	.50	.40	.20
1991 Upper Deck	337	.15	.11	.06
1992 Bowman	315	1.50	1.25	.60
1992 Donruss	133	.08	.06	.03
1992 Fleer	72	.12	.09	.05
1992 Fleer	686	.10	.08	.04
1992 Fleer Ultra	454	.50	.40	.20
1992 Fleer Update	67	2.50	2.00	1.00
1992 Leaf	171	.25	.15	.08
1992 O-Pee-Chee	5	.06	.05	.02
1992 O-Pee-Chee	792	.12	.09	.05
1992 O-Pee-Chee Premier	150	.20	.15	.08
1992 Pinnacle	375	.35	.25	.14
1992 Pinnacle Rookie Idols	18	8.00	6.00	3.25
1992 Score	32	.15	.11	.06
1992 Score Rookie & Traded	7	.60	.45	.25
1992 Studio	260	.30	.25	.12
1992 Topps	5	.06	.05	.02
1992 Topps	792	.12	.09	.05
1992 Topps Gold	5	.45	.35	.20
1992 Topps Gold	792	2.00	1.50	.80
1992 Topps Kids	96	.20	.15	.08

Card	#			
1992 Topps Stadium Club	745	.60	.45	.25
1992 Topps Traded	130	.15	.11	.06
1992 Topps Traded Gold	130	.50	.40	.20
1992 Upper Deck	28	.10	.08	.04
1992 Upper Deck	222	.15	.11	.06
1992 Upper Deck	734	.15	.11	.06
1992 Upper Deck Home Run Heroes	17	.60	.45	.25
1993 Bowman	565	.20	.15	.08
1993 Donruss	643	.15	.11	.06
1993 Donruss Elite	35	25.00	18.00	10.00
1993 Donruss Elite Supers	17	25.00	18.50	10.00
1993 Donruss Spirit of the Game	1	1.00	.75	.40
1993 Donruss Triple Play Gallery	5	2.50	2.00	1.00
1993 Donruss 1992 Blue Jays Commemorative Set	14	.75	.60	.30
1993 Fleer	343	.15	.11	.06
1993 Fleer Final Edition	9DT	.50	.40	.20
1993 Fleer Final Edition	241	.15	.11	.06
1993 Fleer Flair	243	.60	.45	.25
1993 Fleer Golden Moments I	(3)	1.25	.90	.50
1993 Fleer Ultra	589	.30	.25	.12
1993 Leaf	423	.20	.15	.08
1993 Leaf	----	4.00	3.00	1.50
1993 O-Pee-Chee	371	.50	.40	.20
1993 O-Pee-Chee Premier	28	.30	.25	.12
1993 O-Pee-Chee World Champs	17	.75	.60	.30
1993 O-Pee-Chee World Series Heroes	4	1.00	.70	.40
1993 Pinnacle	295	.25	.20	.10
1993 Pinnacle	438	.25	.20	.10
1993 Pinnacle	486	.12	.09	.05
1993 Pinnacle Cooperstown	10	.35	.25	.14
1993 Pinnacle Cooperstown Dufex	10	75.00	56.00	30.00
1993 Pinnacle Home Run Club	32	.75	.60	.30
1993 Score	521	.10	.07	.04
1993 Score	620	.15	.11	.06
1993 Score Select	32	.25	.20	.10
1993 Score Select Rookie/ Traded	9	.60	.45	.25
1993 Studio	77	.25	.20	.10
1993 Topps	131	.20	.15	.08
1993 Topps Black Gold	44	.35	.25	.14
1993 Topps Finest	162	3.00	2.25	1.25
1993 Topps Finest Refractors	162	60.00	45.00	25.00
1993 Topps Gold	131	.40	.30	.15
1993 Topps Stadium Club	206	.30	.25	.12
1993 Topps Stadium Club	609	.30	.25	.12
1993 Topps Stadium Club First Day Production	206	50.00	37.00	20.00
1993 Topps Stadium Club First Day Production	609	55.00	41.00	22.00
1993 Topps Stadium Club Members Only	(28)	1.00	.70	.40
1993 Topps Stadium Club Special	1	.25	.20	.10
1993 Topps Traded	83	.15	.11	.06
1993 Upper Deck	40	.10	.07	.04
1993 Upper Deck	786	.20	.15	.08
1993 Upper Deck "Highlights"	19	5.00	3.75	2.00
1993 Upper Deck Fun Packs	196	.35	.25	.14
1993 Upper Deck SP	252	.60	.45	.25
1993 Upper Deck Then And Now	9	2.00	1.50	.80
1994 Bowman	300	.25	.20	.10
1994 Bowman's Best	6	1.00	.70	.40
1994 Bowman's Best Refractors	6	8.00	6.00	3.25
1994 Donruss	336	.20	.15	.08
1994 Donruss Diamond Kings	29	1.25	.90	.50
1994 Donruss Diamond Kings Super	29	5.00	3.75	2.00
1994 Donruss Special Edition - Gold	336	.50	.40	.20
1994 Donruss Triple Play Medalists	15	1.50	1.25	.60
1994 Donruss Triple Play	260	.15	.11	.06
1994 Fleer	223	.15	.11	.06
1994 Fleer Extra Bases	126	.25	.20	.10
1994 Fleer Extra Bases Game Breakers	30	.25	.20	.10
1994 Fleer Flair	79	.40	.30	.15
1994 Fleer Flair Outfield Power	10	1.50	1.25	.60
1994 Fleer Golden Moments	3	1.50	1.25	.60
1994 Fleer Golden Moments Super	3	7.50	5.50	3.00
1994 Fleer Ultra	92	.15	.11	.06
1994 Fleer Ultra Career Achievement Awards	5	2.00	1.50	.80
1994 Leaf	137	.15	.11	.06
1994 Leaf Limited	52	1.50	1.25	.60
1994 Leaf Statistical Standouts	8	1.50	1.25	.60
1994 O-Pee-Chee	53	.15	.11	.06
1994 Pacific Crown	371	.25	.20	.10
1994 Pinnacle	332	.25	.20	.10
1994 Pinnacle Artist's Proof	332	8.00	6.00	3.25
1994 Pinnacle Museum Collection	332	3.00	2.25	1.25
1994 Pinnacle Tribute	3	2.00	1.50	.80
1994 Score	407	.15	.11	.06
1994 Score	629	.08	.06	.03
1994 Score Select	84	.15	.11	.06
1994 Score Select Salute	2	30.00	22.00	12.00
1994 Sportflics 2000	63	.25	.20	.10
1994 Studio	202	.10	.08	.04
1994 Topps	430	.08	.06	.03
1994 Topps Finest	215	.75	.60	.30
1994 Topps Finest Refractors	215	7.50	5.25	2.75
1994 Topps Finest Superstars	215	5.00	3.75	2.00
1994 Topps Gold	430	.20	.15	.08
1994 Topps Stadium Club	288	.20	.15	.08
1994 Topps Stadium Club	526	.25	.20	.10
1994 Topps Stadium Club Dugout Dirt	2	.50	.40	.20
1994 Topps Stadium Club First Day Production	288	15.00	11.00	6.00
1994 Topps Stadium Club First Day Production	526	10.00	7.50	4.00
1994 Upper Deck	81	.25	.20	.10
1994 Upper Deck Collector's Choice	302	.15	.11	.06
1994 Upper Deck Electric Diamond	81	1.25	.90	.50
1994 Upper Deck Fun Packs	32	.20	.15	.08
1994 Upper Deck Fun Packs	202	.75	.60	.30
1994 Upper Deck SP	187	.40	.30	.15
1994 Upper Deck SP Baseball Die-Cut	187	.60	.45	.25

Carl Yastrzemski

Set	Card #	NM	EX	VG
1960 Topps	148 (R)	175.00	85.00	50.00
1961 Topps	287	65.00	32.50	19.50
1962 Post Cereal	61	45.00	22.00	13.50
1962 Topps	425	145.00	72.50	42.50
1963 Fleer	8	90.00	45.00	27.00
1963 Post Cereal	80	325.00	162.00	97.00
1963 Topps	115	40.00	20.00	12.00
1964 Topps	8	11.00	5.50	3.25
1964 Topps	182	12.00	6.00	3.50
1964 Topps	210	45.00	22.50	13.50
1965 Topps	385	65.00	32.00	19.50
1966 O-Pee-Chee	70	50.00	25.00	15.00
1966 Topps	70	35.00	17.50	10.50
1966 Topps	216	8.00	4.00	2.50
1967 Topps	355	65.00	32.00	19.50
1968 O-Pee-Chee	2	12.75	6.50	3.75
1968 O-Pee-Chee	4	13.50	6.75	4.00
1968 O-Pee-Chee	6	10.25	5.25	3.00
1968 O-Pee-Chee	192	3.50	1.75	1.00
1968 Topps	2	8.00	4.00	2.50
1968 Topps	4	8.00	4.00	2.50
1968 Topps	6	8.00	4.00	2.50
1968 Topps	192a	4.50	2.25	1.25
1968 Topps	192b	6.00	3.00	1.75
1968 Topps	250	26.00	13.00	7.75
1968 Topps	369	7.00	3.50	2.00
1969 O-Pee-Chee	1	17.00	8.50	5.00
1969 O-Pee-Chee	130	32.00	16.00	9.50
1969 Topps	1	8.00	4.00	2.50
1969 Topps	130	18.00	9.00	5.50
1969 Topps	425	9.00	4.50	2.75
1970 O-Pee-Chee	10	25.00	12.50	7.50
1970 O-Pee-Chee	461	12.75	6.50	3.75
1970 Topps	10	15.00	7.50	4.50
1970 Topps	461	8.00	4.00	2.50
1971 O-Pee-Chee	61	1.50	.70	.45
1971 O-Pee-Chee	65	1.50	.70	.45
1971 O-Pee-Chee	530	50.00	25.00	15.00
1971 Topps	61	3.50	1.75	1.00
1971 Topps	65	3.50	1.75	1.00
1971 Topps	530	28.00	14.00	8.00
1972 O-Pee-Chee	37	15.00	7.50	4.50
1972 O-Pee-Chee	38	7.50	3.75	2.25
1972 Topps	37	10.00	5.00	3.00
1972 Topps	38	5.00	2.50	1.50
1973 O-Pee-Chee	245	17.00	8.50	5.00
1973 Topps	245	15.00	7.50	4.50
1974 O-Pee-Chee	280	12.75	6.50	3.75
1974 Topps	280	10.00	5.00	3.00
1975 O-Pee-Chee	205	3.00	1.50	.90
1975 O-Pee-Chee	280	10.25	5.25	3.00
1975 Topps	205	1.25	.60	.40
1975 Topps	280	12.00	6.00	3.50
1975 Topps Mini	205	1.75	.90	.50
1975 Topps Mini	280	10.00	5.00	3.00
1976 O-Pee-Chee	230	8.50	4.25	2.50
1976 Topps	230	7.00	3.50	2.00
1977 O-Pee-Chee	37	6.25	3.25	2.00

Set	Card #			
1977 Topps	434	1.50	.70	.45
1977 Topps	480	6.00	3.00	1.75
1978 O-Pee-Chee	137	4.25	2.25	1.25
1978 Topps	40	4.00	2.00	1.25
1979 O-Pee-Chee	160	3.75	2.00	1.25
1979 Topps	320	4.00	2.00	1.25
1980 O-Pee-Chee	365	1.00	.50	.30
1980 Topps	1	2.00	1.00	.60
1980 Topps	720	1.50	.70	.45

Set	Card #	MT	NM	EX
1981 Donruss	94	1.00	.70	.40
1981 Donruss	214	1.25	.90	.50
1981 Fleer	221	1.00	.70	.40
1981 Fleer	638	1.00	.70	.40
1981 O-Pee-Chee	110	2.50	2.00	1.00
1981 Topps	110	2.00	1.50	.80
1982 Donruss	74	1.00	.70	.40
1982 Fleer	312	1.00	.70	.40
1982 Fleer	633	.35	.25	.14
1982 O-Pee-Chee	72	1.50	1.25	.60
1982 O-Pee-Chee	358	.30	.25	.12
1982 Topps	650	1.50	1.25	.60
1982 Topps	651	.60	.45	.25
1983 Donruss	25	.80	.60	.30
1983 Donruss	326	.80	.60	.30
1983 Fleer	200	1.00	.70	.40
1983 Fleer	629	.25	.20	.10
1983 O-Pee-Chee	4	.75	.60	.30
1983 O-Pee-Chee	126	.30	.25	.12
1983 Topps	550	1.00	.70	.40
1983 Topps	551	.40	.30	.15
1983 Topps All-Star Glossy Set of 40	1	.75	.60	.30
1984 Donruss	B	7.00	5.25	2.75
1984 Fleer	412	.80	.60	.30
1984 Fleer	640	2.00	1.50	.80
1984 Topps	6	.40	.30	.15
1984 Topps All-Star Glossy Set of 22	11	.80	.60	.30
1986 Sportflics Decade Greats	47	1.00	.70	.40
1987 Topps	314	.10	.08	.04
1990 Pacific Legends	61	.50	.40	.20
1990 Topps All-Star Glossy Set of 22	22	.20	.15	.08
1992 Score The Franchise	3	8.00	6.00	3.25
1992 Score The Franchise	4	9.00	6.75	3.50
1993 Score Select Triple Crown	3	25.00	18.00	10.00

Robin Yount

Set	Card #	NM	EX	VG
1975 O-Pee-Chee	223	205.00	102.00	61.00
1975 Topps	223 (R)	150.00	75.00	45.00
1975 Topps Mini	223	200.00	100.00	60.00
1976 O-Pee-Chee	316	55.00	27.00	16.50
1976 Topps	316	50.00	25.00	15.00
1977 O-Pee-Chee	204	32.00	16.00	9.50

Set	Card #	MT	NM	EX
1977 Topps	635	25.00	12.50	7.50
1978 O-Pee-Chee	29	18.00	9.00	5.50
1978 Topps	173	20.00	10.00	6.00
1979 O-Pee-Chee	41	12.75	6.50	3.75
1979 Topps	95	12.00	6.00	3.50
1980 O-Pee-Chee	139	11.00	5.50	3.25
1980 Topps	265	10.00	5.00	3.00
Set	Card #	MT	NM	EX
1981 Donruss	323	4.00	3.00	1.50
1981 Fleer	511	3.00	2.25	1.25
1981 O-Pee-Chee	4	3.75	2.75	1.50
1981 Topps	515	5.00	3.75	2.00
1982 Donruss	510	3.00	2.25	1.25
1982 Fleer	155	3.00	2.25	1.25
1982 O-Pee-Chee	237	3.00	2.25	1.25
1982 Topps	435	4.00	3.00	1.50
1983 Donruss	258	2.50	2.00	1.00
1983 Fleer	51	2.50	2.00	1.00
1983 Fleer	632	.20	.15	.08
1983 O-Pee-Chee	350	2.50	2.00	1.00
1983 O-Pee-Chee	389	.20	.15	.08
1983 Topps	321	.20	.15	.08
1983 Topps	350	3.00	2.25	1.25
1983 Topps	389	.75	.60	.30
1983 Topps All-Star Glossy Set of 40	5	.50	.40	.20
1984 Donruss	1a	3.00	2.25	1.25
1984 Donruss	1b	5.00	3.75	2.00
1984 Donruss	48	8.00	6.00	3.25
1984 Fleer	219	5.00	3.75	2.00
1984 O-Pee-Chee	10	1.50	1.25	.60
1984 Topps	10	2.50	2.00	1.00
1984 Topps All-Star Glossy Set of 22	5	.75	.60	.30
1984 Topps All-Star Glossy Set of 40	36	.50	.40	.20
1985 Donruss	48	3.50	2.75	1.50
1985 Fleer	601	4.00	3.00	1.50
1985 Leaf-Donruss	44	3.50	2.75	1.50
1985 O-Pee-Chee	340	1.00	.70	.40
1985 Topps	340	1.00	.70	.40
1986 Donruss	48	1.75	1.25	.70
1986 Fleer	506	2.00	1.50	.80
1986 Leaf	31	1.75	1.25	.70
1986 O-Pee-Chee	144	.75	.60	.30
1986 Sportflics	42a	150.00	125.00	60.00
1986 Sportflics	42b	1.25	.90	.50
1986 Sportflics	54	1.25	.90	.50
1986 Sportflics	63	.30	.25	.12
1986 Sportflics	71	.30	.25	.12
1986 Sportflics Decade Greats	73	.30	.25	.12
1986 Topps	780	.60	.45	.25
1987 Donruss	126	.60	.45	.25
1987 Fleer	361	1.25	.90	.50
1987 Leaf	67	.60	.45	.25
1987 O-Pee-Chee	76	.30	.25	.12
1987 Sportflics	16	1.50	1.25	.60
1987 Topps	773	.40	.30	.15
1988 Donruss	295	.30	.25	.12
1988 Fleer	178	.60	.45	.25
1988 Leaf	106	.20	.15	.08
1988 O-Pee-Chee	165	.15	.11	.06
1988 Score	160	.35	.25	.14
1988 Sportflics	34	1.00	.70	.40
1988 Topps	165	.20	.15	.08
1988 Topps Big Baseball	66	.30	.25	.12
1989 Bowman	144	.25	.20	.10
1989 Donruss	5	.12	.09	.05
1989 Donruss	55	.25	.20	.10
1989 Fleer	200	.25	.20	.10
1989 O-Pee-Chee	253	.50	.40	.20
1989 Score	151	.25	.20	.10
1989 Sportflics	199	.30	.25	.12
1989 Topps	615	.25	.20	.10
1989 Topps All-Star Glossy Set of 60	38	.40	.30	.15
1989 Topps Big Baseball	249	.25	.20	.10
1989 Upper Deck	285	.80	.60	.30
1990 Bowman	404	.20	.15	.08
1990 Bowman Inserts	(11)	.10	.08	.04
1990 Donruss	146	.20	.15	.08
1990 Fleer	340	.20	.15	.08
1990 Leaf	71	2.00	1.50	.80
1990 O-Pee-Chee	290	.25	.20	.10
1990 O-Pee-Chee	389	.25	.20	.10
1990 Post Cereal	26	.60	.45	.25
1990 Score	320	.25	.20	.10
1990 Sportflics	18	.50	.40	.20
1990 Topps	290	.25	.20	.10
1990 Topps	389	.15	.11	.06
1990 Topps All-Star Glossy Set of 60	15	.40	.30	.15
1990 Topps Big Baseball	59	.20	.15	.08
1990 Upper Deck	567	.50	.40	.20
1991 Bowman	55	.20	.15	.08
1991 Donruss	272	.15	.11	.06
1991 Fleer	601	.15	.11	.06
1991 Fleer Ultra	184	.25	.20	.10
1991 Leaf	116	.25	.20	.10
1991 O-Pee-Chee Premier	131	.20	.15	.08
1991 Score	525	.15	.11	.06
1991 Score	854	.10	.07	.04
1991 Studio	80	.35	.25	.14
1991 Topps	575	.15	.11	.06
1991 Topps Stadium Club	509	1.50	1.25	.60
1991 Upper Deck	344	.20	.15	.08
1992 Bowman	700	2.00	1.50	.80
1992 Donruss	173	.20	.15	.08
1992 Donruss Triple Play	81	.15	.11	.06
1992 Fleer	194	.15	.11	.06
1992 Fleer	708	.20	.15	.08
1992 Fleer Ultra	87	.40	.30	.15
1992 Fleer Update	H2	7.00	5.25	2.75
1992 Leaf	64	.25	.20	.10
1992 O-Pee-Chee	90	.12	.09	.05
1992 O-Pee-Chee Premier	111	.25	.20	.10
1992 Pinnacle	38	.40	.30	.15
1992 Pinnacle	287	.35	.25	.14
1992 Score	525	.12	.09	.05
1992 Studio	200	.30	.25	.12
1992 Topps	90	.12	.09	.05
1992 Topps Gold	90	2.00	1.50	.80
1992 Topps Kids	80	.20	.15	.08
1992 Topps Stadium Club	450	.75	.60	.30
1992 Topps Stadium Club	607	.25	.20	.10
1992 Topps Stadium Club East Coast National	607	25.00	18.50	10.00
1992 Upper Deck	456	.20	.15	.08
1993 Bowman	535	.50	.40	.20
1993 DiamondMarks	(94)	1.00	.70	.40
1993 DiamondMarks Inserts	(8)	15.00	11.00	6.00
1993 Donruss	441	.25	.20	.10
1993 Donruss Diamond Kings	16	2.00	1.50	.80
1993 Donruss Elite	----	75.00	60.00	30.00
1993 Donruss Masters of the Game	15	4.00	3.00	1.50
1993 Donruss Spirit of the Game	20	2.00	1.50	.80
1993 Donruss Triple Play Action Baseball	16	.20	.15	.08
1993 Donruss Triple Play	188	.35	.25	.14
1993 Fleer	260	.15	.11	.06
1993 Fleer Final Edition	10DT	1.00	.75	.40
1993 Fleer Flair	232	1.50	1.25	.60
1993 Fleer Ultra	227	.40	.30	.15
1993 Leaf	188	.50	.40	.20
1993 Leaf Heading for the Hall	3	3.50	2.75	1.50
1993 O-Pee-Chee	365	.60	.45	.25
1993 Pinnacle	118	.40	.30	.15
1993 Pinnacle	293	.30	.25	.12
1993 Pinnacle Cooperstown	3	.50	.40	.20
1993 Pinnacle Cooperstown Dufex	3	125.00	94.00	50.00
1993 Post Cereal	30	.50	.40	.20
1993 Score	47	.20	.15	.08

1993 Score	518	.15	.11	.06
1993 Score Select	22	.25	.20	.10
1993 Score The Franchise	8	5.00	3.75	2.00
1993 Studio	118	.35	.25	.14
1993 Topps	1	.15	.11	.06
1993 Topps Finest	192	6.00	4.50	2.50
1993 Topps Finest Refractors	192	125.00	95.00	50.00
1993 Topps Gold	1	.30	.25	.12
1993 Topps Stadium Club	173	.50	.40	.20
1993 Topps Stadium Club First Day Production	173	60.00	45.00	24.00
1993 Topps Stadium Club I Inserts	1	4.00	3.00	1.50
1993 Upper Deck	43	.15	.11	.06
1993 Upper Deck	587	.20	.15	.08
1993 Upper Deck "Highlights"	20	4.00	3.00	1.50
1993 Upper Deck Diamond Gallery	6	3.00	2.25	1.25
1993 Upper Deck Fun Packs	69	.25	.20	.10
1993 Upper Deck Fun Packs	73	.35	.25	.14
1993 Upper Deck SP	72	1.00	.75	.40
1993 Upper Deck Then And Now	15	2.50	2.00	1.00
1994 Donruss	15	.35	.25	.14
1994 Donruss Anniversary-1984	2	3.50	2.75	1.50
1994 Donruss Special Edition - Gold	15	.75	.60	.30
1994 Donruss Triple Play	60	.20	.15	.08
1994 Fleer	197	.20	.15	.08
1994 Pacific Crown	348	.20	.15	.08
1994 Pacific Crown Jewels of the Crown	1	4.00	3.00	1.50
1994 Score	13	.25	.20	.10
1994 Sportflics 2000	24	.40	.30	.15
1994 Topps	310	.15	.11	.06
1994 Topps Gold	310	.45	.35	.20
1994 Topps Stadium Club	1	.35	.25	.14
1994 Topps Stadium Club First Day Production	1	25.00	18.50	10.00
1994 Upper Deck Diamond Collection	10C	8.00	6.00	3.25
1994 Upper Deck Fun Packs	202	.75	.60	.30

MORE GREAT BOOKS FOR COLLECTORS

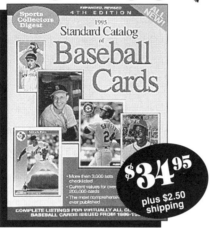

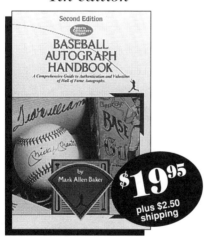

YOUR NEWEST GUIDES TO SPORTS COLLECTIBLES

$16.95

SPORTS EQUIPMENT PRICE GUIDE

Find pricing for collectible baseball, football, basketball and hockey equipment used from 1860 - 1960.
6"x9", 352 pgs., 500 photos

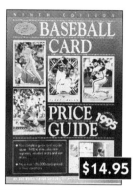

$14.95

BASEBALL CARD PRICE GUIDE, 9th Ed.

Thorough and reliable pricing to evaluate your collection of modern baseball cards. Over 95,000 cards and 285,000 current values.
6"x9", 816 pgs., 1400 photos

$16.95

PREMIUM INSERT SPORTS CARDS

Put a premium on your premium insert sports cards with updated prices from 1960 to date. 600 sets and 10,000 cards are included.
6"x9",, 400 pgs., 400 photos

$19.95

COMPLETE GUIDE TO BOXING MEMORABILIA

Boxing fans can now identify, evaluate and authenticate all their boxing memorabilia with this new handy guide.
6"x9", 320 pgs., 300+ photos

All titles are softcover

$19.95

STANDARD CATALOG OF FOOTBALL, BASKETBALL & HOCKEY CARDS

One convenient catalog for three sports. Over 750 sets and 100,000 cards with updated pricing help to buy, sell, trade and evaluate your collection.
8-1/2"x11", 600 pgs., 500 photos

$14.95

ALL SPORTS ALPHABETICAL PRICE GUIDE

Easily find prospects, stars, Hall of Famers and desirable players. 24,000 collectible cards from 725 popular players of1948 to date, alphabetized, checklisted and priced here.
6"x9", 500 pgs., 725 photos

Shipping: Add $2.50 1st book, $1.50 each additional, $5.00 each foreign. WI residents add 5.5% sales tax.

 **Krause Publications** 700 E. State St., Dept KFB1 Iola, WI 54990-0001
Call in or send check or money order (payable to Krause Publications) today!

Charge Card Holders call toll-free 800-258-0929 Dept. KFB1